P9-CST-669

HEATH

Pre-Algebra

David W. Lowry
Earl G. Ockenga
Walter E. Rucker

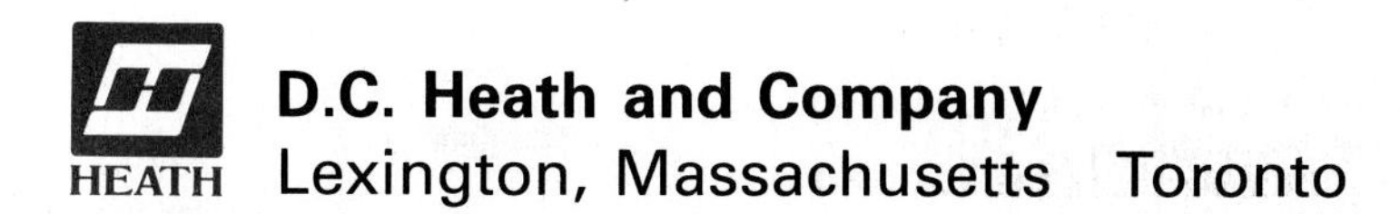
D.C. Heath and Company
Lexington, Massachusetts Toronto

Authors

David W. Lowry
Teacher, Grey Junior High School, Acton, MA

Earl G. Ockenga
Teacher, Price Laboratory School, University of Northern Iowa, Cedar Falls, IA

Walter E. Rucker
Author in residence, D. C. Heath and Company

Project Editor Justine Dombrowski

Book Designer Dawn Ostrer Emerson

Cover Designer Barbara Tonnesen

Production Coordinator Maureen LaRiccia

Cover photos (*from left to right*): Ron Colby/The Stock Market; Guy Savage–Agence Vandystadt/Photo Researchers, Inc.; Warren William/Robert Harding Picture Library

Published simultaneously in Canada.

Printed in the United States of America.

International Standard Book Number: 0-669-09738-1

4 5 6 7 8 9 0

Contents

1 Addition and Subtraction Equations

$a + t = g$

2 Multiplication and Division Equations

$\frac{d}{g} = m$

3 Equations with Decimals

4 Number Properties and Equations

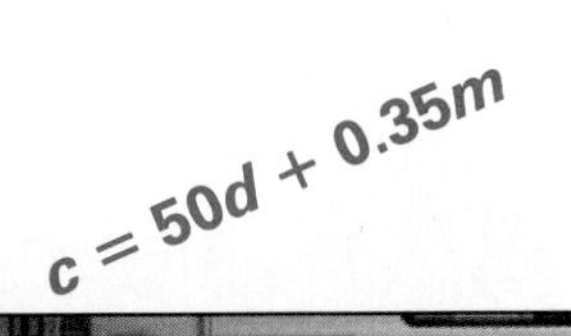

5 Number Theory and Equivalent Fractions

$h = \frac{d^2}{8000}$

6 Addition and Subtraction of Fractions

$w = \frac{s}{8}$

7 Multiplication and Division of Fractions

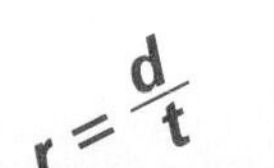

8 Integers and Equations

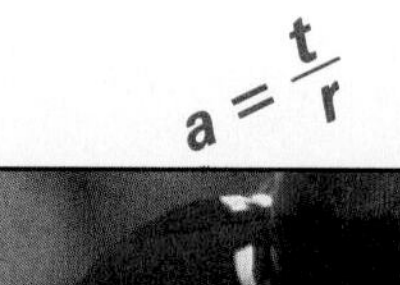

9 Rational Numbers and Equations

10 Ratio, Proportion, and Percent

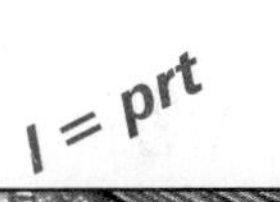

11 Geometry—Perimeter and Area

12 Surface Area and Volume

13 Graphing Equations and Inequalities

$y = \frac{1}{4}x + 40$

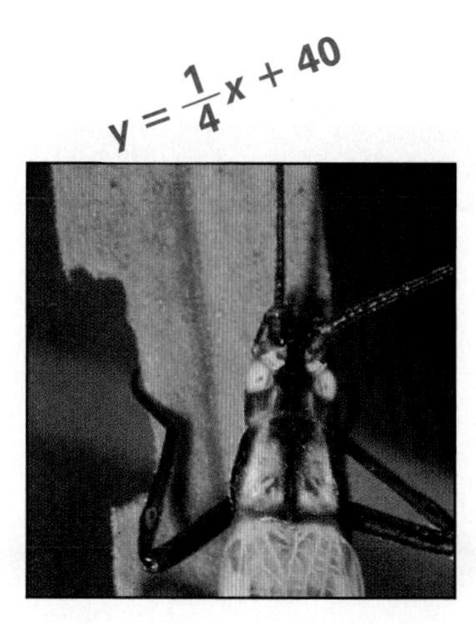

14 Probability and Statistics

$P(4, 6 \text{ or } 6, 4) = \frac{1}{18}$

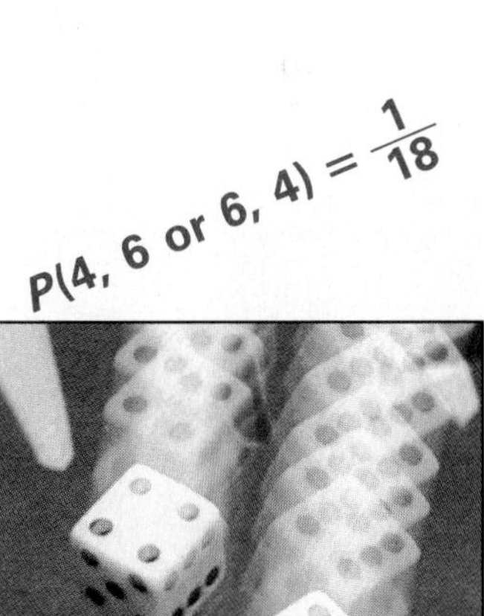

15 Similar and Right Triangles

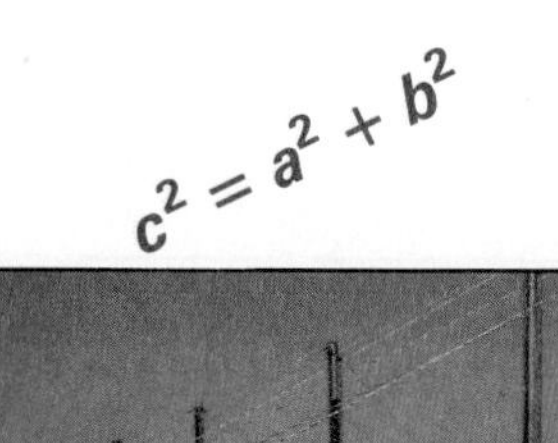

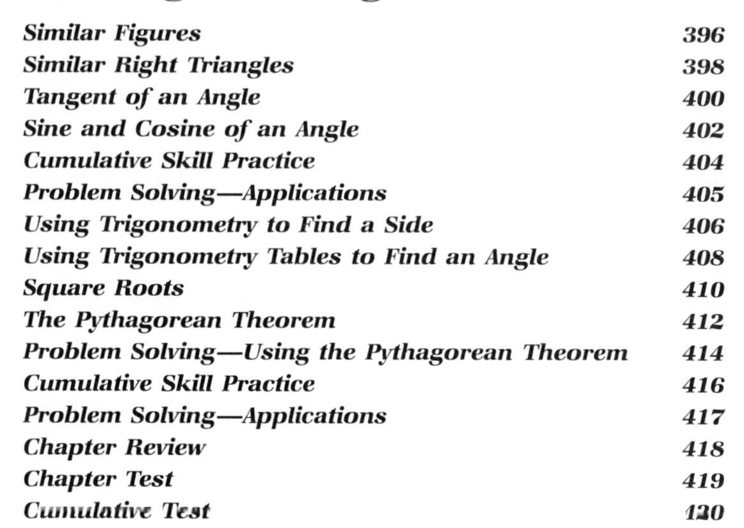

16 BASIC Programming

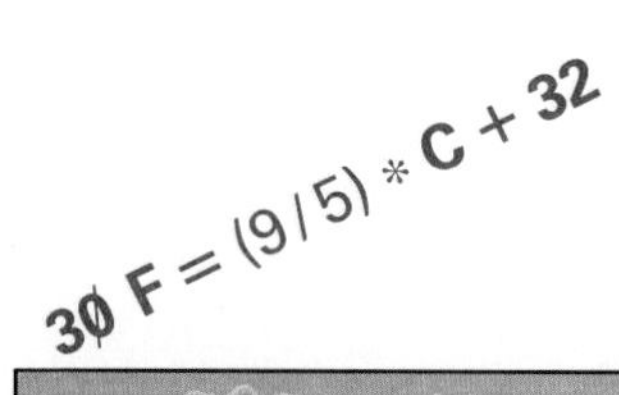

1 Addition and Subtraction Equations

$a + t = g$
Airspeed plus tailwind speed equals ground speed.
(page 19)

Airplane pilots use information about jet streams to arrive at their destination in the shortest amount of time with the most efficient use of fuel.

Variables and Expressions

Alan Alda is **n** years old.

Ringo Starr is **$n - 4$** years old.

Harry Belafonte is **$n + 9$** years old.

Paul Newman is **11** years older than Alda.

Elvis Costello is **18** years younger than Alda.

The letter n is a **variable.** It represents Alan Alda's age in years. Variables, numbers, and operation signs can be combined to form **mathematical expressions.** If Alan Alda is n years old, then Paul Newman's age is given by the expression $n + 11$.

1. Whose age is 9 years more than Alda's age?

2. Whose age is 4 years less than Alda's age?

3. If Alan Alda is n years old, who is $n - 18$ years old?

Here's how to write mathematical expressions for word expressions.

Word expression	Mathematical expression
a number n plus 8 →	$n + 8$
a number r minus 2 →	$r - 2$
a number m less 3 →	$m - 3$
a number s increased by 4 →	$s + 4$
a number t decreased by 1 →	$t - 1$
the sum of a number y and 5 →	$y + 5$
6 less than a number b →	$b - 6$
9 more than a number c →	$c + 9$

Notice that any letter can be used as a variable.

4. Look at the examples above. To read the expression $c + 9$, you can say "9 _?_ than a number c."

5. To read $t - 1$, you can say "a number t _?_ by 1."

Write a mathematical expression for each word expression.

6. 8 more than a number n
7. 7 less than a number w
8. the sum of a number c and 9
9. a number r minus 7
10. 3 increased by a number g
11. a number m decreased by 2
12. a number y less 8
13. the sum of a number e and 10
14. 15 decreased by a number n
15. 6 more than a number d
16. a number c plus 12
17. a number v minus 7
18. a number c increased by 15
19. 10 less than a number u
20. a number r plus a number s
21. a number n minus a number m
22. a number t increased by itself
23. a number c decreased by itself

Let n be Alan Alda's age. Write a mathematical expression for the age that is

24. 6 years more than his age.
25. 4 years less than his age.
26. Alda's age increased by 6 years.
27. his age decreased by 3 years.
28. his age plus 5 years.
29. Alda's age minus 2 years.
★30. his age 1 year ago.
★31. his age 2 years from now.

Problem Solving

Decide whether Expression A or B would be used to complete each sentence.

Expression A: $n + 5$
Expression B: $n - 5$

32. Cindy is 5 years older than Brian. If Brian is n years old, then Cindy is __?__ years old.
33. Together two gifts cost n dollars. If one of the gifts costs 5 dollars, then the other gift costs __?__ dollars.
34. Ann scored 5 more points than Beth. If Beth scored n points, then Ann scored __?__ points.
35. The sale price is $5 less than the regular price. If the regular price is n dollars, then the sale price is __?__ dollars.
36. Today is 5 degrees warmer than yesterday. If today's temperature is n degrees, then yesterday's temperature was __?__ degrees.
37. Maria has $5 less than Troy. If Maria has n dollars, then Troy has __?__ dollars.
38. The regular price is $5 more than the sale price. If the sale price is n dollars, then the regular price is __?__ dollars.
39. You scored 5 fewer points than your friend. If your friend scored n points, then you scored __?__ points.

Evaluating Expressions

The mathematical expressions in this chart show the players' scores for each half of the basketball game. The variables f and s represent the number of points Bird scored in the first and second halves of the game.

	Points scored	
Player	**First half**	**Second half**
Bird	f	s
Parish	$f + 4$	$s - 2$
Maxwell	$f - 3$	$s + 5$
Kite	$f - 2$	$s - 1$
Johnson	f	$s + 3$
McHale	$f + 5$	$s - 4$
Buckner	$f - 8$	$s - 5$
Ainge	$f - 5$	$s - 8$

1. Look at the chart. In the first half, who scored 5 more points than Bird?
2. In the second half, who scored 2 fewer points than Bird?
3. Who scored more points in the first half, Parish or McHale?
4. Who scored more points in the second half, Parish or Kite?

Here's how to evaluate mathematical expressions.

In this game Bird scored 10 points in the first half and 8 points in the second half. To find the number of points each player scored, substitute 10 for f and/or 8 for s in the expression and simplify.

Points Maxwell scored in the first half:

$$f - 3$$
$$10 - 3 = 7$$

Maxwell scored 7 points in the first half.

Points Maxwell scored in the second half:

$$s + 5$$
$$8 + 5 = 13$$

Maxwell scored 13 points in the second half.

Total points Johnson scored in the game:

$$f + s + 3$$
$$10 + 8 + 3 = 21$$

Johnson scored a total of 21 points.

5. Look at the examples above. How many points did Maxwell score in all?
6. Who scored more points in the game, Maxwell or Johnson?

EXERCISES

Evaluate each expression for $r = 5$, $s = 8$, and $t = 6$.
Here are scrambled answers for the next row of exercises: *11 2 3 12*

7. $r + 7$
8. $s - 5$
9. $r + t$
10. $s - t$
11. $s - 4$
12. $r + 1$
13. $s - r$
14. $r - 5$
15. $r + 9$
16. $s - 6$
17. $10 - t$
18. $s - 8$
19. $r + s - 2$
20. $s + t - 5$
21. $s - r + 6$
22. $t + s - r$
23. $r + r + 4$
24. $s - t + 2$
25. $15 - s - t$
26. $s + r - 9$
27. $s + s - 4$
28. $t + s - s$
29. $r + r + r$
30. $s + s + s$
31. $t - r + r$
32. $t + t - s$
33. $14 - r - s$
34. $r - r + r$
35. $12 - s + t$
36. $10 - r + r$
37. $9 + r - t$
38. $r + t - s$
39. $s - t + 9$
40. $10 + r - r$
41. $t - r + t + r$
42. $r + r + r + r$

Evaluate each expression for $w = 3$, $x = 7$, $y = 4$.
Here are scrambled answers for the next two rows of exercises: *10 1 7 11*

43. y decreased by w
44. the sum of x and y
45. x increased by w
46. w plus y
47. w less than x
48. x minus y
49. w decreased by itself
50. the sum of y and w
51. six less than x
52. y more than two
53. the sum of x and 6 decreased by 8
54. the sum of w and 5 increased by 7
55. the sum of w and x decreased by y
56. the sum of w and w increased by x

Problem Solving

Solve. Use the chart on page 4. ***Remember:*** *$f = 10$ and $s = 8$.*

57. How many points did Ainge score in the first half?
58. How many points did Buckner score in the second half?
59. Who scored 15 points in the first half?
60. Who scored 6 points in the second half?
61. How many points did Bird score in all?
62. How many points did Parish score in all?
63. Who scored a total of 19 points in the game?
64. Who scored a total of 15 points?

★65. Who scored a total of $f + s + 1$ points?

★66. Who scored a total of $f + s - 3$ points?

Place Value and Rounding

Antique-Car Auction Attracts 20,000

A total of 19,852 admirers of classic automobiles attended yesterday's antique-car auction.

Some "top dollar" bids were $58,498 for a 1933 Mercedes, $29,553 for a 1936 Packard, $23,464 for a 1908 Stanley Steamer, and $28,127 for a 1936 Ford Convertible.

1933 Mercedes sells for $58,498.

1. Read the article. What was the exact number of people that attended the auction?
2. What rounded number was used in the headline?

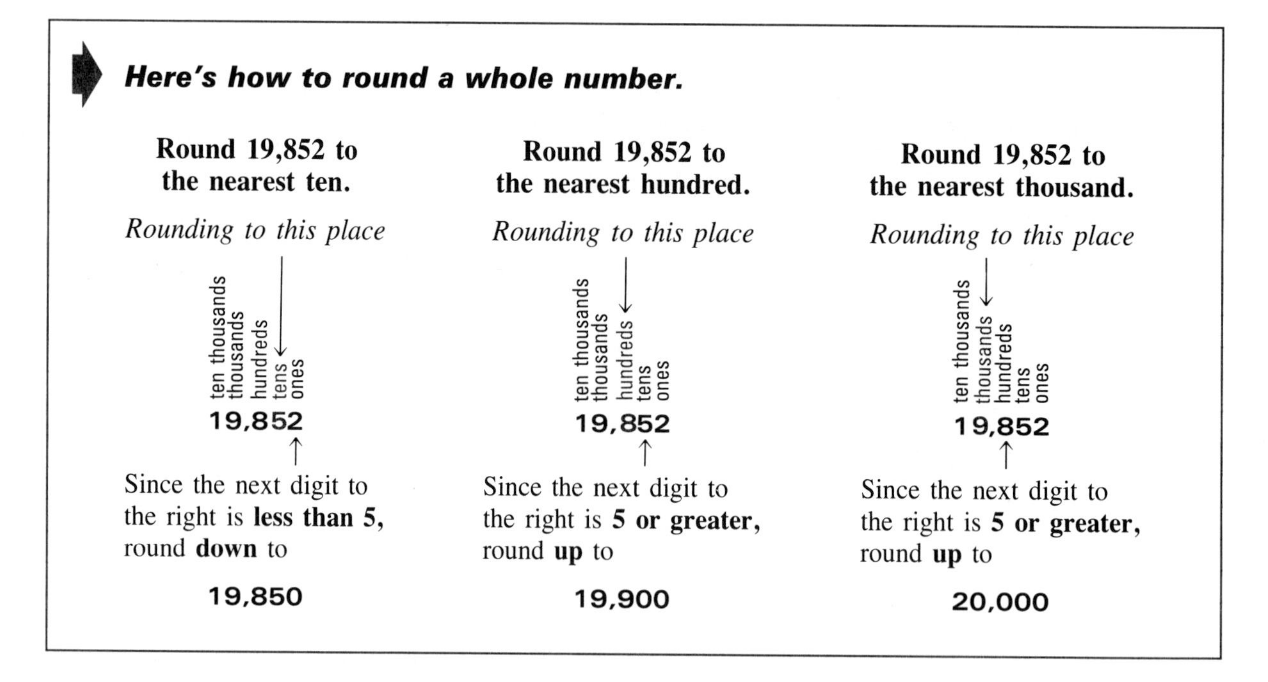

Here's how to round a whole number.

Round 19,852 to the nearest ten.

Rounding to this place

ten thousands, thousands, hundreds, tens, ones

19,852

Since the next digit to the right is **less than 5,** round **down** to

19,850

Round 19,852 to the nearest hundred.

Rounding to this place

ten thousands, thousands, hundreds, tens, ones

19,852

Since the next digit to the right is **5 or greater,** round **up** to

19,900

Round 19,852 to the nearest thousand.

Rounding to this place

ten thousands, thousands, hundreds, tens, ones

19,852

Since the next digit to the right is **5 or greater,** round **up** to

20,000

3. Look at the examples above. In 19,852, which digit is in the ten thousands place? Is the next digit to the right 5 or greater?
4. Round 19,852 to the nearest ten thousand.

EXERCISES

Round to the nearest ten.

5. 93 6. 85 7. 7 8. 496 9. 524

10. 2 11. 3653 12. 5706 13. 6333 14. 7801

Round to the nearest hundred.

15. 278 16. 750 17. 89 18. 369 19. 498

20. 6506 21. 5628 22. 3779 23. 23,950 24. 40,962

Round to the nearest thousand.

25. 5794 26. 8036 27. 768 28. 500 29. 203

30. 26,343 31. 41,560 32. 64,329 33. 50,200 34. 15,470

35. 536,479 36. 163,500 37. 879,999 38. 426,606 39. 799,999

Round to the nearest ten thousand.

40. 87,468 41. 34,600 42. 73,911 43. 9830 44. 67,302

45. 289,700 46. 868,492 47. 523,672 48. 675,000 49. 99,999

Use the newspaper article on page 6. Study each quotation. Tell to what place the person rounded the exact selling price.

50. "The Mercedes sold for $58,000."

51. "The Stanley Steamer sold for $23,500."

52. "The final bid for the most expensive car was nearly $60,000."

53. "The Stanley Steamer sold for more than $20,000."

Challenge

Solve. Use the map and the clues.

54. The greatest collection of antique cars is the Harrah Collection of 1700 cars, estimated to be worth $4 million. Where would you go to see the Harrah Collection?

Clues:

- Sparks is not next to Verdi.
- Carson City is south of Steamboat.
- Steamboat is between Reno and Carson City.
- Verdi is west of Sparks.

The Harrah Collection is in _?_, Nevada.

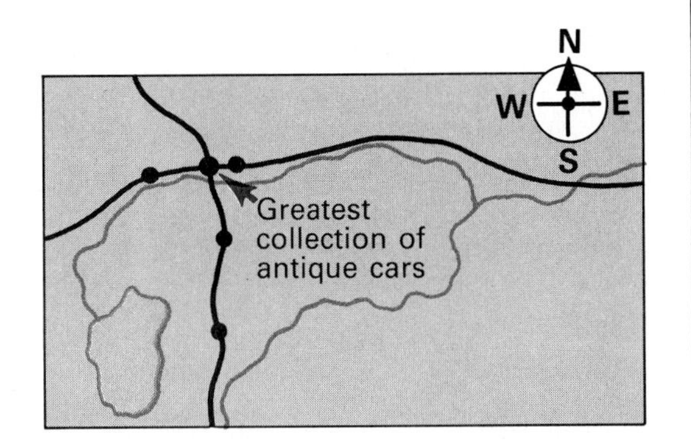

Cumulative Skill Practice

▶ **Write a mathematical expression for each word expression.** *(page 2)*

1. 5 less than a number y
2. 9 more than a number w
3. 7 increased by a number d
4. a number x minus 12
5. the sum of a number b and 4
6. a number t decreased by 8
7. 12 decreased by s
8. the sum of a number f and 15
9. 10 more than a number x
10. a number h less 6
11. a number z minus 18
12. a number m increased by 16
13. a number r plus 17
14. 14 less than a number v
15. a number x minus a number y
16. a number s plus a number t
17. a number k decreased by itself
18. a number q increased by itself

▶ **Evaluate each expression for $x = 7$, $y = 10$, and $z = 8$.** *(page 4)*

19. $y - 4$
20. $x + 5$
21. $y - 10$
22. $x + z$
23. $y - z$
24. $x + 9$
25. $y + z$
26. $x - 6$
27. $y + 8$
28. $x - 0$
29. $12 - z$
30. $z - 7$
31. $y - x + 5$
32. $z + y - x$
33. $x + y - 1$
34. $x + x + 8$
35. $y + z - 6$
36. $y - z + 4$
37. $y + z - 10$
38. $18 - x - z$
39. $z + y - y$
40. $y + y + y$
41. $x + x - y$
42. $x + x + x$
43. $z - x + x$
44. $z + z - y$
45. $y + y - x$
46. $z - z + x$
47. $20 - x - y$
48. $20 - x + y$
49. $20 + x - y$
50. $20 + x + y$

▶ **Round to the nearest thousand.** *(page 6)*

51. 3648
52. 6380
53. 824
54. 949
55. 7500
56. 245
57. 302
58. 9390
59. 35,620
60. 26,374
61. 78,095
62. 53,006
63. 52,720
64. 80,825
65. 73,450
66. 64,921
67. 44,500
68. 17,050
69. 59,500
70. 99,738
71. 521,350
72. 638,487
73. 409,618
74. 647,700
75. 821,068
76. 222,521
77. 375,100
78. 615,603
79. 321,500
80. 935,099
81. 379,500
82. 999,800

Problem Solving—Applications

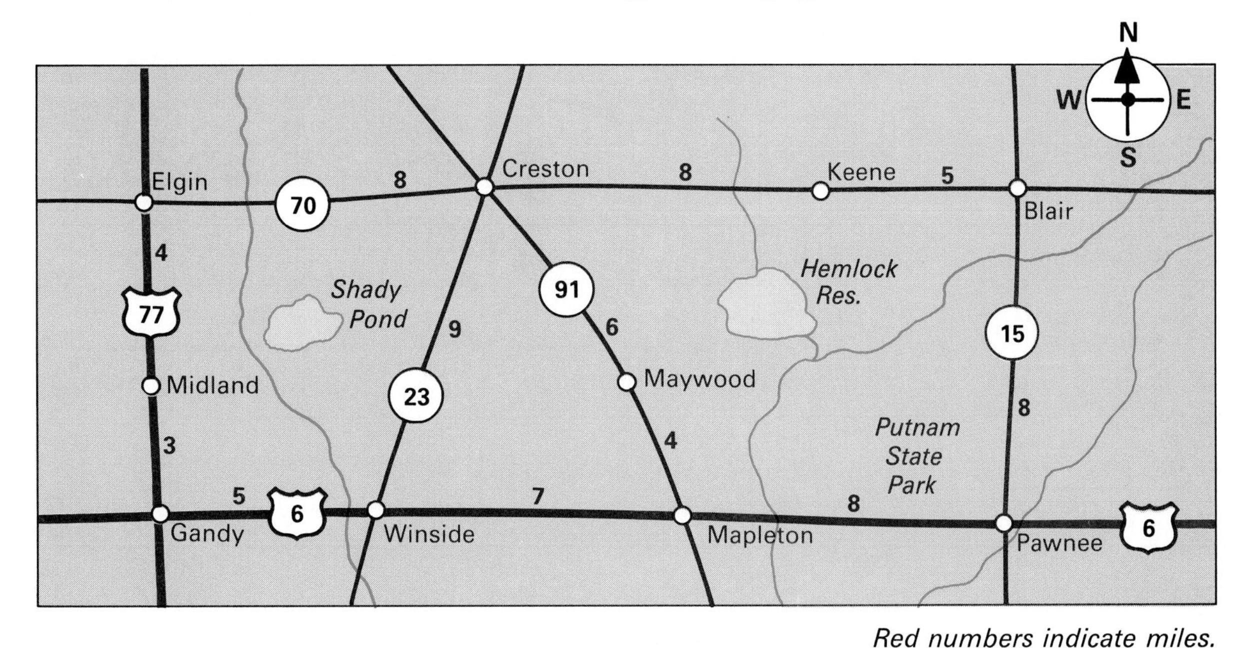

Red numbers indicate miles.

▶ **Use the map to answer the questions.**

1. How far is it from Winside to Pawnee?
2. How many miles is it from Elgin to Blair?
3. Which city is 18 miles from Creston?
4. How far is it from Elgin to Pawnee if you take Highways 70 and 91?
5. You want to take the shortest route from Blair to Winside. Which highways should you take?
6. You are 6 miles east of Mapleton going west on Highway 6. How far are you from Gandy?
7. You are 5 miles northeast of Winside on Highway 23. How far are you from Keene?
8. You are at Grant's Truckstop, 3 miles west of Winside. How far are you from Pawnee?

▶ **Decide whether Expression A, B, or C would be used to complete each sentence.**

Expression A: $n + 8$
Expression B: $n - 8$
Expression C: $8 - n$

9. You are driving east on Highway 70. When you are n miles west of Elgin, you are _?_ miles from Creston.
10. You are on your way from Pawnee to Blair. After driving n miles, you have _?_ miles left to go.
11. It takes 8 minutes to drive from Gandy to Winside. After driving n minutes, it will take _?_ minutes to complete the trip.
12. It's an n-minute drive from Winside to Keene. After driving 8 minutes, it will take _?_ minutes to get to Keene.

Estimating and Computing Sums

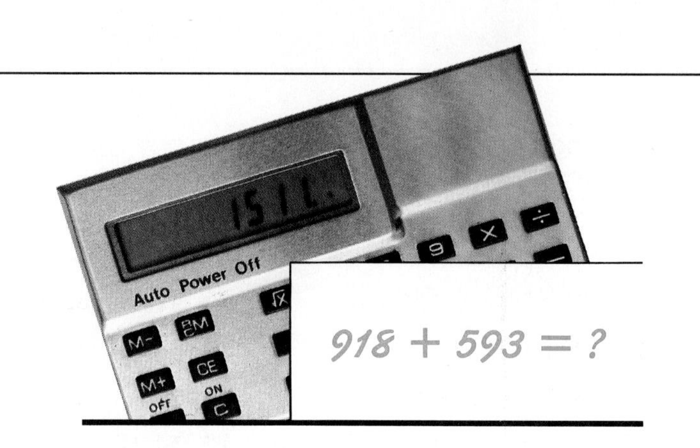

The answer to an addition problem is called the **sum.**

1. The calculator was used to find the sum. What sum is shown on the calculator?
2. Is the sum shown on the calculator reasonable?

Here's how to estimate and compute a sum.

308 + 586 + 890 = ?

To estimate the sum, you could round each number to the nearest hundred.

300 + 600 + 900 = 1800

Line up the digits vertically.

$$\begin{array}{r} 308 \\ 586 \\ +890 \\ \hline \end{array}$$

Add in columns.

$$\begin{array}{r} {}^{11} \\ 308 \\ 586 \\ +890 \\ \hline 1784 \end{array}$$

3. Look at the example above. To estimate the sum, the three numbers were rounded to the nearest __?__.
4. Was the sum close to the estimate?

EXERCISES

Three of the calculator answers are wrong. Find them by estimating.

5. **a.** 415 + 319 — 734 **b.** 729 + 1678 — 2407
 c. 526 + 288 + 617 — 1131 **d.** 926 + 806 + 579 — 2311
 e. 3528 + 6160 — 9688 **f.** 7386 + 6038 — 12424
 g. 53,294 + 26,043 — 79337 **h.** 38,175 + 82,233 — 100408

Add.
Here are scrambled answers for the next two rows of exercises:
1748 1820 830 2348 1428 1730

6. 378 + 452	**7.** 740 + 688	**8.** 945 + 875
9. 227 + 895 + 626	**10.** 426 + 382 + 922	**11.** 758 + 811 + 779
12. 5206 + 1733	**13.** 2983 + 4621	**14.** 5928 + 5928
15. 6342 + 856 + 3200	**16.** 728 + 2366 + 4591	**17.** 8355 + 1788 + 294
18. 36,274 + 46,288	**19.** 50,718 + 29,633	**20.** 72,593 + 82,957

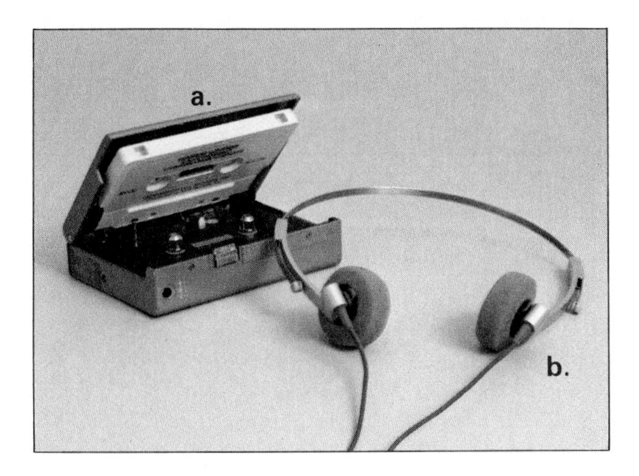

a. **Mini Stereo Cassette Player $79**
Separate left and right volume controls.

b. **Stereo Headphones $24**
Lightweight design. Padded ear cushions.

c. **Personal Stereo Cassette Carrying Case . $17**
Shock padding for maximum protection.

d. **Desk Top Battery Charger $19**
Recharges up to 2 pairs of C or D batteries.

e. **90-Minute Cassette Tapes $6**
Pack of 3.

Use the catalog prices. Evaluate each expression to get the total cost.

21. $a + b$ ($79 ↓ $24 ↓)	**22.** $b + c$ ($24 ↓ $17 ↓)	**23.** $d + e$
24. $c + e$	**25.** $a + c$	**26.** $c + a$
27. $a + b + c$	**28.** $b + c + d$	**29.** $c + d + e$
30. $a + c + d$	**31.** $b + d + e$	**32.** $b + c + e$
33. $a + d + e$	**34.** $a + b + d$	**35.** $e + e + e$
36. $e + e + a$	**37.** $a + b + e$	**38.** $b + e + e$

CALCULATOR

Solve. ***Hint: Make a guess. Use your calculator to check.***

39. Marcie bought four of the five items in the catalog. She spent more than $100 but less than $125. Which item did she *not* buy?

Estimating and Computing Differences

The answer to a subtraction problem is called the **difference.** If you estimate the difference, you will know whether your answer is reasonable.

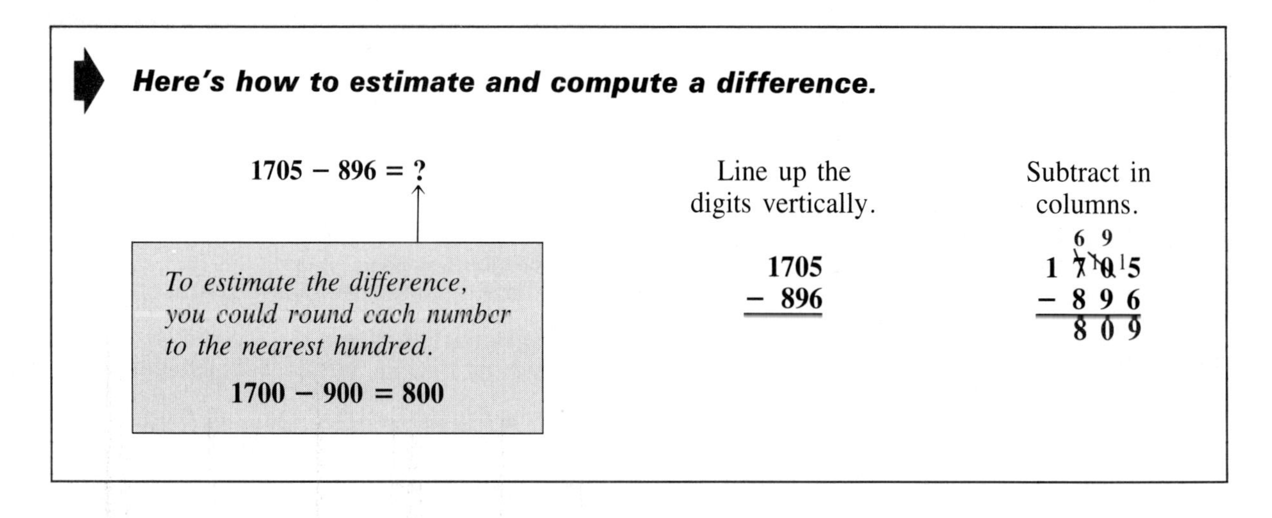

1. Look at the example above. To estimate the difference, the two numbers were rounded to the nearest __?__ .
2. Was the difference close to the estimate?

EXERCISES

▶ **Five of the calculator answers are wrong. Find them by estimating.**

3. **a.** 811 − 229 → 582   **b.** 900 − 194 → 706

c. 1236 − 445 → 791   **d.** 2957 − 965 → 2792

e. 4000 − 1038 → 2962   **f.** 3660 − 1174 → 2486

g. 5821 − 1990 → 3231   **h.** 4988 − 2475 → 2513

i. 30,433 − 14,856 → 15577   **j.** 50,300 − 29,700 → 30600

k. 37,342 − 18,291 → 27051   **l.** 63,977 − 24,099 → 39878

m. 42,396 − 29,142 → 13254   **n.** 38,102 − 10,013 → 18089

▶ **Subtract.**
Here are scrambled answers for the next two rows of exercises:
283 119 635 83 2997 1467

4. 846 − 211
5. 958 − 675
6. 403 − 284
7. 601 − 518
8. 1958 − 491
9. 3628 − 631
10. 5800 − 2619
11. 9000 − 3815
12. 7000 − 5025
13. 36,112 − 8,795
14. 40,116 − 7,221
15. 53,984 − 13,829

▶ **Use your mental math skills.**
Evaluate each expression for $x = 1200$, $y = 900$, and $z = 1300$.
Here are scrambled answers for the next row of exercises: 2100 100 300 2200

16. $x - y$
17. $x + y$
18. $z + y$
19. $z - x$
20. $z - z$
21. $y + y$
22. $z + x + y$
23. $x + z + y$
24. $y + z - x$
25. $z - y + x$
26. $y + x - z$
27. $x + z - y$
28. $x + y + z$
29. $y + x + z$
30. $x + y - x$
31. $z - x + y$

Problem Solving

▶ **Decide whether Expression A, B, or C would be used to complete each sentence.**

Expression A: $n + 10$
Expression B: $n - 10$
Expression C: $10 - n$

32. If you are n years old, then 10 years ago you were _?_ years old.

33. If you are n years old, in 10 years you will be _?_ years old.

34. If you have n dollars and earn 10 dollars, you have _?_ dollars.

35. If you have 10 dollars and spend n dollars, then you have _?_ dollars.

36. You and your friend spent a total of 10 dollars. If you spent n dollars, then your friend spent _?_ dollars.

37. Maria and Brian sold a total of n boxes of candy. If Maria sold 10 boxes, then Brian sold _?_ boxes.

Challenge

▶ **Solve.**

38. Todd is 8 years younger than Raymond. Susan is 6 years older than Todd. Susan is 15 years old. How old is Raymond?

39. Arthur is 7 years older than Barbara. Carol is 4 years younger than Arthur. Carol is 16 years old. How old is Barbara?

Solving Addition Equations

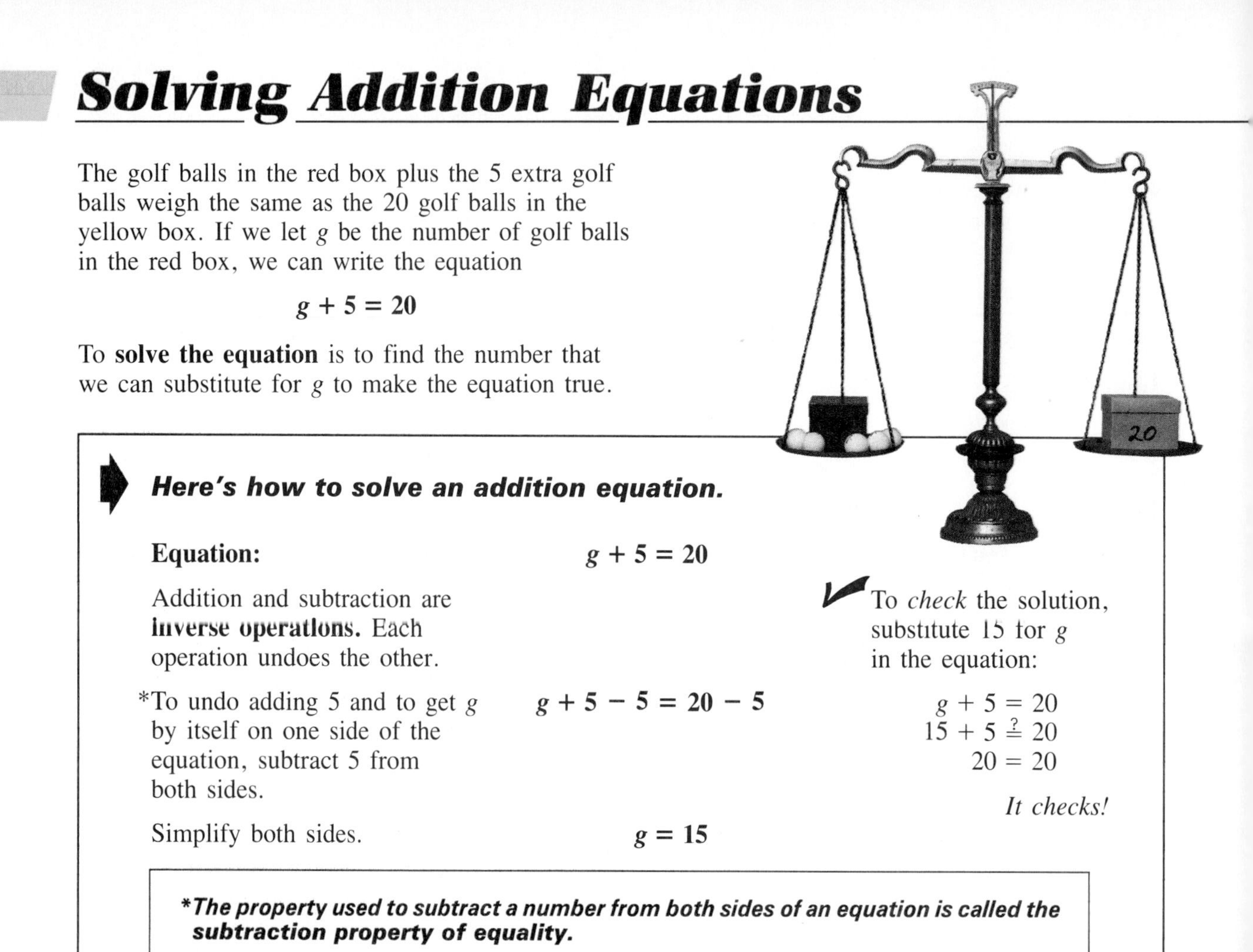

The golf balls in the red box plus the 5 extra golf balls weigh the same as the 20 golf balls in the yellow box. If we let g be the number of golf balls in the red box, we can write the equation

$$g + 5 = 20$$

To **solve the equation** is to find the number that we can substitute for g to make the equation true.

Here's how to solve an addition equation.

Equation: $g + 5 = 20$

Addition and subtraction are **inverse operations.** Each operation undoes the other.

*To undo adding 5 and to get g by itself on one side of the equation, subtract 5 from both sides. $g + 5 - 5 = 20 - 5$

Simplify both sides. $g = 15$

To *check* the solution, substitute 15 for g in the equation:

$$g + 5 = 20$$
$$15 + 5 \stackrel{?}{=} 20$$
$$20 = 20$$

It checks!

The property used to subtract a number from both sides of an equation is called the subtraction property of equality.

1. Look at the example above. To find g, what number was subtracted from both sides of the equation? How many golf balls are in the red box?

2. What number would you subtract from both sides to solve the equation?

a. $n + 6 = 20$ **b.** $m + 10 = 45$ **c.** $e + 15 = 28$

d. $t + 23 = 42$ **e.** $r + 55 = 75$ **f.** $d + 21 = 22$

3. Complete these examples.

a. $c + 8 = 20$
$c + 8 - 8 = 20 - \underline{?}$
$c = 12$

b. $n + 32 = 41$
$n + 32 - 32 = 41 - 32$
$n = \underline{?}$

c. $t + 17 = 80$
$t + 17 - 17 = 80 - 17$
$t = \underline{?}$

d. $a + 3 = 16$
$a + 3 - 3 = 16 - \underline{?}$
$a = 13$

e. $b + 16 = 34$
$b + 16 - \underline{?} = 34 - 16$
$b = 18$

f. $c + 18 = 94$
$c + 18 - 18 = 94 - 18$
$c = \underline{?}$

EXERCISES

▶ **Solve and check.**
Here are scrambled answers for the next two rows of exercises:
9 12 25 10 23 2 22 42

4. $n + 26 = 38$	**5.** $t + 10 = 35$	**6.** $x + 34 = 43$	**7.** $z + 18 = 28$
8. $n + 28 = 50$	**9.** $y + 27 = 50$	**10.** $c + 17 = 59$	**11.** $m + 24 = 26$
12. $y + 35 = 37$	**13.** $d + 32 = 65$	**14.** $w + 77 = 98$	**15.** $m + 4 = 62$
16. $x + 27 = 68$	**17.** $d + 15 = 33$	**18.** $x + 18 = 45$	**19.** $y + 55 = 57$
20. $g + 54 = 66$	**21.** $f + 45 = 78$	**22.** $n + 65 = 72$	**23.** $h + 43 = 89$
24. $x + 14 = 65$	**25.** $m + 11 = 30$	**26.** $t + 18 = 50$	**27.** $h + 33 = 33$
28. $g + 88 = 97$	**29.** $s + 43 = 54$	**30.** $r + 15 = 50$	**31.** $b + 23 = 56$
32. $t + 29 = 76$	**33.** $x + 16 = 17$	**34.** $g + 20 = 99$	**35.** $n + 66 = 77$
36. $t + 77 = 80$	**37.** $c + 46 = 55$	**38.** $x + 24 = 24$	**39.** $f + 21 = 70$
40. $a + 52 = 75$	**41.** $w + 55 = 64$	**42.** $f + 37 = 40$	**43.** $c + 34 = 43$

Problem Solving

▶ **Write an equation and solve the problem.**

44. A number n plus 45 equals 60. What is the number?

45. A number t increased by 14 equals 32. What is the number?

46. The sum of a number y and 15 is 38. What is the number?

47. Five more than a number r is 17. What is the number?

48. When a number t is increased by 18, the result is 50. What is the number?

49. The sum of a number m and 42 is 60. What is the number?

50. Nine more than a number x is 15. What is the number?

51. A number s plus 19 equals 28. What is the number?

Challenge

▶ **Solve. Use the clues.**

52. How much does a golf ball weigh?
Clues:
- Steve guessed 50 grams and missed by 6 grams.
- Holly guessed 40 grams and missed by 4 grams.

53. How much does a tennis ball weigh?
Clues:
- Steve guessed 60 grams and missed by 3 grams.
- Holly guessed 50 grams and missed by 7 grams.

Solving Subtraction Equations

Remember that subtraction undoes addition and addition undoes subtraction. We say that addition and subtraction are **inverse operations.**

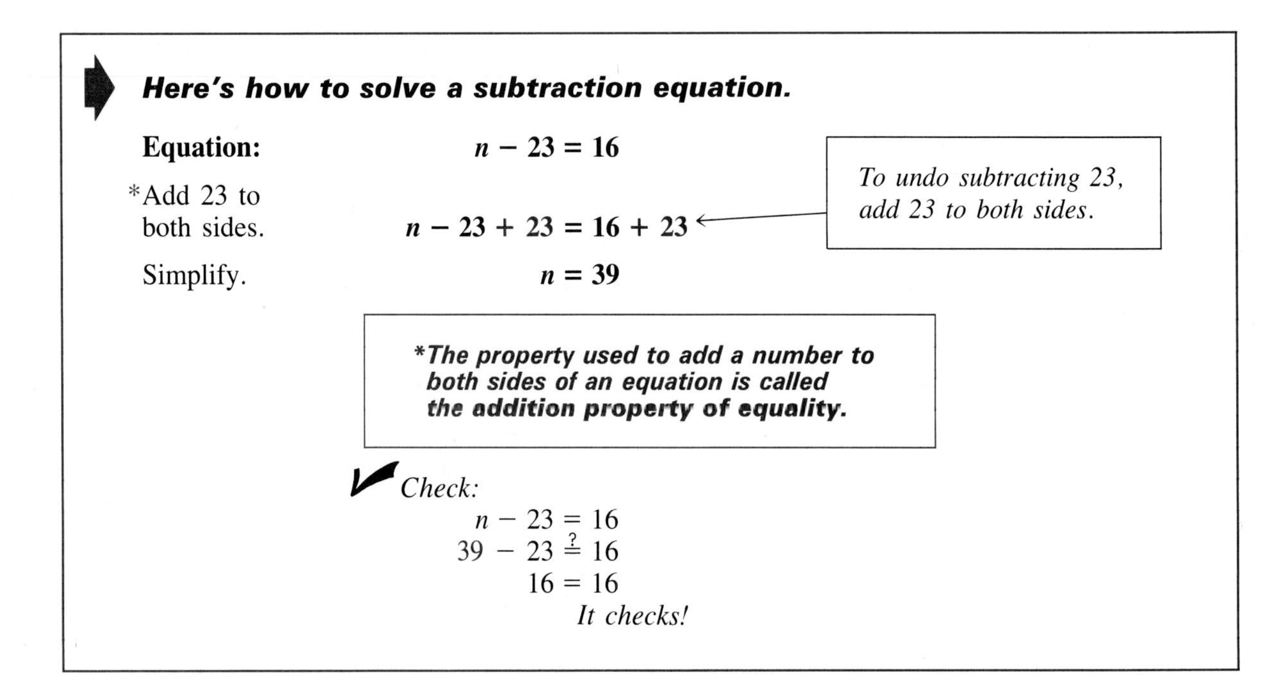

Here's how to solve a subtraction equation.

Equation: $n - 23 = 16$

*Add 23 to both sides. $n - 23 + 23 = 16 + 23$ ← *To undo subtracting 23, add 23 to both sides.*

Simplify. $n = 39$

The property used to add a number to both sides of an equation is called the addition property of equality.

Check:

$n - 23 = 16$

$39 - 23 \stackrel{?}{=} 16$

$16 = 16$

It checks!

1. Look at the example above.

a. To find n, what number was added to both sides of the equation? What does n equal?

b. To check the solution, what number was substituted for n in the equation $n - 23 = 16$?

2. What number would you add to both sides to solve each equation?

a. $a - 7 = 12$ **b.** $b - 46 = 12$ **c.** $c - 23 = 50$

d. $n - 23 = 6$ **e.** $t - 26 = 26$ **f.** $n - 40 = 35$

g. $a - 5 = 78$ **h.** $u - 3 = 12$ **i.** $t - 33 = 76$

3. Complete these examples.

a.
$a - 4 = 12$
$a - 4 + 4 = 12 + \underline{?}$
$a = 16$

b.
$b - 34 = 6$
$b - 34 + \underline{?} = 6 + 34$
$b = 40$

c.
$c - 4 = 67$
$c - 4 + 4 = 67 + 4$
$c = \underline{?}$

d.
$d - 7 = 14$
$d - 7 + 7 = 14 + \underline{?}$
$d = 21$

e.
$m - 43 = 16$
$m - 43 + \underline{?} = 16 + 43$
$m = 59$

f.
$n - 29 = 84$
$n - 29 + 29 = 84 + 29$
$n = \underline{?}$

EXERCISES

▶ **Solve and check.**
Here are scrambled answers for the next two rows of exercises:
51 40 39 40 32 25 20 15

4. $n - 15 = 24$	**5.** $r - 46 = 5$	**6.** $n + 10 = 50$	**7.** $p - 3 = 37$
8. $m + 23 = 38$	**9.** $w + 42 = 67$	**10.** $t - 12 = 8$	**11.** $r - 24 = 8$
12. $x - 7 = 23$	**13.** $d - 19 = 1$	**14.** $y - 20 = 17$	**15.** $n + 11 = 35$
16. $n - 15 = 27$	**17.** $b + 33 = 33$	**18.** $s - 5 = 26$	**19.** $t - 16 = 0$
20. $c - 61 = 62$	**21.** $x - 4 = 17$	**22.** $y + 17 = 20$	**23.** $t - 24 = 56$
24. $r + 33 = 33$	**25.** $w - 56 = 65$	**26.** $a - 22 = 9$	**27.** $x - 45 = 4$
28. $c - 7 = 10$	**29.** $y + 23 = 67$	**30.** $t - 11 = 5$	**31.** $y + 7 = 77$
32. $b - 125 = 3$	**33.** $m - 114 = 20$	**34.** $t + 14 = 108$	**35.** $s - 23 = 123$
36. $v - 205 = 84$	**37.** $g - 112 = 89$	**38.** $e + 113 = 807$	**39.** $b + 78 = 248$
40. $a - 50 = 300$	**41.** $x - 75 = 5$	**42.** $b - 10 = 123$	**43.** $s + 120 = 275$

Problem Solving

▶ **Decide whether Equation A or B would be used to solve each problem. Then solve the problem.**

Equation A: $n + 12 = 56$
Equation B: $n - 12 = 56$

44. Twelve less than a number n is 56. What is the number?

45. Twelve more than a number n is 56. What is the number?

46. The sum of a number n and 12 is 56. What is the number?

47. A number n decreased by 12 is 56. What is the number?

48. Twelve dollars off the regular price is $56. What is the regular price?

49. Twelve dollars more than the sale price is $56. What is the sale price?

50. The regular price decreased by $12 is $56. What is the regular price?

51. The sum of the sale price and a $12 discount is $56. What is the sale price?

Challenge

▶ **Solve.**

52. Jason is 3 years older than Kevin. Laura is 9 years younger than Kevin. Jason was 8 years old 6 years ago. How old is Laura?

53. Debra is 4 years younger than Ellen. Ellen is 7 years older than Frank. Debra will be 18 years old 3 years from now. How old is Frank?

More on Solving Equations

You have solved equations such as $x + 13 = 41$ and $y - 18 = 27$ by either subtracting the same number from both sides or adding the same number to both sides.

Notice that in both equations the variable is on the left side of the equation. In this lesson you will solve some equations that have the variable on the right side of the equation.

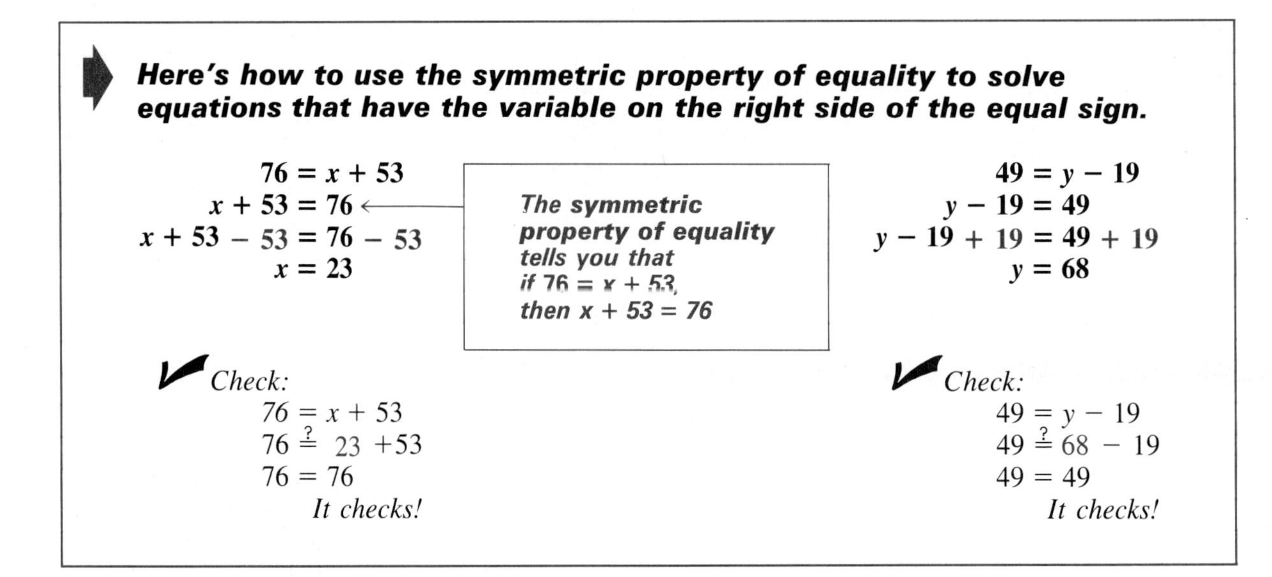

Here's how to use the symmetric property of equality to solve equations that have the variable on the right side of the equal sign.

$$76 = x + 53$$
$$x + 53 = 76$$
$$x + 53 - 53 = 76 - 53$$
$$x = 23$$

The symmetric property of equality tells you that if $76 = x + 53$, then $x + 53 = 76$

$$49 = y - 19$$
$$y - 19 = 49$$
$$y - 19 + 19 = 49 + 19$$
$$y = 68$$

Check:

$76 = x + 53$
$76 \stackrel{?}{=} 23 + 53$
$76 = 76$
It checks!

Check:

$49 = y - 19$
$49 \stackrel{?}{=} 68 - 19$
$49 = 49$
It checks!

1. Look at the examples above.

a. In each first equation, the expression containing the variable is on the __?__ side of the equation.

b. In each second equation, the symmetric property of equality was used to get the expression containing the variable on the __?__ side of the equation.

2. Complete these examples.

a.
$49 = r + 32$
$r + 32 = 49$
$r + 32 - \underline{?} = 49 - 32$
$r = 17$

b.
$93 = s - 36$
$s - 36 = 93$
$s - 36 + 36 = 93 + \underline{?}$
$s = 129$

c.
$66 = t + 37$
$t + 37 = 66$
$t + 37 - 37 = 66 - 37$
$t = \underline{?}$

d.
$72 = n - 80$
$n - 80 = 72$
$n - 80 + \underline{?} = 72 + 80$
$n = 152$

e.
$162 = k + 29$
$k + 29 = 162$
$k + 29 - 29 = 162 - \underline{?}$
$k = 133$

f.
$81 = n - 100$
$n - 100 = 81$
$n - 100 + 100 = 81 + 100$
$n = \underline{?}$

▶ **Solve and check.**

Here are scrambled answers for the next row of exercises: 58 19 37 29

3. $18 = x - 11$	**4.** $a + 32 = 51$	**5.** $q - 26 = 32$	**6.** $56 = w + 19$
7. $f + 74 = 81$	**8.** $65 = u + 59$	**9.** $50 = y - 25$	**10.** $n - 18 = 35$
11. $d - 19 = 80$	**12.** $25 = n - 33$	**13.** $h + 18 = 100$	**14.** $97 = t + 30$
15. $c + 64 = 64$	**16.** $p - 29 = 77$	**17.** $74 = y + 36$	**18.** $32 = m - 0$
19. $r - 36 = 0$	**20.** $m + 53 = 110$	**21.** $0 = z - 41$	**22.** $83 = s + 45$
23. $100 = m + 60$	**24.** $75 = q - 16$	**25.** $e + 65 = 90$	**26.** $c - 74 = 26$
27. $0 = n - 54$	**28.** $j + 75 = 75$	**29.** $m - 30 = 36$	**30.** $73 = n + 57$
31. $80 = q + 27$	**32.** $55 = s - 30$	**33.** $k - 56 = 17$	**34.** $b + 17 = 91$
35. $n + 64 = 155$	**36.** $b - 32 = 100$	**37.** $110 = r + 53$	**38.** $90 = t - 58$
39. $q - 27 = 140$	**40.** $155 = x + 82$	**41.** $115 = u - 23$	**42.** $k + 28 = 117$
43. $100 = v - 46$	**44.** $d + 39 = 153$	**45.** $137 = v + 65$	**46.** $k - 63 = 105$
47. $160 = p + 94$	**48.** $55 = w - 55$		
49. $a + 18 = 29$	**50.** $42 = b + 19$		
51. $d - 14 = 86$	**52.** $f + 8 = 72$		
53. $r - 27 = 87$	**54.** $p + 14 = 21$		

Problem Solving

▶ **Solve.**

55. You're the pilot. If you are flying with the tailwind (a wind that is blowing in the same direction your plane is flying in), will your ground speed be more or less than your airspeed?

*Hint: The **formula** below shows how the airspeed and tailwind speed of a plane are related to its ground speed.*

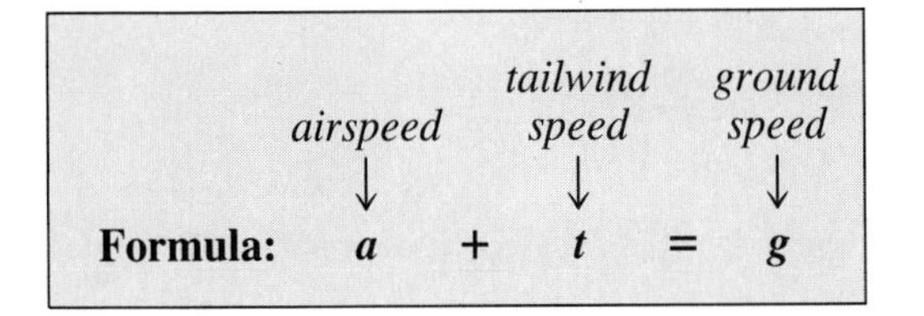

56. Use the formula in exercise 55. Complete the chart.

	a (miles per hour)	t (miles per hour)	g (miles per hour)
a.	350	65	?
b.	175	28	?
c.	240	45	?
d.	?	50	360
e.	?	110	475
f.	?	33	316

Problem Solving—Using Equations

Problems that can be solved with arithmetic can also be solved by writing and solving an equation.

Here's how to use arithmetic or algebra to solve a problem.

Problem: Our football team scored a total of 31 points. We scored 17 points in the second half. How many points did we score in the first half?

Method 1 Using arithmetic

$$\begin{array}{rl} 31 & \leftarrow \textit{Total points} \\ -17 & \leftarrow \textit{Points scored in second half} \\ \hline 14 & \leftarrow \textit{Points scored in first half} \end{array}$$

Fourteen points were scored in the first half.

Method 2 Using algebra

Step 1. Choose a variable. Use it and the facts to represent the numbers in the problem.

Let n = points scored in the first half. Then $n + 17$ = total points scored.

Step 2. Write an equation based on the facts.

$$n + 17 = 31$$

These are two equal expressions for the total score.

Step 3. Solve the equation.

$$n + 17 = 31$$
$$n + 17 - 17 = 31 - 17$$
$$n = 14$$

Fourteen points were scored in the first half.

1. Look at the example above. In Method 1, the number of points scored in the second half was subtracted from the total points to get the number of points scored in the ? half.
2. Look at Method 2.
   a. In Step 1, the variable n equals the number of ? scored in the first half.
   b. In Step 2, both the expression $n + 17$ and the number ? equal the total points scored.
   c. In Step 3, to solve the equation, ? was subtracted from both sides of the equation.
3. To check the solution, ask yourself whether the answer fits the facts in the problem. Did the team score 14 points in the first half?

Decide whether Equation A or B would be used to solve the problem. Then solve the problem.

Equation A: $n + 12 = 30$
Equation B: $n - 12 = 30$

4. The sum of two numbers is 30. One of the numbers is 12. What is the other number? (Let n = the other number.)

5. The difference between two numbers is 30. The lesser number is 12. What is the greater number? (Let n = the greater number.)

6. There are 30 players on the team. Twelve of the players are boys. How many girls are on the team? (Let n = the number of girls.)

7. There are 12 fewer girls than boys in the band. There are 30 girls in the band. How many boys are in the band? (Let n = the number of boys.)

Write an equation and solve the problem.

8. The difference between two numbers is 5. The lesser number is 8. What is the greater number? (Let g = the greater number.)

9. Forty is 17 less than a number. What is the number? (Let n = the number.)

10. You had some money and then you earned 15 dollars. Now you have 28 dollars. How many dollars did you have? (Let d = the dollars you had.)

11. You had some money and then you spent 28 dollars. Now you have 9 dollars. How many dollars did you have before you spent some? (Let d = the dollars you had before you spent some.)

12. The sale price is 7 dollars less than the regular price. The sale price is 48 dollars. What is the regular price? (Let r = the regular price.)

13. The regular price is 8 dollars more than the sale price. The regular price is 55 dollars. What is the sale price? (Let s = the sale price.)

14. You scored 10 more points than your friend. You scored 24 points. How many points did your friend score? (Let f = the points your friend scored.)

15. Ann scored 8 points less than Ted. Ann scored 30 points. How many points did Ted score? (Let t = the points Ted scored.)

16. Tony is 3 inches shorter than George. Tony is 58 inches tall. How tall is George? (Let g = George's height in inches.)

17. Mary is 7 inches taller than Anne. Mary is 60 inches tall. How tall is Anne? (Let a = Anne's height in inches.)

Cumulative Skill Practice

▶ **Three of the calculator answers are wrong. Find them by estimating.** *(page 10)*

1. **a.** $384 + 178$ 562 **b.** $562 + 7519$ 8081

c. $465 + 281 + 673$ 1219 **d.** $806 + 631 + 493$ 1930

e. $4817 + 7093$ 11910 **f.** $8409 + 7860$ 15269

g. $23{,}107 + 46{,}597$ 69704 **h.** $70{,}642 + 19{,}814$ 80456

▶ **Three of the calculator answers are wrong. Find them by estimating.** *(page 12)*

2. **a.** $703 - 276$ 527 **b.** $417 - 384$ 133

c. $6304 - 732$ 5572 **d.** $9031 - 846$ 8185

e. $7081 - 2392$ 4689 **f.** $4732 - 2865$ 2867

g. $76{,}024 - 19{,}863$ 56161 **h.** $84{,}703 - 35{,}619$ 49084

▶ **Solve and check.** *(page 14)*

3. $x + 9 = 17$ **4.** $b + 8 = 15$ **5.** $g + 12 = 20$ **6.** $d + 11 = 25$

7. $j + 12 = 12$ **8.** $r + 0 = 24$ **9.** $y + 15 = 29$ **10.** $f + 19 = 33$

11. $c + 42 = 57$ **12.** $h + 18 = 49$ **13.** $y + 31 = 58$ **14.** $s + 26 = 50$

15. $t + 37 = 65$ **16.** $a + 42 = 85$ **17.** $e + 52 = 52$ **18.** $z + 65 = 84$

▶ **Solve and check.** *(page 16)*

19. $b - 7 = 8$ **20.** $t - 9 = 4$ **21.** $m - 11 = 6$ **22.** $d - 10 = 9$

23. $r - 12 = 16$ **24.** $f - 15 = 27$ **25.** $s - 19 = 15$ **26.** $p - 20 = 25$

27. $h - 25 = 0$ **28.** $h - 21 = 42$ **29.** $c - 36 = 35$ **30.** $v - 39 = 50$

31. $e - 35 = 58$ **32.** $k - 42 = 42$ **33.** $q - 51 = 63$ **34.** $g - 63 = 0$

35. $m - 15 = 28$ **36.** $x - 14 = 80$ **37.** $r - 13 = 80$ **38.** $l - 15 = 15$

▶ **Solve and check.** *(page 18)*

39. $35 = w + 16$ **40.** $18 = u - 21$ **41.** $18 = q + 18$ **42.** $30 = z - 32$

43. $46 = n - 43$ **44.** $53 = x - 25$ **45.** $57 = s + 46$ **46.** $66 = c + 20$

47. $79 = r + 38$ **48.** $39 = p - 42$ **49.** $61 = b - 50$ **50.** $90 = j + 61$

51. $55 = m - 0$ **52.** $48 = v - 71$ **53.** $100 = y + 68$ **54.** $112 = t + 84$

55. $39 = p - 10$ **56.** $14 = d - 18$ **57.** $74 = s + 15$ **58.** $100 = m + 80$

Problem Solving—Applications

You have circled the ads for seven used cars you'd like to look at. Use the circled ads to solve these problems.

1. How many fewer miles has the 1983 Cutlass been driven than the 1979 Cutlass?

2. You have $1775 in one savings account and $965 in another. Do you have enough money to pay cash for the least expensive car you'd like to look at?

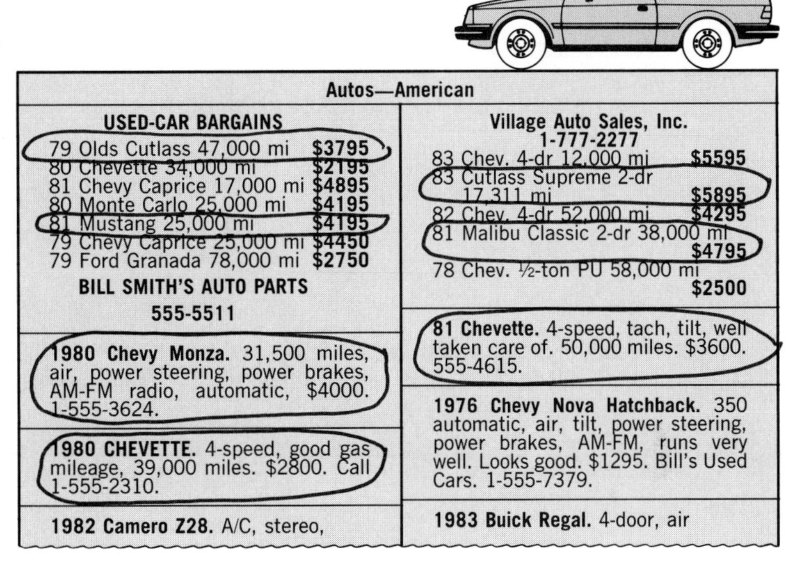

Autos—American

USED-CAR BARGAINS
79 Olds Cutlass 47,000 mi $3795
80 Chevette 34,000 mi $2195
81 Chevy Caprice 17,000 mi $4895
80 Monte Carlo 25,000 mi $4195
81 Mustang 25,000 mi $4195
79 Chevy Caprice 25,000 mi $4450
79 Ford Granada 78,000 mi $2750
BILL SMITH'S AUTO PARTS
555-5511

1980 Chevy Monza. 31,500 miles, air, power steering, power brakes, AM-FM radio, automatic, $4000. 1-555-3624.

1980 CHEVETTE. 4-speed, good gas mileage, 39,000 miles. $2800. Call 1-555-2310.

1982 Camero Z28. A/C, stereo,

Village Auto Sales, Inc.
1-777-2277
83 Chev. 4-dr 12,000 mi $5595
83 Cutlass Supreme 2-dr 17,311 mi $5895
82 Chev. 4-dr 52,000 mi $4295
81 Malibu Classic 2-dr 38,000 mi $4795
78 Chev. ½-ton PU 58,000 mi $2500

81 Chevette. 4-speed, tach, tilt, well taken care of. 50,000 miles. $3600. 555-4615.

1976 Chevy Nova Hatchback. 350 automatic, air, tilt, power steering, power brakes, AM-FM, runs very well. Looks good. $1295. Bill's Used Cars. 1-555-7379.

1983 Buick Regal. 4-door, air

3. You have $2860. How much will you need to borrow to buy the 1981 Mustang?

4. Village Auto Sales guarantees its cars for 7500 miles after the purchase. How many miles will the Cutlass have when the guarantee expires?

Decide whether Equation A or B would be used to solve each problem. Then solve the problem.

Equation A: $n + 125 = 2250$
Equation B: $n - 125 = 2250$

5. One hundred twenty-five dollars off the regular price is $2250. What is the regular price?

6. One hundred twenty-five dollars more than the sale price is $2250. What is the sale price?

7. You will need $125 more than you have in your savings account to buy a car that costs $2250. How much money do you have in your savings account?

8. After buying a car radio for $125, you have $2250 left in your savings account. How much money did you have in your savings account before you bought the radio?

Write an equation and solve the problem.

9. A Cutlass Supreme costs $5895. You have $3500. How much more money do you need to buy the car? (Let m = the money you need.)

10. A Chevy Monza costs $195 less than a Mustang. The Chevy Monza costs $4000. What is the price of the Mustang? (Let m = the price of the Mustang.)

Chapter Review

Here are scrambled answers for the review exercises:

1	*5*	*23*	*600*	*greater*	*less*	*subtract*	*variable*
3	*7*	*477*	*add*	*inverse*	*right*	*symmetric*	
4	*11*	*500*	*expressions*	*left*	*simplify*	*tens*	

1. Variables, numbers, and operation signs can be combined to form mathematical _?_. In the expression $n - 8$ the letter n is called a _?_. A word expression for the mathematical expression is 8 _?_ than a number n. *(page 2)*

2. If you evaluate the expression $x + y - z$ for $x = 6$, $y = 3$, and $z = 5$, you get _?_. If you evaluate the same expression for $x = 7$, $y = 4$, and $z = 10$, you get _?_. *(page 4)*

3. To round the number **56,320** to the nearest hundred, first look at the digit in the _?_ place. Since it is less than _?_, round the hundreds digit down to _?_. *(page 6)*

4. To round the number **76,890** to the nearest thousand, first look at the digit in the hundreds place. Since it is 5 or _?_, round the thousands digit up to _?_. *(page 6)*

5. If you estimate the sum of **221 + 285 + 132** by rounding each number to the nearest hundred, you get _?_. *(page 10)*

6. If you estimate the difference of **894 − 417** by rounding each number to the nearest hundred, you get _?_. If you calculate the exact difference you get _?_. *(page 12)*

7. Addition and subtraction are _?_ operations. Each operation undoes the other. To solve the equation $z + 7 = 18$ you would first _?_ 7 from both sides and then simplify both sides. To check the solution, you would substitute _?_ for z in the equation. *(page 14)*

8. To solve the equation $w - 6 = 17$ you would first _?_ 6 to both sides and then _?_ both sides. To check the solution, you would substitute _?_ for w in the equation. *(page 16)*

9. In the first equation at the right, the expression containing the variable is on the _?_ side of the equation. In the second equation the _?_ property of equality was used to get the expression containing the variable on the _?_ side. *(page 18)*

$$23 = x + 17$$

$$x + 17 = 23$$

Chapter Test

Write a mathematical expression for each word expression. *(page 2)*

1. 6 more than a number n

2. 5 less than a number x

3. 12 decreased by a number y

4. 16 increased by a number c

5. a number r decreased by itself

6. a number d increased by itself

Evaluate each expression for $x = 12$, $y = 10$, and $z = 7$. *(page 4)*

7. $x + z$

8. $x - z$

9. $24 + y$

10. $x - 3$

11. $x + y - z$

12. $x - y + z$

13. $y + y - z$

14. $8 + y - z$

15. $24 - x - y$

16. $24 + x - y$

17. $24 + y - x$

18. $24 - x - x$

Round to the nearest thousand. *(page 6)*

19. 3846

20. 351

21. 4500

22. 9627

23. 32,096

24. 58,742

25. 49,500

26. 638,340

27. 409,600

28. 899,999

Give each sum or difference. *(pages 10, 12)*

29. $209 + 605$

30. $4092 + 6709$

31. $37{,}854 + 37{,}854$

32. $638 - 219$

33. $7203 - 4529$

34. $42{,}003 - 16{,}258$

Solve and check. *(pages 14, 16, 18)*

35. $x + 18 = 32$

36. $z + 27 = 59$

37. $w + 23 = 23$

38. $y + 114 = 150$

39. $b - 14 = 26$

40. $a - 42 = 31$

41. $d - 52 = 0$

42. $c - 125 = 110$

43. $71 = r + 38$

44. $49 = t - 40$

45. $126 = s + 67$

46. $0 = u - 36$

Decide whether Equation A or B would be used to solve each problem. Then solve the problem. *(page 20)*

Equation A: $n + 18 = 26$
Equation B: $n - 18 = 26$

47. The regular price decreased by \$18 is \$26. What is the regular price?

48. The cost was marked up \$18 to get the regular price \$26. What was the cost?

49. You gave 18 of your records to a friend. You then had 26 records. How many records did you have before you gave your friend the records?

50. Before your birthday, you had 18 silver dollars. After your birthday you had 26 silver dollars. How many silver dollars did you get for your birthday?

Cumulative Test
Standardized Format

▶ **Choose the correct letter.**

1. An expression for

14 less than a number n

is

A. $14 - n$
B. $n + 14$
C. $n - 14$
D. none of these

2. An expression for

a number r increased by a number s

is

A. $s - r$
B. $r + s$
C. $r - s$
D. none of these

3. Evaluate $15 - x$ for $x = 7$.

A. 8
B. 22
C. 7
D. none of these

4. Evaluate $c + c - d$ for $c = 9$ and $d = 6$.

A. 3
B. 9
C. 12
D. none of these

5. 5543 rounded to the nearest thousand is

A. 5600
B. 5500
C. 5000
D. none of these

6. 85,000 rounded to the nearest ten thousand is

A. 90,000
B. 85,000
C. 80,000
D. none of these

7. Give the sum.
Hint: Estimate.

367 + 2986 + 5943

A. 6296
B. 9296
C. 12,599
D. 10,599

8. Give the difference.
Hint: Estimate.

5006 − 1738

A. 6744
B. 4268
C. 1244
D. 3268

9. Solve.

$y + 17 = 23$

A. 23
B. 40
C. 6
D. none of these

10. Solve.

$x - 38 = 50$

A. 88
B. 50
C. 12
D. none of these

11. Solve.

$43 = w + 32$

A. 43
B. 75
C. 11
D. none of these

12. Choose the equation.

Sarah scored 12 more points than Paige. How many points did Paige score if Sarah scored 14?

A. $n - 12 = 14$
B. $n - 14 = 12$
C. $n + 12 = 14$
D. $n + 14 = 12$

2 Multiplication and Division Equations

$\frac{d}{g} = m$

Distance traveled in miles divided by gallons used equals miles per gallon.

(page 49)

The gas mileage of a vehicle depends upon many factors, the most important of which is size. The average gas mileage for an automobile is about 15 miles per gallon, while the average gas mileage for a cargo vehicle is about 9 miles per gallon.

Mathematical Expressions

Gold Medal Winners from the 1984 Olympics

A group of high school students were asked to identify these gold medal winners.

Joan Benoit
(recognized by $n \div 2$ students)

Mary Lou Retton
(recognized by $4n$ students)

Greg Louganis
(recognized by n students)

Carl Lewis
(recognized by $4n + 10$ students)

1. Which gold medal winner was recognized by n students?
2. Which gold medal winner was recognized by one half as many students as Greg Louganis?
3. Which athlete was recognized by 4 times as many students as Greg Louganis?
4. Which athlete was recognized by 10 more students than Mary Lou Retton?

Here's how to write multiplication and division expressions.

Word expression		Mathematical expression
3 times a number r	⟶	$3 \times r$, $3(r)$, $3 \cdot r$, or $3r$
5 multiplied by a number t	⟶	$5t$
the product of 4 and a number n	⟶	$4n$
a number n divided by 2	⟶	$n \div 2$ or $\frac{n}{2}$
a number n divided by 6, plus 3	⟶	$\frac{n}{6} + 3$
8 times a number b, minus 2	⟶	$8b - 2$

This form will be used most often. (refers to $3r$)

5. Look at the examples above. To read the expression $3r$, you can say "3 __?__ a number r."
6. To read $\frac{n}{2}$, you can say "a number n __?__ by 2."

Write a mathematical expression for each word expression.

7. 9 times a number n
8. a number r divided by 5
9. a number m multiplied by 2
10. 20 divided by a number s
11. 8 more than a number r
12. the product of 5 and a number k
13. a number e minus 9
14. the sum of a number f and 9
15. 6 divided by a number t
16. a number j decreased by 7
17. the product of a number c and a number d
18. a number k divided by a number e
19. 4 times a number m, plus 6
20. 5 times a number d, minus 3
21. a number s divided by s, plus 3
22. a number n divided by b, minus 5

Suppose that you could name p people who won gold medals at the 1984 Olympic Games. Write a mathematical expression for the number of people that is

23. 6 times as many.
24. your number divided by 6.
25. 4 less than your number.
26. your number increased by 8.
27. 3 times your number, plus 5.
28. your number divided by 5, plus 4.
29. your number divided by 3, minus 4.
30. the product of your number and 5, minus 2.

Problem Solving

Decide whether expression A, B, C, or D would be used to complete each sentence.

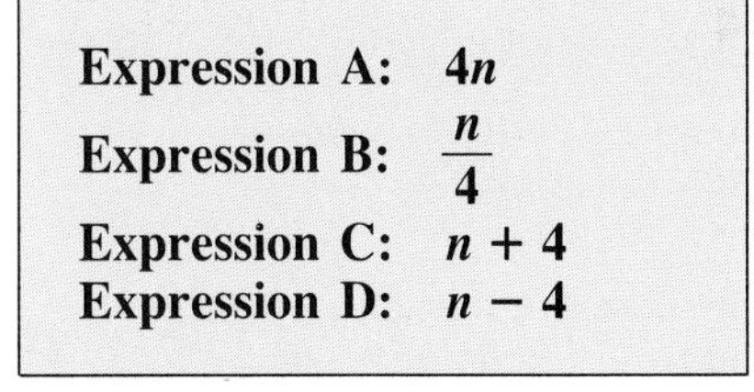
Expression A: $4n$
Expression B: $\frac{n}{4}$
Expression C: $n + 4$
Expression D: $n - 4$

31. You bought n packages of batteries. If each package contained 4 batteries, you bought __?__ batteries.
32. You bought 4 rolls of film. If the 4 rolls of film cost n dollars, each roll costs __?__ dollars.
33. You plan to work n hours. If you have 4 hours left to work, you have already worked __?__ hours.
34. Mia earned 4 dollars less than Andy. If Mia earned n dollars, then Andy earned __?__ dollars.
35. Melissa earned n dollars. If this is 4 times the amount she needs to buy a pocket radio, the pocket radio costs __?__ dollars.
36. Greg earned n dollars. If he worked 4 hours, then he made __?__ dollars per hour.

Evaluating Expressions

Can you recognize the four common objects in these close-up photos?

Photo	Children	Adults
1	c	$3a$
2	$2c$	a
3	$\frac{c}{4}$	$\frac{a}{2}$
4	$3c$	$4a$

Survey Results: Number of children and adults that recognized each photo.

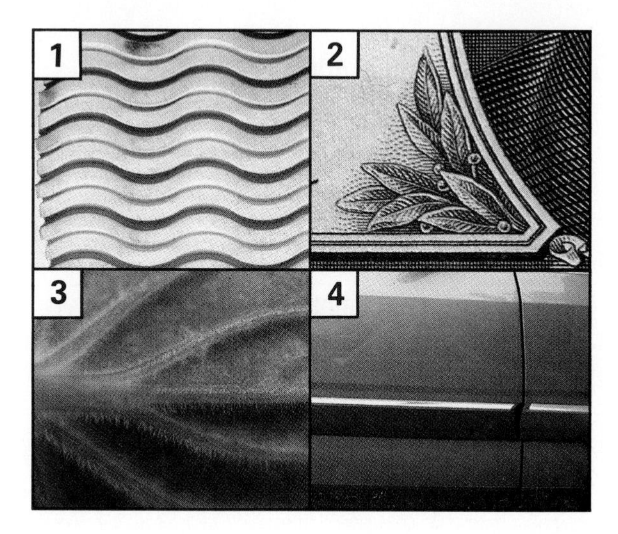

1. Look at the chart. Which photo was recognized by c children?
2. Which photo was recognized by more children, photo 2 or photo 4?
3. Which photo was recognized by more adults, photo 2 or photo 3?

Here's how to evaluate mathematical expressions.

8 children recognized photo 1; 10 adults recognized photo 2. To find the number of people who recognized each photo, substitute 8 for c and 10 for a in the expressions and simplify.

Number of children who recognized photo 4:	$3c$ $3 \times 8 = 24$	Photo 4 was recognized by 24 children.
Number of adults who recognized photo 3:	$\frac{a}{2}$ $\frac{10}{2} = 5$	Photo 3 was recognized by 5 adults.
Number of people who recognized photo 2:	$2c + a$ $2 \times 8 + 10$ $16 + 10 = 26$	Photo 2 was recognized by 26 people.

4. Look at the examples above. How many children recognized photo 4?
5. Which photo did 26 people recognize?

Evaluate each expression for $r = 6$, $s = 8$, and $t = 2$.
Here are scrambled answers for the next row of exercises: 2 30 18 1

6. $5r$ **7.** $\frac{s}{4}$ **8.** $9t$ **9.** $\frac{r}{6}$

10. rs **11.** $\frac{s}{t}$ **12.** rt **13.** $\frac{r}{t}$

14. $4 + r$ **15.** $t - 1$ **16.** $s - r$ **17.** $s - t$

18. $st - 3$ **19.** $7s - 5$ **20.** $\frac{s}{t} + 1$ **21.** $\frac{r}{2} - 2$

22. $\frac{s}{t} + 5$ **23.** $4rt$ **24.** $\frac{20}{t} - 10$ **25.** $4r + 6$

26. $st + r$ **27.** $tr + s$ **28.** $sr + t$ **29.** $tr - t$

30. $2r + s$ **31.** $2s + t$ **32.** $2t + r$ **33.** $tr - s$

34. $\frac{12}{r} + s$ **35.** $\frac{20}{t} - r$ **36.** $\frac{16}{s} + t$ **37.** $\frac{50}{t} - t$

Evaluate each expression for $w = 4$, $x = 5$, and $y = 10$.
Here are scrambled answers for the next two rows of exercises: 9 2 6 50

38. x times y

39. y divided by x

40. w increased by x

41. y decreased by w

42. y minus x

43. the product of x and w

44. seven less than y

45. five more than w

46. w times x, plus 5

47. y divided by 2, minus w

48. twelve divided by w, plus y

49. the product of w and x, minus y

50. x divided by x, increased by w

51. w times w, decreased by y

Problem Solving

Solve. Use the chart on page 30. *Remember:* $c = 8$ and $a = 10$.

52. How many children recognized photo 2?

53. How many adults recognized photo 4?

54. Which photo did 2 children recognize?

55. Which photo did 30 adults recognize?

56. Which photo did 38 people recognize?

57. Which photo did 64 people recognize?

58. Which photo did the most people recognize?

59. Which photo did the fewest people recognize?

Multiplying by Multiples of 10, 100, or 1000

In a survey, people were asked to name one event that is on television once a year. The picture graph shows the results of the survey.

TV SURVEY—Name an event that is on television once a year.	
Academy Awards	
Super Bowl	
Emmy Awards	
Rose Bowl Parade	

KEY: *Each*  *stands for 10 people.*

1. Each  stands for _?_ people.
2. To find the number of people surveyed who picked the Super Bowl, you would multiply _?_ by 10.

Here's how to multiply by multiples of 10, 100, or 1000.

8 × 10 = ?

To multiply a whole number by 10, multiply by 1 and annex 1 zero.

8 × 10 = 80

16 × 100 = ?

To multiply a whole number by 100, multiply by 1 and annex 2 zeros.

16 × 100 = 1600

72 × 1000 = ?

To multiply a whole number by 1000, multiply by 1 and annex 3 zeros.

72 × 1000 = 72,000

Study these examples.

a. $\begin{array}{r} 40 \\ \times 60 \\ \hline 2400 \end{array}$ Multiply 4 × 6. Annex 2 zeros.

b. $\begin{array}{r} 9000 \\ \times 700 \\ \hline 6{,}300{,}000 \end{array}$ Multiply 9 × 7. Annex 5 zeros.

3. Look at the examples above. To multiply 40 by 60, multiply 4 by 6 and annex _?_ zeros.
4. To multiply 9000 by 700, multiply 9 by 7 and annex _?_ zeros.
5. To multiply 800 by 30, multiply 8 by 3 and annex _?_ zeros.

▶ **Multiply.**
Here are scrambled answers for the next row of exercises:
1200 310 15,000 8000

6. 31 × 10	**7.** 40 × 30	**8.** 80 × 100	**9.** 30 × 500
10. 71 × 10	**11.** 20 × 200	**12.** 600 × 40	**13.** 70 × 500
14. 3 × 80	**15.** 8 × 3000	**16.** 60 × 70	**17.** 5 × 200
18. 7 × 4000	**19.** 50 × 80	**20.** 32 × 100	**21.** 6 × 3000
22. 4000 × 2	**23.** 300 × 8	**24.** 700 × 40	**25.** 5000 × 5
26. 600 × 20	**27.** 100 × 30	**28.** 100 × 400	**29.** 6000 × 20
30. 40 × 1000	**31.** 70 × 1000	**32.** 800 × 100	**33.** 9000 × 50
34. 400 × 60	**35.** 1000 × 800	**36.** 300 × 100	**37.** 400 × 600
38. 375 × 100	**39.** 625 × 1000	**40.** 124 × 10	**41.** 426 × 1000
42. 200 × 4000	**43.** 400 × 300	**44.** 900 × 900	**45.** 2000 × 200
46. 70 × 8000	**47.** 4000 × 20	**48.** 8000 × 80	**49.** 50 × 5000

Problem Solving

▶ **Solve. Use the picture graph on page 32.**

50. How many of the people surveyed picked the Rose Bowl Parade as the event that appears on television once a year?

51. How many more people picked the Super Bowl than the Rose Bowl Parade?

52. Which television event was picked by 35 people?

53. Which event was picked by 65 people?

54. Which two events were picked by a total of 150 people?

55. Which two events were picked by a total of 115 people?

Challenge

▶ **Solve.**

56. In what year was the first Super Bowl game played? To find the year, use the clues.

Clues:
- No digit is an 8.
- The hundreds digit is three more than the tens digit.
- The digits in the year add to 23.

Estimating and Computing Products

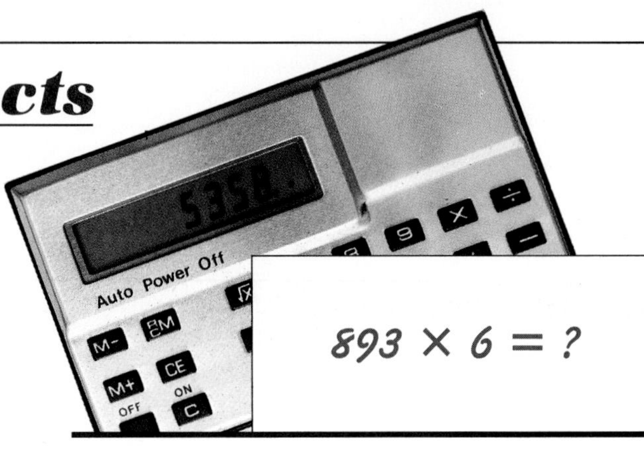

The numbers that you multiply are called **factors.** The answer to a multiplication problem is called the **product.**

1. The calculator was used to find the product. What product is shown on the calculator?
2. Is the product shown on the calculator reasonable?

Here's how to estimate and compute a product.

614 × 8 = ?

To estimate the product, round the greater factor to its first (leading) digit and multiply.

600 × 8 = 4800

Multiply.

$$\begin{array}{r} {\scriptstyle 1\,3} \\ 614 \\ \times \quad 8 \\ \hline 4912 \end{array}$$

3. Look at the example above. To estimate the product, the greater number was rounded to the nearest __?__ .
4. Was the product close to the estimate?

EXERCISES

▶ **Three of the calculator answers are wrong. Find them by estimating.**

5. a.	594 × 8	4752	**b.**	708 × 5	2940
c.	411 × 9	3699	**d.**	893 × 7	6251
e.	3025 × 4	16100	**f.**	4983 × 6	29898
g.	6102 × 5	30510	**h.**	7895 × 8	53160

▶ **Multiply.**

Here are scrambled answers for the next row of exercises: 3090 1180 3970 1610

6. 794×5 **7.** 515×6 **8.** 805×2 **9.** 295×4

10. 487×8 **11.** 621×7 **12.** 487×9 **13.** 590×8

14. 920×5 **15.** 899×8 **16.** 203×9 **17.** 681×7

18. 2015×5 **19.** 3942×8 **20.** 6100×4 **21.** 4137×9

22. 5981×3 **23.** 3899×4 **24.** 5118×6 **25.** 6895×6

26. 4992×8 **27.** 8007×9 **28.** 6887×7 **29.** 9065×5

▶ **Use your mental-math skills. Evaluate each expression for $v = 700$, $w = 500$, $x = 4$, $y = 6$, and $z = 9$.**

Here are scrambled answers for the next row of exercises: 2000 3000 6300 4200

Remember: vy means $v \times y$.

30. vy **31.** wx **32.** vz **33.** wy

34. wz **35.** zw **36.** vx **37.** xv

38. $w + z$ **39.** $z + w$ **40.** $v + x$ **41.** $x + v$

42. $v - y$ **43.** $w - z$ **44.** $w - y$ **45.** $v - w$

46. $v + w + x$ **47.** $x + y + w$ **48.** $v - w - z$ **49.** $v - y - z$

Remember: $3v$ means $3 \times v$.

50. $3v + w$ **51.** $4w + v$ **52.** $5w + v$ **53.** $7w + v$

54. $xv + w$ **55.** $zv + w$ **56.** $xw + v$ **57.** $yw + v$

CALCULATOR

▶ **Look for the pattern. Find the values for b, c, d, r, s, and t. Check with a calculator.**

58.

1 [×] 8 [+] 1 [=] 9

12 [×] 8 [+] 2 [=] 98

123 [×] 8 [+] 3 [=] 987

⋮

b [×] c [+] d [=] 98765432

59.

1 [×] 9 [+] 2 [=] 11

12 [×] 9 [+] 3 [=] 111

123 [×] 9 [+] 4 [=] 1111

⋮

r [×] s [+] t [=] 11111111

More on Estimating and Computing Products

Will you have lived 1 million hours by your 21st birthday?

1. To find the number of hours in 1 year, you would multiply 365 by _?_

2. To compute the number of hours you will have lived by your 21st birthday, you would multiply the number of hours in 1 year by _?_

24 hours = 1 day
365 days = 1 year

Here's how to estimate and compute a product.

365 × 24 = ?

To estimate the product, you can round each factor to the place of its leading digit.

400 × 20 = 8000

Multiply by 4.	Multiply by 20.	Add.
365	365	365
×24	×24	×24
1460	1460	1460
	7300	7300
		8760

3. Look at the example above. Was the product close to the estimate?

4. How many hours are in 1 year?

5. Estimate and compute the number of hours in 21 years.

8760 × 21 = ?

9000 × 20

8760
×21

6. Will you have lived 1 million hours by your 21st birthday?

EXERCISES

Three of the calculator answers are wrong. Find them by estimating.

7. a. 795 × 39 — 31005

b. 513 × 48 — 14624

c. 836 × 478 — 399608

d. 687 × 488 — 223275

e. 2074 × 390 — 80860

f. 8219 × 488 — 4010872

▶ **Multiply.**

Here are scrambled answers for the next row of exercises: 2542 2752 1452 3922

8. 86×32	**9.** 33×44	**10.** 74×53	**11.** 62×41
12. 68×32	**13.** 59×45	**14.** 70×26	**15.** 27×46
16. 268×25	**17.** 452×46	**18.** 398×56	**19.** 903×61
20. 2613×31	**21.** 6530×88	**22.** 4283×75	**23.** 2317×59
24. 695×115	**25.** 834×226	**26.** 654×360	**27.** 505×435
28. 1938×421	**29.** 2706×208	**30.** 4357×581	**31.** 6008×761
32. 3021×222	**33.** 4006×152	**34.** 4105×382	**35.** 2581×304
36. 2910×304	**37.** 3601×102	**38.** 3601×209	**39.** 4816×604

▶ **Use your mental-math skills. Evaluate each expression for $a = 400$, $b = 100$, $c = 80$, $d = 70$, and $e = 20$.**

Here are scrambled answers for the next row of exercises: 1400 8000 1600 7000

40. ce	**41.** de	**42.** ae	**43.** bd
44. ac	**45.** ca	**46.** ab	**47.** ba
48. $a + c$	**49.** $c + a$	**50.** $b + a$	**51.** $a + b$
52. $b - e$	**53.** $a - d$	**54.** $c - 3$	**55.** $a - a$
56. $b + 5$	**57.** $5b$	**58.** $c + 9$	**59.** $c - 9$
60. $8d$	**61.** $d - 8$	**62.** $a + 2$	**63.** $a - 2$
64. $a + b + c$	**65.** $b + c + d$	**66.** $c + d + e$	**67.** $a + c + e$
68. $2a + b$	**69.** $3b + d$	**70.** $4d - e$	**71.** $5c - a$
72. $cd + e$	**73.** $ce + d$	**74.** $ac - b$	**75.** $bc - a$

Problem Solving

▶ **Choose the mathematical expression that fits each of the following word expressions:**

$7n$	$60n$	$24n$
$\frac{n}{7}$	$\frac{n}{60}$	$\frac{n}{24}$

76. hours in n days	**77.** days in n weeks	**78.** minutes in n hours
79. days in n hours	**80.** weeks in n days	**81.** hours in n minutes

Cumulative Skill Practice

▶ **Write a mathematical expression for each word expression.** *(page 2)*

1. 6 more than a number x

2. 4 less than a number y

3. a number r minus 8

4. 7 increased by a number t

5. 8 decreased by a number u

6. 3 more than a number w

7. a number s decreased by 4

8. a number z less 6

9. a number y minus 14

10. the sum of a number c and 18

11. a number q increased by 12

12. a number s plus 15

13. a number x minus a number y

14. a number s plus a number t

15. a number z decreased by itself

16. a number r increased by itself

▶ **Round to the nearest hundred.** *(page 6)*

17. 378 **18.** 450 **19.** 199 **20.** 637

21. 5742 **22.** 8023 **23.** 6052 **24.** 5900

25. 8346 **26.** 6039 **27.** 4499 **28.** 4050

29. 7253 **30.** 4138 **31.** 3333 **32.** 7284

33. 37,168 **34.** 45,600 **35.** 74,811 **36.** 53,275

37. 61,521 **38.** 83,258 **39.** 57,500 **40.** 94,950

41. 69,492 **42.** 75,324 **43.** 89,950 **44.** 65,095

▶ **Solve and check.** *(page 14)*

45. $x + 9 = 15$ **46.** $w + 7 = 23$ **47.** $u + 8 = 32$ **48.** $s + 5 = 27$

49. $a + 10 = 36$ **50.** $y + 15 = 41$ **51.** $e + 23 = 30$ **52.** $b + 41 = 41$

53. $d + 35 = 60$ **54.** $f + 52 = 63$ **55.** $z + 36 = 70$ **56.** $g + 53 = 82$

57. $r + 75 = 93$ **58.** $v + 60 = 86$ **59.** $c + 59 = 95$ **60.** $t + 48 = 76$

▶ **Solve and check.** *(page 16)*

61. $a - 7 = 13$ **62.** $z - 5 = 16$ **63.** $u - 9 = 11$ **64.** $g - 8 = 24$

65. $r - 11 = 18$ **66.** $s - 15 = 32$ **67.** $b - 21 = 53$ **68.** $x - 16 = 45$

69. $f - 35 = 60$ **70.** $h - 43 = 34$ **71.** $v - 29 = 29$ **72.** $d - 40 = 59$

73. $y - 56 = 25$ **74.** $c - 38 = 53$ **75.** $w - 50 = 41$ **76.** $t - 19 = 63$

Problem Solving—Applications

Here is a schedule for direct-dial telephone rates for calls made from Chicago, Illinois, to some other cities in the United States.

FROM CHICAGO TO	8 A.M.—5 P.M. Monday through Friday		5 P.M.—11 P.M. Sunday through Friday		11 P.M.—8 A.M. Every night 8 A.M.—11 P.M. Saturday 8 A.M.—5 P.M. Sunday	
	First Minute	Each Additional Minute	First Minute	Each Additional Minute	First Minute	Each Additional Minute
Atlanta	$.62	$.43	$.38	$.26	$.25	$.18
Detroit	.59	.42	.36	.26	.24	.17
Los Angeles	.64	.44	.39	.27	.26	.18
Minneapolis	.59	.42	.36	.26	.24	.17
St. Louis	.58	.39	.35	.24	.24	.16

Use the rate-schedule information to solve these problems.

1. Susan called her sister in Atlanta. She called at 3 P.M. on Wednesday. They talked for 5 minutes.
   - **a.** What was the cost for the first minute of their call?
   - **b.** What was the cost for the next 4 minutes?
   - **c.** What was the total cost of their 5-minute call?

2. Mike called his grandfather in Los Angeles. He called at 5:45 P.M. on Tuesday. They talked for 8 minutes.
   - **a.** What was the cost for the first minute?
   - **b.** What was the cost for the next 7 minutes?
   - **c.** What was the total cost?

3. Jan called her brother in Detroit. She called at 9 A.M. on Saturday. They talked for 13 minutes. What was the cost?

4. Ruth called her friend in Minneapolis on Sunday. They talked from 8:10 A.M. to 8:17 A.M. What was the cost?

5. A 20-minute call to Atlanta on a weekday before 5 P.M. costs $8.79. How much money can you save if you wait until after 5 P.M. to make the call?

6. Suppose that you called a friend in St. Louis at 10 P.M. on Friday and talked for 15 minutes. How much money could you have saved by calling an hour later?

Let n be the number of additional minutes after the first minute. Write an expression for the cost (in cents) of a call to

7. Minneapolis on a weekday before 5 P.M.

8. Los Angeles at 10 A.M. on a Saturday.

9. Atlanta on a weekday after 5 P.M.

10. Detroit at 1:30 P.M. on a Sunday.

Dividing by a 1-digit Number

MOTORCYCLE FOR SALE

Only 15,200 miles. No money down—pay $1845 in 9 equal monthly payments. Call 999-6275.

1. Read the ad. What is the price of the motorcycle?
2. How many monthly payments would you have to make?
3. To compute how many dollars you would have to pay each month, you would divide 1845 by what number?

Here's how to estimate and compute a quotient (the answer to a division problem).

$$1845 \div 9 = ?$$

To estimate the quotient, find the first digit in the quotient.

$$9\overline{)1845} \quad \text{quotient: } 2$$

Then write 0's in the remaining places.

$$9\overline{)1845} \quad \text{quotient: } 200$$

Not enough thousands. Think 18 hundreds. Divide hundreds.

$$\begin{array}{r} 2 \\ 9\overline{)1845} \\ -18 \end{array}$$

Not enough tens. Think 45 ones.

$$\begin{array}{r} 20 \\ 9\overline{)1845} \\ -18 \\ 45 \end{array}$$

Don't forget the zero!

Divide ones.

$$\begin{array}{r} 205 \\ 9\overline{)1845} \\ -18 \\ 45 \\ -45 \\ 0 \end{array}$$

4. Look at the example above. Is $200 a good estimate for the monthly payment? What is the monthly payment?

EXERCISES

▶ **Four of these calculator answers are wrong. Find them by estimating.**

5. a. $4\overline{)8176}$	2044	**b.** $5\overline{)935}$	187	**c.** $4\overline{)836}$	209
d. $7\overline{)1680}$	24	**e.** $9\overline{)783}$	87	**f.** $4\overline{)3192}$	532
g. $8\overline{)3616}$	452	**h.** $4\overline{)1224}$	36	**i.** $3\overline{)6123}$	241

▶ **Divide.**

Here are scrambled answers for the next row of exercises: 109 604 72 3210

6. $3\overline{)9630}$ **7.** $8\overline{)872}$ **8.** $7\overline{)504}$ **9.** $9\overline{)5436}$

10. $7\overline{)658}$ **11.** $5\overline{)7355}$ **12.** $4\overline{)360}$ **13.** $6\overline{)654}$

14. $9960 \div 8$ **15.** $2961 \div 7$ **16.** $405 \div 9$ **17.** $625 \div 5$

18. $732 \div 4$ **19.** $2400 \div 6$ **20.** $4263 \div 7$ **21.** $9265 \div 5$

22. $3050 \div 5$ **23.** $7448 \div 8$ **24.** $36{,}486 \div 6$ **25.** $64{,}800 \div 8$

26. $55{,}760 \div 8$ **27.** $18{,}633 \div 3$ **28.** $26{,}019 \div 9$ **29.** $43{,}022 \div 7$

▶ **Use your mental-math skills. Evaluate each expression for $r = 1200$, $s = 500$, $t = 2$, $u = 5$, and $v = 4$.**

Here are scrambled answers for the next row of exercises: 250 125 300 600 100

30. $\frac{r}{t}$ **31.** $\frac{s}{u}$ **32.** $\frac{s}{t}$ **33.** $\frac{r}{v}$ **34.** $\frac{s}{v}$

35. rt **36.** su **37.** rv **38.** st **39.** sv

40. $r + s$ **41.** $s + t$ **42.** $u + v$ **43.** $r + v$ **44.** $s + v$

45. $rv + s$ **46.** $st + r$ **47.** $tu - v$ **48.** $uv - t$ **49.** $ru - v$

Challenge

▶ **Copy and complete.**

50.
```
     2■■
 4)■0■4
  -■
   ■■
  -20
    ■4
   -■■
     0
```

51.
```
    ■■■
 ■)152■
  -15
    ■■
   -■7
     0
```

52.
```
    ■■■5
 7)■■■■
  -■
    ■
   -■
    ■■
   -■■
     0
```

Dividing by 2- and 3-digit Numbers

This bag contains $1000. (10,000 dimes)

Could you lift this $1000 bag of dimes?

1. How many dimes are in the bag?
2. The weight of 206 dimes is one pound. To find the number of pounds that you would have to lift, you would divide 10,000 by __?__ .

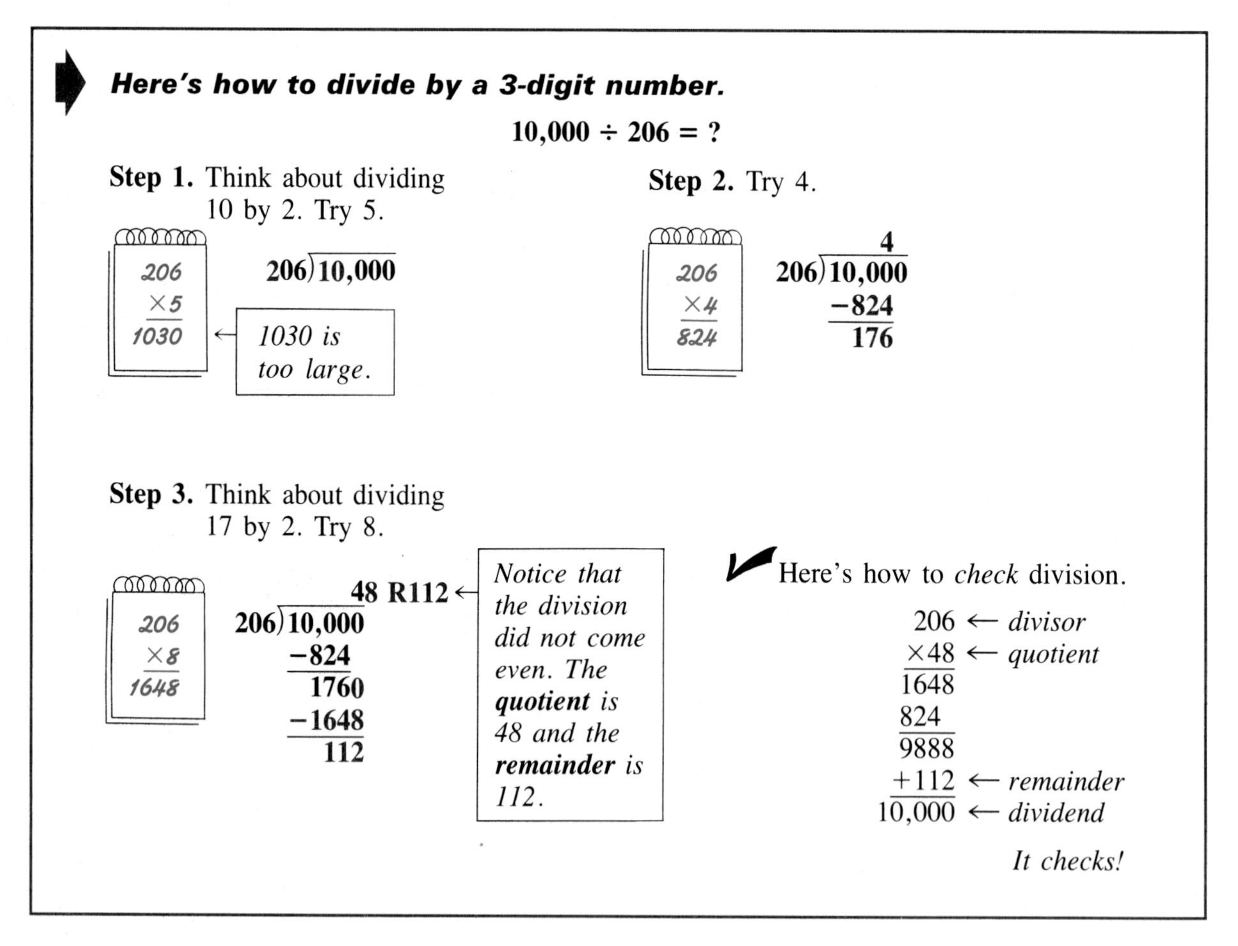

Here's how to divide by a 3-digit number.

10,000 ÷ 206 = ?

Step 1. Think about dividing 10 by 2. Try 5.

206)10,000

1030 is too large.

Step 2. Try 4.


```
      4
206)10,000
    -824
     176
```

Step 3. Think about dividing 17 by 2. Try 8.


```
      48 R112
206)10,000
    -824
     1760
    -1648
      112
```

Notice that the division did not come even. The ***quotient*** *is 48 and the* ***remainder*** *is 112.*

Here's how to *check* division.

```
   206 ← divisor
   ×48 ← quotient
  1648
  824
  9888
  +112 ← remainder
10,000 ← dividend
```

It checks!

3. Look at the example above. Does the $1000 bag of dimes weigh between 48 and 49 pounds?
4. Could you lift a $1000 bag of dimes?

▶ **Find the missing quotient.**

5. $37\overline{)15{,}577}$ (quotient: ▮▮▮)
−148
77
−74
37
−37
0

6. $625\overline{)156{,}260}$ (quotient: ▮▮▮ R10)
−1250
3126
−3125
10
− 0
10

7. $84\overline{)42{,}593}$ (quotient: ▮▮▮ R5)
−420
593
−588
5

▶ **Divide.**
Here are scrambled answers for the next row of exercises: *342* *36 R2* *5 R2* *21*

8. $15\overline{)542}$	**9.** $39\overline{)819}$	**10.** $43\overline{)217}$	**11.** $23\overline{)7866}$
12. $42\overline{)653}$	**13.** $16\overline{)704}$	**14.** $58\overline{)5916}$	**15.** $28\overline{)392}$
16. 3592 ÷ 78	**17.** 5270 ÷ 34	**18.** 1783 ÷ 57	**19.** 15,730 ÷ 80
20. 3875 ÷ 125	**21.** 7834 ÷ 203	**22.** 7538 ÷ 351	**23.** 2994 ÷ 150
24. 62,917 ÷ 521	**25.** 23,229 ÷ 801	**26.** 49,438 ÷ 481	**27.** 39,000 ÷ 365
28. 1260 ÷ 28	**29.** 792 ÷ 14	**30.** 3806 ÷ 17	**31.** 2644 ÷ 62
32. 40,000 ÷ 150	**33.** 53,182 ÷ 225	**34.** 74,281 ÷ 101	**35.** 6724 ÷ 671

CALCULATOR

Here's how to find the remainder when you divide 993 by 24 with a calculator.

Step 1.
Divide.
993 ÷ 24 =
41.375

Step 2.
Subtract the whole-number part of the quotient.
− 41 =
0.375

Step 3.
Multiply by the divisor.
The remainder is 9.
× 24 =
9

▶ **Use a calculator to find the remainder for each division.**

36. 604 ÷ 16	**37.** 195 ÷ 24	**38.** 774 ÷ 96	**39.** 355 ÷ 32
40. 8271 ÷ 192	**41.** 4524 ÷ 125	**42.** 9274 ÷ 250	**43.** 3885 ÷ 444

Solving Multiplication Equations

Each red box contains the same number of golf balls.

1. Two times the number of golf balls in 1 red box weighs the same as how many golf balls?
2. If we let g be the number of golf balls in each red box, we can write the equation

$$2g = \underline{\ ?\ }$$

Here's how to solve a multiplication equation.

Equation: $2g = 14$

*Multiplication and division are inverse operations. To undo multiplying by 2 and to get g by itself on one side of the equation, divide both sides by 2.

$$\frac{2g}{2} = \frac{14}{2}$$

Simplify both sides. $g = 7$

Check the solution by substituting 7 for g in the equation $2g = 14$.

$$2g = 14$$
$$2(7) \stackrel{?}{=} 14$$
$$14 = 14$$

It checks!

The property used to divide both sides of an equation by the same number is called the division property of equality.

3. Look at the example above. To find g, by what number were both sides of the equation divided?
4. By what number would you divide both sides to solve these equations?

   a. $5x = 75$ **b.** $9y = 99$ **c.** $8w = 96$

5. Complete these examples.

   a. $7c = 56$, $\frac{7c}{7} = \frac{56}{?}$, $c = 8$

   b. $10b = 150$, $\frac{10b}{?} = \frac{150}{10}$, $b = 15$

   c. $20a = 220$, $\frac{20a}{20} = \frac{220}{20}$, $a = \underline{\ ?\ }$

EXERCISES

Solve and check.
Here are scrambled answers for the next two rows of exercises:
6 10 12 3 9 34 7 13

6. $4a = 36$	**7.** $12f = 84$	**8.** $6k = 60$	**9.** $15k = 90$
10. $14j = 42$	**11.** $5n = 65$	**12.** $2r = 68$	**13.** $7d = 84$
14. $8y = 120$	**15.** $20c = 200$	**16.** $9v = 108$	**17.** $4h = 44$
18. $5u = 145$	**19.** $25b = 225$	**20.** $17q = 0$	**21.** $10x = 170$
22. $12e = 12$	**23.** $5g = 105$	**24.** $15c = 165$	**25.** $4s = 172$
26. $36t = 216$	**27.** $24j = 480$	**28.** $6w = 186$	**29.** $5z = 200$
30. $10b = 340$	**31.** $12t = 276$	**32.** $9n = 279$	**33.** $7f = 238$
34. $8f = 8$	**35.** $3b = 0$	**36.** $10y = 200$	**37.** $14n = 70$

Solve and check.
Here are scrambled answers for the next two rows of exercises:
56 17 83 41 0 65 50 55

38. $c + 12 = 53$	**39.** $w - 15 = 40$	**40.** $6a = 102$	**41.** $r + 10 = 75$
42. $9j = 0$	**43.** $t + 31 = 87$	**44.** $4n = 200$	**45.** $x - 22 = 61$
46. $z - 28 = 79$	**47.** $7k = 105$	**48.** $d + 21 = 53$	**49.** $5w = 215$
50. $f + 19 = 80$	**51.** $8c = 144$	**52.** $y - 33 = 107$	**53.** $10m = 320$

Problem Solving

Decide whether Equation A, B, or C would be used to solve the problem. Then solve the problem.

Equation A: $n + 16 = 48$
Equation B: $n - 16 = 48$
Equation C: $16n = 48$

54. Sixteen less than a number n is 48. What is the number?

55. Sixteen times a number n is 48. What is the number?

56. Sixteen more than a number n is 48. What is the number?

57. Sarah gave John 16 records. She then had 48 records. How many records did Sarah have before she gave John the records?

58. Alex bought 16 coins for his collection. He then had 48 coins. How many coins did he have in his collection before he bought the coins?

59. Beth bought 16 packages of baseball cards. How many cards were in each package if she bought a total of 48?

Solving Division Equations

Remember that division undoes multiplication and multiplication undoes division. We say that multiplication and division are **inverse operations.**

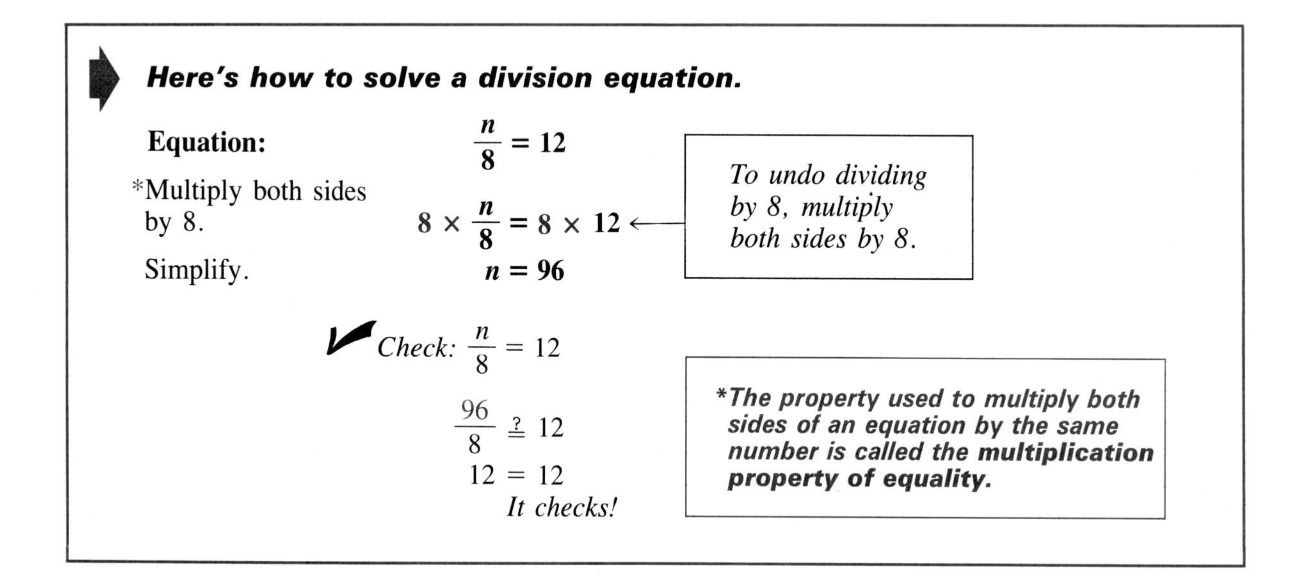

Here's how to solve a division equation.

Equation: $\frac{n}{8} = 12$

*Multiply both sides by 8. $8 \times \frac{n}{8} = 8 \times 12$ ← *To undo dividing by 8, multiply both sides by 8.*

Simplify. $n = 96$

Check: $\frac{n}{8} = 12$

$\frac{96}{8} \stackrel{?}{=} 12$

$12 = 12$

It checks!

The property used to multiply both sides of an equation by the same number is called the multiplication property of equality.

1. Look at the example above.
   a. To find n, what number were both sides of the equation multiplied by? What does n equal?
   b. To check the equation, what number was substituted for n in the equation $\frac{n}{8} = 12$?

2. By what number would you multiply both sides to solve these equations?

   a. $\frac{x}{3} = 11$ b. $\frac{z}{7} = 10$ c. $\frac{y}{5} = 9$

3. Complete these examples.

   a. $\frac{d}{9} = 7$
   $9 \times \frac{d}{9} = \underline{?} \times 7$
   $d = 63$

   b. $\frac{f}{4} = 20$
   $\underline{?} \times \frac{f}{4} = 4 \times 20$
   $f = 80$

   c. $\frac{g}{11} = 9$
   $11 \times \frac{g}{11} = 11 \times 9$
   $g = \underline{?}$

   d. $\frac{h}{6} = 6$
   $6 \times \frac{h}{6} = 6 \times 6$
   $h = \underline{?}$

   e. $\frac{p}{5} = 10$
   $5 \times \frac{p}{5} = 5 \times 10$
   $p = \underline{?}$

   f. $\frac{q}{10} = 30$
   $10 \times \frac{q}{10} = 10 \times 30$
   $q = \underline{?}$

EXERCISES

▶ **Solve and check.**
Here are scrambled answers for the next two rows of exercises:
80 56 72 70 18 66 33 32

4. $\frac{n}{3} = 6$ **5.** $\frac{p}{2} = 16$ **6.** $\frac{h}{4} = 18$ **7.** $\frac{x}{5} = 16$

8. $\frac{r}{6} = 11$ **9.** $\frac{v}{7} = 10$ **10.** $\frac{e}{3} = 11$ **11.** $\frac{b}{2} = 28$

12. $\frac{d}{12} = 12$ **13.** $\frac{k}{4} = 20$ **14.** $\frac{y}{8} = 30$ **15.** $\frac{j}{6} = 15$

16. $\frac{w}{3} = 15$ **17.** $\frac{t}{5} = 21$ **18.** $\frac{a}{2} = 33$ **19.** $\frac{q}{15} = 27$

▶ **Solve and check.**
Here are scrambled answers for the next two rows of exercises:
65 64 0 450 80 11 66 17

20. $x - 26 = 54$ **21.** $n + 19 = 83$ **22.** $10w = 170$ **23.** $9k = 0$

24. $d + 37 = 103$ **25.** $\frac{a}{15} = 30$ **26.** $m - 16 = 49$ **27.** $11c = 121$

28. $\frac{z}{12} = 24$ **29.** $10s = 210$ **30.** $y + 35 = 81$ **31.** $j - 32 = 0$

32. $r + 127 = 221$ **33.** $\frac{w}{8} = 0$ **34.** $f - 72 = 113$ **35.** $16d = 288$

Problem Solving

▶ **Decide whether Equation A, B, C, or D would be used to solve the problem. Then solve the problem.**

Equation A: $n + 32 = 96$
Equation B: $n - 32 = 96$
Equation C: $32n = 96$
Equation D: $\frac{n}{32} = 96$

36. Thirty-two less than a number n is 96. What is the number?

37. The sum of a number n and 32 is 96. What is the number?

38. A number n divided by 32 is 96. What is the number?

39. Thirty-two times a number n is 96. What is the number?

40. Alan worked 32 hours and earned \$96. How much did he earn per hour?

41. Sally bought a tape player and earphones for \$96. The earphones cost \$32. What did she pay for the tape player?

42. After buying a letter sweater for \$32, Mary had \$96. How much money did she have before she bought the sweater?

43. The 32 students in a class contributed an average of 96¢ to a charity. What was the total class contribution?

More on Solving Equations

Variables can be on either side of the equation. In this lesson you will solve some equations that have the variable on the right side.

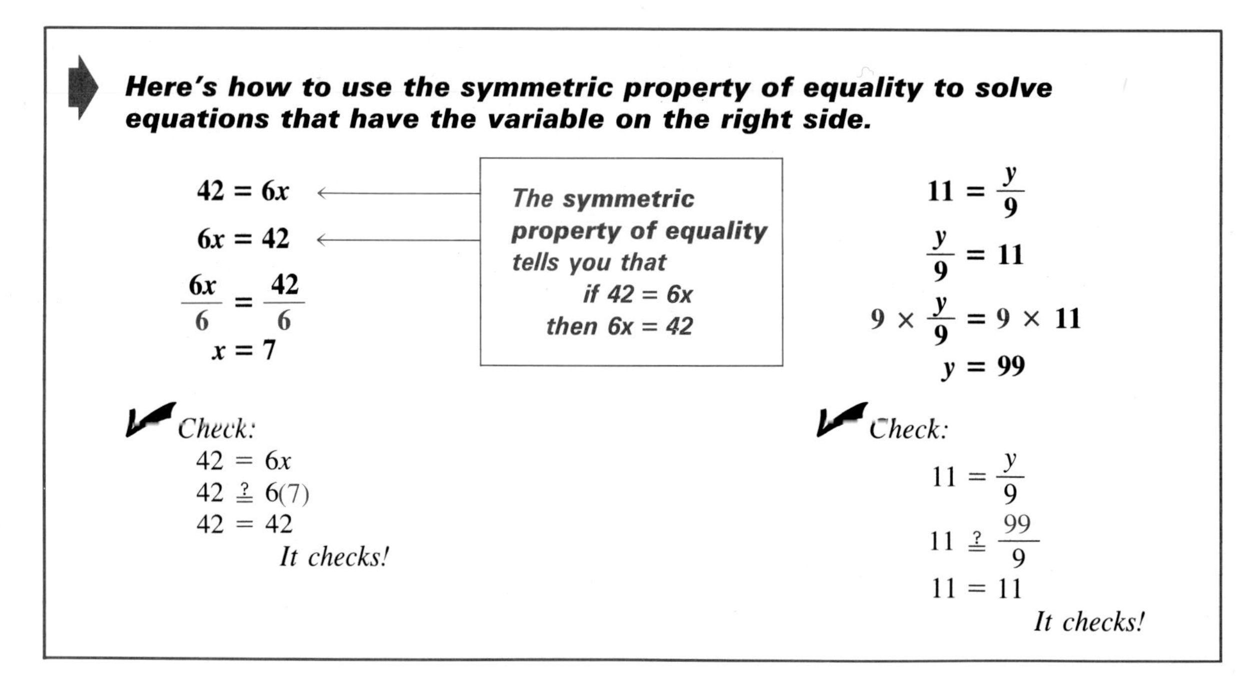

Here's how to use the symmetric property of equality to solve equations that have the variable on the right side.

$$42 = 6x$$
$$6x = 42$$
$$\frac{6x}{6} = \frac{42}{6}$$
$$x = 7$$

The symmetric property of equality tells you that if $42 = 6x$ then $6x = 42$

$$11 = \frac{y}{9}$$
$$\frac{y}{9} = 11$$
$$9 \times \frac{y}{9} = 9 \times 11$$
$$y = 99$$

Check:

$$42 = 6x$$
$$42 \stackrel{?}{=} 6(7)$$
$$42 = 42$$

It checks!

Check:

$$11 = \frac{y}{9}$$
$$11 \stackrel{?}{=} \frac{99}{9}$$
$$11 = 11$$

It checks!

1. Look at the examples above.

a. In each first equation, the expression containing the variable is on the _?_ side of the equation.

b. For each second equation, the symmetric property of equality was used to get the expression containing the variable on the _?_ side of the equation.

2. Complete these examples.

a.
$$84 = v + 19$$
$$v + 19 = 84$$
$$v + 19 - \underline{?} = 84 - 19$$
$$v = 65$$

b.
$$20 = \frac{w}{7}$$
$$\frac{w}{7} = 20$$
$$7 \times \frac{w}{7} = \underline{?} \times 20$$
$$w = 140$$

c.
$$53 = z - 41$$
$$z - 41 = 53$$
$$z - 41 + 41 = 53 + 41$$
$$z = \underline{?}$$

d.
$$38 = r + 17$$
$$r + 17 = 38$$
$$r + 17 - \underline{?} = 38 - 17$$
$$r = 21$$

e.
$$132 = 12t$$
$$12t = 132$$
$$\frac{12t}{12} = \frac{132}{?}$$
$$t = 11$$

f.
$$69 = \frac{m}{3}$$
$$\frac{m}{3} = 69$$
$$3 \times \frac{m}{3} = 3 \times 69$$
$$m = \underline{?}$$

Solve and check.

Here are scrambled answers for the next row of exercises: 23 36 32 4

3. $12 = \frac{a}{3}$ **4.** $32 = 8j$ **5.** $21 = z - 11$ **6.** $36 = j + 13$

7. $0 = 5k$ **8.** $45 = h + 19$ **9.** $15 = \frac{b}{6}$ **10.** $30 = w - 16$

11. $42 = y - 12$ **12.** $11 = \frac{f}{5}$ **13.** $18 = g + 18$ **14.** $42 = 6m$

15. $59 = f + 31$ **16.** $60 = 5n$ **17.** $37 = y - 30$ **18.** $30 = \frac{g}{3}$

19. $96 = 16p$ **20.** $x - 18 = 29$ **21.** $\frac{h}{6} = 12$ **22.** $60 = d + 47$

23. $20 = \frac{c}{10}$ **24.** $c + 34 = 34$ **25.** $4q = 100$ **26.** $40 = n - 40$

27. $b + 29 = 103$ **28.** $200 = 25r$ **29.** $49 = m - 16$ **30.** $\frac{d}{8} = 14$

31. $12s = 156$ **32.** $10 = \frac{e}{12}$ **33.** $115 = d + 32$ **34.** $r - 47 = 0$

35. $z + 105 = 215$ **36.** $w - 52 = 87$ **37.** $20x = 300$ **38.** $\frac{y}{16} = 24$

39. $58 = r - 87$ **40.** $225 = 15t$ **41.** $96 = s + 61$ **42.** $37 = \frac{u}{12}$

43. $22n = 396$ **44.** $\frac{m}{18} = 25$ **45.** $q - 102 = 102$ **46.** $p + 142 = 195$

47. $30 = \frac{w}{12}$ **48.** $56 = y - 73$ **49.** $378 = 18z$ **50.** $29 = \frac{x}{13}$

51. $a + 9 = 27$ **52.** $b - 9 = 27$ **53.** $9c = 27$ **54.** $\frac{d}{9} = 27$

55. $17 = e + 17$ **56.** $17 = f - 17$ **57.** $17 = 17g$ **58.** $17 = \frac{p}{17}$

Problem Solving

Complete the table using the formula.

59. Gas mileage is the number of miles driven for each gallon of gasoline. You can use this formula to compute gas mileage:

Formula: *distance* → $\frac{d}{g} = m$ ← *mileage*
gallons →

	miles (d)	gallons (g)	miles per gallon (m)
a.	208	8	?
b.	330	15	?
c.	?	7	25
d.	?	9	24

Problem Solving—Using Equations

Remember that problems that can be solved with arithmetic can also be solved by writing and solving an equation.

Here's how to use arithmetic or algebra to solve a problem.

Problem: You bought 3 tickets to a Lionel Richie concert. The total cost for the tickets was $54. What was the cost of each ticket?

Method 1. Using arithmetic

$$\mathbf{54} \div \mathbf{3} = \mathbf{18}$$

54 ↑ *total cost*; 3 ↑ *number of tickets*; 18 ↑ *cost of each ticket*

Each ticket costs $18.

Method 2. Using algebra

Step 1. Choose a variable. Use it and the facts to represent the numbers in the problem.

Let t = cost of each ticket.
Then $3t$ = cost of three tickets.

Step 2. Write an equation based on the facts.

$$3t = 54$$

These are equal expressions for the cost of three tickets.

Step 3. Solve the equation.

$$3t = 54$$
$$\frac{3t}{3} = \frac{54}{3}$$
$$t = 18$$

Each ticket costs $18.

1. Look at the example above. In Method 1, the total cost of the tickets was divided by the number of tickets to get the cost of __?__ ticket.
2. Look at Method 2.
   a. In Step 1, the variable t equals the __?__ of each ticket.
   b. In Step 2, both the expression $3t$ and the number __?__ equal the total cost of the tickets.
   c. In Step 3, to solve the equation, each side of the equation was divided by __?__
3. To check the solution, ask yourself whether the answer fits the facts in the problem. Did each ticket cost $18?

EXERCISES

Decide whether Equation A, B, C, or D would be used to solve the problem. Then solve the problem.

Equation A:	$\frac{n}{15} = 75$
Equation B:	$15n = 75$
Equation C:	$n + 15 = 75$
Equation D:	$n - 15 = 75$

4. The product of a number and 15 is 75. What is the number? (Let n = the number.)

5. A number divided by 15 gives a result of 75. What is the number? (Let n = the number.)

6. The sum of a number and 15 is 75. What is the number? (Let n = the number.)

7. When 15 is subtracted from a number the difference is 75. What is the number? (Let n = the number.)

8. Carlo has 15 more records than David. Carlo has 75 records. How many records does David have? (Let n = David's records.)

9. Terri has 15 fewer records than Sue. Terri has 75 records. How many records does Sue have? (Let n = Sue's records.)

10. One hour a store sold 15 times as many tapes as records. The store sold 75 tapes. How many records did it sell? (Let n = the records sold.)

11. The average number of records owned by each of 15 families is 75. How many records do the 15 families own altogether? (Let n = the records owned altogether.)

Write an equation and solve the problem.

12. A number divided by 17 equals 8. What is the number? (Let j = the number.)

13. The product of 11 and a number is 165. What is the number? (Let k = the number.)

14. The sum of two numbers is 86. One of the numbers is 54. What is the other number? (Let n = the number.)

15. The difference between two numbers is 24. The lesser number is 13. What is the greater number? (Let m = the greater number.)

16. You scored 3 times as many points as your friend. You scored 21 points. How many points did your friend score? (Let f = the points your friend scored.)

17. Beth scored 4 times as many points as Ann. Beth scored 36 points. How many points did Ann score? (Let a = the points Ann scored.)

18. Holly's age minus 6 is 23. How old is Holly? (Let h = Holly's age.)

19. Kevin's age divided by 6 is 7. How old is Kevin? (Let k = Kevin's age.)

20. Brad is 6 years younger than Tracey. Brad is 19 years old. How old is Tracey? (Let t = Tracey's age.)

21. Joan is 39 years old. That is 3 times as old as Evan. How old is Evan? (Let e = Evan's age.)

Cumulative Skill Practice

▶ **Write a mathematical expression for each word expression.** *(page 28)*

1. the product of 8 and a number s

2. 6 times a number x

3. a number y divided by 12

4. 10 multiplied by a number t

5. 7 times a number w, plus 5

6. 5 times a number w, plus 7

▶ **Multiply.** *(pages 34, 36)*

7. 811×6 **8.** 689×7 **9.** 409×9 **10.** 2021×5

11. 4119×4 **12.** 6993×8 **13.** 76×21 **14.** 92×43

15. 217×391 **16.** 684×521 **17.** 2958×308 **18.** 6103×492

▶ **Divide.** *(pages 40, 42)*

19. $162 \div 6$ **20.** $280 \div 8$ **21.** $395 \div 5$ **22.** $378 \div 9$

23. $672 \div 12$ **24.** $924 \div 22$ **25.** $1200 \div 30$ **26.** $2322 \div 43$

27. $8798 \div 106$ **28.** $8265 \div 145$ **29.** $26{,}078 \div 221$ **30.** $38{,}556 \div 357$

▶ **Solve and check.** *(page 44)*

31. $6n = 48$ **32.** $8k = 72$ **33.** $4m = 80$ **34.** $7w = 0$

35. $10x = 130$ **36.** $20w = 220$ **37.** $24z = 240$ **38.** $32y = 352$

39. $18r = 486$ **40.** $25t = 500$ **41.** $16s = 496$ **42.** $35u = 665$

▶ **Solve and check.** *(page 46)*

43. $\frac{x}{6} = 9$ **44.** $\frac{m}{7} = 7$ **45.** $\frac{u}{5} = 0$ **46.** $\frac{z}{8} = 5$

47. $\frac{t}{4} = 30$ **48.** $\frac{y}{3} = 36$ **49.** $\frac{p}{12} = 9$ **50.** $\frac{s}{18} = 6$

51. $\frac{r}{10} = 15$ **52.** $\frac{n}{11} = 18$ **53.** $\frac{w}{26} = 22$ **54.** $\frac{v}{21} = 37$

▶ **Solve and check.** *(page 48)*

55. $45 = v + 17$ **56.** $12 = \frac{n}{10}$ **57.** $43 = w - 26$ **58.** $48 = 6x$

59. $35 = \frac{a}{4}$ **60.** $53 = r - 39$ **61.** $108 = 9j$ **62.** $93 = c + 41$

63. $225 = 15z$ **64.** $103 = d + 66$ **65.** $46 = \frac{m}{12}$ **66.** $49 = s - 82$

Problem Solving—Applications

APARTMENTS—FURNISHED

Efficiency Apartment New carpet, spotless. Bus at door, all shopping half block away. **All utilities paid by landlord.** $235 per month. Call 999-1668.

2 or 3 bedrooms, $360 per month, all utilities paid. 104 E. Green. 999-4457. 999-4688.

Quiet 2-bedroom second-floor apartment in private home. Close to downtown. $285 per month plus electricity. After 5 P.M.: 999-8923.

New Building—Now Leasing New furniture & appliances. 3-bedroom apartments have dishwashers. 3 bedrooms—$495 per month Efficiencies—$245 per month **999-5046 or 999-3689**

Unfurnished 2-bedroom apartment. Maximum 3 persons. $345 per month. Phone: Hodges Real Estate, 999-5126.

One-bedroom furnished apartment. Available immediately. $280 per month. 1-888-3355 days.

Solve. Use the ad.

1. How much would you spend per year for the first apartment listed?
2. Suppose that your ''take-home'' pay is $920 each month. How much would you have left after paying the rent on the second apartment listed?
3. The average cost of electricity for the third apartment listed is $86 per month. How much would you spend a year for rent and electricity?
4. The estimated total rent and cost of utilities for a 3-bedroom apartment in the new building is $7464 per year. What is the estimated average monthly utility bill?

Decide whether Equation A, B, C, or D would be used to solve the problem. Then solve the problem.

Equation A: $n + 12 = 156$
Equation B: $n - 12 = 156$
Equation C: $12n = 156$
Equation D: $\frac{n}{12} = 156$

5. During 12 months you spent a total of $156 for water. What was the average per month?
6. For January your heating bill was $156. That was $12 more than your December bill. How much was your December bill?
7. For August your electricity bill was $156. That was $12 less than your July bill. How much was your July bill?
8. After an increase of $12, your rent was $156. What was your rent before the increase?

Write an equation and solve the problem.

9. A 2-bedroom apartment that rents for $417 a month is three times the cost of a 1-bedroom apartment. What is the monthly cost of the 1-bedroom apartment? (Let c = the monthly cost of the 1-bedroom apartment.)
10. The average monthly cost of electricity for an apartment was $83. That was $27 more than the average monthly cost of heat. What was the average monthly cost of heat? (Let h = the average monthly cost of heat.)

Chapter Review

Here are scrambled answers for the review exercises:

8	*5600*	*divide*	*left*	*right*	*times*
9	*15,000*	*equality*	*minus*	*simplify*	*zeros*
19	*add*	*inverse*	*multiply*	*three*	

1. A word expression for the mathematical expression $\mathbf{7w - 3}$ is 7 __?__ a number w, __?__ 3. *(page 28)*

2. If you evaluate the expression $\frac{a}{c} + b$ for $a = 12$, $b = 4$, and $c = 3$, you get __?__. *(page 30)*

3. To multiply a whole number by 1000, you can copy the whole number and annex __?__ zeros. *(page 32)*

4. If you estimate the product of $\mathbf{689 \times 8}$ by rounding the greater factor to the nearest hundred, you get __?__. *(page 34)*

5. If you estimate the product of $\mathbf{487 \times 32}$ by rounding each factor to its leading digit, you get __?__. *(page 36)*

6. To estimate the quotient of $7\overline{)4634}$ you would find the first digit in the quotient and write __?__ in the remaining places. *(page 40)*

7. In this division exercise the quotient is __?__ and the remainder is __?__. To check the division, you would multiply 36 by 19 and __?__ 9. *(page 42)*

$$\begin{array}{r} 19 \text{ R9} \\ 36\overline{)693} \\ -36 \\ \hline 333 \\ -324 \\ \hline 9 \end{array}$$

8. Multiplication and division are __?__ operations. To solve the equation $\mathbf{6v = 84}$ you would first __?__ both sides by 6. Then you would simplify both sides. *(page 44)*

9. To solve the equation $\frac{x}{8} = 17$ you would first __?__ both sides by 8 and then __?__ both sides. *(page 46)*

10. In the first equation at the right the expression containing the variable is on the __?__ side of the equation. For the second equation, the symmetric property of __?__ was used to get the expression containing the variable on the __?__ side. *(page 48)*

$$68 = 4z$$

$$4z = 68$$

Chapter Test

▶ **Write a mathematical expression for each word expression.** *(page 28)*

1. the product of 12 and z

2. 15 multiplied by v

3. a number x divided by 4, minus 10

4. 20 times a number u, plus 14

▶ **Evaluate each expression for $a = 10$, $b = 5$, and $c = 2$.** *(page 30)*

5. abc

6. $ab + c$

7. $ac - b$

8. $bc + a$

9. $ca + b$

10. $\frac{bc}{a}$

11. $\frac{a}{b} + c$

12. $\frac{a}{b} - c$

13. $\frac{a}{c} - b$

14. $\frac{a}{c} + b$

▶ **Give each product.** *(pages 32, 34, 36)*

15. 421×8

16. 793×5

17. 226×10

18. 557×100

19. 831×1000

20. 657×42

21. 3948×61

22. 7255×306

▶ **Give each quotient.** *(pages 40, 42)*

23. $72 \div 6$

24. $96 \div 4$

25. $344 \div 8$

26. $504 \div 7$

27. $972 \div 36$

28. $2788 \div 82$

29. $17{,}155 \div 235$

30. $65{,}163 \div 609$

▶ **Solve and check.** *(pages 44, 46, 48)*

31. $6a = 66$

32. $\frac{c}{3} = 18$

33. $\frac{x}{7} = 20$

34. $212 = 2m$

35. $50 = \frac{u}{5}$

36. $x + 18 = 30$

37. $c - 22 = 40$

38. $63 = x + 29$

39. $47 = m - 18$

40. $21 = 7d$

41. $9k = 108$

42. $4y = 128$

▶ **Decide which equation would be used to solve the problem. Then solve the problem.** *(page 50)*

Equation A: $n + 8 = 24$
Equation B: $n - 8 = 24$
Equation C: $8n = 24$
Equation D: $\frac{n}{8} = 24$

43. You bought 8 gallons of gasoline to fill your 24-gallon tank. How many gallons did you have before you filled the tank?

44. During one week you drove the same toll road 8 times. You paid a total of $24 in tolls. How much was each toll?

45. You bought a windshield-wiper blade for $8. You then had $24. How much money did you have before you bought the blade?

46. It took you 8 hours to drive Stage Coach Trail. You averaged 24 miles per hour. How many miles was Stage Coach Trail?

Cumulative Test
Standardized Format

▶ **Choose the correct letter.**

1. An expression for a number y minus 7 is

A. $y + 7$
B. $7 - y$
C. $y - 7$
D. none of these

2. 38,657 rounded to the nearest hundred is

A. 38,660
B. 38,600
C. 39,000
D. none of these

3. Solve.

$w + 37 = 63$

A. 100
B. 26
C. 37
D. none of these

4. Solve.

$z - 48 = 60$

A. 108
B. 60
C. 12
D. none of these

5. An expression for 9 times a number x, minus 4 is

A. $\frac{x}{9} - 4$
B. $9x + 4$
C. $9x - 4$
D. none of these

6. An expression for a number t divided by 6, plus 12 is

A. $6t + 12$
B. $\frac{t}{6} + 12$
C. $6t - 12$
D. none of these

7. Give the product.

48×29

A. 1392
B. 432
C. 528
D. none of these

8. Give the quotient.

$24{,}308 \div 236$

A. 113
B. 103
C. 1003
D. none of these

9. Solve.

$15n = 105$

A. 90
B. 120
C. 105
D. none of these

10. Solve.

$\frac{m}{12} = 36$

A. 3
B. 24
C. 432
D. none of these

11. Solve.

$319 = 11n$

A. 29
B. 308
C. 3509
D. none of these

12. Choose the equation.

Jerry rode 4 hours in a bike-a-thon. How many miles did he ride if he averaged 8 miles an hour?

A. $n + 4 = 8$
B. $n - 4 = 8$
C. $4n = 8$
D. $\frac{n}{4} = 8$

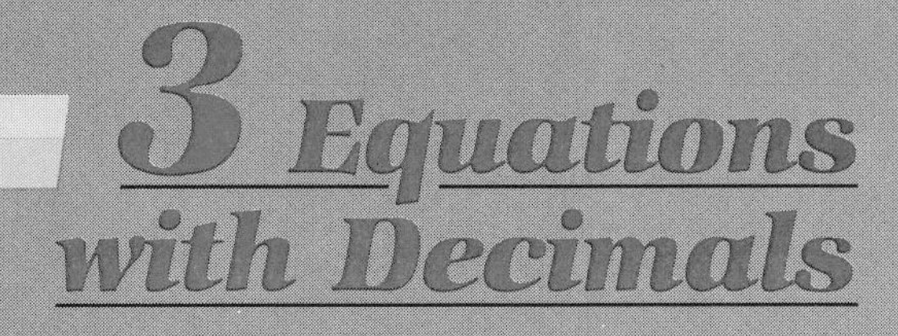

3 Equations with Decimals

$h \cdot w = e$

The number of hours worked times the hourly wage equals earnings.

(page 83)

You increase your earnings by increasing your hourly wage, the number of hours worked, or both. A worker's hourly wage is based on several factors including skill, experience, and the amount of danger involved.

Place Value—Reading Decimals

The decimal shows the number of seconds that it took the winner to sprint 100 yards.

1. In what place is the digit 4?

2. In what place is the last digit?

Here's how to read decimals.

The 100-yard dash took **18 and 46 hundredths** seconds. Notice that the decimal point is read as "and" and the place of the last digit is read last.
Here are some more examples of how to read decimals:

tens	*ones*		*tenths*	*hundredths*	*thousandths*	*ten-thousandths*	
	0	.	4				4 tenths
	9	.	5				9 and 5 tenths
	6	.	2	1			6 and 21 hundredths
4	2	.	0	6			42 and 6 hundredths
	3	.	2	7	4		3 and 274 thousandths
2	5	.	0	0	6	8	25 and 68 ten-thousandths
Decimal							**Short Word-Name**

3. Look at the examples above. To read 42.06, you say "42 and 6 __?__."

4. To read 3.274, you say "3 and 274 __?__."

5. To read 25.0068, you say "25 and 68 __?__."

EXERCISES

▶ **In what place is the last digit?** *Example: 16.7* tenths

6. 3.001
7. 19.42
8. 0.781
9. 12.06
10. 1.3734
11. 23.42
12. 17.6
13. 4.2603
14. 0.0051
15. 72.47
16. 12.008
17. 36.77
18. 9.0004
19. 358.6
20. 49.74
21. 6.352
22. 1364.91
23. 0.007
24. 1.3625
25. 2934.1

▶ **Write the short word name.** *Example: 7.4* 7 and 4 tenths

26. 8.6
27. 15.82
28. 0.325
29. 14.002
30. 6.08
31. 0.054
32. 18.6
33. 5.0074
34. 321.82
35. 0.0476
36. 58.002
37. 866.38
38. 0.0492
39. 0.765
40. 4.2008
41. 470.8
42. 5036.17
43. 4936.2
44. 0.4006
45. 38.0005
46. 629.34
47. 37.004
48. 9.7008
49. 321.6
50. 25.376
51. 48.03
52. 156.2
53. 204.84

▶ **Write the decimal.** *Example: 8 hundredths* 0.08

54. 9 thousandths
55. 32 and 6 tenths
56. 24 and 16 hundredths
57. 9 and 6 hundredths
58. 6 thousandths
59. 114 and 58 hundredths
60. 274 thousandths
61. 62 and 250 thousandths
62. 7 and 42 thousandths
63. 1456 ten-thousandths
64. 944 ten-thousandths
65. 5 and 360 ten-thousandths

Challenge

▶ **Solve.**

66. In a bicycle race, Alice beat Bob by 10.40 seconds. Carol finished ahead of David. Alice finished 5.52 seconds ahead of David but 2.25 seconds behind Carol.

a. Which cyclist won the sprint?

b. Which cyclist came in last?

Rounding Decimals

The gasoline pump shows the total cost and the total number of gallons.

1. What is the total cost?
2. What is the total number of gallons?

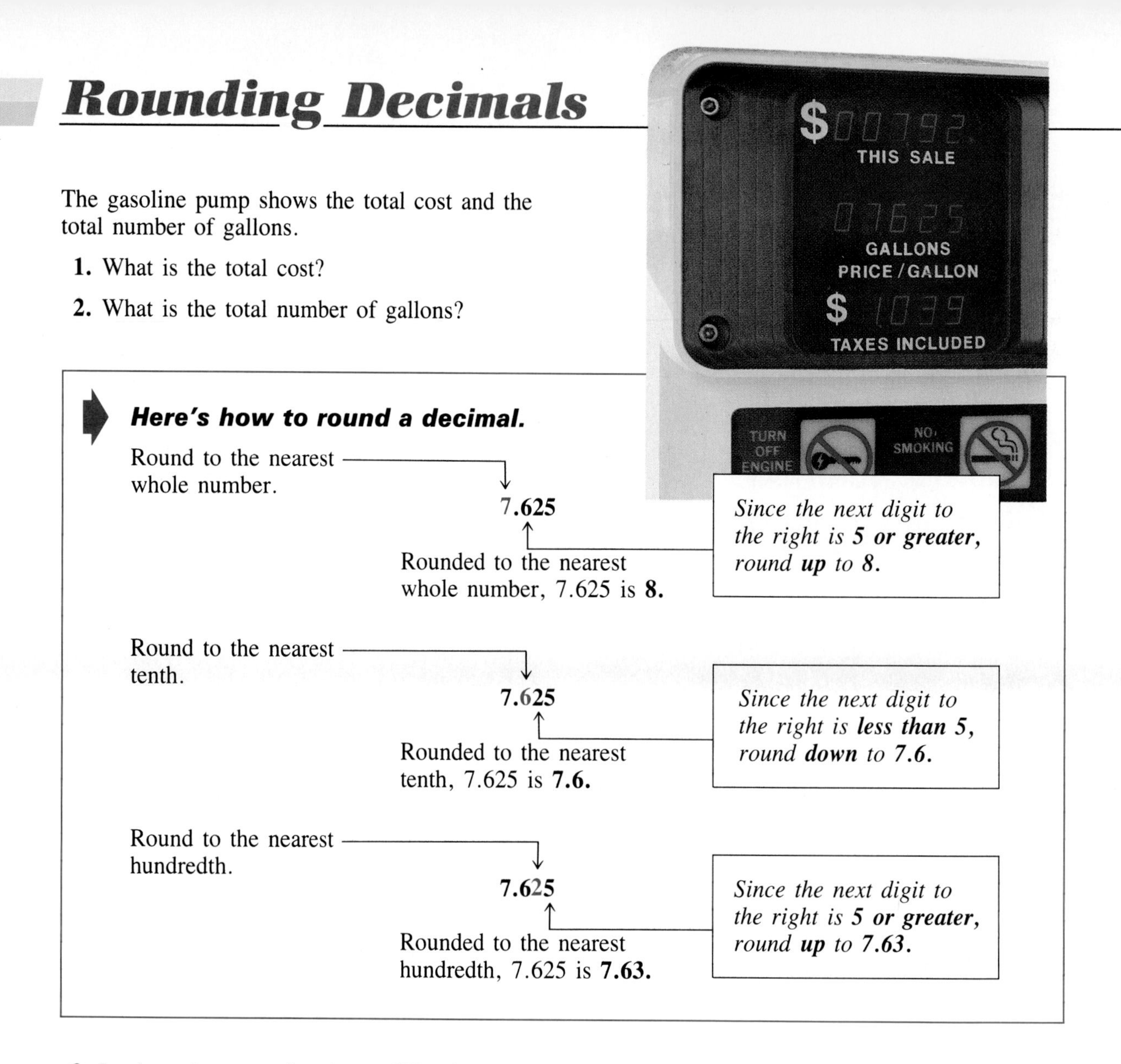

Here's how to round a decimal.

Round to the nearest whole number.

7.625

Rounded to the nearest whole number, 7.625 is **8.**

*Since the next digit to the right is **5 or greater**, round **up** to **8**.*

Round to the nearest tenth.

7.625

Rounded to the nearest tenth, 7.625 is **7.6.**

*Since the next digit to the right is **less than 5**, round **down** to **7.6**.*

Round to the nearest hundredth.

7.625

Rounded to the nearest hundredth, 7.625 is **7.63.**

*Since the next digit to the right is **5 or greater**, round **up** to **7.63**.*

3. Look at the examples above. What is 7.625 rounded to the nearest

   a. whole number? **b.** tenth? **c.** hundredth?

4. What is the total cost rounded to the nearest dollar?

EXERCISES

▶ **Round to the nearest whole number.**

5. 25.6 **6.** 36.3 **7.** 0.38 **8.** 84.44 **9.** 0.94

10. 43.17 **11.** 38.927 **12.** 89.821 **13.** 54.0361 **14.** 38.27

▶ **Round to the nearest tenth.**

15. 3.74 **16.** 36.205 **17.** 8.36 **18.** 0.554 **19.** 9.238

20. 3.470 **21.** 49.183 **22.** 41.08 **23.** 6.452 **24.** 7.1205

25. 605.38 **26.** 714.82 **27.** 0.057 **28.** 27.021 **29.** 64.398

30. 5.395 **31.** 0.321 **32.** 74.563 **33.** 3.106 **34.** 82.0064

▶ **Round to the nearest hundredth.**

35. 16.318 **36.** 42.106 **37.** 2.563 **38.** 72.835 **39.** 25.614

40. 72.573 **41.** 4.3059 **42.** 0.0351 **43.** 6.4745 **44.** 0.018

45. 8.4536 **46.** 0.005 **47.** 27.938 **48.** 165.789 **49.** 17.046

50. 5.2875 **51.** 33.715 **52.** 3.402 **53.** 287.277 **54.** 5.118

▶ **Round to the nearest dollar.**

55. $6.66 **56.** $15.39 **57.** $146.68 **58.** $58.51 **59.** $27.87

60. $42.48 **61.** $55.37 **62.** $138.50 **63.** $99.75 **64.** $14.09

65. $246.58 **66.** $39.49 **67.** $39.94 **68.** $158.99 **69.** $199.79

Challenge

▶ **Use the clues to find the costs of gasoline that are missing in the chart.**

Cost of Regular Gasoline in the United States							
1973	1974	1975	1976	1977	1978	1979	1980
$.40	?	$.57	$.59	$.62	$.63	?	?

70. The cost of gasoline in 1974

Clues:
- The cost rounded to the nearest dime is $.50.
- The sum of the digits in the cost is 8.

71. The cost of gasoline in 1979

Clues:
- The cost rounded to the nearest dime is $.90.
- The sum of the digits in the cost is 14.

72. The cost of gasoline in 1980

Clues:
- The cost rounded to the nearest dime is $1.20.
- The sum of the digits in the cost is 11.

Comparing Decimals

In drag racing, the car that travels a quarter of a mile in the shortest time wins the race.

Two decimals are used to show how a car performs. (See the table.) The first decimal tells the time in seconds that the car took to travel a quarter of a mile. This time is called the *elapsed time*. The second decimal tells the speed (in miles per hour) of the car when it reached the finish line. This speed is called the *terminal speed*.

Car	Driver	Time / Speed (s) / (mph)
Sling Shot	Lee	8.70 / 164.48
Flash Bye	Austin	8.67 / 166.93
Blue Flame	Pace	8.64 / 168.28
Lightning	Dickey	8.66 / 168.63
Jetaway	Marshal	8.72 / 161.72
Old Smokie	Klick	8.71 / 162.37

1. Which car had an elapsed time of 8.70 seconds?

2. Which car had an elapsed time of 8.71 seconds?

3. Which two decimals would you compare to decide whether Sling Shot or Old Smokie had the better (shorter) time?

Here's how to compare decimals.

8.70 ◆ 8.71

Start at the left and compare digits that have the same place value.

Step 1.	**Step 2.**	**Step 3.**
8.70 8.71	**8.70 8.71**	**8.70 < 8.71**
same	*0 is less than 1*	*Read < as "is less than."*

4. Look at the example above. Which car had the better time, Sling Shot or Old Smokie?

5. Check these examples. Have the decimals been compared correctly?

Read > as "is greater than."

▶ Less than (<) or greater than (>)?

6. 0.3 ◆ 0.4
7. 0.009 ◆ 0.007
8. 0.006 ◆ 0.007
9. 21.5 ◆ 21.3
10. 8.75 ◆ 8.57
11. 0.37 ◆ 0.3
12. 0.008 ◆ 0.07
13. 0.4 ◆ 0.03
14. 7.56 ◆ 7.65
15. 35.58 ◆ 35.6
16. 8.3 ◆ 7.99
17. 9.471 ◆ 94.71
18. 0.567 ◆ 1.3
19. 4.06 ◆ 4.006
20. 0.712 ◆ 0.72
21. 43.86 ◆ 43.87
22. 0.78 ◆ 0.87
23. 7.904 ◆ 79.04
24. 36.78 ◆ 35.88
25. 1.1 ◆ 1.06
26. 583.1 ◆ 584
27. 19.05 ◆ 19.005
28. 42.05 ◆ 42.1
29. 0.444 ◆ 0.443
30. 3.605 ◆ 3.65
31. 57.4 ◆ 6.93
32. 0.054 ◆ 0.54
33. 6.72 ◆ 6.78
34. 9.264 ◆ 9.3
35. 4.70 ◆ 4.69
36. 0.03 ◆ 0.005
37. 9.016 ◆ 9.007
38. 6.42 ◆ 6.240

▶ $<$ or $>$? Let $m = 6$, $n = 5$, $r = 4$, and $t = 2$.

39. mn ◆ 29.5
40. rt ◆ 9.5
41. mr ◆ 24.1
42. $m + n$ ◆ 10.3
43. $r + t$ ◆ 6.01
44. $m + r$ ◆ 9.5
45. $m - n$ ◆ 0.95
46. $r - t$ ◆ 2.15
47. $m - r$ ◆ 1.85
48. $m + t$ ◆ $n + t$
49. $m + t$ ◆ $r + t$
50. $r + n$ ◆ $m + n$
51. mn ◆ rn
52. nt ◆ mt
53. rt ◆ nt
54. $m + n$ ◆ $m - n$
55. $m - t$ ◆ $r - t$
56. $n + t$ ◆ $m - t$
57. $m + n$ ◆ nt
58. $m + n$ ◆ rt
59. $n + t$ ◆ mt

Problem Solving

▶ Solve. Use the table on page 62.

60. Which driver had the better (shorter) time, Lee or Austin?

61. Which car won the race?

62. Which car placed second?

63. Who drove the car that placed third?

64. Which car placed last?

65. Rank the cars from first place to last place.

66. What was the terminal speed of the winning car?

67. Did the driver with the fastest terminal speed win the race?

Estimating and Computing Decimal Sums

The red numbers show the miles along a hiking trail. The black numbers show the hiking time in hours and minutes.

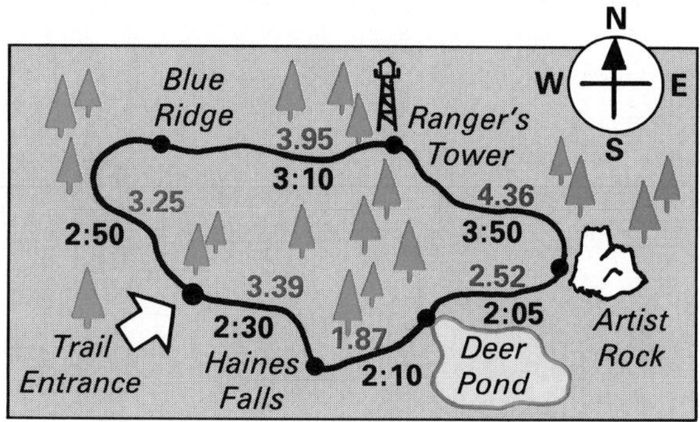

1. How many miles is it from the Trail Entrance to Haines Falls?
2. What two decimals would you add to find the distance from the Trail Entrance past Haines Falls to Deer Pond?

Here's how to add decimals.

3.39 + 1.87 = ?

To estimate the sum, you could round each decimal to the nearest whole number and add.

3 + 2 = 5

Line up the decimal points.

$$\begin{array}{r} 3.39 \\ +1.87 \\ \hline \end{array}$$

Add.

$$\begin{array}{r} {}^{1\,1} \\ 3.39 \\ +1.87 \\ \hline 5.26 \end{array}$$

3. Look at the example above. To estimate the sum, each decimal was rounded to the nearest _?_ number.
4. Was the sum close to the estimate?

EXERCISES

Four of the calculator answers are wrong. Find them by estimating.

5.
- **a.** 68.06 + 9.784 — 77.844
- **b.** 39.842 + 31.063 — 70.905
- **c.** 5.0831 + 3.9142 — 6.9973
- **d.** 54.893 + 15.138 — 70.031
- **e.** 78.566 + 8.167 — 86.733
- **f.** 9.8659 + 7.9301 — 27.7960
- **g.** 56.875 + 13.315 — 70.190
- **h.** 8.844 + 5.222 — 14.066
- **i.** 80.099 + 20.377 — 94.476
- **j.** 5.3429 + 0.728 — 6.0709
- **k.** 13.521 + 1.3521 — 14.8731
- **l.** 36.084 + 11.769 — 53.853

▶ **Give each sum.**

Here are scrambled answers for the next two rows of exercises:

22.41   32.1   26.22   10.2   35.51   23.7

6. 7.3 + 2.9

7. 15.4 + 16.7

8. 13.0 + 9.41

9. 8.3 + 6.9 + 8.5

10. 20.63 + 10.6 + 4.28

11. 15.42 + 3.8 + 7

12. 5.038 + 2.96

13. 18.04 + 2.683

14. 32.4 + 15.067

15. 6.8 + 3.42 + 9.3

16. 26.4 + 21.8 + 7.56

17. 37 + 8.4 + 2.6

18. 3.7 + 17 + 0.9

19. 20 + 4.7 + 0.857

20. 3.8 + 5 + 0.71

21. 0.03 + 0.6 + 8

22. 0.6 + 0.69 + 0.01

23. 16 + 1.6 + 0.517

▶ **Use your mental-math skills. Evaluate each expression to get the total cost.**

24. $a + c$

25. $b + c$

26. $c + e$

27. $d + a$

28. $a + e$

29. $e + a$

30. $b + d$

31. $d + e$

32. $a + c + d$

33. $a + c + e$

34. $c + d + e$

35. $a + b + c$

36. $a + d + e$

37. $b + c + e$

38. $b + d + e$

39. $a + a + e$

40. $d + d + c$

41. $c + c + e$

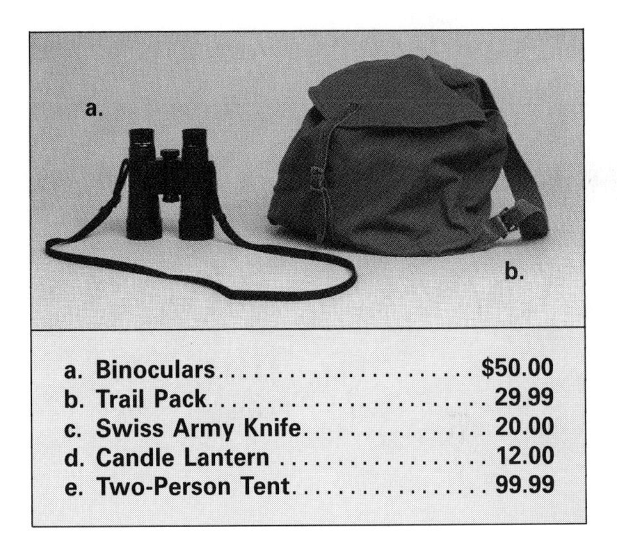

a. Binoculars	$50.00
b. Trail Pack	29.99
c. Swiss Army Knife	20.00
d. Candle Lantern	12.00
e. Two-Person Tent	99.99

Problem Solving

▶ **Solve. Use the map on page 64.**

42. What is the shortest hiking distance from the Trail Entrance to the Ranger's Tower?

43. What is the shortest hiking distance from Blue Ridge to Artist Rock?

44. What is the hiking time from Deer Pond past Artist Rock to the Ranger's Tower?

45. What is the hiking time from the Trail Entrance over Blue Ridge to the Ranger's Tower?

46. You leave Haines Falls at 8:00 A.M. If you plan two 15-minute stops, at what time should you arrive at Artist Rock?

47. You want to arrive at the Trail Entrance by 4:00 P.M. If you plan to take a 15-minute stop at Blue Ridge, what time should you leave the Ranger's Tower?

Estimating and Computing Decimal Differences

Mark's guess

Several students had a contest to see who could come closest to guessing how long a minute is. The results are shown in the table.

Name	Time (seconds)
Mark C.	54.29
Joan G.	57.08
Susan J.	63.41
Alan M.	65.63
David R.	56.79
Nancy T.	64.80

1. How many seconds did Mark guess?
2. From what number would you subtract 54.29 to compute how close Mark came to a minute?

Here's how to subtract decimals.

60 − 54.29 = ?

To estimate the difference, you could round each decimal to the nearest whole number and subtract.

60 − 54 = 6

Line up the decimal points and annex the *0*'s.

$$\begin{array}{r} 60.00 \\ -54.29 \\ \hline \end{array}$$

Subtract.

$$\begin{array}{r} \overset{5}{\cancel{6}}\overset{9}{\cancel{0}}.\overset{9}{\cancel{0}}0 \\ -54.29 \\ \hline 5.71 \end{array}$$

3. Look at the example above. To estimate the difference, each decimal was rounded to the nearest _?_ number.
4. Was the difference close to the estimate?

EXERCISES

▶ **Three of the calculator answers are wrong. Find them by estimating.**

5. a. 87.42 − 4.25 [83.17] **b.** 68.12 − 39.31 [38.81]

c. 6.01 − 2.99 [5.02] **d.** 18.2 − 16.95 [1.25]

e. 243.8 − 22.12 [122.6] **f.** 17.21 − 13.194 [4.016]

Give each difference.

Here are scrambled answers for the next row of exercises: 28.2 2.45 6.25 8.2

6. $6.43 - 0.18$ **7.** $39.6 - 11.4$ **8.** $15 - 6.8$ **9.** $2.93 - 0.48$

10. $1.742 - 0.815$ **11.** $21 - 3.75$ **12.** $69.48 - 27.4$ **13.** $78.4 - 26.95$

14. $62.49 - 35.71$ **15.** $5.74 - 3.8$ **16.** $27 - 10.4$ **17.** $23.75 - 18.8$

18. $8.4 - 5$ **19.** $80.03 - 4.38$ **20.** $6.254 - 0.88$ **21.** $6.83 - 2.7$

22. $28 - 15.7$ **23.** $6.2 - 3.851$ **24.** $7.69 - 0.94$ **25.** $75.25 - 18$

26. $12.692 - 8.95$ **27.** $9.006 - 4.44$ **28.** $100 - 26.7$ **29.** $37.2 - 3.72$

30. $9.304 - 6.91$ **31.** $131 - 106.94$ **32.** $0.361 - 0.087$ **33.** $68 - 62.75$

34. $8.37 - 1.6$ **35.** $10 - 0.42$ **36.** $9.1 - 3.67$ **37.** $65 - 7.8$

Evaluate each expression for $x = 10$, $y = 5.5$, and $z = 12.75$.

Here are scrambled answers for the next row of exercises: 15.5 2.75 4.5 22.75

38. $x - y$ **39.** $z - x$ **40.** $x + y$ **41.** $z + x$

42. $z - y$ **43.** $x - x$ **44.** $y + z$ **45.** $z + y$

46. $y + z - x$ **47.** $z - y + x$ **48.** $y + x - z$ **49.** $x + z - y$

50. $x + y + z$ **51.** $y + x + z$ **52.** $x + y - z$ **53.** $z - x + y$

54. $z + y + x$ **55.** $x - y + z$ **56.** $x + y - y$ **57.** $z + z - y$

58. $x + x - y$ **59.** $y + y + z$ **60.** $z + x - x$ **61.** $y - y + z$

62. $x + x + x$ **63.** $y + y + y$ **64.** $z + z + z$ **65.** $z + z - z$

CALCULATOR

Tell whether you would push the [+] or [−] key to get the answer.

66. 31.5 _?_ 6.7 _?_ 4.3 [=] 33.9

67. 47.2 _?_ 32.8 _?_ 6.7 [=] 21.1

68. 9.34 _?_ 4.68 _?_ 2.14 [=] 2.52

69. 8.73 _?_ 1.29 _?_ 4.37 [=] 5.65

70. 16.71 _?_ 3.48 _?_ 4.52 [=] 17.75

71. 23.74 _?_ 4.68 _?_ 4.35 [=] 23.41

72. 4.074 _?_ 1.032 _?_ 0.751 [=] 5.857

73. 62.14 _?_ 3.47 _?_ 3.46 [=] 62.15

74. 21.74 _?_ 11.38 _?_ 1.93 [=] 31.19

75. 40.89 _?_ 29.28 _?_ 4.06 [=] 7.55

76. 26 _?_ 1.49 _?_ 1.52 [=] 25.97

77. 83 _?_ 2.03 _?_ 1.98 [=] 82.95

Solving Addition and Subtraction Equations

You have learned to solve addition equations by subtracting a *whole number* from both sides, and you have learned to solve subtraction equations by adding a *whole number* to both sides. In this lesson you will solve equations by adding a *decimal* to both sides or by subtracting a *decimal* from both sides.

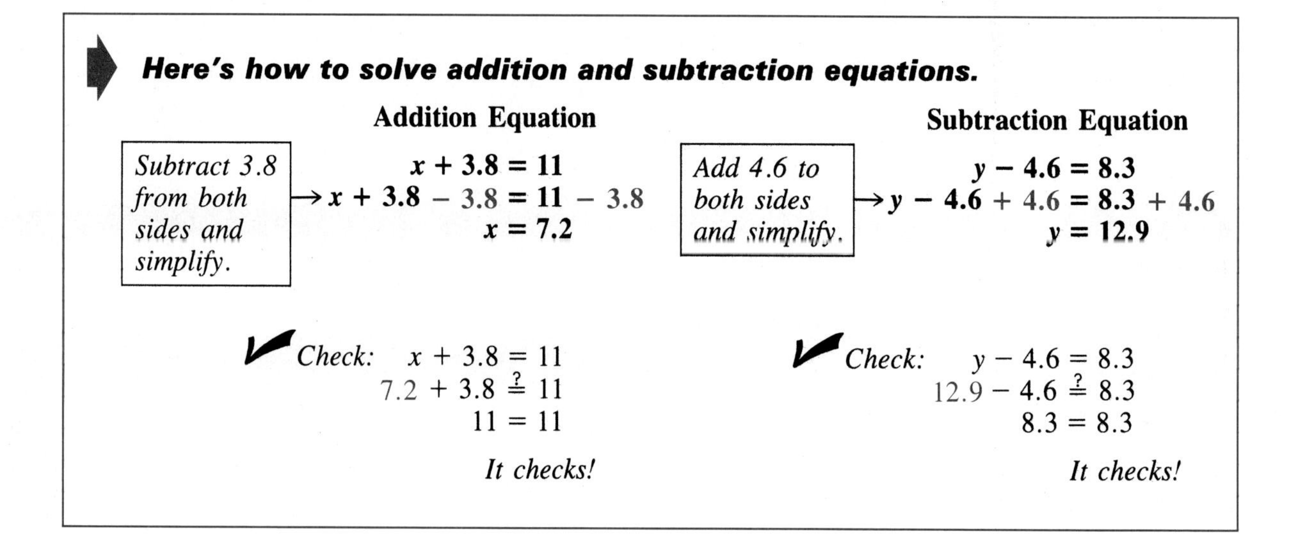

Here's how to solve addition and subtraction equations.

Addition Equation

Subtract 3.8 from both sides and simplify.

$$x + 3.8 = 11$$
$$x + 3.8 - 3.8 = 11 - 3.8$$
$$x = 7.2$$

Check:
$$x + 3.8 = 11$$
$$7.2 + 3.8 \stackrel{?}{=} 11$$
$$11 = 11$$

It checks!

Subtraction Equation

Add 4.6 to both sides and simplify.

$$y - 4.6 = 8.3$$
$$y - 4.6 + 4.6 = 8.3 + 4.6$$
$$y = 12.9$$

Check:
$$y - 4.6 = 8.3$$
$$12.9 - 4.6 \stackrel{?}{=} 8.3$$
$$8.3 = 8.3$$

It checks!

1. Look at the examples above.

a. To find x, what number was subtracted from both sides?

b. To find y, what number was added to both sides?

2. Complete these examples.

a.
$$r + 2.5 = 8$$
$$r + 2.5 - 2.5 = 8 - 2.5$$
$$r = \underline{\ ?\ }$$

b.
$$t - 3.6 = 4$$
$$t - 3.6 + 3.6 = 4 + 3.6$$
$$t = \underline{\ ?\ }$$

c.
$$s + 8.4 = 12.6$$
$$s + 8.4 - 8.4 = 12.6 - \underline{\ ?\ }$$
$$s = \underline{\ ?\ }$$

d.
$$20 = w - 6.4$$
$$w - 6.4 = \underline{\ ?\ }$$
$$w - 6.4 + 6.4 = 20 + 6.4$$
$$w = 26.4$$

symmetric property of equality

e.
$$17.2 = u - 10.9$$
$$u - 10.9 = \underline{\ ?\ }$$
$$u - 10.9 + \underline{\ ?\ } = 17.2 + 10.9$$
$$u = \underline{\ ?\ }$$

f.
$$36.4 = y + 6.48$$
$$y + 6.48 = \underline{\ ?\ }$$
$$y + 6.48 - \underline{\ ?\ } = 36.4 - \underline{\ ?\ }$$
$$y = 29.92$$

▶ **Solve and check.**
Here are scrambled answers for the next row of exercises: *7.9* *25.6* *13.1*

3. $9 = x - 4.1$
4. $a + 5.1 = 13$
5. $g - 4.6 = 21$
6. $24 = w + 9.5$
7. $f + 6.4 = 18$
8. $31 = u + 19.4$
9. $26 = y - 7.2$
10. $h - 18.6 = 20$
11. $d - 3.9 = 4.5$
12. $16.4 = n - 18.6$
13. $h + 13.9 = 28.3$
14. $32.4 = t + 21.7$
15. $c + 5.8 = 9.3$
16. $p - 14.6 = 29.0$
17. $36.5 = y + 36.5$
18. $40.6 = m - 0$
19. $r - 18.2 = 0$
20. $m + 7.8 = 19$
21. $0 = z - 6.3$
22. $21 = s + 17.8$
23. $60 = m + 24.8$
24. $64 = q - 26.8$
25. $s + 33.3 = 50$
26. $c - 18 = 41.7$
27. $0 = n - 8.9$
28. $j + 19.1 = 19.1$
29. $m - 20 = 48.3$
30. $63.4 = n + 27.5$
31. $42.3 = q + 30.4$
32. $16.7 = s - 9.9$
33. $k - 8.3 = 10$
34. $b + 16 = 43.7$
35. $h + 6 = 8.29$
36. $b - 5.6 = 100$
37. $97 = r + 3.58$
38. $68.3 = t - 29.55$
39. $q - 5.8 = 30.75$
40. $40 = x + 22.68$
41. $110 = u - 35.8$
42. $k + 2.6 = 11.89$
43. $100 = v - 85.6$
44. $d + 0.39 = 26$
45. $1.78 = v + 0.94$
46. $h - 21 = 58.6$
47. $43.8 = p + 9.52$
48. $37 = w - 18.66$
49. $g + 0.752 = 3.5$
50. $a - 19.1 = 4.082$

Problem Solving

▶ **Solve.**

51. If you buy a record on sale, do you pay more or less than the regular price?
Hint: The formula below shows how the sale price is related to the regular price and the discount.

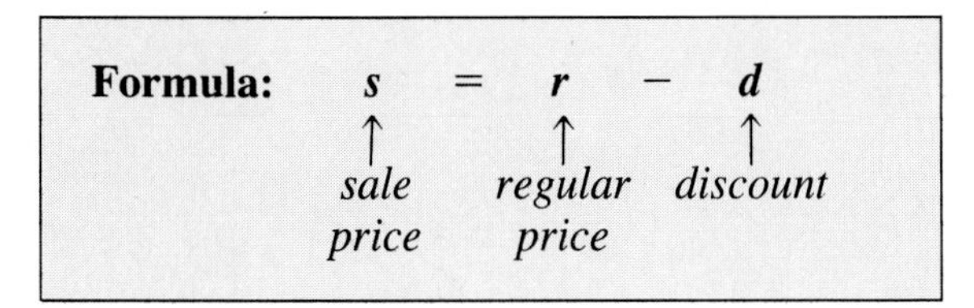

★52. Use the formula to complete this chart.

	Sale price (s)	Regular price (r)	Discount (d)
a.	?	\$8.39	\$2.10
b.	?	\$7.98	\$1.85
c.	\$4.95	?	\$1.67
d.	\$5.50	?	\$2.25
e.	?	\$6.90	\$1.95
f.	\$3.61	?	\$.98
g.	?	\$8.39	\$1.79

Cumulative Skill Practice

Solve and check. *(page 18)*

1. $c - 13 = 41$
2. $d + 16 = 29$
3. $16 = y - 16$
4. $37 = r + 16$
5. $68 = n + 57$
6. $w - 42 = 70$
7. $23 = x - 19$
8. $m + 39 = 81$
9. $64 = y - 82$
10. $s + 53 = 53$
11. $61 = t + 27$
12. $k - 23 = 32$

Write a mathematical expression for each word expression. *(page 28)*

13. the product of 6 and a number n
14. 12 times a number k
15. a number c divided by 20
16. 16 multiplied by a number w
17. 4 times a number t, plus 18
18. 10 times a number y, plus 24
19. a number s divided by 8, minus 12
20. the product of 12 and a number z, plus 29
21. a number p divided by a, plus 9
22. f times a number g, minus 18

Evaluate each expression for $x = 4$, $y = 6$, and $z = 10$. *(page 30)*

23. $xy + z$
24. $yz + x$
25. $xx - y$
26. $yy - z$
27. $5y + x$
28. $6x + z$
29. $8z + y$
30. $xy - z$
31. $\frac{42}{y} + x$
32. $\frac{36}{x} - y$
33. $\frac{36}{y} + z$
34. $\frac{60}{z} - x$

Multiply. *(page 36)*

35. 24×11
36. 29×31
37. 52×18
38. 47×61
39. 108×39
40. 268×54
41. 378×62
42. 680×50
43. 205×196
44. 218×304
45. 438×695
46. 768×540

Divide. *(page 42)*

47. $564 \div 21$
48. $802 \div 37$
49. $900 \div 28$
50. $739 \div 16$
51. $2351 \div 54$
52. $5900 \div 42$
53. $4638 \div 60$
54. $8217 \div 73$
55. $18{,}046 \div 108$
56. $35{,}081 \div 212$
57. $59{,}364 \div 431$
58. $72{,}057 \div 674$

Solve and check. *(page 44)*

59. $3x = 42$
60. $5r = 65$
61. $8v = 80$
62. $6n = 96$
63. $9u = 108$
64. $7m = 105$
65. $4y = 132$
66. $2s = 116$

Problem Solving—Applications

In many banks you can use a computer-operated teller machine to deposit and withdraw money, make payments, and check the balance of your account. To operate the machine, you insert a special card and enter your personal identification number. Directions will then appear on the screen.

Solve.

1. When you withdraw cash, you have to withdraw a multiple of $10 ($10, $20, $30, ...). How much would you withdraw if you needed
   a. $17.75? **b.** $48.53?
   c. $24.00? **d.** $179.25?

2. You request your account balances. They are:

Savings	$695.43
Checking	$381.35

   What is your total balance?

3. Suppose that your checking account had a beginning balance of $806.20. What would your balance be after writing checks for $92.00 and $136.29?

4. Suppose that your checking account had a beginning balance of $577.90. What would your balance be after writing a check for $82.41 and making a deposit of $75.00?

Decide whether Equation A, B, or C would be used to solve each problem. Then solve the problem.

Equation A: $n + 40 = 360$
Equation B: $n - 40 = 360$
Equation C: $40n = 360$

5. After writing a check for $40, your balance was $360. What was your balance before you wrote the check?

6. You deposit $40 in your savings account every week. How many deposits will you need to make to save $360?

7. You make a $40 cash withdrawal from your checking account. You then have $360 left in your account. How much money did you have in your account before the withdrawal?

8. You make a $40 cash deposit to your checking account. Your balance is then $360. How much money did you have in your account before the deposit?

Write an equation and solve the problem.

9. You have $460 in your checking account. You want to buy a television that costs $535. How much more money do you need?
   (Let n = the money you need.)

10. The regular price of a cassette tape player is reduced $118. You pay for the tape player by writing a check for $246. How much was the regular price?
    (Let n = the regular price.)

Estimating and Computing Decimal Products

1. What is the cost of one pound of grapes?
2. To find the cost of 2.4 pounds of grapes, you would multiply 2.4 by what number?

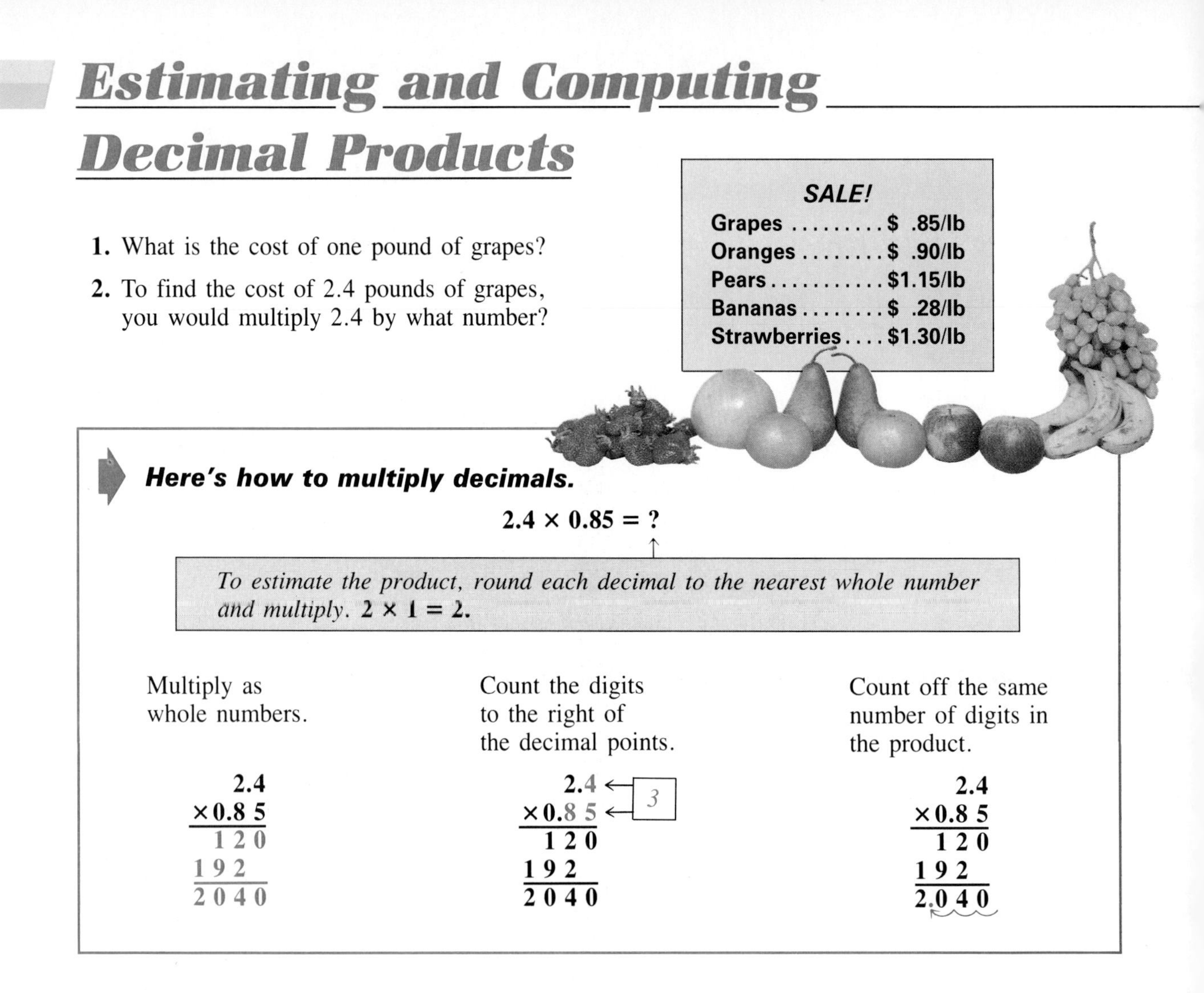

Here's how to multiply decimals.

2.4 × 0.85 = ?

To estimate the product, round each decimal to the nearest whole number and multiply. **2 × 1 = 2.**

Multiply as whole numbers.	Count the digits to the right of the decimal points.	Count off the same number of digits in the product.
2.4 ×0.8 5 1 2 0 1 9 2 2 0 4 0	2.4 ×0.8 5 (3) 1 2 0 1 9 2 2 0 4 0	2.4 ×0.8 5 1 2 0 1 9 2 2.0 4 0

3. Look at the example above. What is the cost of 2.4 pounds of grapes? Was $2 a good estimate?
4. Complete these examples.

a. 9.2 × 1.5

```
   9.2
  ×1.5
  4 _ 0
  _ 2
 _3. _ 0
```

b. 0.31 × 0.27

```
   0.31
  ×0.27
   2 1 _
   _ 2
 0. _ 8 _ 7
```

c. 85 × 0.71

```
    85
  ×0.71
     _5
  _ _ 5
  _0.3_
```

You have to write a zero here to place the decimal point.

Three of the calculator answers are wrong. Find them by estimating.

5. a. 7.1×0.98 6.958 **b.** 5.7×2.1 119.7

c. 2.31×9.85 22.7535 **d.** 3.28×4.6 15.088

e. 19×3.2 6.08 **f.** 8.74×2.1 183.54

Multiply.

Here are scrambled answers for the next row of exercises: *8.4* *33.12* *2.604* *9*

6. 4.8×6.9 **7.** 7.5×1.2 **8.** 4.2×2 **9.** 0.31×8.4

10. 1.8×56 **11.** 7.4×20 **12.** 0.05×0.7 **13.** 0.75×16

14. 7.5×0.42 **15.** 3.5×6.3 **16.** 2.31×0.7 **17.** 8.76×2.6

18. 75.6×4.32 **19.** 0.89×8.76 **20.** 0.006×0.12 **21.** 64.2×9.5

22. 4.15×0.021 **23.** 97.1×0.0025 **24.** 6.4×9.05 **25.** 77×1.4

Use your mental-math skills. Evaluate each expression for $r = 0.2$, $s = 0.6$, $t = 0.08$, $u = 9$, and $v = 0.1$.

26. rs **27.** st **28.** tu **29.** su

30. $r + s$ **31.** $s + t$ **32.** $u + v + s$ **33.** $r + s + t$

34. $s - r$ **35.** $s - v$ **36.** $rs - v$ **37.** $su - r$

Problem Solving

Solve. Use the prices on page 72.

38. How much would 1.7 pounds of oranges cost?

39. How much would 4.5 pounds of bananas cost?

40. A customer paid for 1.6 pounds of pears with a $5 bill. How much change should the customer receive?

41. You paid for 2.6 pounds of strawberries with a $5 bill. You received 4 coins and a bill in change. What were the coins?

Challenge

Use the clues to complete the sentences.

Clues:
- A lemon and a lime cost 31¢.
- A lime and an avocado cost 42¢.
- An avocado and a lemon cost 35¢.

42. Lemons cost __?__¢ each.

43. Limes cost __?__¢ each.

44. Avocados cost __?__¢ each.

Multiplying a Decimal by 10, 100, or 1000

A telephone survey was taken to identify favorite outdoor recreation activities. The bar graph shows the results.

1. What recreational activity was preferred by 1.8 thousand people?
2. What two numbers would you multiply to find how many people preferred bicycling?

Here's how to multiply a decimal by 10, 100, or 1000.

When you multiply a number by 10, 100, or 1000, the product is greater than the number.

2.5 × 10 = ?

Multiplying by 10 moves the decimal point 1 place to the right.

2.5
× 10
25.0

2.5 × 10 = 25.

2.5 × 100 = ?

Multiplying by 100 moves the decimal point 2 places to the right.

2.5 × 100 = 250.

2.5 × 1000 = ?

Multiplying by 1000 moves the decimal point 3 places to the right.

2.5 × 1000 = 2500.

3. Look at the example above. How many people chose bicycling as their favorite outdoor recreation?

EXERCISES

Give the product.

Here are scrambled answers for the next two rows of exercises.

7.2 856 85,600 72 860 7200 8600 8560

4. 7.2×10 **5.** 72×100 **6.** 0.72×10 **7.** 8.56×100

8. 856×100 **9.** 8.56×1000 **10.** 8.6×1000 **11.** 0.86×1000

12. 95×1000 **13.** 0.296×1000 **14.** 2.96×10 **15.** 2.96×100

16. 2.96×1000 **17.** 5.13×10 **18.** 5.13×100 **19.** 5.13×1000

20. 9400×10 **21.** 9400×100 **22.** 9400×1000 **23.** 940×100

24. 83×10 **25.** 83×100 **26.** 83×1000 **27.** 830×100

28. 0.76×1000 **29.** 0.76×100 **30.** 0.76×10 **31.** 7.6×1000

32. 0.09×1000 **33.** 0.09×100 **34.** 0.09×10 **35.** 0.9×10

36. 421×10 **37.** 421×1000 **38.** 421×100 **39.** 42.1×100

40. 64.2×100 **41.** 64.2×1000 **42.** 64.2×10 **43.** 0.642×1000

44. 4.76×1000 **45.** 4.76×10 **46.** 4.76×100 **47.** 476×100

Problem Solving

Solve. Use the bar graph on page 74.

48. Which recreational activity was preferred by the most people?

49. Which activity was preferred by the fewest people?

50. Which activity was preferred by 1300 people?

51. How many people preferred fishing?

52. Which activities were preferred by more than 1500 people?

53. Which activities were preferred by fewer than 2000 people?

54. How many more people preferred bicycling to golf?

55. How many fewer people preferred tennis to fishing?

Challenge

Graph the data given below.

56. a. Construct a bar graph like shown on page 74.

b. Construct a picture graph like shown on page 32.

Students Trying Out For Springfield High School Teams			
Football	42	Girls Gymnastics	30
Boys Basketball	33	Boys Track	43
Girls Basketball	29	Girls Track	37
Boys Gymnastics	25	Baseball	32

Dividing a Decimal by a Whole Number

Time yourself! Can you identify, just from the shape, what product is in each can?

A group of students timed themselves. Their results are shown in the table.

1. How many students recorded their time?
2. What was the total number of seconds?
3. To find the average time, you would divide 94.08 by what number?

Name	Time (seconds)
Craig	12.35
Mike	11.76
Sue	12.58
Dave	11.38
Carolyn	12.02
Earl	11.96
Bonnie	11.28
Bev	10.75
Total	94.08

Here's how to divide a decimal by a whole number. **94.08 ÷ 8 = ?**

Place the decimal point for the quotient.

$$8\overline{)94.08}$$

Divide as you would whole numbers.

$$\begin{array}{r} 11.76 \\ 8\overline{)94.08} \\ -8 \\ \hline 14 \\ -8 \\ \hline 60 \\ -56 \\ \hline 48 \\ -48 \\ \hline 0 \end{array}$$

4. Look at the example above. What is the average time for the students to identify the products?
5. Complete these examples. Round each quotient to the nearest hundredth.

a.

$$\begin{array}{r} 0.0\square\square \\ 9\overline{)0.432} \\ -36 \\ \hline 72 \\ -72 \\ \hline 0 \end{array}$$

You have to write a zero here.

b.

$$\begin{array}{r} 0.\square\square\square \\ 26\overline{)6.280} \\ -5\,2 \\ \hline 1\,08 \\ -1\,04 \\ \hline 40 \\ -26 \\ \hline 14 \end{array}$$

Sometimes the division does not come out even. You can annex a zero here and carry out the division to the next place.

Divide.

Here are scrambled answers for the next row of exercises: 4.2 0.405 2.54 1.24

6. $8.68 \div 7$ **7.** $33.02 \div 13$ **8.** $2.025 \div 5$ **9.** $134.4 \div 32$

10. $10.32 \div 43$ **11.** $38.36 \div 14$ **12.** $24.08 \div 7$ **13.** $358.4 \div 56$

14. $107.01 \div 87$ **15.** $300.51 \div 81$ **16.** $16.5 \div 55$ **17.** $362.25 \div 45$

18. $326.40 \div 80$ **19.** $165.33 \div 9$ **20.** $2722.2 \div 78$ **21.** $616.2 \div 6$

First carry out the division to the thousandths place. Then round the quotient to the nearest hundredth.

Example:

$$8\overline{)6.300} = 0.787 \approx 0.79$$

```
   0.787  ≈ 0.79
8)6.300
 -56
   70
  -64
    60
   -56
     4
```

≈ *means "is approximately equal to"*

22. $6.1 \div 7$ **23.** $17.03 \div 9$ **24.** $8.72 \div 3$

25. $8.2 \div 12$ **26.** $78.66 \div 15$ **27.** $45 \div 64$

28. $15 \div 8$ **29.** $74.2 \div 60$ **30.** $4.27 \div 23$

31. $65.9 \div 9$ **32.** $7.43 \div 14$ **33.** $3.6 \div 7$

34. $4.82 \div 8$ **35.** $2.11 \div 24$ **36.** $8.81 \div 12$

37. $9.25 \div 4$ **38.** $4.82 \div 45$ **39.** $8.8 \div 66$

40. $72 \div 7$ **41.** $16.4 \div 13$ **42.** $4.59 \div 11$

Use your mental-math skills. Evaluate each expression for $r = 2$, $s = 3$, $t = 0.6$, $u = 0.9$, and $v = 1.2$.

43. $\frac{t}{r}$ **44.** $\frac{u}{s}$ **45.** rt **46.** su **47.** tu **48.** sv

49. $r + u$ **50.** $s + v$ **51.** $s + t + r$ **52.** $u + v + s$

53. $u - t$ **54.** $v - u$ **55.** $r + s - t$ **56.** $u + v - r$

Problem Solving

Solve. Use the time chart on page 76.

57. Who identified the products in the least amount of time?

58. Who identified the products in a time that was 0.26 second faster than Carolyn's time?

59. What was the average time for the four boys to identify the products?

60. What was the average time for the four girls to identify the products?

Dividing a Decimal by a Decimal

Knaub Captures Wheel Title

Jim Knaub yesterday broke the Boston Marathon wheelchair record. He completed the 26.2188-mile course in 1.8 hours. Knaub, a 27-year-old resident of Long Beach, California, has been paralyzed since 1977.

The former Cal State Long Beach pole-vaulter and later its track coach attributes his win to a more efficient wheelchair and improved race conditions.

APRIL 19, 1983

Record-setter Jim Knaub cheers his victory.

1. Read the newspaper article. How many miles is the Boston Marathon course?
2. To compute Knaub's speed in miles per hour, you would divide 26.2188 by __?__ .

Here's how to divide a decimal by a decimal. $26.2188 \div 1.8 = ?$

Hard problem!

$1.8\overline{)26.2188}$

divisor ↑ dividend ↑

Multiply both divisor and dividend by 10 to get a whole-number divisor.

$1.8\overline{)26.2188}$

Divide.

$$
\begin{array}{r}
14.566 \\
18\overline{)262.188} \\
-18 \\
\hline
82 \\
-72 \\
\hline
101 \\
-90 \\
\hline
118 \\
-108 \\
\hline
108 \\
-108 \\
\hline
0
\end{array}
$$

3. Look at the example above. To get a whole-number divisor, both decimal points were moved __?__ place(s) to the right.
4. What was Knaub's average speed per hour?

5. Complete these examples.

a. $0.54\overline{)17.28}$ with quotient 32; $-$ ▒▒▒; 1 08; $-$ ▒▒▒; ▒

Move both decimal points 2 places to the right.

b. $0.006\overline{)0.2802}$ with quotient 46.7; $-$ ▒▒; 40; $-$ ▒▒; 4 2; $-$4 2; ▒

Move both decimal points 3 places to the right.

EXERCISES

▶ **Place the decimal point in each quotient.**

6. $0.2\overline{)0.56}$ quotient 28 **7.** $0.06\overline{)4.44}$ quotient 74 **8.** $0.007\overline{)0.0098}$ quotient 14 **9.** $0.4\overline{)6.24}$ quotient 156

10. $1.2\overline{)31.2}$ quotient 26 **11.** $0.3\overline{)0.78}$ quotient 26 **12.** $0.34\overline{)3.570}$ quotient 105 **13.** $0.012\overline{)0.0060}$ quotient 05

▶ **Divide.**

Here are scrambled answers for the next row of exercises: 910 38 6.5 12.7

14. $3.25 \div 0.5$ **15.** $0.76 \div 0.02$ **16.** $5.46 \div 0.006$ **17.** $1.016 \div 0.08$

18. $31.2 \div 0.4$ **19.** $0.57 \div 0.003$ **20.** $0.485 \div 0.5$ **21.** $2.56 \div 0.004$

22. $0.57 \div 0.15$ **23.** $3.91 \div 3.4$ **24.** $0.884 \div 0.26$ **25.** $0.126 \div 2.8$

26. $1.875 \div 0.25$ **27.** $26.22 \div 5.7$ **28.** $23.24 \div 2.8$ **29.** $40.95 \div 9.1$

Problem Solving

▶ **Decide which expression would be used to complete each sentence.**

Expression A: mn
Expression B: $\frac{m}{n}$
Expression C: $\frac{n}{m}$

30. The record for running the n-mile Boston Marathon is m hours. Therefore, the record average speed is __?__ miles per hour.

31. The longest recorded trampoline-bouncing marathon is m hours. The record was set by a team of n people. They averaged __?__ hours per person.

32. The longest distance recorded for walking backwards is __?__ miles at a speed of n miles per hour for m hours.

33. The record for swimming the English Channel by a relay team is m hours by n swimmers. The swimmers averaged __?__ hours apiece.

Dividing a Decimal by 10, 100, or 1000

Try your mental-math skills. Can you fill in the missing numbers in less than 15 seconds?

> **The boat in the picture costs $5000. You can buy it for _?_ $10 bills, or _?_ 100 bills, or _?_ $1000 bills.**

Remember: If you divide a number by 10, 100, or 1000, the quotient is less than the number.

Here's how to divide by 10, 100, or 1000.

5000 ÷ 10 = 500.0 , or 500	Dividing by 10 moves the decimal point 1 place to the left.
5000 ÷ 100 = 50.00 , or 50	Dividing by 100 moves the decimal point 2 places to the left.
5000 ÷ 1000 = 5.000 , or 5	Dividing by 1000 moves the decimal point 3 places to the left.

Other examples:

47.125 ÷ 10 = 4.7125

8.4 ÷ 100 = 0.084 ←

5.25 ÷ 1000 = 0.00525 ←

Some zeros had to be written before the decimal point could be placed in the quotient.

1. Look at the examples above. Dividing by 10 moves the decimal point 1 place to the _?_ .
2. Dividing by 100 moves the decimal point _?_ places to the left.
3. Dividing by 1000 moves the decimal point _?_ places to the left.
4. Divide.
   a. 36.5 ÷ 10 **b.** 6.3 ÷ 100 **c.** 17.2 ÷ 1000

Divide.

5. 76 ÷ 10 **6.** 76 ÷ 100 **7.** 76 ÷ 1000 **8.** 7.6 ÷ 10

9. 217.2 ÷ 10 **10.** 217.2 ÷ 100 **11.** 217.2 ÷ 1000 **12.** 21.72 ÷ 1000

13. 68.1 ÷ 1000 **14.** 68.1 ÷ 100 **15.** 68.1 ÷ 10 **16.** 0.681 ÷ 10

17. 80 ÷ 10 **18.** 80 ÷ 100 **19.** 80 ÷ 1000 **20.** 800 ÷ 10

21. 41.23 ÷ 10 **22.** 41.23 ÷ 100 **23.** 41.23 ÷ 1000 **24.** 4.123 ÷ 1

25. 846 ÷ 1000 **26.** 846 ÷ 100 **27.** 846 ÷ 10 **28.** 84.6 ÷ 1000

29. 214.7 ÷ 1000 **30.** 214.7 ÷ 100 **31.** 214.7 ÷ 10 **32.** 21.47 ÷ 100

33. 2.42 ÷ 10 **34.** 2.42 ÷ 100 **35.** 2.42 ÷ 1000 **36.** 242 ÷ 1000

37. 18.5 ÷ 100 **38.** 18.5 ÷ 1000 **39.** 18.5 ÷ 10 **40.** 1.85 ÷ 10

41. 9 ÷ 1000 **42.** 9 ÷ 100 **43.** 9 ÷ 10 **44.** 90 ÷ 100

45. 3.9 ÷ 100 **46.** 3.9 ÷ 1000 **47.** 3.9 ÷ 10 **48.** 39 ÷ 1000

Problem Solving

Use the sales ad. Complete each sentence.

USED-CAR SALE

'76 Firebird	75,000 mi	$2800
'77 Camaro	42,500 mi	$4400
'78 Mustang	63,100 mi	$5300
'79 Chevy Caprice	54,000 mi	$2500
'80 Monte Carlo	36,400 mi	$6700
'81 Olds Cutlass	38,000 mi	$5900

49. You can buy a 1979 Chevy Caprice for _?_ hundred dollars.

50. The 1978 Mustang costs _?_ hundred dollars.

51. The 1981 Olds Cutlass has been driven _?_ thousand miles.

52. The mileage on the 1977 Camaro is _?_ thousand miles.

53. The 1980 Monte Carlo costs _?_ hundred dollars more than the 1978 Mustang.

54. The 1977 Camaro costs _?_ hundred dollars less than the 1981 Olds Cutlass.

55. The 1976 Firebird has _?_ thousand more miles than the 1979 Chevy Caprice.

Challenge

Study the clues. Use the sales ad above to name the car.

56. *Clues:*
- This car costs more than $5000.
- It has less than 40,000 miles.
- It is older than the 1981 Olds Cutlass.

57. *Clues:*
- This car has more than 40,000 miles.
- It is newer than the 1977 Camaro.
- It costs less than $5000.

Solving Multiplication and Division Equations

You have already solved equations such as

$$12x = 60 \text{ and } \frac{y}{14} = 9$$

In this lesson you will use what you have learned about solving multiplication and division equations to solve equations involving decimals.

Here's how to solve multiplication and division equations involving decimals.

Remember that multiplication and division are inverse operations—that is, division undoes multiplication and multiplication undoes division.

$$\begin{aligned} 0.2n &= 7 \\ \frac{0.2n}{0.2} &= \frac{7}{0.2} \\ n &= 35 \end{aligned}$$

$$0.2\overline{)7.0} = 35; \quad -6,\ 10,\ -10,\ 0$$

Check: $0.2n = 7$

$0.2(35) \stackrel{?}{=} 7$

$7 = 7$

It checks!

$$\begin{aligned} \frac{m}{1.2} &= 8 \\ 1.2 \times \frac{m}{1.2} &= 1.2 \times 8 \\ m &= 9.6 \end{aligned}$$

$$1.2 \times 8 = 9.6$$

Check: $\frac{m}{1.2} = 8$

$\frac{9.6}{1.2} \stackrel{?}{=} 8$

$8 = 8$ *It checks!*

1. Look at the examples above.

a. To find n, what number were both sides of the equation divided by? What does n equal?
b. To find m, what number were both sides of the equation multiplied by? What does m equal?

c. To check the solution, what number was substituted for m in the equation $\frac{m}{1.2} = 8$?

2. Complete these examples.

a.
$$\begin{aligned} 5d &= 13.5 \\ \frac{5d}{5} &= \frac{13.5}{?} \\ d &= 2.7 \end{aligned}$$

b.
$$\begin{aligned} \frac{r}{2.5} &= 12 \\ \underline{?} \times \frac{r}{2.5} &= 2.5 \times 12 \\ r &= 30 \end{aligned}$$

c.
$$\begin{aligned} 6.2 &= \frac{t}{3} \\ \frac{t}{3} &= 6.2 \\ 3 \times \frac{t}{3} &= 3 \times 6.2 \\ t &= \underline{?} \end{aligned}$$

d.
$$\begin{aligned} 1.26 &= 1.4y \\ 1.4y &= \underline{?} \\ \frac{1.4y}{?} &= \frac{1.26}{?} \\ y &= \underline{?} \end{aligned}$$

▶ **Solve and check.**
Here are scrambled answers for the next two rows of exercises:
5 0.6 0.21 0.4 12.4 0.07 5.2 8.4

3. $3r = 1.2$ **4.** $4b = 2.4$ **5.** $6r = 0.42$ **6.** $1.5n = 7.5$

7. $\frac{b}{4.2} = 2$ **8.** $\frac{r}{3.1} = 4$ **9.** $\frac{c}{0.03} = 7$ **10.** $\frac{k}{5.2} = 1$

11. $5j = 4.5$ **12.** $6.4 = 8n$ **13.** $1.4 = 7a$ **14.** $1.2s = 0.36$

15. $3.5 = \frac{n}{6}$ **16.** $\frac{m}{12} = 0.2$ **17.** $\frac{d}{25} = 0.01$ **18.** $2.5 = \frac{e}{3}$

19. $5t = 6$ **20.** $12 = 8r$ **21.** $15 = 6n$ **22.** $2.5k = 12$

▶ **Solve and check.**
Here are scrambled answers for the next two rows of exercises:
8.3 1.1 5.3 2.5 8.5 0.5 15.3 1.2

23. $n + 1.6 = 2.8$ **24.** $t + 0.2 = 8.5$ **25.** $7.5 = m + 5$ **26.** $t + 7.5 = 8$

27. $t - 2.2 = 3.1$ **28.** $9.3 = m - 6$ **29.** $b - 7.5 = 1$ **30.** $0.8 = c - 0.3$

31. $4t = 1.6$ **32.** $\frac{n}{4} = 0.3$ **33.** $a + 2.1 = 2.3$ **34.** $b - 6 = 9.3$

35. $1.5 = \frac{k}{3}$ **36.** $13.8 = 0.6s$

37. $8.5 = y + 6.2$ **38.** $3.3 = c - 1.2$

Problem Solving

▶ **Use the formula to complete the chart.**

You work at a fast-food restaurant. Your earnings depend upon the number of hours you work and your hourly wage (what you are paid per hour). You can use this formula to compute your earnings:

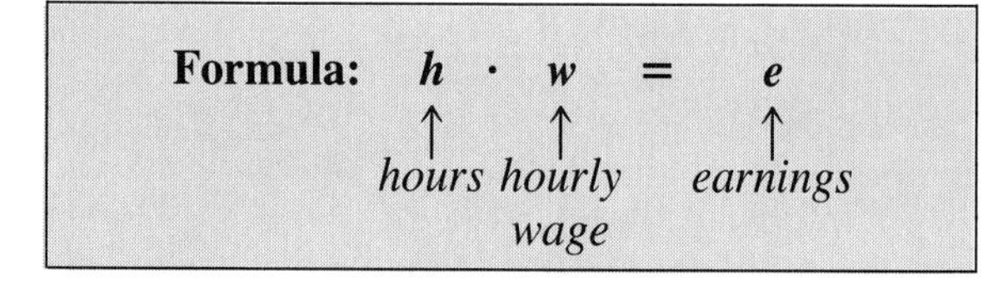

★39.

	h (hours)	*w* (dollars per hour)	*e* (total dollars)
a.	12	5	?
b.	10	4.50	?
c.	40	3.85	?
d.	25	?	100
e.	15	?	57.75
f.	6	?	22.80

Problem Solving—Using Equations

Remember: To write an equation, you need to write two equal expressions. One of the expressions can be just a number.

Here's how to use an equation to solve a problem.

Problem: Ken's distance on the broad jump is 1.75 feet more than Carrie's distance. Ken's distance is 14.5 feet. What is Carrie's distance?

Step 1. Choose a variable. Use it and the facts to represent the numbers in the problem.

Let c = Carrie's distance
Then $c + 1.75$ = Ken's distance

Step 2. Write an equation based on the facts.

$$c + 1.75 = 14.5$$

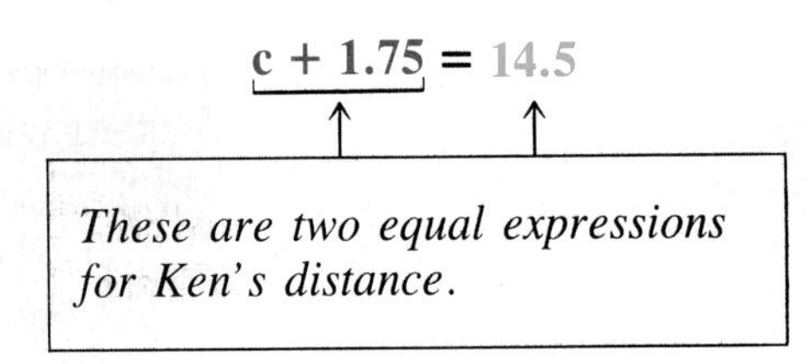

Step 3. Solve the equation.

$$c + 1.75 = 14.5$$
$$c + 1.75 - 1.75 = 14.5 - 1.75$$
$$c = 12.75$$

Carrie jumped 12.75 feet.

1. Look at the example above.

a. In Step 1, we let c equal Carrie's distance. Then Ken's distance equals c + __?__.
b. In Step 2, the two equal expressions for Ken's distance are __?__ and 14.5.
c. An equation for the problem is c + __?__ = __?__.
d. To solve the equation, __?__ was subtracted from both sides of the equation.

2. To check the solution, ask yourself if the answer fits the facts in the problem. Did Carrie jump 12.75 feet?

EXERCISES

Read the facts. Then complete the steps to answer the question.

3. *Facts:* Jackie's shot-put distance was 3.5 feet less than Cindy's. Jackie's shot-put distance was 29 feet.

Question: What was Cindy's shot-put distance?

a. If you let c equal Cindy's shot-put distance, then c − __?__ equals Jackie's distance.

b. Jackie's shot-put distance was __?__ feet.

c. Two equal expressions for Jackie's distance are c − __?__ and 29.

d. To find Cindy's shot-put distance, you can solve the equation $c - 3.5 =$ __?__ .

e. Solve the equation in part d. Cindy's shot-put distance was __?__ feet.

4. *Facts:* Brian threw the discus 90 feet. His distance was 1.2 times as far as Ted's throw.

Question: How far did Ted throw the discus?

a. If you let t equal the distance Ted threw the discus, then __?__ $\cdot\, t$ equals Brian's distance.

b. Brian threw the discus __?__ feet.

c. Two equal expressions for Brian's distance are __?__ $\cdot\, t$ and 90.

d. To find how far Ted threw the discus, you can solve the equation $1.2t =$ __?__ .

e. Solve the equation in part d. Ted threw the discus __?__ feet.

Write an equation and solve the problem.

5. A number increased by 7.4 equals 20.7. What is the number?
(Let c = the number.)

6. A number decreased by 1.36 is 13.29. What is the number?
(Let d = the number.)

7. A number times 4 is 26.4. What is the number?
(Let f = the number.)

8. A number divided by 3.2 is 7.5. What is the number?
(Let g = the number.)

9. The sum of two numbers is 17.6. One of the numbers is 8.2. What is the other number?
(Let n = the other number.)

10. The difference between two numbers is 6.3. The lesser number is 10.9. What is the greater number?
(Let m = the greater number.)

11. The product of two numbers is 6.5. One of the numbers is 1.3. What is the other number?
(Let p = the other number.)

12. When the greater number is divided by the lesser number, the quotient is 1.2. If the lesser number is 5, what is the greater number?
(Let r = the greater number.)

13. Stan ran the 100-yard dash in 13.5 seconds. His time was 1.8 seconds faster than Calvin's time. What was Calvin's time?
(Let c = Calvin's time.)

14. Holly high-jumped 5.5 feet. Her jump was 1.1 times higher than Kari's jump. How high did Kari jump?
(Let k = the height Kari jumped.)

Cumulative Skill Practice

▶ **Solve and check.** *(page 46)*

1. $\frac{c}{3} = 8$ **2.** $\frac{z}{9} = 7$ **3.** $\frac{s}{8} = 11$ **4.** $\frac{b}{6} = 10$

5. $\frac{y}{10} = 15$ **6.** $\frac{v}{4} = 25$ **7.** $\frac{d}{5} = 16$ **8.** $\frac{x}{11} = 42$

9. $\frac{w}{20} = 13$ **10.** $\frac{a}{16} = 16$ **11.** $\frac{t}{24} = 9$ **12.** $\frac{r}{23} = 17$

▶ **Solve and check.** *(page 48)*

13. $\frac{c}{6} = 11$ **14.** $a - 16 = 30$ **15.** $r + 15 = 15$ **16.** $90 = 9x$

17. $72 = s + 20$ **18.** $v + 48 = 165$ **19.** $180 = 20r$ **20.** $46 = g - 22$

21. $20 = \frac{d}{16}$ **22.** $t + 19 = 40$ **23.** $39 = b - 0$ **24.** $416 = 32t$

25. $c - 23 = 85$ **26.** $11w = 33$ **27.** $112 = u + 45$ **28.** $\frac{f}{12} = 17$

29. $18s = 396$ **30.** $4 = \frac{e}{18}$ **31.** $\frac{b}{25} = 12$ **32.** $100 = d - 60$

33. $120 = z + 56$ **34.** $0 = \frac{a}{26}$ **35.** $f - 106 = 111$ **36.** $25y = 475$

▶ **Solve and check.** *(page 68)*

37. $c + 3.8 = 9.9$ **38.** $r - 6.4 = 2.2$ **39.** $6.41 = d + 4.81$ **40.** $8.32 = s - 5.83$

41. $v - 4.3 = 5.76$ **42.** $f + 2.7 = 9$ **43.** $28 = w - 9.37$ **44.** $14.2 = g + 8$

45. $y + 8.26 = 12.9$ **46.** $x - 4.8 = 19.63$ **47.** $16 = a + 2.94$ **48.** $29 = y - 13.74$

▶ **Multiply.** *(page 72)*

49. 8.2×2 **50.** 4.3×0.6 **51.** 7.15×0.8 **52.** 4.62×9

53. 2.54×12 **54.** 6.8×23 **55.** 9.3×2.6 **56.** 5.74×7.8

57. 0.531×1.8 **58.** 14.6×0.49 **59.** 9.74×3.58 **60.** 6.75×0.483

▶ **Divide.** *(page 78)*

61. $2.4 \div 0.8$ **62.** $0.156 \div 0.6$ **63.** $0.567 \div 0.07$ **64.** $0.495 \div 0.09$

65. $5.27 \div 1.7$ **66.** $50.4 \div 4.2$ **67.** $2.3218 \div 0.38$ **68.** $8.584 \div 0.74$

69. $0.00336 \div 0.007$ **70.** $0.09288 \div 0.0018$ **71.** $45.402 \div 9.4$ **72.** $3.4476 \div 0.68$

Problem Solving—Applications

Big Holiday Sale!			
FILM SHOP Color Film			PHOTO FINISHING Color Prints
Size	Exposures	Price	
135	36	\$3.00	Any negative 25¢
135	20	\$2.15	Each additional print 15¢
126	20	\$2.05	5 × 7 enlargement 99¢
110	12	\$1.49	8 × 10 enlargement \$2.59

Solve.

1. What will it cost you to buy a roll of size 110 film and have one print made of each exposure?
2. Your best friend bought 2 rolls of film. She spent \$5.15. How many pictures will she be able to take?
3. You leave 2 rolls of 126 film to be developed. If you order 2 prints of each exposure, how much will the prints cost?
4. What is the average cost per print if you order 12 prints of a negative? Round the answer to the nearest tenth of a cent.

Decide whether Equation A, B, C, or D would be used to solve each problem. Then solve the problem.

Equation A: $n + 12 = 60$
Equation B: $n - 12 = 60$
Equation C: $12n = 60$
Equation D: $\frac{n}{12} = 60$

5. After you take 12 photos, you have 60 exposures left. How many exposures did you have before you took the photos?
6. The average number of photos taken by 12 tourists was 60. How many photos were taken altogether?
7. After you buy a package of 12 flashbulbs, you have a total of 60. How many flashbulbs did you have before you bought the package of 12?
8. During a Thursday night special, you could get a dozen prints made for 60¢. What was the cost per print?

Write an equation and solve the problem.

9. You have 96 photos to mount in an album. If you mount 6 on a page, how many pages will you need? (Let n = the number of pages.)

★10. The average cost per exposure for a 20-exposure roll of film is 11.5¢. What is the price of the roll of film? (Let n = the cost of the roll of film.)

Chapter Review

Here are scrambled answers for the review exercises:

2.5	*24*	*digits*	*greater*	*multiply*	*subtract*	*up*
6	*25*	*divide*	*left*	*right*	*ten-thousandths*	
10	*add*	*down*	*less*	*simplify*	*thousandths*	

1. The short word-name for **17.039** is 17 and 39 _?_. *(page 58)*

2. The short word-name for **25.0015** is 25 and 15 _?_. *(page 58)*

3. To round **6.728** to the nearest whole number, first look at the digit in the tenths place. Since it is _?_ than 5, you would round the decimal _?_ to 7. *(page 60)*

4. To round **6.728** to the nearest tenth, first look at the digit in the hundredths place. Since it is _?_ than 5, you would round the decimal _?_ to 6.7. *(page 60)*

5. To compare the decimals **68.51** ◆ **68.15** start at the left and compare the _?_ that are in the same place. *(page 62)*

6. If you estimate the sum of **15.94 + 9.092** by rounding each decimal to the nearest whole number, you get _?_. *(page 64)*

7. If you estimate the difference of **28.89 − 5.17** by rounding to the nearest whole number, you get _?_. *(page 66)*

8. To solve the equation $x - 3.52 = 4.08$ you would first _?_ 3.52 to both sides, then _?_ both sides. *(page 68)*

9. To solve the equation $x + 4.9 = 6.14$, you would first _?_ 4.9 from both sides and then simplify both sides. *(page 68)*

10. If you estimate the product of **6.17 × 0.94** by rounding each decimal to the nearest whole number, you get _?_. *(page 72)*

11. Multiplying a decimal by 1000 moves the decimal point 3 places to the _?_. Dividing a decimal by 1000 moves the decimal point 3 places to the _?_. *(pages 74, 80)*

12. To find the quotient of $2.8\overline{)22.96}$ you would first _?_ the divisor and dividend by _?_ to get a whole-number divisor. *(page 78)*

13. To solve the equation $2.5y = 8$ you would first _?_ both sides by _?_ and then simplify both sides. *(page 82)*

Chapter Test

Write the short word-name. *(page 58)*

1. 12.7 **2.** 8.92 **3.** 0.064 **4.** 2.0256

Round to the nearest hundredth. *(page 60)*

5. 9.427 **6.** 0.358 **7.** 1.605 **8.** 7.7706 **9.** 0.005 **10.** 6.2982

$<$ **or** $>$**?** *(page 62)*

11. 0.5 ◆ 0.3 **12.** 0.4 ◆ 0.05 **13.** 0.614 ◆ 0.62 **14.** 36.009 ◆ 36.01

Give each sum or difference. *(pages 64, 66)*

15. $8.46 + 3.97$ **16.** $11.46 + 3.855$ **17.** $9.6 + 0.04 + 12.5$ **18.** $15.32 + 0.09 + 6$

19. $2.57 - 0.96$ **20.** $13.5 - 9.16$ **21.** $20 - 9.3$ **22.** $9.075 - 8.88$

Solve and check. *(pages 68, 82)*

23. $x + 2.7 = 5$ **24.** $w - 3.8 = 12.4$ **25.** $z + 9.6 = 12.3$ **26.** $y - 0.58 = 7.4$

27. $33 = t - 4.6$ **28.** $15.7 = u + 8.8$ **29.** $5.27 = n - 8.8$ **30.** $0.06 = n + 0.06$

31. $4a = 9.6$ **32.** $14.4 = 16h$ **33.** $8b = 4.08$ **34.** $184.8 = 28h$

35. $7.2 = \frac{f}{12}$ **36.** $\frac{c}{3.2} = 5$ **37.** $2.7 = \frac{g}{6.6}$ **38.** $\frac{d}{0.6} = 1.34$

Give each product or quotient. *(pages 72, 74, 76, 78, 80)*

39. 1.6×8.4 **40.** 0.05×0.8 **41.** 0.07×1000 **42.** 5.049×100

43. $73.2 \div 8$ **44.** $17.248 \div 5.6$ **45.** $50.32 \div 10$ **46.** $9.31 \div 1000$

First choose the equation and solve the problem. Then reread the problem to see if your answer makes sense.
(page 84)

Equation A: $n + 5 = 42.5$
Equation B: $n - 5 = 42.5$
Equation C: $5n = 42.5$
Equation D: $\frac{n}{5} = 42.5$

47. In one week Alex rode his bicycle 5 times over the same route. He rode 42.5 miles altogether. How many miles long is the route?

48. John rode 5 fewer miles than Maria. If John rode 42.5 miles, how many miles did Maria ride?

49. Jerry rode 5 more miles than Ann. If Jerry rode 42.5 miles, how many miles did Ann ride?

50. While in training, Marty averaged 42.5 miles per day for 5 days. How many miles did she ride during training?

Cumulative Test
Standardized Format

▶ **Choose the correct letter.**

1. Solve.

$79 = y - 37$

A. 116
B. 42
C. 79
D. none of these

2. An expression for a number n divided by 3, minus 8 is

A. $3n - 8$
B. $\frac{n}{3} + 8$
C. $\frac{n}{3} - 8$
D. none of these

3. Evaluate $\frac{48}{y} - x$ for $x = 3$ and $y = 8$.

A. 8
B. 3
C. 9
D. none of these

4. Give the product.

647×208

A. 18,116
B. 17,016
C. 124,576
D. none of these

5. Give the quotient.

$20{,}468 \div 34$

A. 62
B. 620
C. 602
D. none of these

6. Solve.

$16w = 432$

A. 27
B. 416
C. 6912
D. none of these

7. Solve.

$\frac{t}{15} = 75$

A. 1125
B. 60
C. 5
D. none of these

8. Solve.

$340 = 20r$

A. 320
B. 17
C. 6800
D. none of these

9. Solve.

$12.1 = v - 8.93$

A. 3.17
B. 10.14
C. 21.03
D. none of these

10. Give the product.

5.82×1.6

A. 93.12
B. 8.212
C. 4.074
D. none of these

11. Give the quotient.

$12.936 \div 4.62$

A. 0.28
B. 2.8
C. 5.6
D. none of these

12. Choose the equation.

Susan earned $29.25 for working 9 hours. How much did she earn per hour?

A. $n + 9 = 29.25$
B. $n - 9 = 29.25$
C. $9n = 29.25$
D. $\frac{n}{9} = 29.25$

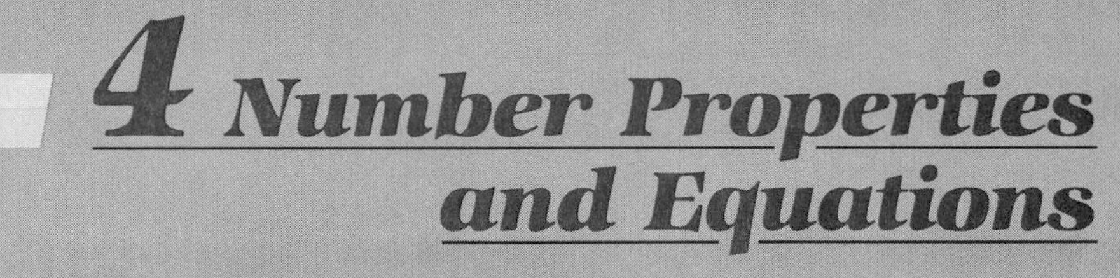

4 Number Properties and Equations

$c = 50d + 0.35m$

Cost equals \$50 a day plus 35¢ a mile.

(page 115)

Many families rent campers when they go on a vacation. Most rental firms charge a daily rate plus a certain amount for each mile driven.

Order of Operations

1. How many NFL decals are there on the three sheets?
2. The number of NFL decals is given by the expression written in red.
   a. If you add first and then multiply, do you get the number of decals?
   b. If you multiply first and then add, do you get the number of decals?
3. Does the expression have a different value when you do the operations in a different order?

$3 + 2 \times 6$

Here's how to simplify expressions having more than one kind of operation:

So that an expression has only one value, we use these rules for the order of operations:

Rule 1. First, do the operation(s) within the grouping symbols, ( ).

Rule 2. Next, work from left to right doing any multiplication and division.

Rule 3. Last, work from left to right doing addition and subtraction.

4. Look at the rules above. Rule 1 tells you to first do the operation(s) within the _?_ symbols.

Example: $\mathbf{8 + 3 \times (4 - 1)}$

↑ *Step 1* (under $4 - 1$)

5. After doing the operation(s) within the grouping symbols, Rule 2 tells you to work from left to right doing any multiplication or division. Rule 3 tells you to do the _?_ and subtraction last.

Step 2 ↓ (above $\times$)

$\mathbf{8 + 3 \times (4 - 1)}$

↑ *Step 3* (under $+$) ↑ *Step 1* (under $-$)

6. Simplify the expression $8 + 3 \times (4 - 1)$.

EXERCISES

▶ **Simplify each expression.**
Hint: The order of operations is shown by the numbered arrows.

7. $12 \overset{\boxed{1}}{\div} 3 \overset{\boxed{2}}{\times} 2$

8. $20 \overset{\boxed{1}}{-} 10 \overset{\boxed{2}}{+} 4$

9. $9 \overset{\boxed{2}}{+} 3 \overset{\boxed{1}}{\times} 5$

10. $16 \overset{\boxed{2}}{+} 8 \overset{\boxed{1}}{\div} 4 \overset{\boxed{3}}{-} 2$

11. $32 \overset{\boxed{1}}{\div} 4 \overset{\boxed{3}}{+} 3 \overset{\boxed{2}}{\times} 10$

12. $8 \overset{\boxed{2}}{+} 6 \overset{\boxed{3}}{-} 4 \overset{\boxed{1}}{\times} 3$

13. $7 \overset{\boxed{2}}{\times} (8 \overset{\boxed{1}}{+} 12)$

14. $(15 \overset{\boxed{1}}{-} 10) \overset{\boxed{2}}{\div} 5$

15. $36 \overset{\boxed{2}}{-} (12 \overset{\boxed{1}}{-} 8)$

16. $(3 \overset{\boxed{1}}{+} 6) \overset{\boxed{3}}{\times} (12 \overset{\boxed{2}}{-} 9)$

17. $(3 \overset{\boxed{1}}{+} 6) \overset{\boxed{2}}{\times} 12 \overset{\boxed{3}}{-} 9$

18. $3 \overset{\boxed{2}}{+} 6 \overset{\boxed{1}}{\times} 12 \overset{\boxed{3}}{-} 9$

19. $16 \div 8 + 4$

20. $6 \times 10 - 3$

21. $24 \times 2 \div 2$

22. $33 - 8 - 6$

23. $16 + 30 \div 5$

24. $18 + 6 \div 3$

25. $45 \div 5 \times 9$

26. $56 + 14 - 10$

27. $37 - 12 + 10$

28. $(75 + 25) \div 10$

29. $96 \times (15 - 13)$

30. $20 \times (30 - 25)$

31. $48 + 8 \div 4 + 4$

32. $(24 + 8) \div 4 + 4$

33. $24 + 8 \div (4 + 4)$

34. $24 + 12 \times 6 - 1$

35. $(24 + 12) \times 6 - 1$

36. $(24 + 12) \times (6 - 1)$

▶ **Evaluate each expression for $m = 4$, $n = 6$, $r = 8$, and $t = 2$.**
Here are scrambled answers for the next row of exercises: 22 100 10

37. $r + m \div t$

38. $3r - t$

39. $(m + n) \cdot (r + t)$

40. $n \div t + r$

41. $r - n - t$

42. $(r + m) \div n$

43. $4m + 2r$

44. $7n - 5t$

45. $5(r - m)$

46. $(t + r) \div (n + m)$

47. $9(n + 3)$

48. $(r - t) \div n$

49. $r \div (n + t) + m$

50. $r + t + m \div t$

51. $9r + 3t$

52. $5(n + m) + t$

53. $(r + t) \div (n - m)$

54. $m + n \div (r - t)$

Challenge

▶ **Solve.**

55. Study the clues to find in what year the first professional football game was played.

Clues:
- The year rounded to the nearest ten is 1900.
- The sum of its digits is 23.

Properties of Addition

1. Choose values for a and b. Substitute your values in these expressions and simplify.

$$a + b \qquad b + a$$

Were your answers the same?

2. Choose values for a, b, and c. Substitute your values in these expressions and simplify.

$$(a + b) + c \qquad a + (b + c)$$

Were your answers the same?

3. Choose a value for a. Substitute your value in these expressions and simplify.

$$a + 0 \qquad a$$

Were your answers the same?

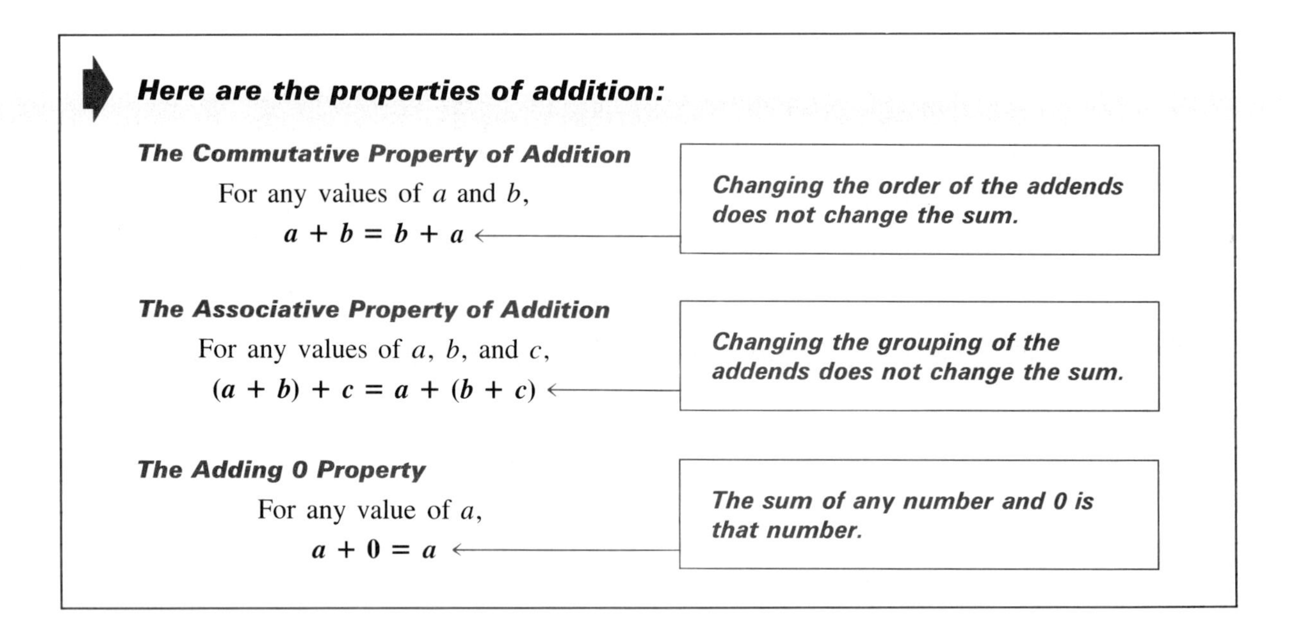

4. Complete these examples of the addition properties.

a. $x + 0 = \underline{\ ?\ }$

b. $r + s = \underline{\ ?\ } + r$

c. $(x + y) + z = x + (y + \underline{\ ?\ })$

d. $c + \underline{\ ?\ } = d + c$

e. $w + \underline{\ ?\ } = w$

f. $(p + \underline{\ ?\ }) + r = p + (q + r)$

g. $\underline{\ ?\ } + c = c + a$

h. $\underline{\ ?\ } + 0 = y$

i. $(\underline{\ ?\ } + s) + v = q + (s + v)$

j. $(k + n) + \underline{\ ?\ } = k + (n + r)$

▶ **Use your mental-math skills. The commutative and associative properties of addition allow you to add numbers in any order. Find these sums.**

5. 12 + 39 + 8
6. 15 + 52 + 35
7. 11 + 29 + 37
8. 59 + 47 + 23
9. 25 + 68 + 75
10. 46 + 70 + 30
11. 19 + 9 + 11 + 6
12. 28 + 9 + 12 + 7
13. 50 + 16 + 50 + 6
14. 11 + 36 + 14 + 23
15. 29 + 56 + 44 + 12
16. 50 + 30 + 70 + 36
17. 45 + 27 + 55 + 7
18. 85 + 53 + 15 + 20
19. 29 + 26 + 18 + 74
20. 60 + 38 + 22 + 40
21. 25 + 34 + 75 + 30
22. 10 + 65 + 90 + 25
23. 36 + 18 + 82 + 21
24. 48 + 29 + 71 + 35
25. 77 + 52 + 23 + 19
26. 70 + 25 + 80 + 20
27. 64 + 75 + 36 + 10
28. 56 + 25 + 75 + 18

▶ **Use your mental-math skills. Evaluate each expression to get the total cost.**

29. $a + c$
30. $b + d$
31. $a + b$
32. $b + c$
33. $c + e$
34. $d + e$
35. $c + c$
36. $d + d$
37. $a + b + c$
38. $b + c + d$
39. $c + d + e$
40. $a + c + d$
41. $b + d + e$
42. $b + c + e$
43. $a + d + e$
44. $a + b + d$
45. $a + a + b$
46. $a + b + b$
47. $b + c + c$
48. $b + d + d$
49. $a + e + e$
50. $e + e + e$

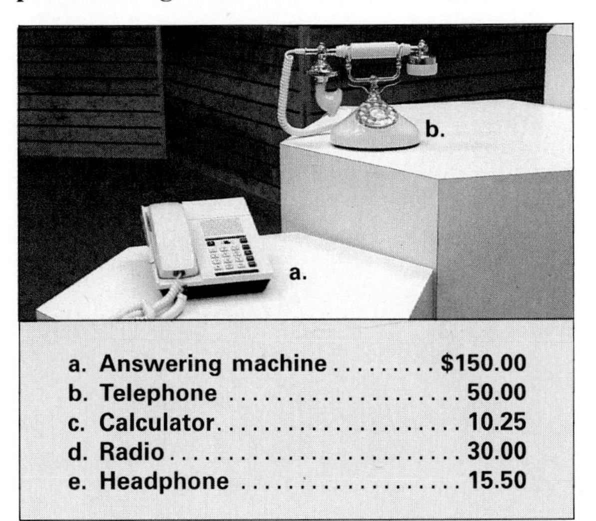

a. Answering machine $150.00
b. Telephone 50.00
c. Calculator..................... 10.25
d. Radio 30.00
e. Headphone 15.50

Challenge

▶ **Solve.**

51. Use the clues to find the cost of a camera.

Clues:
- The camera costs more than $80 but less than $100.
- You can buy it with the same number of $10 bills, $5 bills, and $1 bills.

Properties of Multiplication

1. Choose values for x and y. Substitute your values in these expressions and simplify.

$$xy \qquad yx$$

Were your answers the same?

2. Choose values for x, y, and z. Substitute your values in these expressions and simplify.

$$(xy)z \qquad x(yz)$$

Were your answers the same?

3. Choose a value for x. Substitute your value in these expressions and simplify.

$$x \times 1 \qquad x$$

Were your answers the same?

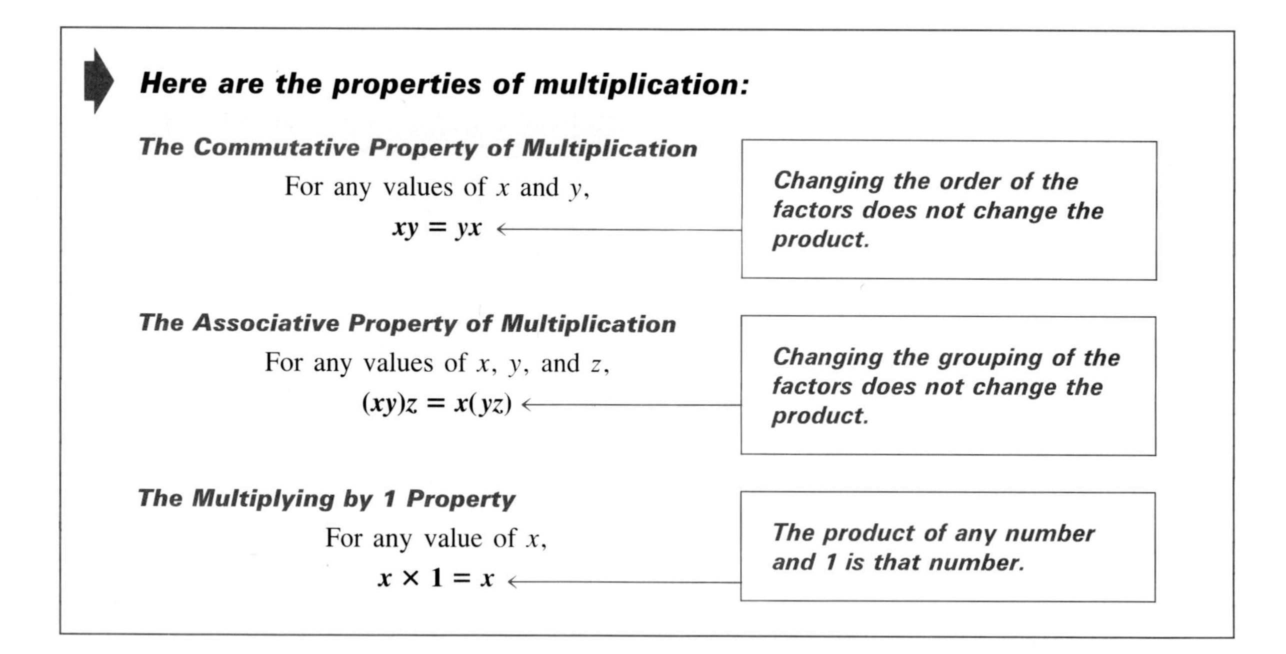

Here are the properties of multiplication:

The Commutative Property of Multiplication

For any values of x and y,

$$xy = yx$$

Changing the order of the factors does not change the product.

The Associative Property of Multiplication

For any values of x, y, and z,

$$(xy)z = x(yz)$$

Changing the grouping of the factors does not change the product.

The Multiplying by 1 Property

For any value of x,

$$x \times 1 = x$$

The product of any number and 1 is that number.

4. Complete these examples of the multiplication properties.

a. $n \times 1 = \underline{\ ?\ }$

b. $ab = b\underline{\ ?\ }$

c. $(rs)t = r(s\underline{\ ?\ })$

d. $m \times \underline{\ ?\ } = n \times m$

e. $k \times \underline{\ ?\ } = k$

f. $(a\underline{\ ?\ })c = a(bc)$

g. $\underline{\ ?\ }r = rj$

h. $\underline{\ ?\ } \times 1 = d$

i. $(\underline{\ ?\ }t)w = r(tw)$

j. $(fa)\underline{\ ?\ } = f(ax)$

EXERCISES

▶ **Use your mental-math skills. The commutative and associative properties of multiplication allow you to multiply numbers in any order. Find these products.**

5. $2 \times 16 \times 5$

6. $5 \times 22 \times 4$

7. $8 \times 7 \times 5$

8. $5 \times 18 \times 20$

9. $10 \times 17 \times 10$

10. $18 \times 25 \times 4$

11. $2 \times 8 \times 5 \times 9$

12. $4 \times 3 \times 6 \times 5$

13. $8 \times 10 \times 6 \times 10$

14. $9 \times 20 \times 8 \times 5$

15. $10 \times 7 \times 9 \times 10$

16. $4 \times 5 \times 25 \times 11$

17. $7 \times 10 \times 7 \times 10$

18. $11 \times 5 \times 8 \times 20$

19. $25 \times 9 \times 4 \times 9$

20. $2 \times 8 \times 50 \times 4$

21. $3 \times 25 \times 4 \times 12$

22. $20 \times 4 \times 15 \times 5$

▶ **Match each property with its example.**

23. The commutative property of addition

24. The associative property of addition

25. The adding 0 property

26. The commutative property of multiplication

27. The associative property of multiplication

28. The multiplying by 1 property

a. $26 + 0 = 26$

b. $18 \times 53 = 53 \times 18$

c. $67 \times 1 = 67$

d. $38 + 9 = 9 + 38$

e. $(19 + 47) + 13 = 19 + (47 + 13)$

f. $(35 \times 18) \times 16 = 35 \times (18 \times 16)$

▶ **Complete these examples of the properties.**

29. $(9 + 18) + 27 = 9 + (\underline{?} + 27)$

30. $(26 \times 18) = \underline{?} \times 26$

31. $73 \times 1 = \underline{?}$

32. $(51 \times 8) \times 10 = \underline{?} \times (8 \times 10)$

33. $92 + 0 = \underline{?}$

34. $12 + 74 = 74 + \underline{?}$

35. $54 \times \underline{?} = 30 \times 54$

36. $(\underline{?} + 16) + 37 = 45 + (16 + 37)$

37. $\underline{?} + 84 = 84 + 27$

38. $\underline{?} + 0 = 88$

39. $(16 \times \underline{?}) \times 38 = 16 \times (62 \times 38)$

40. $\underline{?} \times 1 = 54$

Challenge

▶ **Solve.**

41. John, Beth, Sarah, and David collected a total of 14 bumper stickers. Each had more than 1 sticker. Sarah had the most. John had more than David. Beth had the fewest. How many bumper stickers did each person have?

Solving Equations

You have learned to solve equations such as these:

$y + 12 = 37$ $\quad$ $5y = 95$ $\quad$ $58 = y + 29$ $\quad$ $60 = 12y$

$y - 18 = 54$ $\quad$ $\frac{y}{12} = 20$ $\quad$ $37 = y - 17$ $\quad$ $16 = \frac{y}{11}$

In this lesson you will learn to solve equations such as these:

$15 + x = 37$ $\quad$ $52 = 29 + x$ $\quad$ $x(8) = 120$ $\quad$ $156 = x(12)$

Here's how to use the commutative properties to solve equations:

$$\begin{aligned} 34 &= 19 + n \\ 34 &= n + 19 \\ n + 19 &= 34 \\ n + 19 - 19 &= 34 - 19 \\ n &= 15 \end{aligned}$$

the commutative property of addition

$$\begin{aligned} 210 &= n(7) \\ 210 &= 7n \\ 7n &= 210 \\ \frac{7n}{7} &= \frac{210}{7} \\ n &= 30 \end{aligned}$$

the commutative property of multiplication

Check:

$$\begin{aligned} 34 &= 19 + n \\ 34 &\stackrel{?}{=} 19 + 15 \\ 34 &= 34 \end{aligned}$$

It checks!

Check:

$$\begin{aligned} 210 &= n(7) \\ 210 &\stackrel{?}{=} 30(7) \\ 210 &= 210 \end{aligned}$$

It checks!

1. Complete these examples.

a.
$$\begin{aligned} 14 + r &= 43 \\ r + \underline{\ ?\ } &= 43 \\ r + 14 - 14 &= 43 - 14 \\ r &= 29 \end{aligned}$$

b.
$$\begin{aligned} t(11) &= 132 \\ \underline{\ ?\ }\,t &= 132 \\ \frac{11t}{11} &= \frac{132}{11} \\ t &= 12 \end{aligned}$$

c.
$$\begin{aligned} 54 &= 17 + s \\ 54 &= s + 17 \\ s + 17 &= \underline{\ ?\ } \\ s + 17 - 17 &= 54 - 17 \\ s &= 37 \end{aligned}$$

d.
$$\begin{aligned} 204 &= 17v \\ \underline{\ ?\ }\,v &= 204 \\ \frac{17v}{17} &= \frac{204}{17} \\ v &= 12 \end{aligned}$$

e.
$$\begin{aligned} 26 + u &= 75 \\ u + 26 &= 75 \\ u + 26 - 26 &= 75 - \underline{\ ?\ } \\ u &= 49 \end{aligned}$$

f.
$$\begin{aligned} w(20) &= 280 \\ 20w &= 280 \\ \frac{20w}{20} &= \frac{280}{?} \\ w &= 14 \end{aligned}$$

▶ **Solve and check.**
Here are scrambled answers for the next row of exercises: 8 37 26 11

2. $16 + f = 53$	**3.** $k(15) = 165$	**4.** $160 = z(20)$	**5.** $45 = 19 + a$
6. $220 = w(11)$	**7.** $25 + g = 74$	**8.** $63 = 27 + b$	**9.** $m(25) = 350$
10. $55 = 39 + x$	**11.** $9j = 108$	**12.** $w(9) = 144$	**13.** $19 = v - 12$
14. $288 = t(18)$	**15.** $8 = \frac{f}{16}$	**16.** $51 = t + 16$	**17.** $38 = j(4)$
18. $f - 38 = 38$	**19.** $52 = 48 + c$	**20.** $h(8) = 15$	**21.** $12k = 132$
22. $\frac{p}{6} = 20$	**23.** $12.3 + h = 41$	**24.** $37 = w - 29$	**25.** $20 = 6.4 + d$
26. $35 = t + 35$	**27.** $144 = 16b$	**28.** $b + 19 = 100$	**29.** $34 = 8c$
30. $17 = x - 6.8$	**31.** $5m = 42$	**32.** $22 = \frac{e}{8}$	**33.** $\frac{r}{3} = 4.8$
34. $c + 8.2 = 10$	**35.** $3.6 = \frac{h}{10}$	**36.** $g - 5.6 = 12$	**37.** $0.94 = y - 0.68$
38. $18.5 = 9.2 + e$	**39.** $8 = t + 6.5$	**40.** $p(5) = 67$	**41.** $1.75 + j = 2.65$
42. $h - 8.2 = 9.6$	**43.** $25 = 4d$	**44.** $6.4 = u + 6.4$	**45.** $8n = 41$
46. $1.2 = \frac{g}{12}$	**47.** $\frac{s}{6} = 0.72$	**48.** $d + 16.4 = 20.3$	**49.** $116 = k(8)$
50. $5 = \frac{n}{2.6}$	**51.** $12 = y - 4.6$	**52.** $16 = 12.3 + x$	**53.** $3.5 = j(0.7)$
54. $0.9 = w - 3.5$	**55.** $1.6 = \frac{x}{8}$	**56.** $4.8 = 0.6 + z$	**57.** $8.4 = m(1.2)$

Problem Solving

▶ **Complete the chart using the formula.**

The distance (d) that you travel is equal to the rate *(r)* multiplied by the time *(t)*.

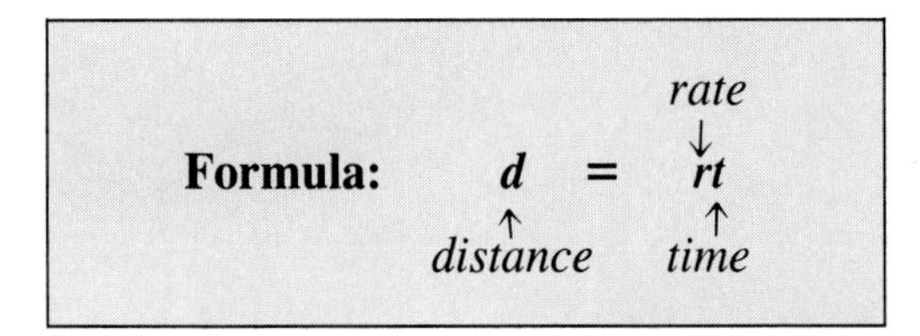

★58.

	d (miles)	*r* (mph)	*t* (hours)
a.	?	43	4
b.	?	52	6
c.	270	54	?
d.	147	49	?
e.	204	?	4

Cumulative Skill Practice

Solve and check. *(page 48)*

1. $11x = 220$	**2.** $15 = \frac{w}{8}$	**3.** $107 = y + 74$	**4.** $z - 38 = 0$
5. $64 = c - 23$	**6.** $600 = 15f$	**7.** $152 = r + 86$	**8.** $43 = \frac{v}{2.1}$
9. $t + 83 = 100$	**10.** $\frac{v}{16} = 21$	**11.** $s - 56 = 204$	**12.** $25u = 750$
13. $40 = \frac{k}{18}$	**14.** $37 = j - 21$	**15.** $232 = \frac{n}{3}$	**16.** $595 = 35z$

Round to the nearest tenth. *(page 60)*

17. 4.83	**18.** 21.805	**19.** 9.48	**20.** 0.661	**21.** 8.147
22. 6.380	**23.** 29.172	**24.** 31.06	**25.** 5.456	**26.** 19.1308
27. 406.29	**28.** 823.74	**29.** 0.059	**30.** 46.032	**31.** 34.296

Less than or greater than? *(page 62)*

32. 4.706 ◆ 4.76	**33.** 68.5 ◆ 7.82	**34.** 0.065 ◆ 0.65	**35.** 7.83 ◆ 7.89
36. 8.375 ◆ 8.4	**37.** 5.80 ◆ 5.79	**38.** 0.002 ◆ 0.004	**39.** 8.027 ◆ 8.008
40. 7.53 ◆ 7.351	**41.** 36.7 ◆ 36.68	**42.** 46.02 ◆ 46.1	**43.** 0.926 ◆ 0.93

Solve and check. *(page 68)*

44. $8.6 = q + 5.3$	**45.** $10 = s - 6.5$	**46.** $k - 4.7 = 12$	**47.** $b + 12 = 21.8$
48. $h + 4 = 6.84$	**49.** $b - 7.7 = 50$	**50.** $83 = r + 9.75$	**51.** $42.6 = t - 21.4$
52. $q - 4.7 = 20.28$	**53.** $30 = x + 26.8$	**54.** $135 = u - 28.4$	**55.** $k + 3.9 = 15.48$
56. $120 = v - 72.6$	**57.** $d + 0.48 = 0.48$	**58.** $1.96 = v + 0.98$	**59.** $h - 32 = 64.8$
60. $57.6 = p + 8.53$	**61.** $45 = w - 16.25$	**62.** $y + 0.381 = 4.6$	**63.** $a - 23.6 = 4.09$

Multiply. *(page 72)*

64. 5.6×0.2	**65.** 8.4×0.5	**66.** 19.7×3	**67.** 0.81×0.7
68. 1.9×21	**69.** 7.4×0.23	**70.** 0.05×0.2	**71.** 0.85×12
72. 48.8×1.6	**73.** 3.91×2.7	**74.** 6.54×0.38	**75.** 0.296×0.97
76. 0.124×6.5	**77.** 0.581×2.06	**78.** 3.814×0.015	**79.** 9.103×4.26

Problem Solving—Applications

In an emergency, a driver might have to stop quickly. The braking distance of a car is the distance traveled after the brakes are applied and until the car comes to a stop. This distance depends upon the type of road surface and the weather conditions.

The graph shows the braking distances for automobiles on wet and dry concrete roads at different speeds.

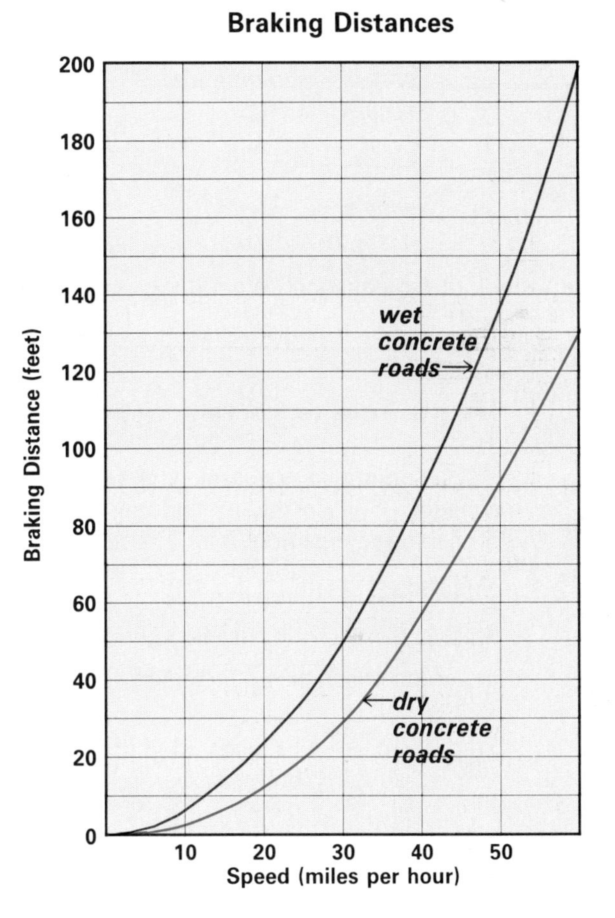

Use the graph to choose the correct answer.

1. Suppose you are driving on dry concrete. About how many feet will your braking distance be if you are traveling 40 miles per hour?
a. 30 **b.** 60 **c.** 90

2. About how many miles per hour was a car traveling on wet concrete if its braking distance was 110 feet?
a. 20 **b.** 35 **c.** 45

3. What is the difference in braking distance between cars traveling 50 miles per hour on wet and dry concrete?
a. about 10 feet
b. about 50 feet
c. about 100 feet

4. Compare the braking distances on dry concrete for speeds of 20 and 40 miles per hour. When the speed is doubled,
a. the braking distance is the same.
b. the braking distance is doubled.
c. the braking distance is more than doubled.

Write an equation and solve the problem.

5. The braking distance on wet asphalt is 1.32 times the braking distance on dry asphalt. When one is driving on wet asphalt at 40 miles per hour, the braking distance is 82.038 feet. What is the braking distance on dry asphalt at 40 miles per hour? (Let d = the braking distance at 40 miles per hour on dry asphalt.)

6. The braking distance on dry concrete is half the braking distance on packed snow. When one is driving on dry concrete at 30 miles per hour, the braking distance is 33.3 feet. What is the braking distance at 30 miles per hour on packed snow? (Let s = the braking distance at 30 miles per hour on packed snow.)

Solving Two-Step Equations

1. What is the cost of 1 record (not including shipping and handling)?
2. How much must be added for shipping and handling?
3. This equation can be used to find the number of records you can get for $30:

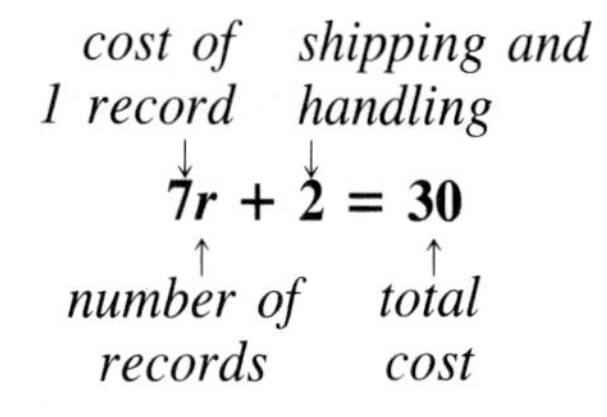

Look at the equation. What does r represent?

➡ *Here's how to solve a two-step equation.*

When solving an equation, you want to get the variable by itself on one side of the equation. You do this by undoing all the operations that were done on the variable. To solve the equation $7r + 2 = 30$, two steps are needed.

Equation: $\mathbf{7r + 2 = 30}$

Step 1. To get $7r$ by itself, subtract 2 from both sides. Then simplify both sides.

$$7r + 2 - 2 = 30 - 2$$
$$7r = 28$$

Step 2. To get r by itself, divide both sides by 7. Then simplify both sides.

$$\frac{7r}{7} = \frac{28}{7}$$
$$r = 4$$

✔ *Check:*

$$7r + 2 = 30$$
$$7(4) + 2 \stackrel{?}{=} 30$$
$$30 = 30$$

It checks!

4. Look at the example above. To find r, first subtract __?__ from both sides of the equation and then divide both sides by __?__ .
5. Check the solution. How many records can you get for $30?

EXERCISES

▶ **Copy and finish solving each equation. Check your solution.**

6.
$$\begin{aligned} 3y + 6 &= 30 \\ 3y + 6 - 6 &= 30 - \underline{?} \\ 3y &= \underline{?} \\ \frac{3y}{3} &= \frac{24}{?} \\ y &= \underline{?} \end{aligned}$$

7.
$$\begin{aligned} 5t - 4 &= 26 \\ 5t - 4 + \underline{?} &= 26 + 4 \\ 5t &= \underline{?} \\ \frac{5t}{?} &= \frac{30}{5} \\ t &= \underline{?} \end{aligned}$$

8.
$$\begin{aligned} 29 &= 7r - 6 \\ 7r - 6 &= \underline{?} \\ 7r - 6 + 6 &= 29 + \underline{?} \\ 7r &= \underline{?} \\ \frac{7r}{7} &= \frac{35}{?} \\ r &= \underline{?} \end{aligned}$$

▶ **Solve and check.**

Here are scrambled answers for the next two rows of exercises:
6 7 2 5 11 4 9 17

9. $4t + 8 = 28$
10. $2n + 5 = 39$
11. $3m - 2 = 25$
12. $27 = 4y + 3$
13. $6b - 3 = 39$
14. $20 = 6k - 4$
15. $32 = 2n + 10$
16. $8c - 2 = 14$
17. $5r - 6 = 29$
18. $22 = 3r + 10$
19. $9y + 10 = 19$
20. $4r + 13 = 41$
21. $6n - 19 = 53$
22. $77 = 10a + 7$
23. $4k - 42 = 18$
24. $5t - 35 = 0$
25. $50 = 5c - 10$
26. $3d + 14 = 35$
27. $19d - 1 = 56$
28. $85 = 15r + 10$
29. $3n + 6.2 = 9.2$
30. $5r + 6.3 = 8.8$
31. $4t - 1.8 = 10.6$
32. $9d - 3.1 = 14.9$
33. $10.2 = 6t - 1.2$
34. $22.3 = 4y + 1.5$
35. $6s - 5.1 = 18.9$
36. $12a + 6.2 = 42.2$
37. $3t + 9 = 21.6$
38. $5x - 2.2 = 10.3$
39. $2r + 23.5 = 53.7$
40. $7t + 6.1 = 9.6$

Problem Solving

▶ **Substitute in the formula to complete this chart.**

You can use this formula to find the cost of buying cassette tapes by mail.

Formula: $8t + s = c$

- t — *number of tapes*
- $8t$ — *cost of 1 tape* (8)
- s — *shipping and handling charge*
- c — *total cost*

★41.

	t (tapes)	s (dollars)	c (dollars)
a.	3	1.65	?
b.	4	2.20	?
c.	?	3.30	51.30
d.	?	2.75	42.75
e.	8	?	68.50
f.	7	?	59.85
g.	9	4.50	?
h.	10	4.75	?
i.	11	?	93.00
j.	?	5.25	101.25

More on Two-Step Equations

If you divide Michael Jackson's age when he first sang in public by 7 and then add 19, you get 20. How old was he then?

You can find how old Michael Jackson was when he first sang in public by writing and solving an equation:

$$\frac{n}{7} + 19 = 20$$

To solve the equation, undo all the operations that were done on the variable.

Here's how to solve a two-step equation.

Equation: $\frac{n}{7} + 19 = 20$

Step 1. To get $\frac{n}{7}$ by itself, subtract 19 from both sides. Then simplify both sides.

$$\frac{n}{7} + 19 - 19 = 20 - 19$$

$$\frac{n}{7} = 1$$

Step 2. To get n by itself, multiply both sides by 7. Then simplify both sides.

$$7 \times \frac{n}{7} = 7 \times 1$$

$$n = 7$$

Check: $\frac{n}{7} + 19 = 20$

$\frac{7}{7} + 19 \stackrel{?}{=} 20$

$1 + 19 \stackrel{?}{=} 20$

$20 = 20$

It checks!

1. Look at the example above. To find n, first subtract __?__ from both sides of the equation and then multiply both sides by __?__.
2. Check the solution. How old was Michael Jackson when he sang for the first time in public?
3. Complete these examples.

a.

$$\frac{r}{5} + 6 = 11$$
$$\frac{r}{5} + 6 - \underline{?} = 11 - 6$$
$$\frac{r}{5} = 5$$
$$(5)\frac{r}{5} = (5)5$$
$$r = 25$$

b.

$$22 = \frac{t}{2} - 9$$
$$\frac{t}{2} - 9 = \underline{?}$$
$$\frac{t}{2} - 9 + 9 = 22 + 9$$
$$\frac{t}{2} = 31$$
$$(2)\frac{t}{2} = (2)31$$
$$t = 62$$

c.

$$45 = 3n + 15$$
$$3n + 15 = 45$$
$$3n + 15 - 15 = 45 - 15$$
$$3n = 30$$
$$\frac{3n}{3} = \frac{30}{?}$$
$$n = 10$$

▶ **Solve and check.**

Here are scrambled answers for the next two rows of exercises:

2 4 7 21 10 27 6 15

4. $\frac{n}{7} + 5 = 8$
5. $\frac{t}{9} - 2 = 1$
6. $10 = \frac{c}{3} + 5$
7. $4 + \frac{r}{2} = 9$
8. $5n + 3 = 23$
9. $3n - 4 = 14$
10. $14 = 8y - 2$
11. $3m + 2 = 23$
12. $\frac{r}{7} - 50 = 20$
13. $\frac{k}{9} + 5 = 6$
14. $\frac{b}{3} + 2 = 11$
15. $24 = \frac{c}{3} + 4$
16. $6n - 1 = 17$
17. $31 = 5t + 6$
18. $12g - 3 = 33$
19. $4y + 7 = 51$
20. $4y + 8 = 16$
21. $\frac{m}{3} - 5 = 10$
22. $10 = \frac{n}{2} + 6$
23. $\frac{n}{3} - 2 = 0$
24. $\frac{n}{8} + 1 = 4$
25. $4x - 6 = 10$
26. $\frac{c}{7} - 5 = 11$
27. $6 = \frac{x}{4} - 14$

Problem Solving

▶ **Decide which equation would be used to solve each problem. Then solve the problem.**

Equation A:	$\frac{n}{4} + 2 = 10$
Equation B:	$\frac{n}{4} - 2 = 10$
Equation C:	$4n + 2 = 10$
Equation D:	$4n - 2 = 10$

28. If you divide Paige's age by 4 and then add 2, you get 10. What is Paige's age?
29. If you multiply Jon's age by 4 and then subtract 2, you get 10. What is Jon's age?
30. Multiply Brian's age by 4, then add 2, and you get 10. What is Brian's age?
31. Divide Wendy's age by 4, then subtract 2, and you get 10. What is Wendy's age?
32. Two more than the product of 4 and Mary's age is 10. How old is Mary?
33. Two less than the quotient of Al's age divided by 4 is 10. How old is Al?

Challenge

▶ **Solve.**

34. Wolfgang Amadeus Mozart is a famous eighteenth-century composer. Follow these steps to find Mozart's age when he first performed in public on the harpsichord and violin:

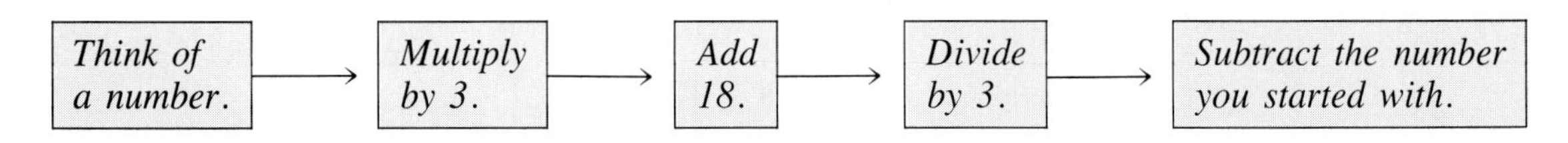

How old was Mozart when he first performed in public?

Distributive Property

1. Choose values for a, b, and c. Substitute your values in these expressions and simplify.

$$a(b + c) \qquad ab + ac$$

Were your answers the same?

> **Here is the property that links multiplication and addition:**
>
> ***The Distributive Property***
> ***For any values of a, b, and c,***
>
> $$a(b + c) = ab + ac$$

2. Complete these examples of the distributive property.

a. $4(2 + 6) = 4(2) + 4(\underline{\ ?\ })$

b. $3(\underline{\ ?\ } + 8) = 3(5) + 3(8)$

c. $9(7) + 9(2) = 9(7 + \underline{\ ?\ })$

d. $12(5) + \underline{\ ?\ }(4) = 12(5 + 4)$

> ***Here's how to use the distributive property to compute mentally.***
>
> Compute **6(17)** mentally.
>
> $$\begin{aligned} 6(17) &= 6(10 + 7) \\ &= 6(10) + 6(7) \\ &= 60 + 42 \\ &= 102 \end{aligned}$$
>
> *Since it is easier to multiply by 10, think of 17 as 10 + 7.*
>
> Compute **8(75) + 8(25)** mentally.
>
> $$\begin{aligned} 8(75) + 8(25) &= 8(75 + 25) \\ &= 8(100) \\ &= 800 \end{aligned}$$
>
> *Notice that 8 is a common factor. Since it is easier to multiply by 100, add first and then multiply.*

3. Look at the examples above.

a. To compute 6(17) mentally, first think of 17 as 10 + __?__, then multiply both 10 and 7 by __?__. Next, add 60 and __?__ to get 102.

b. In the second example, first use the distributive property to restate 8(75) + 8(25) as __?__(75 + 25). Next, add 75 and __?__ to get __?__, then multiply 100 by __?__ to get 800.

Complete these examples of the distributive property.

4. $2(5 + 4) = 2(5) + 2(\underline{?})$
5. $8(9 + 7) = 8(\underline{?}) + 8(7)$
6. $12(3 + \underline{?}) = 12(3) + 12(7)$
7. $11(\underline{?} + 7) = 11(6) + 11(7)$
8. $8(7 + 3) = \underline{?}(7) + 8(3)$
9. $\underline{?}(12 + 4) = 6(12) + 6(4)$
10. $2(9 + 5) = 2(9) + 2(\underline{?})$
11. $15(6 + \underline{?}) = 15(6) + 15(4)$
12. $4(8) + 4(6) = 4(8 + \underline{?})$
13. $9(5) + 9(4) = 9(\underline{?} + 4)$
14. $10(5) + 10(3) = \underline{?}(5 + 3)$
15. $7(\underline{?}) + 7(6) = 7(4 + 6)$
16. $8(3) + \underline{?}(2) = 8(3 + 2)$
17. $4(20) + 4(5) = \underline{?}(20 + 5)$

Compute mentally.

18. $7(23)$
    Hint: $7(20) + 7(3)$
19. $5(16)$
20. $6(14)$
21. $8(31)$
22. $7(15)$
23. $6(42)$
24. $7(41)$
25. $3(34)$
26. $5(103)$
27. $7(202)$
28. $8(406)$
29. $9(204)$
30. $7(8) + 7(2)$
    Hint: $7(8 + 2)$
31. $4(6) + 4(4)$
32. $6(2) + 6(8)$
33. $5(7) + 5(3)$
34. $3(80) + 3(20)$
35. $4(70) + 4(30)$
36. $8(90) + 8(10)$
37. $7(40) + 7(60)$
38. $26(2) + 26(8)$
39. $15(7) + 15(3)$
40. $35(5) + 35(5)$
41. $19(9) + 19(1)$

Evaluate each expression to get the total cost. Use the distributive property whenever it makes your computation easier.

42. $2a + 2c$
    Hint: $2(\$3.75) + 2(\$2.25)$
    $2(\$3.75 + \$2.25)$
    $2(\$6.00)$
43. $3b + 3d$
44. $4c + 4d$
45. $2a + 2b$
46. $2a + 2d$
47. $2b + 2c$
48. $2a + b$
49. $a + 2c$
50. $2b + c$
51. $2d + c$
52. $2a + b + c$

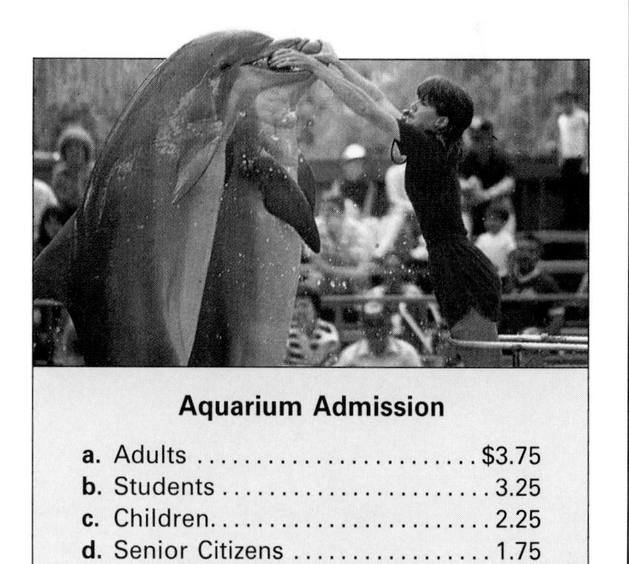

Aquarium Admission

a. Adults	$3.75
b. Students	3.25
c. Children	2.25
d. Senior Citizens	1.75

Simplifying Expressions

The distributive property and the multiplying by 1 property can be used to simplify expressions such as

$$5n + 4n \qquad 8m + m$$

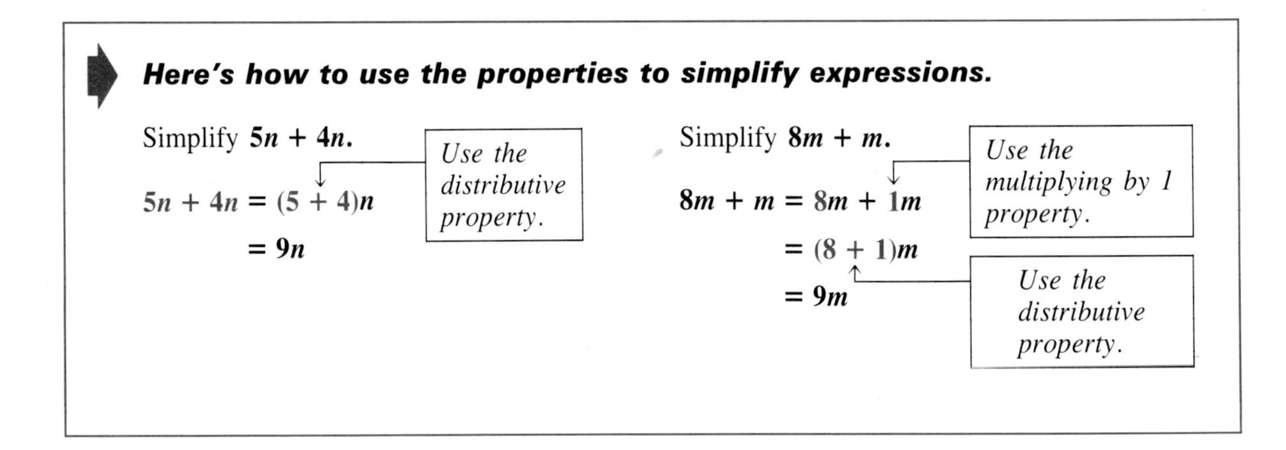

1. Complete these examples.

a. $8n + 3n = (8 + 3)n$
$= \underline{\ ?\ }$

b. $3r + r = (3 + \underline{\ ?\ })r$
$= 4r$

c. $6t + 4t = (6 + 4)\underline{\ ?\ }$
$= 10t$

d. $8k + k = (\underline{\ ?\ } + 1)k$
$= 9k$

e. $2m + m + 3m = (2 + \underline{\ ?\ } + 3)m$
$= 6m$

f. $3b + 4b + 5b = (3 + 4 + 5)b$
$= \underline{\ ?\ }\,b$

Here's how to use a shortcut to simplify expressions.

To simplify these expressions, combine like terms (terms that have the same variable) by adding.

Simplify $\mathbf{5r + 2 + 4r + 8}$.

like terms

$5r + 2 + 4r + 8 = 9r + 10$

like terms

Simplify $\mathbf{6t + 5 + t + 1}$.

like terms

$6t + 5 + t + 1 = 7t + 6$

like terms

EXERCISES

▶ **Simplify.** ***Hint: Combine like terms.***
Here are scrambled answers for the next two rows of exercises:
14n 4n 8n 7n 9n 13n

2. $6n + 2n$
3. $3n + 4n + 7n$
4. $8n + 5n$
5. $5n + n + n$
6. $2n + 3n + 4n$
7. $n + n + n + n$
8. $5a + 2a$
9. $7b + 2b + 3b$
10. $8f + 2f + 3f$
11. $8m + 5m + 3m$
12. $3x + 4x + 2x$
13. $4c + 8c + 3c$
14. $7r + 2r + 5r$
15. $8y + 2y + 12$
16. $12c + 4c + 8$
17. $18g + 4 + 10g$
18. $36r + 16 + 5r$
19. $25t + 9t + 20t$
20. $d + d + 3d$
21. $5a + a + a$
22. $8z + 2z + 6 + 4$
23. $6r + 3r + 5r + 1$
24. $7x + 3 + 2 + 2x$
25. $14c + 10c + 2 + 1$

▶ **Use your mental-math skills. Evaluate each expression for $v = 20$, $w = 60$, $y = 100$, $z = 200$.**

26. $5v + 2v$
27. $2w + 3w$
28. $7y + 3y$
29. $8z + 2z$
30. $6v + 4v$
31. $9w + w$
32. $3v + 2v + 4v$
33. $9w + w + w$
34. $8y + 2y + 3y$
35. $4z + 3z + 5z$
36. $v + 7v + 3v$
37. $7w + 2w + 5w$
38. $2v + 3v + 4v + v$
39. $w + 2w + 3w + w$
40. $2y + 2y + 3y + y$
41. $9z + 2z + 3z + 3z$
42. $10v + 3v + 2v + 4v$
43. $7y + 2y + 5y + 2y$

Challenge

▶ **Solve. Use the signpost.**

44. Which city is $2n + 9$ miles from Dodge?
45. Which city is $5n + 19$ miles from Pierceville?
46. Which city is $5n + 19$ miles from Wichita?
47. How many miles is it from Pratt to Pierceville?

★48. If $n = 34$, how many miles is it from Wichita to Dodge?

Solving Equations Containing Like Terms

Mike bought 6 posters, and Sue bought 4 posters. Each poster cost the same. Together they spent \$12.50. How much did each poster cost?

Let p be the cost of 1 poster. Then $6p$ is the cost of 6 posters, and $4p$ is the cost of 4 posters.

$$6p + 4p = 12.50$$

Here's how to solve an equation that has the same variable in more than one term.

Equation: $6p + 4p = 12.50$

Simplify by combining like terms. → $10p = 12.50$

$$\frac{10p}{10} = \frac{12.50}{10}$$

$$p = 1.25$$

Check: $6p + 4p = 12.50$

$6(1.25) + 4(1.25) \stackrel{?}{=} 12.50$

$12.50 = 12.50$

It checks!

1. Look at the example above. To find p, first combine like terms to get $\underline{?}\,p = 12.50$ and then divide both sides by $\underline{?}$.
2. Check the solution. How much does each poster cost?
3. Complete these examples.

a. $6r + 5r = 44$

$\underline{?}\,r = 44$

$\frac{11r}{11} = \frac{44}{11}$

$r = 4$

b. $c + 2c = 4.50$

$\underline{?}\,c = 4.50$

$\frac{3c}{3} = \frac{4.50}{3}$

$c = 1.50$

c. $36 = 8n + n$

$8n + n = 36$

$9n = 36$

$\frac{9n}{9} = \frac{36}{9}$

$n = \underline{?}$

EXERCISES

▶ **Solve and check.**
Here are scrambled answers for the next row of exercises: 5 16 4 7

4. $5n + 3n = 32$ **5.** $r + 4r = 25$ **6.** $49 = 6t + t$ **7.** $32 = c + c$

8. $6a + a = 140$ **9.** $t + 2t = 39$ **10.** $30 = 8y + 7y$ **11.** $120 = 9n + 6n$

12. $14n + 6n = 240$ **13.** $17w + 5w = 88$ **14.** $63 = 15b + 6b$ **15.** $30 = 12w + 3w$

16. $9n + 3n = 9.6$ **17.** $w + w = 24.6$ **18.** $8.8 = 3r + r$ **19.** $12.04 = 3s + s$

20. $6z + 2z = 1.92$ **21.** $3d + 4d = 2.45$ **22.** $12.6 = 2t + t$ **23.** $2.7 = 5c + c$

▶ **Solve and check.**
Here are scrambled answers for the next row of exercises: 9 2 50 6

24. $\frac{n}{5} + 2 = 12$ **25.** $4h + 5 = 29$ **26.** $2 = \frac{r}{3} - 1$ **27.** $10 = 7t - 4$

28. $15 = t + 6$ **29.** $\frac{d}{2} = 13$ **30.** $2n + 8n = 20$ **31.** $68 = 2f + 18$

32. $\frac{a}{7} + 6 = 7$ **33.** $2b - 6 = 8$ **34.** $8 = \frac{w}{2} + 2$ **35.** $\frac{b}{5} - 2 = 3$

36. $3h + h = 12$ **37.** $10 = \frac{c}{3} - 2$ **38.** $5 = 3n - 4$ **39.** $41 = 12n + 5$

40. $2n + 6.2 = 7.4$ **41.** $\frac{t}{5} - 3.2 = 4.3$ **42.** $n + 1.6 = 28$ **43.** $b - 6 = 9.3$

44. $4b - 2.2 = 10.3$ **45.** $9.6 = 8f + 6.1$ **46.** $9r + 3.1 = 5.8$ **47.** $8x + 2x = 6.6$

Problem Solving

▶ **Decide which equation would be used to solve each problem. Then solve the problem.**

Equation A: $4y + 6 = 7.40$
Equation B: $4y + 6y = 7.40$
Equation C: $4y = 7.40$
Equation D: $y + 4 = 7.40$

48. Four posters cost $7.40. Each poster costs the same. How much does each poster cost?

49. Lee bought 4 pages for his photo album, and Jackie bought 6 pages. Each page cost the same. Together they spent $7.40. How much did one page cost?

50. Janice bought a roll of film and some flash-cubes. She spent $4 for the film. Altogether she spent $7.40. How much did she spend for the flashcubes?

51. Brad bought 4 decals. Each decal cost the same. He also bought a poster for $6. Altogether he spent $7.40. How much did one decal cost?

Problem Solving—Using Equations

In this lesson you will use what you learned about writing simple equations to write two-step equations.

Here's how to use an equation to solve a two-step problem.

Problem: Fran wants to buy a \$58 radio. She already has \$30. If she earns \$4 per hour as a cashier, how many hours must she work to earn the money she needs?

Step 1. Choose a variable. Use it and the facts to represent the numbers in the problem.

Let h = the number of hours Fran must work.

money Fran earns → $4h$; *money she has* → 30

Then $4h + 30$ = the cost of the radio.

Step 2. Write an equation based on the facts.

$$4h + 30 = 58$$

These are two equal expressions for the cost of the radio.

Step 3. Solve the equation.

$$4h + 30 = 58$$
$$4h + 30 - 30 = 58 - 30$$
$$4h = 28$$
$$\frac{4h}{4} = \frac{28}{4}$$
$$h = 7$$

Fran needs to work 7 hours to earn the money she needs.

1. Look at the example above.

a. In Step 1, we let h equal the number of hours Fran must work to earn the money she needs. Then the expression $4h$ + __?__ equals the cost of the radio.
b. In Step 2, the two equal expressions for the cost of the radio are __?__ and 58.
c. An equation for the problem is $4h$ + __?__ = __?__ .

2. To check the solution, ask yourself whether the answer fits the facts in the problem. Does Fran need to work 7 hours to earn the money she needs?

Read the facts. Then complete the steps to answer the question.

3. *Facts:* The cost of a stereo set is \$269. That is \$9 more than 4 times the cost of a camera.

Question: What is the cost of the camera?

a. If you let c equal the cost of the camera, then $4c +$ _?_ equals the cost of the stereo.

b. The stereo costs _?_ dollars.

c. Two equal expressions for the cost of the stereo are $4c +$ _?_ and 269.

d. To find the cost of the camera, you can solve the equation $4c + 9 =$ _?_.

e. Solve the equation in part d. The cost of the camera is _?_ dollars.

4. *Facts:* If you divide the cost of a TV set by 5 and subtract \$13, you get the cost of a tape recorder. The tape recorder costs \$39.

Question: What is the cost of the TV set?

a. If you let t equal the cost of the TV, then $\frac{t}{?} - 13$ equals the cost of the tape recorder.

b. The tape recorder costs _?_ dollars.

c. Two equal expressions for the cost of the tape recorder are $\frac{t}{?} - 13$ and 39.

d. To find the cost of the TV, you can solve the equation $\frac{t}{5} - 13 =$ _?_.

e. Solve the equation in part d. The cost of the TV is _?_ dollars.

Write an equation and solve the problem.

5. If you multiply a number by 7 and subtract 9 from the result, you get 68. What is the number?
(Let n = the number.)

6. If you divide a number by 4 and add 3 to the result, you get 30. What is the number?
(Let k = the number.)

7. If a number is divided by 6 and then 5 is subtracted, the result is 4. What is the number?
(Let m = the number.)

8. If a number is multiplied by 8 and then 17 is added, the result is 65. What is the number?
(Let j = the number.)

9. Two more than 7 times a number is 44. What is the number?
(Let p = the number.)

10. Five less than 6 times a number is 61. What is the number?
(Let f = the number.)

11. The sum of 6 times a number and 10 is 64. What is the number?
(Let r = the number.)

12. If you divide a number by 8 and then add 7, you get 10. What is the number?
(Let d = the number.)

13. Mark earned \$17 picking apples. He earned \$2 more than 3 times what Linda earned. How much money did Linda earn?
(Let e = the money Linda earned.)

14. Tina earned \$26 washing cars. She earned \$2 less than 4 times what Brad earned. How much money did Brad earn?
(Let b = the money Brad earned.)

Cumulative Skill Practice

Give the product. *(page 74)*

1. 0.08×1000
2. 0.08×100
3. 0.08×10
4. 0.8×10
5. 342×10
6. 23×1000
7. 136×100
8. 728×10
9. 56.7×100
10. 39.3×1000
11. 4.37×10
12. 6.593×100
13. 8.3×100
14. 0.65×1000
15. 7.51×10
16. 10.46×1000
17. 5.037×1000
18. 5.037×10
19. 5.037×100
20. 50.37×10

Divide. *(page 78)*

21. $38.36 \div 0.7$
22. $2.634 \div 0.6$
23. $5.067 \div 0.9$
24. $4.584 \div 0.08$
25. $1.473 \div 0.03$
26. $3.605 \div 0.005$
27. $0.2656 \div 0.004$
28. $96.30 \div 0.3$
29. $0.144 \div 1.2$
30. $0.6075 \div 0.15$
31. $28.52 \div 2.3$
32. $1.3995 \div 0.45$
33. $1.2912 \div 2.4$
34. $5.809 \div 0.37$
35. $29.011 \div 6.7$
36. $19.292 \div 5.3$
37. $39.56 \div 0.86$
38. $0.8532 \div 0.79$
39. $73.66 \div 5.8$
40. $2.1471 \div 0.051$

Give the quotient. *(page 80)*

41. $42 \div 10$
42. $356 \div 100$
43. $86 \div 1000$
44. $177 \div 100$
45. $38.51 \div 100$
46. $38.51 \div 10$
47. $38.51 \div 1000$
48. $3.851 \div 10$
49. $421 \div 10$
50. $53.6 \div 100$
51. $12.56 \div 1000$
52. $359.1 \div 100$
53. $466.1 \div 1000$
54. $638 \div 10$
55. $74.9 \div 100$
56. $37.85 \div 10$
57. $529 \div 100$
58. $88.1 \div 1000$
59. $56.92 \div 10$
60. $806.3 \div 1000$

Solve and check. *(page 82)*

61. $5x = 16.8$
62. $w + 5.4 = 9.7$
63. $g - 8.25 = 0$
64. $\frac{n}{6} = 7.1$
65. $c + 0.88 = 1.6$
66. $\frac{p}{8} = 0.12$
67. $10y = 5.63$
68. $h - 42.5 = 60$
69. $j - 3.8 = 5.7$
70. $16k = 0.256$
71. $\frac{q}{22} = 4.03$
72. $d + 6.55 = 42$
73. $\frac{r}{3.6} = 3.2$
74. $m - 2.85 = 4.75$
75. $f + 0.065 = 1.731$
76. $25z = 97.5$
77. $7.42 = d + 3.58$
78. $2.6 = \frac{n}{8}$
79. $42 = m - 8.9$
80. $15.6 = 1.2r$

Problem Solving—Applications

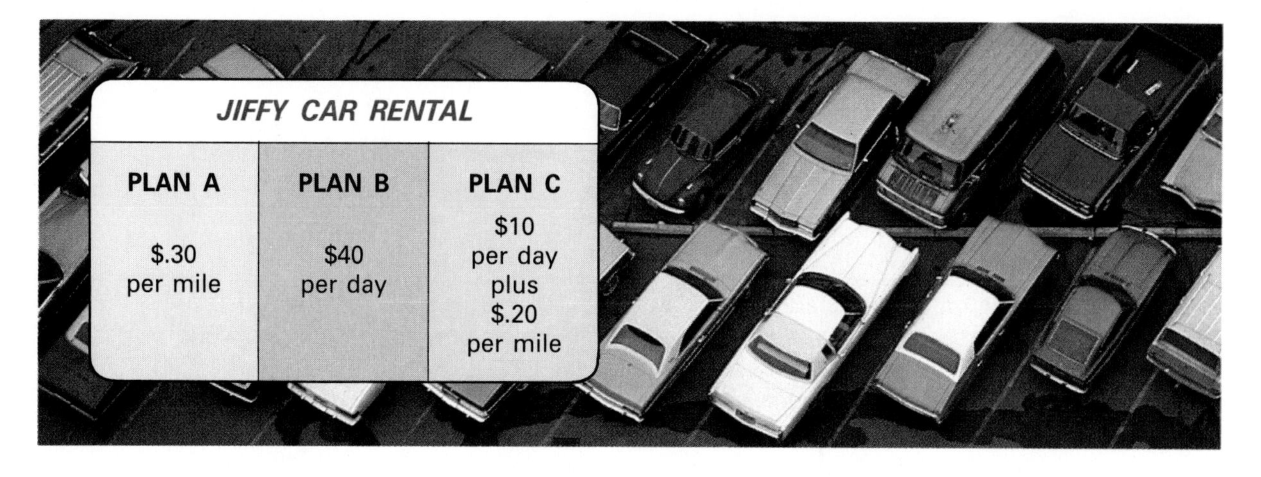

Use the car rental plans to answer the questions.

1. Using Plan A, how much would it cost to rent a car for 500 miles?

2. Using Plan B, how much would it cost to rent a car for 3 days?

3. Using Plan C, how much would it cost to rent a car for 4 days and drive it 1200 miles?

4. You want to rent a car for 2 days and drive it 500 miles. Which is the cheapest plan for you?

Solve. Use the car rental formulas.

5. You rented a car using Plan A. It costs you $24. How many miles did you drive the car?

6. A salesperson used Plan B to rent a car. He paid $280. How many days did he have the car?

Car Rental Formulas

Plan A: $c = 0.30m$ (c = *cost*, m = *miles*)

Plan B: $c = 40d$ (c = *cost*, d = *days*)

Plan C: $c = 10d + 0.20m$ (c = *cost*, d = *days*, m = *miles*)

7. A corporation president rented a car using Plan C. She used the car for 4 days and was charged $200. How many miles did she drive the car?

8. A reporter rented a car using Plan C. He drove the car 660 miles and was charged $162. How many days did he have the car?

9. Which rental plan did Mrs. Williams use? It cost her $60 to rent a car for 3 days and 200 miles.

10. Which rental plan did Ms. Gilbert use? She paid $100 to rent a car for 4 days. She drove it 300 miles.

Chapter Review

Here are scrambled answers for the review exercises:

4	*18*	*addition*	*commutative*	*division*	*like*	*simplify*
5	*add*	*associative*	*distributive*	*grouping*	*multiply*	*subtract*
17	*adding*	*combine*	*divide*	*left*	*multiplying*	

1. The rules for the order of operations tell you to first do the operations within the _?_ symbols. Next, work from left to right doing any multiplication and _?_. Last, work from left to right doing any _?_ and subtraction. *(page 92)*

2. When you simplify $2 + 3 - (8 - 1) \div 7$, the result is _?_. *(page 92)*

3. An example of the commutative property of addition is $a + b = b + a$. An example of the _?_ property of addition is $(a + b) + c = a + (b + c)$. An example of the _?_ 0 property is $a + 0 = a$. *(page 94)*

4. An example of the _?_ property of multiplication is $xy = yx$. An example of the associative property of multiplication is $(xy)z = x(yz)$. An example of the _?_ by 1 property is $x \times 1 = x$. *(page 96)*

5. To solve the equation $46 + n = 83$ you would first use the commutative property of addition. Then you would _?_ 46 from both sides and then _?_ both sides. *(page 98)*

6. To solve the equation $96 = n(4)$ you would first use the commutative property of multiplication. Next, you would use the symmetric property of equality to get the variable on the _?_ side of the equal sign. Finally, you would _?_ both sides by 4 and simplify both sides. *(page 98)*

7. To solve the two-step equation $5r + 18 = 78$ you would first subtract _?_ from both sides and simplify. Then you would divide both sides by _?_ and simplify. *(page 102)*

8. To solve the equation $\frac{t}{7} - 21 = 35$ you would first _?_ 21 to both sides and simplify. Then you would _?_ both sides by 7 and simplify. *(page 104)*

9. The property that links multiplication and addition is called the _?_ property. An example is $a(b + c) = ab + ac$. *(page 106)*

10. To simplify the expression $5x + 7 + 3x + 8$ you would combine _?_ terms by adding. *(page 108)*

11. To solve the equation $8y + 9y = 153$ you would first _?_ like terms. Then you would divide both sides by _?_ and simplify. *(page 110)*

Chapter Test

▶ **Simplify each expression.** *(page 92)*

1. $18 + 6 \div 2$
2. $50 - 25 + 10$
3. $6 \times (13 + 7)$
4. $(6 + 24) \div 3 - 1$
5. $6 + 24 \div 3 - 1$
6. $(6 + 24) \div (3 - 1)$
7. $30 \div (2 + 4) \times 4 - 2$
8. $30 \div 2 + 4 \times 4 - 2$
9. $30 \div 2 + 4 \times (4 - 1)$

▶ **Match each property with its example.** *(pages 94, 96, 106)*

10. The commutative property of addition
11. The associative property of addition
12. The adding 0 property
13. The commutative property of multiplication
14. The associative property of multiplication
15. The multiplying by 1 property
16. The distributive property

a. $(15 \times 10) \times 20 = 15 \times (10 \times 20)$
b. $(12 + 18) + 30 = 12 + (18 + 30)$
c. $22 \times 10 = 10 \times 22$
d. $53 + 38 = 38 + 53$
e. $10 \times (13 + 27) = 10 \times 13 + 10 \times 27$
f. $112 + 0 = 112$
g. $136 \times 1 = 136$

▶ **Solve and check.** *(pages 98, 102, 104)*

17. $22 + x = 47$
18. $y(11) = 198$
19. $109 = 41 + z$
20. $476 = w(17)$
21. $5s - 3 = 57$
22. $40 = 2n + 18$
23. $62 = 6m - 10$
24. $3q + 19 = 79$
25. $\frac{d}{8} - 4 = 19$
26. $\frac{c}{6} + 14 = 23$
27. $10 = \frac{h}{7} - 5$
28. $32 = \frac{q}{5} + 25$

▶ **Simplify.** *(page 108)*

29. $5y + 3y$
30. $6x + x$
31. $z + z + z$
32. $3 + 2a + 5a$
33. $8w + w + 2w$
34. $4t + t + 9$
35. $4s + 2s + 3 + 8$
36. $8u + 6 + 5 + u$

▶ **Solve and check.** *(page 110)*

37. $6n + 2n = 96$
38. $8m + m = 90$
39. $120 = p + 7p$
40. $144 = 4q + 4q$
41. $3y + 5 = 29$
42. $\frac{w}{6} - 10 = 0$
43. $15.6 = 2x - 1.2$
44. $10 = \frac{z}{8} + 5.6$

▶ **First choose the equation and then solve the problem.** *(page 112)*

Equation A: $4n + 6 = 18$
Equation B: $4n - 6 = 18$
Equation C: $\frac{n}{4} + 6 = 18$
Equation D: $\frac{n}{4} - 6 = 18$

45. Six more than 4 times a number is 18. What is the number?
46. Six less than the product of 4 and a number is 18. What is the number?
47. If you divide a number by 4 and then add 6, you get 18. What is the number?
48. If 6 is added to 4 times a number, the result is 18. What is the number?

Cumulative Test
Standardized Format

▶ **Choose the correct letter.**

1. Solve.

$139 = x - 21$

A. 139
B. 160
C. 118
D. none of these

2. Solve.

$51 = \frac{y}{3}$

A. 17
B. 51
C. 153
D. none of these

3. 8.952 rounded to the nearest tenth is

A. 8.95
B. 8.9
C. 9.0
D. none of these

4. $5.623 > \underline{?}$

A. 5.632
B. 56.23
C. 5.700
D. none of these

5. Solve.

$z + 5.4 = 9.75$

A. 9.21
B. 15.15
C. 4.35
D. none of these

6. Give the product.

5.42×0.18

A. 0.9756
B. 0.4878
C. 97.56
D. none of these

7. Give the product.

12.7×1000

A. 127
B. 1270
C. 12,700
D. none of these

8. Give the quotient.

$2.0801 \div 0.61$

A. 341
B. 3.41
C. 0.0341
D. none of these

9. Give the quotient.

$29.74 \div 100$

A. 2974
B. 2.974
C. 0.02974
D. none of these

10. Solve.

$1.2m = 6.48$

A. 5.4
B. 7.776
C. 5.28
D. none of these

11. Solve.

$\frac{y}{2.8} = 58.8$

A. 21
B. 56
C. 164.64
D. none of these

12. Choose the equation.

If you divide John's age by 2 and subtract 6 from the quotient, you get 8. How old is John?

A. $2n + 6 = 8$
B. $2n - 6 = 8$
C. $\frac{n}{2} + 6 = 8$
D. $\frac{n}{2} - 6 = 8$

5 Number Theory and Equivalent Fractions

$$h = \frac{d^2}{8000}$$

The height in miles at which a pilot must fly in order to see d miles is equal to d^2 divided by 8000.

(page 125)

From a height of 528 feet $\left(\frac{1}{10}\text{ mile}\right)$, a pilot can see a distance of about 28 miles. This means that a helicopter pilot can give traffic reports for an entire metropolitan area.

Exponents

Given below are two ways to write the number of blocks. The dot (·) means multiplication.

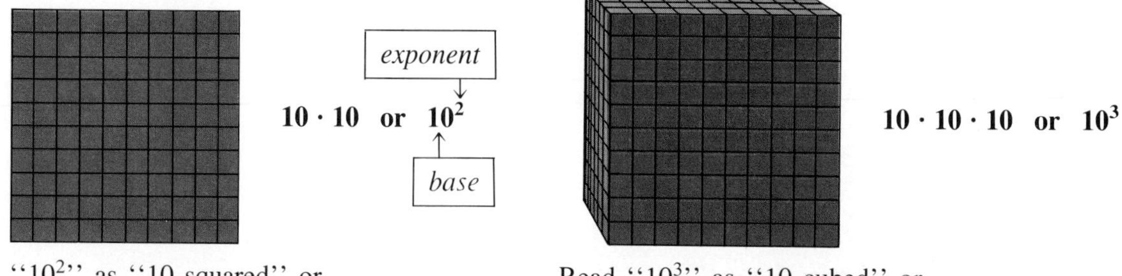

Read "10^2" as "10 squared" or "10 to the second power."

Read "10^3" as "10 cubed" or "10 to the third power."

Notice that instead of writing the same factor several times, you can write the factor once and use an **exponent.** The exponent tells you how many times the **base** is used as a factor.

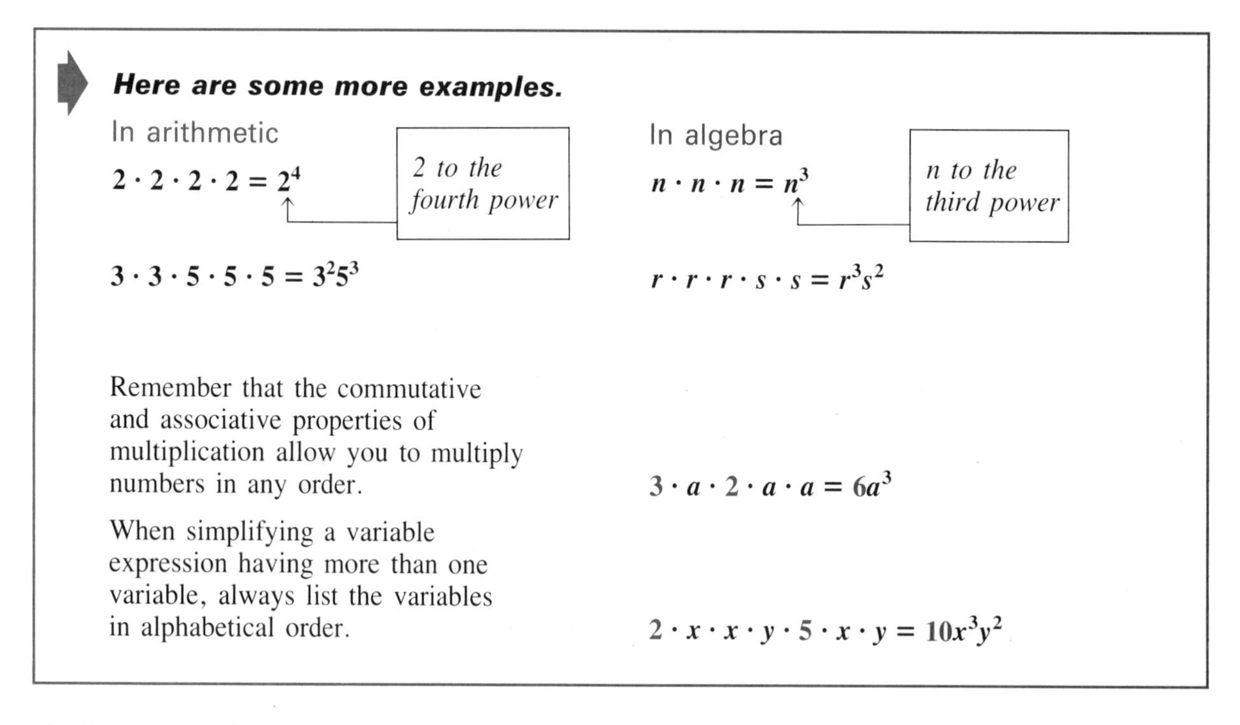

Here are some more examples.

In arithmetic

$2 \cdot 2 \cdot 2 \cdot 2 = 2^4$ — *2 to the fourth power*

$3 \cdot 3 \cdot 5 \cdot 5 \cdot 5 = 3^2 5^3$

In algebra

$n \cdot n \cdot n = n^3$ — *n to the third power*

$r \cdot r \cdot r \cdot s \cdot s = r^3 s^2$

Remember that the commutative and associative properties of multiplication allow you to multiply numbers in any order.

$3 \cdot a \cdot 2 \cdot a \cdot a = 6a^3$

When simplifying a variable expression having more than one variable, always list the variables in alphabetical order.

$2 \cdot x \cdot x \cdot y \cdot 5 \cdot x \cdot y = 10x^3y^2$

1. Complete each example.

a. $5 \cdot 5 \cdot 5 = 5^{?}$

b. $x \cdot x = \underline{?}^{\,2}$

c. $3 \cdot 3 \cdot 4 \cdot 4 \cdot 4 = 3^2 4^{?}$

d. $a \cdot a \cdot a \cdot b \cdot b = a^3 \underline{?}^{\,2}$

e. $4 \cdot a \cdot 3 \cdot a = 12a^{?}$

f. $2 \cdot a \cdot 7 \cdot a \cdot a = \underline{?}\, a^3$

g. $3 \cdot y \cdot x \cdot 3 \cdot y = 9x \underline{?}^{\,2}$

2 **h.** $5 \cdot x \cdot y \cdot y \cdot 3 \cdot y = 15x \underline{?}^{\,3}$

i. $2 \cdot x \cdot 3 \cdot x \cdot x \cdot y = 6x^{?}y$

Write using exponents.

2. $9 \cdot 9 \cdot 9 \cdot 9$ **3.** $4 \cdot 4 \cdot 4$ **4.** $10 \cdot 10$

5. $2 \cdot 2 \cdot 2 \cdot 3 \cdot 3$ **6.** $7 \cdot 7 \cdot 10 \cdot 10$ **7.** $8 \cdot 8 \cdot 10 \cdot 10 \cdot 10$

8. $a \cdot a \cdot b$ **9.** $a \cdot b \cdot b \cdot b$ **10.** $a \cdot a \cdot a \cdot b \cdot b$

11. $x \cdot x \cdot x \cdot y$ **12.** $x \cdot x \cdot y \cdot y \cdot y$ **13.** $x \cdot x \cdot x \cdot y \cdot y$

14. $m \cdot m \cdot n \cdot n \cdot n \cdot n$ **15.** $m \cdot m \cdot m \cdot n \cdot n \cdot n$ **16.** $m \cdot m \cdot m \cdot m \cdot n \cdot n$

Simplify using exponents for the variables.
Here are scrambled answers for the next two rows of exercises:
$21a^2$ $20a^3b$ $6a^2$ $27a^2b$ $30a^3$ $12ab^2$

17. $3 \cdot a \cdot 2 \cdot a$ **18.** $5 \cdot a \cdot a \cdot 6 \cdot a$ **19.** $7 \cdot a \cdot a \cdot 3$

20. $9 \cdot a \cdot 3 \cdot a \cdot b$ **21.** $6 \cdot 2 \cdot a \cdot b \cdot b$ **22.** $a \cdot 5 \cdot a \cdot 4 \cdot a \cdot b$

23. $a \cdot c \cdot c \cdot d \cdot d$ **24.** $2 \cdot c \cdot d \cdot d \cdot d$ **25.** $a \cdot c \cdot c \cdot c \cdot d$

26. $8 \cdot m \cdot m \cdot 2 \cdot n$ **27.** $6 \cdot m \cdot 3 \cdot m \cdot n \cdot n$ **28.** $m \cdot 4 \cdot m \cdot 3 \cdot m \cdot n$

29. $4 \cdot a \cdot b \cdot 3 \cdot a \cdot b$ **30.** $5 \cdot a \cdot a \cdot b \cdot 2 \cdot a$ **31.** $6 \cdot a \cdot b \cdot 4 \cdot a \cdot a \cdot b$

32. $8 \cdot r \cdot s \cdot 9 \cdot r \cdot r$ **33.** $4 \cdot r \cdot r \cdot s \cdot 6 \cdot r \cdot s$ **34.** $7 \cdot r \cdot s \cdot s \cdot 8 \cdot r \cdot r \cdot s$

35. $3 \cdot x \cdot 2 \cdot y \cdot x \cdot y$ **36.** $6 \cdot x \cdot y \cdot 3 \cdot x \cdot y \cdot x$ **37.** $10 \cdot a \cdot b \cdot a \cdot 2 \cdot b$

Problem Solving

Solve.

The distance *(d)* in feet that an object will fall in *t* seconds is given by the following formula:

$$d = 16t^2 \leftarrow$$ *First square t. Then multiply by 16.*

38. Use the formula to complete the chart.

	time in seconds *(t)*	distance in feet *(d)*
a.	1	?
b.	2	?
c.	3	?
d.	4	?
e.	5	?

39. Look at your completed chart. How far does an object fall *during* the first second? During the second second? The third? Why are the distances different?

Divisibility

If you divide 144 by 8, you get a quotient of 18 and a remainder of 0. Since the remainder is 0, we say that 144 is **divisible** by 8.

You can tell whether a whole number is divisible by certain other whole numbers without actually dividing.

Here are some rules for divisibility.

A whole number is divisible by

2 if its last digit is divisible by 2.

Example:

9436 is divisible by 2.

A number that is divisible by 2 is called an **even number.** A number that is not divisible by 2 is called an **odd number.**

3 if the sum of the digits is divisible by 3.

Example:

1545 is divisible by 3.

1 + 5 + 4 + 5 = 15

4 if its last two digits are divisible by 4.

Example:

7316 is divisible by 4.

5 if the last digit is divisible by 5, that is, if the last digit is 0 or 5.

Example:

8490 is divisible by 5.

6 if it is divisible by both 2 and 3.

Example:

5202 is divisible by 6.

8 if its last three digits are divisible by 8.

Example:

6104 is divisible by 8.

9 if the sum of its digits is divisible by 9.

Example:

2835 is divisible by 9.

2 + 8 + 3 + 5 = 18

10 if its last digit is divisible by 10, that is, if the last digit is 0.

Example:

5980 is divisible by 10.

EXERCISES

▶ **Is the number divisible by 2?**

1. 2344 **2.** 2463 **3.** 1670 **4.** 38,166 **5.** 84,998 **6.** 78,367

▶ **Is the number divisible by 3?**

7. 2016 **8.** 3805 **9.** 6822 **10.** 27,492 **11.** 50,646 **12.** 63,275

▶ **Is the number divisible by 4?**

13. 3616 **14.** 7532 **15.** 5314 **16.** 41,342 **17.** 83,560 **18.** 90,388

▶ **Is the number divisible by 5?**

19. 7352 **20.** 6895 **21.** 9070 **22.** 23,842 **23.** 53,295 **24.** 47,000

▶ **Is the number divisible by 6?**

25. 9142 **26.** 4308 **27.** 6183 **28.** 60,210 **29.** 75,444 **30.** 52,890

▶ **Is the number divisible by 8?**

31. 6320 **32.** 5136 **33.** 9208 **34.** 19,176 **35.** 32,048 **36.** 88,436

▶ **Is the number divisible by 9?**

37. 1926 **38.** 5699 **39.** 6237 **40.** 24,894 **41.** 79,254 **42.** 42,783

▶ **Is the number divisible by 10?**

43. 7830 **44.** 5628 **45.** 4864 **46.** 37,480 **47.** 65,370 **48.** 99,880

▶ **True or false?**

49. If a number is divisible by 10, then it is divisible by 5.

50. If a number is divisible by 5, then it is divisible by 10.

51. All numbers divisible by 4 are even numbers.

52. Some numbers divisible by 5 are odd numbers.

Challenge

▶ **Find the whole number.** ***Hint: Make a list.***

53. *Clues:*
- It is a 2-digit number.
- It is greater than 90.
- It is divisible by 2.
- It is divisible by 3.

54. *Clues:*
- It is a 4-digit number.
- It is less than 1060.
- It is divisible by 5.
- It is divisible by 9.

Prime Factorization

A whole number that has exactly two factors is called a **prime number.**

Here are the first few prime numbers:

2 3 5 7 11 13

A whole number (other than 0) that has more than two factors is called a **composite number.**

Here are the first few composite numbers:

4 6 8 9 10 12

0 and 1 are neither prime nor composite. Every number is a factor of 0 ($0 \cdot 1 = 0$, $0 \cdot 2 = 0$, $0 \cdot 3 = 0$, etc.), and the only factor of 1 is 1 itself.

Every composite number can be factored into a product of prime numbers. To express a composite number as a product of prime numbers is to give the **prime factorization** of the number.

Here's how to give the prime factorization of a composite number.

$18 = 2 \cdot 9$ Factor. Since 9 is not prime, factor again.

$= 2 \cdot 3 \cdot 3$ All factors are prime!

$60 = 6 \cdot 10$

$= 2 \cdot 3 \cdot 2 \cdot 5$, or $2^2 \cdot 3 \cdot 5$

1. Look at the first example above. The prime factorization of 18 is $2 \cdot 3 \cdot$ __?__

2. Complete these examples.

a. $52 = 2 \cdot 26$
$= 2 \cdot 2 \cdot$ __?__

b. $72 = 8 \cdot 9$
$= 2 \cdot 2 \cdot$ __?__ $\cdot 3 \cdot 3$

c. $50 = 2 \cdot 25$
$= 2 \cdot$ __?__ $\cdot 5$

Here's how to give the algebraic factorization of an expression.

First write the prime factorization of the whole number, and then write the variables in alphabetical order.

$6a^2 = 2 \cdot 3 \cdot a \cdot a$

$20c^2d = 2 \cdot 2 \cdot 5 \cdot c \cdot c \cdot d$

$10b^3 = 2 \cdot 5 \cdot b \cdot b \cdot b$

$5e^3f^2 = 5 \cdot e \cdot e \cdot e \cdot f \cdot f$

3. Look at the examples above. The algebraic factorization of $6a^2$ is $2 \cdot$ __?__ $\cdot a \cdot a$

4. Complete these examples.

a. $20c^2 = 2 \cdot 2 \cdot 5 \cdot c \cdot$ __?__

b. $9f^3 = 3 \cdot$ __?__ $\cdot f \cdot f \cdot f$

c. $7r^2s^3 = 7 \cdot r \cdot$ __?__ $\cdot s \cdot s \cdot s$

EXERCISES

▶ **Give the prime factorization of each number.** *Example:* **4** *2 · 2*

5. 35 **6.** 9 **7.** 10 **8.** 6 **9.** 15 **10.** 14

11. 24 **12.** 18 **13.** 22 **14.** 20 **15.** 8 **16.** 25

17. 21 **18.** 30 **19.** 12 **20.** 27 **21.** 50 **22.** 28

23. 44 **24.** 26 **25.** 38 **26.** 32 **27.** 16 **28.** 42

29. 48 **30.** 39 **31.** 33 **32.** 36 **33.** 49 **34.** 57

35. 45 **36.** 55 **37.** 58 **38.** 52 **39.** 34 **40.** 46

▶ **Give the prime factorization using exponents.** *Example:* **60** $2^2 \cdot 3 \cdot 5$

41. 25 **42.** 50 **43.** 40 **44.** 35 **45.** 64 **46.** 24

47. 66 **48.** 63 **49.** 54 **50.** 56 **51.** 62 **52.** 74

53. 65 **54.** 75 **55.** 69 **56.** 76 **57.** 70 **58.** 68

▶ **Give the algebraic factorization.** *Example:* $9b^2$ $3 \cdot 3 \cdot b \cdot b$

59. $4x^3$ **60.** $9m^3$ **61.** $10c^2$ **62.** $5a^3$ **63.** $12d$

64. $7f^3$ **65.** $15g^2$ **66.** $42w^2$ **67.** $36y$ **68.** $40x^3$

69. $35t^3$ **70.** $25r^4$ **71.** $32u$ **72.** $27q$ **73.** $45d^3$

74. $14f^2$ **75.** $11g$ **76.** $30h^4$ **77.** $24j^2$ **78.** $11ab^2$

79. $32a^2b$ **80.** $56ab$

81. $7ab^3$ **82.** $38a^2b$

83. $54a^2b^2$ **84.** $22xy^2$

Problem Solving

▶ **Use the formula to complete the chart.**

The height (h) in miles at which a pilot must fly in order to see a distance of d miles is given by the following formula:

$$h = \frac{d^2}{8000}$$ ← *First square d; then divide by 8000.*

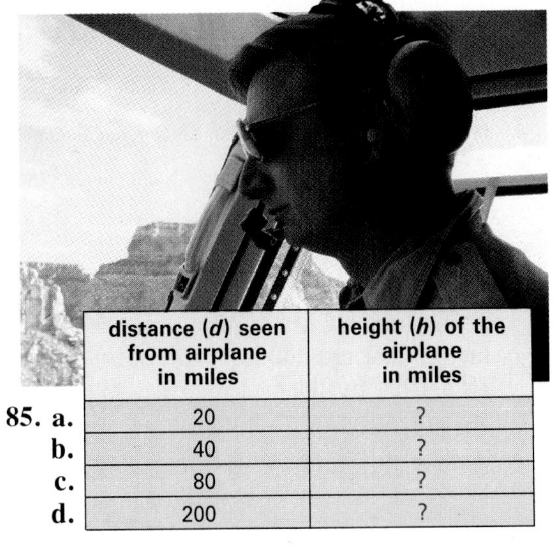

	distance (d) seen from airplane in miles	height (h) of the airplane in miles
85. a.	20	?
b.	40	?
c.	80	?
d.	200	?

Greatest Common Factor and Least Common Multiple

FACTORS OF 18: 1, 2, 3, 6, 9, 18
FACTORS OF 24: 1, 2, 3, 4, 6, 8, 12, 24
1, 2, 3, and 6 are factors of both 18 and 24. They are called **common factors** of 18 and 24.

1. What is the **greatest common factor (GCF)** of 18 and 24?

Here's how to find the GCF by factoring.

In arithmetic you first write the prime factorization of each number.

$$18 = 2 \cdot 3 \cdot 3$$

$$24 = 2 \cdot 2 \cdot 2 \cdot 3$$

Then to find the GCF, multiply the factors that are common to both 18 and 24.

$$\text{GCF} = 2 \cdot 3 = 6$$

In algebra you first write the algebraic factorization of each expression.

$$10r^3s = 2 \cdot 5 \cdot r \cdot r \cdot r \cdot s$$

$$15r^2s^2 = 3 \cdot 5 \cdot r \cdot r \cdot s \cdot s$$

Then to find the GCF, multiply the factors that are common to both $10r^3s$ and $15r^2s^2$.

$$\text{GCF} = 5 \cdot r \cdot r \cdot s = 5r^2s$$

MULTIPLES OF 18: 18, 36, 54, 72, 90, 108, 126, 144, . . .
MULTIPLES OF 24: 24, 48, 72, 96, 120, 144, . . .
72 and 144 are multiples of both 18 and 24. They are called **common multiples** of 18 and 24.

2. What is the **least common multiple (LCM)** of 18 and 24?

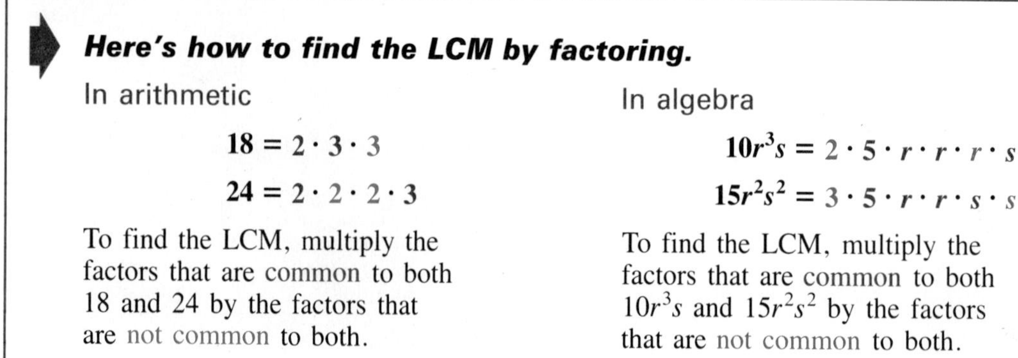

Here's how to find the LCM by factoring.

In arithmetic

$$18 = 2 \cdot 3 \cdot 3$$

$$24 = 2 \cdot 2 \cdot 2 \cdot 3$$

To find the LCM, multiply the factors that are common to both 18 and 24 by the factors that are not common to both.

$$\text{LCM} = 2 \cdot 3 \cdot 3 \cdot 2 \cdot 2 = 72$$

In algebra

$$10r^3s = 2 \cdot 5 \cdot r \cdot r \cdot r \cdot s$$

$$15r^2s^2 = 3 \cdot 5 \cdot r \cdot r \cdot s \cdot s$$

To find the LCM, multiply the factors that are common to both $10r^3s$ and $15r^2s^2$ by the factors that are not common to both.

$$\text{LCM} = 2 \cdot 3 \cdot 5 \cdot r \cdot r \cdot r \cdot s \cdot s = 30r^3s^2$$

EXERCISES

▶ **Give the greatest common factor.**

Here are scrambled answers for the next row of exercises: 8 3 5 4 6

3. 4, 8 **4.** 6, 9 **5.** 12, 18 **6.** 20, 15 **7.** 8, 24

8. 3, 10 **9.** 12, 24 **10.** 25, 20 **11.** 15, 24 **12.** 6, 14

13. 18, 20 **14.** 32, 6 **15.** 36, 24 **16.** 28, 32 **17.** 40, 15

★**18.** 12, 20, 28 ★**19.** 12, 21, 27 ★**20.** 18, 30, 42 ★**21.** 20, 24, 27 ★**22.** 24, 56, 72

Here are scrambled answers for the next row of exercises: 3d 2 d 3

23. 2, $4a$ **24.** 6, $9c$ **25.** $3d$, $12d$ **26.** d, $15d$

27. $6x$, $8x$ **28.** $9y$, $5y$ **29.** $4xy$, x **30.** $10e$, $14e$

31. $10u^2$, $5u$ **32.** $16a^2b$, $20ab$ **33.** $6c^2d$, $15c^2$ **34.** $18y^2$, $6y$

35. $11y^2z$, $25yz$ **36.** $35m^3n$, $25m^2n^2$ **37.** $20ab^2$, $24a^2$ **38.** $27rs$, $36r^2s$

▶ **Give the least common multiple.**

Here are scrambled answers for the next row of exercises: 24 28 6 12 18

39. 2, 3 **40.** 3, 8 **41.** 4, 6 **42.** 6, 9 **43.** 4, 7

44. 4, 5 **45.** 6, 8 **46.** 5, 6 **47.** 7, 5 **48.** 8, 12

49. 6, 12 **50.** 5, 10 **51.** 3, 11 **52.** 7, 6 **53.** 12, 4

★**54.** 5, 8, 10 ★**55.** 3, 4, 10 ★**56.** 6, 8, 9 ★**57.** 4, 5, 6 ★**58.** 6, 10, 15

Here are scrambled answers for the next row of exercises: 18x 10w 16x

59. 5, $10w$ **60.** $9x$, 6 **61.** $4x$, $16x$

62. $6z$, $7z$ **63.** $9b$, $5b^2$ **64.** $12c$, c^2

65. $24d^2e$, $6d$ **66.** $10ab$, $15a^2$ **67.** $12x^2y$, $16xy$

68. $25uv$, $10u^2v^2$ **69.** $11x^2y$, $5x^2y$ **70.** $6w^3x$, w^2x^2

Challenge

▶ **Solve.**

71. Use the clues to find Trent's age.

Clues:
- Brenda is 25.
- The LCM of their ages is 150.
- The GCF of their ages is 5.

Cumulative Skill Practice

▶ **Solve and check.** *(pages 68, 82)*

1. $n + 2.3 = 4.5$ **2.** $x + 0.3 = 9.7$ **3.** $4.6 = m + 2$ **4.** $8 = y + 3.4$

5. $w - 3.5 = 6.4$ **6.** $10.8 = z - 5$ **7.** $c - 7.5 = 0$ **8.** $0.9 = k - 0.4$

9. $4t = 2.4$ **10.** $3b = 10.5$ **11.** $0.72 = 9s$ **12.** $1.44 = 16w$

13. $\frac{b}{1.2} = 5$ **14.** $\frac{m}{3} = 5.6$ **15.** $0.12 = \frac{f}{8}$ **16.** $15 = \frac{h}{0.04}$

▶ **Simplify each expression.** *(page 92)*

17. $12 \div 4 - 1$ **18.** $8 \times 5 - 3$ **19.** $24 - 4 \div 4$

20. $30 - 12 - 6$ **21.** $10 + 16 \div 4$ **22.** $18 + 6 \div 3$

23. $5 + 2 \times 5 - 1$ **24.** $5 \times 2 + 10 \div 2$ **25.** $5 + (3 + 9) \div 6$

26. $(4 + 5) \times 10 - 4$ **27.** $4 + 5 \times 10 - 4$ **28.** $4 + 5 \times (10 - 4)$

29. $16 + 8 \div 4 + 4$ **30.** $(16 + 8) \div 4 + 4$ **31.** $16 + 8 \div (4 + 4)$

32. $(20 + 12) \times 4 - 1$ **33.** $20 + 12 \times (4 - 1)$ **34.** $20 + 12 \times 4 - 1$

▶ **Match each property with its example.** *(pages 94, 96, 106)*

35. The commutative property of addition

36. The associative property of addition

37. The adding 0 property

38. The commutative property of multiplication

39. The associative property of multiplication

40. The multiplying by 1 property

41. The distributive property

a. $134 + 0 = 134$

b. $(80 \times 19) \times 54 = 80 \times (19 \times 54)$

c. $54 + 38 = 38 + 54$

d. $26 \times (44 + 39) = (26 \times 44) + (26 \times 39)$

e. $27 \times 63 = 63 \times 27$

f. $(71 + 45) + 39 = 71 + (45 + 39)$

g. $85 \times 1 = 85$

▶ **Solve and check.** *(page 98)*

42. $23 + g = 91$ **43.** $8d = 104$ **44.** $\frac{d}{6} = 13$ **45.** $x - 47 = 104$

46. $\frac{f}{16} = 10$ **47.** $129 = y - 36$ **48.** $117 = z + 83$ **49.** $153 = j(9)$

50. $35 + x = 71$ **51.** $k(20) = 340$ **52.** $\frac{g}{32} = 6$ **53.** $11 = \frac{f}{16}$

54. $5c = 11.5$ **55.** $r - 8.7 = 15.3$ **56.** $132 = r - 63$ **57.** $18.3 = y + 7.9$

Problem Solving—Applications

Use the price chart to answer the questions.

1. In which year were the fewest Indian Head pennies minted?
2. What is the market value of an 1867 Indian Head penny that is in good condition?
3. How much more is the market value of an 1868 penny that is in fine condition than the market value of one that is in good condition?

Indian Head Pennies			
	Market Value		
Year	Good Condition	Fine Condition	Quantity Minted
1865	$2.50	$6.50	35,429,000
1866	$7.50	$22.50	9,826,500
1867	$7.75	$22.75	9,821,000
1868	$7.25	$22.00	10,266,500
1869	$13.50	$53.50	6,420,000
1870	$13.00	$40.00	5,275,000

Read the facts. Then complete the steps to answer the question.

4. *Facts:* The market value of a 1900 nickel is $2.90. The total market value of three 1930 nickels and the one 1900 nickel is $5.15.

   Question: What is the market value of a 1930 nickel?

   a. Let m equal the market value of a 1930 nickel. Then $\underline{?}\,m + 2.90$ equals the market value of all four coins.

   b. Two equal expressions for the market value of all four coins are $\underline{?}\,m + 2.90$ and 5.15.

   c. To find the market value of a 1930 nickel, you can solve the equation $3m + 2.90 = \underline{?}$.

   d. Solve the equation in part c. What is the market value of a 1930 nickel?

5. *Facts:* The market value of an 1890 nickel is $.80 more than 4 times the market value of a 1910 nickel. The market value of the 1890 nickel is $8.80.

   Question: What is the market value of a 1910 nickel?

   a. Let n equal the market value of a 1910 nickel. Then $4n + \underline{?}$ equals the market value of an 1890 nickel.

   b. Two equal expressions for the market value of an 1890 nickel are $4n + \underline{?}$ and 8.80.

   c. To find the market value of a 1910 nickel, you can solve the equation $4n + .80 = \underline{?}$.

   d. Solve the equation in part c. What is the market value of a 1910 nickel?

Write an equation and solve the problem.

6. The market value of an 1867 Indian Head penny that is in good condition is $.25 more than 6 times the market value of a 1920 nickel. What is the market value of the 1920 nickel? *Hint: Use the price chart to find the market value of the 1867 penny.*

7. You have an 1865 Indian Head penny that is in fine condition. You also have five 1950 nickels in fine condition. Together, your six coins have a market value of $15.25. What is the market value of each 1950 nickel? *Hint: Use the chart to find the market value of the 1865 penny.*

Equivalent Fractions

FAMOUS-FACES QUIZ Whose famous face is in the picture?

Cartoonist

Tennis player

U.S. president

Singer

Twenty-four students took the Famous-Faces Quiz. The results are shown in the chart.

1. What fraction of those surveyed knew that the cartoonist was Walt Disney?
2. What fraction of those surveyed knew that the tennis player was Chris Evert-Lloyd?
3. Fifteen students identified Donna Summer as the singer. Do you agree or disagree that $\frac{5}{8}$, or $\frac{15}{24}$, of those surveyed identified the singer?

Famous face	Fraction who identified face
Cartoonist	$\frac{1}{4}$
Tennis player	$\frac{2}{3}$
U.S. president	$\frac{5}{6}$
Singer	$\frac{5}{8}$

Here's how to change a fraction to an equivalent fraction.

In arithmetic

To change a fraction to an equivalent fraction, you can multiply both numerator and denominator by the same number (not 0).

numerator → **denominator** →
$$\frac{5}{8} = \frac{5 \cdot 3}{8 \cdot 3} = \frac{15}{24}$$

In algebra

To change an algebraic fraction to an equivalent fraction, you can multiply both numerator and denominator by the same number (not 0) or expression.

$$*\ \frac{a}{3b} = \frac{a \cdot 2b}{3b \cdot 2b} = \frac{2ab}{6b^2}$$

*You can assume that the expression in the denominator is not equal to 0.

4. The first example shows that $\frac{5}{8}$ and __?__ are equivalent fractions.
5. To change $\frac{a}{3b}$ to the equivalent fraction $\frac{2ab}{6b^2}$, both numerator and denominator were multiplied by __?__.

6. Complete these examples.

a. $\frac{5}{3} = \frac{5 \cdot 6}{3 \cdot ?} = \frac{30}{18}$

b. $\frac{2}{5} = \frac{2 \cdot ?}{5 \cdot ?} = \frac{6}{15}$

c. $\frac{b}{c} = \frac{b \cdot ?}{c \cdot 2c} = \frac{2bc}{2c^2}$

d. $\frac{2n}{3m} = \frac{2n \cdot ?}{3m \cdot ?} = \frac{4nt}{6mt}$

EXERCISES

▶ **Complete to get an equivalent fraction.**

7. $\frac{4}{3} = \frac{?}{6}$ **8.** $\frac{5}{4} = \frac{?}{12}$ **9.** $\frac{7}{8} = \frac{?}{24}$ **10.** $\frac{3}{4} = \frac{?}{16}$ **11.** $\frac{1}{8} = \frac{?}{48}$

12. $\frac{1}{3} = \frac{?}{18}$ **13.** $\frac{5}{8} = \frac{?}{16}$ **14.** $\frac{7}{8} = \frac{?}{16}$ **15.** $\frac{2}{3} = \frac{?}{18}$ **16.** $\frac{3}{5} = \frac{?}{15}$

17. $\frac{3}{8} = \frac{?}{24}$ **18.** $\frac{7}{2} = \frac{?}{16}$ **19.** $\frac{7}{9} = \frac{?}{54}$ **20.** $\frac{4}{3} = \frac{?}{6}$ **21.** $\frac{5}{6} = \frac{?}{36}$

22. $\frac{16}{5} = \frac{?}{10}$ **23.** $\frac{3}{8} = \frac{?}{24}$ **24.** $\frac{3}{2} = \frac{?}{8}$ **25.** $\frac{1}{7} = \frac{?}{21}$ **26.** $\frac{5}{6} = \frac{?}{18}$

27. $\frac{10}{9} = \frac{?}{45}$ **28.** $\frac{15}{12} = \frac{?}{24}$ **29.** $\frac{1}{3} = \frac{?}{30}$ **30.** $\frac{7}{9} = \frac{?}{45}$ **31.** $\frac{4}{5} = \frac{?}{50}$

▶ **Complete to get an equivalent fraction.**

32. $\frac{2}{a} = \frac{?}{5a}$ **33.** $\frac{5}{d} = \frac{?}{3d}$ **34.** $\frac{2}{b} = \frac{?}{6b}$ **35.** $\frac{10}{d} = \frac{?}{4d}$ **36.** $\frac{4}{g} = \frac{?}{4g}$

37. $\frac{x}{y} = \frac{?}{y^2}$ **38.** $\frac{r^2}{s} = \frac{?}{s^2}$ **39.** $\frac{t}{u^2} = \frac{?}{9u^2}$ **40.** $\frac{3r}{s^2} = \frac{?}{8s^2}$ **41.** $\frac{5m}{3n^2} = \frac{?}{15n^2}$

42. $\frac{4}{x^2y} = \frac{?}{x^2y^2}$ **43.** $\frac{2}{3ac} = \frac{?}{6a^2c}$ **44.** $\frac{7rt}{4} = \frac{?}{4rt}$ **45.** $\frac{3}{5y} = \frac{?}{5yz^2}$ **46.** $\frac{7f}{4g} = \frac{?}{8g^2}$

47. $\frac{5}{7a} = \frac{?}{14ab}$ **48.** $\frac{8m}{3n} = \frac{?}{12mn}$ **49.** $\frac{4}{11c} = \frac{?}{11c^2d}$ **50.** $\frac{9s^2}{8} = \frac{?}{24t}$ **51.** $\frac{5w}{6w} = \frac{?}{24wx}$

Problem Solving

▶ **Solve. Use the chart on page 130.**

52. How many of the 24 students identified the cartoonist?

53. How many of the 24 students identified the singer.

54. How many more students identified the president than the tennis player?

55. Which face was identified by the fewest students? The most students?

Writing Fractions in Lowest Terms

1. What is the greatest common factor (GCF) of 15 and 24?

2. What is the GCF of $8x^2$ and $6xy$?

Here's how to write a fraction in lowest terms.

To write a fraction in lowest terms, divide both terms (the numerator and denominator) by their greatest common factor.

In arithmetic

$$GCF = 3 \quad \frac{15}{24} = \frac{15 \div 3}{24 \div 3} = \frac{5}{8}$$

In algebra

$$GCF = 2x \quad \frac{8x^2}{6xy} = \frac{8x^2 \div 2x}{6xy \div 2x} = \frac{4x}{3y}$$

Notice that a fraction is in lowest terms when the GCF of the numerator and denominator is 1.

3. Look at the example above. To write $\frac{15}{24}$ in lowest terms, the numerator and denominator were __?__ by 3.

4. To write $\frac{8x^2}{6xy}$ in lowest terms, the numerator and denominator were divided by __?__.

If you have difficulty determining the GCF, you can use the following method.

Here's how to write a fraction in lowest terms by factoring and canceling.

In arithmetic

$$\frac{15}{24} = \frac{\overset{1}{\cancel{3}} \cdot 5}{2 \cdot 2 \cdot 2 \cdot \underset{1}{\cancel{3}}} = \frac{5}{8}$$

In algebra

$$\frac{8x^2}{6xy} = \frac{\overset{1}{\cancel{2}} \cdot 2 \cdot 2 \cdot \overset{1}{\cancel{x}} \cdot x}{\underset{1}{\cancel{2}} \cdot 3 \cdot \underset{1}{\cancel{x}} \cdot y} = \frac{4x}{3y}$$

5. Look at the first example above. Canceling a 3 in the numerator and denominator gives the same result as dividing both numerator and denominator by __?__.

6. Look at the second example. Canceling a 2 and an x gives the same result as dividing both terms by __?__.

▶ **Write each fraction in lowest terms.**
Here are scrambled answers for the next row of exercises: $\frac{2}{5}$ $\frac{5}{12}$ $\frac{9}{5}$ $\frac{1}{2}$ $\frac{2}{3}$ $\frac{6}{5}$

7. $\frac{8}{12}$ **8.** $\frac{36}{20}$ **9.** $\frac{16}{40}$ **10.** $\frac{12}{10}$ **11.** $\frac{15}{36}$ **12.** $\frac{20}{40}$

13. $\frac{14}{42}$ **14.** $\frac{20}{36}$ **15.** $\frac{10}{15}$ **16.** $\frac{6}{8}$ **17.** $\frac{4}{6}$ **18.** $\frac{3}{9}$

19. $\frac{22}{33}$ **20.** $\frac{20}{24}$ **21.** $\frac{22}{10}$ **22.** $\frac{40}{30}$ **23.** $\frac{10}{6}$ **24.** $\frac{18}{14}$

25. $\frac{18}{21}$ **26.** $\frac{12}{42}$ **27.** $\frac{25}{20}$ **28.** $\frac{20}{32}$ **29.** $\frac{12}{8}$ **30.** $\frac{10}{24}$

▶ **Write in lowest terms.**
Here are scrambled answers for the next row of exercises: $\frac{2}{3a}$ $\frac{3}{2a}$ $\frac{1}{2a}$ $\frac{3a}{2}$ $\frac{4a}{3}$ $\frac{2a}{3}$

31. $\frac{2}{4a}$ **32.** $\frac{9a}{6}$ **33.** $\frac{8}{12a}$ **34.** $\frac{10a}{15}$ **35.** $\frac{18}{12a}$ **36.** $\frac{20a}{15}$

37. $\frac{a}{ab}$ **38.** $\frac{d}{2d}$ **39.** $\frac{r}{rs}$ **40.** $\frac{x}{4x}$ **41.** $\frac{z}{wz}$ **42.** $\frac{mn}{5n}$

43. $\frac{9rs}{21r^2}$ **44.** $\frac{4jk^2}{7jk}$ **45.** $\frac{13p^2}{10p^2}$ **46.** $\frac{9q}{7q^2}$ **47.** $\frac{16r^2s}{20s}$ **48.** $\frac{11mn}{24mn}$

49. $\frac{20m}{24mn}$ **50.** $\frac{15n}{10m^2n}$ **51.** $\frac{16r^2s}{9rs}$ **52.** $\frac{21m^2}{14n}$ **53.** $\frac{10m}{8m^2}$ **54.** $\frac{9t^2}{24st}$

55. $\frac{16yz^2}{18z}$ **56.** $\frac{y^2z^2}{3z^2}$ **57.** $\frac{9xy^2}{27y}$ **58.** $\frac{7xy}{22xy}$ **59.** $\frac{18jk^2}{12j^2}$ **60.** $\frac{20j^2k}{23j^2k^2}$

Problem Solving

▶ **Solve.**

Ninety people were asked to name a state with great skiing. The circle graph shows the result of the survey.

61. Which state was named by $\frac{1}{6}$ of the people?

62. Which state was named by $\frac{2}{9}$ of the people?

63. Which state was named by $\frac{3}{10}$ of the people?

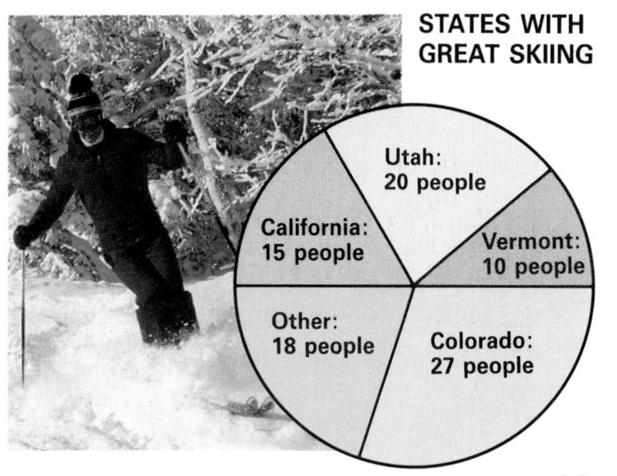

Least Common Denominator

In order to add, subtract, or compare fractions, you will need to know how to find the least common denominator.

Here's how to find the least common denominator of two fractions.

To find the **least common denominator (LCD)** of two fractions, find the least common multiple of the denominators.

In arithmetic

The LCD of $\frac{1}{4}$ and $\frac{5}{6}$ = ?

Find the least common multiple of 4 and 6.

$$4 = 2 \cdot 2$$
$$6 = 2 \cdot 3$$

To find the LCM of the denominators, multiply the factors that are common to both 4 and 6 by the factors that are not common to both.

$$\text{LCM} = 2 \cdot 2 \cdot 3 = 12$$

So, the LCD of $\frac{1}{4}$ and $\frac{5}{6}$ is 12.

In algebra

The LCD of $\frac{2}{b}$ and $\frac{1}{3b}$ = ?

Find the least common multiple of b and $3b$.

$$b = b$$
$$3b = 3 \cdot b$$

To find the LCM of the denominators, multiply the factors that are common to both b and $3b$ by the factors that are not common to both.

$$\text{LCM} = 3 \cdot b = 3b$$

So, the LCD of $\frac{2}{b}$ and $\frac{1}{3b}$ is $3b$.

1. Look at the first example above. To find the LCD of $\frac{1}{4}$ and $\frac{5}{6}$, find the least common multiple of the denominators 4 and __?__. The LCD of $\frac{1}{4}$ and $\frac{5}{6}$ is __?__.

2. To find the LCD of $\frac{2}{b}$ and $\frac{1}{3b}$, find the least common multiple of the denominators __?__ and __?__. The LCD of $\frac{2}{b}$ and $\frac{1}{3b}$ is __?__.

3. Complete these examples.

a. Find the LCD of $\frac{3}{8}, \frac{5}{12}$.

$$8 = 2 \cdot 2 \cdot 2$$
$$12 = 2 \cdot 2 \cdot 3$$

LCM $= 2 \cdot 2 \cdot 2 \cdot 3 =$ __?__

LCD of $\frac{3}{8}, \frac{5}{12}$ is __?__

b. Find the LCD of $\frac{2}{9n}, \frac{1}{6}$.

$$9n = 3 \cdot 3 \cdot n$$
$$6 = 3 \cdot 2$$

LCM $= 3 \cdot 3 \cdot 2 \cdot n =$ __?__

LCD of $\frac{2}{9n}, \frac{1}{6}$ is __?__

c. Find the LCD of $\frac{c}{a^2b}, \frac{c}{ab^2}$.

$$a^2b = a \cdot a \cdot b$$
$$ab^2 = a \cdot b \cdot b$$

LCM $= a \cdot a \cdot b \cdot b = a^2b^2$

LCD of $\frac{c}{a^2b}, \frac{c}{ab^2}$ is __?__

EXERCISES

Find the least common denominator.

Here are scrambled answers for the next row of exercises: 20 18 30 12 8

4. $\frac{2}{3}, \frac{1}{4}$ 5. $\frac{5}{9}, \frac{1}{2}$ 6. $\frac{1}{10}, \frac{3}{4}$ 7. $\frac{1}{2}, \frac{5}{8}$ 8. $\frac{1}{6}, \frac{1}{5}$

9. $\frac{1}{6}, \frac{3}{8}$ 10. $\frac{2}{5}, \frac{3}{10}$ 11. $\frac{4}{3}, \frac{1}{8}$ 12. $\frac{2}{3}, \frac{4}{9}$ 13. $\frac{4}{3}, \frac{5}{6}$

14. $\frac{4}{7}, \frac{1}{4}$ 15. $\frac{2}{9}, \frac{1}{8}$ 16. $\frac{3}{5}, \frac{1}{4}$ 17. $\frac{1}{8}, \frac{3}{10}$ 18. $\frac{1}{7}, \frac{1}{6}$

19. $\frac{1}{2}, \frac{3}{20}$ 20. $\frac{1}{12}, \frac{1}{8}$ 21. $\frac{3}{4}, \frac{7}{6}$ 22. $\frac{5}{9}, \frac{7}{6}$ 23. $\frac{1}{20}, \frac{2}{15}$

24. $\frac{7}{20}, \frac{3}{8}$ 25. $\frac{4}{9}, \frac{1}{15}$ 26. $\frac{1}{10}, \frac{1}{100}$ 27. $\frac{3}{10}, \frac{1}{25}$ 28. $\frac{2}{11}, \frac{1}{33}$

29. $\frac{2}{15}, \frac{1}{10}$ 30. $\frac{1}{15}, \frac{5}{6}$ 31. $\frac{3}{10}, \frac{1}{6}$ 32. $\frac{1}{20}, \frac{3}{25}$ 33. $\frac{2}{25}, \frac{7}{30}$

Find the least common denominator.

Here are scrambled answers for the next row of exercises: $8n^2$ $6n$ $4n$ n^2 $5n$

34. $\frac{3}{n}, \frac{1}{4n}$ 35. $\frac{3}{5n}, \frac{m}{n}$ 36. $\frac{5}{n}, \frac{3}{n^2}$ 37. $\frac{t}{2n}, \frac{3t}{3n}$ 38. $\frac{5}{4n^2}, \frac{3}{8n}$

39. $\frac{1}{3d}, \frac{4a}{d}$ 40. $\frac{7}{8t}, \frac{3}{2t}$ 41. $\frac{t}{r^2}, \frac{4}{4}$ 42. $\frac{7}{2u}, \frac{1}{4}$ 43. $\frac{3}{a}, \frac{4c}{a^3}$

44. $\frac{5}{a^2}, \frac{6b}{4a}$ 45. $\frac{f}{3b}, \frac{2}{6b}$ 46. $\frac{4}{e^2}, \frac{1}{5e^2}$ 47. $\frac{b}{6a}, \frac{b}{3}$ 48. $\frac{7}{c^2}, \frac{1}{c^3}$

49. $\frac{1}{24m}, \frac{3}{8m}$ 50. $\frac{t}{12y^2}, \frac{3}{4y}$ 51. $\frac{3}{r^2}, \frac{4}{r^3}$ 52. $\frac{2}{15r}, \frac{1}{6r^2}$ 53. $\frac{y^2}{z^3}, \frac{y}{z^4}$

54. $\frac{1}{2a}, \frac{1}{3a^2}$ 55. $\frac{3}{5n^2}, \frac{1}{10n}$ 56. $\frac{r}{6t^2}, \frac{s}{4t}$ 57. $\frac{3}{3t^3}, \frac{1}{4t}$ 58. $\frac{a}{9b}, \frac{a^2}{6b^2}$

59. $\frac{1}{ab^2}, \frac{3}{a^2b^2}$ 60. $\frac{t}{u^2v}, \frac{t}{v}$ 61. $\frac{5}{6ab}, \frac{1}{4ab}$ 62. $\frac{7}{8n^2r}, \frac{1}{6nr}$ 63. $\frac{9}{4cd}, \frac{3}{6c^2d}$

Challenge

Solve.

64. The Cycle Shop ordered a shipment of custom motorcycles. The shop received $\frac{1}{3}$ of the motorcycles on Monday and $\frac{3}{8}$ on Saturday. What is the smallest number of motorcycles that could have been ordered?

Comparing Fractions

A group of high school students were asked to name one person whose face appears on United States currency. The circle graph shows the results of the poll.

1. What fraction of the students named George Washington?
2. Whose portrait appears on the bill that was named by $\frac{2}{9}$ of the students?
3. What two fractions would you compare to decide whether more students named Washington or Hamilton?

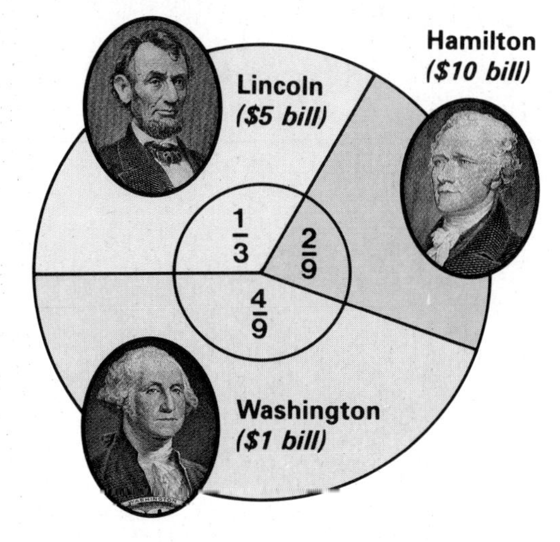

Here's how to compare two fractions.

To compare fractions with a common denominator, compare the numerators.

$$\frac{4}{9} > \frac{2}{9}$$

4 is greater than 2. So, $\frac{4}{9}$ is greater than $\frac{2}{9}$.

To compare fractions with different denominators, compare equivalent fractions with the same denominator.

$$\frac{2}{9} \blacklozenge \frac{1}{3}$$

9 is the LCD.

$$\frac{2}{9} \blacklozenge \frac{1}{3}$$

$$\frac{2}{9} \blacklozenge \frac{3}{9}$$

$$\frac{2}{9} \blacklozenge \frac{1}{3}$$

$$\frac{2}{9} < \frac{3}{9}$$

So, $\frac{2}{9}$ is less than $\frac{1}{3}$.

4. Look at the example above. Did more students name Lincoln or Hamilton?

▶ $<$ or $>$?

5. $\frac{2}{3} \blacklozenge \frac{1}{3}$
6. $\frac{5}{9} \blacklozenge \frac{7}{9}$
7. $\frac{5}{7} \blacklozenge \frac{3}{7}$
8. $\frac{5}{4} \blacklozenge \frac{7}{4}$
9. $\frac{2}{5} \blacklozenge \frac{3}{5}$
10. $\frac{8}{8} \blacklozenge \frac{9}{8}$
11. $\frac{7}{4} \blacklozenge \frac{8}{4}$
12. $\frac{0}{9} \blacklozenge \frac{1}{9}$
13. $\frac{7}{8} \blacklozenge \frac{5}{8}$
14. $\frac{6}{5} \blacklozenge \frac{7}{5}$
15. $\frac{0}{5} \blacklozenge \frac{1}{5}$
16. $\frac{11}{10} \blacklozenge \frac{13}{10}$
17. $\frac{7}{9} \blacklozenge \frac{2}{9}$
18. $\frac{3}{8} \blacklozenge \frac{2}{8}$
19. $\frac{7}{6} \blacklozenge \frac{6}{6}$

▶ $<$, $>$, or $=$? ***Hint: First, write equivalent fractions with the same denominator.***

20. $\frac{1}{5} \blacklozenge \frac{3}{10}$ ↑ $\boxed{\frac{2}{10}}$ $\boxed{\frac{3}{10}}$
21. $\frac{5}{8} \blacklozenge \frac{3}{4}$ ↑ $\boxed{\frac{5}{8}}$ $\boxed{\frac{6}{8}}$
22. $\frac{1}{3} \blacklozenge \frac{2}{7}$ ↑ $\boxed{\frac{7}{21}}$ $\boxed{\frac{6}{21}}$
23. $\frac{1}{4} \blacklozenge \frac{1}{3}$ ↑ $\boxed{\frac{?}{12}}$ $\boxed{\frac{?}{12}}$
24. $\frac{5}{4} \blacklozenge \frac{8}{7}$ ↑ $\boxed{\frac{?}{28}}$ $\boxed{\frac{?}{28}}$
25. $\frac{2}{5} \blacklozenge \frac{1}{4}$
26. $\frac{2}{9} \blacklozenge \frac{6}{27}$
27. $\frac{1}{7} \blacklozenge \frac{1}{8}$
28. $\frac{3}{5} \blacklozenge \frac{3}{10}$
29. $\frac{3}{10} \blacklozenge \frac{1}{3}$
30. $\frac{0}{3} \blacklozenge \frac{0}{7}$
31. $\frac{2}{3} \blacklozenge \frac{7}{9}$
32. $\frac{3}{4} \blacklozenge \frac{3}{5}$
33. $\frac{5}{6} \blacklozenge \frac{3}{4}$
34. $\frac{3}{4} \blacklozenge \frac{2}{3}$
35. $\frac{15}{12} \blacklozenge \frac{5}{4}$
36. $\frac{7}{8} \blacklozenge \frac{8}{9}$
37. $\frac{4}{7} \blacklozenge \frac{5}{8}$
38. $\frac{9}{16} \blacklozenge \frac{5}{8}$
39. $\frac{3}{7} \blacklozenge \frac{9}{21}$
40. $\frac{51}{100} \blacklozenge \frac{5}{10}$
41. $\frac{69}{1000} \blacklozenge \frac{6}{100}$
42. $\frac{9}{100} \blacklozenge \frac{1}{10}$
43. $\frac{8}{100} \blacklozenge \frac{88}{1000}$
44. $\frac{7}{10} \blacklozenge \frac{69}{100}$
45. $\frac{4}{15} \blacklozenge \frac{7}{20}$
46. $\frac{9}{8} \blacklozenge \frac{13}{12}$
47. $\frac{8}{11} \blacklozenge \frac{5}{7}$
48. $\frac{9}{13} \blacklozenge \frac{2}{3}$
49. $\frac{6}{5} \blacklozenge \frac{9}{8}$

▶ $<$, $>$, or $=$? **Let $a = 4$, $b = 5$, $c = 3$, $d = 9$.**

50. $\frac{1}{a} \blacklozenge \frac{3}{a}$
51. $\frac{8}{b} \blacklozenge \frac{7}{b}$
52. $\frac{3}{c} \blacklozenge \frac{4}{c}$
53. $\frac{c}{4} \blacklozenge \frac{c}{5}$
54. $\frac{d}{6} \blacklozenge \frac{d}{5}$
55. $\frac{b+1}{c} \blacklozenge \frac{b}{c}$
56. $\frac{a}{b} \blacklozenge \frac{a+1}{b}$
57. $\frac{c+1}{d} \blacklozenge \frac{c+2}{d}$
58. $\frac{c-1}{d} \blacklozenge \frac{c}{d}$
59. $\frac{b}{c} \blacklozenge \frac{b-1}{c}$

CALCULATOR

▶ $<$, $>$, or $=$? ***Hint: Divide to find the decimal name for each fraction.***

$\boxed{142 \div 355 =}$ ↓

60. $\frac{142}{355} \blacklozenge \frac{123}{300}$
61. $\frac{2103}{2804} \blacklozenge \frac{2739}{3652}$
62. $\frac{1316}{1175} \blacklozenge \frac{1634}{2451}$
63. $\frac{1597}{2397} \blacklozenge \frac{1634}{2451}$

Problem Solving—Using Equations

In this lesson you will solve problems by writing equations to represent the facts in given situations.

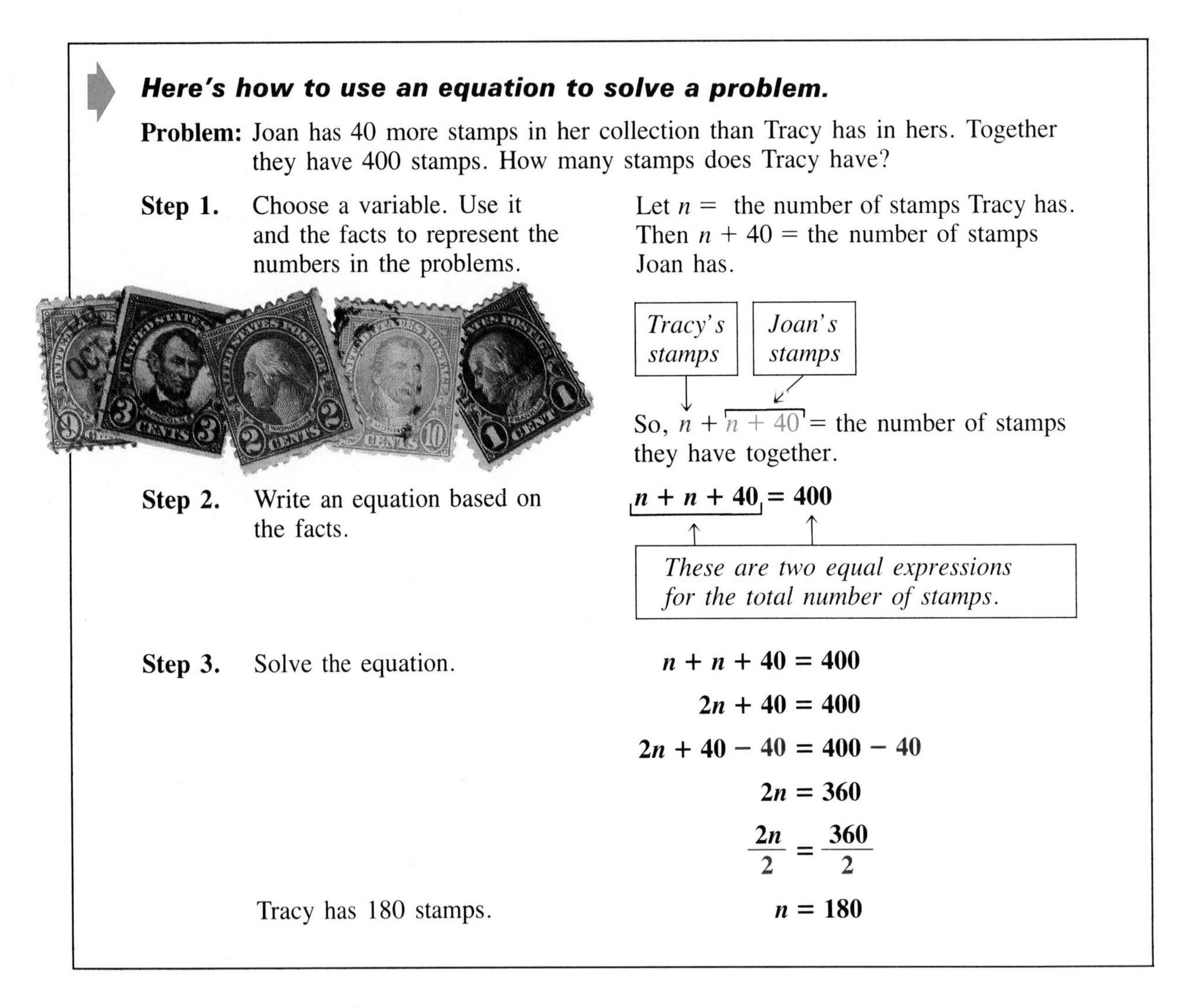

Here's how to use an equation to solve a problem.

Problem: Joan has 40 more stamps in her collection than Tracy has in hers. Together they have 400 stamps. How many stamps does Tracy have?

Step 1. Choose a variable. Use it and the facts to represent the numbers in the problems.

Let n = the number of stamps Tracy has. Then $n + 40$ = the number of stamps Joan has.

Tracy's stamps *Joan's stamps*

So, $n + n + 40$ = the number of stamps they have together.

Step 2. Write an equation based on the facts.

$$\mathbf{n + n + 40 = 400}$$

These are two equal expressions for the total number of stamps.

Step 3. Solve the equation.

$$n + n + 40 = 400$$
$$2n + 40 = 400$$
$$2n + 40 - 40 = 400 - 40$$
$$2n = 360$$
$$\frac{2n}{2} = \frac{360}{2}$$

Tracy has 180 stamps.

$$n = 180$$

1. Look at the example above.

a. In Step 1, we let n equal the number of stamps Tracy has. Then the expression $n +$ __?__ equals the number of stamps Joan has and __?__ $+ n + 40$ equals the number of stamps Tracy and Joan have together.

b. In Step 2, the two equal expressions for the total number of stamps are __?__ and 400.

c. An equation for the problem is $n + n + 40 = 400$, or __?__ $n + 40 =$ __?__.

Read the facts. Then complete the steps to answer the question.

2. *Facts:* Craig has 20 more dimes in his collection than Sue has in hers. Together they have 150 dimes.

Question: How many dimes does Sue have?

a. If you let d equal the number of dimes that Sue has, then d + _?_ equals the number of dimes that Craig has and $d + d$ + _?_ equals the total number of dimes Sue and Craig have.

b. To find the number of dimes Sue has, you can solve the equation $d + d + 20 =$ _?_.

c. Solve the equation in part b. Sue has _?_ dimes.

3. *Facts:* Mike has 30 fewer nickels in his collection than Kim has in hers. Together they have 124 nickels.

Question: How many nickels does Kim have?

a. If you let n equal the number of nickels that Kim has, then n − _?_ equals the number of nickels that Mike has and $n + n$ − _?_ equals the total number of nickels Kim and Mike have.

b. To find the number of nickels Kim has, you can solve the equation $n + n - 30 =$ _?_.

c. Solve the equation in part b. Kim has _?_ nickels.

Write an equation and solve the problem.

4. Jim scored 8 fewer points than Danny scored. Together they scored 44 points. How many points did Danny score? (Let d = the number of points that Danny scored.)

5. Angela scored 9 more points than Julie scored. Together they scored 77 points. How many points did Julie score? (Let j = the number of points that Julie scored.)

6. A bottle cost 70¢ more than a cork. Together they cost 90¢. How much did the cork cost? (Let c = the cost of the cork.)

7. An eraser cost 10¢ less than a pencil. Together they cost 80¢. How much did the pencil cost? (Let p = the cost of the pencil.)

8. Together Juan and Lisa weigh 262 pounds. Juan weighs 20 pounds more than Lisa. How much does Lisa weigh? (Let w = Lisa's weight in pounds.)

9. Together Theresa and Vince weigh 267 pounds. Theresa weighs 45 pounds less than Vince. How much does Vince weigh? (Let v = Vince's weight in pounds.)

10. There are 52 students on the bus. There are 4 more boys than girls on the bus. How many girls are on the bus? (Let g = the number of girls on the bus.)

11. There are 128 pages in the book. There are 6 fewer pages without drawings than pages with drawings. How many pages with drawings are there? (Let d = the number of pages with drawings.)

Cumulative Skill Practice

Solve and check. *(page 102)*

1. $3x + 6 = 21$
2. $2n + 10 = 34$
3. $5m - 6 = 49$
4. $4y - 11 = 89$
5. $39 = 7c + 18$
6. $75 = 6k - 15$
7. $18 = 12d + 18$
8. $0 = 5n - 60$
9. $3j + 25 = 100$
10. $20q - 10 = 130$
11. $136 = 10r + 16$
12. $100 = 5t + 5$
13. $2y + 1.4 = 5$
14. $4x - 3.4 = 5.8$
15. $8.1 = 5n - 6.4$
16. $1.7 = 6b - 4.3$
17. $8n - 0.5 = 0.3$
18. $18.4 = 3f - 0.2$
19. $15.9 = 5m + 7.4$
20. $12z - 8.5 = 1.1$

Solve and check. *(page 104)*

21. $\frac{x}{4} + 9 = 17$
22. $5g + 3 = 88$
23. $39 = 2n - 5$
24. $4 = \frac{g}{3} - 5$
25. $9 = \frac{s}{7} + 8$
26. $78 = 4j + 18$
27. $\frac{y}{6} - 4 = 21$
28. $11m - 20 = 90$
29. $18 = \frac{r}{2} + 16$
30. $6n - 3 = 33$
31. $42 = 5j + 2$
32. $\frac{w}{3} - 10 = 15$
33. $12a + 0.6 = 12.6$
34. $\frac{z}{5} - 1.8 = 2.3$
35. $1.8 = \frac{b}{3} + 1.8$
36. $25.8 = 18d + 9.6$
37. $\frac{c}{7} + 0.9 = 5.2$
38. $2u + 1.7 = 4.5$
39. $8.5 = \frac{a}{4} + 8.5$
40. $0.86 = 12t - 0.58$

Simplify. *(page 108)*

41. $5a + 3a$
42. $7n + 11n$
43. $3c + c$
44. $3f + 2f + 4f$
45. $9x + 3x + x$
46. $8y + y + y$
47. $13w + 4w + 6$
48. $12z + z - 8$
49. $r + r + 11$
50. $6k + 4k + 8 + 3$
51. $5n + n + 6 + 11$
52. $3j + j + 10 - 4$
53. $t + 3t + 4t + 3t$
54. $x + x + 3x + x$
55. $5n + 8 + n + 7$

Solve and check. *(page 110)*

56. $4x + 2x = 66$
57. $5a + 3a = 120$
58. $2y + 8y = 160$
59. $3b + 2b = 65$
60. $7n + n = 136$
61. $m + 11m = 252$
62. $g + g = 46$
63. $c + 20c = 105$
64. $108 = 3j + 3j$
65. $130 = k + 9k$
66. $0 = d + d$
67. $125 = 13c + 12c$
68. $w + w = 4.8$
69. $9e + e = 7.9$
70. $12.5 = 3w + 2w$
71. $1.21 = 5z + 6z$
72. $9m + 8m = 8.5$
73. $j + j = 12.4$
74. $0.88 = 5c + 3c$
75. $12.45 = g + 4g$

Problem Solving—Applications

In the scorebook each X represents a field goal made during the game and is worth 2 points.
Each ● represents a successful free throw and is worth 1 point.
Each O represents a missed free throw.

Team NORTH

Player	Points
Johnson, B.	X ● X X ● O
Campbell, T.	X X X ●
Miller, R.	X X O X X X ●
Lewis, E.	X ● X X ● X
Ramires, L.	● O X
McCrory, P.	X X ● O X X

Team SOUTH

Player	Points
Watkins, G.	● O O X X X ●
Krzak, D.	X O O O X X
Reiter, A.	X X X ● ● O
Martin, M.	● ● X O O
Tate, C.	X ● X X X O X
Woodrow, P.	X ● X X ● ●

Use the scoreboard information to solve these problems.

1. Which player on the North team made 4 field goals and 1 free throw?
2. Which South player scored a total of 9 points?
3. How many points did Reiter score?
4. How many more points did Lewis score than Johnson?
5. Who was the high scorer for North?
6. Who was the high scorer for South?
7. How many points did North score?
8. Which team won the game?

Solve. Use the basketball-scoring formula.

9. How many points did a team score if they made 27 field goals and 7 free throws?
10. The home team scored 57 points. They made 21 field goals. How many free throws did the team make?
11. The visiting team scored 63 points. They made 11 free throws. How many field goals did the visiting team make?
12. A team scored 88 points. They made 7 free throws in the first half and 9 in the second half. How many field goals did they make in the game?
13. Another team scored 71 points. They made 18 field goals in the first half and 14 in the second half. How many free throws did they make in the game?

Basketball-Scoring Formula

$$T = 2g + f$$

T ↑ *total points*; g ↑ *field goals*; f ↑ *free throws*

Chapter Review

Here are scrambled answers for the review exercises:

2	12	2y	composite	equivalent	multiply
3	36	algebraic	denominator	exponent	numerators
5	2c	base	digits	factorization	power
6	$2c^2$	common	divide	multiple	prime

1. In 4^3, 4 is called the __?__ and 3 is called the __?__. The exponent tells you how many times the base is used as a factor. You can read n^3 as "n to the third __?__." *(page 120)*

2. A whole number is divisible by 2 if its last digit is divisible by __?__. A whole number is divisible by 6 if it is divisible by both 2 and __?__. A whole number is divisible by 9 if the sum of its __?__ is divisible by 9. *(page 122)*

3. A whole number that has exactly two factors is called a __?__ number. A whole number (other than 0) that has more than two factors is called a __?__ number. The prime __?__ of 24 is $2 \cdot 2 \cdot 2 \cdot 3$. The __?__ factorization of $6a^2b$ is $2 \cdot 3 \cdot a \cdot a \cdot b$. *(page 124)*

4. Look at the prime factorization of these two numbers: $12 = 2 \cdot 2 \cdot 3$ $\quad 18 = 2 \cdot 3 \cdot 3$
To find the greatest common factor, __?__ the factors that are common to both 12 and 18. The GCF is __?__.
To find the least common multiple, multiply the factors that are common to both 12 and 18 by the factors that are not __?__ to both. The LCM is __?__. *(page 126)*

5. To change a fraction to an equivalent fraction, you can multiply both numerator and __?__ by the same number (not 0). If you multiply both the numerator and denominator of $\frac{x}{4y}$ by __?__ you get the equivalent fraction $\frac{2xy}{8y^2}$. *(page 130)*

6. To write a fraction in lowest terms, __?__ both terms by their greatest common factor. To write $\frac{10}{25}$ in lowest terms, you would divide both terms by __?__. To write $\frac{4c^2}{6cd}$ in lowest terms, you would divide both terms by __?__. *(page 132)*

7. To find the least common denominator of two fractions, find the least common __?__ of the denominators. The least common denominator of $\frac{3}{4}$ and $\frac{1}{6}$ is __?__. The least common denominator of $\frac{b}{2}$ and $\frac{3b}{c^2}$ is __?__. *(page 134)*

8. To compare fractions with a common denominator, compare the __?__. To compare fractions with different denominators, compare __?__ fractions with the same denominator. *(page 136)*

Chapter Test

Write using exponents. *(page 120)*

1. $7 \cdot 7 \cdot 7$
2. $8 \cdot 8 \cdot 10 \cdot 10 \cdot 10$
3. $x \cdot x \cdot x \cdot y$
4. $y \cdot 3 \cdot x \cdot y \cdot x \cdot y$

True or false? *(page 122)*

5. 635 is divisible by 5.
6. 1305 is divisible by 9.
7. 2842 is divisible by 8.
8. 3064 is divisible by 6.

Give the prime factorization or algebraic factorization. *(page 124)*

9. 6
10. 18
11. 24
12. 42
13. $20a^2$
14. $12a^3$
15. $21a^2b$
16. $30ab^2$

Give the greatest common factor and the least common multiple. *(page 126)*

17. 8, 24
18. 15, 20
19. $9x$, 12
20. $7x^2$, $5xy^2$

Complete to get an equivalent fraction. *(page 130)*

21. $\frac{5}{3} = \frac{?}{15}$
22. $\frac{7}{9} = \frac{?}{36}$
23. $\frac{10}{t} = \frac{?}{3t^2}$
24. $\frac{9s}{2t} = \frac{?}{4st^2}$

Write in lowest terms. *(page 132)*

25. $\frac{9}{12}$
26. $\frac{15}{10}$
27. $\frac{27}{45}$
28. $\frac{8}{4y}$
29. $\frac{3xy^2}{15y}$
30. $\frac{12x^2y}{20xy^2}$

Give the least common denominator. *(page 134)*

31. $\frac{5}{12}, \frac{3}{8}$
32. $\frac{4}{9}, \frac{7}{6}$
33. $\frac{1}{3w}, \frac{1}{4w^2}$
34. $\frac{3}{5wx}, \frac{1}{4w^2}$

$<$ or $>$? *(page 136)*

35. $\frac{3}{8}$ ◆ $\frac{5}{8}$
36. $\frac{1}{2}$ ◆ $\frac{1}{3}$
37. $\frac{2}{3}$ ◆ $\frac{3}{4}$
38. $\frac{6}{5}$ ◆ $\frac{9}{8}$

First choose the equation and solve the problem. Then reread the problem to see if your answer makes sense.

Equation A: $n + n + 3 = 33$
Equation B: $n + n - 3 = 33$

39. Bill has 3 fewer dollars than Carol. Together they have 33 dollars. How many dollars does Carol have? (Let n = the number of dollars Carol has.)

40. Jan has 3 more dollars than Wendy. Together they have 33 dollars. How many dollars does Wendy have? (Let n = the number of dollars Wendy has.)

Cumulative Test

Standardized Format

▶ **Choose the correct letter.**

1. Solve.

$6.3 = \frac{x}{3}$

A. 3.2
B. 2.1
C. 9.3
D. none of these

2. $24 + 6 \div (3 - 2) = ?$

A. 8
B. 30
C. 24
D. none of these

3. An example of the distributive property is

A. $(5 \times 6) \times 3 = 5 \times (6 \times 3)$
B. $27 + 39 = 39 + 27$
C. $2 \times (4 + 6) = (2 \times 4) + (2 \times 6)$
D. $8 + (3 \times 0) = (8 \times 3) + (8 \times 0)$

4. An example of the associative property of addition is

A. $23 + 74 = 74 + 23$
B. $(1 + 9) + 6 = 1 + (9 + 6)$
C. $(5 \times 6) \times 7 = 5 \times (6 \times 7)$
D. $136 + 0 = 136$

5. Solve.

$83 = 21 + r$

A. 62
B. 83
C. 104
D. none of these

6. Solve.

$128 = j(4)$

A. 124
B. 32
C. 512
D. none of these

7. Solve.

$8b - 32 = 88$

A. 7
B. 15
C. 120
D. none of these

8. Solve.

$9.6 = \frac{b}{2} + 6.4$

A. 32
B. 1.6
C. 6.4
D. none of these

9. Simplify.

$9x + 3x$

A. $12x$
B. 12
C. $6x$
D. none of these

10. Simplify.

$5y + 8 + y + 7$

A. $21y$
B. $14y + 7$
C. $6y + 15$
D. none of these

11. Solve.

$7.5 = g + 4g$

A. 1.5
B. 2.5
C. 37.5
D. none of these

12. Choose the equation.

You bought 3 tickets and your friend bought 2 tickets. Together, you and your friend spent \$12.50. How much did each ticket cost?

A. $\frac{n}{3} + 2 = 12.50$
B. $\frac{n}{2} + 3 = 12.50$
C. $3n + 2n = 12.50$
D. $3n + 2 = 12.50$

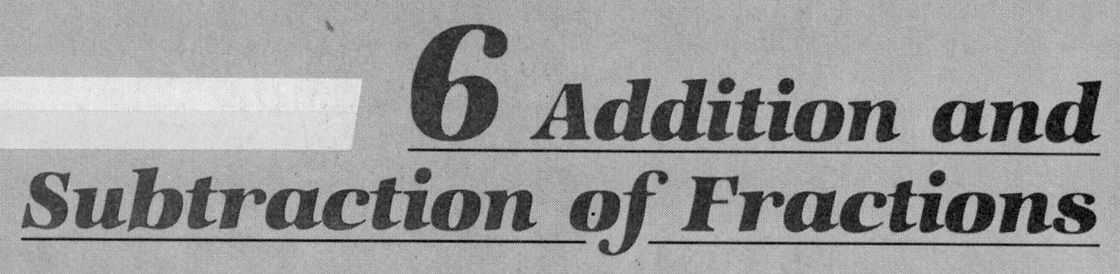

6 Addition and Subtraction of Fractions

$w = \frac{s}{8}$

The amount of water (in inches) obtained from melting snow is equal to the amount of snow (in inches) divided by 8.
(page 149)

On February 6–7, 1978, a record-breaking snowfall occurred in Boston. A total of 30 inches of snow fell during a 24-hour period. We could use the above formula to determine how many inches of rain this amount of snow is equivalent to.

Writing Whole Numbers and Mixed Numbers as Fractions

1. Look at a whole page of ads.

Does $1 = \frac{4}{4}$?

2. Look at 2 whole pages.

Does $2 = \frac{8}{4}$?

Yearbook Ads

3. In all, there are ads on 2 whole pages plus __?__ fourths of a page. The mixed number $2\frac{3}{4}$ can be used to tell how many pages of ads. Read "$2\frac{3}{4}$" as "2 and $\frac{3}{4}$."

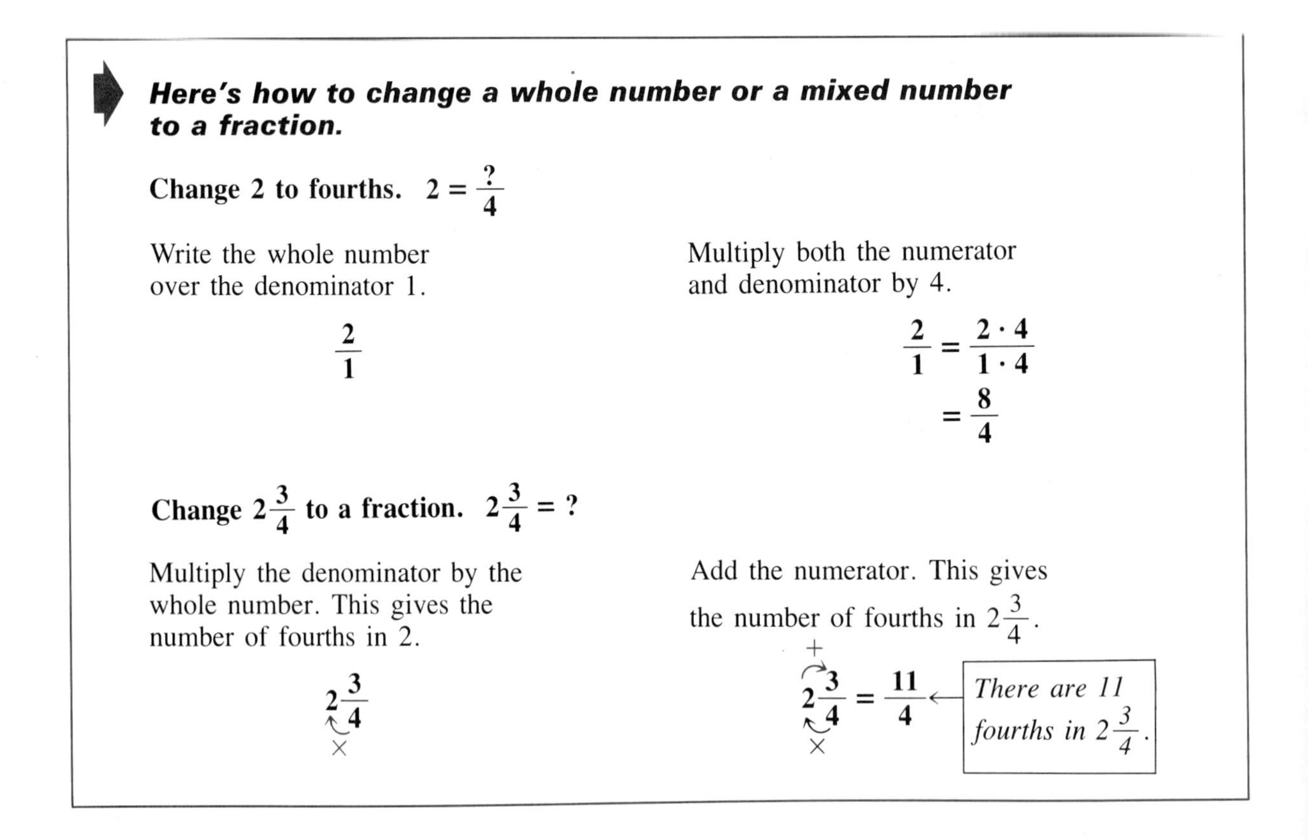

Here's how to change a whole number or a mixed number to a fraction.

Change 2 to fourths. $2 = \frac{?}{4}$

Write the whole number over the denominator 1.

$$\frac{2}{1}$$

Multiply both the numerator and denominator by 4.

$$\frac{2}{1} = \frac{2 \cdot 4}{1 \cdot 4} = \frac{8}{4}$$

Change $2\frac{3}{4}$ to a fraction. $2\frac{3}{4} = ?$

Multiply the denominator by the whole number. This gives the number of fourths in 2.

$$2\frac{3}{4} \quad (\times)$$

Add the numerator. This gives the number of fourths in $2\frac{3}{4}$.

$$2\frac{3}{4} = \frac{11}{4}$$

There are 11 fourths in $2\frac{3}{4}$.

4. Look at the second example above. To change $2\frac{3}{4}$ to a fraction, you would first __?__ 4 by 2 and then __?__ 3.

Change to halves.
Here are scrambled answers for the next row of exercises: $\frac{18}{2}$ $\frac{6}{2}$ $\frac{2}{2}$ $\frac{10}{2}$ $\frac{8}{2}$ $\frac{12}{2}$

5. 4 **6.** 1 **7.** 6 **8.** 9 **9.** 5 **10.** 3

11. 7 **12.** 12 **13.** 16 **14.** 2 **15.** 20 **16.** 10

Change to fifths.

17. 3 **18.** 5 **19.** 1 **20.** 2 **21.** 7 **22.** 4

23. 12 **24.** 8 **25.** 11 **26.** 20 **27.** 9 **28.** 25

Change each mixed number to a fraction.

29. $1\frac{1}{2}$ **30.** $2\frac{1}{3}$ **31.** $1\frac{1}{3}$ **32.** $2\frac{1}{4}$ **33.** $2\frac{1}{2}$ **34.** $1\frac{1}{4}$

35. $1\frac{3}{4}$ **36.** $1\frac{2}{5}$ **37.** $2\frac{4}{5}$ **38.** $1\frac{2}{3}$ **39.** $3\frac{1}{3}$ **40.** $8\frac{1}{6}$

41. $6\frac{3}{4}$ **42.** $6\frac{5}{6}$ **43.** $5\frac{3}{4}$ **44.** $10\frac{1}{8}$ **45.** $5\frac{1}{6}$ **46.** $5\frac{2}{5}$

47. $13\frac{1}{2}$ **48.** $20\frac{3}{8}$ **49.** $16\frac{1}{2}$ **50.** $25\frac{1}{4}$ **51.** $11\frac{3}{5}$ **52.** $12\frac{2}{3}$

Problem Solving

Solve. Use the information in the chart.

53. Who sold $1\frac{1}{4}$ pages of ads?

54. Who sold 2 pages of ads?

55. Which two people sold a total of 4 pages of ads?

56. Which two people sold a total of $3\frac{1}{4}$ pages of ads?

Salesperson	Number of $\frac{1}{4}$-page ads sold
Kim Arnez	7
David Berg	5
Mio Clark	8
Steve Mason	1
Marcia Sanchez	9

Challenge

Solve.

57. David sold his $\frac{1}{4}$-page ads two days before yesterday. Mio sold her ads the day after David did. The day after tomorrow is Friday. On what day did Mio sell her ads?

Writing Fractions as Whole Numbers or as Mixed Numbers

A fraction can be changed to a whole number or mixed number if the denominator is less than or equal to the numerator.

Notice that 4 photos cover $\frac{4}{4}$, or 1, page of the album and 7 photos cover $\frac{7}{4}$, or $1\frac{3}{4}$, pages of the album.

Here's how to change a fraction to a whole number or mixed number.

To change a fraction to a whole number or mixed number, divide the numerator by the denominator.

$$\frac{15}{3} = ?$$

Number of thirds in one → $3\overline{)15}$ with quotient 5 ← *Number of thirds in all*

$$\frac{15}{3} = 5$$

$$\frac{17}{5} = ?$$

$$\begin{array}{r} 3 \\ 5\overline{)17} \\ -15 \\ \hline 2 \end{array}$$

2 ← *Number of fifths left over*

$$\frac{17}{5} = 3\frac{2}{5}$$

EXERCISES

▶ **Change each fraction to a whole number.**
Here are scrambled answers for the next row of exercises: 6 4 8 1 3 5

1. $\frac{6}{6}$	**2.** $\frac{8}{2}$	**3.** $\frac{5}{1}$	**4.** $\frac{9}{3}$	**5.** $\frac{24}{4}$	**6.** $\frac{24}{3}$
7. $\frac{12}{3}$	**8.** $\frac{50}{10}$	**9.** $\frac{32}{4}$	**10.** $\frac{36}{6}$	**11.** $\frac{28}{2}$	**12.** $\frac{40}{8}$
13. $\frac{75}{5}$	**14.** $\frac{48}{4}$	**15.** $\frac{42}{2}$	**16.** $\frac{64}{8}$	**17.** $\frac{30}{3}$	**18.** $\frac{40}{10}$

Change each fraction to a whole number or mixed number.

Here are scrambled answers for the next row of exercises: $1\frac{1}{4}$ $1\frac{5}{6}$ 2 9 3 $1\frac{1}{2}$

19. $\frac{9}{3}$ **20.** $\frac{16}{8}$ **21.** $\frac{5}{4}$ **22.** $\frac{3}{2}$ **23.** $\frac{11}{6}$ **24.** $\frac{81}{9}$

25. $\frac{13}{5}$ **26.** $\frac{7}{4}$ **27.** $\frac{11}{9}$ **28.** $\frac{13}{10}$ **29.** $\frac{5}{2}$ **30.** $\frac{10}{3}$

31. $\frac{16}{4}$ **32.** $\frac{17}{8}$ **33.** $\frac{11}{2}$ **34.** $\frac{14}{3}$ **35.** $\frac{27}{10}$ **36.** $\frac{19}{5}$

37. $\frac{27}{7}$ **38.** $\frac{15}{4}$ **39.** $\frac{18}{3}$ **40.** $\frac{30}{6}$ **41.** $\frac{35}{5}$ **42.** $\frac{36}{6}$

43. $\frac{25}{3}$ **44.** $\frac{36}{4}$ **45.** $\frac{35}{2}$ **46.** $\frac{29}{6}$ **47.** $\frac{37}{10}$ **48.** $\frac{19}{6}$

49. $\frac{144}{12}$ **50.** $\frac{182}{25}$ **51.** $\frac{137}{20}$ **52.** $\frac{195}{16}$ **53.** $\frac{225}{15}$ **54.** $\frac{253}{35}$

Problem Solving

Solve.

55. If you melt 1 inch of snow, do you get more or less than 1 inch of water? *Hint: The formula below shows that 8 inches of snow contains 1 inch of water.*

	inches of water		*inches of snow*
Formula:	w	$=$	$\frac{s}{8}$

56. Substitute in the formula above to complete this chart. Write the number of inches as a whole number or mixed number.

	Inches of snow (s)	Inches of water (w)
a.	11	?
b.	25	?
c.	43	?
d.	?	3
e.	?	7

Writing Fractions and Mixed Numbers in Simplest Form

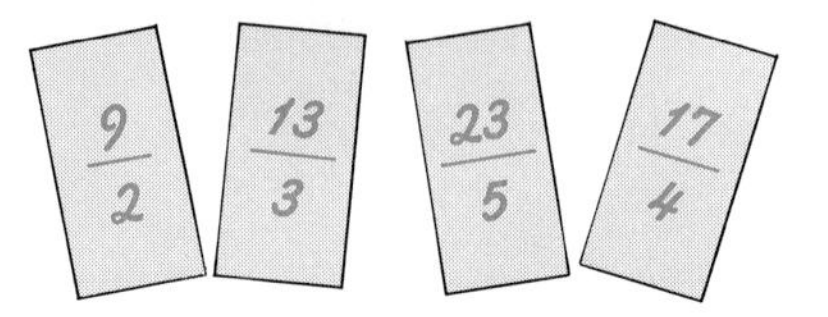

If the numerator of a fraction is greater than the denominator, then the fraction is greater than 1. These fractions are greater than 1.

1. Think about a fraction that has a numerator equal to its denominator. Is the fraction equal to 1?
2. Think about a fraction that has a numerator less than its denominator. Is the fraction less than 1?

Here's how to write fractions and mixed numbers in simplest form.

In arithmetic

Write fractions less than 1 in lowest terms.

$$\frac{10}{15} = \frac{2}{3}$$

In algebra

Write algebraic fractions in lowest terms.

$$\frac{10a^2}{6ab} = \frac{5a}{3b}$$

Write mixed numbers with the fraction part less than 1 and in lowest terms.

$$4\frac{6}{8} = 4\frac{3}{4}$$

Write fractions that are greater than or equal to 1 as a whole number or as a mixed number in simplest form.

$$\frac{24}{4} = 6 \qquad \frac{17}{5} = 3\frac{2}{5}$$

EXERCISES

Write in simplest form.

Here are scrambled answers for the next row of exercises: $\frac{3}{5}$ $\frac{5}{6}$ $\frac{1}{6}$ $\frac{1}{2}$ $\frac{3}{4}$ $\frac{4}{5}$

3. $\frac{6}{8}$ **4.** $\frac{15}{18}$ **5.** $\frac{6}{10}$ **6.** $\frac{5}{10}$ **7.** $\frac{20}{25}$ **8.** $\frac{2}{12}$

9. $\frac{16}{24}$ **10.** $\frac{10}{12}$ **11.** $\frac{6}{18}$ **12.** $\frac{6}{9}$ **13.** $\frac{8}{14}$ **14.** $\frac{5}{20}$

▶ **Write in simplest form.**

15. $2\frac{4}{6}$ **16.** $3\frac{6}{8}$ **17.** $5\frac{10}{12}$ **18.** $2\frac{2}{4}$ **19.** $4\frac{2}{6}$ **20.** $4\frac{2}{8}$

21. $6\frac{5}{10}$ **22.** $5\frac{3}{12}$ **23.** $7\frac{10}{15}$ **24.** $2\frac{3}{9}$ **25.** $8\frac{8}{10}$ **26.** $5\frac{9}{12}$

27. $6\frac{10}{15}$ **28.** $4\frac{4}{8}$ **29.** $2\frac{7}{14}$ **30.** $5\frac{8}{24}$ **31.** $9\frac{8}{64}$ **32.** $3\frac{15}{30}$

▶ **Write in simplest form.**

33. $\frac{6}{3}$ **34.** $\frac{9}{2}$ **35.** $\frac{17}{3}$ **36.** $\frac{8}{10}$ **37.** $\frac{33}{6}$ **38.** $\frac{8}{12}$

39. $\frac{10}{2}$ **40.** $\frac{8}{3}$ **41.** $\frac{15}{4}$ **42.** $\frac{10}{8}$ **43.** $\frac{36}{3}$ **44.** $\frac{6}{24}$

45. $\frac{12}{4}$ **46.** $\frac{12}{8}$ **47.** $\frac{7}{4}$ **48.** $\frac{16}{3}$ **49.** $\frac{24}{36}$ **50.** $\frac{8}{1}$

51. $\frac{20}{4}$ **52.** $\frac{9}{5}$ **53.** $\frac{15}{10}$ **54.** $\frac{3}{6}$ **55.** $\frac{18}{5}$ **56.** $\frac{10}{25}$

57. $\frac{36a}{3b}$ **58.** $\frac{10x^2}{3xy}$ **59.** $\frac{16x}{12xy^2}$ **60.** $\frac{9b^2}{8b}$ **61.** $\frac{22rs}{16s^2}$ **62.** $\frac{25cd}{10cd}$

63. $\frac{24ab}{32b^2}$ **64.** $\frac{24m^2}{8n^2}$ **65.** $\frac{32xy}{24y^2}$ **66.** $\frac{18c}{12d^2}$ **67.** $\frac{14a}{7a}$ **68.** $\frac{6r}{rs}$

69. $\frac{8m^2}{10m}$ **70.** $\frac{12c^2}{9c}$ **71.** $\frac{35m^2}{7m^2n^2}$ **72.** $\frac{35st^2}{15st}$ **73.** $\frac{24y^2z}{8yz}$ **74.** $\frac{21a^2b}{14b^2}$

Challenge

▶ **One algebraic fraction in each box does not belong. Which one is it?**
Hint: Write each fraction in simplest form.

75. $\frac{25r}{35q^2}$ $\frac{15r^2}{21q}$ $\frac{5qr^3}{7q^2r}$

76. $\frac{6mn^3}{9m^2n}$ $\frac{10m^3n^2}{15m^2}$ $\frac{18m^2n^4}{27m^3n^2}$

77. $\frac{24st^2}{32ts}$ $\frac{15mt}{20mt^2}$ $\frac{21rt}{28r}$

78. $\frac{16a^2b^2c}{20a^3bc}$ $\frac{8a^3bc^3}{10a^4bc^3}$ $\frac{28ab^3c^2}{35a^2b^2c^2}$

Writing Quotients as Mixed Numbers

You can predict your adult height by first multiplying your present height (in inches) by 100 and then dividing the answer by the growth factor found in the table.

Age (years)		12	13	14	15	16
Growth Factor	Girl	91	95	98	99	100
	Boy	82	86	90	94	97

1. On his 14th birthday, Kevin was 60 inches tall. To predict his adult height, you would first multiply 60 by what number?
2. Which number in the table is the growth factor for Kevin?
3. To predict Kevin's adult height, you would divide what number by 90?

Here's how to write a quotient as a mixed number.

6000 ÷ 90 = ?

Divide.

$$\begin{array}{r} 66 \\ 90\overline{)6000} \\ -540 \\ \hline 600 \\ -540 \\ \hline 60 \end{array}$$

Write the quotient as a mixed number.

$$\begin{array}{r} 66\frac{60}{90} \\ 90\overline{)6000} \\ -540 \\ \hline 600 \\ -540 \\ \hline 60 \end{array}$$

Write the remainder over the divisor.

Write the mixed number in simplest form.

$$\begin{array}{r} 66\frac{60}{90} = 66\frac{2}{3} \\ 90\overline{)6000} \\ -540 \\ \hline 600 \\ -540 \\ \hline 60 \end{array}$$

4. Look at the second step in the example above. To write the quotient as a mixed number, you write the remainder over the __?__.
5. What should Kevin's adult height be? Give your answer as a mixed number.
6. Complete these examples.

a.
$$\begin{array}{r} 26\frac{2}{?} \\ 5\overline{)132} \\ -10 \\ \hline 32 \\ -30 \\ \hline 2 \end{array}$$

b.
$$\begin{array}{r} 36\frac{?}{3} \\ 3\overline{)109} \\ -9 \\ \hline 19 \\ -18 \\ \hline 1 \end{array}$$

c.
$$\begin{array}{r} 97\frac{?}{?} \\ 6\overline{)587} \\ -54 \\ \hline 47 \\ -42 \\ \hline 5 \end{array}$$

EXERCISES

▶ **Divide. Write each quotient as a mixed number in simplest form.**

Here are scrambled answers for the next row of exercises: $3\frac{1}{6}$ $4\frac{1}{2}$ $4\frac{3}{5}$ $6\frac{1}{2}$ $20\frac{1}{2}$

7. $5\overline{)23}$	**8.** $6\overline{)19}$	**9.** $4\overline{)26}$	**10.** $8\overline{)36}$	**11.** $2\overline{)41}$
12. $5\overline{)52}$	**13.** $9\overline{)60}$	**14.** $6\overline{)63}$	**15.** $8\overline{)52}$	**16.** $6\overline{)46}$
17. $7\overline{)65}$	**18.** $4\overline{)66}$	**19.** $10\overline{)185}$	**20.** $16\overline{)200}$	**21.** $12\overline{)192}$
22. $20\overline{)215}$	**23.** $335 \div 25$	**24.** $252 \div 24$	**25.** $384 \div 18$	**26.** $424 \div 32$
27. $73 \div 2$	**28.** $84 \div 9$	**29.** $90 \div 4$	**30.** $99 \div 6$	**31.** $58 \div 8$
32. $47 \div 3$	**33.** $78 \div 5$	**34.** $54 \div 7$	**35.** $66 \div 5$	**36.** $82 \div 4$
37. $91 \div 6$	**38.** $75 \div 9$	**39.** $120 \div 13$	**40.** $135 \div 11$	**41.** $220 \div 15$

Problem Solving

▶ **Solve. Use the table on page 152.**

42. A 12-year-old girl is 60 inches tall. What should her adult height be? Give the answer as a mixed number.

43. A 15-year-old boy is 64 inches tall. What should his adult height be? Give the answer as a mixed number.

44. **a.** What is your height to the nearest inch?
b. What is your growth factor?

45. Your adult height (in inches) should be between what two whole numbers?

46. At what age do girls usually attain their adult height?

47. Do boys usually attain their adult height earlier or later than girls?

48. Who should be the taller adult, a 12-year-old girl who is 56 inches tall or a 13-year-old girl who is 58 inches tall?

49. Who should be the taller adult, a 15-year-old girl who is 66 inches tall or a 15-year-old boy who is 65 inches tall?

▶ **Solve.**

You can use the following formula to find the desired weight for a given height of a young adult.

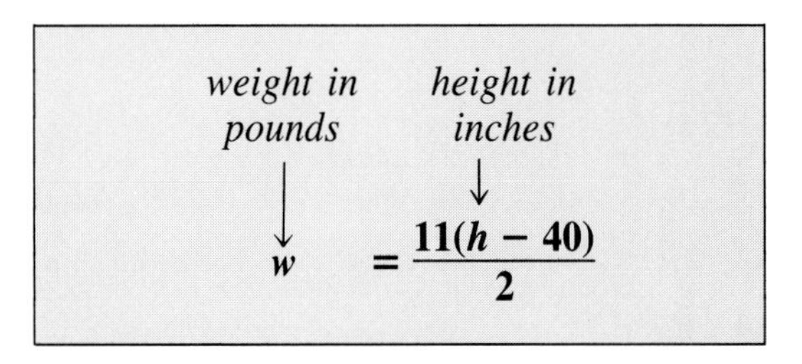

50. Substitute in the formula to complete the chart below. Give answers as whole numbers or mixed numbers.

	Height in inches *(h)*	Weight in pounds *(w)*
a.	60	?
b.	63	?
c.	66	?
d.	69	?
e.	72	?

Cumulative Skill Practice

▶ **Solve and check.** *(page 104)*

1. $3y - 6 = 15$ **2.** $\frac{k}{8} + 1 = 3$ **3.** $5x + 6 = 41$ **4.** $\frac{n}{4} - 3 = 0$

5. $44 = 6m + 2$ **6.** $2 = \frac{j}{3} - 2$ **7.** $10 = \frac{r}{12} + 6$ **8.** $56 = 12y - 4$

9. $\frac{d}{3} + 15 = 21$ **10.** $1 = \frac{k}{4} - 14$ **11.** $11p + 12 = 111$ **12.** $152 = 16r - 8$

13. $5t + 4.3 = 11.7$ **14.** $\frac{n}{6} - 1.5 = 2.4$ **15.** $18.4 = 4w + 5.6$ **16.** $0.6 = \frac{z}{8} - 2.7$

▶ **Simplify.** *(page 108)*

17. $7k + 5k$ **18.** $11j + j$ **19.** $r + r$

20. $3s + 2s + 2s$ **21.** $5x + 3x + x$ **22.** $t + t + t$

23. $5y + 4y + 3$ **24.** $5y + 4 + 3$ **25.** $5y + 4y + 3y$

26. $b + 4b + 3b + 2b$ **27.** $n + n + 4n + 6n$ **28.** $3j + 2j + 9 - 6$

▶ **Solve and check.** *(page 110)*

29. $3x + 2x = 105$ **30.** $2w + 4w = 102$ **31.** $7z + z = 144$ **32.** $y + y = 86$

33. $105 = 3b + 4b$ **34.** $220 = 9f + f$ **35.** $162 = c + 8c$ **36.** $104 = c + c$

37. $g + 3g = 6.4$ **38.** $6h + 4h = 12.5$ **39.** $8.4 = j + 7j$ **40.** $16.3 = k + k$

41. $4d - 3.8 = 6.2$ **42.** $10 = 5f + 7.4$ **43.** $\frac{n}{2} + 6.1 = 20.7$ **44.** $14.5 = \frac{q}{3} - 2.5$

▶ **Write using exponents.** *(page 120)*

45. $4 \cdot 4 \cdot 4$ **46.** $10 \cdot 10$ **47.** $6 \cdot 6 \cdot 8 \cdot 8$

48. $a \cdot a \cdot b$ **49.** $x \cdot x \cdot x \cdot y \cdot y$ **50.** $3 \cdot x \cdot x \cdot y$

51. $2 \cdot y \cdot z \cdot y \cdot z$ **52.** $6 \cdot r \cdot s \cdot s \cdot s$ **53.** $z \cdot y \cdot 6 \cdot y \cdot z \cdot y$

▶ **Give the prime or algebraic factorization.** *(page 124)*

54. 6 **55.** 14 **56.** 18 **57.** 16 **58.** 24 **59.** 42

60. 36 **61.** 45 **62.** 48 **63.** $9x^2$ **64.** $10g^3$ **65.** $15d$

66. $11c^3$ **67.** $8n^3$ **68.** $20xy^2$ **69.** $25r^2s^2$ **70.** $18cd^3$ **71.** $27y^3z^2$

Problem Solving—Applications

Use the bar graph to solve the problems.

1. Which item cost \$.90 more in 1985 than it did in 1975?
2. Which item cost \$1.20 less in 1975 than it did in 1985?
3. Which had the greater increase in price from 1975 to 1985, a Mother's Day card or a spiral notebook?
4. In which year could you have paid for 3 spiral notebooks with a \$5 bill and received \$3.20 in change?
5. In 1975, would \$2.00 have been enough money to buy 3 soft drinks, a Mother's Day card, and a 45-RPM record?

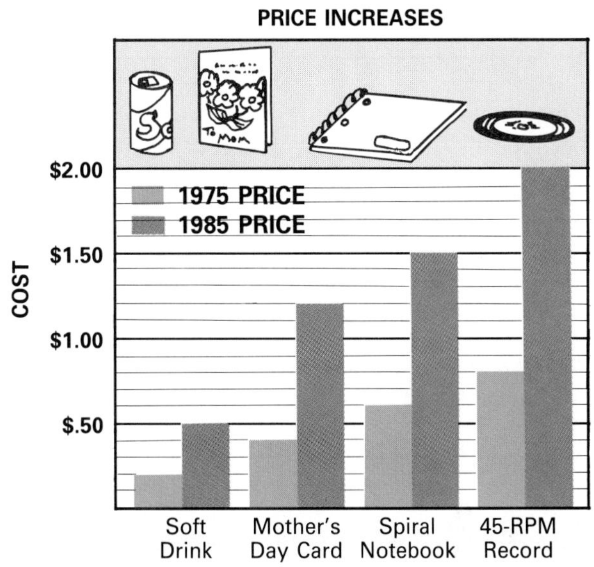

PRICE INCREASES

Read the facts. Then complete the steps to answer the question.

6. *Facts:* The cost of a movie ticket in 1985 was \$3.50. That is \$.50 more than 2 times the cost of a 1975 movie ticket.
Question: What was the cost of a movie ticket in 1975?
   - **a.** Let t equal the cost of a 1975 ticket. Then $\underline{?}\ t + 0.50$ equals the cost of a 1985 ticket.
   - **b.** Two equal expressions for the cost of a 1985 ticket are $\underline{?}\ t + 0.50$ and 3.50.
   - **c.** To find the cost of a 1975 ticket, you can solve the equation $2t + 0.50 = \underline{?}$.
   - **d.** Solve the equation in part c. What was the cost of a ticket in 1975?

7. *Facts:* The cost of a burger in 1985 was \$1.20. That is \$.30 less than 3 times the cost of a burger in 1975.
Question: What was the cost of a burger in 1975?
   - **a.** Let p equal the cost of a burger in 1975. Then $3p - \underline{?}$ equals the cost of a burger in 1985.
   - **b.** Two equal expressions for the cost of a burger in 1985 are $3p - \underline{?}$ and 1.20.
   - **c.** To find the cost of a burger in 1975, you can solve the equation $3p - 0.30 = \underline{?}$.
   - **d.** Solve the equation in part c. What was the cost of a burger in 1975?

Write an equation and solve the problem.

8. The cost of a spiral notebook in 1985 was \$.40 less than 2 times the cost of a spiral notebook in 1980. What was the cost of a spiral notebook in 1980? *Hint: Use the bar graph to find the cost of a 1985 spiral notebook.*
(Let n = the cost of a notebook in 1980.)

9. If you multiply the cost of a 45-RPM record in 1980 by 1.5 and then add \$.05, you get the cost of a 45-RPM record in 1985. What was the cost of a 45-RPM record in 1980? *Hint: Use the bar graph to find the cost of a 45-RPM record in 1985.*
(Let m = the cost of a record in 1980.)

Adding and Subtracting Fractions with Common Denominators

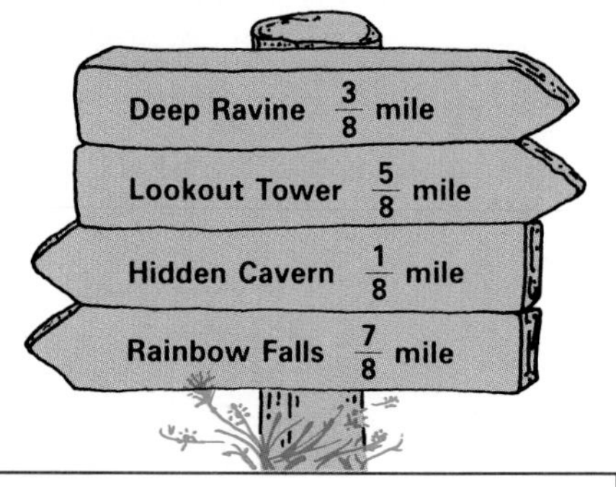

This sign at the trail entrance shows the distance between the trail entrance and four scenic points.

1. What is the hiking distance to Deep Ravine?
2. What two fractions would you add to compute the distance from the Lookout Tower to Rainbow Falls?

Here's how to add fractions with common denominators.

To add fractions with common denominators, write the sum of the numerators over the common denominator.

In arithmetic

$$\frac{5}{8} + \frac{7}{8} = \frac{12}{8} = 1\frac{1}{2} \leftarrow \text{simplest form}$$

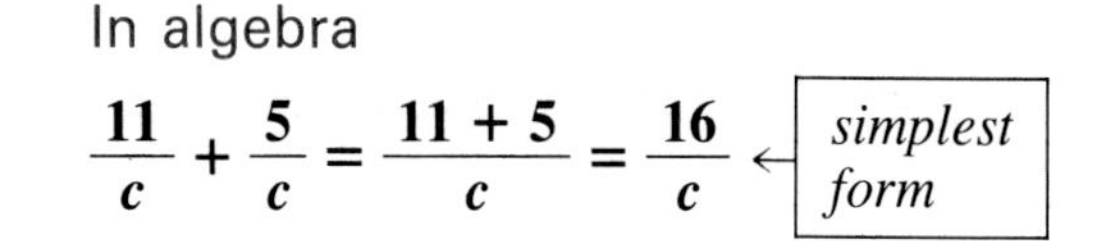

In algebra

$$\frac{11}{c} + \frac{5}{c} = \frac{11 + 5}{c} = \frac{16}{c} \leftarrow \text{simplest form}$$

3. Look at the first example above. How far is it from Lookout Tower to Rainbow Falls?
4. Complete these examples.

a. $\frac{3}{5} + \frac{4}{5} = \frac{?}{5} = 1\frac{?}{5}$ **b.** $\frac{r}{t} + \frac{s}{t} = \frac{r + s}{?}$ **c.** $\frac{7}{z} + \frac{8}{z} = \frac{7 + 8}{?} = \frac{?}{z}$

5. Look at the sign. What two fractions would you subtract to compute the distance from Deep Ravine to Lookout Tower?

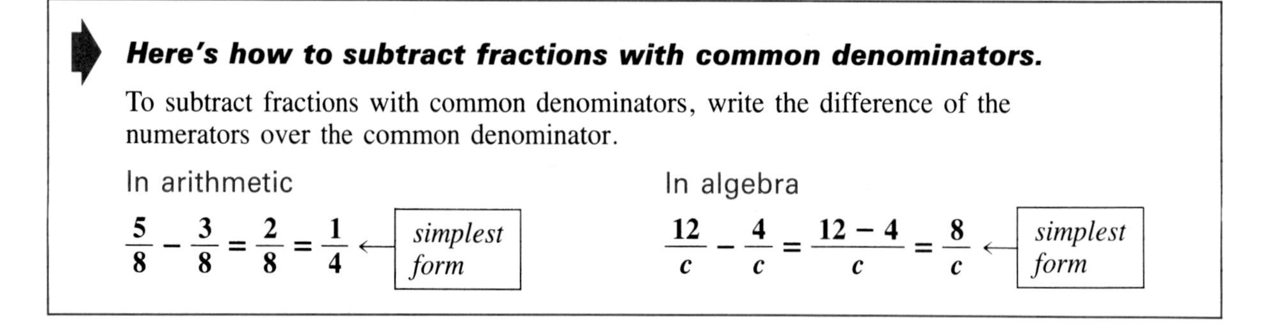

Here's how to subtract fractions with common denominators.

To subtract fractions with common denominators, write the difference of the numerators over the common denominator.

In arithmetic

$$\frac{5}{8} - \frac{3}{8} = \frac{2}{8} = \frac{1}{4} \leftarrow \text{simplest form}$$

In algebra

$$\frac{12}{c} - \frac{4}{c} = \frac{12 - 4}{c} = \frac{8}{c} \leftarrow \text{simplest form}$$

6. Look at the example above. How far is it from Deep Ravine to Lookout Tower?

EXERCISES

Give each sum in simplest form.
Here are scrambled answers for the next row of exercises: $\frac{2}{3}$ $1\frac{1}{4}$ $1\frac{2}{7}$ 1 $1\frac{1}{7}$

7. $\frac{1}{3}+\frac{1}{3}$ **8.** $\frac{4}{7}+\frac{5}{7}$ **9.** $\frac{5}{6}+\frac{1}{6}$ **10.** $\frac{6}{7}+\frac{2}{7}$ **11.** $\frac{3}{4}+\frac{2}{4}$

12. $\frac{3}{8}+\frac{7}{8}$ **13.** $\frac{1}{4}+\frac{3}{4}$ **14.** $\frac{3}{10}+\frac{1}{10}$ **15.** $\frac{7}{16}+\frac{5}{16}$ **16.** $\frac{1}{8}+\frac{1}{8}$

17. $\frac{b}{d}+\frac{c}{d}$ **18.** $\frac{r}{t}+\frac{s}{t}$ **19.** $\frac{2a}{c}+\frac{3}{c}$ **20.** $\frac{3x}{y}+\frac{w}{y}$ **21.** $\frac{3b}{d}+\frac{7}{d}$

22. $\frac{5}{a^2}+\frac{7}{a^2}$ **23.** $\frac{10}{xy}+\frac{6}{xy}$ **24.** $\frac{12}{pq}+\frac{3}{pq}$ **25.** $\frac{18}{k^2}+\frac{6}{k^2}$ **26.** $\frac{20}{a^2b}+\frac{12}{a^2b}$

Give each difference in simplest form.
Here are scrambled answers for the next row of exercises: $\frac{1}{3}$ $\frac{2}{3}$ 0 2 $\frac{1}{5}$

27. $\frac{4}{15}-\frac{1}{15}$ **28.** $\frac{5}{9}-\frac{2}{9}$ **29.** $\frac{7}{12}-\frac{7}{12}$ **30.** $\frac{10}{9}-\frac{4}{9}$ **31.** $\frac{11}{4}-\frac{3}{4}$

32. $\frac{9}{8}-\frac{3}{8}$ **33.** $\frac{6}{4}-\frac{2}{4}$ **34.** $\frac{12}{10}-\frac{7}{10}$ **35.** $\frac{11}{12}-\frac{7}{12}$ **36.** $\frac{8}{3}-\frac{2}{3}$

37. $\frac{r}{t}-\frac{s}{t}$ **38.** $\frac{a}{d}-\frac{c}{d}$ **39.** $\frac{3x}{y}-\frac{w}{y}$ **40.** $\frac{a}{g}-\frac{2b}{g}$ **41.** $\frac{4d}{e}-\frac{5}{e}$

42. $\frac{11}{w^2}-\frac{4}{w^2}$ **43.** $\frac{9}{mn}-\frac{3}{mn}$ **44.** $\frac{20}{rs}-\frac{14}{rs}$ **45.** $\frac{16}{j^2}-\frac{2}{j^2}$ **46.** $\frac{25}{c^2d}-\frac{8}{c^2d}$

Evaluate each expression for $a = 1$, $b = 2$, $c = 3$, $d = 4$, and $e = 6$. Write the answer in simplest form.

47. $\frac{a}{e}+\frac{b}{e}$ **48.** $\frac{b}{d}+\frac{c}{d}$ **49.** $\frac{c}{b}+\frac{a}{b}$ **50.** $\frac{d}{e}+\frac{d}{e}$ **51.** $\frac{a}{c}+\frac{d}{c}$

52. $\frac{b}{c}+\frac{d}{c}-\frac{a}{c}$ **53.** $\frac{b}{d}+\frac{c}{d}-\frac{a}{d}$ **54.** $\frac{d}{e}+\frac{b}{e}-\frac{a}{e}$ **55.** $\frac{e}{d}+\frac{c}{d}-\frac{b}{d}$

Problem Solving

Solve. Use the trail sign on page 156.

56. What is the hiking distance from Deep Ravine to Rainbow Falls?

57. What is the hiking distance from Hidden Cavern to Rainbow Falls?

58. How far is a round trip from the trail entrance to Rainbow Falls and back again?

★59. If you hiked at 1 mile per hour, could you hike from Hidden Cavern to Lookout Tower in less than $\frac{1}{2}$ hour?

Adding and Subtracting Fractions with Different Denominators

As part of their driver's test, a group of students were asked to identify 20 road signs. The table shows the results.

1. Which two fractions would you add to find what fraction of the students identified 19 or more road signs?

Signs identified	Number of students	Fraction of students
20	𝍸 I	$\frac{1}{8}$
19	𝍸 𝍸 𝍸 𝍸	$\frac{5}{12}$
18	𝍸 𝍸 II	$\frac{1}{4}$
17	𝍸 III	$\frac{1}{6}$
16 or fewer	II	$\frac{1}{24}$

Here's how to add fractions with different denominators.

To add fractions with different denominators, find the least common denominator, change to equivalent fractions, and add.

In arithmetic

$$\frac{5}{12} + \frac{1}{8} = \frac{10}{24} + \frac{3}{24} = \frac{13}{24}$$

The LCD is 24.

In algebra

$$\frac{a}{6} + \frac{b}{4} = \frac{2a}{12} + \frac{3b}{12} = \frac{2a + 3b}{12}$$

The LCD is 12.

2. Look at the first example above. What fraction of the students identified 19 or more signs?
3. What fraction would you subtract from 1 to find the fraction of students who did not identify all 20 signs?

Here's how to subtract fractions with different denominators.

To subtract fractions with different denominators, find the least common denominator, change to equivalent fractions, and subtract.

In arithmetic

$$1 - \frac{1}{8} = \frac{8}{8} - \frac{1}{8} = \frac{7}{8}$$

The LCD is 8.

In algebra

$$\frac{x}{6} - \frac{y}{9} = \frac{3x}{18} - \frac{2y}{18} = \frac{3x - 2y}{18}$$

The LCD is 18.

4. Look at the first example above. What fraction of the students did not identify all 20 signs?

Give each sum in simplest form.
Here are scrambled answers for the next row of exercises:

$1\frac{1}{15}$ $1\frac{5}{24}$ $\frac{5}{8}$ $1\frac{1}{8}$ $\frac{5}{6}$

5. $\frac{1}{2}+\frac{1}{3}$ **6.** $\frac{3}{8}+\frac{1}{4}$ **7.** $\frac{2}{5}+\frac{2}{3}$ **8.** $\frac{5}{8}+\frac{1}{2}$ **9.** $\frac{5}{6}+\frac{3}{8}$

10. $\frac{5}{9}+\frac{1}{6}$ **11.** $\frac{3}{5}+\frac{1}{5}$ **12.** $\frac{7}{16}+\frac{1}{2}$ **13.** $\frac{5}{8}+\frac{1}{6}$ **14.** $\frac{2}{5}+\frac{1}{4}$

15. $\frac{a}{2}+\frac{b}{3}$ **16.** $\frac{n}{3}+\frac{3}{4}$ **17.** $\frac{c}{4}+\frac{d}{2}$ **18.** $\frac{5}{3}+\frac{k}{5}$ **19.** $\frac{r}{4}+\frac{s}{5}$

20. $\frac{2f}{5}+\frac{g}{6}$ **21.** $\frac{4}{5}+\frac{3q}{2}$ **22.** $\frac{3s}{4}+\frac{5}{6}$ **23.** $\frac{u}{5}+\frac{5v}{8}$ **24.** $\frac{5n}{2}+\frac{1}{8}$

25. $\frac{5b}{6}+\frac{7c}{9}$ **26.** $\frac{3r}{8}+\frac{5s}{4}$ **27.** $\frac{3g}{5}+\frac{7a}{10}$ **28.** $\frac{11m}{6}+\frac{7n}{3}$ **29.** $\frac{2x}{9}+\frac{7y}{12}$

Give each difference in simplest form.
Here are scrambled answers for the next row of exercises:

$\frac{3}{10}$ $\frac{7}{24}$ $\frac{1}{4}$ $\frac{1}{9}$ $\frac{5}{12}$

30. $\frac{3}{4}-\frac{1}{3}$ **31.** $\frac{7}{12}-\frac{1}{3}$ **32.** $\frac{5}{8}-\frac{1}{3}$ **33.** $\frac{9}{10}-\frac{3}{5}$ **34.** $\frac{2}{3}-\frac{5}{9}$

35. $\frac{2}{3}-\frac{7}{12}$ **36.** $\frac{5}{6}-\frac{2}{3}$ **37.** $\frac{7}{10}-\frac{1}{5}$ **38.** $\frac{1}{2}-\frac{1}{3}$ **39.** $\frac{7}{8}-\frac{0}{6}$

40. $\frac{c}{4}-\frac{d}{2}$ **41.** $\frac{m}{5}-\frac{1}{6}$ **42.** $\frac{k}{2}-\frac{5}{3}$ **43.** $\frac{x}{6}-\frac{y}{4}$ **44.** $\frac{u}{2}-\frac{v}{8}$

45. $\frac{2a}{3}-\frac{b}{4}$ **46.** $\frac{7c}{8}-\frac{d}{4}$ **47.** $\frac{3k}{2}-\frac{2}{5}$ **48.** $\frac{y}{3}-\frac{4z}{5}$ **49.** $\frac{5n}{6}-\frac{1}{3}$

50. $\frac{5c}{6}-\frac{7d}{9}$ **51.** $\frac{3x}{4}-\frac{2y}{5}$ **52.** $\frac{5r}{12}-\frac{2t}{9}$ **53.** $\frac{2m}{5}-\frac{7n}{8}$ **54.** $\frac{4j}{5}-\frac{9k}{10}$

Problem Solving

Solve. Use the table on page 158.

55. What fraction of the students identified 17 or fewer road signs?

56. What fraction of the students missed 2 or fewer of the road signs?

57. What fraction of the students identified 17 or more of the road signs?

58. What fraction of the students missed at least 1 of the road signs?

Adding and Subtracting Mixed Numbers without Regrouping

1. A balloonist who weighs $145\frac{1}{2}$ pounds plans to take $23\frac{1}{4}$ pounds of equipment on a balloon ride. What would you do to compute the total weight of the balloonist and the equipment?

2. Suppose that you are in a balloon that is 1000 feet above the ground. Suppose also that your friend is in a balloon that is 200 feet above the ground. What would you do to compute how much farther you can see than your friend? Look at the chart.

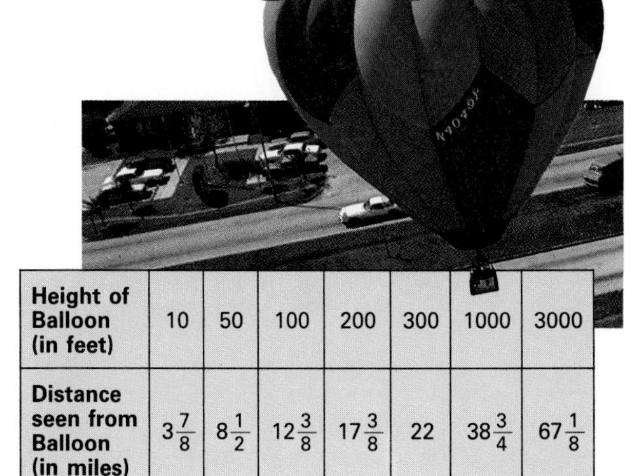

Height of Balloon (in feet)	10	50	100	200	300	1000	3000
Distance seen from Balloon (in miles)	$3\frac{7}{8}$	$8\frac{1}{2}$	$12\frac{3}{8}$	$17\frac{3}{8}$	22	$38\frac{3}{4}$	$67\frac{1}{8}$

Here's how to add and subtract mixed numbers.

To add (or subtract) mixed numbers with different denominators, first write fractions with a common denominator. Next add (or subtract) the equivalent fractions. Then add (or subtract) the whole numbers.

$$145\frac{1}{2} + 23\frac{1}{4} = ? \qquad\qquad 38\frac{3}{4} - 17\frac{3}{8} = ?$$

$$\begin{array}{rcr} 145\frac{1}{2} & = & 145\frac{2}{4} \\ +23\frac{1}{4} & = & +\ 23\frac{1}{4} \\ \hline & & 168\frac{3}{4} \end{array}$$

Change to a common denominator. Add the fractions. Add the whole numbers.

$$\begin{array}{rcr} 38\frac{3}{4} & = & 38\frac{6}{8} \\ -17\frac{3}{8} & = & -17\frac{3}{8} \\ \hline & & 21\frac{3}{8} \end{array}$$

Change to a common denominator. Subtract the fractions. Subtract the whole numbers.

3. Look at the examples above. What is the total weight? How much farther can you see?

4. Complete these examples.

a. $$\begin{array}{r} 4\frac{2}{5} \\ +2\frac{1}{5} \\ \hline 6\ \underline{?} \end{array}$$

b. $$\begin{array}{rcr} 4\frac{1}{6} & = & 4\frac{4}{24} \\ +2\frac{3}{8} & = & +2\frac{9}{24} \\ \hline & & \underline{?}\ \frac{13}{24} \end{array}$$

c. $$\begin{array}{r} 8\frac{7}{9} \\ -3\frac{1}{9} \\ \hline 5\frac{6}{9} = 5\ \underline{?} \end{array}$$

d. $$\begin{array}{rcr} 10\frac{1}{3} & = & 10\frac{4}{12} \\ -\ 2\frac{1}{4} & = & -\ 2\ \underline{?} \\ \hline & & 8\frac{1}{12} \end{array}$$

EXERCISES

▶ **Add. Write the sum in simplest form.**
Here are scrambled answers for the next row of exercises: $5\frac{7}{8}$ $6\frac{7}{8}$ $7\frac{19}{20}$ $4\frac{5}{6}$

5. $3\frac{1}{3} + 1\frac{1}{2}$ **6.** $4\frac{1}{2} + 2\frac{3}{8}$ **7.** $1\frac{3}{4} + 4\frac{1}{8}$ **8.** $5\frac{3}{4} + 2\frac{1}{5}$

9. $4\frac{1}{2} + 3\frac{1}{5}$ **10.** $4\frac{1}{3} + 8\frac{1}{5}$ **11.** $8\frac{5}{12} + 1\frac{1}{8}$ **12.** $6 + 3\frac{3}{8}$

13. $7\frac{3}{8} + 9\frac{1}{6}$ **14.** $9\frac{1}{5} + 5\frac{3}{10}$ **15.** $2\frac{1}{8} + 2\frac{3}{8}$ **16.** $2\frac{5}{8} + 1\frac{1}{5}$

17. $1\frac{1}{4} + 3\frac{2}{5}$ **18.** $6\frac{1}{2} + 3\frac{1}{9}$ **19.** $3\frac{5}{12} + 4\frac{1}{2}$ **20.** $8\frac{1}{6} + 2\frac{5}{9}$

▶ **Subtract. Write the difference in simplest form.**
Here are scrambled answers for the next row of exercises: $3\frac{1}{8}$ $1\frac{1}{4}$ $2\frac{3}{8}$ $4\frac{1}{4}$

21. $4\frac{5}{8} - 2\frac{1}{4}$ **22.** $2\frac{1}{2} - 1\frac{1}{4}$ **23.** $5\frac{7}{8} - 2\frac{3}{4}$ **24.** $6\frac{3}{4} - 2\frac{1}{2}$

25. $7\frac{1}{2} - 4\frac{1}{8}$ **26.** $5\frac{1}{3} - 2\frac{1}{4}$ **27.** $15\frac{1}{2} - 8\frac{1}{4}$ **28.** $83\frac{1}{2} - 12\frac{3}{10}$

29. $15\frac{3}{4} - 6\frac{5}{8}$ **30.** $8\frac{4}{5} - 1\frac{1}{4}$ **31.** $2\frac{7}{10} - 1\frac{3}{5}$ **32.** $18\frac{1}{4} - 8\frac{1}{6}$

33. $5\frac{7}{8} - 4\frac{1}{2}$ **34.** $6\frac{4}{9} - 4\frac{1}{3}$ **35.** $9\frac{5}{8} - 2\frac{1}{6}$ **36.** $9\frac{7}{10} - 3\frac{1}{4}$

Problem Solving

▶ **First choose the equation and solve the problem. Then reread the problem to see if your answer makes sense.**

Equation A: $n + 1\frac{1}{4} = 2\frac{1}{2}$

Equation B: $n - 1\frac{1}{4} = 2\frac{1}{2}$

37. Your hot-air balloon is $1\frac{1}{4}$ miles above another balloon. If you are at a height of $2\frac{1}{2}$ miles, what is the height of the other balloonist?

38. The difference in height of two balloons is $2\frac{1}{2}$ miles. If the lower balloon is at a height of $1\frac{1}{4}$ miles, what is the height of the other balloon?

39. Your balloon landed $1\frac{1}{4}$ miles closer to the target than another balloon did. If you were $2\frac{1}{2}$ miles from the target, how far was the other balloon from the target?

40. Your balloon ride took $1\frac{1}{4}$ hours less time than your friend's ride did. If your ride took $2\frac{1}{2}$ hours, how many hours did your friend's ride take?

Adding and Subtracting Mixed Numbers with Regrouping

1. You have a 6-week-old dachshund and a 7-week-old sheepdog. What two mixed numbers would you add to find the total number of cups of food you should feed them each day?

2. What two numbers would you subtract to find how much more food each day you should feed a 14-week-old sheepdog than a 12-week-old poodle?

Recommended Daily Amounts of Food			
Dog Size		Age 5–9 weeks	Age 10–15 weeks
Small	Chihuahua, Dachshund	$1\frac{2}{3}$ cups	$2\frac{1}{4}$ cups
Medium	Poodle, Boston Terrier	$2\frac{3}{4}$ cups	$4\frac{1}{2}$ cups
Large	Labrador Retriever, Sheepdog	$3\frac{1}{2}$ cups	$6\frac{1}{3}$ cups

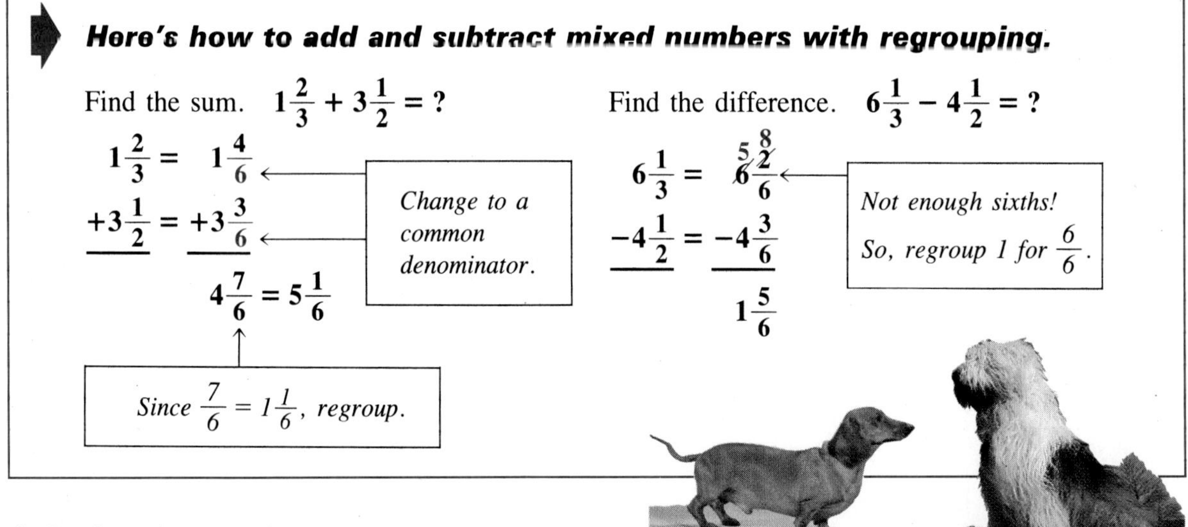

Here's how to add and subtract mixed numbers with regrouping.

Find the sum. $1\frac{2}{3} + 3\frac{1}{2} = ?$

$$\begin{aligned} 1\frac{2}{3} &= 1\frac{4}{6} \\ +3\frac{1}{2} &= +3\frac{3}{6} \\ & \quad 4\frac{7}{6} = 5\frac{1}{6} \end{aligned}$$

Change to a common denominator.

Since $\frac{7}{6} = 1\frac{1}{6}$, regroup.

Find the difference. $6\frac{1}{3} - 4\frac{1}{2} = ?$

$$\begin{aligned} 6\frac{1}{3} &= \overset{5}{\cancel{6}}\frac{\overset{8}{\cancel{2}}}{6} \\ -4\frac{1}{2} &= -4\frac{3}{6} \\ & \quad 1\frac{5}{6} \end{aligned}$$

Not enough sixths! So, regroup 1 for $\frac{6}{6}$.

3. Look at the examples above.

   a. How many cups of food should you feed a 6-week-old dachshund and a 7-week-old sheepdog each day?

   b. How much more food each day should you feed a 14-week-old sheepdog than a 12-week-old poodle?

4. Complete these examples.

   a. $$\begin{aligned} 4\frac{5}{6} &= 4\frac{20}{24} \\ +4\frac{3}{8} &= +4\frac{9}{24} \\ & \quad 8\frac{29}{24} = 9\frac{?}{?} \end{aligned}$$

   b. $$\begin{aligned} 14 &= 13\frac{2}{2} \\ -3\frac{1}{2} &= -3\frac{1}{2} \\ & \quad ?\frac{1}{2} \end{aligned}$$

   Regroup 1 for $\frac{2}{2}$.

   c. $$\begin{aligned} 6\frac{1}{2} &= \overset{5?}{\cancel{6}}\frac{\cancel{4}}{8} \\ -2\frac{7}{8} &= -2\frac{7}{8} \\ & \quad 3\frac{5}{8} \end{aligned}$$

Add. Write the sum in simplest form.
Here are scrambled answers for the next row of exercises: $9\frac{3}{8}$ $6\frac{7}{8}$ $6\frac{1}{6}$ $5\frac{1}{2}$ $9\frac{1}{8}$

5. $4\frac{2}{3} + 1\frac{1}{2}$ **6.** $2\frac{1}{2} + 6\frac{5}{8}$ **7.** $3\frac{3}{4} + 5\frac{5}{8}$ **8.** $1\frac{1}{8} + 5\frac{3}{4}$ **9.** $2\frac{5}{6} + 2\frac{2}{3}$

10. $6\frac{3}{5} + 2\frac{3}{10}$ **11.** $3\frac{1}{5} + 6\frac{7}{10}$ **12.** $2\frac{9}{10} + 4\frac{1}{2}$ **13.** $2\frac{1}{2} + 5\frac{2}{5}$ **14.** $7\frac{11}{12} + 2\frac{1}{4}$

15. $2\frac{1}{6} + 2\frac{7}{8}$ **16.** $3\frac{5}{8} + 2\frac{1}{2}$ **17.** $1\frac{1}{4} + 3\frac{4}{5}$ **18.** $6\frac{1}{2} + 3\frac{2}{3}$ **19.** $3\frac{7}{12} + 4\frac{1}{2}$

Subtract. Write the difference in simplest form.
Here are scrambled answers for the next row of exercises: $4\frac{3}{8}$ $2\frac{3}{4}$ $2\frac{1}{4}$ $4\frac{3}{4}$ $4\frac{7}{8}$

20. $13\frac{1}{4} - 8\frac{1}{2}$ **21.** $7\frac{1}{8} - 2\frac{3}{4}$ **22.** $10 - 5\frac{1}{8}$ **23.** $6\frac{5}{8} - 3\frac{7}{8}$ **24.** $9\frac{1}{8} - 6\frac{7}{8}$

25. $8\frac{1}{3} - 2\frac{1}{2}$ **26.** $10\frac{1}{4} - 1\frac{2}{3}$ **27.** $7\frac{7}{8} - 1\frac{3}{4}$ **28.** $15\frac{1}{6} - 3\frac{2}{3}$ **29.** $9 - 7\frac{1}{2}$

30. $20 - 8\frac{3}{4}$ **31.** $5\frac{5}{8} - 2\frac{3}{4}$ **32.** $4\frac{2}{3} - 1\frac{1}{2}$ **33.** $4\frac{1}{10} - 3\frac{1}{2}$ **34.** $9\frac{2}{3} - 8\frac{1}{2}$

35. $2\frac{2}{9} - 1\frac{1}{3}$ **36.** $18 - 8\frac{5}{8}$ **37.** $6\frac{1}{2} - 2\frac{1}{8}$ **38.** $9\frac{1}{10} - 5\frac{3}{5}$ **39.** $10\frac{1}{4} - 5\frac{2}{3}$

Problem Solving

Solve. Use the chart on page 162.

40. Would $9\frac{1}{2}$ cups of food each day be enough food for an 8-week-old sheepdog and a 12-week-old labrador retriever?

41. If dog food costs 18¢ per cup, how much does it cost each day to feed a 15-week-old chihuahua and a 5-week-old Boston terrier?

CALCULATOR

Find and correct the two wrong answers.

42. a. Six tenths plus two hundredths minus three and twelve hundredths plus five and four tenths equals

2.75

b. Sixteen hundredths plus two and eight tenths minus one and six hundredths minus seven tenths equals

1.2

c. Nine and five hundredths minus sixty-four hundredths minus five tenths plus three and two hundredths equals

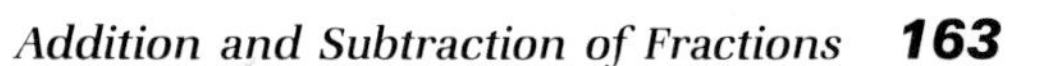

Problem Solving—Using Equations

In earlier chapters you wrote addition and subtraction equations with whole numbers to solve problems. You can use the same method to write equations with mixed numbers.

Here's how to use an equation to solve a problem.

Problem: Steve is $4\frac{1}{2}$ inches taller than Tina. He is $67\frac{3}{4}$ inches tall. How tall is Tina?

Step 1. Choose a variable. Use it and the facts to represent the numbers in the problem.

Let t = Tina's height in inches. Then $t + 4\frac{1}{2}$ = Steve's height in inches.

Step 2. Write an equation based on the facts.

$$t + 4\frac{1}{2} = 67\frac{3}{4}$$

These are two equal expressions for Steve's height.

Step 3. Solve the equation.

$$t + 4\frac{1}{2} = 67\frac{3}{4}$$

$$t + 4\frac{1}{2} - 4\frac{1}{2} = 67\frac{3}{4} - 4\frac{1}{2}$$

$$t = 63\frac{1}{4}$$

Tina is $63\frac{1}{4}$ inches tall.

1. Look at the example above.

a. In Step 1, we let t equal __?__ height in inches. Then the expression t + __?__ equals Steve's height in inches.

b. In Step 2, the two equal expressions for Steve's height in inches are __?__ and __?__.

c. An equation for the problem is __?__.

2. To check the solution, ask yourself if the answer fits the facts. Is Tina $63\frac{1}{4}$ inches tall?

First choose the equation and solve the problem. Then reread the problem to see if your answer makes sense.

Equation A: $n + 5\frac{3}{4} = 68\frac{1}{2}$

Equation B: $n - 5\frac{3}{4} = 68\frac{1}{2}$

3. If Arlo grows $5\frac{3}{4}$ inches, he will be as tall as Karen. If Karen is $68\frac{1}{2}$ inches tall, how tall is Arlo?

4. April is $5\frac{3}{4}$ inches shorter than Brad. If April is $68\frac{1}{2}$ inches tall, how tall is Brad?

5. The sum of a number n and $5\frac{3}{4}$ is $68\frac{1}{2}$. What is the number?

6. A number n decreased by $5\frac{3}{4}$ is $68\frac{1}{2}$. What is the number?

7. A number n increased by $5\frac{3}{4}$ is $68\frac{1}{2}$. What is the number?

8. A number n minus $5\frac{3}{4}$ equals $68\frac{1}{2}$. What is the number?

9. The difference between two numbers is $68\frac{1}{2}$. If the smaller number is $5\frac{3}{4}$, what is the larger number?

10. $5\frac{3}{4}$ more than a number n is $68\frac{1}{2}$. What is the number?

Write an equation and solve the problem.

11. A number decreased by $3\frac{1}{8}$ is $14\frac{1}{2}$. What is the number?
(Let n = the number.)

12. A number increased by $12\frac{3}{10}$ is $20\frac{2}{5}$. What is the number?
(Let m = the number.)

13. The sum of two numbers is $20\frac{2}{3}$. If one of the numbers is $6\frac{1}{2}$, what is the other number?
(Let n = the other number.)

14. The difference between two numbers is $2\frac{3}{5}$. If the smaller number is $6\frac{7}{10}$, what is the larger number?
(Let n = the larger number.)

15. Jan worked $3\frac{1}{2}$ more hours than Sara did. If Jan worked $26\frac{1}{4}$ hours, how many hours did Sara work?
(Let s = the number of hours Sara worked.)

16. Dan worked $10\frac{3}{4}$ hours less than Jenny did. If Dan worked $28\frac{1}{2}$ hours, how many hours did Jenny work?
(Let j = the number of hours Jenny worked.)

17. Carrie worked 5 more than twice as many hours as Hal. If she worked 43 hours, how many hours did Hal work?
(Let h = the number of hours Hal worked.)

18. Larry worked 3 times as many hours as Emily. Together they worked 64 hours. How many hours did Emily work?
(Let n = the number of hours Emily worked.)

Cumulative Skill Practice

Give the greatest common factor. *(page 126)*

1. 10, 15 **2.** 16, 6 **3.** 7, 27 **4.** 48, 32 **5.** 12, 18

6. $3, 6c$ **7.** $5a, a$ **8.** $10y, 22y$ **9.** $5w, 10w^2$ **10.** $3y^2, 7y$

11. $9xy, x^2$ **12.** $5u^2v^2, 15u^2$ **13.** $12c^2d, 18cd^2$ **14.** $x^3y^2, 3x^2y$ **15.** $40e^3f, 25e^2f^2$

Complete to get an equivalent fraction. *(page 130)*

16. $\frac{5}{8} = \frac{?}{32}$ **17.** $\frac{3}{4} = \frac{?}{32}$ **18.** $\frac{7}{8} = \frac{?}{24}$ **19.** $\frac{5}{9} = \frac{?}{36}$ **20.** $\frac{7}{16} = \frac{?}{48}$

21. $\frac{5}{c} = \frac{?}{3c}$ **22.** $\frac{b}{4} = \frac{?}{4b}$ **23.** $\frac{3r}{2s} = \frac{?}{8s^2}$ **24.** $\frac{5y}{2x} = \frac{?}{6xy}$ **25.** $\frac{3a}{4b} = \frac{?}{12b^2}$

26. $\frac{3mn}{m^2n} = \frac{?}{5m^2n^2}$ **27.** $\frac{8y}{3yz} = \frac{?}{6y^2z}$ **28.** $\frac{3a^2b}{7} = \frac{?}{21b}$ **29.** $\frac{8fg}{3} = \frac{?}{12fg}$ **30.** $\frac{6y^2}{5x} = \frac{?}{20xy}$

Write in lowest terms. *(page 132)*

31. $\frac{5}{20}$ **32.** $\frac{15}{18}$ **33.** $\frac{20}{15}$ **34.** $\frac{24}{36}$ **35.** $\frac{14}{42}$ **36.** $\frac{54}{48}$

37. $\frac{y}{y^2}$ **38.** $\frac{8}{6w}$ **39.** $\frac{yz}{3z}$ **40.** $\frac{6rs}{8r^2}$ **41.** $\frac{2c^2d^2}{9cd}$ **42.** $\frac{15a^2b}{5ab}$

43. $\frac{16}{20a^2b}$ **44.** $\frac{16st}{24s}$ **45.** $\frac{w^3x^2}{5w^2}$ **46.** $\frac{8m^3}{24n^2}$ **47.** $\frac{36st^3}{29st}$ **48.** $\frac{48x^2y}{36xy^2}$

Find the least common denominator. *(page 134)*

49. $\frac{2}{3}, \frac{5}{6}$ **50.** $\frac{3}{5}, \frac{3}{4}$ **51.** $\frac{5}{2}, \frac{2}{9}$ **52.** $\frac{4}{6}, \frac{4}{9}$ **53.** $\frac{5}{12}, \frac{13}{18}$

54. $\frac{9}{14}, \frac{5}{7}$ **55.** $\frac{16}{15}, \frac{10}{20}$ **56.** $\frac{6}{5m}, \frac{3}{m}$ **57.** $\frac{4}{x^2}, \frac{6}{x}$ **58.** $\frac{4}{8b}, \frac{a}{2}$

59. $\frac{1}{a^2b}, \frac{3}{ab}$ **60.** $\frac{r}{tu^2}, \frac{s}{t^2}$ **61.** $\frac{9}{4yz}, \frac{x}{3yz}$ **62.** $\frac{4}{3c^2d}, \frac{1}{6cd}$ **63.** $\frac{h}{6jk^2}, \frac{3h}{9j^2k}$

$<$ or $>$? *(page 136)*

64. $\frac{3}{4} \blacklozenge \frac{1}{4}$ **65.** $\frac{2}{5} \blacklozenge \frac{3}{5}$ **66.** $\frac{4}{9} \blacklozenge \frac{5}{9}$ **67.** $\frac{3}{2} \blacklozenge \frac{5}{4}$ **68.** $\frac{1}{3} \blacklozenge \frac{2}{7}$

69. $\frac{3}{8} \blacklozenge \frac{3}{4}$ **70.** $\frac{1}{6} \blacklozenge \frac{1}{8}$ **71.** $\frac{1}{4} \blacklozenge \frac{3}{8}$ **72.** $\frac{5}{12} \blacklozenge \frac{3}{10}$ **73.** $\frac{2}{5} \blacklozenge \frac{1}{4}$

74. $\frac{3}{4} \blacklozenge \frac{2}{3}$ **75.** $\frac{7}{8} \blacklozenge \frac{8}{9}$ **76.** $\frac{5}{12} \blacklozenge \frac{11}{24}$ **77.** $\frac{7}{10} \blacklozenge \frac{2}{3}$ **78.** $\frac{9}{4} \blacklozenge \frac{9}{2}$

Problem Solving—Applications

The amount you pay for a TV is the **retail price.** What the appliance store paid was the **wholesale price.** The difference between the retail price and the wholesale price is the **markup.**

Look at the price tags. The store used this letter code to keep the wholesale prices a secret.

Wholesale Price Code

A	B	C	D	E	F	G	H	I	J	K
1	2	3	4	5	6	7	8	9	0	.

▶ **Use the price-tag information and the wholesale-price code to solve these problems.**

1. What is the wholesale price of the TV that costs $319.99?
2. What is the wholesale price of the TV that costs $389.99?
3. What is the markup on the $319.99 TV?
4. What is the markup on the $389.99 TV?
5. If the store adds $287.75 to a refrigerator that is coded DFCKDI, what is the retail price?
6. What wholesale price code would appear on a $729.95 refrigerator that has been marked up $279.89?

▶ **Solve. Use either the retail price or sale price formula.**

7. Find m if $r = \$189.79$ and $w = \$78.45$.
8. Find p if $s = \$278.88$ and $d = \$33.79$.
9. What is the wholesale price of a microwave oven that has a $207.50 markup and a retail price of $669.95?
10. A toaster that is on sale for $37.99 has been discounted $9.99. What is the regular price?
11. With a $7.50-off coupon you can buy a coffee maker for $39.59. What is the regular price?

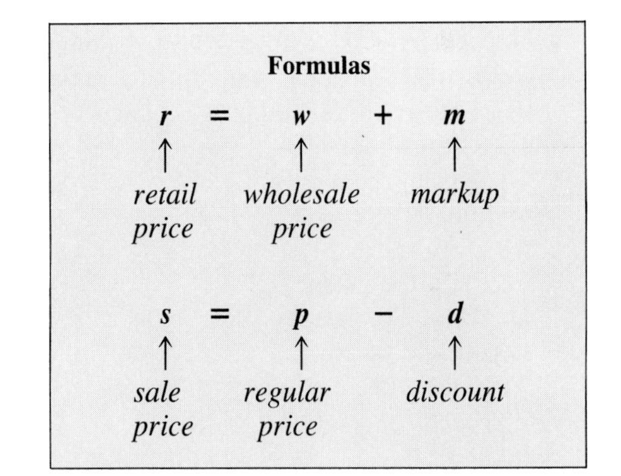
Formulas

$r = w + m$

r ↑ *retail price*; w ↑ *wholesale price*; m ↑ *markup*

$s = p - d$

s ↑ *sale price*; p ↑ *regular price*; d ↑ *discount*

★12. The markup on a dishwasher is $176.95. The wholesale price is $314.85. If the dishwasher is on sale at $99.99 off the retail price, what is the sale price?

Chapter Review

Here are scrambled answers for the review exercises:

1	*add*	*divide*	*form*	*numerators*	*subtract*
2	*common*	*divisor*	*least*	*regroup*	*sum*
3	*denominator*	*equivalent*	*lowest*	*remainder*	*terms*
5	*difference*	*fraction*	*multiply*	*simplest*	*whole*

1. To change a whole number to a fraction, write the whole number over the denominator 1 and _?_ both numerator and _?_ by the same number. To change $\mathbf{3\frac{5}{6}}$ to a fraction, multiply 6 by _?_ and add _?_ to the product. *(page 146)*

2. To change $\mathbf{\frac{14}{3}}$ to a mixed number, you would first _?_ 14 by 3. The remainder _?_ tells the number of thirds left over. *(page 148)*

$$\begin{array}{r} 4 \\ 3\overline{)14} \\ -12 \\ \hline 2 \end{array}$$

3. To write fractions and mixed numbers in simplest form: Write fractions less than 1 in _?_ terms. Write algebraic fractions in lowest _?_. Write mixed numbers with the _?_ part less than 1 and in lowest terms. *(page 150)*

4. To write a quotient as a mixed number, first divide and then write the _?_ over the _?_. *(page 152)*

5. To add fractions with common denominators, write the _?_ of the numerators over the _?_ denominator. To subtract fractions with common denominators, write the _?_ of the _?_ over the common denominator. *(page 156)*

6. To add fractions with different denominators, find the _?_ common denominator, change to equivalent fractions, and _?_. To subtract fractions with different denominators, find the least common denominator, change to _?_ fractions, and _?_. *(page 158)*

7. To find this sum, you would first add the fractions and then add the whole numbers. The last step would be to write the sum in _?_ form. *(page 160)*

$$\begin{array}{rcr} 4\frac{1}{2} & = & 4\frac{3}{6} \\ +3\frac{1}{6} & = & +3\frac{1}{6} \\ \hline \end{array}$$

8. To find this difference, you would first subtract the fractions and then subtract the _?_ numbers. The last step would be to write the difference in simplest _?_. *(page 160)*

$$\begin{array}{rcr} 5\frac{2}{3} & = & 5\frac{4}{6} \\ -2\frac{1}{6} & = & -2\frac{1}{6} \\ \hline \end{array}$$

9. To find this sum, you would next _?_ $\frac{5}{4}$ for $1\frac{1}{4}$. *(page 162)*

$$\begin{array}{rcr} 5\frac{1}{2} & = & 5\frac{2}{4} \\ +2\frac{3}{4} & = & +2\frac{3}{4} \\ \hline & & 7\frac{5}{4} \end{array}$$

10. To find this difference, you would next regroup _?_ for $\frac{8}{8}$ and then subtract. *(page 162)*

$$\begin{array}{rcr} 6\frac{1}{8} & = & 6\frac{1}{8} \\ -3\frac{1}{4} & = & -3\frac{2}{8} \\ \hline \end{array}$$

Chapter Test

▶ **Change each mixed number to a fraction.** *(page 146)*

1. $1\frac{1}{3}$ **2.** $1\frac{3}{4}$ **3.** $2\frac{1}{5}$ **4.** $3\frac{2}{3}$ **5.** $2\frac{5}{6}$ **6.** $4\frac{5}{8}$

▶ **Change each fraction to a whole number or mixed number.** *(page 148)*

7. $\frac{4}{2}$ **8.** $\frac{5}{3}$ **9.** $\frac{12}{4}$ **10.** $\frac{15}{4}$ **11.** $\frac{17}{6}$ **12.** $\frac{29}{8}$

▶ **Write in simplest form.** *(page 150)*

13. $\frac{9}{3}$ **14.** $\frac{12}{16}$ **15.** $\frac{18}{3}$ **16.** $\frac{13}{4}$ **17.** $\frac{15}{20}$ **18.** $\frac{22}{8}$

▶ **Divide. Write each quotient as a mixed number.** *(page 152)*

19. $54 \div 8$ **20.** $94 \div 6$ **21.** $150 \div 12$ **22.** $284 \div 24$

▶ **Give each sum or difference in simplest form.** *(pages 156, 158, 160, 162)*

23. $\frac{1}{8} + \frac{5}{8}$ **24.** $\frac{5}{6} + \frac{5}{6}$ **25.** $\frac{r}{s} - \frac{t}{s}$ **26.** $\frac{8}{ab} + \frac{4}{ab}$ **27.** $\frac{5a}{b^2c} - \frac{d}{b^2c}$

28. $\frac{1}{3} - \frac{1}{4}$ **29.** $\frac{3}{8} + \frac{3}{4}$ **30.** $\frac{c}{6} + \frac{d}{3}$ **31.** $\frac{3x}{4} - \frac{y}{6}$ **32.** $\frac{2k}{9} + \frac{5j}{12}$

33. $2\frac{1}{2} + 1\frac{1}{4}$ **34.** $15\frac{5}{6} + 11\frac{1}{8}$ **35.** $8\frac{5}{8} - 2\frac{1}{4}$ **36.** $10\frac{2}{3} - 6\frac{1}{2}$ **37.** $18\frac{7}{8} - 12\frac{1}{3}$

38. $5\frac{3}{4} + 2\frac{1}{3}$ **39.** $10\frac{5}{6} + 5\frac{2}{5}$ **40.** $6 - 4\frac{3}{5}$ **41.** $12\frac{1}{5} - 8\frac{7}{10}$ **42.** $20\frac{1}{4} - 13\frac{5}{6}$

▶ **First choose the equation and solve the problem. Then reread the problem to see if your answer makes sense.**

Equation A: $n + 3\frac{1}{2} = 6\frac{3}{4}$

Equation B: $n - 3\frac{1}{2} = 6\frac{3}{4}$

Equation C: $n - 6\frac{3}{4} = 3\frac{1}{2}$

43. A number decreased by $3\frac{1}{2}$ is $6\frac{3}{4}$. What is the number?

44. A number increased by $3\frac{1}{2}$ is $6\frac{3}{4}$. What is the number?

45. The difference between two numbers is $3\frac{1}{2}$. If the smaller number is $6\frac{3}{4}$, what is the larger number?

46. The sum of two numbers is $6\frac{3}{4}$. If one of the numbers is $3\frac{1}{2}$, what is the other number?

Cumulative Test

Standardized Format

▶ **Choose the correct letter.**

1. Solve.

$10 = \frac{y}{3} - 5$

A. 5
B. 15
C. 45
D. none of these

2. $5x + 2 + 1 + 2x = \underline{?}$

A. $3x + 5$
B. $5x + 3$
C. $2x + 3$
D. none of these

3. Solve.

$16.4 = n + n$

A. 8.2
B. 32.8
C. 16.4
D. none of these

4. $r \cdot r \cdot r \cdot s \cdot s = \underline{?}$

A. r^2s^3
B. r^3s
C. r^3s^2
D. none of these

5. The algebraic factorization of $15x^2y$ is

A. $15 \cdot x \cdot x \cdot y$
B. $3 \cdot 5 \cdot x^2 \cdot y$
C. $3 \cdot 5 \cdot x \cdot x \cdot y$
D. none of these

6. The greatest common factor of $5a$ and $10a^2$ is

A. $5a$
B. $5a^2$
C. $10a^2$
D. none of these

7. Complete.

$\frac{3c}{2d} = \frac{?}{4cd}$

A. $2c$
B. $4c$
C. $2cd$
D. none of these

8. $\frac{16}{48}$ written in lowest terms is

A. $\frac{8}{24}$
B. $\frac{4}{12}$
C. $\frac{1}{3}$
D. none of these

9. $\frac{24x^2y}{18xy^2}$ written in lowest terms is

A. $\frac{4x^2y}{3xy}$
B. $\frac{4xy}{3y}$
C. $\frac{4x}{3y}$
D. none of these

10. The least common denominator of $\frac{n}{3}$ and $\frac{n}{6m}$ is

A. $6m$
B. $3m$
C. 3
D. none of these

11. $\frac{5}{6} < \underline{?}$

A. $\frac{2}{3}$
B. $\frac{3}{4}$
C. $\frac{5}{6}$
D. $\frac{7}{8}$

12. Choose the equation.

You had \$18. After being paid for working 6 hours, you then had a total of \$39. How much were you paid per hour?

A. $\frac{n}{6} + 18 = 39$
B. $\frac{n}{6} - 18 = 39$
C. $6n + 18 = 39$
D. $6n - 18 = 39$

7 Multiplication and Division of Fractions

$r = \frac{d}{t}$

Rate in miles per hour equals distance in miles divided by time in hours.

(page 179)

Cross-country bicyclists use the formula above to calculate how fast they must travel to reach a certain destination in a given amount of time.

Multiplying Fractions

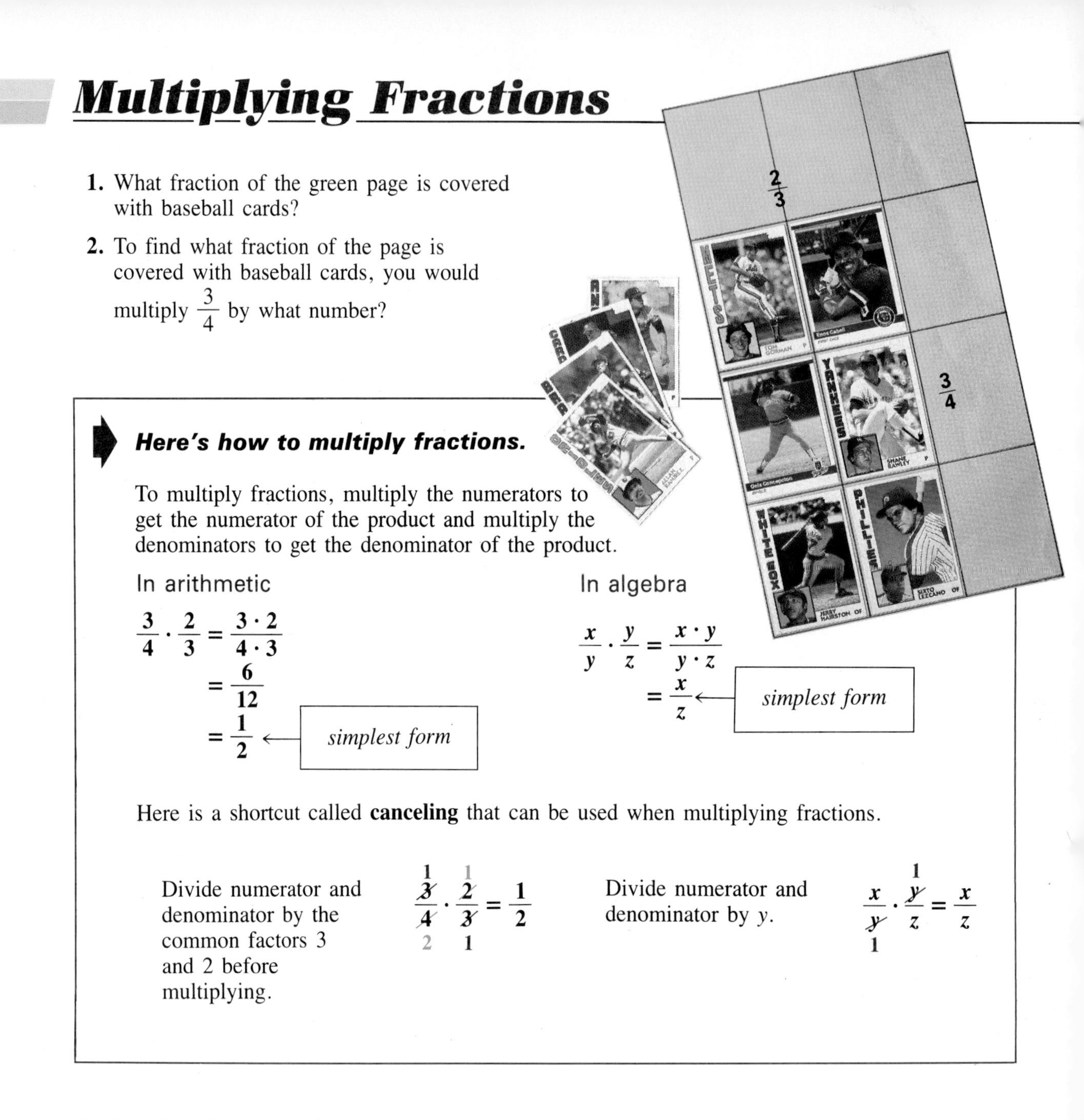

1. What fraction of the green page is covered with baseball cards?
2. To find what fraction of the page is covered with baseball cards, you would multiply $\frac{3}{4}$ by what number?

➡ *Here's how to multiply fractions.*

To multiply fractions, multiply the numerators to get the numerator of the product and multiply the denominators to get the denominator of the product.

In arithmetic

$$\frac{3}{4} \cdot \frac{2}{3} = \frac{3 \cdot 2}{4 \cdot 3} = \frac{6}{12} = \frac{1}{2} \leftarrow \boxed{\textit{simplest form}}$$

In algebra

$$\frac{x}{y} \cdot \frac{y}{z} = \frac{x \cdot y}{y \cdot z} = \frac{x}{z} \leftarrow \boxed{\textit{simplest form}}$$

Here is a shortcut called **canceling** that can be used when multiplying fractions.

Divide numerator and denominator by the common factors 3 and 2 before multiplying.

$$\frac{\overset{1}{\cancel{3}}}{\underset{2}{\cancel{4}}} \cdot \frac{\overset{1}{\cancel{2}}}{\underset{1}{\cancel{3}}} = \frac{1}{2}$$

Divide numerator and denominator by y.

$$\frac{x}{\underset{1}{\cancel{y}}} \cdot \frac{\overset{1}{\cancel{y}}}{z} = \frac{x}{z}$$

3. Complete these examples.

a. $\frac{5}{\underset{2}{\cancel{6}}} \cdot \overset{1}{\cancel{3}} = \frac{5}{2}$

$= 2\frac{?}{2}$

b. $\frac{\overset{3}{\cancel{6}}}{\underset{1}{\cancel{5}}} \cdot \frac{\overset{3}{\cancel{15}}}{\underset{4}{\cancel{8}}} = \frac{9}{4}$

$= 2\frac{?}{4}$

c. $\overset{1}{\cancel{y}} \cdot \frac{t}{\underset{1}{\cancel{y}}} = \underline{\ ?\ }$

d. $\frac{\overset{1}{\cancel{2}}a}{\underset{b}{\cancel{b^2}}} \cdot \frac{\overset{1}{\cancel{b}}}{\underset{2}{\cancel{4}}} = \frac{?}{2b}$

EXERCISES

▶ **Give each product in simplest form.**
Here are scrambled answers for the next row of exercises: $2\frac{1}{4}$ $\frac{1}{2}$ 6 1 $\frac{3}{8}$ $\frac{1}{4}$

4. $\frac{3}{2} \cdot \frac{1}{4}$
5. $\frac{5}{8} \cdot \frac{4}{5}$
6. $\frac{1}{3} \cdot \frac{3}{4}$
7. $\frac{3}{4} \cdot 3$
8. $\frac{5}{2} \cdot \frac{2}{5}$
9. $\frac{9}{2} \cdot \frac{4}{3}$
10. $6 \cdot \frac{3}{10}$
11. $\frac{1}{2} \cdot \frac{1}{3}$
12. $2 \cdot \frac{1}{2}$
13. $5 \cdot \frac{2}{5}$
14. $\frac{5}{8} \cdot \frac{2}{5}$
15. $\frac{1}{4} \cdot \frac{1}{4}$
16. $\frac{2}{3} \cdot 2$
17. $\frac{5}{12} \cdot \frac{3}{2}$
18. $\frac{1}{2} \cdot \frac{2}{5}$
19. $\frac{1}{2} \cdot \frac{1}{2}$
20. $\frac{3}{2} \cdot \frac{0}{2}$
21. $\frac{3}{5} \cdot \frac{1}{3}$
22. $\frac{3}{5} \cdot \frac{5}{3}$
23. $\frac{7}{10} \cdot \frac{5}{4}$
24. $\frac{11}{12} \cdot 3$
25. $4 \cdot \frac{3}{4}$
26. $\frac{6}{5} \cdot \frac{15}{2}$
27. $\frac{1}{2} \cdot \frac{2}{3}$
28. $\frac{3}{8} \cdot \frac{3}{8}$
29. $3 \cdot \frac{3}{4}$
30. $3 \cdot \frac{5}{6}$
31. $\frac{2}{3} \cdot \frac{3}{2}$
32. $\frac{4}{3} \cdot \frac{3}{4}$
33. $\frac{5}{16} \cdot \frac{4}{5}$

▶ **Give each product in simplest form.**
Here are scrambled answers for the next row of exercises: $\frac{p}{q}$ $\frac{2n}{mp}$ $\frac{u^2}{xy}$ $\frac{uv}{xy}$ $\frac{2m}{n^2}$

34. $\frac{u}{x} \cdot \frac{v}{y}$
35. $\frac{6}{q} \cdot \frac{p}{6}$
36. $\frac{u}{x} \cdot \frac{u}{y}$
37. $\frac{m}{n} \cdot \frac{2}{n}$
38. $\frac{n}{m} \cdot \frac{2}{p}$
39. $\frac{x}{5} \cdot \frac{1}{x}$
40. $\frac{b}{a} \cdot c$
41. $\frac{8}{j} \cdot 3$
42. $\frac{m}{3} \cdot \frac{9}{n}$
43. $\frac{5}{j} \cdot \frac{k}{10}$
44. $\frac{2}{5} \cdot \frac{15}{w}$
45. $12 \cdot \frac{5x}{3}$
46. $\frac{6}{5} \cdot \frac{5u}{v}$
47. $\frac{2u}{y} \cdot \frac{v}{2y}$
48. $\frac{4}{9} \cdot \frac{3x}{y}$
49. $\frac{v}{2w} \cdot \frac{2}{z}$
50. $\frac{r}{s} \cdot \frac{s}{r}$
51. $\frac{x}{y} \cdot \frac{y}{x}$
52. $\frac{a}{b} \cdot \frac{b}{a}$
53. $\frac{2}{9e} \cdot \frac{3d}{4}$
54. $\frac{4v}{3} \cdot \frac{1}{8}$
55. $\frac{2r}{s} \cdot \frac{8}{2r}$
56. $\frac{a}{c} \cdot \frac{b}{a^2}$
57. $\frac{b^2}{15} \cdot \frac{1}{b}$
58. $\frac{9}{c} \cdot \frac{c^2}{4}$
59. $\frac{a}{b^2} \cdot \frac{2b}{3}$
60. $\frac{3c}{b} \cdot \frac{b}{c^2}$
61. $\frac{s^2}{r} \cdot \frac{r}{s}$
62. $\frac{m}{n} \cdot \frac{n^2}{3}$
63. $\frac{7}{d} \cdot \frac{3d}{e}$

Challenge

▶ **Study the clues to find the final score.**

64. *Clues:*
- After 6 complete innings, the Cardinals were leading the Cubs 5 to 2.
- Only one team scored in the last 3 innings.
- The winning team won by 3 runs.

65. *Clues:*
- After 8 complete innings, the Orioles were leading the Indians 3 to 1.
- The game went extra innings.
- Both teams scored after the 8th inning.
- A total of 7 runs was scored.

Multiplying Mixed Numbers

1. How much flour is needed to make a recipe of pizza dough?

2. Suppose that you want to make $1\frac{1}{2}$ times the recipe. What two mixed numbers would you multiply to find how much flour is needed?

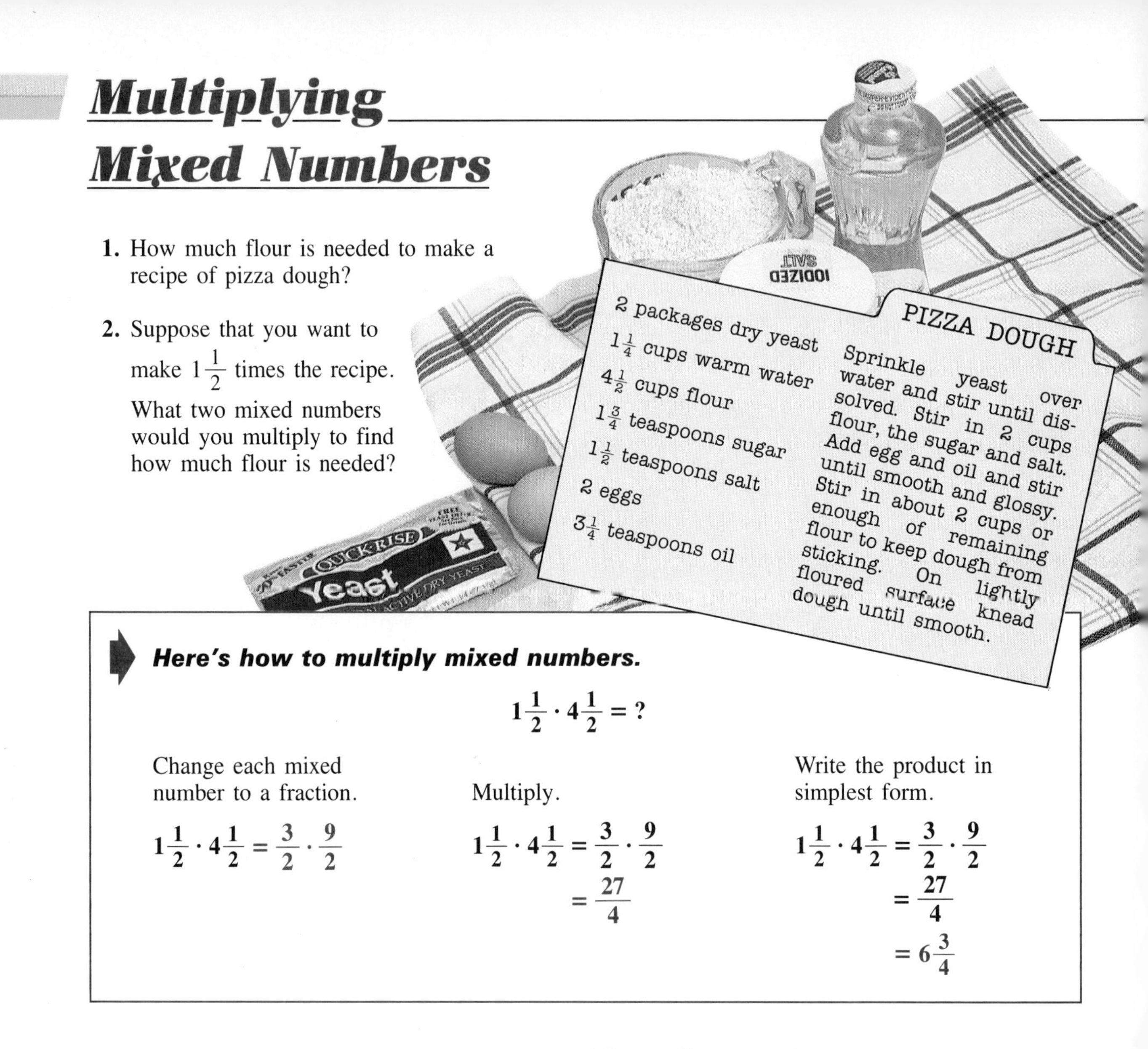

Here's how to multiply mixed numbers.

$$1\frac{1}{2} \cdot 4\frac{1}{2} = ?$$

Change each mixed number to a fraction.

$$1\frac{1}{2} \cdot 4\frac{1}{2} = \frac{3}{2} \cdot \frac{9}{2}$$

Multiply.

$$1\frac{1}{2} \cdot 4\frac{1}{2} = \frac{3}{2} \cdot \frac{9}{2} = \frac{27}{4}$$

Write the product in simplest form.

$$1\frac{1}{2} \cdot 4\frac{1}{2} = \frac{3}{2} \cdot \frac{9}{2} = \frac{27}{4} = 6\frac{3}{4}$$

3. Look at the example above. How many cups of flour will you need? Does the answer seem reasonable?

4. Complete these examples.

a. $3\frac{1}{3} \cdot 1\frac{1}{6} = \frac{\overset{5}{\cancel{10}}}{3} \cdot \frac{7}{\underset{3}{\cancel{6}}} = \frac{35}{9} = \underline{\ ?\ }$

b. $5\frac{3}{4} \cdot 2\frac{2}{3} = \frac{23}{\underset{1}{\cancel{4}}} \cdot \frac{\overset{2}{\cancel{8}}}{3} = \underline{\ ?\ } = 15\frac{1}{3}$

c. $2\frac{5}{6} \cdot 9 = \frac{17}{\underset{2}{\cancel{6}}} \cdot \overset{\underline{?}}{\cancel{9}} = \frac{51}{2} = 25\frac{1}{2}$

EXERCISES

▶ **Give each product in simplest form.**
Here are scrambled answers for the next row of exercises: $6\frac{1}{4}$ $4\frac{1}{6}$ 2 $7\frac{7}{8}$ $6\frac{1}{8}$

5. $1\frac{2}{3} \cdot 2\frac{1}{2}$ **6.** $3\frac{1}{2} \cdot 1\frac{3}{4}$ **7.** $2\frac{1}{4} \cdot 3\frac{1}{2}$ **8.** $1\frac{1}{2} \cdot 1\frac{1}{3}$ **9.** $2\frac{1}{2} \cdot 2\frac{1}{2}$

10. $2\frac{2}{3} \cdot 3\frac{1}{6}$ **11.** $2 \cdot 3\frac{1}{2}$ **12.** $4\frac{1}{3} \cdot 3\frac{1}{2}$ **13.** $3\frac{3}{4} \cdot 6$ **14.** $1\frac{1}{3} \cdot 6$

15. $3\frac{1}{6} \cdot 2\frac{3}{4}$ **16.** $5\frac{3}{4} \cdot 2\frac{1}{2}$ **17.** $2\frac{4}{5} \cdot 3$ **18.** $4\frac{1}{2} \cdot 3$ **19.** $3\frac{2}{3} \cdot 4\frac{1}{3}$

20. $2\frac{3}{4} \cdot 2$ **21.** $5\frac{1}{2} \cdot 4\frac{3}{4}$ **22.** $4\frac{1}{5} \cdot 5\frac{3}{8}$ **23.** $2\frac{1}{5} \cdot 3$ **24.** $1\frac{1}{2} \cdot 2\frac{1}{3}$

25. $2\frac{3}{8} \cdot 4$ **26.** $3\frac{3}{8} \cdot 6\frac{3}{4}$ **27.** $2\frac{1}{2} \cdot 3\frac{1}{2}$ **28.** $1\frac{2}{3} \cdot 6$ **29.** $1\frac{5}{8} \cdot 4\frac{1}{2}$

30. $3\frac{1}{3} \cdot 4\frac{1}{3}$ **31.** $2\frac{1}{3} \cdot 4\frac{1}{2}$ **32.** $3 \cdot 5\frac{2}{3}$ **33.** $2\frac{1}{5} \cdot 1\frac{1}{2}$ **34.** $4 \cdot 2\frac{1}{2}$

Problem Solving

▶ **Solve. Use the recipe on page 174.**

35. How much sugar is needed to double the recipe?

36. How much oil is needed to triple the recipe?

37. Suppose that you wanted to make $2\frac{1}{2}$ times the recipe. How much flour would you need?

38. Suppose that you wanted to make $1\frac{3}{4}$ times the recipe. How much water would you need?

39. You have 12 cups of flour. Can you make $2\frac{3}{4}$ times the recipe?

40. You have 4 teaspoons of salt. How much more do you need to make $3\frac{1}{2}$ times the recipe?

Challenge

▶ **Solve.**

41. One of your friends ate $\frac{1}{2}$ of your pieces of pizza. Another friend ate $\frac{1}{2}$ of the remaining pieces. A third friend ate the 3 pieces that were left. How many pieces of pizza did you have to begin with?

Dividing Fractions

This bicyclist is making some practice runs on a track. The distance around the track is $\frac{1}{5}$ of a mile. She rode a total of 2 miles while making her practice runs.

1. a. Divide to find how many practice runs she made.

$$\underset{\text{miles}}{2} \div \underset{\text{miles around the track}}{\frac{1}{5}} = \underset{\text{runs}}{\underline{\ ?\ }}$$

b. Multiply to find how many practice runs she made.

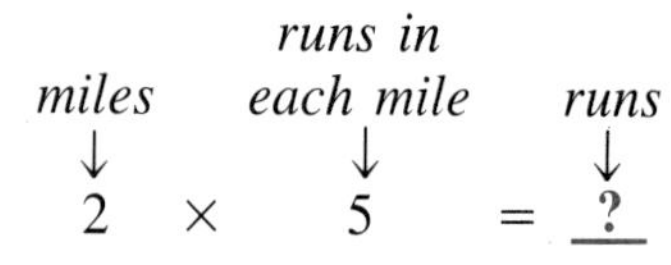

$$\underset{\text{miles}}{2} \times \underset{\text{runs in each mile}}{5} = \underset{\text{runs}}{\underline{\ ?\ }}$$

2. Look at exercise 1. Dividing by $\frac{1}{5}$ is the same as multiplying by what number?

Time Out! Two numbers are reciprocals if their product is 1.

Since $5 \cdot \frac{1}{5} = 1$, **5** is the reciprocal of $\mathbf{\frac{1}{5}}$ and $\mathbf{\frac{1}{5}}$ is the reciprocal of **5**.

Since $\frac{2}{3} \cdot \frac{3}{2} = 1$, $\mathbf{\frac{2}{3}}$ is the reciprocal of $\mathbf{\frac{3}{2}}$ and $\mathbf{\frac{3}{2}}$ is the reciprocal of $\mathbf{\frac{2}{3}}$.

For a fraction not equal to 0, find the reciprocal by inverting the fraction.

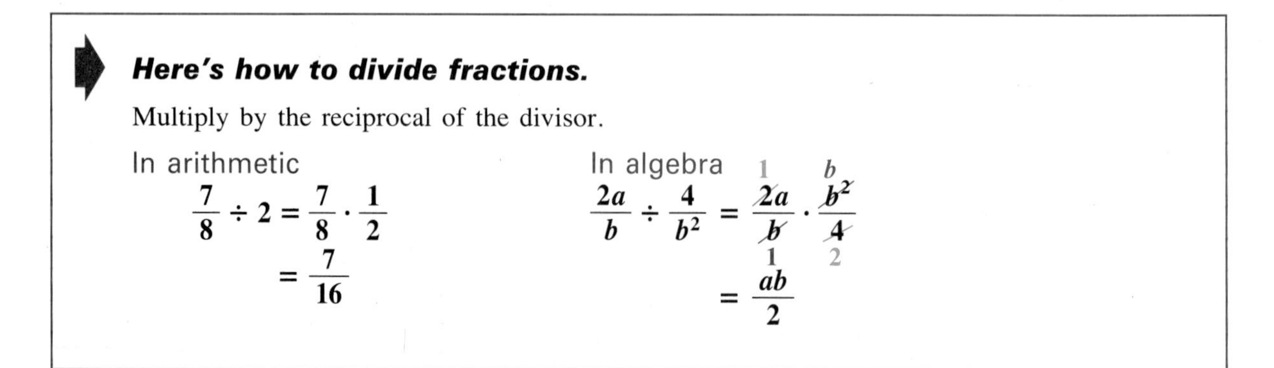

Here's how to divide fractions.

Multiply by the reciprocal of the divisor.

In arithmetic

$$\frac{7}{8} \div 2 = \frac{7}{8} \cdot \frac{1}{2} = \frac{7}{16}$$

In algebra

$$\frac{2a}{b} \div \frac{4}{b^2} = \frac{\overset{1}{\cancel{2}}a}{\underset{1}{\cancel{b}}} \cdot \frac{\overset{b}{\cancel{b^2}}}{\underset{2}{\cancel{4}}} = \frac{ab}{2}$$

3. Complete these examples.

a. $\frac{3}{5} \div \frac{9}{10} = \frac{\overset{1}{\cancel{3}}}{\underset{1}{\cancel{5}}} \cdot \frac{\overset{2}{\cancel{10}}}{\underset{3}{\cancel{9}}}$
$= \underline{\ ?\ }$

b. $\frac{x}{w} \div \frac{y}{z} = \frac{x}{w} \cdot \frac{z}{y}$
$= \frac{xz}{?}$

c. $\frac{3r}{s} \div \frac{4}{rs} = \frac{3r}{\underset{1}{\cancel{s}}} \cdot \frac{r\overset{1}{\cancel{s}}}{4}$
$= \underline{\ ?\ }$

EXERCISES

▶ **Give the reciprocal of each number.**

4. 2 **5.** $\frac{1}{8}$ **6.** $\frac{1}{6}$ **7.** $\frac{3}{2}$ **8.** $\frac{4}{7}$ **9.** $\frac{3}{5}$

▶ **Give each quotient in simplest form.**

Here are scrambled answers for the next row of exercises: $1 \quad \frac{1}{6} \quad 1\frac{1}{8} \quad \frac{9}{16} \quad \frac{2}{3}$

10. $\frac{2}{3} \div 4 \leftarrow \boxed{\frac{2}{3} \cdot \frac{1}{4}}$ **11.** $\frac{3}{4} \div \frac{2}{3}$ **12.** $\frac{7}{5} \div \frac{7}{5}$ **13.** $\frac{3}{8} \div \frac{2}{3}$ **14.** $\frac{2}{9} \div \frac{1}{3}$

15. $\frac{5}{9} \div \frac{1}{3}$ **16.** $\frac{5}{8} \div 2$ **17.** $\frac{4}{5} \div \frac{3}{3}$ **18.** $\frac{2}{3} \div \frac{5}{9}$ **19.** $5 \div \frac{2}{5}$ **20.** $\frac{2}{7} \div \frac{4}{5}$

21. $\frac{3}{5} \div \frac{2}{5}$ **22.** $\frac{3}{2} \div \frac{2}{3}$ **23.** $\frac{7}{9} \div \frac{4}{3}$ **24.** $\frac{2}{5} \div 5$ **25.** $\frac{7}{8} \div \frac{3}{4}$ **26.** $\frac{3}{7} \div \frac{7}{9}$

27. $4 \div \frac{5}{8}$ **28.** $\frac{9}{4} \div \frac{7}{8}$ **29.** $6 \div \frac{3}{2}$ **30.** $\frac{0}{2} \div \frac{9}{4}$ **31.** $\frac{7}{8} \div \frac{5}{16}$ **32.** $8 \div \frac{1}{2}$

Here are scrambled answers for the next row of exercises: $\frac{t}{rs} \quad \frac{yz}{x^2} \quad \frac{a}{cd} \quad \frac{ad}{bc}$

33. $\frac{a}{b} \div \frac{c}{d} \leftarrow \boxed{\frac{a}{b} \cdot \frac{d}{c}}$ **34.** $\frac{1}{r} \div \frac{s}{t}$ **35.** $\frac{a}{c} \div d$ **36.** $\frac{y}{x} \div \frac{x}{z}$

37. $\frac{r}{s} \div \frac{4}{r}$ **38.** $\frac{2}{a} \div \frac{b}{c}$ **39.** $\frac{3m}{n} \div \frac{2}{q}$ **40.** $\frac{r}{s} \div \frac{5t}{2}$ **41.** $\frac{6d}{e} \div f$

42. $\frac{3x}{2y} \div \frac{5}{6y}$ **43.** $\frac{m}{p} \div \frac{m}{2q}$ **44.** $\frac{c^2}{d} \div \frac{c}{d}$ **45.** $\frac{x}{9y} \div \frac{z}{3y}$ **46.** $\frac{4a}{3b^2} \div \frac{6a}{b}$

Challenge

▶ **Solve.**

47. In a bicycle race, Mike's time was 0.74 second faster than Al's; Kim's time was 0.39 second slower than Mike's; Craig's time was 0.23 second slower than Kim's.

a. Rank the four riders from fastest to slowest. *Hint: Make a sketch.*

b. How much faster was Craig's time than Al's?

Dividing Mixed Numbers

1. How many miles long is Green Lake Trail?
2. How many hours does it take to hike Green Lake Trail?
3. To find how many miles per hour you would average when hiking Green Lake Trail, you would divide $3\frac{3}{4}$ by what number?

TRAIL RULES AND INFORMATION

All children under 12 years of age must be accompanied by an adult.
All litter is to be carried out by hikers.
All trails are closed at 6:00 P.M.

TRAIL NAME	DISTANCE *(miles)*	HIKING TIME *(hours)*
Lone Pine	$5\frac{1}{2}$	$2\frac{1}{2}$
Silver Falls	5	$3\frac{3}{4}$
Green Lake	$3\frac{3}{4}$	$1\frac{1}{4}$

Here's how to divide mixed numbers.

Change each mixed number to a fraction.

$$3\frac{3}{4} \div 1\frac{1}{4} = \frac{15}{4} \div \frac{5}{4}$$

Divide.

$$3\frac{3}{4} \div 1\frac{1}{4} = \frac{15}{4} \div \frac{5}{4}$$

$$= \frac{\overset{3}{\cancel{15}}}{\underset{1}{\cancel{4}}} \cdot \frac{\overset{1}{\cancel{4}}}{\underset{1}{\cancel{5}}}$$

Write the quotient in simplest form.

$$3\frac{3}{4} \div 1\frac{1}{4} = \frac{15}{4} \div \frac{5}{4}$$

$$= \frac{\overset{3}{\cancel{15}}}{\underset{1}{\cancel{4}}} \cdot \frac{\overset{1}{\cancel{4}}}{\underset{1}{\cancel{5}}}$$

$$= 3$$

4. Look at the example above. How many miles per hour would you average while hiking Green Lake Trail?
5. Complete these examples.

a. $5\frac{1}{4} \div 2\frac{1}{2} = \frac{21}{4} \div \frac{5}{2}$

$= \frac{21}{\underset{2}{\cancel{4}}} \cdot \frac{\overset{1}{\cancel{2}}}{5}$

$= \frac{21}{10}$

$= 2\,\underline{?}$

b. $4\frac{2}{3} \div 2\frac{1}{4} = \frac{14}{3} \div \frac{9}{4}$

$= \frac{14}{3} \cdot \underline{?}$

$= \frac{56}{27}$

$= 2\frac{2}{27}$

c. $3\frac{1}{8} \div 1\frac{3}{4} = \frac{25}{8} \div \underline{?}$

$= \frac{25}{\underset{2}{\cancel{8}}} \cdot \frac{\overset{1}{\cancel{4}}}{7}$

$= \frac{25}{14}$

$= 1\frac{11}{14}$

▶ **Give each quotient in simplest form.**
Here are scrambled answers for the next row of exercises: $1\frac{1}{4}$ $4\frac{1}{8}$ $1\frac{4}{5}$ $2\frac{1}{7}$ $2\frac{1}{4}$

6. $2\frac{1}{4} \div 1\frac{1}{4}$ **7.** $5\frac{1}{2} \div 1\frac{1}{3}$ **8.** $5 \div 2\frac{1}{3}$ **9.** $4\frac{1}{2} \div 2$ **10.** $2\frac{1}{2} \div 2$

11. $6\frac{1}{2} \div 2\frac{2}{3}$ **12.** $6\frac{1}{2} \div 2\frac{1}{4}$ **13.** $8 \div 2\frac{1}{4}$ **14.** $6\frac{1}{4} \div 1\frac{1}{4}$ **15.** $1\frac{1}{6} \div 1\frac{1}{2}$

16. $5\frac{7}{8} \div 1\frac{3}{4}$ **17.** $7 \div 2\frac{1}{3}$ **18.** $4\frac{1}{3} \div 2\frac{1}{2}$ **19.** $2 \div 1\frac{1}{2}$ **20.** $4\frac{1}{2} \div 4$

21. $2\frac{3}{8} \div 1\frac{1}{3}$ **22.** $6\frac{3}{4} \div 3$ **23.** $1\frac{1}{5} \div 5$ **24.** $8\frac{1}{2} \div 1\frac{3}{4}$ **25.** $6 \div 1\frac{1}{2}$

26. $3\frac{3}{5} \div 1\frac{1}{5}$ **27.** $6\frac{2}{3} \div 2$ **28.** $9\frac{1}{4} \div 2\frac{1}{4}$ **29.** $8 \div 2\frac{1}{2}$ **30.** $2 \div \frac{2}{3}$

31. $6 \div 4\frac{1}{2}$ **32.** $9 \div 2\frac{1}{4}$ **33.** $2\frac{1}{3} \div 2\frac{1}{3}$ **34.** $2\frac{1}{2} \div 1\frac{1}{4}$ **35.** $3\frac{1}{2} \div 3\frac{1}{2}$

36. $1\frac{1}{2} \div 2$ **37.** $7\frac{1}{2} \div 1\frac{1}{2}$ **38.** $3\frac{2}{3} \div 1\frac{1}{3}$ **39.** $6 \div 1\frac{1}{3}$ **40.** $1\frac{1}{2} \div \frac{1}{2}$

Problem Solving

▶ **Solve. Use the information on page 178.**

41. How much longer is Silver Falls Trail than Green Lake Trail?

42. How much longer is Lone Pine Trail than Green Lake Trail?

43. How many hours would you need to hike the two shorter trails?

44. It is 12 noon. Can you hike the two longer trails before the trails close?

45. How many miles per hour would you average while hiking Silver Falls Trail?

46. Which trail is the most difficult to hike (slowest average hiking rate)?

47. You can use the following formula to find your hiking rate.

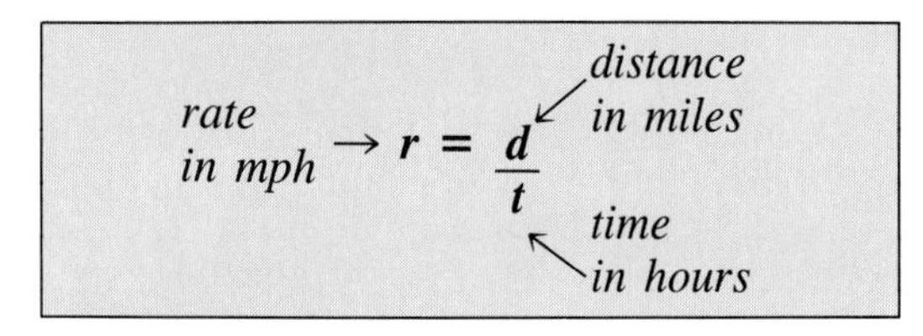

Substitute in the formula above to complete this chart. Give answers in simplest form.

	Distance in miles (d)	Time in hours (t)	Rate in mph (r)
a.	6	$2\frac{1}{2}$	?
b.	$4\frac{3}{4}$	2	?
c.	$6\frac{1}{2}$	$2\frac{1}{4}$	?
d.	?	2	$1\frac{2}{3}$
e.	?	3	$2\frac{3}{5}$

Cumulative Skill Practice

Solve and check. *(page 98)*

1. $19 + g = 74$ **2.** $n(9) = 108$ **3.** $135 = v - 26$ **4.** $20 = \frac{x}{17}$

5. $j - 83 = 26$ **6.** $16t = 176$ **7.** $m + 74 = 117$ **8.** $\frac{s}{18} = 31$

9. $57 = k(3)$ **10.** $19 = h - 34$ **11.** $25 = \frac{t}{16}$ **12.** $91 = 47 + j$

13. $15 = t + 9.4$ **14.** $42 = r - 18.6$ **15.** $2.1 = \frac{v}{11}$ **16.** $15.35 = q(5)$

Solve and check. *(page 104)*

17. $\frac{n}{3} + 9 = 26$ **18.** $\frac{t}{4} - 6 = 41$ **19.** $12 = \frac{d}{3} + 5$ **20.** $20 + \frac{r}{5} = 32$

21. $4x + 10 = 58$ **22.** $72 = 3k + 12$ **23.** $60 = 11j - 17$ **24.** $15t - 30 = 0$

25. $3n + 5.8 = 9.4$ **26.** $\frac{n}{7} + 6.5 = 8.1$ **27.** $15.6 = \frac{a}{5} - 2.4$ **28.** $7.5 = 4n - 14.5$

Solve and check. *(page 110)*

29. $2a + 3a = 35$ **30.** $48 = 2x + 2x$ **31.** $5n + n = 72$ **32.** $156 = 8m + 4m$

33. $c + c = 74$ **34.** $4b + 6b = 120$ **35.** $136 = y + 3y$ **36.** $h + 11h = 252$

37. $9k + 2k = 264$ **38.** $225 = 11m + 4m$ **39.** $200 = 19a + a$ **40.** $14j + 2j = 272$

41. $4n + n = 7.5$ **42.** $12.6 = z + 2z$ **43.** $6h + 2h = 20.8$ **44.** $32.5 = p + p$

Give the algebraic factorization. *(page 124)*

45. $10a^2$ **46.** $6d^2$ **47.** $3b^3$ **48.** $8d$ **49.** $7g^3$

50. $35n^2$ **51.** $24w$ **52.** $40z^3$ **53.** $25n^3$ **54.** $10x^4$

55. $27k$ **56.** $42b^3$ **57.** $7g^4$ **58.** $52b^2$ **59.** $7r^2s$

60. $4x^2y$ **61.** $10yz^2$ **62.** $8r^2s$ **63.** $12u^2v^2$ **64.** $14a^2b^2$

Give the least common multiple. *(page 126)*

65. 8, 12 **66.** 9, 12 **67.** 16, 12 **68.** 18, 12 **69.** 25, 20 **70.** 24, 16

71. $5, 10x$ **72.** $8, 24c$ **73.** $10, 5y$ **74.** $3z, 9$ **75.** $6w, 9$ **76.** $8y, 12$

77. $k, 7k$ **78.** $9j, j$ **79.** $n, 12n$ **80.** $8f, f^2$ **81.** $g^2, 3g$ **82.** $7h, h^2$

83. $9b, 2b^2$ **84.** $3a, 5a^2$ **85.** $6c, 9c^2$ **86.** $5ab, a^2$ **87.** $3m^2n, mn$ **88.** $7c^2d, 5cd^2$

Problem Solving—Applications

▶ **Use the information in the ad to solve the problems.**

1. How many books of trading stamps do you need to get a Spincast reel and binoculars?

2. You have $3\frac{1}{4}$ books of trading stamps. How many more books do you need to get a camera?

3. If you save $\frac{1}{4}$ book of stamps each month, how many months will it take you to get a flashlight?

4. Randy saved $1\frac{1}{2}$ books of stamps and his sister saved $2\frac{3}{4}$ books. How many more books do they need to get a camera?

5. It takes 1600 stamps to fill a trading-stamp book. You have 1200 stamps. What fraction of a book have you filled?

6. Rita has saved 4000 stamps. How many more stamps does she need in order to get a camera? (*Remember:* It takes 1600 stamps to fill a book.)

▶ **Write an equation and solve the problem.**

7. It takes $5\frac{1}{2}$ books of trading stamps to get a pocket radio. That is $\frac{1}{2}$ book more than 2 times the number of books needed to get a football. How many books of stamps do you need to get a football?
(Let f = the number of books needed to get the football.)

8. It takes a total of 7 books of stamps to get a basketball and a Frisbee. A basketball takes 3 times as many books of stamps as a Frisbee. How many books of stamps do you need to get a Frisbee?
(Let f = the number of books needed to get the Frisbee.)

9. It takes $12\frac{1}{2}$ books to get a telescope. That is $2\frac{1}{2}$ books more than 5 times the number of books needed to get a soccerball. How many books are needed to get a soccerball?
(Let s = the number of books needed to get a soccerball.)

10. You need a total of 12 books to get a bowling ball and bag. The ball takes 7 times as many books as the bag. How many books are needed to get the bag?
(Let b = the number of books needed to get the bag.)

Finding a Fraction of a Whole Number

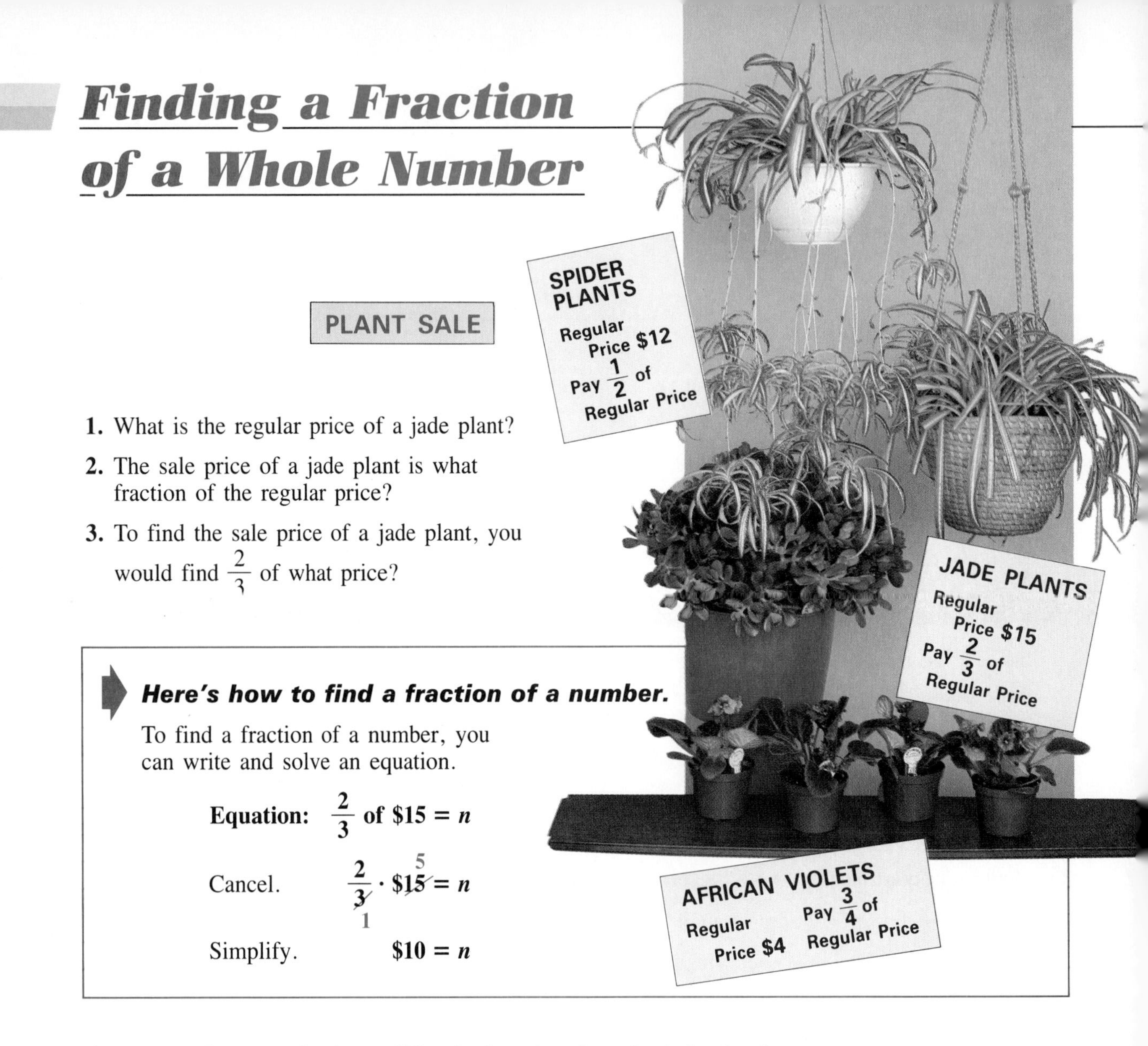

1. What is the regular price of a jade plant?
2. The sale price of a jade plant is what fraction of the regular price?
3. To find the sale price of a jade plant, you would find $\frac{2}{3}$ of what price?

Here's how to find a fraction of a number.

To find a fraction of a number, you can write and solve an equation.

Equation: $\frac{2}{3}$ **of \$15 =** n

Cancel. $\frac{2}{\cancel{3}_1} \cdot \$\cancel{15}^5 = n$

Simplify. $\$10 = n$

4. Look at the example above. What is the sale price of a jade plant?
5. Complete these examples.

a. $\frac{1}{4}$ of $15 = n$

$\frac{1}{4} \cdot \frac{15}{1} = n$

$\frac{15}{4} = n$

$\underline{?} = n$

b. $\frac{5}{8}$ of $48 = n$

$\frac{5}{\cancel{8}_1} \cdot \cancel{48}^6 = n$

$\underline{?} = n$

c. $\frac{7}{10}$ of $55 = n$

$\frac{7}{\cancel{10}_2} \cdot \cancel{55}^{11} = n$

$\underline{?} = n$

$38\frac{1}{2} = n$

Solve. Give answers in simplest form.
Here are scrambled answers for the next row of exercises: $6\frac{2}{3}$ $4\frac{4}{5}$ 4 54

6. $\frac{1}{3}$ of $12 = n$ **7.** $\frac{2}{3}$ of $10 = n$ **8.** $\frac{2}{5}$ of $12 = n$ **9.** $\frac{9}{10}$ of $60 = n$

10. $\frac{5}{6}$ of $30 = n$ **11.** $\frac{1}{5}$ of $18 = n$ **12.** $\frac{5}{8}$ of $56 = n$ **13.** $\frac{2}{5}$ of $55 = n$

14. $\frac{3}{4}$ of $36 = n$ **15.** $\frac{3}{8}$ of $21 = n$ **16.** $\frac{1}{3}$ of $63 = n$ **17.** $\frac{7}{10}$ of $80 = n$

18. $\frac{9}{10}$ of $\$200 = n$ **19.** $\frac{1}{2}$ of $\$38 = n$ **20.** $\frac{2}{3}$ of $\$39 = n$ **21.** $\frac{4}{9}$ of $\$81 = n$

22. $\frac{7}{8}$ of $\$64 = n$ **23.** $\frac{3}{8}$ of $\$16 = n$ **24.** $\frac{3}{10}$ of $\$90 = n$ **25.** $\frac{7}{8}$ of $\$32 = n$

26. $\frac{1}{5}$ of $24 = n$ **27.** $\frac{2}{3}$ of $18 = n$ **28.** $\frac{3}{4}$ of $40 = n$ **29.** $\frac{1}{2}$ of $31 = n$

Give answers to the nearest cent.

30. $\frac{2}{5}$ of $\$11 = n$ **31.** $\frac{1}{5}$ of $\$16 = n$ **32.** $\frac{2}{3}$ of $\$20 = n$ **33.** $\frac{3}{4}$ of $\$10 = n$

34. $\frac{2}{3}$ of $\$40 = n$ **35.** $\frac{5}{8}$ of $\$21 = n$ **36.** $\frac{1}{6}$ of $\$20 = n$ **37.** $\frac{5}{6}$ of $\$25 = n$

Problem Solving

Solve. Use the ad on page 182.

38. What is the sale price of a spider plant?

40. How much would you save by buying a jade plant on sale?

39. What is the sale price of an African violet?

41. Which plants are on sale for $\frac{1}{4}$ off the regular price?

CALCULATOR

42. Which calculator keys did Diane and Tony push to find $\frac{15}{22}$ of 121?

a. Diane's method:

121 _?_ 22 _?_ 15 = 82.5

b. Tony's method:

121 _?_ 15 _?_ 22 = 82.5

43. Use either Diane's or Tony's method to find n.

a. $\frac{14}{25}$ of $420 = n$ **b.** $\frac{27}{48}$ of $120 = n$

c. $\frac{135}{182}$ of $637 = n$ **d.** $\frac{63}{80}$ of $992 = n$

e. $\frac{144}{315}$ of $63 = n$ **f.** $\frac{130}{234}$ of $175.5 = n$

Multiplying a Whole Number by a Mixed Number

1. How many inches are there in 2 feet?
2. How many inches are there in $\frac{1}{2}$ of a foot?
3. If you know the number of inches in 2 feet and the number of inches in $\frac{1}{2}$ of a foot, how could you find the number of inches in $2\frac{1}{2}$ feet?

1 yard (yd) = 3 feet (ft)
1 ft = 12 inches (in.)
1 yd = 36 in.

Here's how to find the number of inches in $2\frac{1}{2}$ feet.

Regular Method

Change the mixed number to a fraction and multiply.

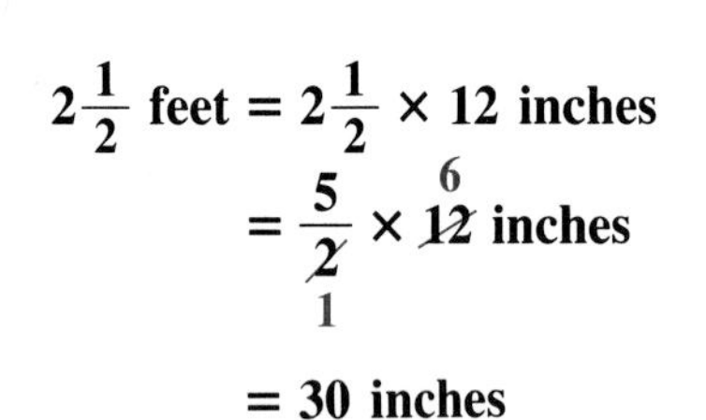

$$2\frac{1}{2} \text{ feet} = 2\frac{1}{2} \times 12 \text{ inches}$$
$$= \frac{5}{\cancel{2}_1} \times \cancel{12}^{6} \text{ inches}$$
$$= 30 \text{ inches}$$

Shortcut Method

First find the number of inches in 2 feet and in $\frac{1}{2}$ of a foot. Then add.

2×12 *inches*	$\frac{1}{2} \times 12$ *inches*

$$2\frac{1}{2} \text{ feet} = 24 \text{ inches} + 6 \text{ inches}$$
$$= 30 \text{ inches}$$

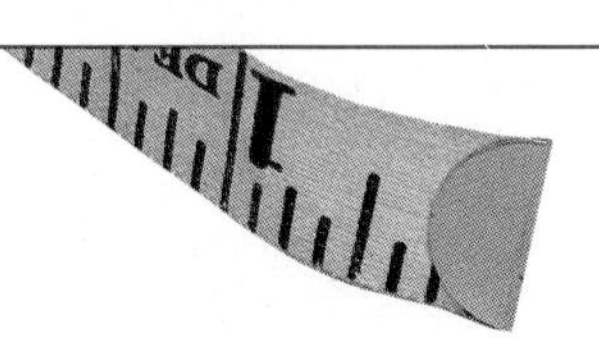

4. Look at the example above.
   a. How many inches are in $2\frac{1}{2}$ feet?
   b. Does the answer make sense? Is it between the number of inches in 2 feet (24) and the number of inches in 3 feet (36)?

▶ **Complete.**
Here are scrambled answers for the next row of exercises: 11 28 18 4

5. $1\frac{1}{2}$ ft = $\underline{?}$ in. **6.** $1\frac{1}{3}$ yd = $\underline{?}$ ft **7.** $2\frac{1}{3}$ ft = $\underline{?}$ in. **8.** $3\frac{2}{3}$ yd = $\underline{?}$ ft

9. $1\frac{1}{3}$ ft = $\underline{?}$ in. **10.** $2\frac{2}{3}$ yd = $\underline{?}$ ft **11.** $1\frac{1}{2}$ yd = $\underline{?}$ in. **12.** $2\frac{1}{3}$ yd = $\underline{?}$ ft

13. $2\frac{1}{4}$ yd = $\underline{?}$ in. **14.** $1\frac{3}{4}$ ft = $\underline{?}$ in. **15.** $3\frac{2}{3}$ ft = $\underline{?}$ in. **16.** $5\frac{1}{3}$ yd = $\underline{?}$ ft

17. $2\frac{1}{2}$ days = $\underline{?}$ h **18.** $4\frac{1}{2}$ h = $\underline{?}$ min

19. $1\frac{1}{3}$ h = $\underline{?}$ min **20.** $1\frac{1}{2}$ min = $\underline{?}$ s

21. $2\frac{3}{10}$ h = $\underline{?}$ min **22.** $2\frac{2}{3}$ days = $\underline{?}$ h

23. $1\frac{2}{3}$ min = $\underline{?}$ s **24.** $3\frac{1}{3}$ days = $\underline{?}$ h

1 day = 24 hours (h)
1 h = 60 minutes (min)
1 min = 60 seconds (s)

1 gallon (gal) = 4 quarts (qt)
1 qt = 2 pints (pt)
1 pt = 2 cups (c)

25. $2\frac{1}{2}$ gal = $\underline{?}$ qt **26.** $1\frac{1}{2}$ qt = $\underline{?}$ pt

27. $3\frac{1}{2}$ pt = $\underline{?}$ c **28.** $3\frac{1}{2}$ qt = $\underline{?}$ pt

29. $1\frac{3}{4}$ gal = $\underline{?}$ qt **30.** $2\frac{1}{2}$ pt = $\underline{?}$ c

31. $5\frac{1}{2}$ gal = $\underline{?}$ qt **32.** $5\frac{1}{2}$ qt = $\underline{?}$ pt

33. $7\frac{1}{2}$ pt = $\underline{?}$ c **34.** $3\frac{1}{2}$ gal = $\underline{?}$ qt

Problem Solving

▶ **Give an expression to complete each sentence.**

35. There are $\underline{?}$ hours in d days.

36. There are $\underline{?}$ hours in m minutes.

37. There are $\underline{?}$ minutes in s seconds.

38. There are $\underline{?}$ seconds in m minutes.

39. There are $\underline{?}$ inches in f feet.

40. There are $\underline{?}$ yards in i inches.

41. There are $\underline{?}$ inches in y yards.

42. There are $\underline{?}$ yards in f feet.

43. There are $\underline{?}$ pints in q quarts.

44. There are $\underline{?}$ cups in p pints.

45. There are $\underline{?}$ pints in c cups.

46. There are $\underline{?}$ quarts in g gallons.

Finding a Number When a Fraction of It Is Known

1. What is the sale price of the Women's Joggers?
2. The sale price of the Women's Joggers is what fraction of the regular price?
3. Is the regular price of the Women's Joggers more or less than $18?

Here's how to find the number when a fraction of it is known.

To find the number when a fraction of it is known, you can write and solve an equation.

Equation: $\frac{3}{4}$ **of** $n = 18$

$\frac{3}{4}n = 18$

Divide both sides by $\frac{3}{4}$.

$$\frac{\frac{3}{4}n}{\frac{3}{4}} = \frac{18}{\frac{3}{4}}$$

Simplify.

$$n = \overset{6}{\cancel{18}} \cdot \frac{4}{\underset{1}{\cancel{3}}}$$

To divide by $\frac{3}{4}$, multiply by $\frac{4}{3}$.

Simplify.

$$n = 24$$

Check:

$$\frac{3}{4}n = 18$$

$$\frac{3}{4} \cdot 24 \stackrel{?}{=} 18$$

$$\frac{3}{\underset{1}{\cancel{4}}} \cdot \overset{6}{\cancel{24}} \stackrel{?}{=} 18$$

$18 = 18$ *It checks!*

4. Look at the example above. What is the regular price of the Women's Joggers?
5. Complete these examples.

a. $\frac{2}{5}n = 38$

$$\frac{\frac{2}{5}n}{\frac{2}{5}} = \frac{38}{\frac{2}{5}}$$

$$n = \overset{19}{\cancel{38}} \cdot \frac{5}{\underset{1}{\cancel{2}}}$$

$n = \underline{\ ?\ }$

b. $\frac{2}{3}n = 15$

$$\frac{\frac{2}{3}n}{\frac{2}{3}} = \frac{15}{\frac{2}{3}}$$

$n = 15 \cdot \underline{\ ?\ }$

$n = 22\frac{1}{2}$

c. $\frac{4}{3}n = 10$

$$\frac{\frac{4}{3}n}{\frac{4}{3}} = \frac{10}{\frac{4}{3}}$$

$n = 10 \cdot \underline{\ ?\ }$

$n = \underline{\ ?\ }$

Solve. Give answers in simplest form.
Here are scrambled answers for the next row of exercises: $10\frac{2}{3}$ 24 20 15 30

6. $\frac{1}{3}n = 8$ **7.** $\frac{2}{3}n = 10$ **8.** $\frac{3}{4}n = 15$ **9.** $\frac{3}{8}n = 4$ **10.** $\frac{2}{5}n = 12$

11. $\frac{4}{3}n = 48$ **12.** $\frac{1}{4}n = 6$ **13.** $\frac{3}{5}n = 15$ **14.** $\frac{1}{7}n = 9$ **15.** $\frac{5}{2}n = 20$

16. $\frac{6}{5}n = 10$ **17.** $\frac{7}{9}n = 28$ **18.** $\frac{2}{5}n = 11$ **19.** $\frac{7}{8}n = 10$ **20.** $\frac{4}{5}n = 22$

21. $\frac{1}{2}n = 17$ **22.** $\frac{3}{2}n = 9$ **23.** $\frac{2}{9}n = 20$ **24.** $\frac{1}{5}n = 13$ **25.** $\frac{5}{6}n = 60$

26. $\frac{5}{2}n = 6$ **27.** $\frac{4}{5}n = 30$ **28.** $\frac{2}{3}n = 15$ **29.** $\frac{1}{5}n = 5$ **30.** $\frac{2}{3}n = \$20$

Problem Solving

Solve. Use the ad on page 186.

31. What is the regular price of the Men's Joggers?

32. What is the regular price of the Basketball Shoes?

33. What is the difference in the regular price of the Men's Joggers and the Women's Joggers?

★34. How much would you save by buying the Basketball Shoes on sale?

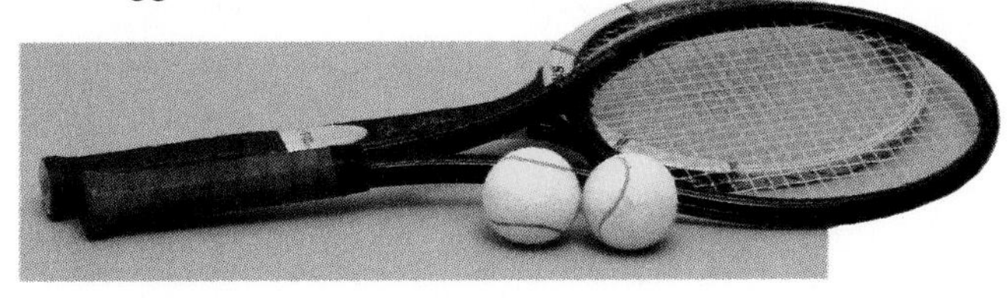

First choose the equation and solve the problem. Then reread the problem to see if your answer makes sense.

Equation A: $\frac{4}{5} \cdot 24 = n$

Equation B: $\frac{4}{5}n = 24$

Equation C: $\frac{4}{5} \cdot 80 = n$

Equation D: $\frac{4}{5}n = 80$

35. There were 24 tennis rackets on sale for $\frac{4}{5}$ of the regular price. What was the sale price of a racket that usually sold for $80?

36. A 24-pound, two-person tent was on sale for $\frac{4}{5}$ of its regular price. The sale price was $80. What was the regular price?

37. During the sale, $\frac{4}{5}$ of the $80 ski jackets were sold. How many ski jackets were on sale in all if 24 of them were sold?

38. There were 80 pairs of tennis shoes on sale for $\frac{4}{5}$ of the regular price. The regular price was $24. What was the sale price?

Problem Solving—Using Equations

In this lesson you will write equations involving fractions to solve problems.
Remember: To write an equation, you need to use two equal expressions.

TRADEMARKS SURVEY
Can you identify these automakers?

Here's how to use an equation to solve a problem.

Problem: An advertising agency made the trademarks survey to determine which trademarks people remember. Two thirds of the adults who took part in the survey correctly identified all four companies by their trademarks. How many adults took part in the survey if 54 identified the trademarks?

Step 1. Choose a variable. Use it and the facts to represent the numbers in the problem.

Let n = the number of adults who took part in the survey.
Then $\frac{2}{3}n$ = the number of adults who correctly identified all four trademarks.

Step 2. Write an equation based on the facts.

$$\frac{2}{3}n = 54$$

$\frac{2}{3}n$ and 54 are equal expressions for the number of adults who identified all four trademarks.

Step 3. Solve the equation.

$$\frac{2}{3}n = 54$$

$$\frac{\frac{2}{3}n}{\frac{2}{3}} = \frac{54}{\frac{2}{3}}$$

$$n = \overset{27}{\cancel{54}} \cdot \frac{3}{\underset{1}{\cancel{2}}}$$

$$n = 81$$

A total of 81 adults took part in the survey.

Look at the example above.

1. In Step 1, we let __?__ equal the number of adults who took part in the survey. Then the expression __?__ equals the number of adults who identified all four trademarks.
2. In Step 2, the two equal expressions for the number of adults who identified all four trademarks are __?__ and __?__.
3. An equation for the problem is __?__.

Equation A:	$\frac{3}{4}(60) = n$
Equation B:	$\frac{3}{4}n = 60$
Equation C:	$4n + 8 = 60$
Equation D:	$4n + 8 = 100$

▶ **Decide whether Equation A, B, C, or D would be used to solve each problem. Then solve the problem.**

4. Three fourths of the 60 people 15 to 18 years old identified all four companies in the trademarks survey. In the age group 14 or under, three fourths of the group, or 60 people, identified the trademarks.

a. How many people 15 to 18 identified the trademarks?

b. How many people 14 or under took part in the survey?

5. In a recent survey, 60 out of 100 adults could identify the trademark of their automobile. That is 8 more than 4 times the number of people who could identify the trademark of their car-insurance company. The number of adults surveyed was 8 more than 4 times the number of people who could identify their automobile-tire trademark.

a. How many people could identify their car-insurance company trademark?

b. How many people could identify their automobile-tire trademark?

▶ **Write an equation and solve the problem.**

6. One third of a number is 14. What is the number?
(Let n = the number.)

7. The product of two numbers is 40. If one number is $\frac{2}{5}$, what is the other number?
(Let m = the other number.)

8. A number increased by one eighth is three fourths. What is the number?
(Let r = the number.)

9. A number decreased by one third is one half. What is the number?
(Let t = the number.)

10. Ten more than 3 times a number is 55. What is the number?
(Let u = the number.)

11. Divide a number by 3, then subtract 6, and you get 1. What is the number?
(Let v = the number.)

12. Connie has saved two thirds of the cost of a sweater she wants. How much does the sweater cost if she has saved $26?
(Let c = the cost of the sweater.)

13. Angela has $3 more than twice as many dollars as Keith. If Angela has $15, how many dollars does Keith have?
(Let k = the number of dollars Keith has.)

14. Three fifths of a number is 1. What is the number?
(Let a = the number.)

★**15.** Two thirds of a number is $\frac{4}{5}$. What is the number?
(Let b = the number.)

Cumulative Skill Practice

▶ **Write in lowest terms.** *(page 132)*

1. $\frac{8}{24}$ **2.** $\frac{12}{10}$ **3.** $\frac{20}{36}$ **4.** $\frac{25}{10}$ **5.** $\frac{18}{27}$ **6.** $\frac{36}{42}$

7. $\frac{y}{y^2}$ **8.** $\frac{8}{6x}$ **9.** $\frac{4a}{6b}$ **10.** $\frac{xy}{3x}$ **11.** $\frac{12cd}{4c^2}$ **12.** $\frac{15}{18f^2}$

13. $\frac{9r}{3s}$ **14.** $\frac{x^2y}{12y^2}$ **15.** $\frac{20c}{25cd}$ **16.** $\frac{9y^3}{4y^2}$ **17.** $\frac{25mn^2}{20m^2}$ **18.** $\frac{16r^2s}{24s^2r}$

▶ **Find the least common denominator.** *(page 134)*

19. $\frac{2}{5}, \frac{3}{10}$ **20.** $\frac{5}{8}, \frac{1}{2}$ **21.** $\frac{4}{3}, \frac{5}{6}$ **22.** $\frac{1}{12}, \frac{3}{8}$ **23.** $\frac{5}{9}, \frac{5}{6}$

24. $\frac{1}{a}, \frac{3}{4a}$ **25.** $\frac{2}{c}, \frac{5}{8c}$ **26.** $\frac{b}{5d}, \frac{3}{d}$ **27.** $\frac{4}{3m}, \frac{5}{2m}$ **28.** $\frac{3}{2m^2}, \frac{7}{m}$

29. $\frac{p}{m^2}, \frac{q}{mn}$ **30.** $\frac{r}{6t^2}, \frac{s}{4t}$ **31.** $\frac{a}{3cd}, \frac{a}{2d}$ **32.** $\frac{x}{6wz}, \frac{y}{z^2}$ **33.** $\frac{2c}{5a^2b}, \frac{3d}{4ab^2}$

▶ **Write in simplest form.** *(page 150)*

34. $\frac{9}{3}$ **35.** $\frac{6}{9}$ **36.** $\frac{15}{2}$ **37.** $\frac{15}{5}$ **38.** $\frac{15}{20}$ **39.** $\frac{23}{3}$

40. $\frac{30}{4}$ **41.** $\frac{24}{4}$ **42.** $\frac{15}{18}$ **43.** $\frac{38}{5}$ **44.** $\frac{50}{8}$ **45.** $\frac{42}{6}$

46. $\frac{6a}{2b}$ **47.** $\frac{9x^2}{12y}$ **48.** $\frac{10cd^2}{15c}$ **49.** $\frac{9x^2}{3x^2}$ **50.** $\frac{4rs}{12r}$ **51.** $\frac{8mn^2}{3m}$

▶ **Give each sum in simplest form.** *(page 158)*

52. $\frac{1}{4} + \frac{3}{8}$ **53.** $\frac{2}{3} + \frac{1}{6}$ **54.** $\frac{3}{10} + \frac{1}{5}$ **55.** $\frac{3}{4} + \frac{2}{3}$ **56.** $\frac{5}{9} + \frac{1}{6}$

57. $\frac{r}{2} + \frac{s}{4}$ **58.** $\frac{m}{5} + \frac{n}{2}$ **59.** $\frac{p}{3} + \frac{q}{4}$ **60.** $\frac{3}{4} + \frac{k}{5}$ **61.** $\frac{r}{6} + \frac{5}{9}$

62. $\frac{5n}{8} + \frac{n}{3}$ **63.** $\frac{2x}{5} + \frac{y}{6}$ **64.** $\frac{7r}{12} + \frac{s}{9}$ **65.** $\frac{5m}{18} + \frac{5n}{12}$ **66.** $\frac{3y}{16} + \frac{7z}{20}$

▶ **Give each difference in simplest form.** *(page 158)*

67. $\frac{2}{3} - \frac{1}{2}$ **68.** $\frac{5}{12} - \frac{1}{4}$ **69.** $\frac{3}{4} - \frac{2}{3}$ **70.** $\frac{11}{12} - \frac{5}{9}$ **71.** $\frac{15}{16} - \frac{5}{12}$

72. $\frac{r}{6} - \frac{s}{3}$ **73.** $\frac{m}{2} - \frac{n}{5}$ **74.** $\frac{x}{4} - \frac{y}{3}$ **75.** $\frac{3a}{4} - \frac{a}{6}$ **76.** $\frac{m}{5} - \frac{5n}{7}$

Problem Solving—Applications

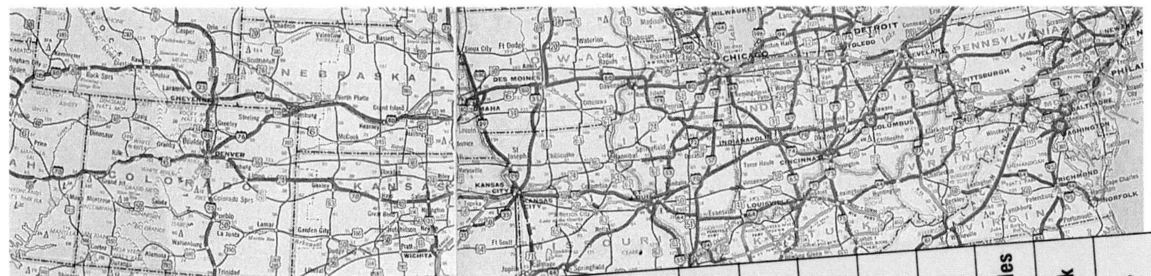

▶ **Use the mileage chart to solve the problems.**

MILEAGE CHART	Baltimore	Chicago	Cleveland	Denver	Houston	Los Angeles	New York	St. Louis
Baltimore		668	343	1621	1412	2636	196	817
Chicago	668		335	996	1067	2054	802	288
Cleveland	343	335		1321	1273	2367	473	546
Denver	1621	996	1321		1019	1059	1771	586
Houston	1412	1067	1273	1019		1538	1608	794
Los Angeles	2636	2054	2367	1059	1538		2786	1848
New York	196	802	473	1771	1608	2786		966
St. Louis	817	288	546	586	794	1848	966	

1. It is 802 miles from New York to Chicago. How far is it from New York to Denver?
2. How far is it from New York to Los Angeles?
3. You first drive from Cleveland to Chicago and then from Chicago to Houston. What is the total mileage?
4. What is the total mileage of a Houston–Denver–Los Angeles trip?
5. How much farther is Chicago from Houston than from New York?
6. When you are 450 miles from Los Angeles on a Denver–Los Angeles trip, how many miles have you driven?

▶ **Solve. Use the mileage chart and the formulas.**

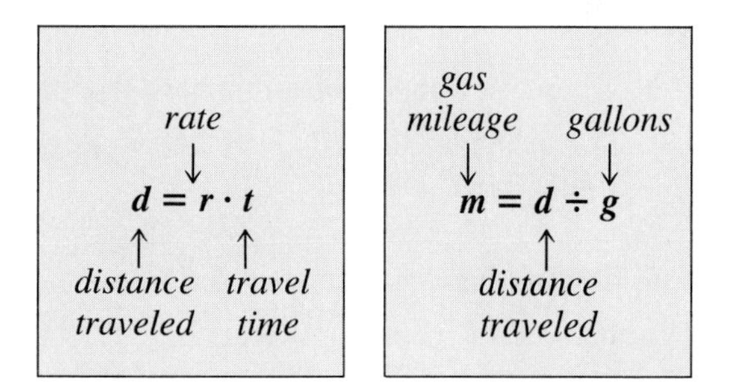

7. You and a friend want to drive from Houston to St. Louis to Chicago in less than 20 hours. Can you do it by traveling at a rate of 50 miles per hour?
8. You leave Houston and plan to drive 50 miles per hour. Will you be in St. Louis in less than 14 hours?
9. You leave St. Louis at 1:00 P.M. and plan to drive 50 miles per hour on your trip to Chicago. Will you reach Chicago by 7:00 P.M.?
10. Your car holds 12.5 gallons of gasoline. If your gas mileage averages 25 miles per gallon, can you drive from St. Louis to Chicago without stopping for gas?
11. If your car gets 25 miles per gallon of gasoline, how many gallons of gas will you need to get from Houston to St. Louis to Chicago?

Chapter Review

Here are scrambled answers for the review exercises:

1	*18*	*add*	*canceling*	*mixed*	*reciprocal*
2	*36*	*denominator*	*equation*	*multiply*	*simplest*
10	*a*	*divide*	*fraction*	*product*	*simplify*

1. To multiply fractions, multiply the numerators to get the numerator of the product and multiply the denominators to get the __?__ of the product. To find the products at the right, a shortcut called __?__ was used before the fractions were multiplied. *(page 172)*

$$\frac{\overset{1}{\cancel{2}}}{5} \cdot \frac{3}{\underset{2}{\cancel{4}}} = \frac{3}{?} \qquad \frac{\overset{1}{a}}{\underset{1}{\cancel{b}}} \cdot \frac{\overset{1}{\cancel{b}}}{\underset{a}{\cancel{a^2}}} = \frac{?}{a}$$

2. To multiply mixed numbers, change each mixed number to a __?__ and multiply. The last step in finding the product at the right would be to write the product in __?__ form. *(page 174)*

$$3\frac{2}{3} \cdot 4\frac{1}{2} = \frac{11}{\underset{1}{\cancel{3}}} \cdot \frac{\overset{3}{\cancel{9}}}{2} = \frac{33}{2}$$

3. Two numbers are reciprocals if their __?__ is 1. To divide by a fraction, __?__ by its reciprocal. To find the quotient of $\frac{3}{8} \div \frac{1}{2}$, you would multiply $\frac{3}{8}$ by __?__. To find the quotient of $\frac{a^2}{b} \div \frac{1}{a}$ you would multiply $\frac{a^2}{b}$ by __?__. *(page 176)*

4. To divide mixed numbers, change each __?__ number to a fraction and __?__. The next step in finding the quotient at the right would be to multiply $\frac{14}{3}$ by the __?__ of $\frac{7}{2}$. *(page 178)*

$$4\frac{2}{3} \div 3\frac{1}{2} = \frac{14}{3} \div \frac{7}{2}$$

5. To find a fraction of a number, you can write and solve an __?__. For example, to find $\frac{3}{4}$ **of 24,** you can solve the equation at the right. *(page 182)*

$$\frac{3}{4} \text{ of } 24 = n$$
$$\frac{3}{\underset{1}{\cancel{4}}} \cdot \overset{6}{\cancel{24}} = n$$
$$? = n$$

6. To find how many inches are in $3\frac{1}{4}$ feet, you could first find the number of inches in 3 feet, next find the number of inches in $\frac{1}{4}$ of a foot, and then __?__. *(page 184)*

7. To find the number when a fraction of it is known, you can write and solve an equation. For example, if you know $\frac{2}{3}$ of a number is 36, you can solve the equation at the right to find the number. To __?__ the right side of the last equation, you would multiply __?__ by $\frac{3}{2}$. *(page 186)*

$$\frac{2}{3} \text{ of } n = 36$$
$$\frac{2}{3}n = 36$$
$$\frac{\frac{2}{3}n}{\frac{2}{3}} = \frac{36}{\frac{2}{3}}$$

Chapter Test

Give each product in simplest form. *(pages 172, 174)*

1. $8 \cdot \frac{3}{4}$
2. $\frac{7}{16} \cdot \frac{12}{5}$
3. $15 \cdot \frac{2x}{3}$
4. $\frac{4m}{3n} \cdot \frac{p}{2m}$
5. $\frac{j}{2h} \cdot \frac{h^2}{j}$
6. $1\frac{1}{2} \cdot 3$
7. $2\frac{1}{3} \cdot 1\frac{1}{4}$
8. $2\frac{2}{3} \cdot 2\frac{2}{3}$
9. $2\frac{3}{4} \cdot 3\frac{1}{6}$
10. $4\frac{2}{3} \cdot 2\frac{5}{6}$

Give each quotient in simplest form. *(pages 176, 178)*

11. $\frac{7}{5} \div 3$
12. $\frac{7}{4} \div \frac{3}{8}$
13. $\frac{a}{b} \div \frac{1}{b}$
14. $\frac{3r}{s} \div \frac{5}{2r}$
15. $\frac{2z^2}{w} \div \frac{8z}{3w}$
16. $7\frac{1}{2} \div 1\frac{1}{4}$
17. $4\frac{2}{3} \div 4$
18. $5\frac{1}{2} \div 1\frac{1}{3}$
19. $3\frac{5}{6} \div 1\frac{2}{3}$
20. $6\frac{7}{8} \div 2\frac{3}{4}$

Solve. Give answers in simplest form. *(page 182)*

21. $\frac{1}{5}$ of $35 = n$
22. $\frac{2}{3}$ of $24 = n$
23. $\frac{6}{5}$ of $60 = n$
24. $\frac{7}{8}$ of $56 = n$

Complete. *(page 184)*

25. $2\frac{1}{2}$ ft = ___?___ in.
26. $1\frac{3}{4}$ days = ___?___ h
27. $4\frac{3}{4}$ min = ___?___ s
28. $3\frac{1}{2}$ gal = ___?___ qt

Solve. Give answers in simplest form. *(page 186)*

29. $\frac{1}{4}n = 20$
30. $\frac{2}{3}n = 42$
31. $\frac{9}{8}n = 72$
32. $\frac{5}{6}n = 60$

First choose the equation and solve the problem. Then reread the problem to see if your answer makes sense. *(page 187)*

Equation A: $\frac{3}{4} \cdot 36 = n$

Equation B: $\frac{3}{4}n = 36$

Equation C: $\frac{3}{4} \cdot 48 = n$

Equation D: $\frac{3}{4}n = 48$

33. The Stereo Shop put 48 pocket radios on sale for $\frac{3}{4}$ of the regular price. What was the sale price if the regular price was $36?
34. During the sale, $\frac{3}{4}$ of the $36 speakers were sold. How many of the speakers were on sale including the 48 that were sold?
35. There were 36 tape players on sale for $\frac{3}{4}$ of the regular price. The regular price was $48. What was the sale price?
36. Forty-eight headsets were on sale for $\frac{3}{4}$ of the regular price. The sale price was $36. What was the regular price?

Cumulative Test
Standardized Format

Choose the correct letter.

1. Solve.

$58 = 26 + j$

A. 32 B. 84 C. 58 D. none of these

2. Solve.

$12 = \frac{n}{6} - 4$

A. 72 B. 48 C. 96 D. none of these

3. Solve.

$60 = 3c + c$

A. 15 B. 240 C. 20 D. none of these

4. The algebraic factorization of $30rs^2$ is

A. $30 \cdot r \cdot s \cdot s$
B. $3 \cdot 10 \cdot r \cdot s \cdot s$
C. $2 \cdot 3 \cdot 5 \cdot r \cdot r \cdot s$
D. none of these

5. The least common multiple of $5y$ and $2y^2$ is

A. $10y$
B. $10y^2$
C. $5y^2$
D. none of these

6. $\frac{15ab^2}{25a}$ written in lowest terms is

A. $\frac{3ab^2}{5a}$ B. $\frac{3b^2}{5a}$ C. $\frac{3b^2}{5}$ D. none of these

7. The least common denominator of $\frac{a}{3c}$ and $\frac{b}{5c^2}$ is

A. 15 B. $15c$ C. $15c^2$ D. none of these

8. $\frac{20}{8}$ written in simplest form is

A. $\frac{10}{4}$ B. $\frac{5}{2}$ C. $2\frac{4}{8}$ D. none of these

9. Give the sum.

$\frac{2}{3} + \frac{3}{4}$

A. $1\frac{5}{12}$ B. $\frac{5}{7}$ C. $\frac{5}{12}$ D. none of these

10. Give the sum.

$\frac{a}{5} + \frac{b}{3}$

A. $\frac{a + 6}{15}$
B. $\frac{3a + b}{15}$
C. $\frac{3a + 5b}{15}$
D. none of these

11. Give the difference.

$\frac{3x}{4} - \frac{y}{6}$

A. $\frac{9x - 2y}{12}$
B. $\frac{3x - y}{12}$
C. $\frac{3x - 2y}{12}$
D. none of these

12. Choose the equation.

Twelve more than the quotient of a number divided by 6 is 18. What is the number?

A. $6n + 12 = 18$
B. $6n - 12 = 18$
C. $\frac{n}{6} - 12 = 18$
D. $\frac{n}{6} + 12 = 18$

8 Integers and Equations

$$a = \frac{t}{r}$$

A football player's average rushing yardage equals the player's total yards gained or lost divided by the number of times the player carried the ball.

(page 213)

Walter Payton, a leading rusher in the NFL, broke the record formerly held by Jim Brown for total lifetime yards gained. However, Jim Brown still holds the record for the greatest average rushing yardage, 5.2 yards.

Ordering and Comparing Integers

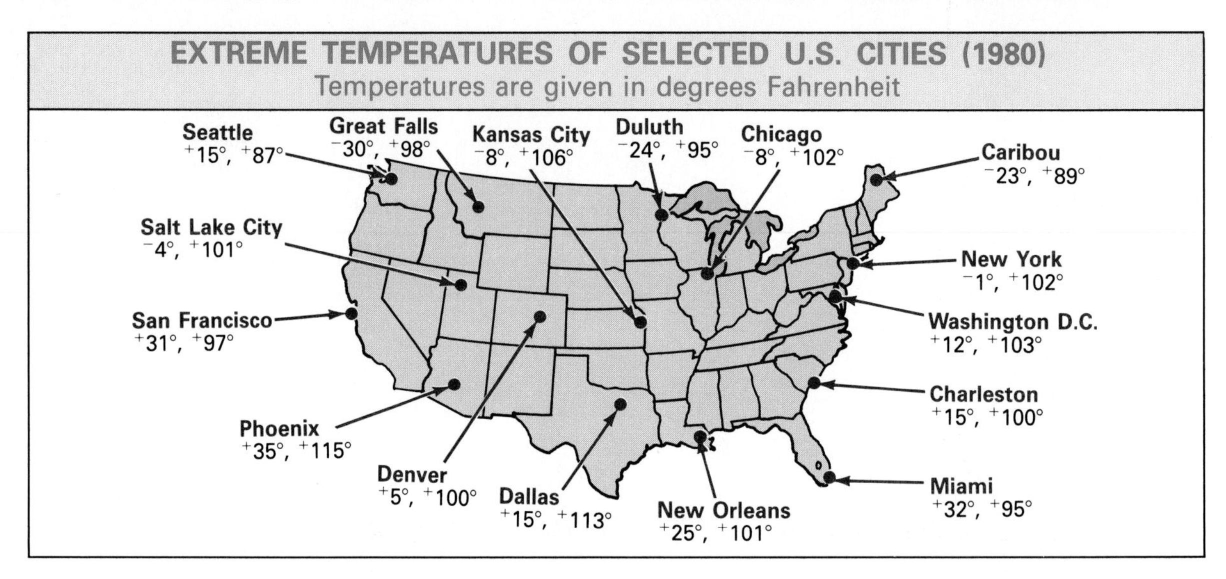

1. The low temperature for Phoenix is 35 degrees above zero, which can be written as $^{+}35°$ ("positive thirty-five degrees"). What is the low temperature for Dallas?

2. The low temperature for Kansas City is 8 degrees below zero, which can be written as $^{-}8°$ ("negative eight degrees"). What is the low temperature for Great Falls?

Here's how to use the number line to compare two integers.

$^{-}6$ $^{-}5$ $^{-}4$ $^{-}3$ $^{-}2$ $^{-}1$ 0 $^{+}1$ $^{+}2$ $^{+}3$ $^{+}4$ $^{+}5$ $^{+}6$

← *smaller* *larger* →

As you move to the right, the integers get larger.
As you move to the left, the integers get smaller.

The number line shows that $^{-}4 < {}^{-}1$ $^{-}1 < {}^{+}2$ $0 > {}^{-}3$ $^{+}3 > {}^{-}5$

↑ *is less than* ↑ *is greater than*

3. Look at the examples above.

a. Is $^{-}4$ less than or greater than $^{-}1$? **b.** Is 0 less than or greater than $^{-}3$?

4. Which number in each pair is farther from 0?

a. $^{-}3$, $^{+}2$ **b.** $^{+}4$, $^{+}5$ **c.** $^{-}4$, $^{-}2$ **d.** $^{+}5$, $^{-}3$

▶ $<$ or $>$?

5. $^{+}3$ ◆ $^{+}5$	**6.** $^{+}3$ ◆ $^{-}5$	**7.** $^{-}2$ ◆ $^{+}4$	**8.** $^{-}2$ ◆ $^{-}4$	**9.** $^{-}5$ ◆ $^{+}6$
10. $^{+}4$ ◆ $^{-}2$	**11.** $^{-}4$ ◆ $^{+}2$	**12.** $^{-}3$ ◆ $^{-}2$	**13.** $^{+}3$ ◆ $^{+}2$	**14.** $^{-}3$ ◆ 0
15. $^{-}9$ ◆ $^{+}6$	**16.** 0 ◆ $^{+}8$	**17.** 0 ◆ $^{-}8$	**18.** $^{+}10$ ◆ $^{-}7$	**19.** $^{-}4$ ◆ $^{-}12$
20. $^{-}17$ ◆ $^{+}19$	**21.** $^{+}17$ ◆ $^{-}19$	**22.** $^{+}17$ ◆ $^{+}19$	**23.** $^{-}17$ ◆ $^{-}19$	**24.** $^{+}17$ ◆ 0
25. $^{+}18$ ◆ $^{+}11$	**26.** $^{-}13$ ◆ $^{+}10$	**27.** $^{+}16$ ◆ $^{-}19$	**28.** $^{-}25$ ◆ 0	**29.** 0 ◆ $^{+}18$
30. $^{-}21$ ◆ $^{+}13$	**31.** $^{+}24$ ◆ $^{-}29$	**32.** $^{-}32$ ◆ $^{-}26$	**33.** $^{+}30$ ◆ $^{+}28$	**34.** $^{-}30$ ◆ $^{+}18$

▶ **Complete.**

35. All __?__ integers are greater than 0.

36. All __?__ integers are less than 0.

37. __?__ is neither positive nor negative.

38. Zero is __?__ than any negative integer.

39. A negative integer is __?__ than any positive integer.

40. A positive integer is __?__ than any negative integer.

Problem Solving

▶ **Solve. Use the information on page 196.**

41. Which city has the highest high temperature?

42. Which city has the lowest low temperature?

43. Which city has the highest low temperature?

44. Which city has the lowest high temperature?

45. List the low temperatures in order from least to greatest. (If two or more cities have the same low temperature, tell the number of cities with that low temperature.)

46. List the high temperatures in order from least to greatest. (If two or more cities have the same high temperature, tell the number of cities with that high temperature.)

▶ **Solve.**

47. The relationship between a temperature in degrees Celsius (C) and the temperature in degrees Fahrenheit (F) is given by the following formula:

$$9C = 5F - 160$$

Substitute in the formula above to complete this chart.

	C (degrees Celsius)	*F* (degrees Fahrenheit)
a.	?	32
b.	?	50
c.	?	59
d.	25	?
e.	30	?
f.	100	?

Adding Integers

Imagine some small particles that have either a positive electrical charge or a negative electrical charge. The positive charges and negative charges are opposites. This means that when one positive charge and one negative charge are put together, the result is no charge, or a charge of 0.

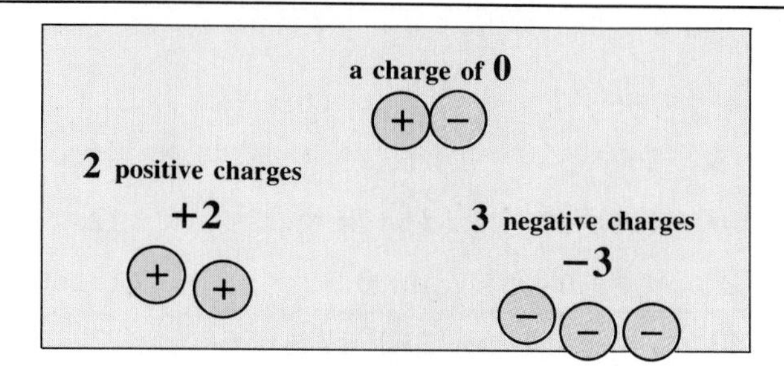

1. Look at the picture below. What is the charge when four positive charges and one negative charge are combined?

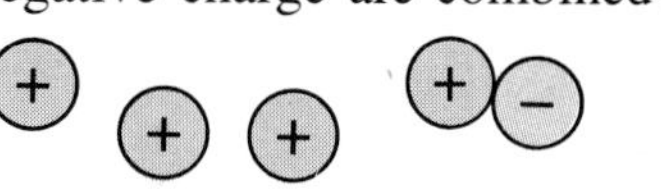

2. Look at the picture below. What is the charge when three positive charges and four negative charges are combined?

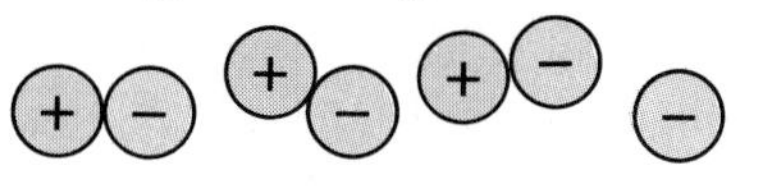

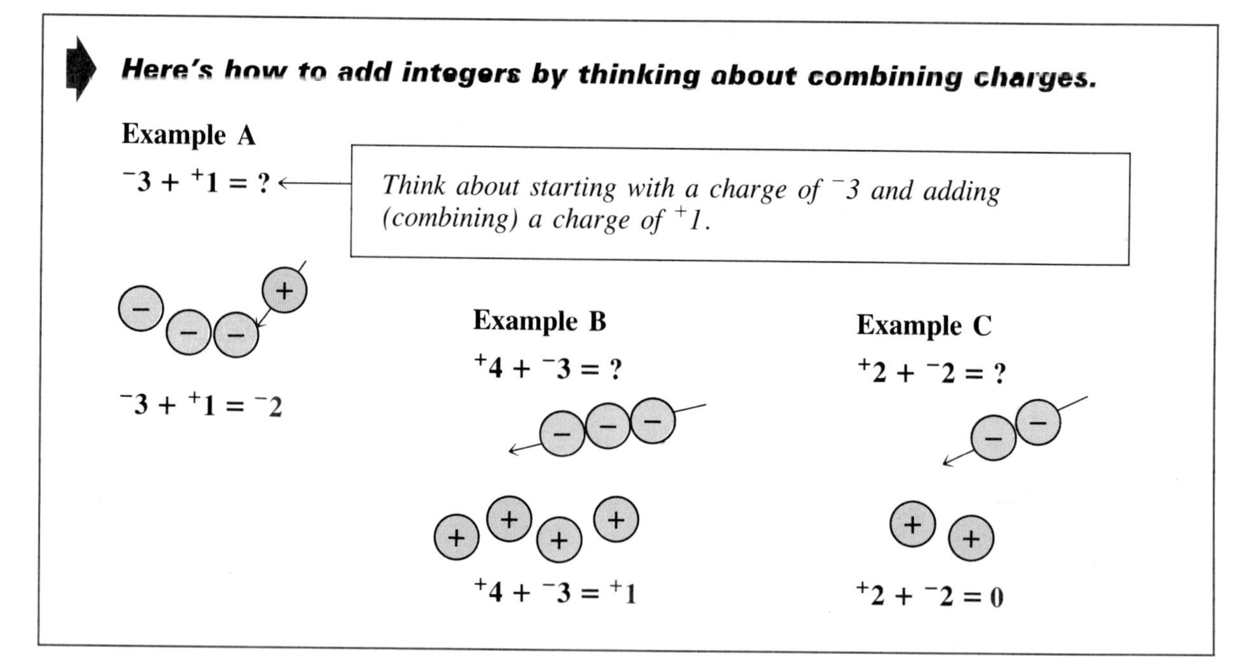

3. Look at the examples above.

a. What is the sum of $^{-}3$ and $^{+}1$?

b. What is the sum of $^{+}4$ and $^{-}3$?

4. If the sum of two numbers is 0, then one number is the **opposite** of the other. Look at Example C. What is the sum of $^{+}2$ and $^{-}2$? Are they opposites?

5. What is the opposite of $^{+}8$? of $^{-}6$? of 0?

You can use the following rules to add integers:

Adding an Integer and 0

- The sum of any integer and 0 is that integer.

Adding Two Positive Integers

- Disregard the positive signs and add the numbers.
- The sign of the sum will be positive.

Adding Two Negative Integers

- Disregard the negative signs and add the numbers.
- The sign of the sum will be negative.

Adding a Positive and a Negative Integer

- Disregard the signs and subtract the smaller number from the larger.
- Determine the sign of the addend farther from zero. This will be the sign of the sum.

EXERCISES

▶ **Give each sum.**

Here are scrambled answers for the next row of exercises: $0 \quad {}^{+}9 \quad {}^{+}4 \quad {}^{+}2 \quad {}^{-}9$

6. ${}^{+}7 + {}^{+}2$ **7.** ${}^{+}6 + {}^{-}2$ **8.** ${}^{-}2 + {}^{+}2$ **9.** ${}^{-}4 + {}^{-}5$ **10.** ${}^{+}5 + {}^{-}3$

11. ${}^{+}8 + {}^{-}1$ **12.** ${}^{-}6 + {}^{+}5$ **13.** ${}^{-}6 + {}^{-}2$ **14.** ${}^{+}9 + {}^{-}1$ **15.** ${}^{+}8 + {}^{-}8$

16. ${}^{-}6 + {}^{+}4$ **17.** ${}^{+}6 + {}^{+}4$ **18.** ${}^{-}6 + {}^{-}4$ **19.** ${}^{+}6 + {}^{-}4$ **20.** ${}^{+}7 + {}^{-}9$

21. ${}^{-}15 + {}^{-}10$ **22.** ${}^{-}20 + {}^{+}14$ **23.** ${}^{+}30 + {}^{-}22$ **24.** ${}^{-}37 + 0$ **25.** ${}^{-}50 + {}^{-}48$

26. ${}^{+}16 + {}^{-}19$ **27.** ${}^{-}34 + {}^{-}19$ **28.** ${}^{+}46 + {}^{-}48$ **29.** ${}^{+}26 + {}^{-}26$ **30.** $0 + {}^{-}68$

▶ **Evaluate each expression for $w = {}^{-}20$, $x = {}^{+}22$, $y = {}^{-}22$ and $z = {}^{+}25$.**

31. $w + x$ **32.** $x + y$ **33.** $y + x$ **34.** $w + y$ **35.** $y + w$

36. $x + x$ **37.** $z + w$ **38.** $w + z$ **39.** $z + x$ **40.** $x + z$

41. $x + y + y$ **42.** $x + x + z$ **43.** $w + x + x$ **44.** $z + z + z$ **45.** $w + w + w$

▶ **True or false?**

46. The sum of two positive numbers is always positive.

47. The sum of two negative numbers is always positive.

48. The sum of a positive number and a negative number is always positive.

49. The sum of two opposites is 0.

Subtracting Integers

Look at the picture at the right to answer the following questions.

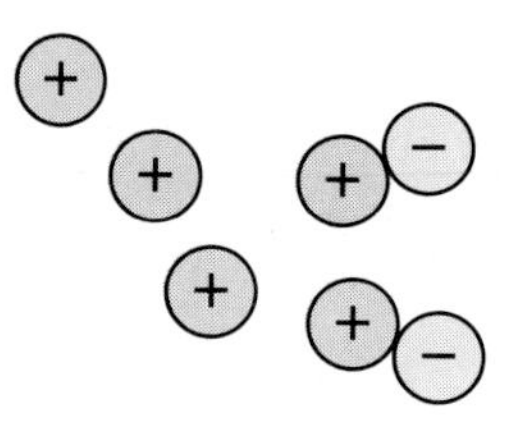

1. What is the charge of the particles?
2. a. Suppose that you removed a charge of $^{+}1$. What would the charge be then?
   b. Suppose instead that you added a charge of $^{-}1$. What would the charge be then?
3. a. Suppose instead that you removed a charge of $^{-}2$. What would the charge be then?
   b. Suppose instead that you added a charge of $^{+}2$. What would the charge be then?

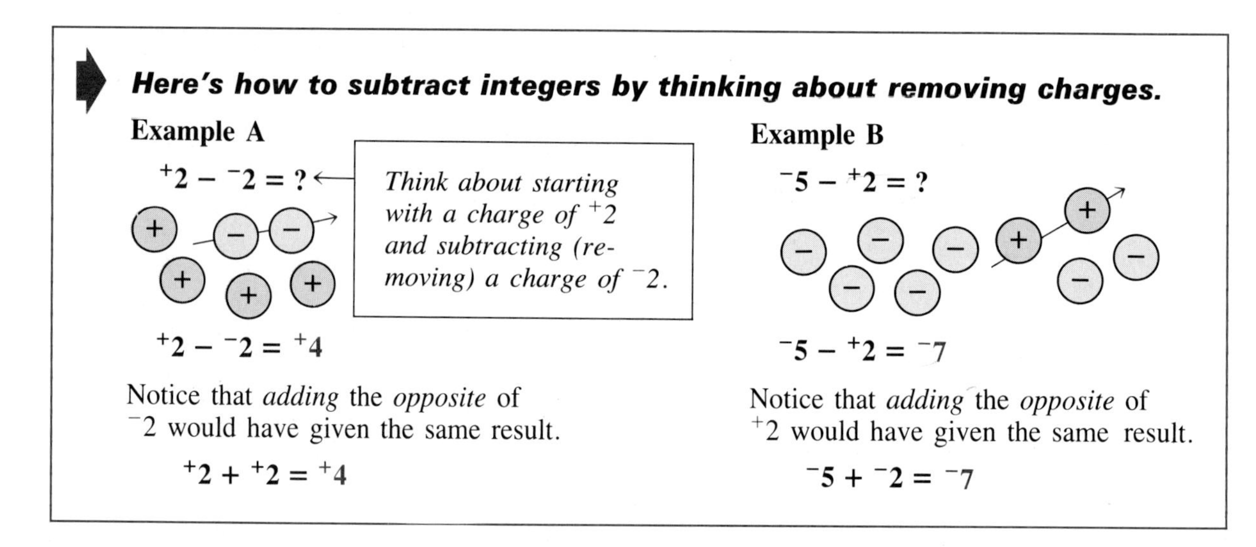

Here's how to subtract integers by thinking about removing charges.

Example A

$^{+}2 - ^{-}2 = ?$

Think about starting with a charge of $^{+}2$ and subtracting (removing) a charge of $^{-}2$.

$^{+}2 - ^{-}2 = ^{+}4$

Notice that *adding* the *opposite* of $^{-}2$ would have given the same result.

$^{+}2 + ^{+}2 = ^{+}4$

Example B

$^{-}5 - ^{+}2 = ?$

$^{-}5 - ^{+}2 = ^{-}7$

Notice that *adding* the *opposite* of $^{+}2$ would have given the same result.

$^{-}5 + ^{-}2 = ^{-}7$

4. Complete.
   a. To subtract $^{+}7$, you could add __?__.
   b. To subtract $^{-}6$, you could add __?__.

You can use the following rule to subtract integers:

- To subtract an integer, add the opposite of the integer.

5. Complete these examples.

a. $^{-}8 - ^{+}5 = ^{-}8 + ^{-}5$
$= \underline{?}$

b. $^{+}10 - ^{-}7 = ^{+}10 + ^{+}7$
$= \underline{?}$

c. $^{-}7 - ^{-}12 = ^{-}7 + ^{+}12$
$= \underline{?}$

EXERCISES

Give each difference.

Here are scrambled answers for the next row of exercises: $^{-}9$ $^{-}16$ $^{+}9$ $^{-}5$ $^{-}3$

6. $^{+}7 - {}^{+}2$ **7.** $^{-}8 - {}^{-}5$ **8.** $^{-}3 - {}^{+}6$ **9.** $^{+}4 - {}^{+}9$ **10.** $^{-}10 - {}^{+}6$

11. $^{-}4 - {}^{-}8$ **12.** $^{+}6 - {}^{+}3$ **13.** $^{-}7 - {}^{+}6$ **14.** $^{+}9 - 0$ **15.** $0 - {}^{+}6$

16. $^{+}7 - {}^{-}3$ **17.** $0 - {}^{-}9$ **18.** $^{+}7 - {}^{+}9$ **19.** $^{-}5 - {}^{+}5$ **20.** $^{-}3 - {}^{+}5$

21. $^{-}8 - {}^{+}3$ **22.** $^{+}6 - {}^{+}7$ **23.** $^{+}4 - {}^{-}3$ **24.** $^{-}4 - {}^{-}3$ **25.** $^{-}9 - {}^{+}3$

26. $^{+}8 - 0$ **27.** $0 - {}^{+}9$ **28.** $^{-}7 - {}^{+}5$ **29.** $^{+}2 - {}^{+}9$ **30.** $^{-}11 - {}^{-}6$

31. $^{-}3 - {}^{+}9$ **32.** $^{-}9 - {}^{+}5$ **33.** $^{+}6 - {}^{-}3$ **34.** $^{+}3 - {}^{+}9$ **35.** $^{-}8 - {}^{+}8$

36. $^{-}10 - {}^{+}12$ **37.** $^{+}14 - {}^{-}12$ **38.** $^{-}14 - {}^{-}18$ **39.** $^{+}15 - {}^{+}15$ **40.** $^{-}21 - {}^{-}13$

41. $^{+}18 - {}^{+}18$ **42.** $^{+}18 - {}^{+}15$ **43.** $^{-}19 - {}^{+}11$ **44.** $^{-}17 - {}^{-}13$ **45.** $^{-}16 - {}^{+}18$

Simplify.

Here are scrambled answers for the next row of exercises: $^{+}27$ $^{-}6$ $^{-}21$ $^{+}2$

46. $^{-}10 + {}^{-}11$ **47.** $^{+}12 - {}^{-}15$ **48.** $^{+}16 - {}^{+}14$ **49.** $^{-}18 + {}^{+}12$

50. $^{-}13 - {}^{+}12$ **51.** $^{+}14 + 0$ **52.** $0 + {}^{-}17$ **53.** $^{+}11 + {}^{+}11$

54. $^{+}11 - {}^{+}11$ **55.** $^{+}25 + {}^{+}11$ **56.** $^{-}20 - {}^{+}14$ **57.** $^{+}27 - {}^{-}27$

58. $({}^{+}6 + {}^{+}3) - {}^{-}4$ **59.** $^{+}6 + ({}^{+}3 - {}^{-}4)$ **60.** $^{+}9 + ({}^{+}8 + {}^{+}6)$

61. $^{+}9 + ({}^{+}8 - {}^{+}6)$ **62.** $({}^{-}5 - {}^{+}8) + {}^{+}2$ **63.** $^{-}5 - ({}^{+}8 + {}^{+}2)$

64. $({}^{-}12 - {}^{-}10) - {}^{-}15$ **65.** $^{-}12 - ({}^{-}10 - {}^{-}15)$ **66.** $({}^{+}18 - {}^{-}20) + {}^{-}12$

67. $^{-}23 + ({}^{+}19 + 0)$ **68.** $({}^{+}27 - {}^{+}27) - {}^{-}31$ **69.** $^{-}36 + ({}^{-}29 + {}^{+}29)$

Write a mathematical expression for each word expression.

70. the sum of y and $^{-}8$

71. a number t minus $^{+}11$

72. $^{+}6$ increased by a number n

73. a number k decreased by $^{+}8$

74. a number s less $^{+}7$

75. $^{-}10$ decreased by a number v

76. $^{+}3$ more than a number b

77. a number c plus $^{-}15$

78. a number w minus $^{-}21$

79. a number j increased by $^{+}20$

80. a number x plus a number y

81. a number d minus a number b

82. c subtracted from a number r

83. c minus r

84. a number a added to itself

85. a number h subtracted from itself

86. $^{-}3$ less than a number d

87. a number t added to $^{-}1$

Multiplying Integers

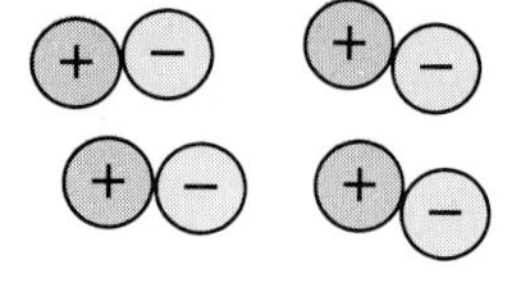

Look at the picture at the right to answer the following questions.

1. What is the charge of the particles?
2. Suppose that you put in 2 sets of $^{+}2$ charges.

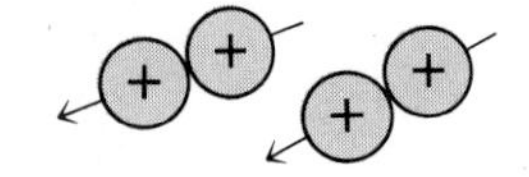

   What would the charge be then?

3. Suppose instead that you took out 2 sets of $^{-}2$. What would the charge be then?

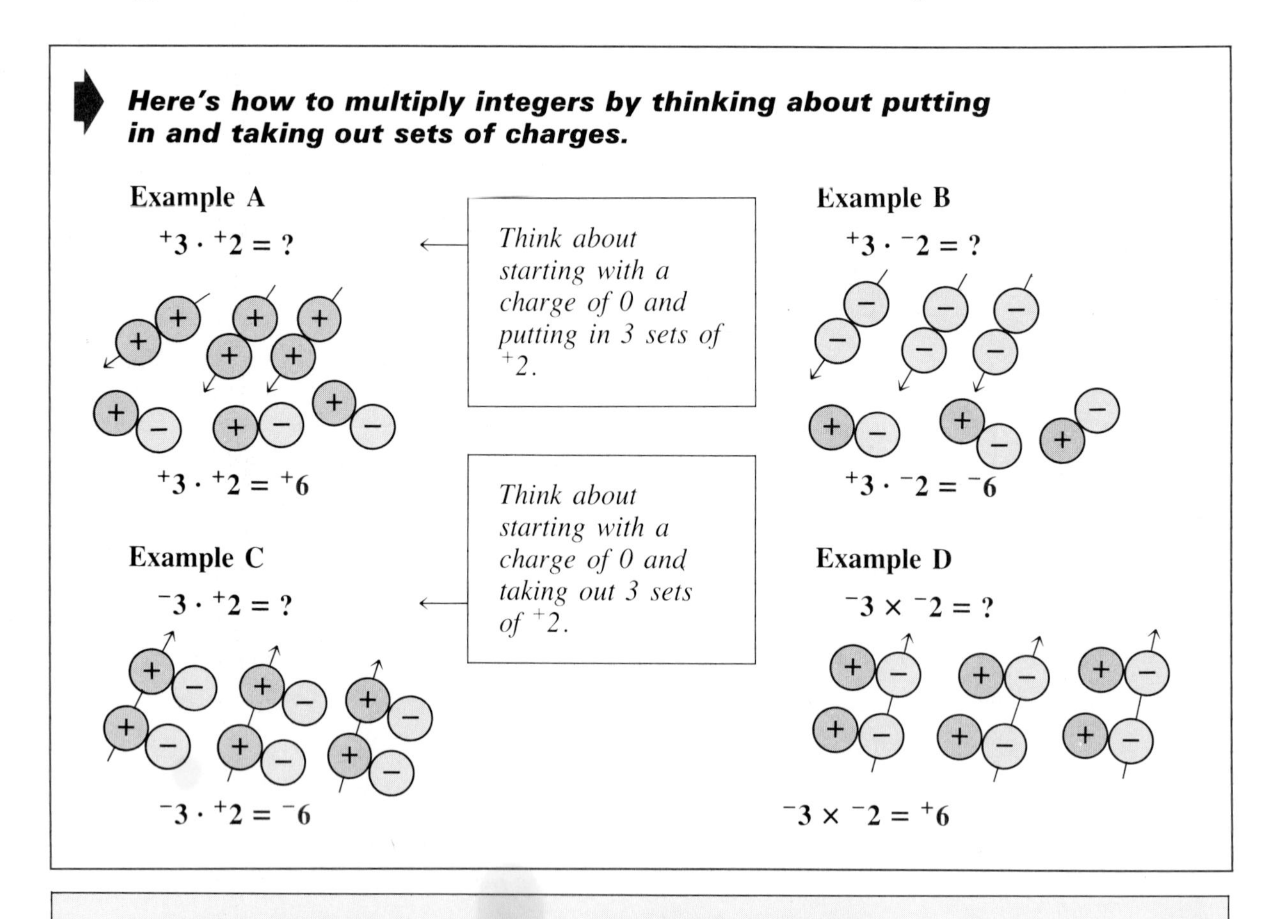

Here's how to multiply integers by thinking about putting in and taking out sets of charges.

Example A

$^{+}3 \cdot {}^{+}2 = ?$

$^{+}3 \cdot {}^{+}2 = {}^{+}6$

Think about starting with a charge of 0 and putting in 3 sets of $^{+}2$.

Example B

$^{+}3 \cdot {}^{-}2 = ?$

$^{+}3 \cdot {}^{-}2 = {}^{-}6$

Example C

$^{-}3 \cdot {}^{+}2 = ?$

$^{-}3 \cdot {}^{+}2 = {}^{-}6$

Think about starting with a charge of 0 and taking out 3 sets of $^{+}2$.

Example D

$^{-}3 \times {}^{-}2 = ?$

$^{-}3 \times {}^{-}2 = {}^{+}6$

You can use the following rules to multiply integers:

- The product of two integers with the ***same*** sign is ***positive.***
- The product of two integers with ***different*** signs is ***negative.***
- The product of any integer and 0 is 0.

4. The product of a positive integer and a positive integer is a __?__ integer.

5. The product of a positive integer and a negative integer is a __?__ integer.

6. The product of a negative integer and negative integer is a __?__ integer.

7. The product of an integer and 0 is __?__.

EXERCISES

▶ **Give each product.**
Here are scrambled answers for the next row of exercises: $^{+}15$ $^{-}8$ $^{+}28$ $^{-}24$ 0

8. $^{-}5 \cdot 0$ **9.** $^{-}6 \cdot {}^{+}4$ **10.** $^{+}3 \cdot {}^{+}5$ **11.** $^{+}1 \cdot {}^{-}8$ **12.** $^{-}4 \cdot {}^{-}7$

13. $^{-}4 \cdot {}^{+}2$ **14.** $^{+}9 \cdot {}^{+}5$ **15.** $^{+}8 \cdot {}^{+}8$ **16.** $^{-}7 \cdot {}^{+}7$ **17.** $0 \cdot {}^{-}8$

18. $^{+}9 \cdot {}^{-}3$ **19.** $^{-}8 \cdot {}^{-}5$ **20.** $^{-}2 \cdot {}^{+}5$ **21.** $^{+}8 \cdot {}^{+}9$ **22.** $^{+}3 \cdot {}^{-}5$

23. $^{+}6 \cdot {}^{-}4$ **24.** $^{-}7 \cdot {}^{+}8$ **25.** $0 \cdot 0$ **26.** $^{-}3 \cdot {}^{-}3$ **27.** $^{+}7 \cdot 0$

28. $^{+}9 \cdot {}^{-}9$ **29.** $^{+}2 \cdot {}^{+}6$ **30.** $^{-}6 \cdot {}^{+}4$ **31.** $^{+}4 \cdot {}^{-}7$ **32.** $^{-}9 \cdot {}^{-}8$

33. $^{-}3 \cdot {}^{+}5$ **34.** $^{+}7 \cdot {}^{-}6$ **35.** $^{-}8 \cdot {}^{+}4$ **36.** $^{+}9 \cdot {}^{+}6$ **37.** $^{-}6 \cdot {}^{-}4$

38. $^{-}12 \cdot {}^{+}12$ **39.** $^{+}18 \cdot {}^{+}11$ **40.** $^{-}15 \cdot {}^{-}10$ **41.** $^{-}16 \cdot {}^{+}14$ **42.** $^{+}18 \cdot {}^{-}18$

▶ **Evaluate each expression for $a = {}^{-}6$, $b = {}^{-}3$, $c = 0$, and $d = {}^{+}8$.**
Here are scrambled answers for the next row of exercises: $^{+}3$ $^{-}48$ $^{-}9$ $^{+}8$

43. $a + b$ **44.** $c - b$ **45.** ad **46.** $d + c$

47. cb **48.** $a + c$ **49.** $d - b$ **50.** da

51. $a - b$ **52.** bb **53.** $b + d$ **54.** $d - a$

55. $a(b + c)$ **56.** $ab + ac$ **57.** $a(b - c)$ **58.** $ab - ac$

59. $(a + b) + c$ **60.** $a + (b + c)$ **61.** $(a - b) - d$ **62.** $a - (b - d)$

Challenge

▶ **Simplify. Let $m = {}^{+}3$, $n = {}^{-}3$, $r = {}^{-}2$, $s = {}^{-}1$, $t = {}^{-}10$, and $u = {}^{+}10$.**
Here are scrambled answers for the next row of exercises: $^{+}1$ $^{+}9$ $^{-}8$ $^{+}100$

63. $n^2 \leftarrow \boxed{{}^{-}3 \cdot {}^{-}3}$ **64.** $r^3 \leftarrow \boxed{{}^{-}2 \cdot {}^{-}2 \cdot {}^{-}2}$ **65.** s^2 **66.** t^2

67. n^3 **68.** u^3 **69.** r^4 **70.** u^4

71. m^3 **72.** u^5 **73.** r^5 **74.** r^6

75. s^3 **76.** s^4 **77.** s^5 **78.** s^6

Dividing Integers

1. What would you multiply $^{+}7$ by to get $^{+}35$?
2. What would you multiply $^{-}6$ by to get $^{-}54$?
3. What would you multiply $^{-}12$ by to get 0?

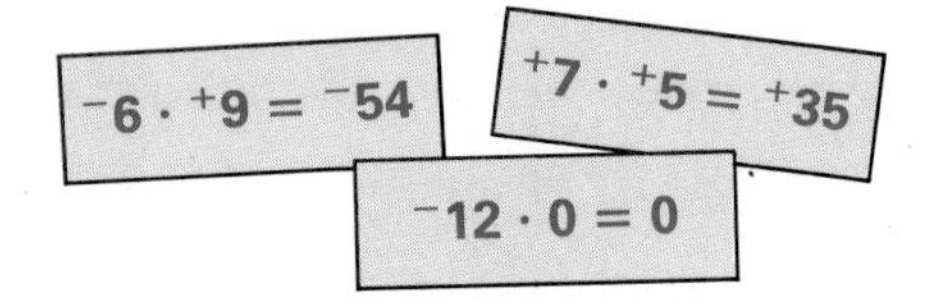

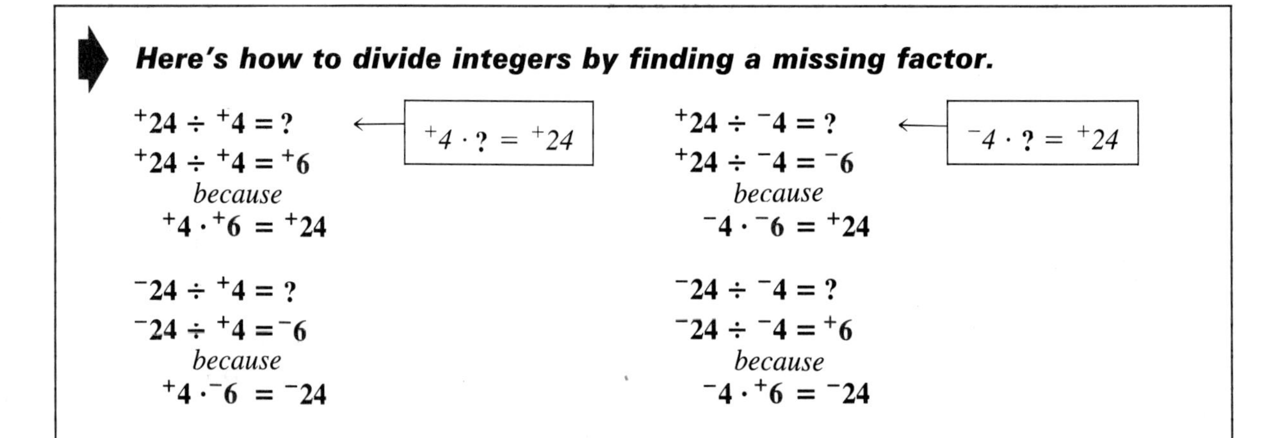

Here's how to divide integers by finding a missing factor.

$^{+}24 \div {}^{+}4 = ?$ ← $^{+}4 \cdot ? = {}^{+}24$

$^{+}24 \div {}^{+}4 = {}^{+}6$

because

$^{+}4 \cdot {}^{+}6 = {}^{+}24$

$^{+}24 \div {}^{-}4 = ?$ ← $^{-}4 \cdot ? = {}^{+}24$

$^{+}24 \div {}^{-}4 = {}^{-}6$

because

$^{-}4 \cdot {}^{-}6 = {}^{+}24$

$^{-}24 \div {}^{+}4 = ?$

$^{-}24 \div {}^{+}4 = {}^{-}6$

because

$^{+}4 \cdot {}^{-}6 = {}^{-}24$

$^{-}24 \div {}^{-}4 = ?$

$^{-}24 \div {}^{-}4 = {}^{+}6$

because

$^{-}4 \cdot {}^{+}6 = {}^{-}24$

You can use the following rules to divide integers:

- The quotient of two integers with the ***same*** sign is ***positive.***
- The quotient of two integers with ***different*** signs is ***negative.***
- The quotient of 0 divided by any nonzero integer is 0.

4. If you divide a positive integer by a positive integer, the quotient will be __?__.
5. If you divide a negative integer by a negative integer, the quotient will be __?__.
6. If you divide a positive integer by a negative integer, the quotient will be __?__.
7. If you divide a negative integer by a positive integer, the quotient will be __?__.

EXERCISES

▶ **Give each quotient.**

Here are scrambled answers for the next row of exercises: $^{+}8$ $^{-}4$ $^{+}10$ $^{+}6$ $^{-}8$

8. $^{+}20 \div {}^{+}2$
9. $^{+}24 \div {}^{-}3$
10. $^{-}30 \div {}^{-}5$
11. $^{-}36 \div {}^{+}9$
12. $^{-}56 \div {}^{-}7$
13. $^{+}14 \div {}^{-}2$
14. $^{+}27 \div {}^{+}9$
15. $^{-}42 \div {}^{-}6$
16. $0 \div {}^{+}7$
17. $^{+}28 \div {}^{-}4$
18. $^{-}64 \div {}^{-}8$
19. $^{+}45 \div {}^{+}9$
20. $^{+}18 \div {}^{-}9$
21. $^{-}48 \div {}^{+}8$
22. $^{+}25 \div {}^{-}5$

Give each quotient.

> *Remember:* $\frac{^{+}36}{^{-}9}$ *means* $^{+}36 \div {}^{-}9$

23. $\frac{^{+}36}{^{-}9}$
24. $\frac{^{+}49}{^{-}7}$
25. $\frac{^{+}32}{^{-}8}$
26. $\frac{^{-}36}{^{-}6}$
27. $\frac{0}{^{+}7}$
28. $\frac{^{+}63}{^{-}9}$
29. $\frac{^{-}63}{^{-}7}$
30. $\frac{^{-}30}{^{+}5}$
31. $\frac{^{+}64}{^{+}8}$
32. $\frac{^{-}45}{^{+}9}$
33. $\frac{^{+}56}{^{-}8}$
34. $\frac{^{-}48}{^{-}6}$
35. $\frac{^{+}42}{^{-}7}$
36. $\frac{^{-}72}{^{+}9}$

TIME OUT!! From this point on we will no longer write the raised plus sign when writing a positive integer.

Simplify.
Here are scrambled answers for the next row of exercises: 4 $^{-}7$ 21 $^{-}108$ $^{-}5$

37. $3 + 18$
38. $21 - 17$
39. $\frac{25}{^{-}5}$
40. $^{-}9 \cdot 12$
41. $20 - 27$
42. $\frac{80}{^{-}10}$
43. $^{-}10 \cdot {}^{-}10$
44. $^{-}12 + {}^{-}14$
45. $^{-}26 - {}^{-}2$
46. $^{-}28 \cdot 0$
47. $^{-}45 + 20$
48. $\frac{^{-}72}{^{-}4}$
49. $48 - {}^{-}30$
50. $3 \cdot {}^{-}35$
51. $16 + {}^{-}28$

Evaluate each expression for $r = {}^{-}48$, $s = 12$, $t = {}^{-}6$, and $u = 3$.
Here are scrambled answers for the next row of exercises: 42 4 $^{-}18$ $^{-}36$ 8

52. $r + s$
53. $t - r$
54. tu
55. $\frac{r}{t}$
56. $\frac{s}{u}$
57. $r - st$
58. $\frac{r}{u} - s$
59. $tu + ts$
60. $u(t + s)$
61. $u(s - t)$
62. $r(t - t)$
63. $tu - \frac{s}{s}$
64. $\frac{t}{t} + \frac{u}{u}$
65. $s^2 - \frac{s}{t}$
66. $t^2 + u^2$

CALCULATOR

Here's how to use a +/− (change sign) key to add and subtract integers.

Example. Find $^{-}16 + 4$.
16 [+/−] + 4 = −12

Example. Find $18 - {}^{-}34$.
18 − 34 [+/−] = 52

67. Find the sum or difference.

a. $^{-}312 + 57$
b. $497 + {}^{-}291$
c. $402 - {}^{-}108$
d. $^{-}117 - 43$
e. $^{-}47 + {}^{-}102$
f. $^{-}123 + 516$
g. $^{-}106 - {}^{-}85$
h. $72 - {}^{-}112$
i. $(36 + {}^{-}41) + {}^{-}82$
j. $({}^{-}45 - 17) + {}^{-}35$

Cumulative Skill Practice

Give the prime factorization using exponents. *(page 124)*

1. 4 **2.** 9 **3.** 18 **4.** 8 **5.** 25 **6.** 24

7. 27 **8.** 28 **9.** 44 **10.** 36 **11.** 40 **12.** 63

13. 72 **14.** 125 **15.** 100 **16.** 64 **17.** 180 **18.** 225

Give the greatest common factor. *(page 126)*

19. 12, 16 **20.** 45, 30 **21.** 72, 60 **22.** 3, 30

23. $16c$, 20 **24.** 52, $13a$ **25.** d, $11d$ **26.** $8e$, $12e$

27. $8x$, $11x^2$ **28.** $24z$, $18z^2$ **29.** $7w^2$, $42w$ **30.** $12yz$, $18y^2$

31. $10u^2v$, $15uv^2$ **32.** $18a^2b$, $24b^2$ **33.** $12c^2d^2$, $15cd^2$ **34.** $48r^2s^3$, $36r^3s^2$

Find the least common denominator. *(page 134)*

35. $\frac{3}{5}, \frac{7}{10}$ **36.** $\frac{5}{4}, \frac{1}{2}$ **37.** $\frac{11}{3}, \frac{7}{6}$ **38.** $\frac{5}{16}, \frac{7}{8}$

39. $\frac{3}{2}, \frac{2}{5x}$ **40.** $\frac{9}{c}, \frac{5}{3c}$ **41.** $\frac{5}{12d}, \frac{1}{8d}$ **42.** $\frac{11}{5k}, \frac{17}{3k}$

43. $\frac{r}{s^2}, \frac{t}{3s}$ **44.** $\frac{m}{6n^2}, \frac{p}{4n}$ **45.** $\frac{c}{5de}, \frac{c}{3de}$ **46.** $\frac{p}{8gr}, \frac{3p}{r^2}$

Write in simplest form. *(page 150)*

47. $\frac{12}{3}$ **48.** $\frac{6}{8}$ **49.** $\frac{13}{2}$ **50.** $\frac{18}{6}$ **51.** $\frac{20}{30}$ **52.** $\frac{27}{6}$

53. $\frac{5a}{3a}$ **54.** $\frac{2c}{11c}$ **55.** $\frac{3d}{8d^2}$ **56.** $\frac{5rs}{10r}$ **57.** $\frac{5a}{15ab}$ **58.** $\frac{36uv}{24v}$

59. $\frac{7c^2}{12c}$ **60.** $\frac{12rs^2}{18r}$ **61.** $\frac{16y^2}{4y^2}$ **62.** $\frac{9ab^2}{12a}$ **63.** $\frac{7mn^2}{4m}$ **64.** $\frac{9yz^2}{4y^2z}$

Give each sum or difference in simplest form. *(page 158)*

65. $\frac{1}{8} + \frac{3}{4}$ **66.** $\frac{1}{3} + \frac{1}{2}$ **67.** $\frac{3}{4} - \frac{2}{3}$ **68.** $\frac{5}{6} - \frac{4}{9}$

69. $\frac{a}{3} + \frac{b}{6}$ **70.** $\frac{m}{12} + \frac{n}{8}$ **71.** $\frac{3x}{10} + \frac{4}{15}$ **72.** $\frac{w}{12} + \frac{35}{18}$

73. $\frac{x}{4} - \frac{y}{6}$ **74.** $\frac{a}{3} - \frac{b}{8}$ **75.** $\frac{2j}{9} - \frac{k}{6}$ **76.** $\frac{m}{12} - \frac{3n}{16}$

Problem Solving—Applications

Use the information in the chart to solve the problems.

1. How many pounds of Delicious apples can you buy for $1.80?
2. A customer bought $1\frac{1}{4}$ pounds of Granny Smith apples and $2\frac{1}{2}$ pounds of McIntosh apples. What was the total cost?
3. How much does a 6-pound bag of apples cost if it is $\frac{1}{3}$ Granny Smith apples and $\frac{2}{3}$ Delicious apples?

	POUNDS				
APPLES	$\frac{1}{4}$	$\frac{1}{2}$	$\frac{3}{4}$	1	2
Granny Smith	$.25	$.50	$.75	$1.00	$2.00
Delicious	$.15	$.30	$.45	$.60	$1.20
McIntosh	$.18	$.36	$.54	$.72	$1.44

Read the facts. Then complete the steps to answer the question.

4. *Facts:* You bought a $1.44 bag of apples and a 4-pound bag of peaches. You spent a total of $5.00.

   Question: What is the cost of one pound of peaches?

   a. Let c equal the cost of one pound of peaches. Then __?__ c equals the cost of four pounds of peaches. So __?__ $c + 1.44$ equals the total cost of the apples and peaches.

   b. Two equal expressions for the total cost are __?__ $c + 1.44$ and 5.

   c. To find the cost of one pound of peaches, you can solve the equation $4c + 1.44 =$ __?__.

   d. Solve the equation in part c. What is the cost of one pound of peaches?

5. *Facts:* You bought a cantaloupe at $1.20 per pound and a $2.20 box of strawberries. You spent a total of $5.20.

   Question: What is the weight of the cantaloupe?

   a. Let p equal the weight of the cantaloupe in pounds. Then __?__ p equals the cost of the cantaloupe. So __?__ $p + 2.20$ equals the total cost of the cantaloupe and strawberries.

   b. Two equal expressions for the total cost are __?__ $p + 2.20$ and 5.20.

   c. To find the weight of the cantaloupe, you can solve the equation $1.20p + 2.20 =$ __?__.

   d. Solve the equation in part c. What is the weight of the cantaloupe?

Write an equation and solve the problem.

6. You bought a 15-pound watermelon and a $3.50 bag of oranges. You spent a total of $7.85. How much did the watermelon cost per pound?
   (Let c equal the cost of one pound of watermelon.)

7. You paid $5.73 for a $1.89 melon and a bag of cherries. The cherries cost $1.20 a pound. How many pounds of cherries did you buy?
   (Let p equal the number of pounds of cherries you bought.)

Writing Numbers in Scientific Notation

- A regular pencil can draw a line **2,210,000** inches long before it runs out.
- Top speed for some species of snails is **0.00036** mile per hour.

The large and small numbers in the facts above can be written in **scientific notation.** Here are the numbers expressed in scientific notation:

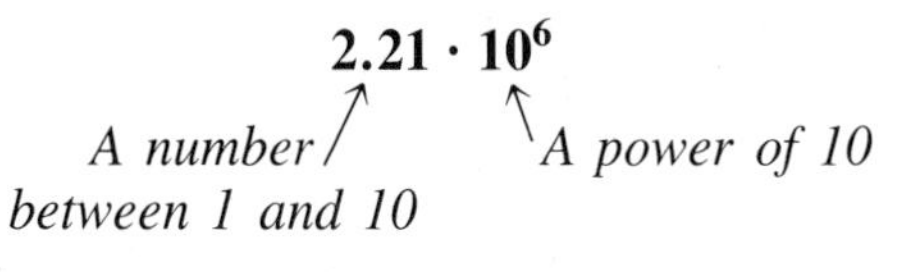

$\mathbf{3.6 \cdot 10^{-4}}$

Read as "3.6 times 10 to the negative 4th power."

Notice that scientific notation is based on positive and negative powers of 10.

Positive (+) powers of 10:	$10^1 = 10$ $10^2 = 100$ $10^3 = 1000$ $10^4 = 10{,}000$ *and so on*	**Negative (−) powers of 10:**	$10^{-1} = 0.1$ $10^{-2} = 0.01$ $10^{-3} = 0.001$ $10^{-4} = 0.0001$ *and so on*

Here's how to write numbers in scientific notation.

Write **61,000,000** and **0.0000875** in scientific notation.

		Large number	Small number
Step 1.	Locate the decimal point to get a number between 1 and 10.	**6.1000000** ↑	**0.00008.75** ↑
Step 2.	Count the number of places the decimal point will move to get a number between 1 and 10.	**6.1000000** *7 places to the left*	**0.00008.75** *5 places to the right*
Step 3.	Write the number as a product of a number between 1 and 10 and a power of 10.	$\mathbf{6.1 \cdot 10^7}$	$\mathbf{8.75 \cdot 10^{-5}}$

1. Look at the examples above. To express a number in scientific notation, write it as a product so that the first factor is between __?__ and 10 and the second factor is a power of __?__.

2. Complete these examples.

a. $36{,}000 = \underline{?} \cdot 10^4$ **b.** $0.0085 = \underline{?} \cdot 10^{-3}$ **c.** $405{,}000 = \underline{?} \cdot 10^5$
d. $0.000125 = \underline{?} \cdot 10^{-4}$ **e.** $8{,}000{,}000 = \underline{?} \cdot 10^6$ **f.** $0.00009 = \underline{?} \cdot 10^{-5}$

EXERCISES

Give each missing exponent.

3. $40{,}000{,}000 = 4 \cdot 10^{?}$
4. $100{,}000 = 1 \cdot 10^{?}$
5. $326{,}000 = 3.26 \cdot 10^{?}$
6. $7{,}400{,}000 = 7.4 \cdot 10^{?}$
7. $83{,}700 = 8.37 \cdot 10^{?}$
8. $1420 = 1.42 \cdot 10^{?}$
9. $140{,}000 = 1.4 \cdot 10^{?}$
10. $32{,}040{,}000 = 3.204 \cdot 10^{?}$
11. $860{,}000{,}000 = 8.6 \cdot 10^{?}$
12. $23{,}450 = 2.345 \cdot 10^{?}$
13. $0.00039 = 3.9 \cdot 10^{?}$
14. $0.00008 = 8 \cdot 10^{?}$
15. $0.0000083 = 8.3 \cdot 10^{?}$
16. $0.00239 = 2.39 \cdot 10^{?}$
17. $0.032 = 3.2 \cdot 10^{?}$
18. $0.000302 = 3.02 \cdot 10^{?}$
19. $0.000000558 = 5.58 \cdot 10^{?}$
20. $0.00008 = 8 \cdot 10^{?}$

Write in scientific notation.

21. 31,000
22. 400,000
23. 5,460,000
24. 8800
25. 236,000
26. 85,000,000
27. 51,000
28. 9,634,000
29. 700,000,000
30. 302,000
31. 1,110,000
32. 70,000,000
33. 400
34. 82,000
35. 6,060,000
36. 327,400
37. 990,000
38. 1,830,000
39. 1400
40. 30,000
41. 0.00075
42. 0.00381
43. 0.00006
44. 0.00075
45. 0.0317
46. 0.0000043
47. 0.00649
48. 0.000045
49. 0.0012
50. 0.006632
51. 0.0375
52. 0.00002
53. 0.000025
54. 0.0125
55. 0.0000075
56. 0.0005

Write each number in scientific notation.

57. There are about 380,000,000,000 telephones in the world.
58. An average-size thundercloud holds about 6,000,000,000,000 raindrops.
59. The water level of the ocean rises about 0.0029 of a foot every year.
60. The thickness of a human hair is about 0.00366 of a foot.
61. Lightning strikes the earth about 8,640,000 times every day.
62. The sun is about 4,500,000,000 years old.
63. It takes 0.00025 of a second for a stick of dynamite to detonate.
64. The earth weighs about 11,980,000,000,000,000,000,000,000 pounds.

Solving Addition and Subtraction Equations

You have already solved equations such as

$$x + 37 = 54 \qquad y - 24 = 16$$

In this lesson you will use what you have learned about solving addition and subtraction equations to solve equations involving integers.

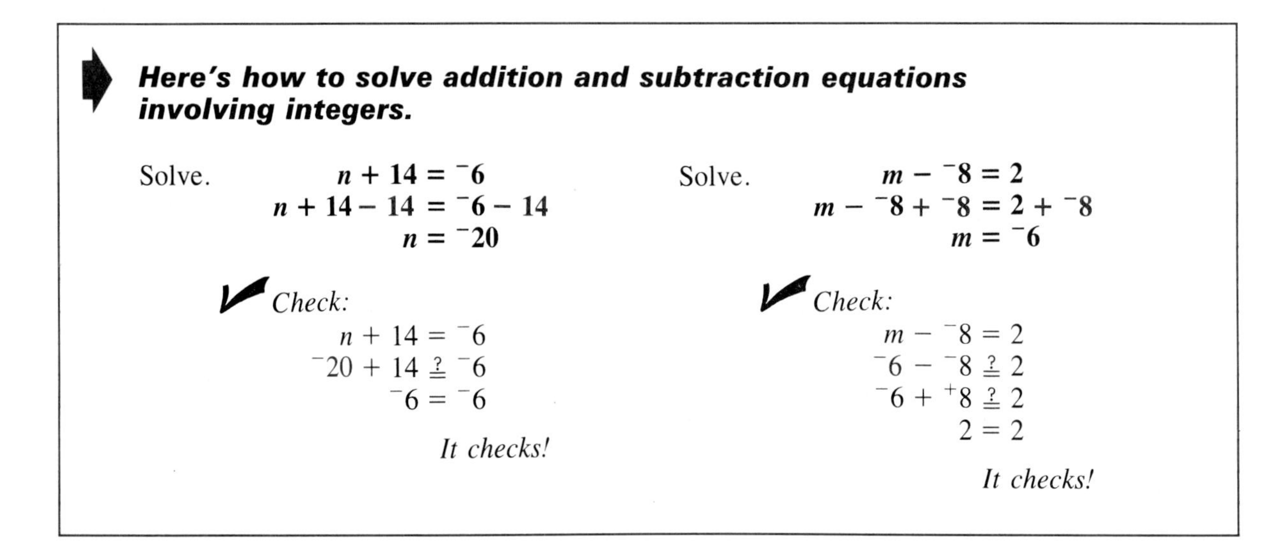

Here's how to solve addition and subtraction equations involving integers.

Solve.

$$\begin{aligned} n + 14 &= {}^-6 \\ n + 14 - 14 &= {}^-6 - 14 \\ n &= {}^-20 \end{aligned}$$

Check:

$$\begin{aligned} n + 14 &= {}^-6 \\ {}^-20 + 14 &\stackrel{?}{=} {}^-6 \\ {}^-6 &= {}^-6 \end{aligned}$$

It checks!

Solve.

$$\begin{aligned} m - {}^-8 &= 2 \\ m - {}^-8 + {}^-8 &= 2 + {}^-8 \\ m &= {}^-6 \end{aligned}$$

Check:

$$\begin{aligned} m - {}^-8 &= 2 \\ {}^-6 - {}^-8 &\stackrel{?}{=} 2 \\ {}^-6 + {}^+8 &\stackrel{?}{=} 2 \\ 2 &= 2 \end{aligned}$$

It checks!

1. Look at the examples above.

a. To find n, what number was subtracted from both sides of the equation? What does n equal?

b. To find m, what number was added to both sides of the equation? What does m equal?

c. To check the solution, what number was substituted for m in the equation $m - {}^-8 = 2$?

2. Complete these examples.

a.
$$\begin{aligned} r + {}^-4 &= 10 \\ r + {}^-4 - {}^-4 &= 10 - \underline{\ ?\ } \\ r &= 14 \end{aligned}$$

b.
$$\begin{aligned} s - 7 &= {}^-5 \\ s - 7 + \underline{\ ?\ } &= {}^-5 + 7 \\ s &= 2 \end{aligned}$$

c.
$$\begin{aligned} t + 8 &= {}^-20 \\ t + 8 - 8 &= {}^-20 - 8 \\ t &= \underline{\ ?\ } \end{aligned}$$

d.
$$\begin{aligned} {}^-28 &= u + {}^-10 \leftarrow \\ u + {}^-10 &= {}^-28 \leftarrow \\ u + {}^-10 - \underline{\ ?\ } &= {}^-28 - {}^-10 \\ u &= \underline{\ ?\ } \end{aligned}$$

symmetric property of equality

e.
$$\begin{aligned} 15 &= v - {}^-18 \\ v - {}^-18 &= 15 \\ v - {}^-18 + {}^-18 &= 15 + \underline{\ ?\ } \\ v &= \underline{\ ?\ } \end{aligned}$$

f.
$$\begin{aligned} 5 + w &= {}^-10 \\ w + \underline{\ ?\ } &= {}^-10 \\ w + 5 - 5 &= {}^-10 - \underline{\ ?\ } \\ w &= \underline{\ ?\ } \end{aligned}$$

EXERCISES

▶ **Solve and check.**

Here are scrambled answers for the next two rows of exercises:
$^{-}10$ 14 26 $^{-}17$ 0 $^{-}32$ 21 $^{-}19$

3. $f + 12 = {}^{-}5$	**4.** $b + {}^{-}4 = 10$	**5.** ${}^{-}12 = y + 20$	**6.** $12 + z = 2$
7. $x - 6 = 15$	**8.** $w + {}^{-}6 = 20$	**9.** ${}^{-}23 = r - 4$	**10.** $p - {}^{-}2 = 2$
11. $r + 15 = {}^{-}25$	**12.** $k + 20 = 0$	**13.** $0 = c + {}^{-}46$	**14.** $5 + p = {}^{-}8$
15. $s - 19 = 18$	**16.** $g - 5 = {}^{-}6$	**17.** ${}^{-}40 = b - 35$	**18.** $n - 25 = 38$
19. $x + 16 = 9$	**20.** $d + {}^{-}18 = 4$	**21.** $a + 18 = {}^{-}15$	**22.** $n + {}^{-}4 = {}^{-}9$
23. $p - 8 = {}^{-}3$	**24.** $m - 8 = {}^{-}2$	**25.** $t - 1 = 5$	**26.** $x - 45 = 54$
27. $m + 6 = {}^{-}8$	**28.** ${}^{-}1 = q + 9$	**29.** ${}^{-}32 + b = 0$	**30.** $e + 10 = 3$
31. $c - {}^{-}7 = {}^{-}3$	**32.** $m - 100 = 0$	**33.** $a - {}^{-}2 = 9$	**34.** ${}^{-}11 = y - 6$
35. $w + {}^{-}3 = {}^{-}9$	**36.** $6 + y = {}^{-}2$	**37.** $10 = y + {}^{-}10$	**38.** ${}^{-}13 = s + 14$
39. $y - 17 = 14$	**40.** ${}^{-}4 = b - 3$	**41.** $y - 20 = 1$	**42.** $n - 4 = {}^{-}1$
43. $t + 5 = 1$	**44.** ${}^{-}2 = y + 6$	**45.** ${}^{-}10 + y = {}^{-}10$	**46.** $s + {}^{-}14 = {}^{-}13$
47. $n - {}^{-}7 = 16$	**48.** $4 = z - 5$	**49.** $0 = d - {}^{-}8$	**50.** $w - 6 = 20$
51. $a + 3 = 3$	**52.** ${}^{-}4 = {}^{-}9 + n$	**53.** ${}^{-}7 = b - 5$	**54.** $t - 8 = 8$

Problem Solving

▶ **Decide which equation would be used to solve each problem. Then solve the problem.**

Equation A: $30 + n = 20$
Equation B: ${}^{-}30 + n = 20$
Equation C: $30 + n = {}^{-}20$
Equation D: ${}^{-}30 + n = {}^{-}20$

55. In a card game, Randy made 30 points on his first hand. After the second hand, his total score was 20 points. What was his score on the second hand?

56. A checking account had a balance of $^{-}30$ dollars. (It was overdrawn.) After a deposit was made, the account had a balance of 20 dollars. How much money was deposited?

57. The temperature at 2 P.M. was 30°F. By 11 P.M. it had changed to $^{-}20$°F. What was the change in temperature?

58. A scuba diver is at the $^{-}30$-foot level. How many feet will she have to rise to be at the $^{-}20$ foot level?

59. The sum of a number and $^{-}30$ is 20. What is the number?

60. When a number is added to 30, the sum is $^{-}20$. What is the number?

61. 30 increased by a number is 20. What is the number?

62. $^{-}30$ plus a number equals 20. What is the number?

Solving Multiplication and Division Equations

Remember that multiplication and division are inverse operations. That is, division undoes multiplication and multiplication undoes division.

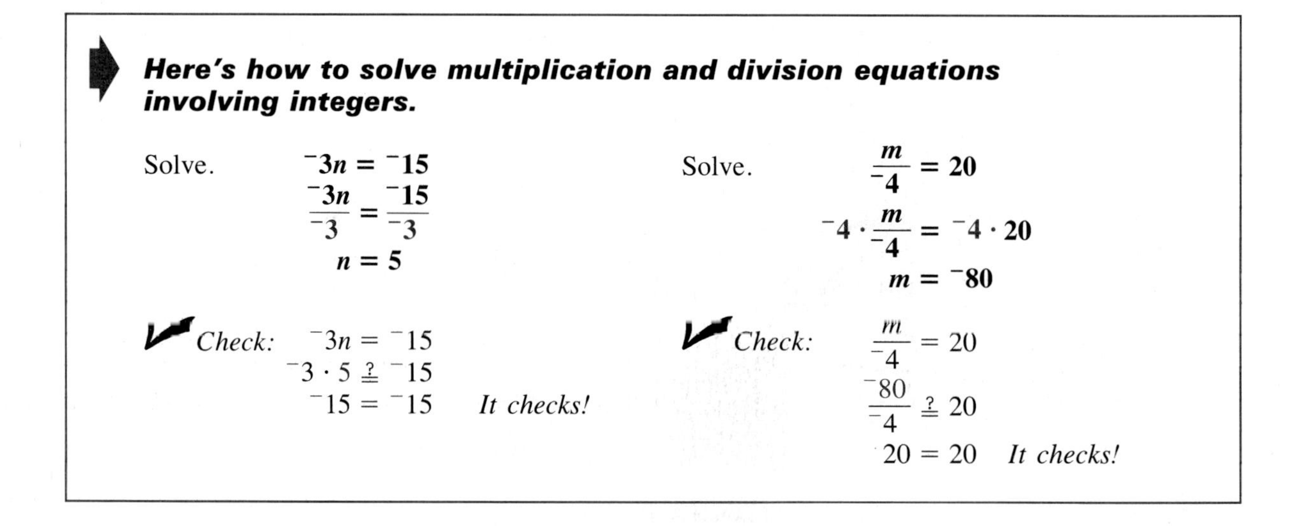

Here's how to solve multiplication and division equations involving integers.

Solve. $\mathbf{{}^{-}3n = {}^{-}15}$

$$\frac{{}^{-}3n}{{}^{-}3} = \frac{{}^{-}15}{{}^{-}3}$$

$$n = 5$$

Check:

$${}^{-}3n = {}^{-}15$$

$${}^{-}3 \cdot 5 \stackrel{?}{=} {}^{-}15$$

$${}^{-}15 = {}^{-}15$$

It checks!

Solve. $\mathbf{\frac{m}{{}^{-}4} = 20}$

$${}^{-}4 \cdot \frac{m}{{}^{-}4} = {}^{-}4 \cdot 20$$

$$m = {}^{-}80$$

Check:

$$\frac{m}{{}^{-}4} = 20$$

$$\frac{{}^{-}80}{{}^{-}4} \stackrel{?}{=} 20$$

$$20 = 20$$

It checks!

1. Look at the examples above.

a. To find n, both sides of the equation were divided by what number? What does n equal?

b. To find m, both sides of the equation were multiplied by what number? What does m equal?

c. To check the solution, what number was substituted for m in the equation $\frac{m}{{}^{-}4} = 20$?

2. Complete these examples.

a. $9r = {}^{-}72$

$$\frac{9r}{9} = \frac{{}^{-}72}{9}$$

$$r = \underline{\ ?\ }$$

b. $\frac{s}{7} = {}^{-}3$

$$7 \cdot \frac{s}{7} = 7 \cdot {}^{-}3$$

$$s = \underline{\ ?\ }$$

c. ${}^{-}12t = 60$

$$\frac{{}^{-}12t}{{}^{-}12} = \frac{60}{?}$$

$$t = \underline{\ ?\ }$$

d. $42 = {}^{-}6t$

$${}^{-}6t = 42$$

$$\frac{{}^{-}6t}{?} = \frac{42}{{}^{-}6}$$

$$t = \underline{\ ?\ }$$

e. ${}^{-}5 = \frac{u}{{}^{-}3}$

$$\frac{u}{{}^{-}3} = {}^{-}5$$

$${}^{-}3 \cdot \frac{u}{{}^{-}3} = \underline{\ ?\ } \cdot {}^{-}5$$

$$u = \underline{\ ?\ }$$

f. $7 = \frac{v}{{}^{-}5}$

$$\frac{v}{{}^{-}5} = \underline{\ ?\ }$$

$${}^{-}5 \cdot \frac{v}{{}^{-}5} = \underline{\ ?\ } \cdot 7$$

$$v = \underline{\ ?\ }$$

EXERCISES

▶ **Solve and check.**
Here are scrambled answers for the next row of exercises: 7 ⁻1 ⁻3 22 ⁻8

3. $^{-}2x = 6$ **4.** $30t = {}^{-}30$ **5.** $^{-}21 = {}^{-}3t$ **6.** $9y = {}^{-}72$ **7.** $^{-}330 = {}^{-}15y$

8. $\frac{b}{^{-}3} = 4$ **9.** $\frac{n}{6} = {}^{-}3$ **10.** $\frac{n}{^{-}2} = {}^{-}5$ **11.** $15 = \frac{a}{2}$ **12.** $0 = \frac{n}{6}$

13. $^{-}4s = {}^{-}40$ **14.** $57 = 3t$ **15.** $^{-}6c = {}^{-}66$ **16.** $7n = {}^{-}7$ **17.** $^{-}192 = {}^{-}24w$

18. $\frac{x}{4} = {}^{-}9$ **19.** $9 = \frac{n}{^{-}7}$ **20.** $\frac{y}{^{-}10} = 5$ **21.** $\frac{t}{^{-}8} = {}^{-}1$ **22.** $^{-}11 = \frac{y}{^{-}6}$

23. $7h = {}^{-}77$ **24.** $^{-}5 = {}^{-}5c$ **25.** $15t = 30$ **26.** $^{-}9w = 270$ **27.** $32j = 0$

▶ **Solve and check.**
Here are scrambled answers for the next row of exercises: 19 ⁻3 ⁻7 ⁻12

28. $n + 7 = 4$ **29.** $t - 12 = 7$ **30.** $^{-}6n = 42$ **31.** $a + 6 = {}^{-}6$

32. $\frac{x}{3} = {}^{-}6$ **33.** $m - 9 = {}^{-}8$ **34.** $^{-}9x = {}^{-}81$ **35.** $\frac{r}{^{-}5} = {}^{-}2$

36. $5g = {}^{-}25$ **37.** $40 = {}^{-}10b$ **38.** $12 = {}^{-}6 + r$ **39.** $t - 15 = {}^{-}10$

40. $\frac{y}{8} = {}^{-}3$ **41.** $^{-}20 = \frac{y}{^{-}10}$

42. $3 + r = {}^{-}3$ **43.** $h - 11 = 3$

44. $^{-}55 = {}^{-}5g$ **45.** $\frac{t}{9} = 11$

46. $c + 7 = {}^{-}3$ **47.** $d - 4 = {}^{-}5$

Problem Solving

You can use this formula to find a football player's average rushing yardage.

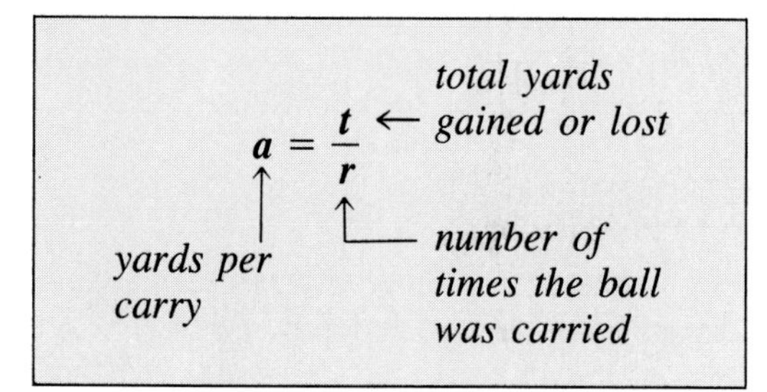

48. Substitute in the formula to complete this chart.

	Total Yardage *(t)*	Number of Carries *(r)*	Yards per Carry *(a)*
a.	56	7	?
b.	⁻32	8	?
c.	?	12	3
d.	?	9	⁻2

Solving Two-Step Equations

Starting at 35 feet below the surface ($^{-}35$ feet), a diver begins descending, moving at a rate of $^{-}15$ feet per minute. At that rate, how many minutes will it take him to reach a depth of $^{-}140$ feet?

1. At what depth was the diver before he started descending at a rate of $^{-}15$ feet per minute?

2. This equation can be used to find how many minutes it will take the diver to reach a depth of $^{-}140$ feet.

$$\underset{\substack{\uparrow \\ \textit{minutes} \\ \textit{of descent}}}{\overset{\substack{\textit{rate of} \\ \textit{descent} \\ \downarrow}}{^{-}15}m} + \overset{\substack{\textit{starting} \\ \textit{depth} \\ \swarrow}}{^{-}35} = \underset{\substack{\uparrow \\ \textit{final} \\ \textit{depth}}}{^{-}140}$$

Look at the equation. What does the variable m represent?

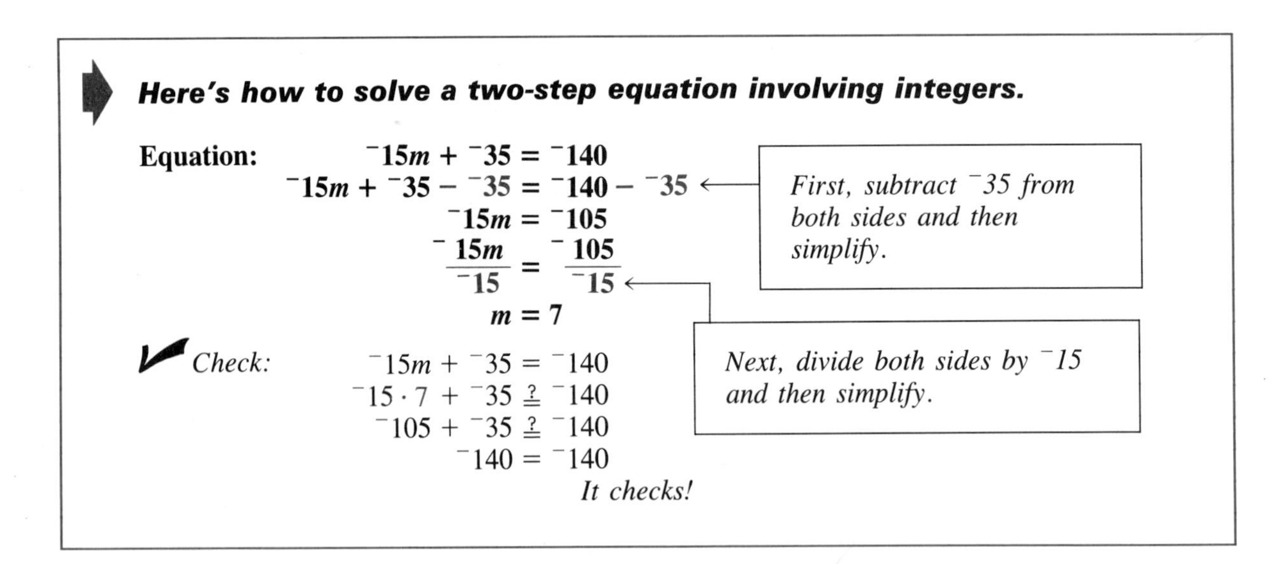

Here's how to solve a two-step equation involving integers.

Equation:

$$\begin{aligned} ^{-}15m + {}^{-}35 &= {}^{-}140 \\ ^{-}15m + {}^{-}35 - {}^{-}35 &= {}^{-}140 - {}^{-}35 \\ ^{-}15m &= {}^{-}105 \\ \frac{^{-}15m}{^{-}15} &= \frac{^{-}105}{^{-}15} \\ m &= 7 \end{aligned}$$

First, subtract $^{-}35$ from both sides and then simplify.

Next, divide both sides by $^{-}15$ and then simplify.

Check:

$$\begin{aligned} ^{-}15m + {}^{-}35 &= {}^{-}140 \\ ^{-}15 \cdot 7 + {}^{-}35 &\stackrel{?}{=} {}^{-}140 \\ ^{-}105 + {}^{-}35 &\stackrel{?}{=} {}^{-}140 \\ ^{-}140 &= {}^{-}140 \end{aligned}$$

It checks!

3. Look at the example above. To find m, first subtract __?__ from both sides of the equation and then divide both sides by __?__ .

4. Check the solution. How many minutes will it take the diver to descend to a depth of $^{-}140$ feet?

▶ **Copy and finish solving each equation. Check your solution.**

5.
$$^{-}4c - 80 = {}^{-}60$$
$$^{-}4c - 80 + 80 = {}^{-}60 + \underline{?}$$
$$^{-}4c = \underline{?}$$
$$\frac{^{-}4c}{^{-}4} = \frac{20}{?}$$
$$c = \underline{?}$$

6.
$$\frac{d}{^{-}6} + 14 = 26$$
$$\frac{d}{^{-}6} + 14 - \underline{?} = 26 - 14$$
$$\frac{d}{^{-}6} = \underline{?}$$
$$\underline{?} \cdot \frac{d}{^{-}6} = {}^{-}6 \cdot 12$$
$$d = \underline{?}$$

7.
$$\frac{e}{4} - 8 = {}^{-}40$$
$$\frac{e}{4} - 8 + 8 = {}^{-}40 + \underline{?}$$
$$\frac{e}{4} = \underline{?}$$
$$4 \cdot \frac{e}{4} = \underline{?} \cdot {}^{-}32$$
$$e = \underline{?}$$

▶ **Solve and check.**
Here are scrambled answers for the next two rows of exercises:
⁻16 5 2 ⁻14 ⁻3 ⁻12 ⁻4 ⁻35

8. $5n - 30 = {}^{-}20$ **9.** $^{-}3m + 5 = {}^{-}10$ **10.** $2d - 14 = {}^{-}20$ **11.** $9e + 6 = {}^{-}30$

12. $\frac{m}{2} + 5 = {}^{-}2$ **13.** $\frac{f}{^{-}3} + 2 = 6$ **14.** $\frac{h}{4} + 6 = 2$ **15.** $\frac{j}{^{-}5} - 3 = 4$

16. $3r + 8 = 2$ **17.** $^{-}5t + 10 = {}^{-}15$ **18.** $^{-}4u - 2 = {}^{-}30$ **19.** $\frac{m}{3} + 7 = 5$

20. $\frac{n}{3} + 20 = 18$ **21.** $\frac{y}{^{-}4} - 2 = 10$ **22.** $\frac{s}{^{-}7} + 3 = 4$ **23.** $\frac{n}{7} + {}^{-}5 = 0$

24. $3y - 5 = 7$ **25.** $^{-}5t + 7 = 27$ **26.** $6a - 12 = {}^{-}36$ **27.** $^{-}4x + 8 = 0$

28. $\frac{d}{3} - 4 = 5$ **29.** $\frac{n}{^{-}2} + 7 = 8$ **30.** $\frac{m}{^{-}4} - 3 = {}^{-}4$ **31.** $\frac{y}{^{-}6} - 3 = 4$

32. $^{-}3q - 4 = 5$ **33.** $2r - {}^{-}6 = {}^{-}4$ **34.** $^{-}7b + 10 = {}^{-}11$ **35.** $5c - 2 = {}^{-}37$

36. $\frac{t}{^{-}3} - 2 = {}^{-}4$ **37.** $\frac{m}{5} - {}^{-}6 = {}^{-}1$ **38.** $\frac{n}{9} + {}^{-}7 = 0$ **39.** $\frac{y}{^{-}4} + {}^{-}8 = 1$

40. $^{-}3r + 9 = 0$ **41.** $^{-}7s + 10 = {}^{-}4$ **42.** $6t - 8 = {}^{-}20$ **43.** $^{-}9w + 8 = 8$

Challenge

▶ **Use the clues to complete each sentence.**

44. The deepest-diving bird, the emperor penguin, can reach a depth of ___?___ feet.

Clues:
- The number is between ⁻810 and ⁻899.
- One of its digits is a 0.
- Its digits add to 15.

45. The deepest-diving mammal, the bull sperm whale, can reach a depth of ___?___ feet.

Clues:
- The number is between ⁻3710 and ⁻3910.
- One of its digits is a 2.
- Its digits add to 12.

Problem Solving—Using Equations

Earlier you have written equations to solve problems involving whole numbers. In this lesson you will write equations involving integers.

Here's how to use an equation to solve a problem.

Problem: Chicago's highest temperature was 123°F more than Chicago's lowest temperature. The highest temperature was 104°F. What was Chicago's lowest temperature?

Step 1. Choose a variable. Use it and the facts to represent the numbers in the problem.

Let n = Chicago's lowest temperature.
Then $n + 123$ = Chicago's highest temperature.

Step 2. Write an equation based on the facts.

$$\underbrace{n + 123} = 104$$

These are two equal expressions for Chicago's highest temperature.

Step 3. Solve the equation.

$$n + 123 = 104$$
$$n + 123 - 123 = 104 - 123$$
$$n = {}^{-}19$$

1. Look at the example above.

a. In Step 1, we let n equal Chicago's ? temperature. Then Chicago's highest temperature equals n + ? .

b. In Step 2, the two equal expressions for Chicago's highest temperature are ? and ? .

c. An equation for the problem is ? .

d. To solve the equation, ? was subtracted from both sides of the equation.

2. To check the solution, ask yourself whether the answer fits the facts in the problem. Was Chicago's lowest temperature $^{-}19$°F?

Read the facts. Then complete the steps to answer the question.

3. *Facts:* A record for extreme temperatures in a 24-hour period was set in Browning, Montana, in 1916. The temperature dropped 100 degrees. The low temperature was $^{-}56$°F.

Question: What was the high temperature?

a. If you let t equal the high temperature, then $t - \underline{?}$ equals the low temperature.

b. Two equal expressions for the low temperature are $t - \underline{?}$ and $^{-}56$.

c. To find the high temperature, you can solve the equation $t - 100 = \underline{?}$.

d. Solve the equation in part c. The high temperature was $\underline{?}$.

4. *Facts:* A most unusual rise in temperature occurred on January 22, 1943, in Spearfish, South Dakota. From 7:30 A.M. to 7:32 A.M. the temperature rose 49°F. The temperature at 7:32 was 45°F.

Question: What was the temperature at 7:30?

a. If you let n equal the temperature at 7:30 A.M., then $n + \underline{?}$ equals the temperature at 7:32 A.M.

b. Two equal expressions for the temperature at 7:32 A.M. are $n + \underline{?}$ and 45.

c. To find the temperature at 7:30 A.M., you can solve the equation $n + 49 = \underline{?}$.

d. Solve the equation in part c. The temperature at 7:30 A.M. was $\underline{?}$.

Write an equation and solve the problem.

5. A number increased by 9 equals $^{-}7$. What is the number?
(Let d = the number.)

6. A number decreased by 5 equals $^{-}9$. What is the number?
(Let e = the number.)

7. A number times $^{-}12$ equals $^{-}72$. What is the number?
(Let f = the number.)

8. A number divided by 8 equals $^{-}25$. What is the number?
(Let g = the number.)

9. The sum of two numbers is $^{-}12$. One of the numbers is $^{-}9$. What is the other number?
(Let j = the other number.)

10. The product of two numbers is $^{-}85$. One of the numbers is 5. What is the other number?
(Let k = the other number.)

11. Multiply a number by 4, then subtract 8, and you get $^{-}32$. What is the number?
(Let t = the number.)

12. Divide a number by $^{-}6$, then add 12, and you get 19. What is the number?
(Let u = the number.)

13. From last night to this morning the temperature dropped 18°F. The temperature this morning was 7°F. What was the temperature last night?
(Let n = the temperature last night.)

14. From this morning to this afternoon, the temperature rose 21°F. The temperature this afternoon was 12°F. What was the temperature this morning?
(Let m = the temperature this morning.)

Cumulative Skill Practice

▶ **Give the product in simplest form.** *(page 172)*

1. $\frac{1}{3} \cdot \frac{1}{n}$ **2.** $\frac{3}{8} \cdot \frac{1}{3}$ **3.** $6 \cdot \frac{2}{3}$ **4.** $\frac{5}{16} \cdot \frac{4}{3}$ **5.** $\frac{5}{8} \cdot \frac{12}{7}$

6. $\frac{y}{3} \cdot \frac{1}{y}$ **7.** $18 \cdot \frac{z}{3}$ **8.** $\frac{5}{8} \cdot \frac{4z}{5}$ **9.** $\frac{3}{4j} \cdot \frac{6}{5k}$ **10.** $\frac{r}{s} \cdot \frac{2s}{5r}$

11. $\frac{m}{n^2} \cdot \frac{3n}{m}$ **12.** $\frac{s}{t} \cdot \frac{t}{s}$ **13.** $\frac{a}{b} \cdot \frac{b^2}{5}$ **14.** $\frac{5y}{x} \cdot \frac{x}{2z}$ **15.** $\frac{4m}{n} \cdot \frac{5n}{10m^2}$

▶ **Give the quotient in simplest form.** *(page 176)*

16. $\frac{5}{4} \div \frac{1}{4}$ **17.** $\frac{4}{9} \div \frac{2}{5}$ **18.** $\frac{5}{6} \div \frac{8}{3}$ **19.** $\frac{4}{5} \div 3$ **20.** $\frac{9}{8} \div \frac{3}{4}$

21. $\frac{3}{x} \div \frac{2}{x}$ **22.** $\frac{6}{r} \div \frac{3}{s}$ **23.** $\frac{m}{6} \div \frac{n}{9}$ **24.** $\frac{2a}{b} \div \frac{a}{5}$ **25.** $\frac{m}{n} \div \frac{3n}{2}$

26. $\frac{4y}{z} \div \frac{2y}{z}$ **27.** $\frac{p}{r} \div \frac{2q}{3s}$ **28.** $\frac{s}{t} \div \frac{s^2}{t}$ **29.** $\frac{a}{5b} \div \frac{a^2}{10b}$ **30.** $\frac{12x}{3y} \div \frac{4x}{6y^2}$

▶ **Solve. Give the answer in simplest form.** *(page 182)*

31. $\frac{1}{3}$ of $24 = n$ **32.** $\frac{1}{2}$ of $42 = n$ **33.** $\frac{3}{4}$ of $40 = n$ **34.** $\frac{2}{3}$ of $36 = n$

35. $\frac{5}{8}$ of $32 = n$ **36.** $\frac{5}{6}$ of $60 = n$ **37.** $\frac{5}{2}$ of $20 = n$ **38.** $\frac{7}{8}$ of $56 = n$

39. $\frac{4}{5}$ of $16 = n$ **40.** $\frac{9}{2}$ of $21 = n$ **41.** $\frac{7}{4}$ of $25 = n$ **42.** $\frac{3}{5}$ of $34 = n$

▶ **Complete.** *(page 184)*

43. $2\frac{1}{4}$ ft = __?__ in. **44.** $2\frac{2}{3}$ yd = __?__ ft **45.** $2\frac{3}{4}$ yd = __?__ in. **46.** $2\frac{2}{3}$ days = __?__ h

47. $1\frac{2}{5}$ min = __?__ s **48.** $2\frac{3}{10}$ h = __?__ min **49.** $1\frac{1}{2}$ gal = __?__ qt **50.** $1\frac{1}{2}$ qt = __?__ c

▶ **Solve. Give the answer in simplest form.** *(page 186)*

51. $\frac{1}{2}n = 6$ **52.** $\frac{1}{4}n = 15$ **53.** $\frac{3}{4}n = 36$ **54.** $\frac{2}{3}n = 42$

55. $\frac{3}{8}n = 33$ **56.** $\frac{3}{2}n = 48$ **57.** $\frac{7}{4}n = 49$ **58.** $\frac{5}{2}n = 65$

59. $\frac{5}{12}n = 31$ **60.** $\frac{5}{6}n = 48$ **61.** $\frac{4}{5}n = 72$ **62.** $\frac{5}{4}n = 72$

Problem Solving—Applications

TV COMMERCIALS		
Time Slot	Price per minute	
	Local Station	National Network
9:00–noon	$200	$35,000
12:30–3:30	360	60,000
3:30–5:30	440	75,000
7:00–10:00	800	150,000
10:30–midnight	480	90,000

Use the information in the chart to solve the problem.

1. During the 9:00–noon time slot, one minute of commercial time on the local TV station costs $200. What is the cost for the same time on the national TV network?
2. What does it cost to buy 4 minutes of commercial time on the local TV station during the 3:30–5:30 time slot?
3. What does it cost to buy $1\frac{1}{2}$ minutes of commercial time on the national TV network during the 7:00–10:00 time slot?
4. Is $500 enough money to buy $1\frac{1}{2}$ minutes of commercial time on the local TV station during the 12:30–3:30 time slot?
5. During what time slot would 3 minutes of commercial time on the local TV station cost a total of $1440?
6. During what time slot would $2\frac{1}{2}$ minutes of commercial time on the national TV network cost a total of $187,500?

When the local TV station televises a football game, it sells commercial time to advertisers. Suppose the game costs $4500 to televise and there are 15 minutes of commercial time. To find the profit the station will make from televising the game, you can use the formula at the right.

$$P = 15n - 4500$$

↑ *Profit* (P) ↑ *price per minute* (n)

Use the formula to solve these problems.

7. How much profit will the TV station make on the game if the price for one minute of commercial time is $360?
8. Find the profit if the price for one minute of commercial time is $440.
9. If the price for one minute of commercial time is $250, will the TV station make a profit or take a loss on the game? How much of a profit or a loss?
10. To make a profit of $4500 on televising the game, how much must the TV station charge per minute of commercial time?

Chapter Review

Here are scrambled answers for the review exercises:

$^{-}15$	$^{-}4$	1	add	greater	negative	same
$^{-}10$	$^{-}3$	5	combining	larger	nonzero	simplify
$^{-}8$	$^{-}1$	10	different	less	opposite	subtract
$^{-}6$	0	15	divide	multiply	positive	

1. As you move to the right on the number line shown below, the integers get __?__ .

$^{-}4 \quad ^{-}3 \quad ^{-}2 \quad ^{-}1 \quad 0 \quad ^{+}1 \quad ^{+}2 \quad ^{+}3 \quad ^{+}4$

$^{-}2$ is __?__ than $^{-}1$.
$^{+}3$ is __?__ than 0. *(page 196)*

2. To add integers you can think about __?__ charges.

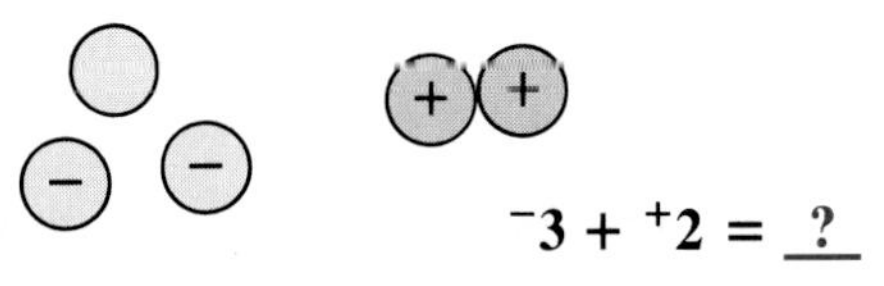

$\mathbf{^{-}3 + {}^{+}2 =}$ __?__

If the sum of two numbers is 0, then one number is the __?__ of the other. *(page 198)*

3. To subtract an integer, __?__ the opposite of the integer. To subtract $^{+}6$, you would add __?__.
$\mathbf{^{-}4 - {}^{+}6 =}$ __?__ *(page 200)*

4. The product of two integers with the same signs is __?__. The product of two integers with different signs is __?__. The product of any integer and 0 is __?__. $\mathbf{^{-}8 \cdot {}^{+}1 =}$ __?__ *(page 202)*

5. The quotient of two integers with the __?__ sign is positive. The quotient of two integers with __?__ signs is negative. The quotient of 0 divided by any __?__ integer is 0.
$\mathbf{^{+}24 \div {}^{-}6 =}$ __?__ *(page 204)*

6. To express a number in scientific notation, you write it as a product so that the first factor is between __?__ and 10 and the second factor is a power of __?__.

$\mathbf{390{,}000 = 3.9 \times 10^{?}}$ $\qquad$ $\mathbf{0.00465 = 4.65 \times 10^{?}}$ *(page 208)*

7. To solve the equation $\mathbf{x + {}^{-}12 = {}^{-}3}$, you would first __?__ $^{-}12$ from both sides and then __?__ both sides. *(page 210)*

8. To solve the equation $\mathbf{^{-}15y = 60}$, you would first __?__ both sides by __?__ and then simplify both sides. *(page 212)*

9. To solve the equation $\mathbf{\frac{t}{^{-}5} - 15 = {}^{-}6}$, you would first add __?__ to both sides and then simplify both sides. Next you would __?__ both sides by $^{-}5$ and simplify both sides. *(page 214)*

Chapter Test

▶ $<$ or $>$? *(page 196)*

1. ${}^{+}8$ ◆ ${}^{+}11$	**2.** ${}^{-}8$ ◆ ${}^{-}11$	**3.** 0 ◆ ${}^{-}9$	**4.** ${}^{-}6$ ◆ ${}^{+}5$

▶ **Give the sum or difference.** *(pages 198, 200)*

5. ${}^{+}8 + {}^{+}9$	**6.** ${}^{+}11 + {}^{-}4$	**7.** ${}^{-}16 + {}^{-}10$	**8.** ${}^{-}12 + {}^{+}12$
9. ${}^{+}11 - {}^{+}7$	**10.** ${}^{+}15 - {}^{-}12$	**11.** ${}^{-}20 - {}^{+}6$	**12.** ${}^{-}14 - {}^{-}22$

▶ **Give the product or quotient.** *(pages 202, 204)*

13. ${}^{+}6 \cdot {}^{-}3$	**14.** ${}^{-}10 \cdot {}^{-}6$	**15.** ${}^{-}8 \cdot {}^{+}5$	**16.** ${}^{+}6 \cdot {}^{+}9$
17. ${}^{+}21 \div {}^{+}3$	**18.** ${}^{+}42 \div {}^{-}6$	**19.** $0 \div {}^{-}9$	**20.** ${}^{-}60 \div {}^{-}12$

▶ **Write in scientific notation.** *(page 208)*

21. 27,000	**22.** 500,000	**23.** 3,200,000	**24.** 683,000,000
25. 0.0054	**26.** 0.0381	**27.** 0.00067	**28.** 0.0000097

▶ **Solve and check.** *(pages 210, 212, 214)*

29. $f + 11 = 8$	**30.** $13 + g = {}^{-}4$	**31.** $s - {}^{-}2 = 8$	**32.** ${}^{-}3 = g - {}^{-}8$
33. ${}^{-}3k = 42$	**34.** ${}^{-}9m = {}^{-}90$	**35.** $\frac{t}{{}^{-}2} = 16$	**36.** ${}^{-}21 = \frac{v}{{}^{-}4}$
37. $4n - 8 = {}^{-}48$	**38.** ${}^{-}5m + 8 = {}^{-}2$	**39.** $6k + 3 = 3$	**40.** ${}^{-}12j - {}^{-}3 = {}^{-}45$
41. $\frac{x}{6} + 3 = 3$	**42.** $\frac{w}{{}^{-}4} - 8 = 2$	**43.** $\frac{c}{{}^{-}3} - {}^{-}4 = 10$	**44.** $\frac{f}{{}^{-}5} + {}^{-}3 = 15$

▶ **First choose the equation and solve the problem. Then reread the problem to see if your answer makes sense.**

Equation A: $n + 5 = {}^{-}10$
Equation B: $n - 5 = {}^{-}10$
Equation C: $5n = {}^{-}10$
Equation D: $\frac{n}{5} = {}^{-}10$

45. The product of two numbers is ${}^{-}10$. One of the numbers is 5. What is the other number?

46. The sum of two numbers is ${}^{-}10$. One of the numbers is 5. What is the other number?

47. A number divided by 5 equals ${}^{-}10$. What is the number?

48. A number increased by 5 equals ${}^{-}10$. What is the number?

Cumulative Test

Standardized Format

▶ **Choose the correct letter.**

1. The prime factorization of 72 is

A. $8 \cdot 9$
B. $2^3 \cdot 9$
C. $2^3 \cdot 3^2$
D. none of these

2. The greatest common factor of $18x^2y$ and $27xy^2$ is

A. $9x^2y^2$
B. $9xy^2$
C. $9x^2y$
D. none of these

3. The least common denominator of $\frac{x}{8y}$ and $\frac{x}{12y^2}$ is

A. $4y$
B. $24y^2$
C. $24y$
D. none of these

4. $\frac{12ab^2}{9b}$ written in simplest form is

A. $\frac{4ab}{3}$
B. $\frac{4ab^2}{3b}$
C. $\frac{4ab^2}{3}$
D. none of these

5. Give the sum.

$\frac{r}{6} + \frac{s}{9}$

A. $\frac{r+s}{15}$
B. $\frac{r+s}{18}$
C. $\frac{2r+s}{18}$
D. none of these

6. Give the difference.

$\frac{2m}{9} - \frac{n}{4}$

A. $\frac{2m-n}{5}$
B. $\frac{2m-n}{36}$
C. $\frac{8m-9n}{36}$
D. none of these

7. Give the product.

$\frac{x}{y} \cdot \frac{y}{3z}$

A. $\frac{x}{3z}$
B. $\frac{3xz}{y^2}$
C. $\frac{y^2}{3xz}$
D. none of these

8. Give the quotient.

$\frac{j^2}{4k} \div \frac{j}{8k}$

A. $\frac{j^3}{8k}$
B. $\frac{j}{2}$
C. $\frac{2}{j}$
D. none of these

9. Solve.

$\frac{5}{6}$ of $n = 36$

A. 30
B. 36
C. $43\frac{1}{5}$
D. none of these

10. $4\frac{3}{5}$ min = __?__ s

A. 276
B. 270
C. 138
D. none of these

11. Solve.

$\frac{7}{5}n = 50$

A. 70
B. $35\frac{5}{7}$
C. 35
D. none of these

12. Choose the equation.

You bought an \$18 shirt and 3 pairs of blue jeans. You spent a total of \$69. How much did you pay for each pair of jeans?

A. $\frac{j}{3} + 18 = 69$
B. $\frac{j}{3} - 18 = 69$
C. $3j - 18 = 69$
D. $3j + 18 = 69$

9 Rational Numbers and Equations

$b = c \cdot h \cdot w$

The number of calories a person burns during an activity equals the number of calories burned per pound in one hour (for that activity) times the number of hours times the person's weight in pounds.

(page 245)

One hour of dancing burns 2.2 calories per pound. A 120-pound person burns 132 calories during a half hour of dancing, while a 150-pound person burns 165 calories.

Rational Numbers

A number that can be written as the quotient of two integers (divisor not 0) is called a **rational number.**

A rational number is used to show the net change in the price of a stock (the difference between yesterday's closing price and today's closing price). If a stock had a net change of $^{+}\frac{1}{2}$, the price of each share went **up** $\frac{1}{2}$ of a dollar. If a stock had a net change of $^{-}1\frac{1}{8}$, the price of each share went **down** $1\frac{1}{8}$ dollars.

DAILY STOCK QUOTATIONS

Stock	Close	Net Change
Disney	52	$^{+}\frac{1}{2}$
DuPont	55	$^{+}\frac{1}{4}$
Exxon	$42\frac{1}{2}$	$^{-}\frac{3}{8}$
Ford	$44\frac{1}{8}$	$^{+}1\frac{1}{4}$
IBM	$125\frac{1}{4}$	$^{-}1\frac{1}{8}$
Kroger	$35\frac{7}{8}$	$^{+}\frac{3}{4}$
Mobil	$32\frac{3}{4}$	$^{-}1$
Sears	$34\frac{5}{8}$	$^{+}\frac{3}{8}$
TWA	$10\frac{1}{4}$	$^{+}1\frac{1}{2}$

1. What was the net change of DuPont? Of Mobil?
2. Which company had the greater gain, Disney or Kroger?

Here's how to compare two rational numbers. Notice that we will not use the raised plus sign when writing a positive rational number.

$^{-}2 \quad ^{-}1\frac{1}{2} \quad ^{-}1\frac{1}{8} \quad ^{-}1 \quad ^{-}\frac{3}{8} \quad 0 \quad \frac{1}{4} \quad \frac{3}{8} \quad \frac{1}{2} \quad \frac{3}{4} \quad 1 \quad 1\frac{1}{4} \quad 1\frac{1}{2} \quad 2$

As you move to the **right** on this number line, the rational numbers get **larger.**

As you move to the **left,** the rational numbers get **smaller.**

The number line shows that

$$^{-}1\frac{1}{8} < {}^{-}\frac{3}{8} \qquad {}^{-}\frac{3}{8} < 0 \qquad \frac{3}{4} > \frac{1}{4} \qquad 1\frac{1}{2} > {}^{-}2$$

To compare rational numbers with different denominators, compare equivalent rational numbers with the same denominator.

$$\frac{3}{8} \blacklozenge \frac{1}{2} \qquad {}^{-}\frac{2}{3} \blacklozenge {}^{-}\frac{3}{4} \qquad 2\frac{1}{3} \blacklozenge 2\frac{3}{8}$$

$$\frac{3}{8} < \frac{4}{8} \qquad {}^{-}\frac{8}{12} > {}^{-}\frac{9}{12} \qquad 2\frac{8}{24} < 2\frac{9}{24}$$

3. Look at the example above. Is $^{-}\frac{3}{8}$ less than or greater than $\frac{1}{2}$?
4. a. Is 0 less than any positive rational number?

   b. Is 0 greater than any negative rational number?

Write each of these rational numbers in simplest fractional form.
Here are scrambled answers for the next row of exercises:

$\frac{^-1}{2}$ $\quad 3 \quad$ $\frac{5}{6}$ $\quad ^-2 \quad$ $^-3\frac{1}{2}$ $\quad$ $3\frac{1}{3}$

5. $\frac{^-8}{4}$ **6.** $\frac{10}{12}$ **7.** $\frac{9}{3}$ **8.** $\frac{^-3}{6}$ **9.** $\frac{10}{3}$ **10.** $\frac{^-14}{4}$

11. $\frac{^-4}{24}$ **12.** $\frac{18}{3}$ **13.** $\frac{^-19}{3}$ **14.** $\frac{6}{30}$ **15.** $\frac{24}{4}$ **16.** $\frac{^-15}{25}$

17. $\frac{18}{12}$ **18.** $\frac{^-22}{4}$ **19.** $\frac{^-20}{5}$ **20.** $\frac{^-8}{18}$ **21.** $\frac{9}{6}$ **22.** $\frac{^-20}{35}$

23. $\frac{^-11}{2}$ **24.** $\frac{17}{5}$ **25.** $\frac{^-18}{24}$ **26.** $\frac{30}{6}$ **27.** $\frac{^-42}{7}$ **28.** $\frac{^-30}{8}$

29. $\frac{^-9}{9}$ **30.** $\frac{15}{18}$ **31.** $\frac{0}{4}$ **32.** $\frac{^-8}{20}$ **33.** $\frac{10}{6}$ **34.** $\frac{^-25}{20}$

$<$, $=$, or $>$?

35. $^-8$ ◆ $^-6$ **36.** 8 ◆ 6 **37.** $^-9$ ◆ $^-10$ **38.** 9 ◆ 10

39. $\frac{2}{3}$ ◆ $\frac{3}{4}$ **40.** $\frac{^-2}{3}$ ◆ $\frac{^-3}{4}$ **41.** $\frac{7}{8}$ ◆ $\frac{5}{6}$ **42.** $\frac{^-7}{8}$ ◆ $\frac{^-5}{6}$

43. 0 ◆ $\frac{2}{5}$ **44.** 0 ◆ $\frac{^-2}{5}$ **45.** $^-4$ ◆ $^-4\frac{1}{3}$ **46.** 4 ◆ $4\frac{1}{3}$

47. $2\frac{2}{3}$ ◆ 3 **48.** $^-5\frac{5}{6}$ ◆ $^-5$ **49.** 7 ◆ $^-8\frac{2}{3}$ **50.** $^-7$ ◆ $8\frac{2}{3}$

51. $^-1\frac{1}{3}$ ◆ $\frac{3}{4}$ **52.** $2\frac{5}{8}$ ◆ $\frac{^-1}{2}$ **53.** $^-4$ ◆ $^-4\frac{1}{3}$ **54.** $5\frac{5}{6}$ ◆ 5

55. $^-2\frac{3}{4}$ ◆ $^-2\frac{5}{8}$ **56.** $5\frac{1}{4}$ ◆ $5\frac{1}{3}$ **57.** $^-6\frac{2}{3}$ ◆ $^-6\frac{3}{4}$ **58.** $8\frac{5}{8}$ ◆ $8\frac{1}{2}$

Problem Solving

Solve. Use the daily stock quotations on page 224.

59. Which stock went down $1 per share?

60. Which stock went up 50¢ a share?

61. Suppose that you owned 100 shares of Dupont. By how much did the value of your shares increase?

62. Suppose that you owned 100 shares of Mobil. By how much did the value of your shares decrease?

★63. If you owned 100 shares of Ford and 100 shares of Mobil, what would your total net change (in dollars) be for the day?

★64. If you owned 200 shares of TWA and 400 shares of Mobil, what would your total net change (in dollars) be for the day?

Writing Rational Numbers

A chili recipe calls for $\frac{3}{4}$ pound of ground pork. You have 0.75 pound of ground pork. To decide whether you have the proper amount for the recipe, you can change $\frac{3}{4}$ to a decimal.

Here's how to write a rational number in decimal form.

To write a rational number in decimal form, divide the numerator by the denominator.

$\frac{3}{4} = ?$

$$\begin{array}{r} 0.75 \\ 4\overline{)3.00} \\ -28 \\ \hline 20 \\ -20 \\ \hline 0 \end{array}$$

$\frac{3}{4} = 0.75$

Notice that the division came to an end, or terminated. For this reason 0.75 is called a ***terminating decimal.***

$\frac{^-4}{11} = ?$

$$\begin{array}{r} 0.3636 \\ 11\overline{)4.0000} \\ -33 \\ \hline 70 \\ -66 \\ \hline 40 \\ -33 \\ \hline 70 \\ -66 \\ \hline 4 \end{array}$$

$\frac{^-4}{11} = {}^-0.\overline{36}$

Notice that the division did not come to an end. The bar over the "$\overline{36}$" tells you that the 36 repeats. For this reason $^-0.\overline{36}$ is called a ***repeating decimal.***

$^-2\frac{2}{3} = ?$

First change $\frac{2}{3}$ to a decimal.

$$\begin{array}{r} 0.66 \\ 3\overline{)2.00} \\ -18 \\ \hline 20 \\ -18 \\ \hline 2 \end{array}$$

Since $\frac{2}{3} = 0.\overline{6}$

$^-2\frac{2}{3} = {}^-2.\overline{6}$

1. Look at the example above. Is $\frac{3}{4}$ pound the same as 0.75 pound?

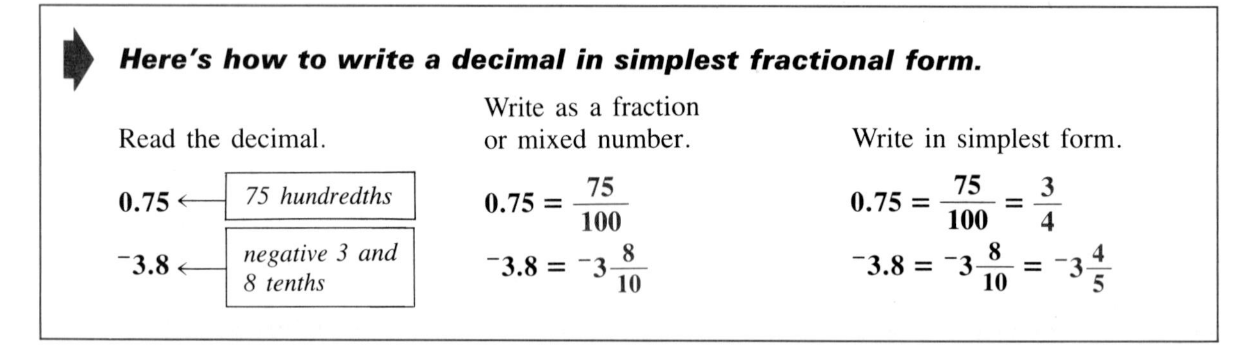

Here's how to write a decimal in simplest fractional form.

Read the decimal.	Write as a fraction or mixed number.	Write in simplest form.
0.75 ← *75 hundredths*	$0.75 = \frac{75}{100}$	$0.75 = \frac{75}{100} = \frac{3}{4}$
$^-3.8$ ← *negative 3 and 8 tenths*	$^-3.8 = {}^-3\frac{8}{10}$	$^-3.8 = {}^-3\frac{8}{10} = {}^-3\frac{4}{5}$

▶ **Write each rational number in decimal form.**
Here are scrambled answers for the next row of exercises:
$2.\overline{6}$ $0.\overline{3}$ 0.5 $^-0.8$ $^-1.75$ $^-0.\overline{4}$

2. $\frac{1}{2}$ **3.** $\frac{^-7}{4}$ **4.** $\frac{1}{3}$ **5.** $\frac{^-4}{5}$ **6.** $\frac{8}{3}$ **7.** $\frac{^-4}{9}$

8. $\frac{^-15}{2}$ **9.** $\frac{7}{2}$ **10.** $\frac{^-9}{8}$ **11.** $\frac{15}{4}$ **12.** $\frac{^-8}{3}$ **13.** $\frac{11}{6}$

14. $\frac{^-8}{9}$ **15.** $\frac{5}{11}$ **16.** $\frac{^-13}{10}$ **17.** $\frac{17}{12}$ **18.** $\frac{^-19}{16}$ **19.** $\frac{25}{12}$

20. $2\frac{1}{2}$ ← *Hint: First change $\frac{1}{2}$ to a decimal.* **21.** $^-4\frac{1}{3}$ **22.** $3\frac{3}{5}$ **23.** $^-6\frac{5}{6}$

▶ **Write each decimal in simplest fractional form.**
Here are scrambled answers for the next row of exercises: $\frac{^-1}{4}$ $\frac{^-1}{8}$ $\frac{3}{5}$ $\frac{3}{4}$ $\frac{^-1}{2}$

24. 0.6 **25.** $^-0.25$ **26.** $^-0.5$ **27.** 0.75 **28.** $^-0.125$

29. 0.8 **30.** $^-0.24$ **31.** 0.48 **32.** $^-0.9$ **33.** 0.150

34. $^-0.35$ **35.** 0.375 **36.** $^-0.72$ **37.** $^-0.4$ **38.** 0.16

39. 2.25 **40.** $^-1.4$ **41.** 2.40 **42.** $^-5.5$ **43.** 9.35

44. $^-7.8$ **45.** 3.75 **46.** $^-6.08$ **47.** $^-4.375$ **48.** $^-1.625$

Problem Solving

▶ **Solve.**

49. The chili recipe calls for $\frac{3}{4}$ pound of pork and $2\frac{1}{2}$ pounds of beef. Pork costs $1.40 a pound. Beef costs $2.40 a pound.

a. How many pounds of meat does the recipe call for?
b. How much will the pork cost?
c. How much will the beef cost?

CALCULATOR

▶ **Write each rational number in decimal form.**

50. a. $\frac{1}{11}$ **b.** $\frac{2}{11}$ **c.** $\frac{3}{11}$ **d.** $\frac{4}{11}$ **e.** $\frac{5}{11}$

▶ **Write each decimal in simplest fractional form.** ***Hint: Look for a pattern in exercise 50.***

51. a. $\frac{?}{?} = 0.\overline{54}$ **b.** $\frac{?}{?} = 0.\overline{63}$ **c.** $\frac{?}{?} = 0.\overline{72}$ **d.** $\frac{?}{?} = 0.\overline{81}$

Adding and Subtracting Rational Numbers

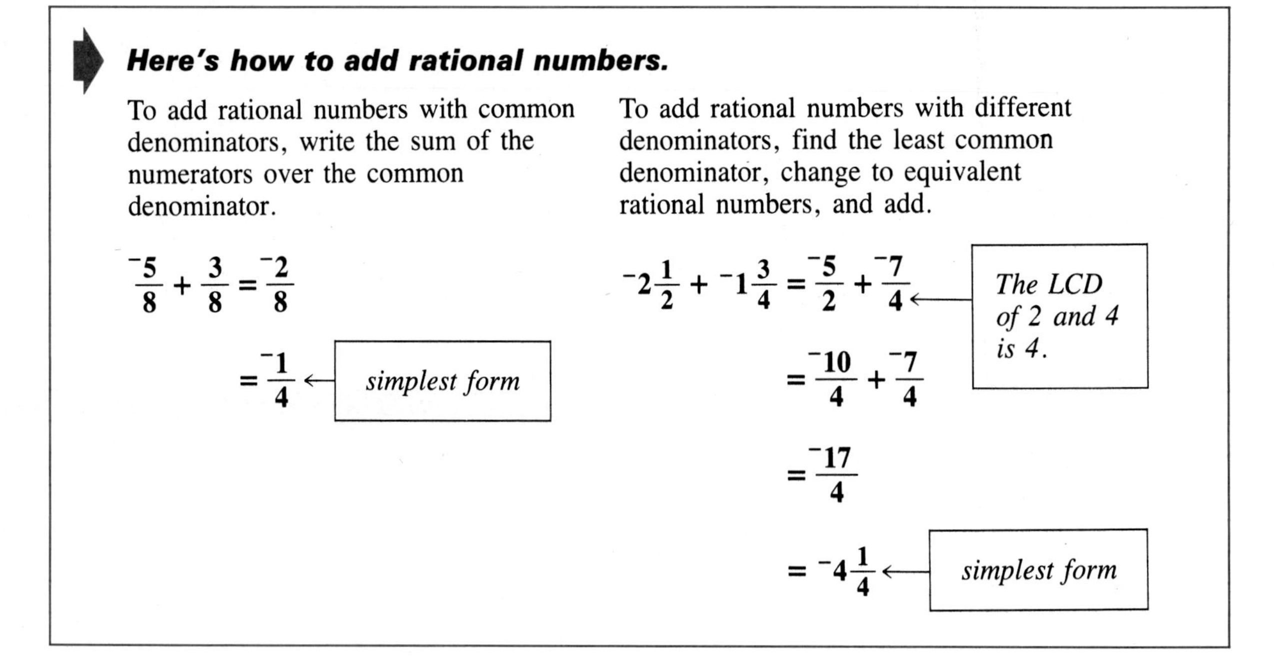

Here's how to add rational numbers.

To add rational numbers with common denominators, write the sum of the numerators over the common denominator.

$$\frac{^-5}{8} + \frac{3}{8} = \frac{^-2}{8}$$

$$= \frac{^-1}{4} \leftarrow$$ *simplest form*

To add rational numbers with different denominators, find the least common denominator, change to equivalent rational numbers, and add.

$$^-2\frac{1}{2} + {^-1}\frac{3}{4} = \frac{^-5}{2} + \frac{^-7}{4} \leftarrow$$ *The LCD of 2 and 4 is 4.*

$$= \frac{^-10}{4} + \frac{^-7}{4}$$

$$= \frac{^-17}{4}$$

$$= {^-4}\frac{1}{4} \leftarrow$$ *simplest form*

Here's how to subtract rational numbers.

To subtract a rational number, add the opposite of the rational number.

$$\frac{5}{16} - \frac{13}{16} = \frac{5}{16} + \frac{^-13}{16}$$

$$= \frac{^-8}{16}$$

$$= \frac{^-1}{2} \leftarrow$$ *simplest form*

$$^-3\frac{2}{3} - {^-1}\frac{3}{4} = \frac{^-11}{3} - \frac{^-7}{4}$$

$$= \frac{^-11}{3} + \frac{7}{4} \leftarrow$$ *The LCD of 3 and 4 is 12.*

$$= \frac{^-44}{12} + \frac{21}{12}$$

$$= \frac{^-23}{12}$$

$$= {^-1}\frac{11}{12} \leftarrow$$ *simplest form*

Give each sum in simplest form.
Here are scrambled answers for the next row of exercises: $\frac{^{-}7}{16}$ $\frac{^{-}1}{8}$ $1\frac{1}{16}$ $\frac{^{-}1}{5}$ $\frac{^{-}13}{20}$

1. $\frac{2}{5} + \frac{^{-}3}{5}$ **2.** $\frac{^{-}1}{2} + \frac{3}{8}$ **3.** $\frac{3}{16} + \frac{7}{8}$ **4.** $\frac{^{-}1}{4} + \frac{^{-}2}{5}$ **5.** $\frac{5}{16} + \frac{^{-}3}{4}$

6. $\frac{1}{2} + \frac{2}{9}$ **7.** $\frac{^{-}2}{3} + \frac{1}{4}$ **8.** $\frac{^{-}5}{12} + \frac{^{-}1}{3}$ **9.** $\frac{1}{10} + \frac{^{-}2}{5}$ **10.** $\frac{^{-}3}{8} + \frac{5}{24}$

11. $\frac{^{-}2}{5} + \frac{^{-}3}{20}$ **12.** $\frac{1}{6} + \frac{^{-}5}{9}$ **13.** $\frac{7}{8} + \frac{5}{6}$ **14.** $\frac{^{-}9}{10} + \frac{7}{10}$ **15.** $\frac{5}{12} + \frac{^{-}5}{8}$

16. $^{-}3\frac{1}{5} + 4\frac{2}{5}$ **17.** $^{-}4\frac{1}{2} + {}^{-}3\frac{1}{4}$ **18.** $5\frac{7}{8} + {}^{-}3$ **19.** $3\frac{2}{3} + {}^{-}2\frac{2}{3}$ **20.** $^{-}8 + {}^{-}6\frac{2}{5}$

21. $^{-}5\frac{1}{2} + 2\frac{3}{4}$ **22.** $3\frac{7}{8} + {}^{-}4\frac{1}{6}$ **23.** $^{-}6\frac{7}{10} + 4\frac{3}{4}$ **24.** $^{-}8\frac{11}{12} + {}^{-}2\frac{2}{3}$ **25.** $4\frac{5}{8} + {}^{-}2\frac{2}{3}$

Give each difference in simplest form.
Here are scrambled answers for the next row of exercises: $1\frac{1}{6}$ $\frac{^{-}14}{15}$ $\frac{1}{8}$ $\frac{11}{12}$ $\frac{^{-}13}{18}$

26. $\frac{2}{3} - \frac{^{-}1}{4}$ **27.** $\frac{^{-}3}{5} - \frac{1}{3}$ **28.** $\frac{^{-}3}{8} - \frac{^{-}1}{2}$ **29.** $\frac{^{-}1}{2} - \frac{2}{9}$ **30.** $\frac{5}{12} - \frac{^{-}3}{4}$

31. $\frac{^{-}1}{2} - \frac{1}{6}$ **32.** $\frac{2}{15} - \frac{^{-}3}{5}$ **33.** $\frac{1}{4} - \frac{2}{5}$ **34.** $\frac{^{-}1}{10} - \frac{^{-}2}{5}$ **35.** $\frac{^{-}11}{20} - \frac{2}{5}$

36. $\frac{5}{6} - \frac{^{-}7}{8}$ **37.** $\frac{11}{12} - \frac{5}{8}$ **38.** $\frac{^{-}9}{16} - \frac{^{-}5}{12}$ **39.** $\frac{3}{8} - \frac{9}{20}$ **40.** $\frac{5}{9} - \frac{^{-}7}{12}$

41. $4\frac{3}{5} - {}^{-}2\frac{1}{5}$ **42.** $8\frac{3}{4} - 5\frac{1}{2}$ **43.** $^{-}9 - 4\frac{3}{4}$ **44.** $4\frac{1}{2} - 7$ **45.** $^{-}6\frac{3}{5} - {}^{-}8\frac{2}{3}$

46. $8\frac{5}{8} - {}^{-}10\frac{2}{3}$ **47.** $6\frac{5}{6} - 4\frac{1}{8}$ **48.** $^{-}6\frac{3}{5} - {}^{-}9\frac{1}{2}$ **49.** $^{-}8\frac{11}{12} - 9\frac{7}{8}$ **50.** $3\frac{5}{8} - {}^{-}9\frac{5}{6}$

Challenge

Solve.

51. Suppose that you have 8 pennies that look alike. However, one of the pennies is counterfeit and is slightly heavier than each of the other 7. Tell how you could use a balance just **two** times to find the counterfeit penny.

Multiplying and Dividing Rational Numbers

Here's how to multiply rational numbers.

To multiply rational numbers, multiply the numerators to get the numerator of the product and multiply the denominators to get the denominator of the product.

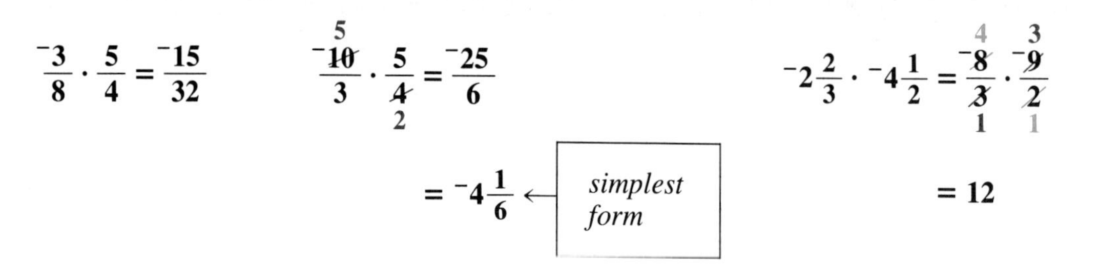

$$\frac{^-3}{8} \cdot \frac{5}{4} = \frac{^-15}{32}$$

$$\frac{^-\cancel{10}^{5}}{3} \cdot \frac{5}{\cancel{4}_{2}} = \frac{^-25}{6} = {^-4}\frac{1}{6}$$ ← *simplest form*

$$^-2\frac{2}{3} \cdot {^-4}\frac{1}{2} = \frac{^-\cancel{8}^{4}}{\cancel{3}_{1}} \cdot \frac{^-\cancel{9}^{3}}{\cancel{2}_{1}} = 12$$

1. Look at the third example above.
   a. $^-2\frac{2}{3}$ and $^-4\frac{1}{2}$ were first written as $\frac{^-8}{3}$ and __?__ .
   b. Next, the shortcut called __?__ was used.
   c. Finally, the product was written in __?__ form.

Here's how to divide rational numbers.

Remember that two numbers are reciprocals if their product is 1.
To divide by a rational number, multiply by its reciprocal.

$$\frac{5}{3} \div \frac{^-2}{5} = \frac{5}{3} \cdot \frac{^-5}{2} = \frac{^-25}{6} = {^-4}\frac{1}{6}$$ ← *simplest form*

$$\frac{^-7}{8} \div \frac{3}{4} = \frac{^-7}{\cancel{8}_{2}} \cdot \frac{\cancel{4}^{1}}{3} = \frac{^-7}{6} = {^-1}\frac{1}{6}$$

$$^-4\frac{2}{3} \div {^-5}\frac{3}{5} = \frac{^-14}{3} \div \frac{^-28}{5} = \frac{^-\cancel{14}^{1}}{3} \cdot \frac{^-5}{\cancel{28}_{2}} = \frac{5}{6}$$

EXERCISES

▶ **Give each product in simplest form.**
Here are scrambled answers for the next row of exercises: $^{-}2\frac{2}{15}$ $\quad \frac{^{-}3}{20}$ $\quad 1$ $\quad \frac{1}{6}$ $\quad 1\frac{1}{2}$

2. $\frac{^{-}3}{4} \cdot \frac{1}{5}$ **3.** $\frac{^{-}1}{3} \cdot \frac{^{-}1}{2}$ **4.** $\frac{1}{4} \cdot 4$ **5.** $\frac{^{-}8}{3} \cdot \frac{4}{5}$ **6.** $\frac{9}{10} \cdot \frac{5}{3}$

7. $\frac{5}{6} \cdot \frac{^{-}3}{4}$ **8.** $\frac{^{-}7}{8} \cdot \frac{9}{2}$ **9.** $\frac{6}{5} \cdot \frac{5}{6}$ **10.** $\frac{^{-}7}{4} \cdot \frac{^{-}7}{4}$ **11.** $^{-}8 \cdot \frac{5}{6}$

12. $2 \cdot {}^{-}1\frac{1}{2}$ **13.** $2\frac{2}{3} \cdot 4$ **14.** $^{-}1\frac{3}{4} \cdot 1\frac{3}{4}$ **15.** $^{-}1\frac{5}{6} \cdot {}^{-}2\frac{1}{3}$ **16.** $3\frac{1}{4} \cdot {}^{-}3\frac{3}{4}$

17. $4\frac{1}{6} \cdot 2\frac{1}{3}$ **18.** $^{-}1\frac{1}{2} \cdot {}^{-}1\frac{3}{4}$ **19.** $2\frac{2}{3} \cdot {}^{-}1\frac{3}{4}$ **20.** $^{-}4\frac{1}{2} \cdot 2\frac{3}{8}$ **21.** $3\frac{1}{8} \cdot {}^{-}3\frac{3}{4}$

▶ **Give each quotient in simplest form.**
Here are scrambled answers for the next row of exercises: $1\frac{1}{2}$ $\quad \frac{^{-}3}{8}$ $\quad {}^{-}3$ $\quad {}^{-}1\frac{1}{3}$ $\quad 1\frac{1}{4}$

22. $\frac{^{-}3}{4} \div \frac{1}{4}$ **23.** $\frac{1}{2} \div \frac{1}{3}$ **24.** $\frac{^{-}5}{6} \div \frac{^{-}2}{3}$ **25.** $\frac{2}{3} \div \frac{^{-}1}{2}$ **26.** $\frac{^{-}3}{10} \div \frac{4}{5}$

27. $\frac{3}{4} \div \frac{1}{2}$ **28.** $^{-}6 \div \frac{3}{4}$ **29.** $\frac{5}{8} \div {}^{-}3$ **30.** $\frac{^{-}5}{6} \div {}^{-}4$ **31.** $\frac{5}{8} \div \frac{2}{3}$

32. $5 \div {}^{-}2\frac{1}{2}$ **33.** $^{-}2\frac{1}{2} \div 1\frac{1}{4}$ **34.** $^{-}2\frac{1}{3} \div {}^{-}1\frac{1}{4}$ **35.** $2\frac{7}{8} \div 3\frac{1}{4}$ **36.** $3\frac{5}{6} \div {}^{-}2\frac{1}{3}$

37. $^{-}5\frac{3}{4} \div {}^{-}2\frac{2}{3}$ **38.** $6\frac{2}{3} \div 5\frac{1}{3}$ **39.** $^{-}4\frac{5}{6} \div 4$ **40.** $4\frac{1}{4} \div {}^{-}3\frac{1}{8}$ **41.** $^{-}3\frac{1}{2} \div {}^{-}1\frac{3}{4}$

Problem Solving

The reaction distance is the distance that you travel during the time it takes you to move your foot from the accelerator to the brake pedal. This formula shows the relationship between reaction distance and speed.

$$\mathbf{d} = \frac{\mathbf{11s}}{\mathbf{10}}$$

d: reaction distance in feet; s: speed in miles per hour

42. What would your approximate reaction distance be if you were driving

a. 20 mph? **b.** 30 mph? **c.** 40 mph? **d.** 50 mph?

★**43.** How fast would you be driving if your reaction distance was

a. 27.5 ft? **b.** 49.5 ft? **c.** 60.5 ft? **d.** 57.75 ft?

Cumulative Skill Practice

Find the least common denominator. *(page 134)*

1. $\frac{5}{6}, \frac{3}{4}$
2. $\frac{4}{9}, \frac{2}{3}$
3. $\frac{1}{8}, \frac{4}{3}$
4. $\frac{3}{10}, \frac{2}{5}$
5. $\frac{3}{8}, \frac{1}{6}$
6. $\frac{3}{a}, \frac{2}{3a}$
7. $\frac{a}{2b}, \frac{c}{b}$
8. $\frac{3}{8}, \frac{5}{64}$
9. $\frac{8}{2m^2}, \frac{7}{m}$
10. $\frac{1}{a^2b}, \frac{5}{ab^2}$

Write in simplest form. *(page 150)*

11. $\frac{24}{6}$
12. $\frac{30}{4}$
13. $\frac{39}{5}$
14. $\frac{21}{7}$
15. $\frac{40}{6}$
16. $\frac{42}{3}$
17. $\frac{4a}{6b}$
18. $\frac{12x}{16x}$
19. $\frac{7b^2}{4b}$
20. $\frac{10f}{4g}$
21. $\frac{28m}{8n}$
22. $\frac{5w}{3w^2}$
23. $\frac{3x}{2xy}$
24. $\frac{7pq}{3pq^2}$
25. $\frac{10m^2}{13mn^2}$
26. $\frac{5xy^2}{15xy}$
27. $\frac{24ab}{30a^2b^2}$
28. $\frac{18cd^2}{24c^2d}$

Give each sum or difference in simplest form. *(page 158)*

29. $\frac{2}{3} + \frac{1}{3}$
30. $\frac{5}{9} + \frac{5}{6}$
31. $\frac{5}{9} - \frac{2}{9}$
32. $\frac{9}{10} - \frac{2}{5}$
33. $\frac{2}{3} - \frac{3}{10}$
34. $\frac{a}{4} + \frac{b}{2}$
35. $\frac{r}{3} + \frac{s}{4}$
36. $\frac{2x}{3} + \frac{y}{6}$
37. $\frac{2m}{5} + \frac{n}{2}$
38. $\frac{3r}{2} + \frac{2s}{9}$
39. $\frac{p}{5} - \frac{q}{6}$
40. $\frac{t}{2} - \frac{u}{8}$
41. $\frac{3a}{4} - \frac{b}{2}$
42. $\frac{2x}{5} - \frac{7y}{8}$
43. $\frac{4m}{9} - \frac{5n}{6}$

Give each product in simplest form. *(page 172)*

44. $\frac{4}{3} \cdot \frac{4}{3}$
45. $\frac{3}{5} \cdot \frac{1}{3}$
46. $4 \cdot \frac{3}{2}$
47. $\frac{5}{12} \cdot \frac{3}{2}$
48. $\frac{7}{8} \cdot \frac{4}{5}$
49. $\frac{x}{5} \cdot \frac{1}{x}$
50. $12 \cdot \frac{y}{3}$
51. $\frac{3}{8} \cdot \frac{4y}{3}$
52. $\frac{2}{3d} \cdot \frac{3}{7f}$
53. $\frac{a}{b} \cdot \frac{2b}{5a}$
54. $\frac{a}{b^2} \cdot \frac{2b}{a}$
55. $\frac{x}{y} \cdot \frac{y}{x}$
56. $\frac{m}{n} \cdot \frac{n^2}{3}$
57. $\frac{2y}{z} \cdot \frac{z}{2w}$
58. $\frac{4d}{e} \cdot \frac{3e}{10d^2}$

Give each quotient in simplest form. *(page 176)*

59. $\frac{3}{2} \div \frac{1}{2}$
60. $\frac{4}{5} \div \frac{2}{3}$
61. $\frac{5}{6} \div \frac{4}{3}$
62. $\frac{7}{8} \div 2$
63. $6 \div \frac{5}{2}$
64. $\frac{2}{a} \div \frac{3}{a}$
65. $\frac{4}{b} \div \frac{2}{c}$
66. $\frac{j}{4} \div \frac{k}{6}$
67. $\frac{2y}{z} \div \frac{y}{3}$
68. $\frac{a}{6} \div \frac{2b}{3}$
69. $\frac{2y}{z} \div \frac{4y}{z}$
70. $\frac{m}{p} \div \frac{3m}{2q}$
71. $\frac{d^2}{e} \div \frac{d}{e}$
72. $\frac{x}{9y} \div \frac{x^2}{6y}$
73. $\frac{9a}{2b} \div \frac{3a}{8b^2}$

Problem Solving—Applications

NOVELTY ITEMS

TALKING TEETH
They walk, clickety-clack, and yackety-yak.
clickety, clack
$2.50

MINI SPY CAMERA
Fits in the palm of your hand.
$1.95

BAG OF LAUGHS
Press button for recorded series of laughs.
HA HA HA
Just For Laughs
$3.95

PHONY ARM CAST
A sympathy winner and great excuse.
$2.95

BALD HEAD WIG
$1.50

VENUS FLYTRAP
Eats flies, bugs, insects—even meat.
$1.75

SALES-TAX TABLE

Amount of Sale	Tax	Amount of Sale	Tax
$ .00 to 0.12	$.00	$3.88 to 4.12	$.16
.13 to 0.37	.01	4.13 to 4.37	.17
.38 to 0.62	.02	4.38 to 4.62	.18
.63 to 0.87	.03	4.63 to 4.87	.19
.88 to 1.12	.04	4.88 to 5.12	.20
1.13 to 1.37	.05	5.13 to 5.37	.21
1.38 to 1.62	.06	5.38 to 5.62	.22
1.63 to 1.87	.07	5.63 to 5.87	.23
1.88 to 2.12	.08	5.88 to 6.12	.24
2.13 to 2.37	.09	6.13 to 6.37	.25
2.38 to 2.62	.10	6.38 to 6.62	.26
2.63 to 2.87	.11	6.63 to 6.87	.27
2.88 to 3.12	.12	6.88 to 7.12	.28
3.13 to 3.37	.13	7.13 to 7.37	.29
3.38 to 3.62	.14	7.38 to 7.62	.30
3.63 to 3.87	.15	7.63 to 7.87	.31

▶ **Use the information in the ad and the sales-tax table to solve the problem.**

1. The sales tax on a Mini Spy Camera is $.08. What is the sales tax on a Phony Arm Cast?

2. Scott bought a Phony Arm Cast and a Bag of Laughs. What was the total cost, including sales tax?

3. If you have $5.90, do you have enough money to buy a Bag of Laughs and a Venus Flytrap? *Hint: Don't forget the sales tax.*

4. Cristy bought 3 Bags of Laughs and 2 Phony Arm Casts. She paid with a $20 bill and received $1.54 change. What was the sales tax on the total?

▶ **Write an equation and solve the problem.**

5. Joan bought 3 of the same novelty item. The sales tax was $.18. The total cost, including the sales tax, was $4.68. What novelty item did she buy?
(Let n = the cost of one of the novelty items Joan bought.)

6. Marty bought 4 of the same novelty item. The sales tax was $.28. The total cost, including the sales tax, was $7.28. What novelty item did he buy?
(Let m = the cost of one of the novelty items Marty bought.)

★ 7. Phil bought a Mini Spy Camera and some Venus Flytraps. The sales tax was $.29. How many flytraps did he buy if the total cost, including the sales tax, was $7.49?
(Let v = the number of flytraps Phil bought.)

★ 8. Anne bought some Bald Head Wigs and a Phony Arm Cast. The sales tax was $.24. How many wigs did she buy if the total cost, including the sales tax, was $6.19?
(Let b = the number of wigs Anne bought.)

Solving Equations Having Rational Solutions

Here's how to solve equations having rational solutions.

Equation: $3x - 2 = 0$

Add 2 to both sides. $3x - 2 + 2 = 0 + 2$

Simplify. $3x = 2$

Divide both sides by 3. $\frac{3x}{3} = \frac{2}{3}$

Simplify. $x = \frac{2}{3}$

Check:

$$3x - 2 = 0$$
$$3 \cdot \frac{2}{3} - 2 \stackrel{?}{=} 0$$
$$2 - 2 \stackrel{?}{=} 0$$
$$0 = 0$$

It checks!

Equation: $^{-}5x + 7 = 23$

Subtract 7 from both sides. $^{-}5x + 7 - 7 = 23 - 7$

Simplify. $^{-}5x = 16$

Divide both sides by $^{-}5$. $\frac{^{-}5x}{^{-}5} = \frac{16}{^{-}5}$

Simplify. $x = {}^{-}3\frac{1}{5}$

Check:

$$^{-}5x + 7 = 23$$
$$^{-}5 \cdot {}^{-}3\frac{1}{5} + 7 \stackrel{?}{=} 23$$
$$^{-}5 \cdot \frac{^{-}16}{5} + 7 \stackrel{?}{=} 23$$
$$16 + 7 \stackrel{?}{=} 23$$
$$23 = 23$$

It checks!

Equation: $9 - 4x = {}^{-}5$

To subtract, add the opposite. → $9 + {}^{-}4x = {}^{-}5$ ← *commutative property of addition*

$^{-}4x + 9 = {}^{-}5$ ← *commutative property of addition*

Subtract 9 from both sides. $^{-}4x + 9 - 9 = {}^{-}5 - 9$

Simplify. $^{-}4x = {}^{-}14$

Divide both sides by $^{-}4$. $\frac{^{-}4x}{^{-}4} = \frac{^{-}14}{^{-}4}$

Simplify. $x = 3\frac{1}{2}$

Check:

$$9 - 4x = {}^{-}5$$
$$9 - 4 \cdot 3\frac{1}{2} \stackrel{?}{=} {}^{-}5$$
$$9 - \overset{2}{\cancel{4}} \cdot \frac{7}{\underset{1}{\cancel{2}}} \stackrel{?}{=} {}^{-}5$$
$$9 - 14 \stackrel{?}{=} {}^{-}5$$
$$^{-}5 = {}^{-}5$$

It checks!

1. Complete these examples.

a.
$$\begin{aligned} 5x - 4 &= 8 \\ 5x - 4 + 4 &= 8 + 4 \\ 5x &= \underline{\ ?\ } \\ \frac{5x}{5} &= \frac{12}{?} \\ x &= 2\frac{2}{5} \end{aligned}$$

b.
$$\begin{aligned} {}^-9y - 5 &= 1 \\ {}^-9y - 5 + 5 &= 1 + \underline{\ ?\ } \\ {}^-9y &= 6 \\ \frac{{}^-9y}{{}^-9} &= \frac{?}{{}^-9} \\ y &= \frac{{}^-2}{3} \end{aligned}$$

c.
$$\begin{aligned} 6 - 8z &= {}^-10 \\ 6 + {}^-8z &= {}^-10 \\ {}^-8z + 6 &= \underline{\ ?\ } \\ {}^-8z + 6 - 6 &= {}^-10 - \underline{\ ?\ } \\ {}^-8z &= {}^-16 \\ \frac{{}^-8z}{{}^-8} &= \frac{{}^-16}{?} \\ z &= 2 \end{aligned}$$

EXERCISES

▶ **Solve and check.**
Here are scrambled answers for the next two rows of exercises:

$^-1\frac{5}{7}$ $\quad$ $^-4\frac{2}{3}$ $\quad$ 3 $\quad$ $\frac{^-4}{7}$ $\quad$ $1\frac{2}{3}$ $\quad$ $^-3\frac{4}{5}$ $\quad$ $^-3$ $\quad$ 4

2. $3n + 8 = 13$	**3.** $4a - 3 = 9$	**4.** ${}^-8 - 5n = 7$	**5.** $9 + 7z = {}^-3$
6. ${}^-5b - 12 = 7$	**7.** ${}^-12 + 5a = 8$	**8.** ${}^-7p + 11 = 15$	**9.** ${}^-10 - 6s = 18$
10. $6q + 13 = {}^-9$	**11.** $9 - 8p = 0$	**12.** $10d - 5 = 0$	**13.** ${}^-10 + 12b = 8$
14. $16 + 7c = 10$	**15.** ${}^-12e - 18 = 5$	**16.** ${}^-8r + 16 = 20$	**17.** $18 - 7r = 12$
18. $10f - 7 = 11$	**19.** ${}^-15 - 6q = 15$	**20.** $14 + 9d = 13$	**21.** $15s + 10 = 12$
22. $12 - 8r = {}^-3$	**23.** ${}^-7g - 16 = {}^-12$	**24.** ${}^-16t + 50 = 0$	**25.** ${}^-10 + 8e = {}^-2$
26. $12u + 18 = 32$	**27.** $18 + 12f = {}^-6$	**28.** $8h - 10 = {}^-19$	**29.** $16 - 4t = {}^-20$
30. ${}^-21 + 11j = 21$	**31.** ${}^-15j - 9 = 15$	**32.** ${}^-20 - 11u = {}^-10$	**33.** ${}^-18v + 12 = 12$
34. $24 - 15v = 16$	**35.** $25 + 4k = {}^-17$	**36.** $20w + 24 = 6$	**37.** $20k - 12 = 26$

Problem Solving

▶ **First choose the equation and solve the problem. Then reread the problem to see if your answer makes sense.**

Equation A: $5n - 6 = 4$
Equation B: $6 - 5n = 4$
Equation C: $6n - 5 = 4$
Equation D: $5 - 6n = 4$

38. If 5 is subtracted from 6 times a number, the difference is 4. What is the number?

39. If 6 times a number is subtracted from 5, the difference is 4. What is the number?

40. If 6 is subtracted from 5 times a number, the difference is 4. What is the number?

41. If you subtract the product of 5 times a number from 6, the difference is 4. What is the number?

Simplifying Expressions

In this lesson you will use the distributive property, the multiplying by 1 property, and the definition of subtraction to simplify expressions such as

$$^{-}5a - 3a \qquad\qquad 12c - c$$

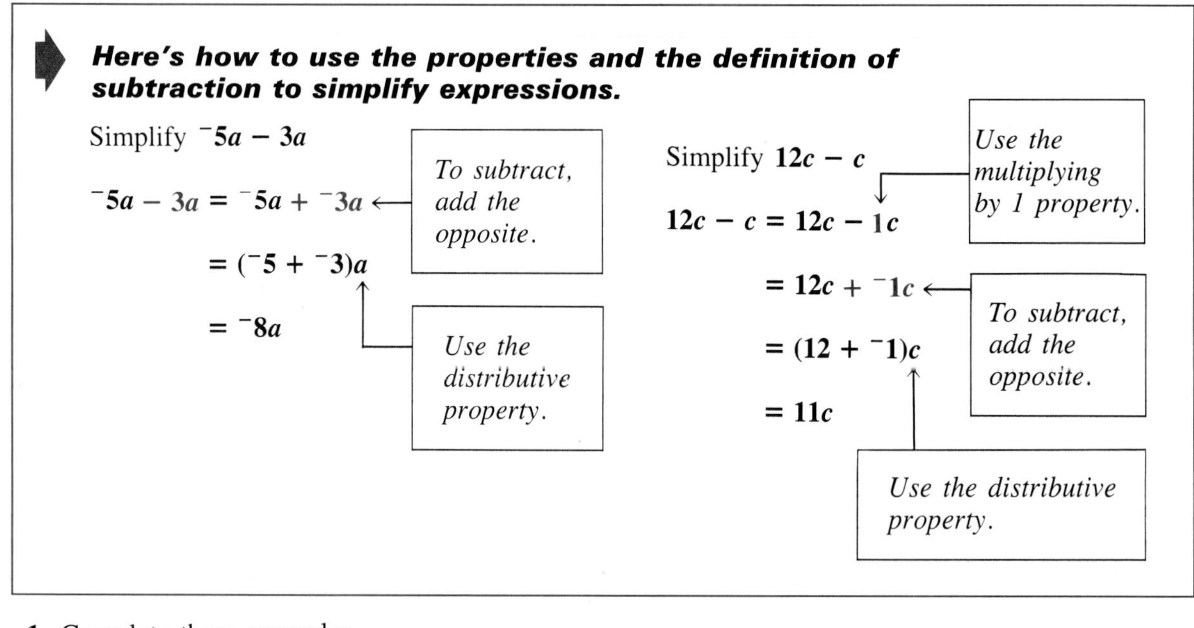

1. Complete these examples.

a. $^{-}5x + 3x = ({}^{-}5 + 3)x$
$= \underline{\ ?\ }\ x$

b. $8z - 8z = 8z + {}^{-}8z$
$= (8 + {}^{-}8)z$
$= \underline{\ ?\ }\ z$
$= 0$

c. $16w - w = 16w - 1w$
$= 16w + {}^{-}1w$
$= (16 + \underline{\ ?\ })w$
$= 15w$

Here's how to use a shortcut to simplify expressions.

To simplify these expressions, first change each subtraction to adding the opposite and then combine like terms (terms that have the same variable) by adding.

Simplify $4a + 3 - 6a$

$4a + 3 - 6a = 4a + 3 + {}^{-}6a$ (*like terms*: $4a$ and ${}^{-}6a$)

$= {}^{-}2a + 3$

Simplify $7b + 8 - b - 6$

$7b + 8 - b - 6 = 7b + 8 + {}^{-}1b + {}^{-}6$ (*like terms*: $7b$ and ${}^{-}1b$; *like terms*: 8 and ${}^{-}6$)

$= 6b + 2$

EXERCISES

▶ **Simplify by combining like terms.**
Here are scrambled answers for the next two rows of exercises:
$11n - 6$ $9n$ $8n + 3$ $^-11n - 6$ $7n$ 0

2. $6n + 3n$ **3.** $8n - n$ **4.** $9n - 9n$

5. $8n + 3n - 6$ **6.** $^-8n - 3n - 6$ **7.** $8n - 3 + 6$

8. $3x + 11x$ **9.** $3x - 11x$ **10.** $^-3x - 11x$

11. $9y - 4y + 7$ **12.** $9y + 4y - 7$ **13.** $9y - 4 - 7$

14. $8 + 3w - 5$ **15.** $8w + 3 - 5$ **16.** $8 + 3w - 5w$

17. $10z - 12 - 6z$ **18.** $10z - 12z - 6$

19. $^-8r - r - 15$ **20.** $^-8r + r - 15$

21. $12t - 12t + 8$ **22.** $12t - 12 + 8t$

23. $5a + 3a + 9 - 8$ **24.** $5a + 3 + 9a - 8$

25. $11c - 4c + 12 - 12$ **26.** $11c - 4 + 10 - 12c$

27. $14j - 14j + 8 - 3$ **28.** $14j - 14 + 8j - 3$

29. $18m - 6 - m + 8$ **30.** $18m - 6m - 1 + 8$

31. $15p - 12 - 15p - 6$ **32.** $15p - 12p - 15 - 6$

33. $20t - 17 - 20t - 18$ **34.** $20t - 17t - 20 - 18$

35. $24r - 24r + 21 - 21$ **36.** $24 - 24r + 21r - 21$

Problem Solving

Suppose that you throw a baseball upward at the rate of 64 feet per second (about 44 miles per hour). The formula below gives the distance that the ball would be above the ground in t seconds.

distance in feet (d)

Formula: $d = 64t - 16t^2$

time in seconds after ball is thrown (t)

★**37.** Use the formula to complete the chart.

	Time in seconds (t)	Distance in feet (d)
a.	0	?
b.	1	?
c.	2	?
d.	3	?
e.	4	?

★**38.** How high would the ball be after 1 second? After 3 seconds? Why are they the same?

Solving Equations

Jan bought 4 cassette tapes. Allison bought 3 cassette tapes and a \$7 storage box for her tapes. Each cassette costs the same. If they spent \$63 together, how much did they spend for each cassette?

If you let c be the cost in dollars of each cassette, you can solve the problem by solving the equation

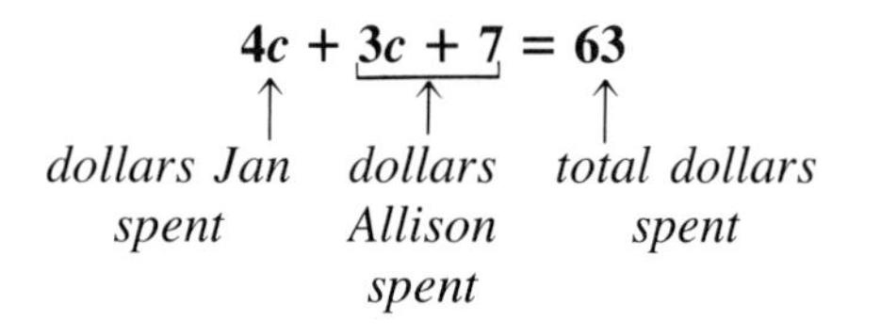

Here's how to solve an equation that has the same variable in more than one term.

Equation:	$4c + 3c + 7 = 63$	
Combine like terms.	$7c + 7 = 63$	
Subtract 7 from both sides.	$7c + 7 - 7 = 63 - 7$	✔ *Check:*
Simplify.	$7c = 56$	$4c + 3c + 7 = 63$ $4 \cdot 8 + 3 \cdot 8 + 7 \stackrel{?}{=} 63$
Divide both sides by 7.	$\frac{7c}{7} = \frac{56}{7}$	$32 + 24 + 7 \stackrel{?}{=} 63$ $63 = 63$
Simplify.	$c = 8$	*It checks!*

1. Look at the example above. The first step in solving the equation was to __?__ like terms.
2. How much did each cassette cost? Does the answer seem reasonable?
3. Complete these examples.

a.
$$5y - 3y + 4 = 9$$
$$\underline{?}\ y + 4 = 9$$
$$2y + 4 - 4 = 9 - 4$$
$$2y = 5$$
$$\frac{2y}{2} = \frac{5}{?}$$
$$y = 2\frac{1}{2}$$

b.
$$6x + 5 - 3x = {}^-12$$
$$\underline{?}\ x + 5 = {}^-12$$
$$3x + 5 - 5 = {}^-12 - 5$$
$$3x = {}^-17$$
$$\frac{3x}{3} = \frac{{}^-17}{3}$$
$$x = \underline{?}$$

c.
$$16 + 4z - 6z = {}^-19$$
$${}^-2z + \underline{?} = {}^-19$$
$${}^-2z + 16 - 16 = {}^-19 - 16$$
$${}^-2z = {}^-35$$
$$\frac{{}^-2z}{{}^-2} = \frac{{}^-35}{?}$$
$$z = 17\frac{1}{2}$$

EXERCISES

▶ **Solve and check.**
Here are scrambled answers for the next two rows of exercises:

$2\frac{3}{7}$ $\quad ^{-}6 \quad$ $\frac{5}{9}$ $\quad 3 \quad$ $^{-}1\frac{3}{7}$ $\quad ^{-}4$

4. $7x + 4x = 33$
5. $9y - y = {}^{-}48$
6. $z - 5z = 16$
7. $7j + 2j - 5 = 0$
8. $^{-}5k - 2k - 4 = 6$
9. $7d - 2 + 5 = 20$
10. $4x + 10x = 28$
11. $4x - 10x = 28$
12. $^{-}4x - 10x = 28$
13. $8y - 3y + 6 = {}^{-}10$
14. $8y + 3y - 6 = {}^{-}10$
15. $8y - 3 - 6 = {}^{-}10$
16. $9 + 4w - 6 = 12$
17. $9w + 4 - 6 = 12$
18. $9 + 4w - 6w = 12$
19. $8z - 10 - 4z = {}^{-}20$
20. $8z - 10z - 4 = {}^{-}20$
21. $8 - 10z - 4z = {}^{-}20$
22. $^{-}6r - r - 13 = {}^{-}18$
23. $^{-}6r + r - 13 = {}^{-}18$
24. $^{-}6r + 1 - 13r = {}^{-}18$
25. $12t - t + 5 = 6$
26. $12t - 1 + 5t = 6$
27. $12 - t + 5t = 6$
28. $6a + 4a + 9 = 0$
29. $6a + 4 + 9a = 0$
30. $6a + 4 + 9 = 0$
31. $12c - 5c + 11 = {}^{-}4$
32. $12c - 5 + 11 = {}^{-}4$
33. $12c - 5 + 11c = {}^{-}4$
34. $15j - 10j + 8 = 11$
35. $15j - 10 + 8j = 11$
36. $15j - 10 + 8 = 11$
37. $18m - 6 - m = {}^{-}16$
38. $18m - 6m - 1 = {}^{-}16$
39. $18 - 6m - m = {}^{-}16$
40. $15q - 18 - 12q = 9$
41. $15q - 18q - 12 = 9$
42. $15 - 18q - 12q = 9$
43. $8a + 6 - 5a = 6$
44. $10 - 3b + 2 = {}^{-}9$
45. $c - 9 + c = {}^{-}12$

Problem Solving

▶ **First choose the equation and solve the problem. Then reread the problem to see if your answer makes sense.**

Equation A:	$4n + 1 = 27$
Equation B:	$4n - 1 = 27$
Equation C:	$4n + n = 27$
Equation D:	$4n - n = 27$

46. Sarah bought 4 cassette tapes and John bought 1 cassette tape. Together they spent \$27. If each tape cost the same, how much did one tape cost?

47. Susan bought 4 cassette tapes. One dollar was deducted from the total cost because she had a discount coupon. She paid \$27 for the tapes. If each tape cost the same, how much did one tape cost?

48. David bought 4 cassette tapes. Kirk bought 1 cassette tape. The difference between the amounts they spent was \$27. If each tape cost the same, how much did one tape cost?

49. Allison bought 4 cassette tapes and a \$1 bottle of tape cleaner. She paid a total of \$27. If each tape cost the same, how much did one tape cost?

More on Solving Equations

The cheerleaders at Winchester High School sold gym shorts and caps to raise money for new uniforms. Robert bought 2 pairs of gym shorts and a \$3 cap. Scott bought 1 pair of gym shorts and a \$2 cap. Robert paid for both orders with a \$20 bill. He got \$3 back in change. What was the cost of each pair of gym shorts?

If you let g be the cost in dollars of a pair of gym shorts, you can solve the problem by solving the equation

$$\underbrace{2g + 3}_{\text{dollars Robert spent}} + \underbrace{g + 2}_{\text{dollars Scott spent}} = \underbrace{20 - 3}_{\text{total dollars spent}}$$

Here's how to solve an equation that has several terms on each side of the equation.

Equation:	$2g + 3 + g + 2 = 20 - 3$
Combine like terms.	$3g + 5 = 17$
Subtract 5 from both sides.	$3g + 5 - 5 = 17 - 5$
Simplify.	$3g = 12$
Divide both sides by 3.	$\frac{3g}{3} = \frac{12}{3}$
Simplify.	$g = 4$

Check:

$2g + 3 + g + 2 = 20 - 3$

$2 \cdot 4 + 3 + 4 + 2 \stackrel{?}{=} 17$

$8 + 3 + 4 + 2 \stackrel{?}{=} 17$

$17 = 17$

It checks!

1. Look at the example above. The first step in solving the equation was to __?__ like terms on each side of the equation.
2. What was the cost of each pair of gym shorts? Does the answer seem reasonable?

3. Complete these examples.

a. $5x - 2x + 9 = {}^{-}7 + 10$

$\underline{\ ?\ }x + 9 = 3$

$3x + 9 - 9 = 3 - 9$

$3x = {}^{-}6$

$\frac{3x}{3} = \frac{{}^{-}6}{3}$

$x = \underline{\ ?\ }$

b. $13 - 6w + 21 - w = {}^{-}15 - 40$

${}^{-}7\underline{\ ?\ } + 34 = {}^{-}55$

${}^{-}7w + 34 - 34 = {}^{-}55 - 34$

${}^{-}7w = {}^{-}89$

$\frac{{}^{-}7w}{{}^{-}7} = \frac{{}^{-}89}{{}^{-}7}$

$w = \underline{\ ?\ }$

EXERCISES

▶ **Solve and check.**

Here are scrambled answers for the next three rows of exercises: $1 \quad {}^{-}1\frac{5}{11} \quad {}^{-}3\frac{1}{2} \quad 1\frac{5}{7} \quad 1\frac{7}{8} \quad {}^{-}4\frac{4}{5}$

4. $3y + 5y = {}^{-}3 + 18$

5. $12x - x = {}^{-}9 - 7$

6. $w - 8w = 19 - 26$

7. $3k + 4k - 8 = 10 - 6$

8. $11j + j + 9 = {}^{-}23 - 10$

9. $5e - 9 + 18 = 2 - 17$

10. $2a - 3a + 7 = {}^{-}4 - 20$

11. $2a - 3 + 7a = {}^{-}4 - 20$

12. $2 - 3a + 7a = {}^{-}4 - 20$

13. $5n - 8n - 4 = 15 - 27$

14. $5n - 8 - 4n = 15 - 27$

15. $5 - 8n - 4n = 15 - 27$

16. ${}^{-}12r + 3r - 10 = {}^{-}16 + 30$

17. ${}^{-}12r + 3 - 10r = {}^{-}16 + 30$

18. ${}^{-}12 + 3r - 10r = {}^{-}16 + 30$

19. $5s + 3s - 8 + 2 = 21 - 9$

20. $5s - 3 - 8s + 2 = 21 - 9$

21. $5 - 3s - 8 + 2s = 21 - 9$

22. $4n - n + 9 = {}^{-}20$

23. ${}^{-}12 + j = {}^{-}3$

24. ${}^{-}7n + 5 + 6n = 0$

25. $15 - n = {}^{-}11$

26. $11 - 6p = {}^{-}10$

27. $4 + 2y + 3y = 0$

Challenge

▶ **Solve.**

28. Sandra is a cheerleader at Winchester High School. She knows a number of different cheers. Study the clues to find out how many different cheers she knows.

Clues:
- She knows fewer than 40 cheers.
- If you divide the number of cheers by 5, the remainder is 1.
- If you divide the number of cheers by 4, the remainder is 3.
- If you divide the number of cheers by 3, the remainder is 1.

Problem Solving—Using Formulas

When you push down or let up on the accelerator of a car, the car changes its speed. The change in speed that the car experiences during a period of time is called **acceleration.** Acceleration is positive when speed increases; it is negative when speed decreases. To find acceleration, you can use this formula:

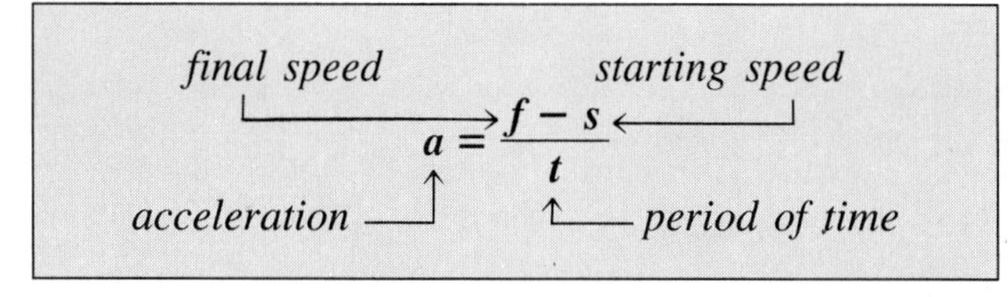

Here's how to use the acceleration formula to solve problems.

Problem A A car's speed is increased from 30 miles per hour to 45 miles per hour in 10 seconds. Find the acceleration.

Write the formula. $a = \frac{f - s}{t}$

Substitute 45 for f, 30 for s, and 10 for t. $a = \frac{45 - 30}{10}$

Simplify. $= \frac{15}{10}$ or $1\frac{1}{2}$

The car accelerates $1\frac{1}{2}$ miles per hour each second.

Problem B A car's speed is decreased from 55 miles per hour to 30 miles per hour in 6 seconds. Find the acceleration.

Write the formula. $a = \frac{f - s}{t}$

Substitute values for f, s, and t. $a = \frac{30 - 55}{6}$

Simplify. $= \frac{^{-}25}{6}$ or $^{-}4\frac{1}{6}$

The acceleration is $^{-}4\frac{1}{6}$ miles per hour each second.

When acceleration is negative, it is called **deceleration.**

Use the formula $a = \frac{f - s}{t}$ to complete each statement.

1. If a car increases its speed from 10 miles per hour to 32 miles per hour in 5 seconds, its acceleration is _?_ miles per hour each second.
2. If a car decreases its speed from 33 miles per hour to 22 miles per hour in 3 seconds, its acceleration is _?_ miles per hour each second.
3. If a motorcycle goes from 40 miles per hour to 10 miles per hour in 4 seconds, its acceleration is _?_ miles per hour each second.
4. If a bicycle goes from 4 miles per hour to 12 miles per hour in 9 seconds, its acceleration is _?_ mile per hour each second.
5. If a car goes from a standstill to 40 miles per hour in 9 seconds, its acceleration is _?_ miles per hour each second.
6. If a car traveling 50 miles per hour is stopped in 4 seconds, its acceleration is _?_ miles per hour each second.

Solve. Use the distance formula at the right.

7. A trucker drove 8.5 hours at an average speed of 44 miles per hour. How many miles did she drive?
8. A salesperson drove 6.25 hours at an average speed of 48 miles per hour. How far did he drive?
9. You drove 3.5 hours at an average speed of 40 miles per hour. How far did you drive?
10. If you drove 125 miles at an average speed of 50 miles per hour, how many hours would it take?
11. How many minutes does it take an airplane to travel 450 miles at 12 miles per minute?

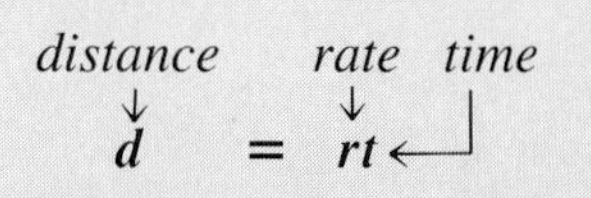

The distance (d) traveled is equal to the rate (r) of speed times the time (t) it takes to travel the distance.

Cumulative Skill Practice

Solve. Give the answer in simplest form. *(page 182)*

1. $\frac{3}{8}$ of $40 = n$ **2.** $\frac{5}{6}$ of $120 = n$ **3.** $\frac{7}{8}$ of $96 = n$ **4.** $\frac{3}{2}$ of $150 = n$

5. $\frac{3}{5}$ of $12 = n$ **6.** $\frac{7}{2}$ of $15 = n$ **7.** $\frac{9}{4}$ of $22 = n$ **8.** $\frac{2}{5}$ of $34 = n$

Complete. *(page 184)*

9. $2\frac{1}{2}$ ft = __?__ in. **10.** $1\frac{2}{3}$ yd = __?__ ft **11.** $3\frac{1}{4}$ yd = __?__ in.

12. $1\frac{1}{3}$ days = __?__ h **13.** $2\frac{2}{3}$ h = __?__ min **14.** $3\frac{1}{2}$ days = __?__ h

15. $1\frac{3}{4}$ min = __?__ s **16.** $1\frac{5}{6}$ h = __?__ min **17.** $2\frac{1}{5}$ min = __?__ s

18. $1\frac{1}{4}$ gal = __?__ qt **19.** $2\frac{1}{2}$ qt = __?__ pt **20.** $1\frac{1}{2}$ gal = __?__ pt

Solve. Give the answer in simplest form. *(page 186)*

21. $\frac{3}{8}n = 36$ **22.** $\frac{5}{8}n = 45$ **23.** $\frac{5}{6}n = 75$ **24.** $\frac{4}{5}n = 48$

25. $\frac{2}{3}n = 33$ **26.** $\frac{5}{2}n = 42$ **27.** $\frac{7}{8}n = 50$ **28.** $\frac{7}{4}n = 65$

Write in scientific notation. *(page 208)*

29. 14,000 **30.** 23,800 **31.** 120,000 **32.** 395,000

33. 5,800,000 **34.** 9,630,000 **35.** 18,000,000 **36.** 427,000,000

37. 0.0083 **38.** 0.052 **39.** 0.00084 **40.** 0.0009

41. 0.000178 **42.** 0.0000258 **43.** 0.005286 **44.** 0.0000718

Solve and check. *(page 214)*

45. $1 = {}^{-}7w + 15$ **46.** ${}^{-}10 = {}^{-}6z - 4$ **47.** ${}^{-}9 = 4k - 9$ **48.** $18 = 5j + 33$

49. ${}^{-}12 = \frac{k}{3} + 9$ **50.** $16 = \frac{h}{{}^{-}3} - 8$ **51.** $20 = \frac{d}{{}^{-}5} + 18$ **52.** ${}^{-}24 = \frac{c}{9} - 24$

53. ${}^{-}5r - 7 = 8$ **54.** ${}^{-}3t + 9 = 27$ **55.** $\frac{x}{{}^{-}4} + 21 = 30$ **56.** $\frac{y}{{}^{-}8} - 12 = {}^{-}40$

Problem Solving—Applications

Want to Lose Weight? Exercise and Burn Off Calories!

When you exercise, you burn off calories. The total calories burned depends on the type of exercise, how long you exercise, and your weight.

Here is a list of activities and the number of calories you burn per pound for each hour of exercise.

Activity	Calories burned per pound in one hour
Bicycling	1.6
Dancing	2.2
Football	3.6
Skiing	5.2
Swimming	4.1
Tennis	2.6
Walking	2.1

Solve. Use the information in the article.

1. Jackie walks 1.5 hours each day. She weighs 110 pounds. How many calories does she burn during each walk?
   Hint: Substitute in the formula.
   $b = 2.1 \times 1.5 \times 110$

2. Frank swims 0.5 hour each day. He weighs 140 pounds. How many calories does he burn off during each swim?
   Hint: $b = 4.1 \times 0.5 \times 140$

3. Cindy likes to ski. How many calories does she burn off while skiing 2 hours? Cindy weighs 120 pounds.

4. Chad plays football. How many calories does he burn off while playing a 2-hour game? Chad weighs 180 pounds.

5. Laura and Jim like to dance. How many more calories will Jim burn off than Laura while dancing 1.5 hours? Laura weighs 105 pounds and Jim weighs 140 pounds.

6. Brian and Polly play tennis. How many more calories will Brian burn off than Polly during a 1-hour tennis match? Brian weighs 150 pounds, and Polly weighs 125 pounds.

7. To lose a pound, you have to burn 3500 calories. How many hours would a 175-pound person have to walk to lose one pound? Round your answer to the nearest tenth.

8. How many hours of tennis would a 180-pound person have to play to lose 5 pounds? Remember, you need to burn 3500 calories to lose one pound. Round your answer to the nearest tenth.

Chapter Review

Here are scrambled answers for the review exercises:

$^-4$	8	common	divide	numerators	repeating
$^-3$	12	compare	equivalent	opposite	subtraction
5	addition	denominators	like	rational	terminating
7	combine	distributive	multiply	reciprocal	terms

1. A number that can be written as the quotient of two integers (divisor not 0) is called a _?_ number. To _?_ rational numbers with different denominators, you compare equivalent rational numbers with the same denominators. *(page 224)*

2. To write a rational number in decimal form, _?_ the numerator by the denominator. If the division comes to an end, the decimal is called a _?_ decimal. If the division does not come to an end, the decimal is called a _?_ decimal. *(page 226)*

3. To add rational numbers with different denominators, find the least _?_ denominator, change to _?_ rational numbers, and add. To subtract a rational number add the _?_ of the rational number. *(page 228)*

4. To multiply rational numbers, multiply the _?_ to get the numerator of the product and multiply the _?_ to get the denominator of the product. To divide by a rational number, multiply by its _?_. To find the quotient of $\frac{7}{8} \div \frac{^-3}{2}$, you would _?_ $\frac{7}{8}$ by $\frac{^-2}{3}$. *(page 230)*

5. To solve the equation $8 - 3y = 7$, you would first change the _?_ to adding the opposite. Next, you would use the commutative property of _?_. Finally, you would subtract _?_ from both sides and then divide both sides by _?_. *(page 234)*

6. The next step in simplifying this expression is to use the _?_ property.

$$\begin{aligned} 15a - a &= 15a - 1a \\ &= 15a + {}^-1a \end{aligned}$$

To simplify the expression $6b - 2b$, you can first change the subtraction to adding the opposite and then combine _?_ terms by adding. *(page 236)*

7. To solve the equation $8x - 3x + 7 = {}^-5$, you would first _?_ like terms. Next, you would subtract _?_ from both sides. Finally, you would divide both sides by _?_. *(page 238)*

8. To solve the equation $5y - 12 - 9y = 12 - 20$, you would first combine like _?_ on both sides of the equal sign. Next, you would add _?_ to both sides. Finally, you would divide both sides by _?_. *(page 240)*

Chapter Test

▶ **$<$, $=$, or $>$?** *(page 224)*

1. $\frac{1}{4} \blacklozenge \frac{^-5}{8}$ **2.** $\frac{^-2}{3} \blacklozenge 0$ **3.** $^-3 \blacklozenge {}^-3\frac{3}{8}$ **4.** $\frac{^-7}{4} \blacklozenge {}^-1\frac{3}{4}$

▶ **Write each rational number in decimal form.** *(page 226)*

5. $\frac{1}{2}$ **6.** $\frac{^-2}{3}$ **7.** $\frac{^-17}{8}$ **8.** $2\frac{5}{6}$

▶ **Write each decimal in simplest fractional form.** *(page 226)*

9. 0.6 **10.** $^-0.25$ **11.** 3.75 **12.** 1.375

▶ **Give each sum or difference in simplest form.** *(page 228)*

13. $\frac{3}{5} + \frac{^-1}{5}$ **14.** $\frac{^-5}{6} + \frac{^-5}{8}$ **15.** $\frac{^-5}{8} - \frac{1}{8}$ **16.** $\frac{7}{8} - \frac{^-2}{3}$

▶ **Give each product or quotient in simplest form.** *(page 230)*

17. $\frac{^-1}{5} \cdot \frac{^-1}{4}$ **18.** $^-3\frac{1}{2} \cdot 2\frac{3}{4}$ **19.** $\frac{3}{8} \div \frac{1}{8}$ **20.** $^-4\frac{3}{4} \div 2\frac{1}{8}$

▶ **Solve and check.** *(page 234)*

21. $5x + 3 = 11$ **22.** $^-6y - 2 = 17$ **23.** $8 + 9w = {}^-20$ **24.** $7 - 10z = {}^-1$

▶ **Simplify by combining like terms.** *(page 236)*

25. $7a + 5a$ **26.** $6f - f - 3$ **27.** $15 - h + 10h - 4$

▶ **Solve and check.** *(pages 238, 240)*

28. $2n + 3n - 6 = {}^-8$ **29.** $7n - n + 10 = 16$ **30.** $3p + 8 - 4 = 0$

31. $5x + 3x = 8 - 10$ **32.** $5y - y + 4 = 6 - 12$ **33.** $9w + w = 15 + 9$

▶ **First choose the equation and solve the problem. Then reread the problem to see if your answer makes sense.** *(page 239)*

Equation A: $8n + 4n = {}^-32$
Equation B: $8n + 4 = {}^-32$
Equation C: $8n - 4 = {}^-32$

34. Four less than the product of 8 and a number n is $^-32$. What is the number?

35. The sum of 8 times a number n and 4 times a number n is $^-32$. What is the number?

36. The sum of 8 times a number n and 4 is $^-32$. What is the number?

37. Eight times a number n increased by 4 times a number n is $^-32$. What is the number?

Cumulative Test
Standardized Format

▶ **Choose the correct letter.**

1. The least common denominator of $\frac{3x}{4y^2z}$ and $\frac{3}{yz}$ is

A. $4yz$ B. $4y^2z$
C. $4y^2z^2$ D. none of these

2. $\frac{5a}{10a^2b}$ written in simplest form is

A. $\frac{a}{2a^2b}$ B. $\frac{5}{10ab}$
C. $\frac{1}{2ab}$ D. none of these

3. Give the sum.
$\frac{3a}{2} + \frac{b}{3}$

A. $\frac{3a + b}{6}$ B. $\frac{9a + b}{6}$
C. $\frac{3a + 2b}{6}$ D. none of these

4. Give the difference.
$\frac{2x}{3} - \frac{5y}{4}$

A. $\frac{8x - 15y}{12}$ B. $\frac{2x - 5y}{12}$
C. $\frac{8x - 5y}{12}$ D. none of these

5. Give the product.
$\frac{2c}{d} \cdot \frac{d}{2f}$

A. $\frac{4cf}{d^2}$ B. $\frac{cd}{f}$
C. $\frac{c}{f}$ D. none of these

6. Give the quotient.
$\frac{m}{3n} \div \frac{5m}{n^2}$

A. $\frac{n}{15}$ B. $\frac{5m^2}{3n^2}$
C. $\frac{n^2}{15m}$ D. none of these

7. Solve.
$\frac{2}{3}$ of $20 = n$

A. 20 B. $13\frac{1}{3}$
C. 30 D. none of these

8. $4\frac{2}{3}$ yd = __?__ ft

A. 13
B. 28
C. 56
D. none of these

9. Solve.
$\frac{5}{2}$ of $n = 40$

A. 16 B. 40
C. 100 D. none of these

10. 0.000875 written in scientific notation is

A. $8.75 \cdot 10^4$
B. $0.875 \cdot 10^{-3}$
C. $8.75 \cdot 10^{-4}$
D. none of these

11. Solve.
$24 = \frac{y}{^{-}2} - 6$

A. $^{-}60$
B. $^{-}36$
C. $^{-}15$
D. none of these

12. Choose the equation.

You worked 5 hours on Friday and 4 hours on Saturday. After spending $9 of what you earned, you had $27 left. How much did you earn per hour?

A. $5n + 4n + 9 = 27$
B. $5n + 4n - 9 = 27$
C. $5n - 4n + 9 = 27$
D. $5n - 4n - 9 = 27$

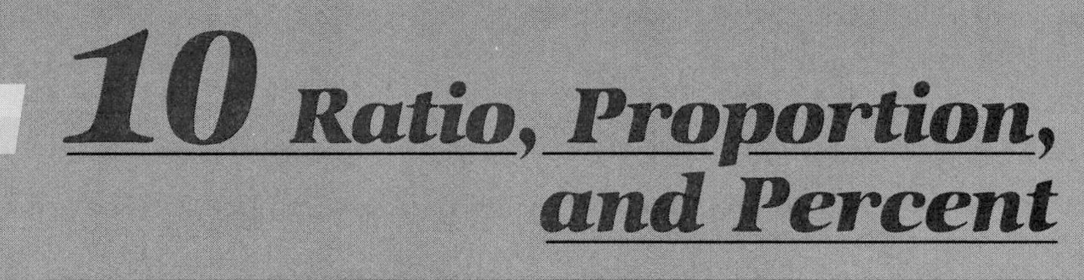

10 Ratio, Proportion, and Percent

I = prt

Interest equals principal times rate times time.

(page 270)

When you put money in a savings account, the bank pays you interest on the principal (the amount in your account). When you borrow money from the bank, you pay the bank interest on the principal (the amount you borrow).

Ratios

Country	Number of Stamps
Austria	24
Canada	96
Denmark	18
France	60
Great Britain	72
Russia	64
United States	120
West Germany	66

You can use a **ratio** to compare two numbers. The table shows how many stamps John has from each of the eight countries. The ratio of Austrian stamps to Canadian stamps is 24 to 96. Here are three ways to write the ratio:

24 to 96 $\qquad \mathbf{\frac{24}{96}} \qquad$ **24:96**

Read each ratio as "24 to 96."

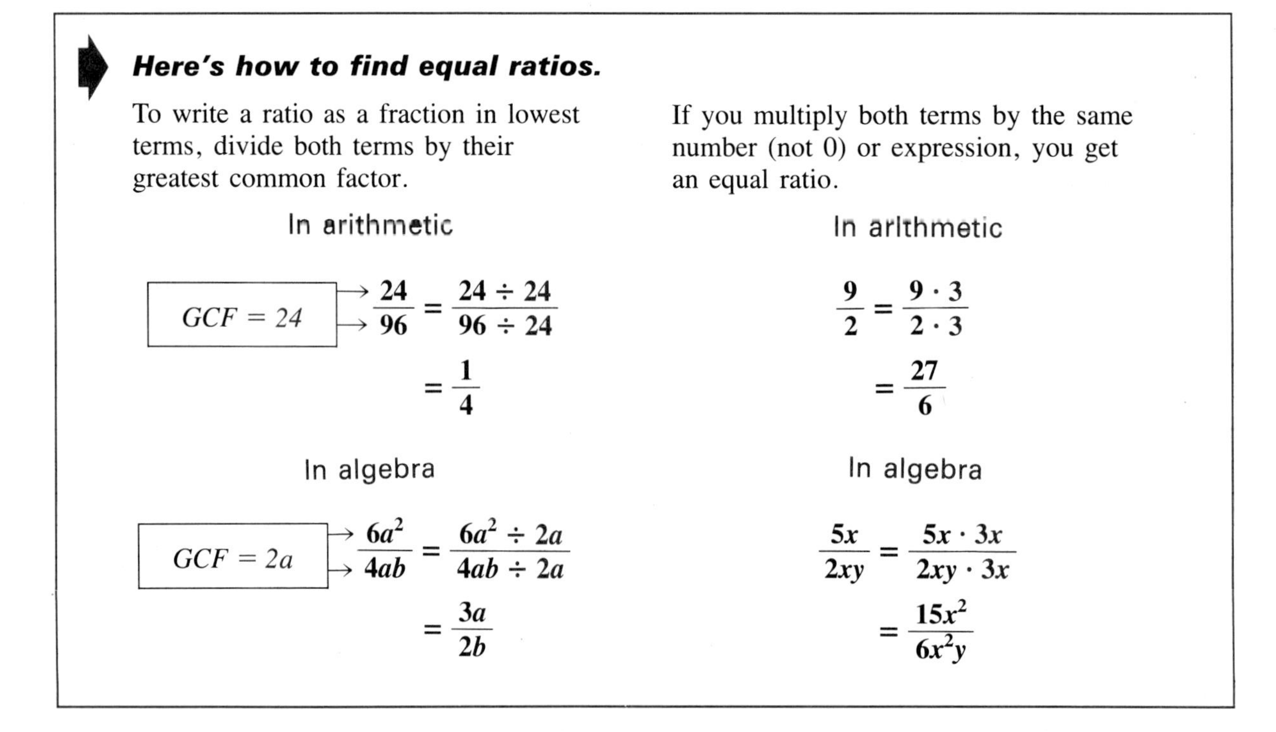

Here's how to find equal ratios.

To write a ratio as a fraction in lowest terms, divide both terms by their greatest common factor.

In arithmetic

GCF = 24

$$\frac{24}{96} = \frac{24 \div 24}{96 \div 24} = \frac{1}{4}$$

In algebra

GCF = 2a

$$\frac{6a^2}{4ab} = \frac{6a^2 \div 2a}{4ab \div 2a} = \frac{3a}{2b}$$

If you multiply both terms by the same number (not 0) or expression, you get an equal ratio.

In arithmetic

$$\frac{9}{2} = \frac{9 \cdot 3}{2 \cdot 3} = \frac{27}{6}$$

In algebra

$$\frac{5x}{2xy} = \frac{5x \cdot 3x}{2xy \cdot 3x} = \frac{15x^2}{6x^2y}$$

1. Look at the example above. What is the ratio of Austrian stamps to Canadian stamps written in lowest terms?

2. To write $\frac{6a^2}{4ab}$ in lowest terms, both terms were divided by the GCF which is _?_.

3. If you multiply both terms by the same number (not 0) or expression, you get an _?_ ratio.

4. Both terms of $\frac{5x}{2xy}$ were multiplied by _?_ to get the equal ratio $\frac{15x^2}{6x^2y}$.

5. Complete these examples.

   a. $\frac{30}{40} = \frac{?}{4}$ $\qquad$ b. $\frac{6}{5} = \frac{?}{15}$ $\qquad$ c. $\frac{ab^2}{2ab} = \frac{?}{2}$ $\qquad$ d. $\frac{3x}{5y} = \frac{?}{10y^2}$

EXERCISES

▶ **Give each ratio as a fraction in lowest terms.**
Here are scrambled answers for the next row of exercises: $\frac{4}{3}$ $\frac{1}{4}$ $\frac{5}{2}$ $\frac{1}{2}$ $\frac{4}{9}$

6. 4 to 8 **7.** 3 to 12 **8.** 15 to 6 **9.** 8 to 6 **10.** 16 to 36

11. $\frac{14}{21}$ **12.** $\frac{10}{4}$ **13.** $\frac{16}{6}$ **14.** $\frac{9}{45}$ **15.** $\frac{18}{27}$

16. 12:20 **17.** 14:8 **18.** 18:32 **19.** 12:18 **20.** 24:18

21. $2a$ to $4b$ **22.** $9x$ to $6x$ **23.** cd to c^2 **24.** $2r^2$ to $8rs$ **25.** $6m^2$ to $8mn^2$

26. $\frac{8c}{24d}$ **27.** $\frac{24j}{16j}$ **28.** $\frac{5ab}{2a^2}$ **29.** $\frac{16yz}{12z^2}$ **30.** $\frac{18s^2t^2}{24st}$

31. $15m:25n$ **32.** $32x:28x$ **33.** $12cd^2:18d$ **34.** $24a:16ab^2$ **35.** $36jh^2:20j^2h$

▶ **Complete to get an equal ratio.**

36. $\frac{3}{4} = \frac{?}{8}$ **37.** $\frac{8}{5} = \frac{?}{15}$ **38.** $\frac{7}{8} = \frac{?}{24}$ **39.** $\frac{1}{3} = \frac{?}{18}$ **40.** $\frac{5}{2} = \frac{?}{16}$

41. $\frac{3}{2} = \frac{?}{24}$ **42.** $\frac{5}{4} = \frac{?}{12}$ **43.** $\frac{1}{2} = \frac{?}{18}$ **44.** $\frac{3}{4} = \frac{?}{16}$ **45.** $\frac{11}{2} = \frac{?}{20}$

46. $\frac{4}{5} = \frac{?}{40}$ **47.** $\frac{5}{6} = \frac{?}{30}$ **48.** $\frac{9}{4} = \frac{?}{24}$ **49.** $\frac{2}{5} = \frac{?}{50}$ **50.** $\frac{10}{3} = \frac{?}{18}$

51. $\frac{3}{b} = \frac{?}{7b}$ **52.** $\frac{5}{x} = \frac{?}{xy}$ **53.** $\frac{n}{8} = \frac{?}{8m}$ **54.** $\frac{12}{c} = \frac{?}{c^2}$ **55.** $\frac{w}{6} = \frac{?}{6z^2}$

56. $\frac{a}{b} = \frac{?}{2b^2}$ **57.** $\frac{j^2}{k} = \frac{?}{10k^2}$ **58.** $\frac{t^2}{s} = \frac{?}{4s^2}$ **59.** $\frac{5m}{3n} = \frac{?}{15mn}$ **60.** $\frac{8x^2y}{3x} = \frac{?}{18x}$

61. $\frac{3cd}{c^2d} = \frac{?}{c^2d^2}$ **62.** $\frac{2rs^2}{3rs} = \frac{?}{9r^2s}$ **63.** $\frac{9}{4a} = \frac{?}{12a^2b^3}$ **64.** $\frac{3m}{8n} = \frac{?}{24mn^2}$ **65.** $\frac{7x^2y}{3} = \frac{?}{15y}$

Problem Solving

▶ **Solve. Use the chart on page 250.**

66. What is the ratio in lowest terms of French stamps to British stamps?

67. What is the ratio in lowest terms of British stamps to French stamps?

68. How many United States stamps are there for each French stamp?

69. How many British stamps are there for every 8 Russian stamps?

70. For every 20 United States stamps, there are 3 stamps from which country?

71. What is the ratio in lowest terms of foreign stamps to United States stamps?

Proportions

The Douglas Chicago *was flown in 1924 by a team of U.S. Army pilots who were the first to fly around the world.*

Suppose that you decided to build a model of the Douglas Chicago that is $\frac{1}{10}$ the size of the real airplane. To decide how wide the wingspan should be, you could solve a proportion. A **proportion** is an equation that states that two ratios are equal.

wingspan of model airplane → $\frac{n}{50} = \frac{1}{10}$ ← *model airplane*

wingspan of real airplane → 50; 10 ← *real airplane*

Note: ***When setting up a proportion, make sure that the ratios are in the same order.***

1. Look at the proportion above. If you think about equal ratios, what must n equal?
2. Therefore, if your model is $\frac{1}{10}$ the size of the real airplane, what should the wingspan of the model be?

The Lockheed Vega *was flown in 1932 by Amelia Earhart who became the first woman to fly across the Atlantic solo and nonstop.*

Suppose you decide to build a model of the Lockheed Vega that is $\frac{3}{8}$ the size of the real airplane. To decide how wide the wingspan should be, you could solve this proportion: $\frac{n}{41} = \frac{3}{8}$

3. Is this proportion easy to solve by thinking about equal ratios?

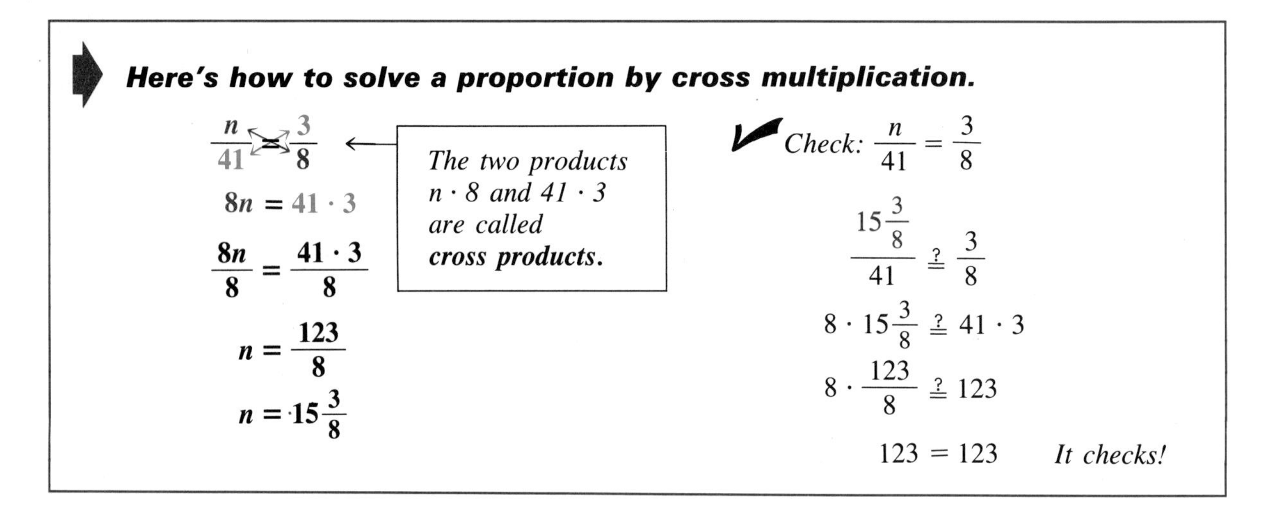

Here's how to solve a proportion by cross multiplication.

$$\frac{n}{41} = \frac{3}{8}$$

$$8n = 41 \cdot 3$$

$$\frac{8n}{8} = \frac{41 \cdot 3}{8}$$

$$n = \frac{123}{8}$$

$$n = 15\frac{3}{8}$$

The two products $n \cdot 8$ and $41 \cdot 3$ are called ***cross products.***

Check: $\frac{n}{41} = \frac{3}{8}$

$$\frac{15\frac{3}{8}}{41} \stackrel{?}{=} \frac{3}{8}$$

$$8 \cdot 15\frac{3}{8} \stackrel{?}{=} 41 \cdot 3$$

$$8 \cdot \frac{123}{8} \stackrel{?}{=} 123$$

$$123 = 123$$ *It checks!*

4. Look at the example above. If your model is $\frac{3}{8}$ the size of the real Lockheed Vega, what should the wingspan of the model be?

5. Complete these examples.

a. $\frac{n}{8} \times \frac{3}{5}$

$5n = 8 \cdot 3$

$\frac{5n}{5} = \frac{24}{5}$

$n = \underline{?}$

b. $\frac{8}{6} \times \frac{4}{n}$

$8n = 6 \cdot 4$

$\frac{8n}{8} = \frac{?}{8}$

$n = 3$

c. $\frac{5}{2} \times \frac{n}{7}$

$2n = 5 \cdot \underline{?}$

$2n = 35$

$\frac{2n}{2} = \frac{35}{2}$

$n = 17\frac{1}{2}$

d. $\frac{2}{n} \times \frac{4}{1\frac{1}{2}}$

$\underline{?}\, n = 2 \cdot 1\frac{1}{2}$

$4n = 3$

$\frac{4n}{4} = \frac{3}{4}$

$n = \frac{3}{4}$

EXERCISES

▶ **Solve each proportion by thinking about equal ratios or by cross multiplication. Give answers in simplest form.**

Here are scrambled answers for the next row of exercises: $2\frac{11}{12}$ 18 16 $1\frac{3}{5}$ $2\frac{1}{10}$

6. $\frac{1}{2} = \frac{8}{n}$ **7.** $\frac{2}{3} = \frac{12}{n}$ **8.** $\frac{n}{8} = \frac{2}{10}$ **9.** $\frac{7}{n} = \frac{12}{5}$ **10.** $\frac{3}{10} = \frac{n}{7}$

11. $\frac{9}{11} = \frac{n}{7}$ **12.** $\frac{13}{4} = \frac{10}{n}$ **13.** $\frac{n}{18} = \frac{6}{3}$ **14.** $\frac{11}{n} = \frac{18}{5}$ **15.** $\frac{16}{5} = \frac{20}{n}$

16. $\frac{n}{9} = \frac{14}{3}$ **17.** $\frac{20}{n} = \frac{14}{11}$ **18.** $\frac{9}{15} = \frac{n}{18}$ **19.** $\frac{16}{5} = \frac{30}{n}$ **20.** $\frac{18}{n} = \frac{9}{4}$

21. $\frac{1\frac{1}{2}}{3} = \frac{n}{2}$ **22.** $\frac{10}{7} = \frac{1\frac{1}{4}}{n}$ **23.** $\frac{4}{n} = \frac{8}{2\frac{3}{4}}$ **24.** $\frac{n}{2\frac{1}{2}} = \frac{4}{6}$ **25.** $\frac{5}{4} = \frac{1\frac{1}{4}}{n}$

26. $\frac{7}{8} = \frac{5\frac{2}{3}}{n}$ **27.** $\frac{4}{n} = \frac{2\frac{1}{3}}{5}$ **28.** $\frac{2}{3\frac{1}{4}} = \frac{n}{9}$ **29.** $\frac{n}{3} = \frac{8}{1\frac{1}{2}}$ **30.** $\frac{n}{5} = \frac{2}{6\frac{1}{5}}$

Problem Solving

▶ **Solve. Use the information on page 252.**

31. Suppose you decide to make a model of the Lockheed Vega that is $\frac{1}{30}$ the size of the real airplane.

a. What should the wingspan of the model be?

b. How long should the model be?

32. Suppose you decide to make a model of the Douglas Chicago that is $\frac{3}{20}$ the size of the real airplane.

a. What should the wingspan of the model be?

b. How long should the model be?

33. A model of the Lockheed Vega has a wingspan of 3 feet. What should the length be?

34. A model of the Douglas Chicago has a length of $4\frac{7}{16}$ feet. What should the wingspan be?

Rates

A **rate** is a ratio of two quantities.

You spent \$11.13 for 8 gallons of gasoline.

Rate: $\frac{\$11.13}{8 \text{ gal}}$

Read as "\$11.13 per 8 gallons."

Here's how to use proportions to solve rate problems.

Problem A If you spent \$11.13 for 8 gallons of gasoline, how much would you spend for 14 gallons?

Remember: When setting up a proportion, you must be sure that the ratios are in the same order!

dollars → $\frac{11.13}{8} = \frac{n}{14}$ ← *dollars*
gallons → ← *gallons*

$$8n = 11.13 \cdot 14$$

$$8n = 155.82$$

$$n \approx 19.48$$

$8\overline{)155.8200}$ = 19.4775

Read ≈ as "is approximately equal to."

At the given rate, you would spend \$19.48 for 14 gallons of gasoline.

Problem B You drive 196 miles in 4 hours. At that rate, how many hours will it take you to drive 340 miles?

miles → $\frac{196}{4} = \frac{340}{n}$ ← *miles*
hours → ← *hours*

$$196n = 4 \cdot 340$$

$$196n = 1360$$

$$n \approx 6.94$$

$196\overline{)1360.0000}$ = 6.9387

At the given rate, it would take you about 6.94 hours to drive 340 miles.

EXERCISES

▶ Solve by using proportions. If an answer does not come out evenly, round it to the nearest hundredth.

1. You spend $18 for 12 gallons of gasoline. At that price,

a. how many gallons could you buy for $13?

Hint: $\frac{18}{12} = \frac{13}{n}$

b. how many gallons could you buy for $7.50?

c. how much would 6 gallons cost?

d. how much would 11.4 gallons cost?

2. You drive 128 miles in 3 hours. At that speed,

a. how many miles could you drive in 4 hours?

Hint: $\frac{128}{3} = \frac{n}{4}$

b. how many miles could you drive in 9 hours?

c. how many hours would it take you to drive 300 miles?

d. how many hours would it take you to drive 186 miles?

3. You drive 124 miles and use 4.8 gallons of gasoline. At that rate,

a. how many miles could you drive on 10 gallons?

b. how many miles could you drive on 13 gallons?

c. how many gallons would you need for 400 miles?

d. how many gallons would you need for 280 miles?

4. You spend $3.60 to drive 110 miles on a toll road. At that rate,

a. how many miles could you drive for $1.80?

b. how many miles could you drive for $3.00?

c. how much would it cost to drive 180 miles?

d. how much would it cost to drive 95 miles?

5. During the first 2 days of your trip you spend $43 for meals. At that rate,

a. how much will your meals cost for 7 days?

b. how many days of meals could you buy for $200?

6. You drive 4 hours and use 8.2 gallons of gasoline. At that rate,

a. how many hours could you drive on 10 gallons?

b. how many gallons would you need to drive 9 hours?

★7. You want to be in Chicago by 12 noon. At 9:30 A.M. you are 127 miles from Chicago and you are traveling at the rate of 54 miles per hour. Will you be on time if you keep driving at the same rate?

★8. At 2:45 P.M. you are 117 miles from Tampa. You want to be in Tampa at 5:00 P.M. How many miles per hour must you average to be on time?

Changing a Percent to a Fraction

The circle graph shows how Roberto budgeted his money. Notice that $12\frac{1}{2}\%$ $\left(12\frac{1}{2}\text{ percent}\right)$ of his earnings is spent for records. This means that $12\frac{1}{2}¢$ out of each $100¢$ is spent for records. *Percent* means "per 100."

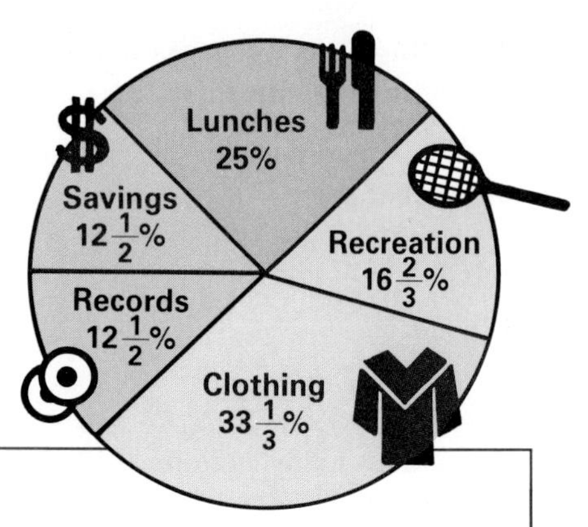

1. What percent is budgeted for lunches?
2. What percent is budgeted for recreation?

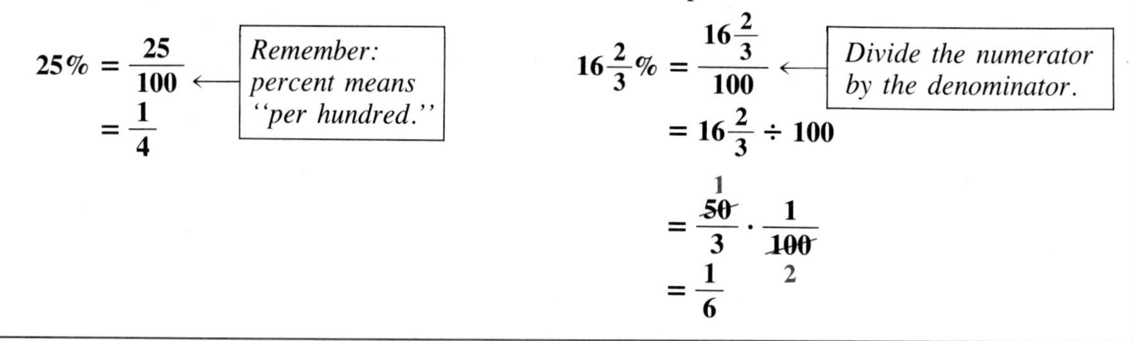

Here's how to change a percent to a fraction.

To change a percent to a fraction, first write the percent as a fraction with a denominator of 100. Then write the fraction in simplest form.

Fraction spent for lunches

$$\mathbf{25\% = \frac{25}{100} = \frac{1}{4}}$$

Remember: percent means "per hundred."

Fraction spent for recreation

$$\mathbf{16\frac{2}{3}\% = \frac{16\frac{2}{3}}{100} = 16\frac{2}{3} \div 100 = \frac{\overset{1}{\cancel{50}}}{3} \cdot \frac{1}{\underset{2}{\cancel{100}}} = \frac{1}{6}}$$

Divide the numerator by the denominator.

3. Look at the example above. What fraction of the budget is spent for lunches? What fraction is spent for recreation?

4. Complete these examples.

a. $20\% = \frac{20}{100} = \underline{?}$

b. $75\% = \frac{?}{100} = \frac{3}{4}$

c. $150\% = \frac{150}{?} = \frac{3}{2} = 1\frac{1}{2}$

d. $37\frac{1}{2}\% = \frac{37\frac{1}{2}}{100} = 37\frac{1}{2} \div 100 = \frac{\overset{3}{\cancel{75}}}{2} \cdot \frac{1}{\underset{4}{\cancel{100}}} = \underline{?}$

e. $8\frac{1}{3}\% = \frac{8\frac{1}{3}}{100} = 8\frac{1}{3} \div 100 = \frac{25}{3} \cdot \underline{?} = \frac{1}{12}$

f. $83\frac{1}{3}\% = \frac{?}{100} = 83\frac{1}{3} \div 100 = \frac{?}{3} \cdot \frac{1}{100} = \frac{5}{6}$

EXERCISES

▶ **Change to a fraction, whole number, or mixed number. Give each answer in simplest form.**
Here are scrambled answers for the next row of exercises:

$\frac{7}{10}$ 1 $\frac{1}{2}$ $\frac{1}{4}$ $1\frac{1}{4}$ $\frac{18}{25}$

5. 25%	**6.** 125%	**7.** 50%	**8.** 100%	**9.** 70%	**10.** 72%
11. 15%	**12.** 32%	**13.** 220%	**14.** 66%	**15.** 44%	**16.** 48%
17. 20%	**18.** 120%	**19.** 60%	**20.** 300%	**21.** 225%	**22.** 175%
23. 74%	**24.** 16%	**25.** 150%	**26.** 96%	**27.** 250%	**28.** 375%
29. 85%	**30.** 75%	**31.** 10%	**32.** 325%	**33.** 160%	**34.** 40%
35. 110%	**36.** 30%	**37.** 400%	**38.** 200%	**39.** 90%	**40.** 35%
41. 45%	**42.** 350%	**43.** 210%	**44.** 5%	**45.** 275%	**46.** 80%
47. $18\frac{3}{4}\%$	**48.** $8\frac{1}{3}\%$	**49.** $81\frac{1}{4}\%$	**50.** $66\frac{2}{3}\%$	**51.** $62\frac{1}{2}\%$	**52.** $116\frac{2}{3}\%$
53. $206\frac{1}{4}\%$	**54.** $33\frac{1}{3}\%$	**55.** $187\frac{1}{2}\%$	**56.** $106\frac{1}{4}\%$	**57.** $162\frac{1}{2}\%$	**58.** $233\frac{1}{3}\%$
59. $137\frac{1}{2}\%$	**60.** $87\frac{1}{2}\%$	**61.** $16\frac{2}{3}\%$	**62.** $166\frac{2}{3}\%$	**63.** $133\frac{1}{3}\%$	**64.** 212%

Problem Solving

▶ **Solve. Use the graph on page 256.**

65. For what two items did Roberto budget half his money?

66. For which item did Roberto budget the greatest percent of his money?

67. What fraction of Roberto's money is spent for clothing?

68. What fraction of Roberto's money is spent for records?

69. What fraction of Roberto's money is budgeted for either clothing or records? *Hint: Use your answers from exercises 67 and 68.*

70. What fraction of Roberto's money is not budgeted for savings?

★**71.** Suppose that Roberto received $24. How much would be budgeted for

a. lunches? **b.** recreation? **c.** clothing? **d.** records? **e.** savings?

★**72.** Suppose that out of one paycheck Roberto could spend $16 for clothing. For what amount was the paycheck?

Changing a Fraction to a Percent

Look at the football helmets. Can you name the team for each helmet? This question was part of a football survey. The tally below shows the results.

Name	Number of Teams Named Correctly
Jane	卌 卌 卌 ǀ
Ruth	卌 卌 ǀǀǀǀ
Mel	卌 卌 ǀǀ
David	卌 卌 卌 ǀǀǀ
Tom	卌 卌 卌 ǀǀ
Amy	卌 卌 卌 卌

1. How many teams did Mel name correctly?
2. How many teams are there in all?
3. What fraction of the teams did Mel name correctly?
4. What fraction of the teams did Jane name correctly?

Here's how to change a fraction to a percent.

Changing Mel's fraction to a percent

Method 1. Change to an equivalent fraction with a denominator of 100. Then write as a percent.

$$\frac{1}{2} = \frac{50}{100}$$
$$= 50\%$$

Changing Jane's fraction to a percent

Method 2. Since there is no whole number that you can multiply by 3 to get the denominator of 100, solve a proportion.

$$\frac{2}{3} = \frac{n}{100}$$
$$3n = 200$$
$$n = 66\frac{2}{3}$$

$$\frac{2}{3} = \frac{66\frac{2}{3}}{100}$$
$$= 66\frac{2}{3}\%$$

5. Look at the examples above. What percent of the teams did Mel name correctly? What percent did Jane name correctly?
6. Which method would you use to change $\frac{2}{5}$ to a percent? To change $\frac{1}{12}$ to a percent?

Change to a percent. ***Hint: First change to an equivalent fraction with a denominator of 100.***
Here are scrambled answers for the next row of exercises:
225% 40% 60% 90% 50% 125%

7. $\frac{2}{5}$ **8.** $\frac{9}{4}$ **9.** $\frac{9}{10}$ **10.** $\frac{3}{5}$ **11.** $\frac{5}{4}$ **12.** $\frac{1}{2}$

13. $\frac{1}{5}$ **14.** $\frac{1}{4}$ **15.** $\frac{4}{5}$ **16.** 1 **17.** $\frac{1}{10}$ **18.** $\frac{3}{10}$

19. $\frac{3}{2}$ **20.** 2 **21.** $\frac{7}{5}$ **22.** $\frac{3}{4}$ **23.** $\frac{5}{2}$ **24.** $\frac{13}{4}$

Change to a percent. ***Hint: You may need to solve a proportion.***
Here are scrambled answers for the next row of exercises:
175% $16\frac{2}{3}\%$ $33\frac{1}{3}\%$ *120%* $133\frac{1}{3}\%$ $83\frac{1}{3}\%$

25. $\frac{1}{3}$ **26.** $\frac{1}{6}$ **27.** $\frac{7}{4}$ **28.** $\frac{6}{5}$ **29.** $\frac{5}{6}$ **30.** $\frac{4}{3}$

31. $\frac{9}{16}$ **32.** $\frac{9}{25}$ **33.** $\frac{5}{9}$ **34.** $\frac{7}{2}$ **35.** $\frac{2}{3}$ **36.** $\frac{3}{8}$

37. $\frac{4}{9}$ **38.** $\frac{9}{20}$ **39.** $\frac{31}{50}$ **40.** $\frac{5}{3}$ **41.** $\frac{5}{12}$ **42.** $\frac{1}{12}$

43. $\frac{7}{25}$ **44.** $\frac{17}{10}$ **45.** $\frac{7}{8}$ **46.** 3 **47.** $\frac{5}{8}$ **48.** $\frac{11}{25}$

49. $\frac{8}{3}$ **50.** $\frac{2}{5}$ **51.** $\frac{7}{6}$ **52.** $\frac{13}{10}$ **53.** $\frac{11}{12}$ **54.** $\frac{9}{5}$

55. $\frac{9}{2}$ **56.** $\frac{17}{20}$ **57.** $\frac{7}{3}$ **58.** $\frac{8}{5}$ **59.** $\frac{11}{6}$ **60.** $\frac{7}{20}$

Problem Solving

Solve. Use the survey results on page 258.

61. What percent of the teams did Tom name correctly?

62. What percent of the teams did Ruth name correctly?

63. What percent of those surveyed knew more than 15 teams?

64. What percent of those surveyed knew 15 or fewer teams?

65. What percent of the teams did Amy miss?

66. How much greater was David's percent than Mel's percent?

67. Allison got $41\frac{2}{3}\%$ of the teams correct. What fraction of the teams did she name correctly?

★**68.** John named $87\frac{1}{2}\%$ of the teams correctly. How many teams did he miss?

Cumulative Skill Practice

▶ **Give the prime factorization using exponents.** *(page 124)*

1. 9 **2.** 4 **3.** 12 **4.** 20 **5.** 27 **6.** 24

7. 25 **8.** 100 **9.** 48 **10.** 16 **11.** 64 **12.** 96

13. 144 **14.** 32 **15.** 240 **16.** 243 **17.** 160 **18.** 128

19. 60 **20.** 480 **21.** 72 **22.** 180 **23.** 360 **24.** 200

▶ **Give the greatest common factor.** *(page 126)*

25. 3, 16 **26.** 18, 12 **27.** 25, 30 **28.** 60, 40

29. 48, 16 **30.** 4, $8c$ **31.** 24, $13d$ **32.** $9x$, $16x$

33. $12y$, y **34.** $6z$, $9z$ **35.** $24a$, $16a$ **36.** $10c$, $13c^2$

37. $5b^2$, $3b$ **38.** $24d$, $21d^2$ **39.** $36f$, $9f^2$ **40.** $15xy$, $18x^2$

41. $15w^2z$, $25wz^2$ **42.** $42m^2n$, $28n^2$ **43.** $32p^2q^2$, $24pq^2$ **44.** $40x^2y^3$, $25xy^2$

▶ **Write in lowest terms.** *(page 132)*

45. $\frac{9}{27}$ **46.** $\frac{15}{12}$ **47.** $\frac{21}{35}$ **48.** $\frac{48}{36}$ **49.** $\frac{28}{42}$ **50.** $\frac{25}{40}$

51. $\frac{z}{z^2}$ **52.** $\frac{9}{6y}$ **53.** $\frac{5n}{15m}$ **54.** $\frac{ab}{5b}$ **55.** $\frac{20mn}{4m^2}$ **56.** $\frac{21}{24h^2}$

57. $\frac{18x}{6y}$ **58.** $\frac{r^2s}{10s^2}$ **59.** $\frac{36p}{42pq}$ **60.** $\frac{17a^3}{3a^2}$ **61.** $\frac{35yz^2}{15y^2}$ **62.** $\frac{18s^2t}{48s^2t^2}$

▶ **Write in scientific notation.** *(page 208)*

63. 18,000 **64.** 5,200 **65.** 390,000 **66.** 14,600,000

67. 9,640,000 **68.** 865,000 **69.** 61,000,000 **70.** 591,000,000

71. 0.014 **72.** 0.0096 **73.** 0.0004 **74.** 0.00084

75. 0.000256 **76.** 0.001472 **77.** 0.0000313 **78.** 0.006173

▶ **Solve and check.** *(page 214)*

79. $4y + y = {}^{-}21$ **80.** $6x - 5 = {}^{-}41$ **81.** $\frac{n}{4} + 3 = {}^{-}10$ **82.** $\frac{m}{7} - 12 = {}^{-}15$

83. $4 = {}^{-}5k + 24$ **84.** ${}^{-}16 = {}^{-}3j - 1$ **85.** ${}^{-}12 = 7z - 12$ **86.** $23 = 12c - 25$

87. ${}^{-}6 = \frac{a}{2} + 6$ **88.** $15 = \frac{d}{{}^{-}2} + 20$ **89.** $30 = \frac{f}{{}^{-}6} + 21$ **90.** ${}^{-}32 = \frac{b}{8} - 25$

91. ${}^{-}11s - 5 = 17$ **92.** ${}^{-}8t + 16 = 40$ **93.** $\frac{y}{{}^{-}9} + 15 = 23$ **94.** $\frac{x}{{}^{-}7} - 28 = {}^{-}36$

Problem Solving—Applications

A map is an example of a scale drawing. On this map, 1 centimeter stands for 130 kilometers. To find the actual air distance between cities, we can measure a distance on the map and solve a proportion.

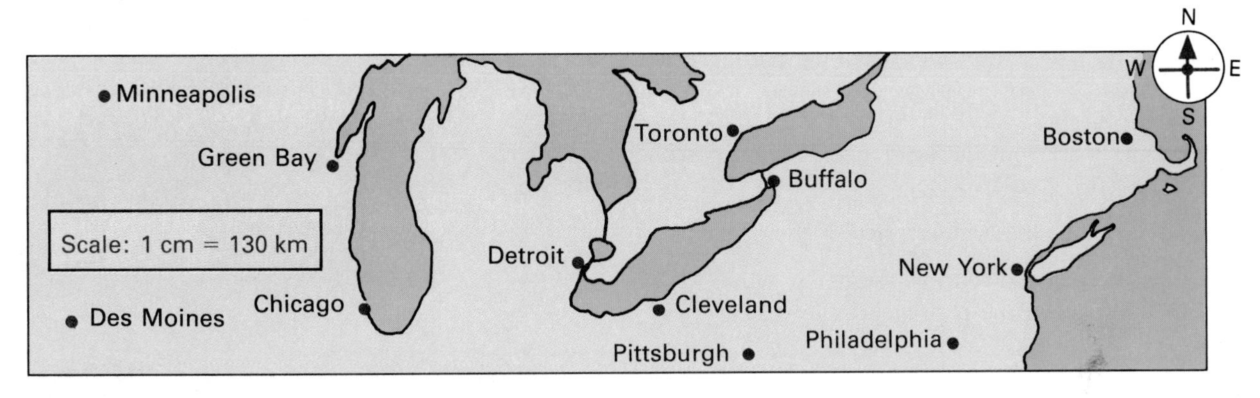

Example: The distance from Chicago to Boston on the map is 10.4 centimeters. What is the actual air distance from Chicago to Boston?

cm on map → / *actual km* → $\frac{1}{130} = \frac{10.4}{n}$ ← *cm on map* / ← *actual km*

$n = 10.4(130)$

$n = 1352$

The actual air distance from Chicago to Boston is 1352 kilometers.

Find the actual air distance between the cities. The map distances are given.

1. Chicago to Des Moines, 3.9 cm
2. New York to Chicago, 8.7 cm
3. New York to Detroit, 5.8 cm
4. Toronto to Minneapolis, 8.3 cm
5. Buffalo to Des Moines, 9.4 cm
6. Philadelphia to Buffalo, 3.3 cm
7. Toronto to Philadelphia, 4.1 cm
8. Detroit to Chicago, 2.9 cm

Use your answers to exercises 1–8 to solve.

9. How far is it from New York to Detroit to Chicago?
10. How far is it from New York to Chicago to Des Moines?
11. How much farther is it from Toronto to Minneapolis than from Toronto to Philadelphia?
12. How much farther is it from Buffalo to Des Moines than from Buffalo to Philadelphia?

Solve. Use a ruler and the map.

13. How far is it from Detroit to Minneapolis?
14. How far is it from Cleveland to Boston?
15. Which city is about 1150 kilometers east of Des Moines?
16. Which city is about 1750 kilometers west of Boston?

Finding a Percent of a Number

To find the sale price of an item, you can first compute the discount. The discount is the amount that is subtracted from the regular price.

1. What is the regular price of the blouse?
2. The discount on the blouse is what percent of the regular price?
3. What is the regular price of the sweater?
4. The discount on the sweater is what percent of the regular price?

Here's how to find a percent of a number.

To find a percent of a number, change the percent to a fraction or decimal and multiply.

Discount on Blouse

20% of $15 = *n*

Change the percent to a fraction and multiply.

20% of $15 = *n*

$\frac{1}{\cancel{5}_1} \cdot \$\cancel{15}^{3} = n$

$3 = *n*

Discount on Sweater

18% of $42 = *n*

Change the percent to a decimal and multiply.

18% of $42 = *n*

0.18 · $42 = *n*

$7.56 = *n*

Notice that to change a percent to a decimal, you can move the decimal point two places to the left and remove the percent sign.

5. Look at the first example above. What is the discount on the blouse? What is the sale price of the blouse?
6. Look at the second example. What is the discount on the sweater? What is the sale price of the sweater?
7. Complete these examples.

a. 25% of $36 = *n*

$\frac{1}{4} \cdot \$\underline{\ ?\ } = n$

$9 = *n*

b. 29% of $47 = *n*

0.29 · $\underline{ ? } = *n*

$13.63 = *n*

c. 80% of $65 = *n*

$\frac{4}{?} \cdot \$65 = n$

$52 = *n*

EXERCISES

▶ **Solve by changing the percent to a fraction and multiplying.**
Here are scrambled answers for the next row of exercises: 15 18 10

8. 50% of 36 = n **9.** 25% of 40 = n **10.** 60% of 25 = n

11. 75% of 24 = n **12.** 30% of 60 = n **13.** 10% of 80 = n

14. 75% of 32 = n **15.** 100% of 24 = n **16.** 150% of 18 = n

▶ **Solve by changing the percent to a decimal and multiplying.**
Here are scrambled answers for the next row of exercises: 128.7 4.68 49.92

17. 32% of 156 = n **18.** 9% of 52 = n **19.** 78% of 165 = n

20. 5.6% of 61 = n **21.** 8.75% of 46 = n **22.** 12.5% of 132 = n

23. 0.75% of 50 = n **24.** 0.35% of 21.5 = n **25.** 14.8% of 36.7 = n

▶ **Solve. *Hint: First try to decide which method would be easier.***

26. 25% of 73 = n **27.** 14% of 32 = n **28.** 80% of 20 = n

29. 10% of 125 = n **30.** 16.5% of 80 = n **31.** 20% of 50 = n

Problem Solving

▶ **Solve.**

32. Blue jeans that regularly sell for $24 are on sale for 25% off. How much is the discount?

33. Running shoes are on sale for 22% off the regular price. What is the sale price if the regular price is $42?

34. The regular price of a coat is $65. You have $40. How much more money do you need to buy the coat if it is on sale for 20% off the regular price?

35. A sweater that regularly sold for $48 was put on sale for 30% off. A week later you bought the sweater for 10% off the *sale price*. How much did you pay for the sweater?

CALCULATOR

36. Which calculator key did Robin and Jeff push to find 37% of 114?

Robin's method:
0.37 _?_ 114 [=] 42.18

Jeff's method:
114 _?_ 37 [%] 42.18

37. Use either Robin's or Jeff's method to find n.

a. 42% of 86 = n **b.** 89% of 72 = n

c. 7.6% of 14.2 = n **d.** 55.3% of 19.6 = n

e. 106% of 8.9 = n **f.** 214% of 35.1 = n

Finding the Number When a Percent Is Known

Name Carol Hansen
Number correct 52
Percent correct 80%

Part A. True or false?
T 1. The RED LIGHT requires a stop at the marked stop line. If there is no marked stop line, stop before entering the crosswalk on the near side of the intersection.
~~T~~ F 2. The YELLOW LIGHT warns that the signal is changing from green to red. When the red light appears, you are prohibited from enter-

1. What percent of the questions did Carol get correct on her driver's license test?
2. How many questions did Carol get correct?
3. Were there more or fewer than 52 questions on the test?

Here's how to find the number when a percent is known.

To find the number of questions on the test, you could solve the equation 80% of $n = 52$.

Change the percent to a fraction and solve the equation.

$$\mathbf{80\% \text{ of } n = 52}$$

$$\frac{4}{5}n = 52$$

$$\frac{\frac{4}{5}n}{\frac{4}{5}} = \frac{52}{\frac{4}{5}}$$

$$n = \overset{13}{\cancel{52}} \cdot \frac{5}{\underset{1}{\cancel{4}}}$$

$$n = 65$$

Change the percent to a decimal and solve the equation.

$$\mathbf{80\% \text{ of } n = 52}$$

$$0.80n = 52$$

$$\frac{0.80n}{0.80} = \frac{52}{0.80}$$

$$n = 65$$

4. Look at the example above. How many questions were on the test?
5. Complete these examples.

a. 75% of $n = 60$

$$\frac{3}{4}n = 60$$

$$\frac{\frac{3}{4}n}{\frac{3}{4}} = \frac{60}{\frac{3}{4}}$$

$$n = \overset{20}{\cancel{60}} \cdot \frac{4}{\underset{1}{\cancel{3}}}$$

$$n = \underline{?}$$

b. 42% of $n = 63$

$$0.42n = 63$$

$$\frac{0.42n}{0.42} = \frac{63}{0.42}$$

$$n = \underline{?}$$

c. 31% of $n = 72$

$$0.31n = 72$$

$$\frac{0.31n}{0.31} = \frac{72}{?}$$

$$n \approx 232.3$$

The answer was rounded to the nearest tenth.

▶ **Change the percent to a fraction and solve.**
Here are scrambled answers for the next row of exercises: 64 70 75

6. 20% of $n = 15$ **7.** 75% of $n = 48$ **8.** 60% of $n = 42$

9. 6% of $n = 12$ **10.** 9% of $n = 45$ **11.** 30% of $n = 15$

▶ **Change the percent to a decimal and solve. Round each answer to the nearest tenth.**
Here are scrambled answers for the next row of exercises: 50.5 81.6 20.3

12. 12.5% of $n = 10.2$ **13.** 6.4% of $n = 1.3$ **14.** 9.3% of $n = 4.7$

15. 0.5% of $n = 0.9$ **16.** 0.8% of $n = 1.3$ **17.** 1.2% of $n = 4.2$

18. 125% of $n = 2.3$ **19.** 175% of $n = 12.4$ **20.** 150% of $n = 10.5$

Problem Solving

▶ **Solve.**

21. You took a test that had 72 questions. You got 18 questions wrong.

a. What fraction of the questions did you get right?

b. What percent of the questions did you get right?

22. You took a test that had 120 questions. You got 80% of the questions right. How many questions did you get right?
Hint: 80% of $120 = n$

23. You got 60 questions on a test right. You scored 75%. How many questions were on the test?
Hint: 75% of $n = 60$.

24. You scored 90% on a test. You got 135 of the questions right. How many questions were on the test?

Challenge

▶ **Solve.**

The approximate distance (d) in feet that it takes you to stop a car traveling at the rate of r miles per hour is given by the formula:

Formula: $d \approx \frac{6r^2}{100}$

25. About how many feet would it take you to stop a car traveling at the rate of

a. 20 mph?

b. 35 mph?

c. 45 mph?

d. 55 mph?

Proportion and Percent

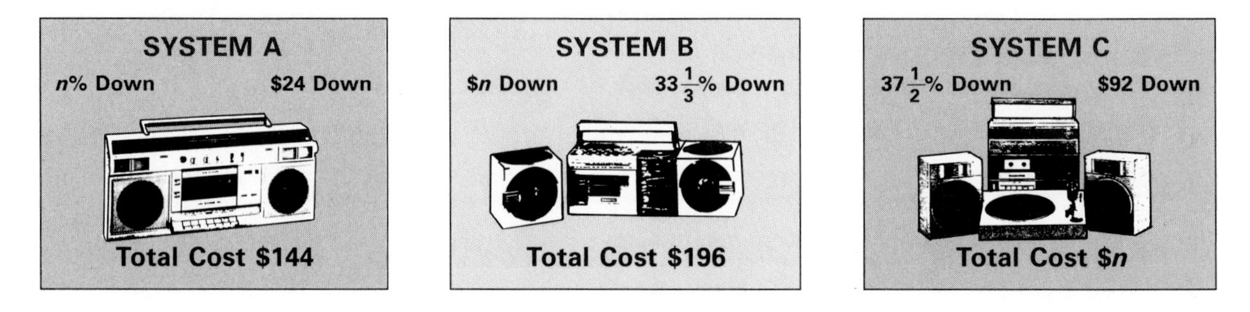

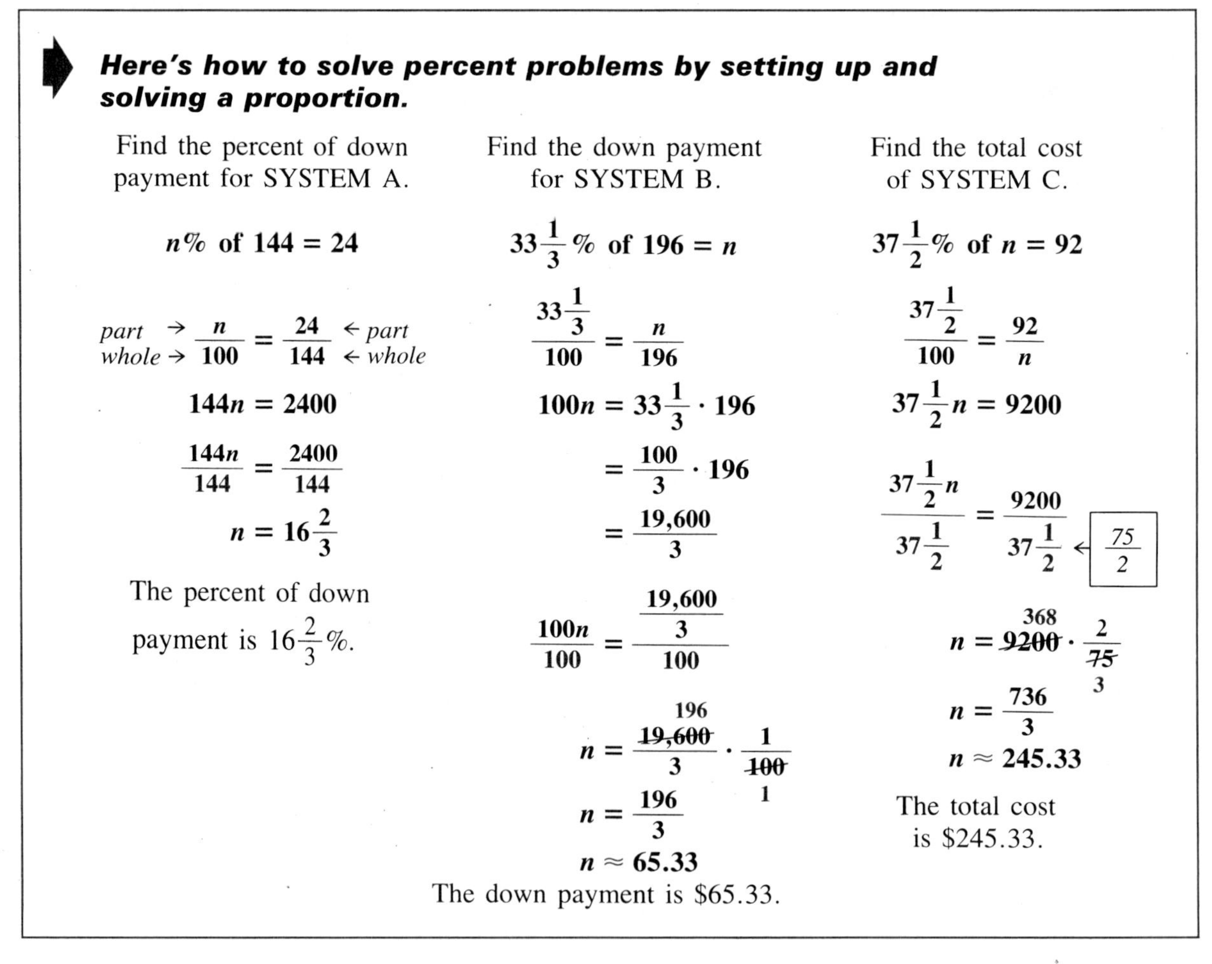

Here's how to solve percent problems by setting up and solving a proportion.

Find the percent of down payment for SYSTEM A.

$$n\% \text{ of } 144 = 24$$

$$\begin{matrix}\textit{part} \rightarrow \\ \textit{whole} \rightarrow\end{matrix} \frac{n}{100} = \frac{24}{144} \begin{matrix}\leftarrow \textit{part} \\ \leftarrow \textit{whole}\end{matrix}$$

$$144n = 2400$$

$$\frac{144n}{144} = \frac{2400}{144}$$

$$n = 16\frac{2}{3}$$

The percent of down payment is $16\frac{2}{3}\%$.

Find the down payment for SYSTEM B.

$$33\frac{1}{3}\% \text{ of } 196 = n$$

$$\frac{33\frac{1}{3}}{100} = \frac{n}{196}$$

$$100n = 33\frac{1}{3} \cdot 196$$

$$= \frac{100}{3} \cdot 196$$

$$= \frac{19{,}600}{3}$$

$$\frac{100n}{100} = \frac{\frac{19{,}600}{3}}{100}$$

$$n = \frac{\overset{196}{\cancel{19{,}600}}}{3} \cdot \frac{1}{\underset{1}{\cancel{100}}}$$

$$n = \frac{196}{3}$$

$$n \approx 65.33$$

The down payment is $65.33.

Find the total cost of SYSTEM C.

$$37\frac{1}{2}\% \text{ of } n = 92$$

$$\frac{37\frac{1}{2}}{100} = \frac{92}{n}$$

$$37\frac{1}{2}n = 9200$$

$$\frac{37\frac{1}{2}n}{37\frac{1}{2}} = \frac{9200}{37\frac{1}{2}} \leftarrow \boxed{\frac{75}{2}}$$

$$n = \overset{368}{\cancel{9200}} \cdot \frac{2}{\underset{3}{\cancel{75}}}$$

$$n = \frac{736}{3}$$

$$n \approx 245.33$$

The total cost is $245.33.

1. Complete these proportions.

a. $n\%$ of $132 = 56$

$$\frac{n}{?} = \frac{56}{?}$$

b. 29% of $157 = n$

$$\frac{?}{100} = \frac{?}{157}$$

c. $62\frac{1}{2}\%$ of $n = 72$

$$\frac{?}{100} = \frac{?}{?}$$

Solve. *Here are scrambled answers for the next row of exercises: 75 125 5*

2. $n\%$ of $4 = 3$
3. $n\%$ of $4 = 5$
4. $n\%$ of $20 = 1$
5. $n\%$ of $8 = 4$
6. $n\%$ of $16 = 4$
7. $n\%$ of $1 = 5$

Solve. *Here are scrambled answers for the next row of exercises: 0.32 0.075 0.36*

8. $2\frac{2}{3}\%$ of $12 = n$
9. $1\frac{1}{4}\%$ of $6 = n$
10. $4\frac{1}{2}\%$ of $8 = n$
11. $16\frac{2}{3}\%$ of $72 = n$
12. $33\frac{1}{3}\%$ of $42 = n$
13. $8\frac{1}{3}\%$ of $96 = n$

Solve. *Here are scrambled answers for the next row of exercises: 34 45 48*

14. 20% of $n = 9$
15. 25% of $n = 12$
16. 50% of $n = 17$
17. 9% of $n = 36$
18. 1% of $n = 2.56$
19. 24% of $n = 12.48$
20. $12\frac{1}{2}\%$ of $n = 6$
21. $16\frac{2}{3}\%$ of $n = 24$
22. $33\frac{1}{3}\%$ of $n = 17$

Solve. *Here are scrambled answers for the next row of exercises: 120 $31\frac{1}{4}$ 6*

23. $12\frac{1}{2}\%$ of $n = 15$
24. $16\frac{2}{3}\%$ of $36 = n$
25. $n\%$ of $16 = 5$
26. 25% of $44 = n$
27. $n\%$ of $8 = 7$
28. 22% of $n = 11$
29. $33\frac{1}{3}\%$ of $18 = n$
30. 50% of $n = 19$
31. $8\frac{1}{3}\%$ of $60 = n$
32. 5% of $n = 15$
33. $n\%$ of $9 = 6$
34. 12.5% of $n = 3$
35. $n\%$ of $48 = 36$
36. 75% of $52 = n$
37. 40% of $n = 36$
38. $16\frac{2}{3}\%$ of $72 = n$
39. $n\%$ of $120 = 50$
40. 150% of $n = 51$

Problem Solving

Solve.

41. A stereo system that costs $224 has a down payment of $56. What percent of the total cost is the down payment?

42. A car radio sells for $275. The down payment is 25% of the selling price. How much is the down payment?

43. A set of speakers can be purchased for a down payment of $24. The down payment is $16\frac{2}{3}\%$ of the price. What is the price of speakers?

44. A tape deck sells for $279. The down payment is $33\frac{1}{3}\%$ of the selling price. How much is the down payment?

Percent of Increase and Decrease

1. **a.** What was the balance of the account at month 1?

   b. Did the balance of the account increase or decrease from month 1 to month 2?

   c. By how many dollars did the balance increase or decrease from month 1 to month 2?

2. **a.** What was the balance of the account at month 4?

   b. Did the balance of the account increase or decrease from month 4 to month 5?

   c. By how many dollars did the balance increase or decrease from month 4 to month 5?

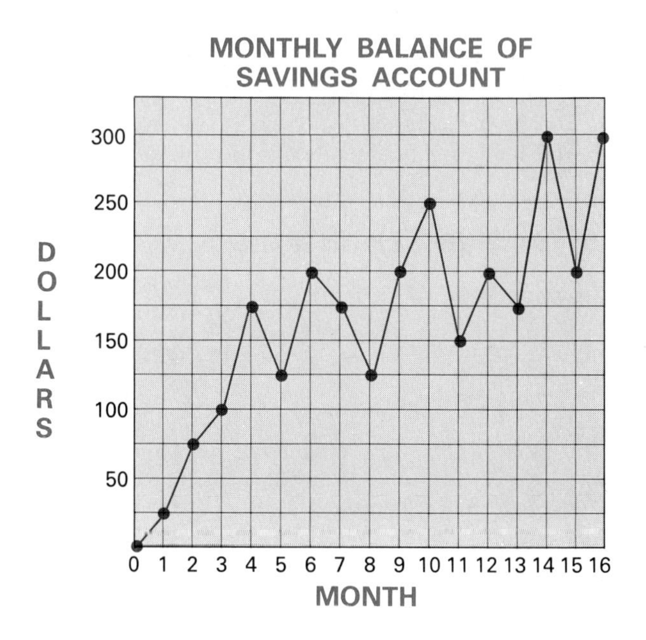

Here's how to find a percent of increase or decrease.

The percent of **increase** from month 1 to month 2

dollars of increase ⟶ 50 ; *dollars **before** increase* ⟶ 25

$$\frac{50}{25} = \frac{n}{100}$$

$$25n = 5000$$

$$\frac{25n}{25} = \frac{5000}{25}$$

$$n = 200$$

The monthly balance **increased** 200%.

The percent of **decrease** from month 4 to month 5

dollars of decrease ⟶ 50 ; *dollars **before** decrease* ⟶ 175

$$\frac{50}{175} = \frac{n}{100}$$

$$175n = 5000$$

$$\frac{175n}{175} = \frac{5000}{175}$$

$$n \approx 28.6$$

The monthly balance **decreased** about 28.6%.

3. Complete.

   a. The percent of increase from 82 to 96 can be found by solving the proportion

   $$\frac{?}{82} = \frac{n}{100}$$

   b. The percent of decrease from 120 to 108 can be found by solving the proportion

   $$\frac{12}{?} = \frac{n}{100}$$

▶ **Find the percent of increase or decrease. Use *i* to indicate increase and *d* to indicate decrease. Give answers to the nearest tenth of a percent.**
Here are scrambled answers for the next two rows of exercises:
50% i   123.7% i   100% i   22.5% d   25% d   36.2% d

4. from 24 to 36
5. from 80 to 60
6. from 38 to 85
7. from 116 to 74
8. from 32 to 64
9. from 160 to 124
10. from 28 to 37
11. from 100 to 81
12. from 38 to 106
13. from 135 to 99
14. from 208 to 187
15. from 120 to 169
16. from 212 to 90
17. from 178 to 256
18. from 160 to 80
19. from 80 to 160
20. from 50 to 125
21. from 125 to 50
22. from 220 to 150
23. from 150 to 220
24. from 184 to 0

Problem Solving

▶ **Solve. Refer to the graph on page 268.**

25. What was the percent of increase from month 2 to month 3?

26. What was the percent of decrease month 7 to month 8?

27. a. By how many *dollars* did the account increase from month 3 to month 4?

b. By how many *dollars* did the account increase from month 5 to month 6?

c. Is the percent of increase from month 3 to month 4 the same as the percent of increase from month 5 to 6?

28. a. By how many *dollars* did the account decrease from month 10 to month 11?

b. By how many *dollars* did the account decrease from month 14 to month 15?

c. Is the percent of decrease from month 10 to month 11 the same as the percent of increase from month 5 to 6?

29. Is the percent of decrease from month 14 to month 15 the same as the percent of increase from month 15 to month 16?

30. Is the percent of increase from month 1 to month 2 the same as the percent of increase from month 11 to month 12?

Challenge

▶ **Solve.**

31. Ellen was earning $100 a week when she received a 10% increase in pay. Six months later she had to take a 10% decrease in pay. How much was she paid then?

32. Arthur was earning $100 a week when he had to take a 10% decrease in pay. Six months later he received a 10% increase in pay. How much was he paid then?

Problem Solving—Using Formulas

When you borrow money from a bank, credit union, or loan company, you pay for the use of it. The amount you pay is called **interest.** The interest paid depends on the **principal** (the amount borrowed), the **rate** (percent of interest charged), and the **time** for which the money is borrowed.

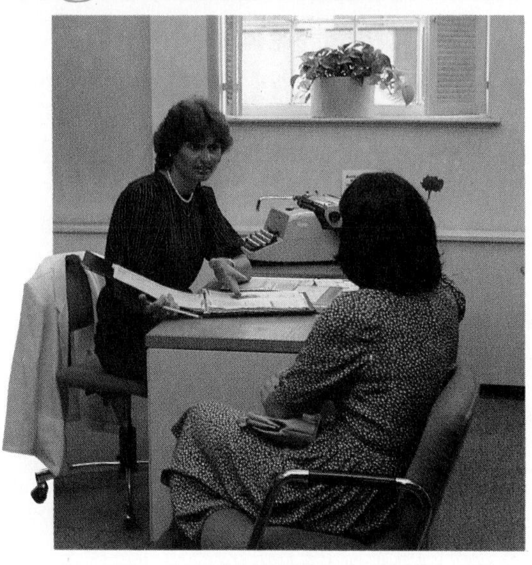

To compute the interest on a loan, you can use this formula:

Simple interest formula: $I = p \cdot r \cdot t$ (*I* = *Interest*, *p* = *principal*, *r* = *rate*, *t* = *time*)

Here's how to use the simple interest formula to solve problems.

Problem A In order to buy a car, you have to borrow \$1250 for 3 years. The yearly interest rate is 14%. How much interest will you owe at the end of 3 years?

Write the formula. $I = prt$

Substitute 1250 for p, 0.14 for r, and 3 for t. $I = (1250)(0.14)(3)$

Simplify. $= 525$

The interest will be \$525.

Problem B Brian borrowed \$400 for 6 months. He paid \$32 in interest. What was the interest rate per year?

Write the formula. $I = prt$

Substitute values for I, p, and t. $32 = (400)(r)(0.5)$ ← *The time units must be the same. Since you are finding the yearly rate, use 0.5 of a year for* t.

$= 200r$

Divide both sides by 200. $\frac{200r}{200} = \frac{32}{200}$

$r = 0.16$

$= 16\%$

The interest rate was 16% per year.

Use the formula $I = prt$ to solve each problem.

1. Jill needs $1600. She borrows the money from a bank for 3 years. If the yearly interest rate is 14%, how much interest will she owe at the end of 3 years?

2. Mark needs $650. He borrows the money from a credit union for 2 years at 13% yearly interest. How much interest will Mark owe at the end of 2 years?

3. Dan borrows $5000 for 4 years to buy a car. The yearly interest rate is 11%. How much interest will he owe at the end of 4 years?

4. David borrows $120 from a friend. He agrees to pay 10% interest per year for 1.5 years. How much interest will David owe at the end of 1.5 years?

5. Beth borrows $2000 from a loan company at 16% yearly interest. How much interest will she owe at the end of 30 months? *Hint: 30 months = 2.5 years*

6. Miekka borrows $450. She agrees to pay 12% yearly interest. How much interest will she owe at the end of 6 months? *Hint: 6 months = 0.5 year*

7. Seth borrowed $600 for 2 years. He paid $120 in interest. What was the interest rate per year?

8. Diane borrowed $1000 for 3 years. She paid $375 in interest. What was the interest rate per year?

Solve. Use the total-amount formula at the right.

Total amount owed		*principal*		*interest*
↓		↓		↓
A	=	p	+	prt

When a loan is due, the total amount (A) owed is equal to the principal (p) plus the interest (prt).

9. Troy borrows $500 at a yearly rate of 12%. What will be the total amount he owes when the loan is due in 2 years?

10. Sonya borrows $3000 at a yearly rate of 15%. What will be the total amount she owes when the loan is due in 4 years?

11. Chad borrows $300 at 16% interest per year. What will be the total amount he owes when the loan is due in 1.5 years?

12. What is the total amount you will have to repay if you borrow $8000 at 12% interest per year for 5 years?

13. What is the total amount you will have to repay if you borrow $8000 at 12% interest per year for 10 years?

★14. What is the total amount you will have to repay if you borrow $6000 at 12.5% interest per year for 8 years?

★15. You have to repay $6000 for the principal you borrowed at 12.5% for 8 years. How much was the principal?

Cumulative Skill Practice

▶ **Give each sum or difference in simplest form.** *(page 228)*

1. $\frac{4}{9} + \frac{^-3}{9}$ **2.** $\frac{^-1}{4} + \frac{3}{8}$ **3.** $\frac{5}{12} + \frac{^-5}{6}$ **4.** $\frac{^-3}{4} + \frac{^-1}{2}$

5. $\frac{^-3}{10} + \frac{^-2}{5}$ **6.** $\frac{5}{7} + \frac{2}{7}$ **7.** $\frac{9}{32} + \frac{^-11}{16}$ **8.** $\frac{^-3}{16} + \frac{7}{8}$

9. $\frac{2}{3} - \frac{^-3}{4}$ **10.** $\frac{^-5}{8} - \frac{^-3}{4}$ **11.** $\frac{^-7}{10} - \frac{1}{5}$ **12.** $\frac{2}{5} - \frac{9}{10}$

13. $\frac{^-5}{6} - \frac{7}{8}$ **14.** $\frac{^-8}{9} - \frac{^-2}{3}$ **15.** $\frac{7}{12} - \frac{5}{8}$ **16.** $\frac{^-11}{16} - \frac{7}{8}$

▶ **Give each product or quotient in simplest form.** *(page 230)*

17. $\frac{1}{3} \cdot \frac{1}{8}$ **18.** $\frac{^-1}{4} \cdot \frac{2}{5}$ **19.** $\frac{5}{12} \cdot {^-5}$ **20.** $\frac{^-8}{5} \cdot \frac{3}{4}$

21. $\frac{^-7}{8} \cdot \frac{^-4}{5}$ **22.** $\frac{^-5}{9} \cdot \frac{^-3}{10}$ **23.** $8 \cdot \frac{^-3}{4}$ **24.** $\frac{^-8}{5} \cdot \frac{15}{16}$

25. $\frac{2}{3} \div \frac{^-5}{6}$ **26.** $\frac{^-4}{5} \div \frac{3}{10}$ **27.** $\frac{1}{2} \div \frac{3}{4}$ **28.** $8 \div \frac{2}{3}$

29. $\frac{^-5}{6} \div 4$ **30.** $\frac{^-7}{12} \div \frac{^-14}{3}$ **31.** $\frac{7}{8} \div \frac{^-21}{16}$ **32.** $\frac{^-7}{8} \div \frac{5}{32}$

▶ **Simplify by combining terms.** *(page 236)*

33. $5x + x$ **34.** $9y - y$ **35.** $4z - 4z$

36. ${^-3}w + 5w - 8$ **37.** ${^-3}w + 5 - 8$ **38.** ${^-3} + 5w - 8$

39. ${^-7}r - r - 8$ **40.** ${^-7}r + r - 18$ **41.** ${^-7}r + 1 - 8$

▶ **Solve and check.** *(page 238)*

42. $5f + f = {^-17}$ **43.** $9h - h = 10$ **44.** $7e - 8 = {^-8}$

45. $6x + x - 4 = 21$ **46.** $6x + 1 - 4x = 21$ **47.** $6 + x - 4x = 21$

48. $9y - 2y + 4 = {^-3}$ **49.** $9 - 2y + 4y = {^-3}$ **50.** $9y - 2 + 4y = {^-3}$

▶ **Solve and check.** *(page 240)*

51. $5b - 2b + 7 = {^-5} + 11$ **52.** $5b - 2 + 7b = {^-5} + 11$

53. ${^-3}d + 8 - 4d = 18 - 20$ **54.** ${^-3} + 8d - 4d = 18 - 20$

55. $8 - 4a + 9 - 4a = {^-3} + 21$ **56.** $3c - c - 6 - 11 = {^-18} - 12$

Problem Solving—Applications

The interest on savings accounts is often compounded annually, semiannually, quarterly, or even daily. In this way, you earn interest on your interest. When the interest is compounded daily, interest is added to the account each day.

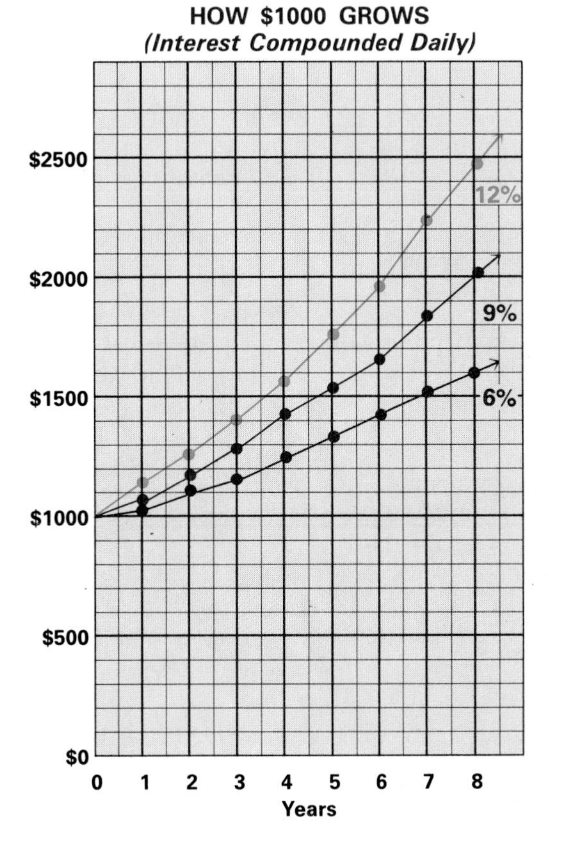

Use the graph to answer the questions.

1. At 6% interest, about how much would a $1000 deposit be worth at the end of 3 years? 5 years? 7 years?
2. At 9% interest, about how much would a $1000 deposit be worth at the end of 3 years? 5 years? 7 years?
3. At 12% interest, about how much would a $1000 deposit be worth at the end of 3 years? 5 years? 7 years?
4. About how many years does it take to double a $1000 deposit at 9% interest?
5. About how many years does it take to double a $1000 deposit at 12% interest?

CALCULATOR

Here is how to use the formula below to find the amount in a savings account after 5 years when $1000 is deposited at 6% per year, compounded annually.

$$A = P(1 + i)^n$$

A = amount in the account
P = original deposit
i = interest rate per year, expressed as a decimal
n = number of years compounded

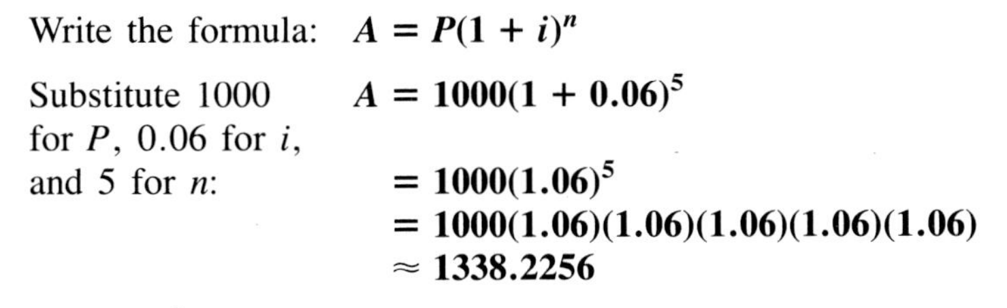

Write the formula: $A = P(1 + i)^n$

Substitute 1000 for P, 0.06 for i, and 5 for n: $A = 1000(1 + 0.06)^5$

$= 1000(1.06)^5$

$= 1000(1.06)(1.06)(1.06)(1.06)(1.06)$

≈ 1338.2256

The amount is $1338.23.

Use the formula and a calculator to find the total savings.

6. Find the amount for $1000 deposited for 5 years at 9% per year compounded annually.
7. Find the amount for $1000 deposited for 5 years at 12% per year compounded annually.

Chapter Review

Here are scrambled answers for the review exercises:

4	*60*	*decrease*	*factor*	*percent*	*solve*
7	*85*	*denominator*	*form*	*rate*	
12	*100*	*divide*	*fraction*	*ratios*	
25	*144*	*equivalent*	*increase*	*simplify*	

1. To write a ratio as a fraction in lowest terms, divide both terms by their greatest common _?_ . $\frac{3x^2}{4x}$ written as a fraction in lowest terms is $\frac{3x}{?}$. *(page 250)*

2. A proportion is an equation that states that two _?_ are equal. To finish solving this proportion, you would next _?_ both sides by 9 and then simplify both sides. *(page 252)*

$$\frac{n}{7} = \frac{5}{9}$$
$$9n = 35$$

3. A _?_ is a ratio of two quantities. Suppose that you drive 203 miles in 5 hours. To find how many miles you would drive at that rate in 7 hours, you could solve the proportion $\frac{203}{5} = \frac{n}{?}$. *(page 254)*

4. To change a percent to a _?_ , first write the percent as a fraction with a _?_ of 100. Then write the fraction in simplest _?_ . To change a fraction to a _?_ , change the fraction to an _?_ fraction with a denominator of 100. Then write as a percent. *(pages 256, 258)*

5. To solve the equation **25% of 38 = *n*,** you could change _?_ % to $\frac{1}{4}$ or 0.25 and multiply. *(page 262)*

6. To find the number when a percent is known, you can change the percent to a fraction or decimal and _?_ the equation. To finish solving this example, you would divide both sides by $\frac{3}{4}$ and then _?_ both sides. *(page 264)*

$$75\% \text{ of } n = 51$$
$$\frac{3}{4}n = 51$$

7. You can solve percent problems by setting up and solving a proportion. *(page 266)*

Problem: $n\%$ of $132 = 60$ Proportion: $\frac{n}{100} = \frac{?}{132}$

Problem: $16\frac{2}{3}\%$ of $144 = n$ Proportion: $\frac{16\frac{2}{3}}{100} = \frac{n}{?}$

Problem: $87\frac{1}{2}\%$ of $n = 77$ Proportion: $\frac{87\frac{1}{2}}{?} = \frac{77}{n}$

8. To find the percent of _?_ from **28 to 40,** you could solve the proportion $\frac{?}{28} = \frac{n}{100}$. To find the percent of _?_ from **85 to 68,** you could solve the proportion $\frac{17}{?} = \frac{n}{100}$. *(page 268)*

Chapter Test

Complete to get an equal ratio. *(page 250)*

1. $\frac{2}{3} = \frac{?}{15}$ 2. $\frac{35}{50} = \frac{?}{10}$ 3. $\frac{2a}{b} = \frac{?}{3b}$ 4. $\frac{4xy}{6x^2} = \frac{?}{3x}$ 5. $\frac{2c}{9cd} = \frac{?}{18c^2d}$

Solve each proportion. *(page 252)*

6. $\frac{2}{5} = \frac{n}{20}$ 7. $\frac{8}{n} = \frac{4}{13}$ 8. $\frac{n}{8} = \frac{15}{4}$ 9. $\frac{20}{11} = \frac{7}{n}$ 10. $\frac{n}{21} = \frac{9}{16}$

Solve by using proportions. If your answer does not come out evenly, round it to the nearest hundredth. *(page 254)*

You drive 126 miles in 3 hours. At that speed, how many

11. miles could you drive in 4 hours?

12. miles could you drive in 5 hours?

13. hours would it take to drive 100 miles?

14. hours would it take to drive 240 miles?

Change to a fraction, whole number, or mixed number. Give each answer in simplest form. *(page 256)*

15. 75% **16.** 16% **17.** 150% **18.** $37\frac{1}{2}\%$ **19.** $8\frac{1}{3}\%$ **20.** 200%

Change to a percent. *(page 258)*

21. $\frac{2}{5}$ **22.** $\frac{7}{4}$ **23.** $\frac{1}{3}$ **24.** $\frac{7}{8}$ **25.** $\frac{11}{6}$ **26.** 1

Solve. If necessary, round your answer to the nearest tenth. *(pages 262, 264, 266)*

27. 20% of $65 = n$ **28.** 125% of $64 = n$ **29.** 18% of $35 = n$ **30.** 24.5% of $75 = n$

31. 25% of $n = 31$ **32.** 40% of $n = 78$ **33.** 63% of $n = 82$ **34.** 71% of $n = 139$

35. $16\frac{2}{3}\%$ of $40 = n$ **36.** $66\frac{2}{3}\%$ of $36 = n$ **37.** $n\%$ of $56 = 49$ **38.** $137\frac{1}{2}\%$ of $n = 77$

Find the percent of increase or decrease. *(page 268)*

39. from 18 to 27 **40.** from 30 to 40 **41.** from 56 to 42 **42.** from 72 to 62

Use the formula $I = prt$ to solve each problem. *(page 270)*

43. Arthur borrowed $2500 for 1.5 years. The yearly interest rate was 13%. How much interest did he owe at the end of 1.5 years?

44. Carol borrowed $1500 for 2 years. She paid $345 in interest. What was the interest rate per year?

Cumulative Test
Standardized Format

▶ **Choose the correct letter.**

1. The prime factorization of 108 is

A. $2 \cdot 54$
B. $2^2 \cdot 27$
C. $2^2 \cdot 3^3$
D. none of these

2. The greatest common factor of $28cd^2$ and $42c^2d$ is

A. $7cd$
B. $14cd$
C. $14c^2d^2$
D. none of these

3. $\frac{28xy^2}{21y^2}$ written in lowest terms is

A. $\frac{28x}{21}$
B. $\frac{4x}{3}$
C. $\frac{4xy^2}{3y^2}$
D. none of these

4. 8,400,000 written in scientific notation is

A. $84 \cdot 10^5$
B. $0.84 \cdot 10^7$
C. $8.4 \cdot 10^{-6}$
D. none of these

5. 0.000563 written in scientific notation is

A. $5.63 \cdot 10^{-4}$
B. $56.3 \cdot 10^{-5}$
C. $5.63 \cdot 10^{-5}$
D. none of these

6. Solve.

$^-12 = \frac{x}{^-3} + 5$

A. 51
B. 21
C. -51
D. none of these

7. Give the difference.

$\frac{^-5}{12} - \frac{^-2}{3}$

A. $\frac{^-1}{3}$
B. $\frac{1}{3}$
C. $^-1\frac{1}{12}$
D. none of these

8. Give the quotient.

$\frac{^-5}{6} \div \frac{20}{3}$

A. $-5\frac{5}{9}$
B. -8
C. $\frac{^-1}{8}$
D. none of these

9. Simplify by combining like terms.

$3x - 5 - x + 3$

A. $4x - 2$
B. $2x + 2$
C. $4x + 2$
D. none of these

10. Solve.

$5y - 8 + y = {}^-7$

A. $\frac{1}{6}$
B. $^-2\frac{1}{2}$
C. $\frac{1}{4}$
D. none of these

11. Solve.

$4z + 9 - z = 13 + 12$

A. $3\frac{1}{3}$
B. $5\frac{1}{3}$
C. 2
D. none of these

12. Choose the equation.

You had \$36. You bought 6 tickets for the school play on Monday and 3 tickets on Tuesday. You then had \$9 left.

How much did you pay for each ticket?

A. $36 - 6n - 3n = 9$
B. $36 + 6n + 3n = 9$
C. $36 - 6n + 3n = 9$
D. $36 + 6n - 3n = 9$

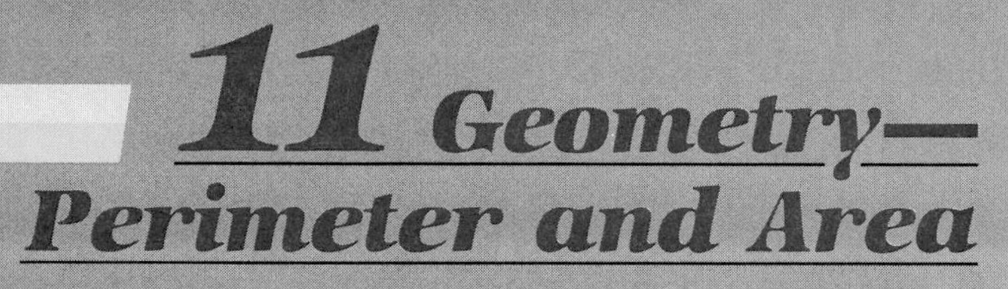

11 Geometry—Perimeter and Area

$A = \pi r^2$

The area of a circle equals π (approximately equal to 3.14) times the radius squared.

(page 300)

The photograph above was taken in Nebraska, south of Morrill. This giant irrigation circle has a radius of about 500 yards. You can use this fact and the formula above to estimate the area of the circle.

Measuring and Classifying Angles

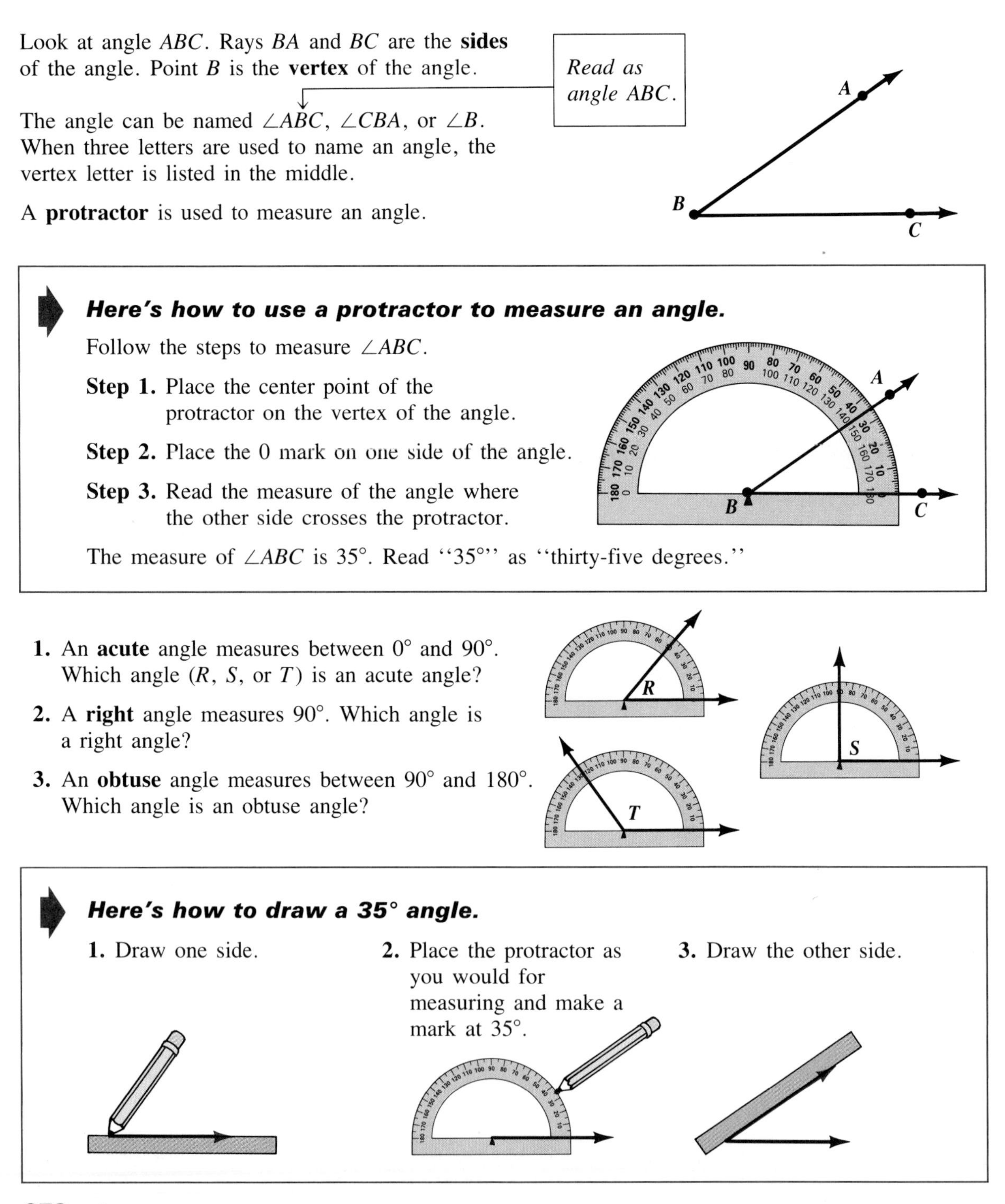

Look at angle *ABC*. Rays *BA* and *BC* are the **sides** of the angle. Point *B* is the **vertex** of the angle.

The angle can be named $\angle ABC$, $\angle CBA$, or $\angle B$. When three letters are used to name an angle, the vertex letter is listed in the middle.

Read as angle ABC.

A **protractor** is used to measure an angle.

Here's how to use a protractor to measure an angle.

Follow the steps to measure $\angle ABC$.

Step 1. Place the center point of the protractor on the vertex of the angle.

Step 2. Place the 0 mark on one side of the angle.

Step 3. Read the measure of the angle where the other side crosses the protractor.

The measure of $\angle ABC$ is 35°. Read "35°" as "thirty-five degrees."

1. An **acute** angle measures between 0° and 90°. Which angle (*R*, *S*, or *T*) is an acute angle?
2. A **right** angle measures 90°. Which angle is a right angle?
3. An **obtuse** angle measures between 90° and 180°. Which angle is an obtuse angle?

Here's how to draw a 35° angle.

1. Draw one side.
2. Place the protractor as you would for measuring and make a mark at 35°.
3. Draw the other side.

▶ **Tell whether each angle is acute, right, or obtuse.**

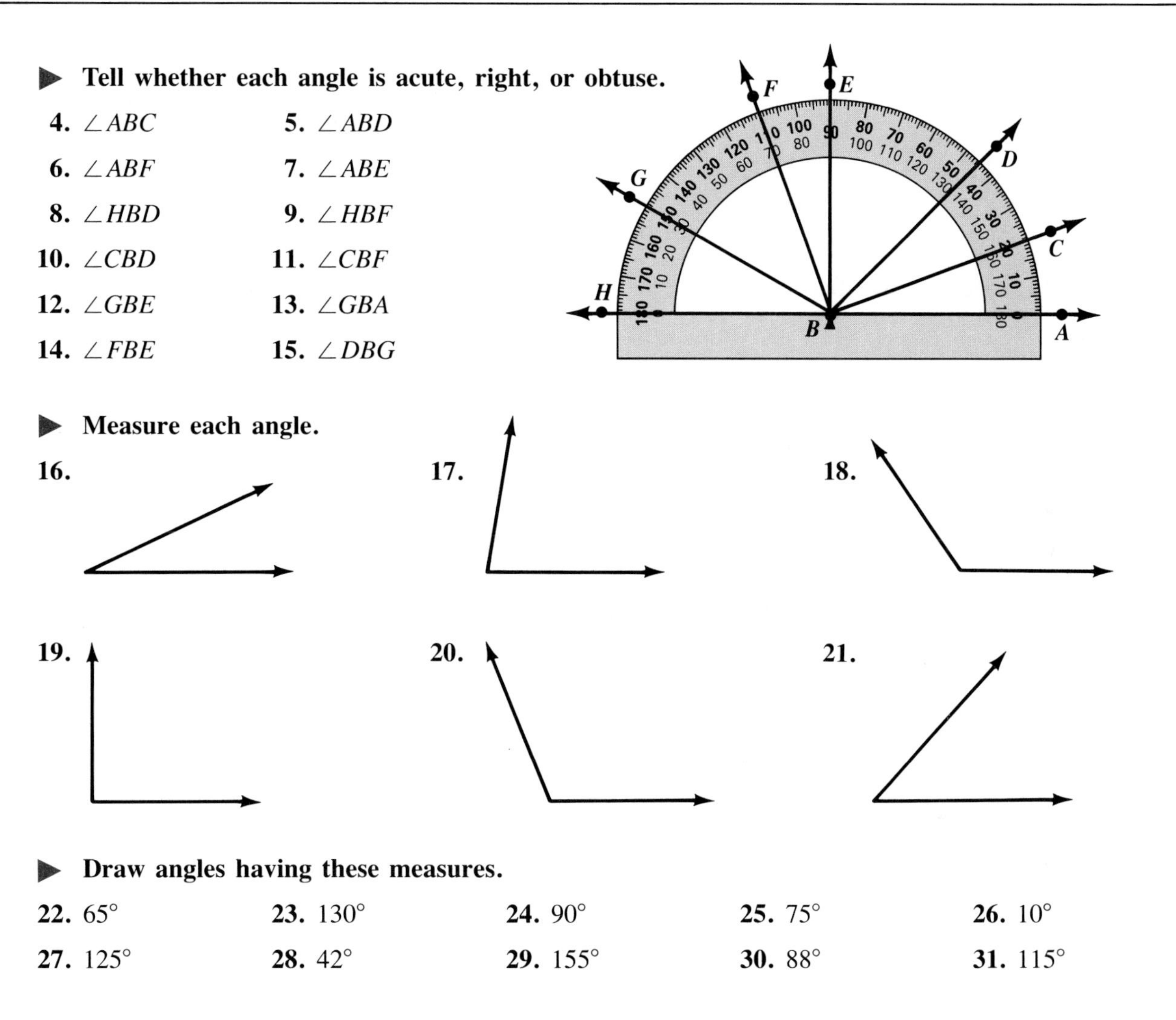

4. $\angle ABC$ **5.** $\angle ABD$

6. $\angle ABF$ **7.** $\angle ABE$

8. $\angle HBD$ **9.** $\angle HBF$

10. $\angle CBD$ **11.** $\angle CBF$

12. $\angle GBE$ **13.** $\angle GBA$

14. $\angle FBE$ **15.** $\angle DBG$

▶ **Measure each angle.**

16. **17.** **18.**

19. **20.** **21.**

▶ **Draw angles having these measures.**

22. 65° **23.** 130° **24.** 90° **25.** 75° **26.** 10°

27. 125° **28.** 42° **29.** 155° **30.** 88° **31.** 115°

Challenge

▶ **Use the code to check your answer to the question.**

32. *Question:*
If 30 people can measure 30 angles in 30 seconds, how long will it take one person to measure one angle?

Answer:

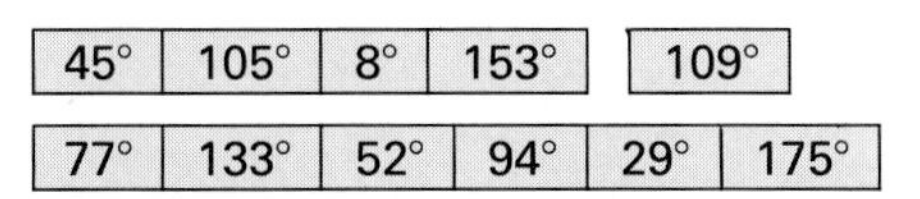

45°	105°	8°	153°		109°
77°	133°	52°	94°	29°	175°

CODE:

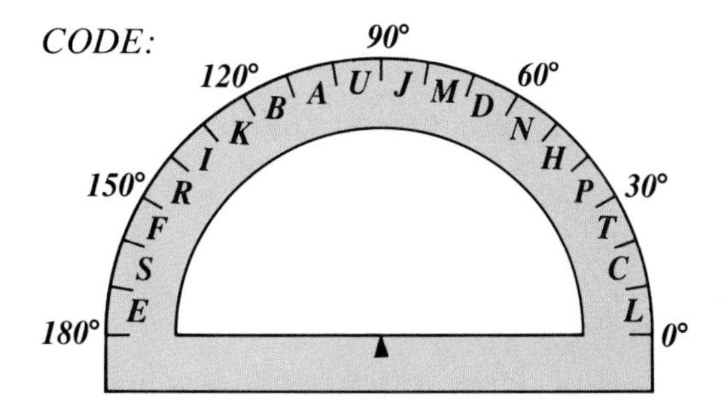

Parallel and Perpendicular Lines

Look at the design at the right.
Line r is **perpendicular** to line t.
Line u is **parallel** to line v.

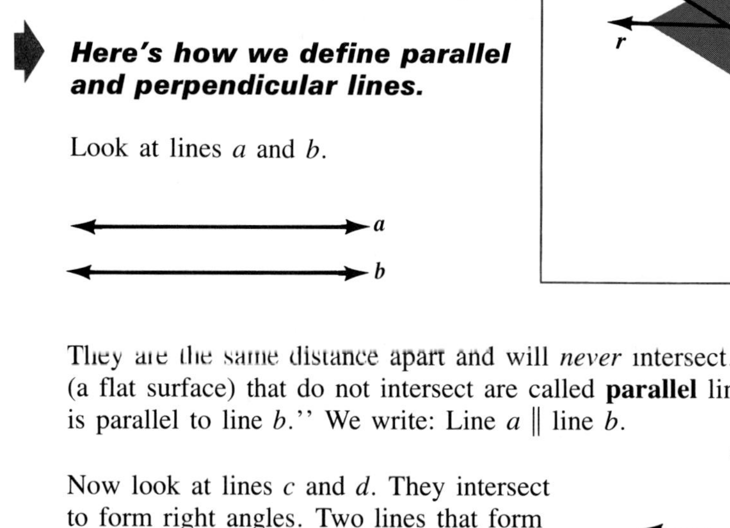

Here's how we define parallel and perpendicular lines.

Look at lines a and b.

They are the same distance apart and will *never* intersect. Two lines in a plane (a flat surface) that do not intersect are called **parallel** lines. We say: "Line a is parallel to line b." We write: Line $a \parallel$ line b.

Now look at lines c and d. They intersect to form right angles. Two lines that form right angles are called **perpendicular** lines. We say: "Line c is perpendicular to line d." We write: Line $c \perp$ line d.

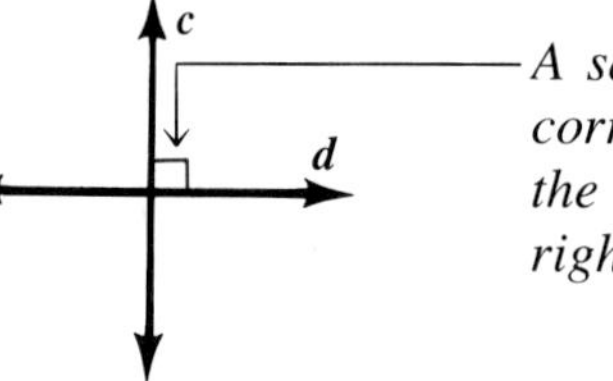

A square corner means the angle is a right angle.

EXERCISES

True or false?

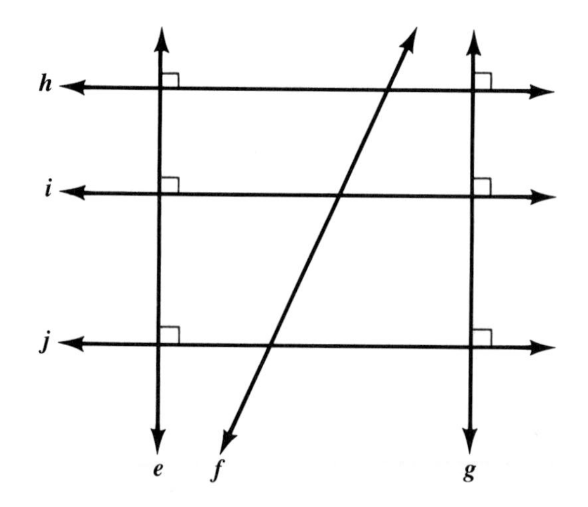

1. Line h is parallel to line j.
2. Line j is perpendicular to line f.
3. Line e is parallel to line f.
4. Line i is perpendicular to line g.
5. Line h is perpendicular to line j.
6. Line j is parallel to line h.
7. There are 24 right angles in the drawing.
8. There are 8 acute angles in the drawing.

True or false?

9. Line $k \perp$ line m.
10. Line $p \parallel$ line k.
11. Line $l \perp$ line n.
12. Line $n \parallel$ line p.
13. Line $j \parallel$ line k.
14. Line $m \perp$ line j.
15. Line $j \parallel$ line p.
16. Lines l and m intersect.
17. There are 20 right angles in the drawing.
18. There are 16 acute angles in the drawing.

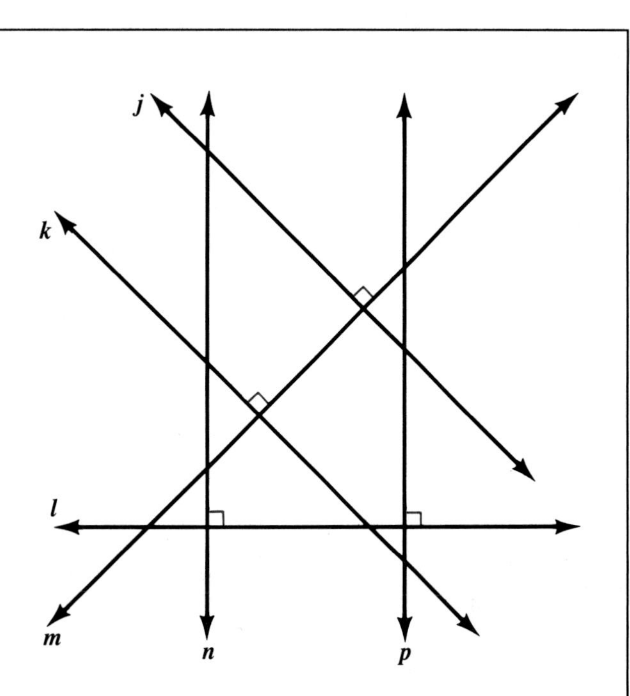

Problem Solving

Make a drawing. Then answer the questions.

19. Draw two perpendicular lines. How many right angles can you find?
20. Draw two intersecting lines that are not perpendicular. How many obtuse angles can you find?
21. Draw two parallel lines. Now draw a line that is perpendicular to the two parallel lines. How many right angles can you find?
22. Draw three parallel lines. Now draw a line that intersects the three parallel lines but is not perpendicular to the parallel lines.
    a. How many right angles can you find?
    b. How many acute angles can you find?
    c. How many obtuse angles can you find?

Challenge

23. Make a larger copy of this design. *Hint: Start with two perpendicular lines and mark off 12 evenly spaced units on each line.*

Polygons

1. Look at the map. Which lot has 4 sides all the same length?
2. Which lot has exactly 1 pair of parallel sides?
3. Which lot has 2 pairs of parallel sides but no right angles?

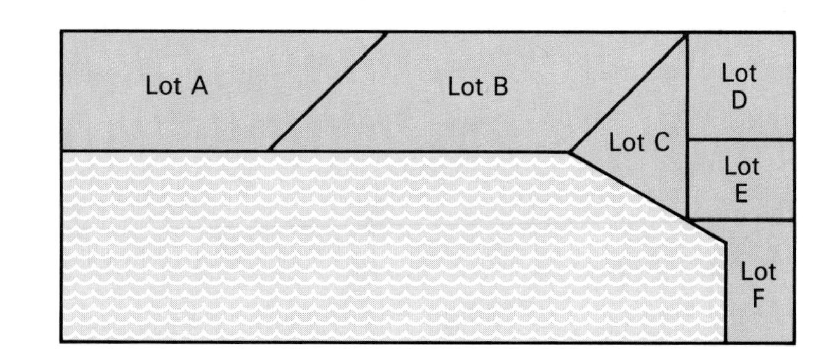

Here's how polygons (closed shapes with straight sides) are named.

Name of Polygon	*Description*	*Examples*
Triangle	3 sides	
Square	4 sides the same length 4 right angles	
Rectangle	4 sides 4 right angles	A square is also a rectangle.
Parallelogram	4 sides 2 pairs of parallel sides	A rectangle is also a parallelogram.
Trapezoid	4 sides Exactly 1 pair of parallel sides	
Pentagon	5 sides	
Hexagon	6 sides	

4. Use the map and the chart above to answer these questions.
   a. Which lot is a triangle?
   b. Which lot is a square?
   c. Which 2 lots are rectangles?
   d. Which 3 lots are parallelograms?
   e. Which lot is a trapezoid?
   f. Which lot is a pentagon?

▶ **Use the chart on page 282 to name each polygon. Some shapes have more than one name.**

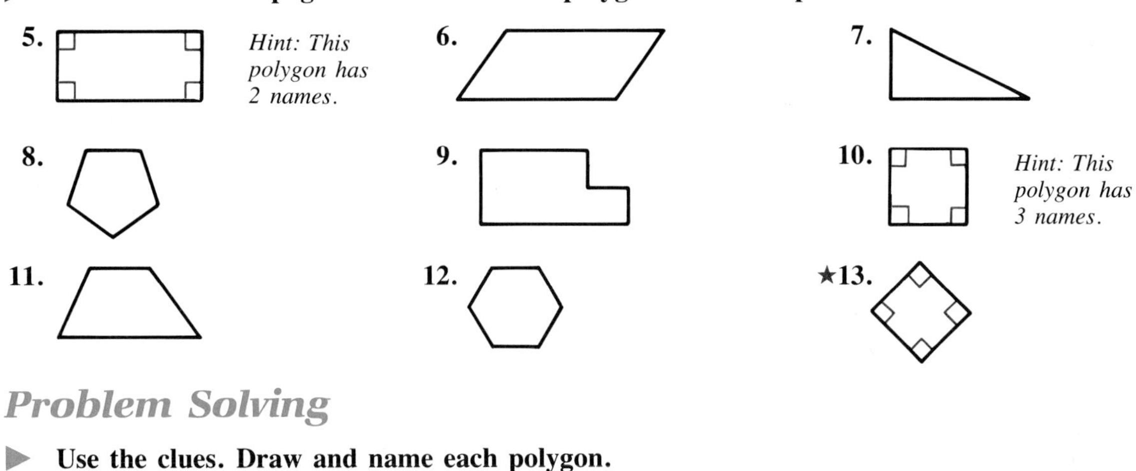

Problem Solving

▶ **Use the clues. Draw and name each polygon.**

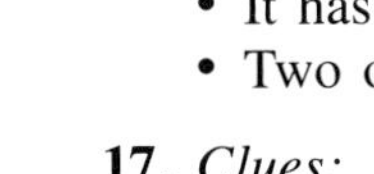

14. *Clues:*
- This polygon has 4 sides.
- It has 4 right angles.
- All its sides are the same length.

15. *Clues:*
- This polygon has 1 right angle.
- It has 3 sides.
- Two of its sides are the same length.

16. *Clues:*
- This polygon has no right angle.
- It has 4 sides.
- It has 2 pairs of parallel sides.

17. *Clues:*
- This polygon has 2 right angles.
- It has 4 sides.
- It has 1 obtuse angle.
- It has 1 acute angle.

Challenge

▶ **Use the clues. Tell who lives on each lot.**

18.

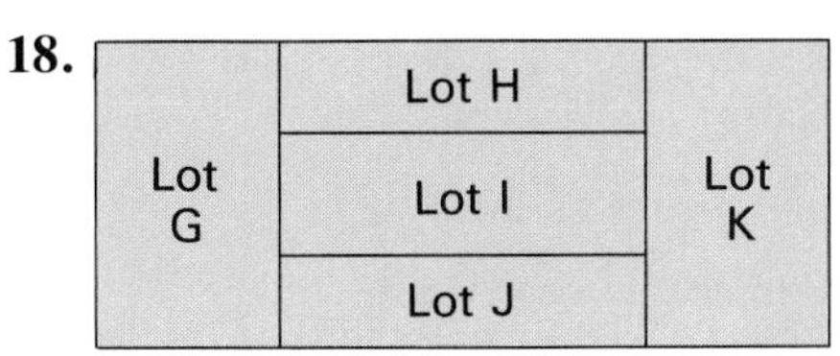

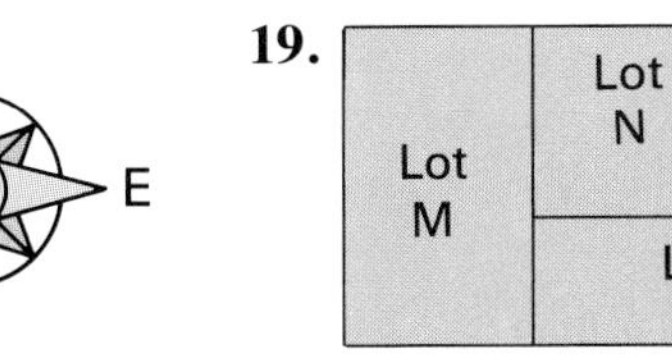

Clues:
- Fran's lot is between Mary's lot and Bill's lot.
- Bill's lot is north of Mary's lot and east of Kevin's lot.
- Laura's lot is not next to Kevin's lot.

19.

Lot M | Lot N | Lot P | Lot R | Lot S

Clues:
- Arlo's lot is west of David's lot and east of Betty's lot.
- Cindy's lot is west of David's lot and east of Rita's lot.
- Betty's lot is north of Cindy's lot and west of Arlo's lot.

Metric Units of Length

These units are used to measure length in the metric system:

1 kilometer (km) = 1000 meters
1 hectometer (hm) = 100 meters
1 dekameter (dam) = 10 meters
1 meter (m) = 1 meter
1 decimeter (dm) = 0.1 meter
1 centimeter (cm) = 0.01 meter
1 millimeter (mm) = 0.001 meter

Note: The units listed in red are used most often.

In the metric system, the **meter** (m) is the basic unit of length. The chart shows the relationships between different metric units.

Here's how to estimate length in the metric system.

From the top of the Ferris wheel, a person can see about 5 city blocks— that's about 1 **kilometer.**

The length of a seat on the Ferris wheel is about 1 **meter.**

The width of an index fingernail is about 1 **centimeter.**

The thickness of an eyeglass lens is about 1 **millimeter.**

EXERCISES

Choose mm, cm, m, or km.

1. The height of a Ferris wheel is 15 __?__.
2. The height of a person is 185 __?__.
3. The thickness of a dime is 1 __?__.
4. The length of a river is 450 __?__.
5. The length of a tennis court is 20 __?__.
6. The length of a paper clip is 3 __?__.
7. The width of a door is 0.6 __?__.
8. The length of a new pencil is 190 __?__.
9. The distance between two cities is 120 __?__.
10. The length of a hiking trail is 12.5 __?__.
11. The height of a kitchen counter is 0.95 __?__.
12. The width of a dollar bill is 66 __?__.
13. The height of a stepladder is 3.05 __?__.
14. The width of a newspaper is 33 __?__.
15. The distance across a room is 9.5 __?__.
16. The length of a tennis racket is 655 __?__.

Which measurement is reasonable?

17. Height of a ten-story building:
a. 33 cm **b.** 33 m **c.** 33 km

18. Length of an automobile:
a. 4.85 cm **b.** 4.85 m **c.** 4.85 mm

19. Length of a dollar bill:
a. 16 mm **b.** 16 cm **c.** 16 m

20. Length of a baseball bat:
a. 95 mm **b.** 95 cm **c.** 95 m

21. Height of a bicycle:
a. 0.95 cm **b.** 0.95 m **c.** 0.95 km

22. Width of a thumb:
a. 20 mm **b.** 20 cm **c.** 20 m

23. Thickness of a nickel:
a. 2 mm **b.** 2 cm **c.** 2 m

24. Thickness of a dollar bill:
a. 0.1 mm **b.** 0.1 cm **c.** 0.1 m

Problem Solving

Solve. Use the map distances.

25. How far is it from

a. Miami to Tallahassee through Orlando?

b. Tampa to Jacksonville through Orlando?

26. How much farther is it from

a. Orlando to Miami than from Orlando to Jacksonville?

b. Tallahassee to Orlando than from Orlando to Miami?

Challenge

Use the code to answer the question.

CODE:

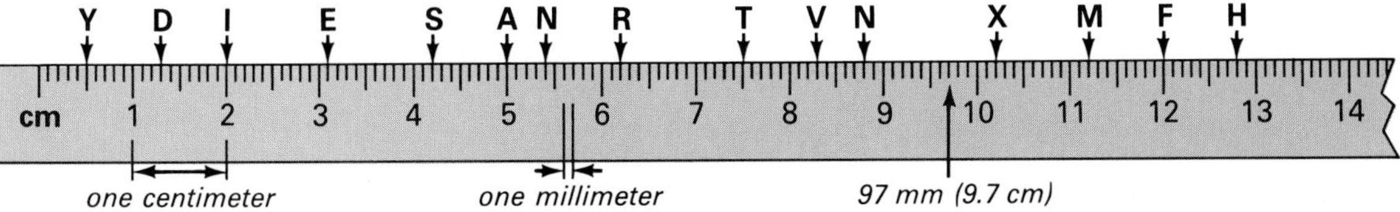

27. *Question:* What is the height of the world's largest Ferris wheel?

Answer:

4.2 cm	20 mm	10.2 cm	75 mm	0.5 cm

–

7.5 cm	128 mm	6.2 cm	31 mm	3.1 cm

50 mm	54 mm	13 mm

120 mm	2 cm	8.3 cm	3.1 cm

–

75 mm	31 mm	5.4 cm	7.5 cm	128 mm	4.2 cm

11.2 cm	3.1 cm	7.5 cm	31 mm	62 mm	42 mm

Changing Units in the Metric System

Who Grew the Longer Beard?

Here are the facts you will need to know to change from one metric unit of length to another.

10 mm = 1 cm
100 cm = 1 m
1000 mm = 1 m
1000 m = 1 km

Here's how to change from one unit of length to another.

To change units in the metric system, multiply or divide by 10, 100, or 1000.

Ivan's beard

0.13 m = ? cm

Think: Since we are changing to a smaller unit, we should get a larger number. Therefore, we should multiply.

Remember: 1 m = 100 cm

0.13 m = 13 cm
× 100

Joe's beard

125 mm = ? cm

Think: Now we are changing to a larger unit, so we should get a smaller number. Therefore, we should divide.

Remember: 10 mm = 1 cm

125 mm = 12.5 cm
÷ 10

1. Look at the examples above.
   a. To change from meters to centimeters, multiply by _?_.
   b. To change from millimeters to centimeters, divide by _?_.

2. Who grew the longer beard, Ivan or Joe?

3. Complete these examples.

   a. 1825 m = **?** km

   Think: Changing smaller to larger units, so divide.

   Remember: 1000 m = _?_ km
   1825 m = _?_ km
   ÷ 1000

   b. 9.65 km = **?** m

   Think: Changing larger to smaller units, so multiply.

   Remember: 1 km = _?_ m
   9.65 km = _?_ m
   × 1000

▶ **Copy and complete.**

4. 6 cm = ? mm

5. 4 m = ? cm

6. 9 km = ? m

7. 54 cm = ? m

8. 36 mm = ? cm

9. 25 km = ? m

10. 2485 m = ? mm

11. 3.5 km = ? m

12. 2.9 cm = ? mm

13. 58 m = ? cm

14. 4.6 m = ? cm

15. 250 cm = ? m

16. 83 mm = ? cm

17. 2.75 km = ? m

18. 2763 m = ? km

19. 75 m = ? cm

20. 28 mm = ? cm

21. 12.6 cm = ? mm

22. 750 km = ? m

23. 900 mm = ? m

24. 0.8 m = ? mm

25. 8 cm + 4 mm = ? mm

26. 40 cm + 4 mm = ? mm

27. 60 cm + 5 mm = ? mm

28. 20 cm + 15 mm = ? cm

29. 6 m + 25 cm = ? cm

30. 8 m + 175 cm = ? cm

31. 5 m + 50 cm = ? m

32. 6 m + 400 cm = ? m

Problem Solving

▶ **Solve.**

33. Researchers say a man's beard grows an average of 0.038 of a centimeter a day. How many millimeters per day is that?

34. In one year, a man's beard grows an average of 138 millimeters. How many centimeters per year is that?

35. During the average lifetime, a man spends approximately 3350 hours removing 838 centimeters of whiskers. How many meters of whiskers is that?

36. The longest beard belonged to Hans Langseth of Barney, North Dakota. He let his whiskers grow to a length of 5.33 meters. How many centimeters is that?

▶ **Choose the expression that describes each of the following.**

$10n$	$100n$	$1000n$
$\frac{n}{10}$	$\frac{n}{100}$	$\frac{n}{1000}$

37. centimeters in n meters

38. millimeters in n meters

39. meters in n kilometers

40. millimeters in n centimeters

41. meters in n centimeters

42. kilometers in n meters

43. centimeters in n millimeters

44. meters in n millimeters

Perimeter

The **perimeter** of a polygon is the distance around the polygon.

To find the perimeter of this tennis court, add the lengths of its sides.

$$11 + 23.8 + 11 + 23.8 = 69.6$$

The perimeter of the tennis court is 69.6 m.

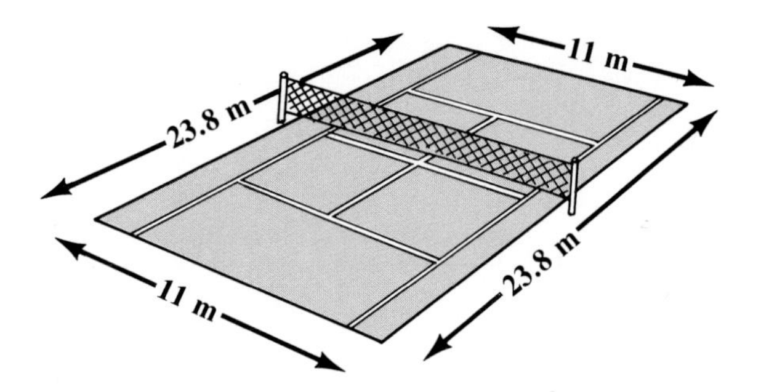

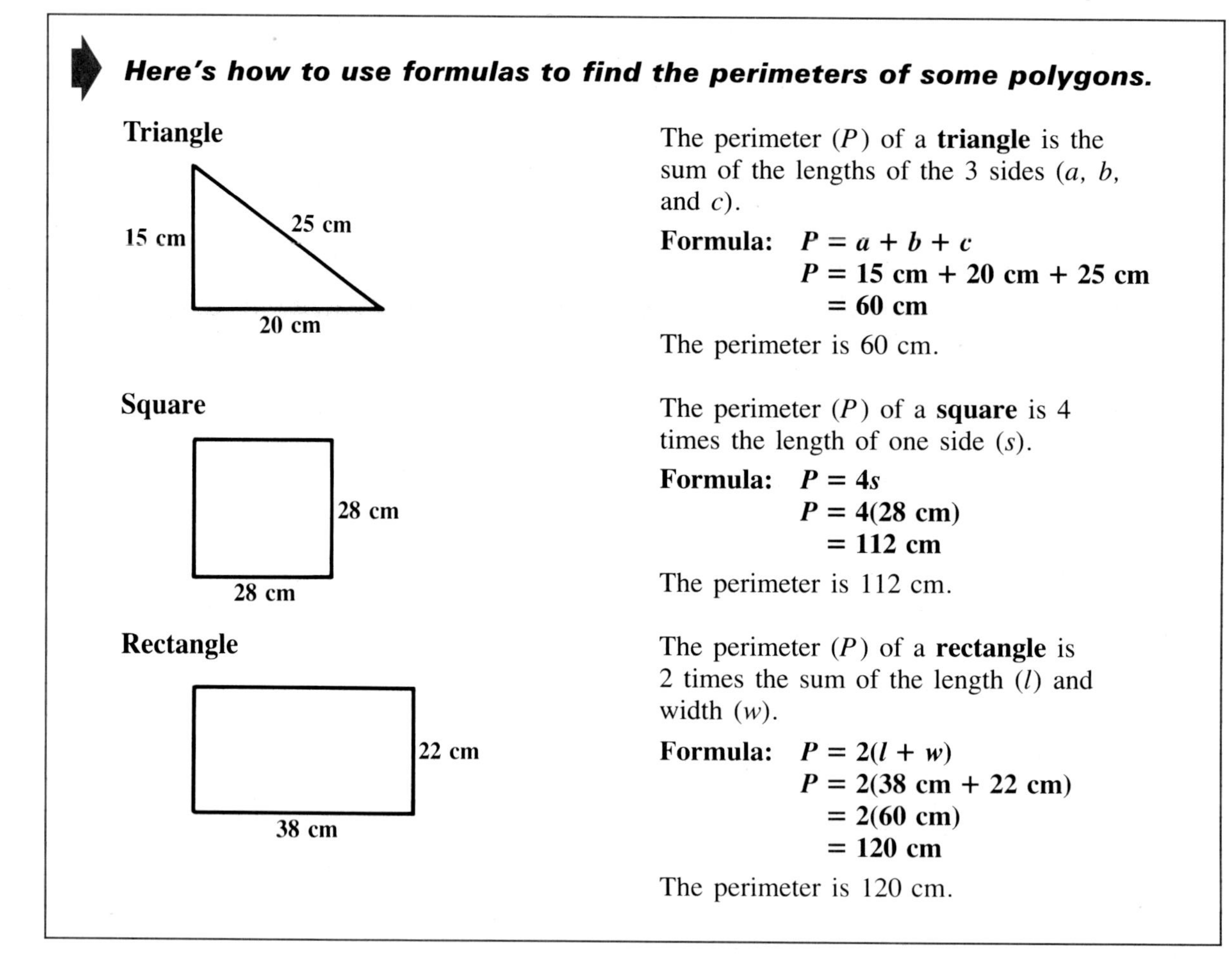

Here's how to use formulas to find the perimeters of some polygons.

Triangle

The perimeter (P) of a **triangle** is the sum of the lengths of the 3 sides (a, b, and c).

Formula: $P = a + b + c$

$P = 15 \text{ cm} + 20 \text{ cm} + 25 \text{ cm}$

$= 60 \text{ cm}$

The perimeter is 60 cm.

Square

The perimeter (P) of a **square** is 4 times the length of one side (s).

Formula: $P = 4s$

$P = 4(28 \text{ cm})$

$= 112 \text{ cm}$

The perimeter is 112 cm.

Rectangle

The perimeter (P) of a **rectangle** is 2 times the sum of the length (l) and width (w).

Formula: $P = 2(l + w)$

$P = 2(38 \text{ cm} + 22 \text{ cm})$

$= 2(60 \text{ cm})$

$= 120 \text{ cm}$

The perimeter is 120 cm.

1. Look at the examples above. What is the formula for the perimeter of a square? What does the letter s represent?
2. What is the formula for the perimeter of a rectangle? What do the letters l and w represent?

Find each perimeter.

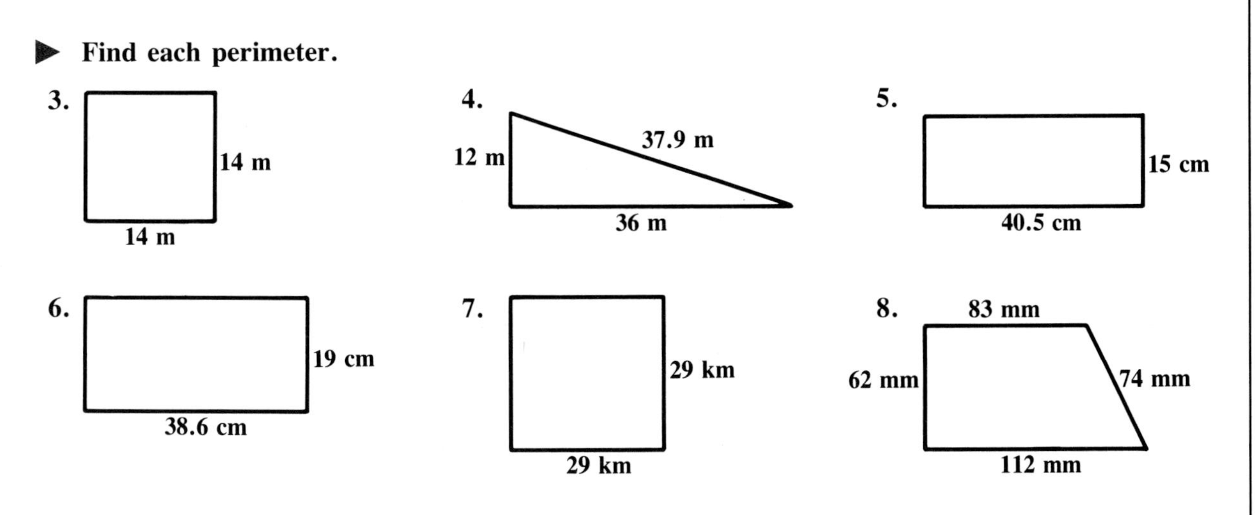

Substitute in the formula $P = a + b + c$, $P = 4s$, or $P = 2(l + w)$ to find the missing measure.

9. $s = 6$ m
$P =$?

10. $s = 7.5$ cm
$P =$?

11. $s =$?
$P = 48$ km

12. $l = 10$ cm
$w = 7$ cm
$P =$?

13. $l = 2.5$ m
$w = 1.9$ m
$P =$?

14. $l = 9$ km
$w =$?
$P = 26$ km

15. $a = 14$ m
$b = 25$ m
$c = 12$ m
$P =$?

16. $a = 9.5$ cm
$b = 10.2$ cm
$c = 18.7$ cm
$P =$?

17. $a = 250$ mm
$b = 168$ mm
$c =$?
$P = 562$ mm

Problem Solving

Solve.

18. How many meters of fence are needed to enclose a rectangular yard that is 25 meters by 18 meters?

19. How many centimeters of framing are needed to frame a painting that is 75 centimeters long and 55 centimeters wide?

20. A square photograph, 35 centimeters on each side, is to be framed. How many centimeters of framing are needed?

21. The perimeter of a rectangular pen is 120 meters. If the length is 45 meters, what is the width?

22. The perimeter of a square room is 52 meters. What is the length of each side of the room?

23. The perimeter of a triangular yard is 250 meters. The longest side is 112 meters and the shortest side is 55 meters. How long is the third side?

Circumference

The **radius** of the wheel is 10 inches. The **diameter** of the wheel is 20 inches. Notice that the diameter is twice the radius.

The distance around a circle is called the **circumference.** The circumference of any circle is a little more than 3 times the length of its diameter.

Here's how to use formulas to find the circumference of a circle.

To find the circumference (C), multiply π (read as "pi") by the diameter (d). We will use 3.14 as a decimal approximation for π.

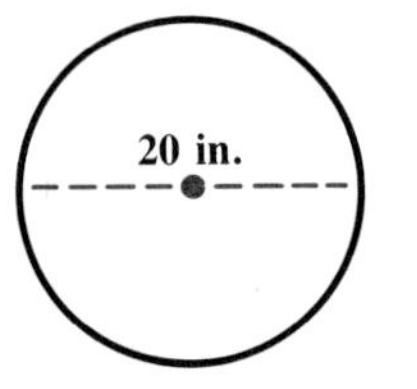

Formula: $C = \pi d$

$C \approx 3.14\ (20\text{ in.})$

$\approx 62.8\text{ in.}$

Since the diameter is twice the radius, we also can find the circumference by multiplying 2π by the radius (r).

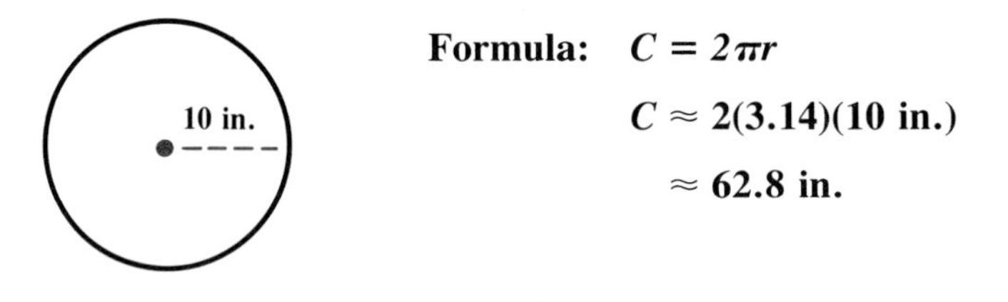

Formula: $C = 2\pi r$

$C \approx 2(3.14)(10\text{ in.})$

$\approx 62.8\text{ in.}$

1. Look at the examples above. A decimal approximation for π is _?_.

2. One formula for finding circumference is $C = \pi d$. Another formula is $C =$ _?_.

3. To compute in inches the circumference of a circle having a 36-inch diameter, you would multiply 3.14 by _?_.

4. To compute in feet the circumference of a circle having a 4-foot radius, you would take 2 times 3.14 times _?_.

▶ **Find the circumference. Use 3.14 for π.**

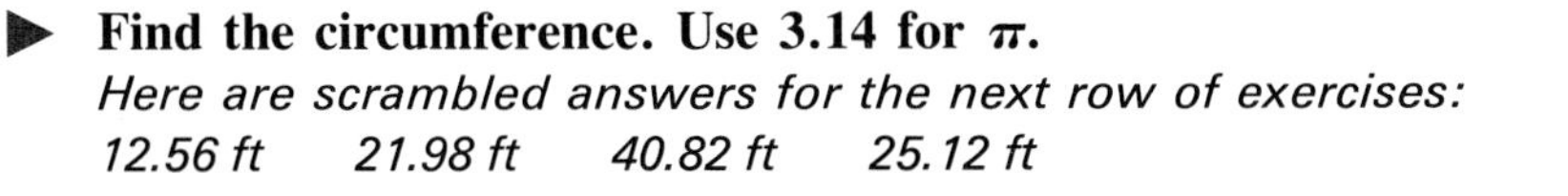

Here are scrambled answers for the next row of exercises:

12.56 ft   21.98 ft   40.82 ft   25.12 ft

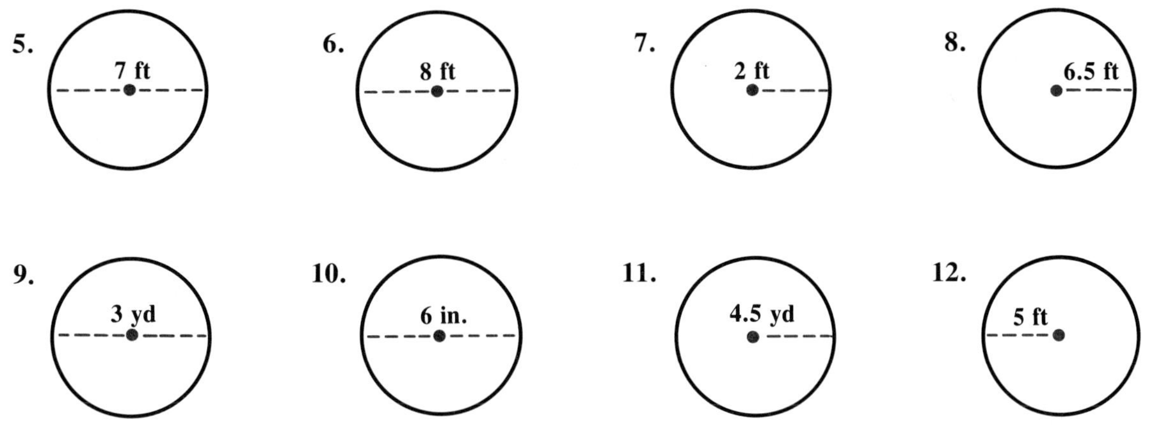

▶ **Substitute in the formula $C = \pi d$ or $C = 2\pi r$ to find the missing measure.**

13. $r = 12$ in.
$\pi \approx 3.14$
$C \approx$?

14. $d = 7$ ft
$\pi \approx 3.14$
$C \approx$?

15. $r = 40$ yd
$\pi \approx 3.14$
$C \approx$?

16. $d = 4$ ft
$\pi \approx 3.14$
$C \approx$?

17. $r = 100$ in.
$\pi \approx 3.14$
$C \approx$?

18. $d = 2.5$ ft
$\pi \approx 3.14$
$C \approx$?

19. $r =$?
$\pi \approx 3.14$
$C \approx 9.42$ yd

20. $d =$?
$\pi \approx 3.14$
$C \approx 502.4$ ft

21. $r =$?
$\pi \approx 3.14$
$C \approx 18.84$ in.

Challenge

▶ **Compute the length of each track.**

22.

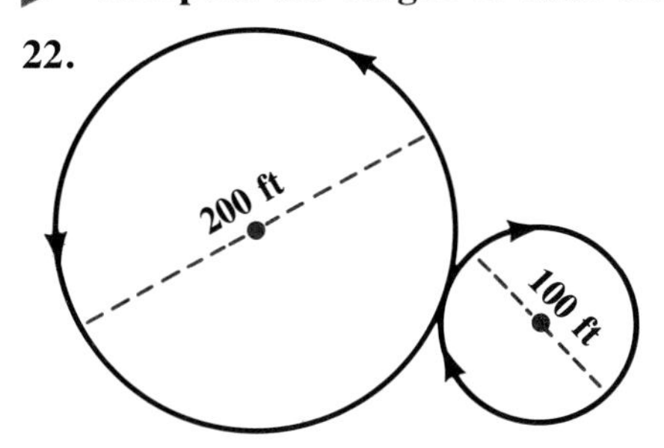

23.

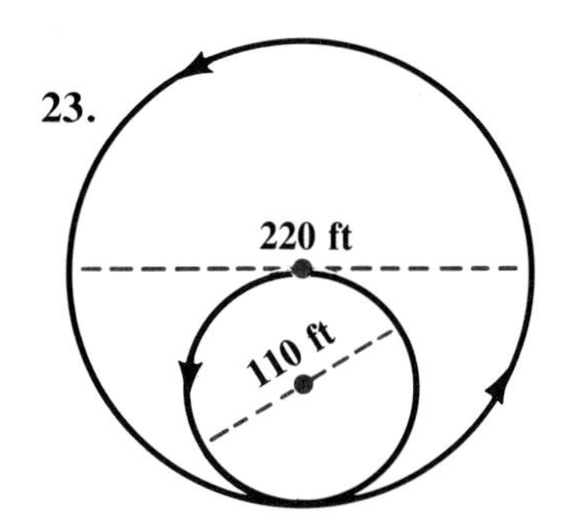

Cumulative Skill Practice

▶ **Simplifying by combining like terms.** *(page 236)*

1. $7c + c$
2. $8x - x$
3. $5n - 5n$
4. $^{-}5d + 4d - 3$
5. $^{-}5d + 4 - 3d$
6. $^{-}5 + 4d - 3$
7. $^{-}10s - s - 8$
8. $^{-}10s + s - 8$
9. $^{-}10s + 1 - 8$
10. $12k - 10 + 6k - 7$
11. $12 - 10k + 6k - 7$
12. $12k - 10 + 6 - 7k$

▶ **Solve and check.** *(page 238)*

13. $4n + n = {}^{-}9$
14. $6r - r = 15$
15. $12v - 18 = {}^{-}18$
16. $11 + 5w - 6 = {}^{-}8$
17. $11 + 5w - 6w = {}^{-}8$
18. $11w + 5 - 6w = {}^{-}8$
19. $^{-}9c + 6 - 3c = 15$
20. $^{-}9 + 6c - 3 = 15$
21. $^{-}9 + 6c - 3c = 15$

▶ **Solve and check.** *(page 240)*

22. $5x + 4x = 8 - 16$
23. $10x - x = {}^{-}5 + 16$
24. $w - 7w = 9 - 15$
25. $3n - 7n - 2 = 12 + 18$
26. $3n - 7 - 2n = 12 + 18$
27. $3 - 7n - 2n = 12 + 18$
28. $8y + 11 - 5y - 10 = {}^{-}29$
29. $8y + 16 - 10y = {}^{-}9 - 20$
30. $13 + 11y - 10y = {}^{-}9 - 20$
31. $^{-}4t + 6 + t - 7 = 14$
32. $^{-}4 + 6t + t - 7 = 14$
33. $^{-}4 + 6 + t - 7t = {}^{-}16 + 30$

▶ **Complete to get an equal ratio.** *(page 250)*

34. $\frac{5}{6} = \frac{?}{18}$
35. $\frac{3}{10} = \frac{?}{40}$
36. $\frac{3}{8} = \frac{?}{16}$
37. $\frac{4}{5} = \frac{?}{25}$
38. $\frac{9}{2} = \frac{?}{20}$
39. $\frac{4}{y} = \frac{?}{2y}$
40. $\frac{3}{w} = \frac{?}{4w}$
41. $\frac{j}{5} = \frac{?}{5k}$
42. $\frac{a}{b} = \frac{?}{b^2}$
43. $\frac{r}{s} = \frac{?}{3s^2}$
44. $\frac{a}{4b} = \frac{?}{12b^2}$
45. $\frac{6m}{2n} = \frac{?}{12n^2}$
46. $\frac{4w}{9xy} = \frac{?}{18xy^2}$
47. $\frac{w}{4} = \frac{?}{20xy}$
48. $\frac{5a}{6bc^2} = \frac{?}{18b^2c^2}$

▶ **Solve each proportion.** *(page 252)*

49. $\frac{n}{5} = \frac{2}{7}$
50. $\frac{8}{n} = \frac{4}{9}$
51. $\frac{8}{12} = \frac{n}{6}$
52. $\frac{9}{7} = \frac{8}{n}$
53. $\frac{n}{10} = \frac{12}{5}$
54. $\frac{11}{3} = \frac{n}{5}$
55. $\frac{15}{19} = \frac{10}{n}$
56. $\frac{n}{10} = \frac{12}{7}$
57. $\frac{20}{n} = \frac{16}{8}$
58. $\frac{18}{21} = \frac{n}{12}$
59. $\frac{4}{3\frac{1}{3}} = \frac{3}{n}$
60. $\frac{n}{2\frac{1}{2}} = \frac{8}{5}$
61. $\frac{12}{n} = \frac{6\frac{1}{8}}{4}$
62. $\frac{10}{2\frac{2}{3}} = \frac{n}{2}$
63. $\frac{7\frac{1}{2}}{5} = \frac{16}{n}$

Problem Solving—Applications

▶ **Use the ticket prices to solve each problem.**

1. How much would you spend for 4 loop-the-loop tickets and 3 roller-coaster tickets?

2. Craig spent \$6.40 on Ferris-wheel tickets and dizzy-swing tickets. He had 5 rides on the dizzy swing. How many rides did he have on the Ferris wheel?

3. Regina bought 8 roller-coaster tickets. She gave the clerk \$10. How much change did she receive?

4. Randy had \$9. He spent $\frac{2}{3}$ of his money on dizzy-swing tickets. How many dizzy-swing tickets did he buy?

5. Gina had \$10.20. She spent 50% of her money for Ferris-wheel tickets. How many rides did she have on the Ferris wheel?

6. Lanny had \$12. He spent 75% of his money on roller-coaster tickets. How many rides did he have on the roller coaster?

▶ **Decide which equation would be used to solve each problem. Then solve the problem.**

Equation A: $n + 4 = 8.80$
Equation B: $4n + 6n = 8.80$
Equation C: $4n = 8.80$
Equation D: $4n + 6 = 8.80$

7. Four house-of-horror tickets cost \$8.80. How much did each ticket cost?

8. Anita bought 4 merry-go-round tickets and Wendy bought 6. Together they spent \$8.80. How much did each ticket cost?

9. John bought some tilt-a-whirl tickets and some pizza. He spent \$4 for the tilt-a-whirl tickets. Altogether he spent \$8.80. How much did he spend for the pizza?

10. Charlene bought 4 bumper-car tickets. She also bought a teddy bear for \$6. Altogether she spent \$8.80. How much did one bumper-car ticket cost?

▶ **Write an equation and solve the problem.**

11. Sidney spent \$4 more than 3 times as much as Jill. If Sidney spent \$16.30, how much did Jill spend?
(Let j = the amount Jill spent.)

12. Anne spent \$2.20 less than 4 times as much as Bill. If Anne spent \$9.20, how much did Bill spend?
(Let b = the amount Bill spent.)

Area—Squares and Rectangles

The **area** of a region is the number of square units that it takes to cover the region.

1 square centimeter

A

B

1. Count the squares. The area of rectangle A is ? square centimeters.
2. What is the area of square B?

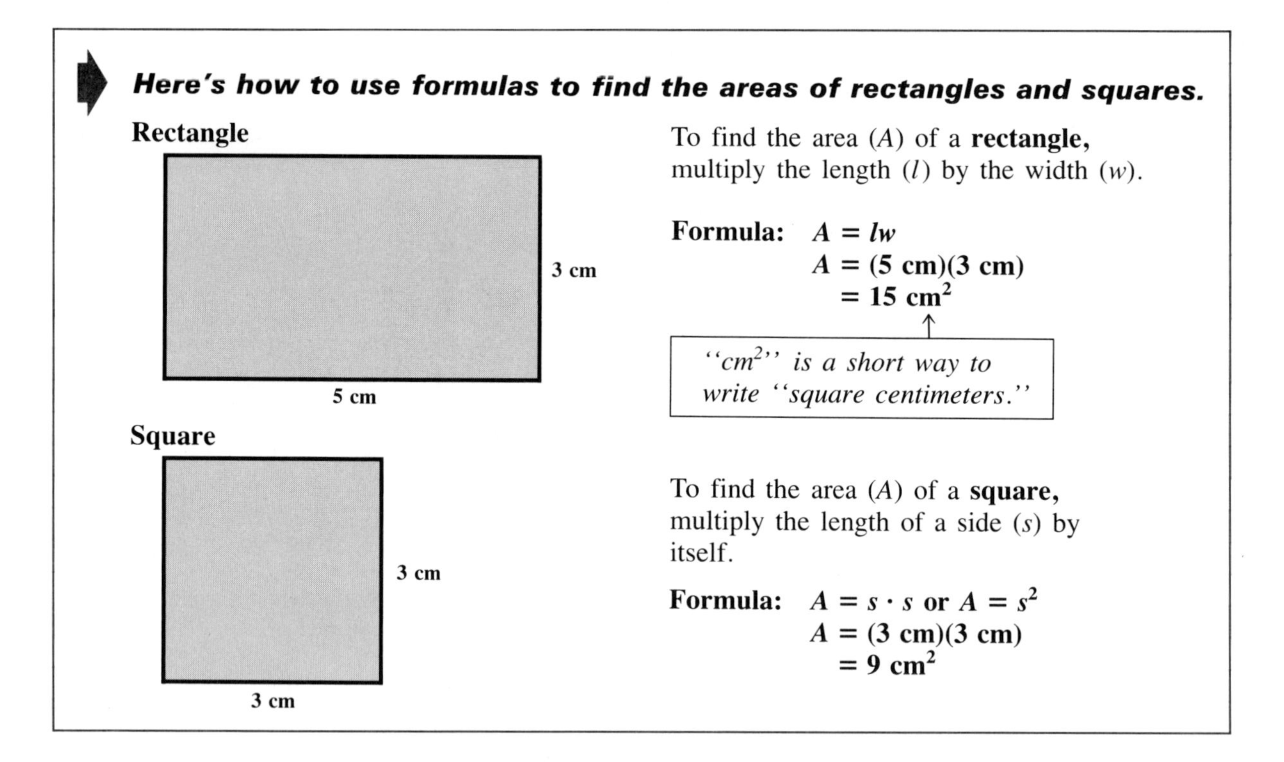

Here's how to use formulas to find the areas of rectangles and squares.

Rectangle

To find the area (A) of a **rectangle,** multiply the length (l) by the width (w).

Formula: $A = lw$
$A = (5 \text{ cm})(3 \text{ cm})$
$= 15 \text{ cm}^2$

"cm^2" is a short way to write "square centimeters."

Square

To find the area (A) of a **square,** multiply the length of a side (s) by itself.

Formula: $A = s \cdot s$ or $A = s^2$
$A = (3 \text{ cm})(3 \text{ cm})$
$= 9 \text{ cm}^2$

3. Look at the examples above. What is the formula for the area of a rectangle? What does each letter represent?
4. If the length and width of a rectangle are 15 meters and 9 meters, the area is 135 ? meters.
5. If the side of a square is 12 centimeters, its area is ? square centimeters.

EXERCISES

▶ **Find the area.**

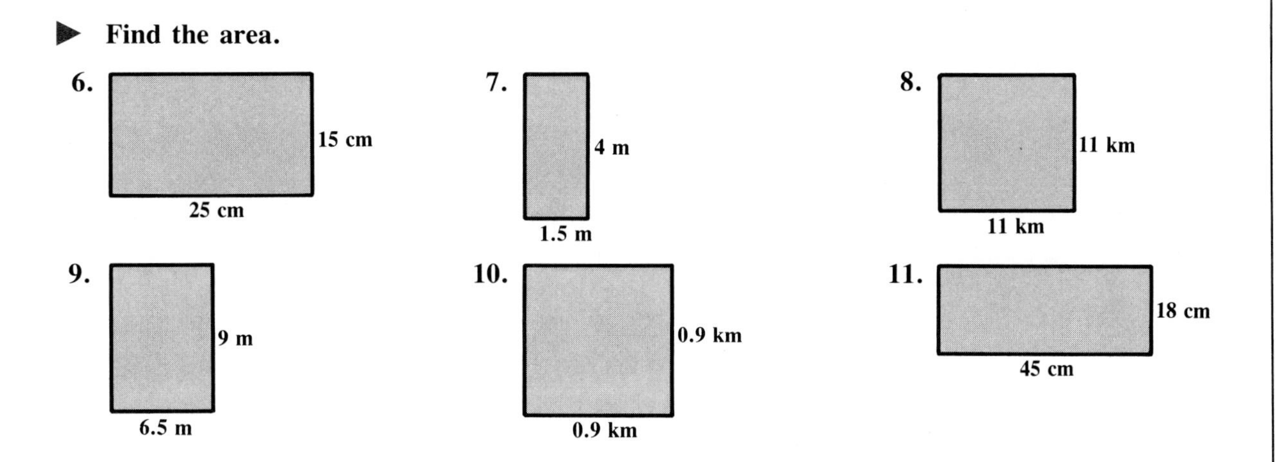

▶ **Substitute in the formula $A = lw$ or $A = s^2$ to find the missing measure.**

12. $l = 35$ cm
$w = 12$ cm
$A = \underline{?}$

13. $l = 2.6$ m
$w = 1.5$ m
$A = \underline{?}$

14. $l = 25$ km
$w = 12$ km
$A = \underline{?}$

15. $l = 10$ cm
$w = 8.4$ cm
$A = \underline{?}$

16. $l = 30$ m
$w = 20$ m
$A = \underline{?}$

17. $l = 2.5$ km
$w = 1.6$ km
$A = \underline{?}$

18. $s = 30$ m
$A = \underline{?}$

19. $s = 8.5$ cm
$A = \underline{?}$

20. $s = 2.2$ km
$A = \underline{?}$

21. $s = 3.4$ m
$A = \underline{?}$

22. $s = 0.8$ cm
$A = \underline{?}$

23. $s = 0.3$ km
$A = \underline{?}$

24. $l = \underline{?}$
$w = 14$ cm
$A = 126\ \text{cm}^2$

25. $l = \underline{?}$
$w = 6.5$ m
$A = 78\ \text{m}^2$

26. $l = 15$ km
$w = \underline{?}$
$A = 93\ \text{km}^2$

Problem Solving

▶ **Tell whether the problem is about perimeter or area. Then solve the problem.**

27. How many 1-foot-square tiles are needed to cover an 18-foot by 12-foot family room?

28. How much molding is needed to go around a 24-foot by 16-foot ceiling?

29. How many yards of fencing are needed to enclose a 30-yard by 25-yard field?

30. How many square feet of sod are needed to cover an 80-foot by 105-foot lawn?

31. How much does it cost to paint a floor that is 15 feet by 25 feet? A $5.90 quart of paint covers about 125 square feet.

32. How much does it cost to frame a 25-foot by 2-foot poster? Framing costs $1.25 a foot.

Area—Parallelograms

To find the area of a parallelogram, we can cut the parallelogram into two pieces **(Step 1)** and rearrange the pieces to make a rectangle with the same area **(Step 2).**

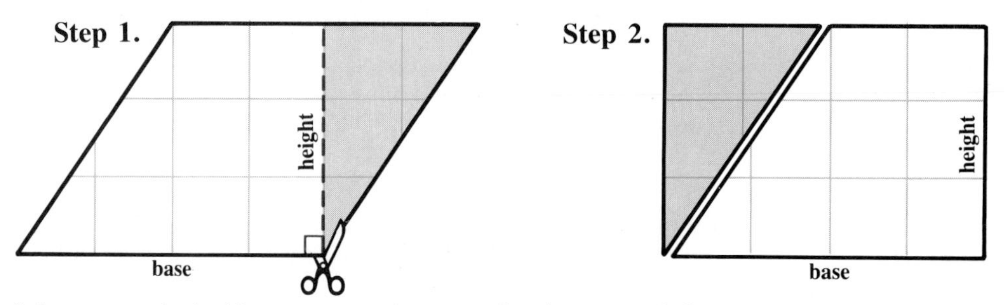

The area of the rectangle is 12 square centimeters. So the area of the parallelogram is also 12 square centimeters.

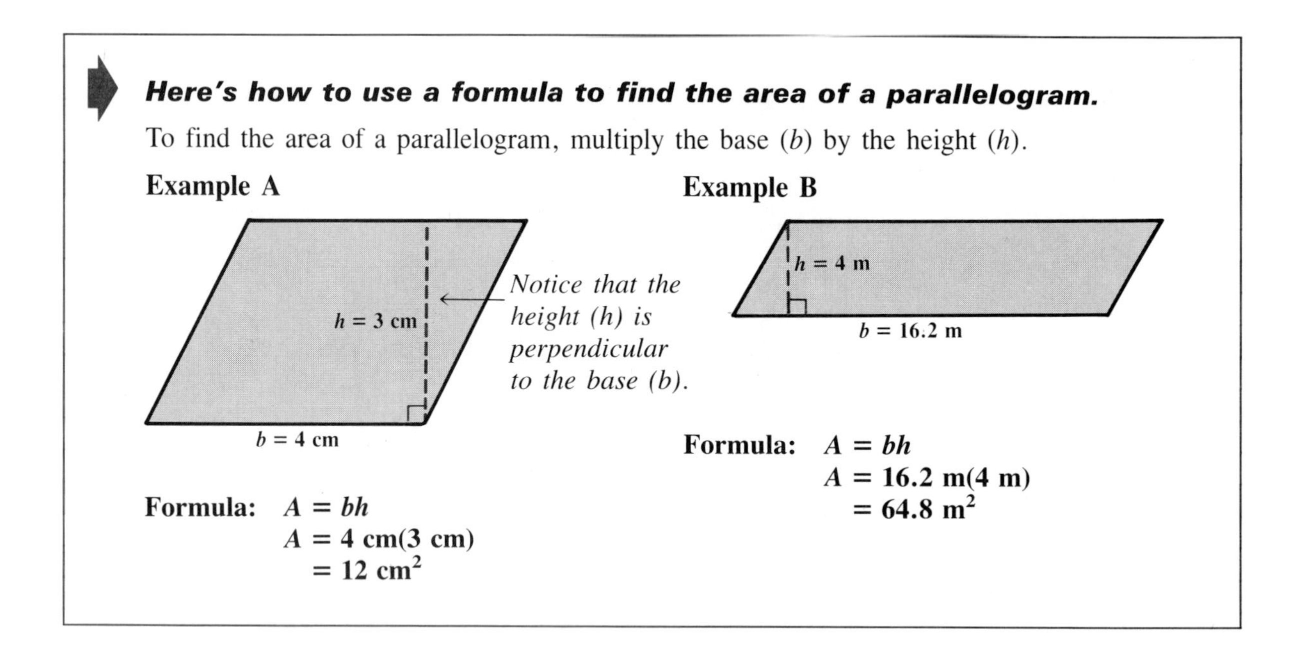

1. Look at the examples above. What is the formula for the area of a parallelogram? What does each letter represent?
2. If the base and height of a parallelogram are 25 centimeters and 20 centimeters, the area is 500 square __?__.
3. If the base and height of a parallelogram are 8.4 meters and 3 meters, the area is __?__ square meters.

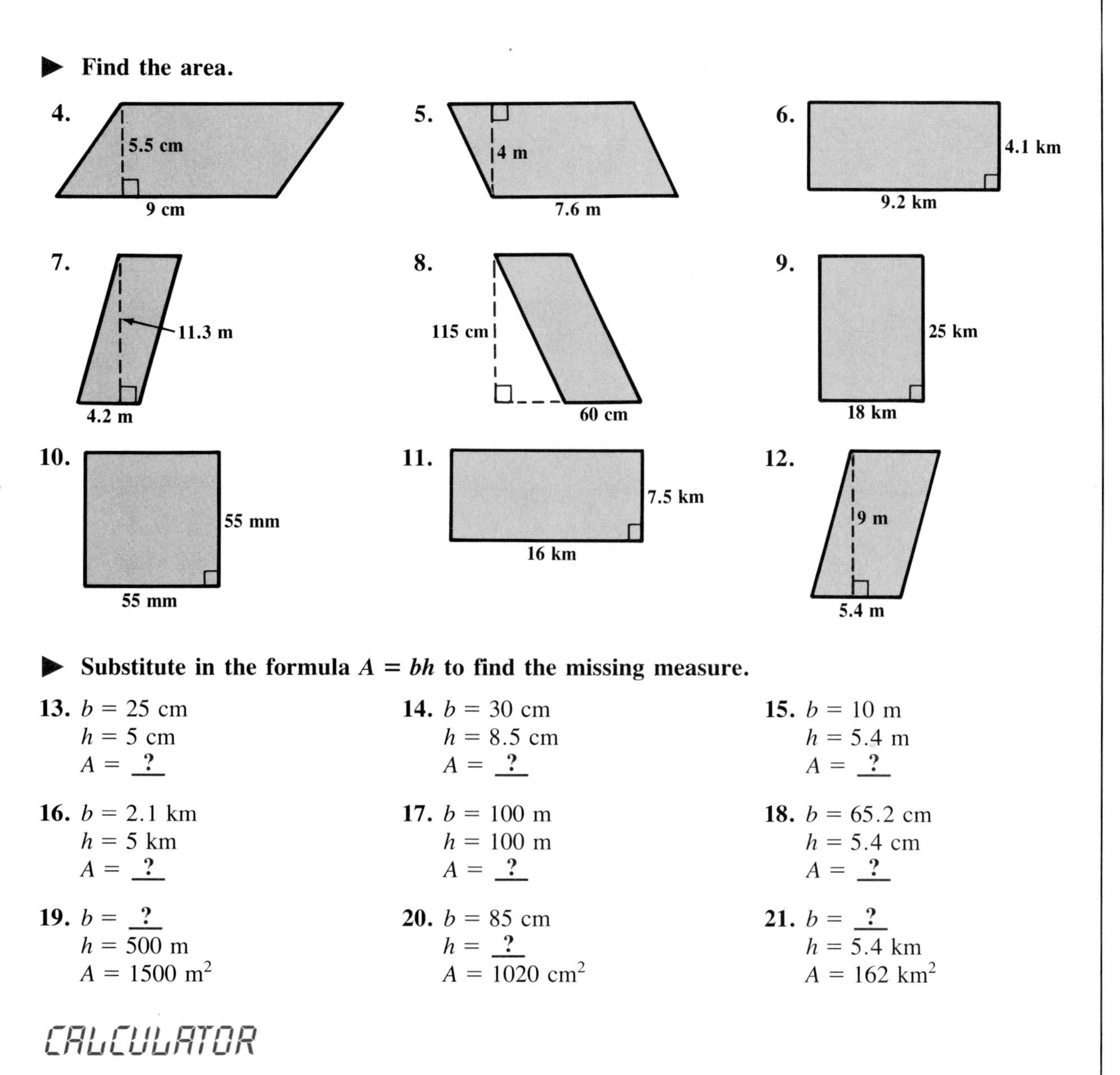

▶ **Substitute in the formula $A = bh$ to find the missing measure.**

13. $b = 25$ cm
$h = 5$ cm
$A = \underline{\ ?\ }$

14. $b = 30$ cm
$h = 8.5$ cm
$A = \underline{\ ?\ }$

15. $b = 10$ m
$h = 5.4$ m
$A = \underline{\ ?\ }$

16. $b = 2.1$ km
$h = 5$ km
$A = \underline{\ ?\ }$

17. $b = 100$ m
$h = 100$ m
$A = \underline{\ ?\ }$

18. $b = 65.2$ cm
$h = 5.4$ cm
$A = \underline{\ ?\ }$

19. $b = \underline{\ ?\ }$
$h = 500$ m
$A = 1500\ m^2$

20. $b = 85$ cm
$h = \underline{\ ?\ }$
$A = 1020\ cm^2$

21. $b = \underline{\ ?\ }$
$h = 5.4$ km
$A = 162\ km^2$

CALCULATOR

▶ **Find the length of the side of the square.** ***Hint: Estimate. Compute the area using a calculator. Repeat until you get the answer.***

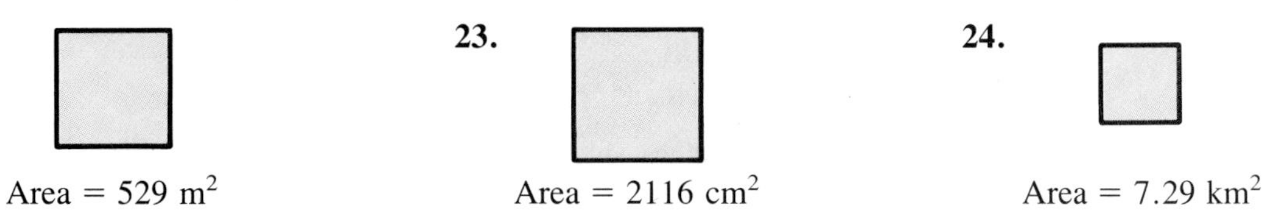

Area = $529\ m^2$

Area = $2116\ cm^2$

Area = $7.29\ km^2$

Area—Triangles

To find the area of a triangle, think about cutting a parallelogram into two triangles that have the same area.

The area of the parallelogram is 12 square inches. The area of each triangle is half of 12 square inches or 6 square inches.

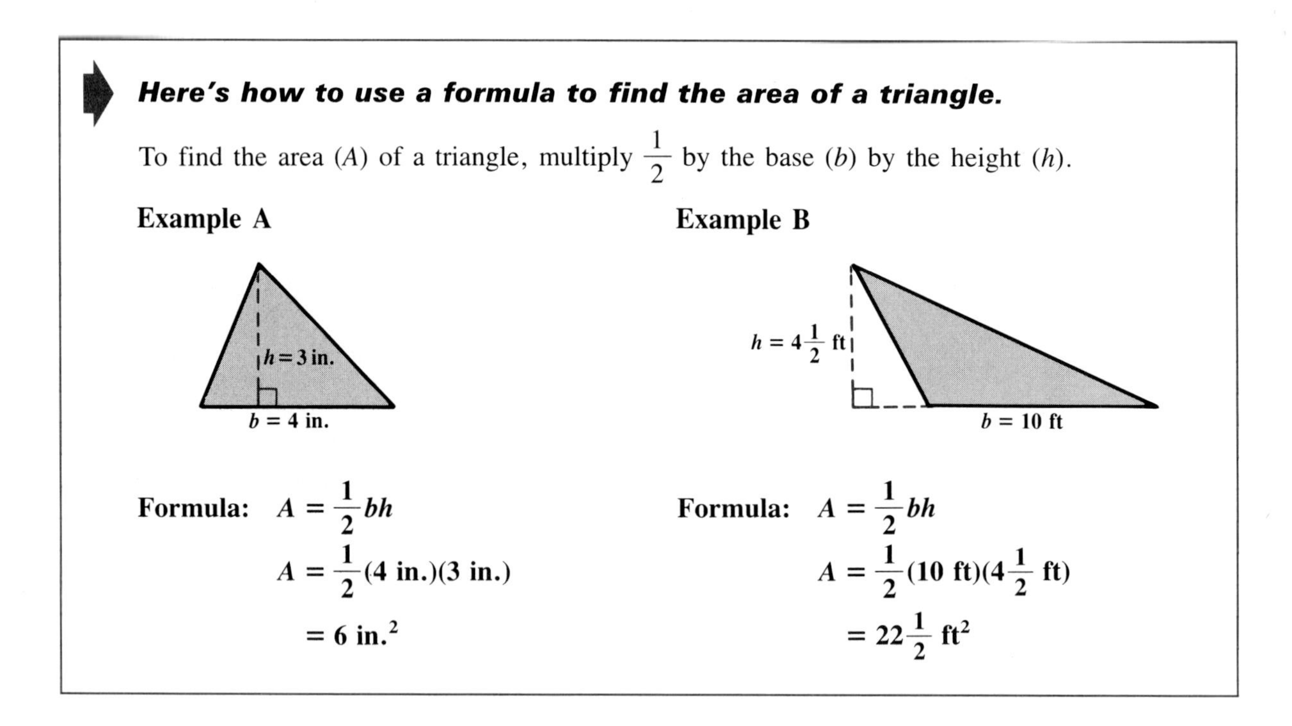

Here's how to use a formula to find the area of a triangle.

To find the area (A) of a triangle, multiply $\frac{1}{2}$ by the base (b) by the height (h).

Example A

Formula: $A = \frac{1}{2}bh$

$A = \frac{1}{2}(4 \text{ in.})(3 \text{ in.})$

$= 6 \text{ in.}^2$

Example B

Formula: $A = \frac{1}{2}bh$

$A = \frac{1}{2}(10 \text{ ft})(4\frac{1}{2} \text{ ft})$

$= 22\frac{1}{2} \text{ ft}^2$

1. Look at the examples above. For any triangle, the area is equal to one half the base times the ? .
2. If the base and height of a triangle are 5 yards and 7 yards, the area is $17\frac{1}{2}$ square ? .
3. If the base and height of a triangle are 12 inches and 9 inches, the area is ? square inches.

▶ **Find the area.**

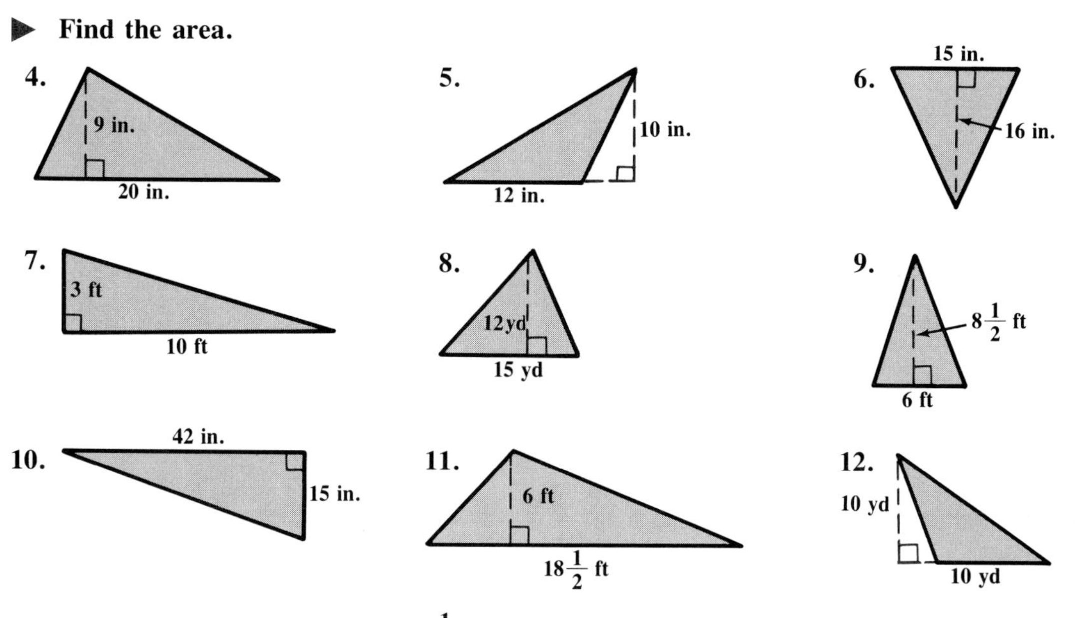

▶ **Substitute in the formula $A = \frac{1}{2}bh$ to find the missing measure.**

13. $b = 40$ yd
$h = 9$ yd
$A = \underline{?}$

14. $b = 28$ ft
$h = 20$ ft
$A = \underline{?}$

15. $b = 16$ yd
$h = 4\frac{1}{2}$ yd
$A = \underline{?}$

16. $b = 8$ in.
$h = \underline{?}$
$A = 20 \text{ in.}^2$

17. $b = 30$ ft
$h = \underline{?}$
$A = 180 \text{ ft}^2$

18. $b = \underline{?}$
$h = 20$ yd
$A = 100 \text{ yd}^2$

Challenge

▶ **Use the code to check your answer to the question.**

19. *Question:* If triangles sell at four for 10¢, how much would five triangles cost at double the price?

Answer:

$1\frac{1}{2}$ ft^2	2 ft^2	4 ft^2	5 ft^2	$1\frac{1}{2}$ ft^2	12 ft^2

–

$4\frac{1}{2}$ ft^2	1 ft^2	3 ft^2	4 ft^2

7 ft^2	4 ft^2	5 ft^2	$1\frac{1}{2}$ ft^2	10 ft^2

CODE:

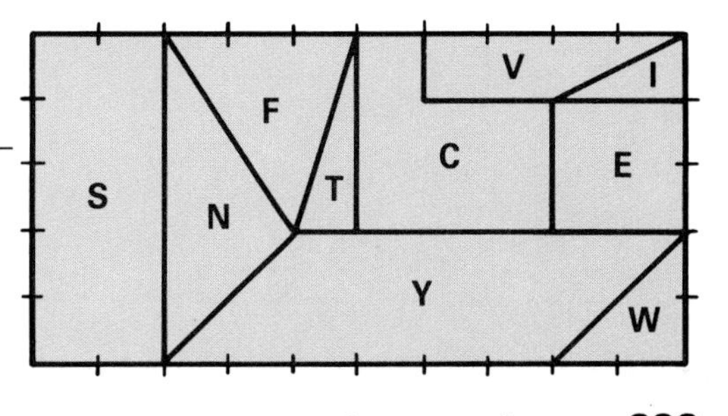

Area—Circles

Here's a method you can use to estimate the area of a circle.

1. Look at the drawing at the right.

a. The area of the red square is 18 square centimeters. What is the area of the green square?

b. The circle is larger than the red square and smaller than the green square. You can estimate the area of the circle by finding the average of the areas of the squares. What is the average?

2. Estimate the area of the circle by counting squares. Is the area of the circle about 27 square centimeters?

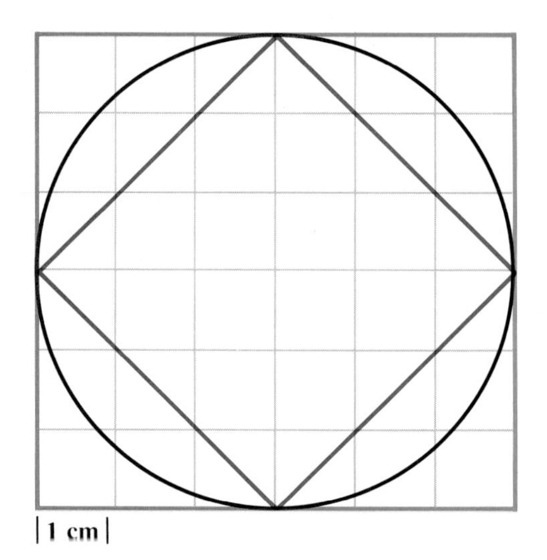

Here's how to use a formula to find the area of a circle.

To find the area (A) of a circle, multiply π (about 3.14) by the square of the radius (r).

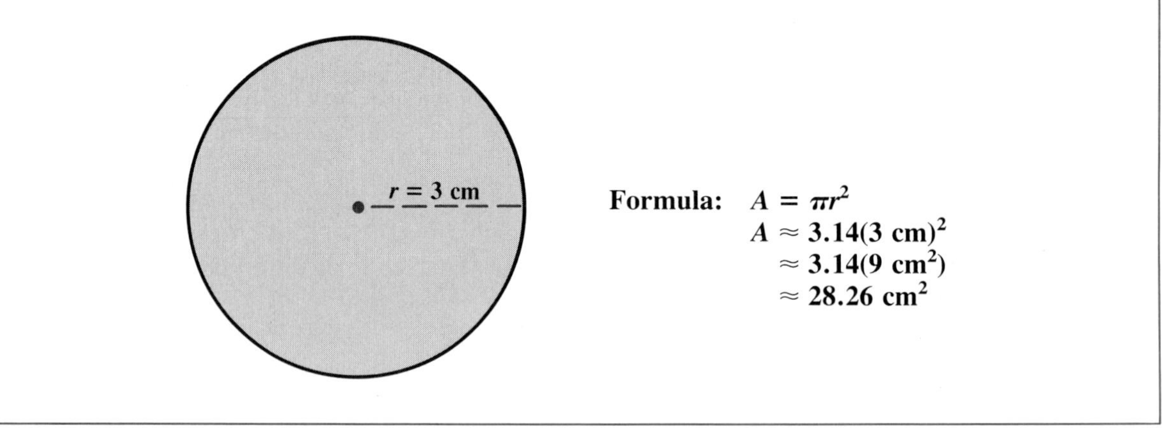

Formula:

$$A = \pi r^2$$
$$A \approx 3.14(3\text{ cm})^2$$
$$\approx 3.14(9\text{ cm}^2)$$
$$\approx 28.26\text{ cm}^2$$

3. Look at the example above. For any circle, the area equals π times the square of the ___?___.

4. In the formula $A = \pi r^2$, r^2 means ___?___ times ___?___.

5. If the radius of a circle is 5 centimeters, its area is 3.14 $(5\text{ cm})^2$, or 78.5 square ___?___.

6. If the radius of a circle is 10 meters, its area is 3.14 $(10\text{ m})^2$, or ___?___ square meters.

▶ **Find the area. Use 3.14 for π.**

Here are scrambled answers for the next row of exercises:

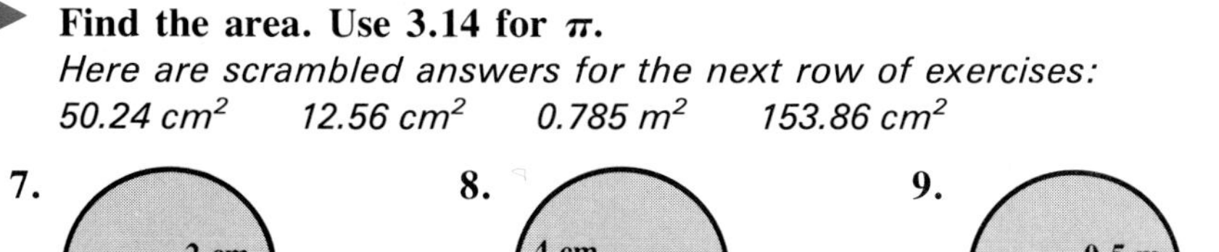

50.24 cm² 12.56 cm² 0.785 m² 153.86 cm²

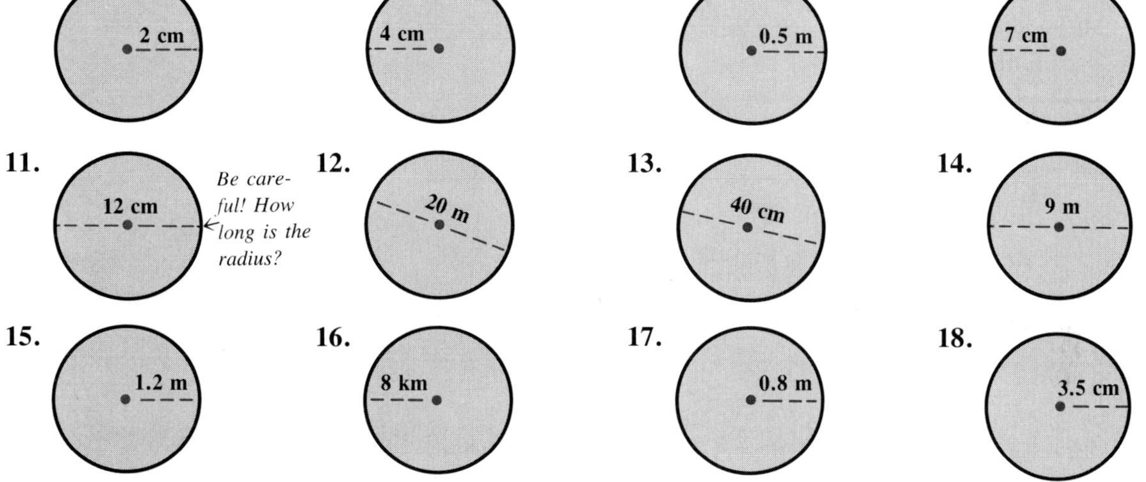

▶ **Substitute in the formula $A = \pi r^2$ to find the missing area.**

19. $r = 5$ cm
$\pi \approx 3.14$
$A \approx$?

20. $r = 1.2$ m
$\pi \approx 3.14$
$A \approx$?

21. $r = 30$ km
$\pi \approx 3.14$
$A \approx$?

22. $r = 0.4$ m
$\pi \approx 3.14$
$A \approx$?

Problem Solving

▶ **Solve.**

23. A round table top has a radius of 80 centimeters. What is its area?

24. A round mirror has a radius of 35 centimeters. What is its area?

25. A circular platform has a diameter of 2 meters. What is its area?

26. A circular swimming pool has a diameter of 8.8 meters. What is its area?

Challenge

▶ **Add or subtract to find the area of each shaded part.**

27.

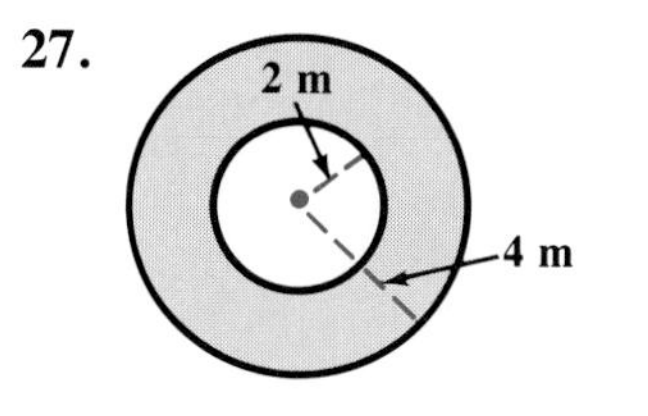

28.

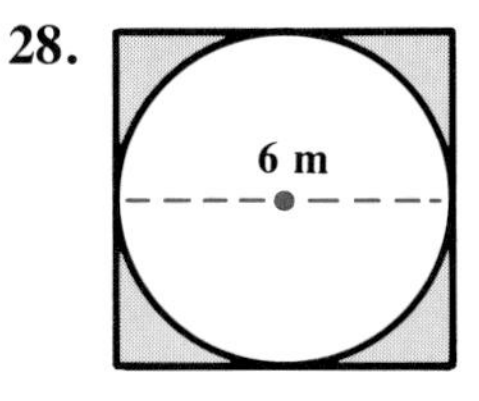

★29.

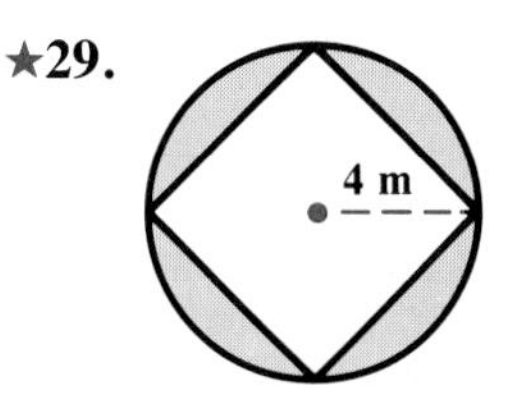

Problem Solving—Drawing a Picture

In this lesson you will solve perimeter problems by writing equations. In solving these problems, it will be helpful to use drawings that picture the facts in the problem.

Here's how to use a drawing and an equation to solve a perimeter problem.

Problem: A rectangle is 12 centimeters longer than it is wide. What is the width of the rectangle if its perimeter is 96 centimeters?

Step 1. Choose a variable. Use it and a drawing to picture the facts in the problem.

Let w = the width of the rectangle.
Let $w + 12$ = the length of the rectangle.

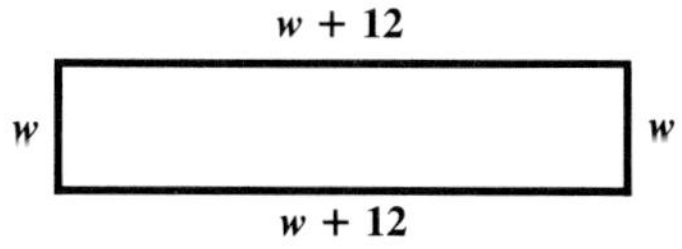

Step 2. Write an equation based on the facts.

$$w + w + 12 + w + w + 12 = 96$$

These are two equal expressions for the perimeter of the rectangle.

Step 3. Solve the equation.

$$w + w + 12 + w + w + 12 = 96$$
$$4w + 24 = 96$$
$$4w + 24 - 24 = 96 - 24$$
$$4w = 72$$
$$\frac{4w}{4} = \frac{72}{4}$$
$$w = 18$$

The width of the rectangle is 18 centimeters.

1. Look at the example above.

a. In Step 1, we let w equal the width of the rectangle. Then w + __?__ equals the length of the rectangle.

b. In Step 2, the two equal expressions for the perimeter are __?__ and 96.

c. An equation for the problem is $w + w + 12 + w + w + 12 =$ __?__.

2. To check the solution, ask yourself if the answer fits the facts in the problem. If the width is 18 centimeters, what is the length? Is the sum of the two widths and two lengths equal to 96 centimeters?

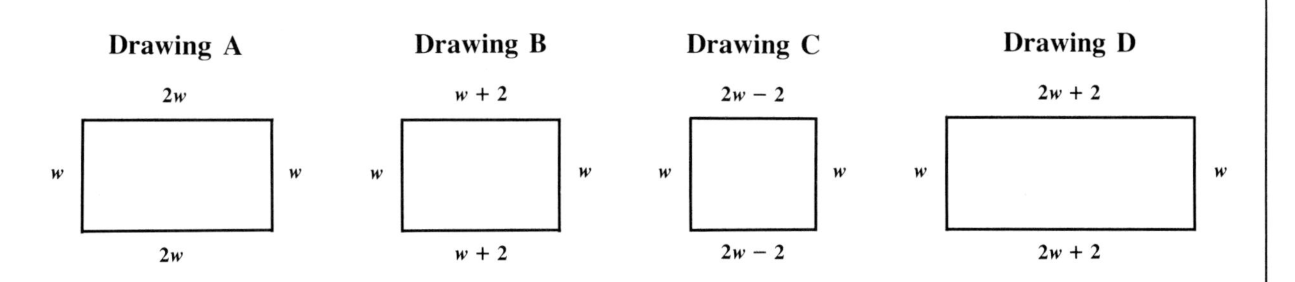

▶ **Decide which drawing above would be used to picture the facts in each problem. Then use the drawing to write an equation and solve the problem.**

3. The length of a rectangle is 2 centimeters more than its width (w). What is its width if its perimeter is 60 centimeters?

4. The length of a rectangle is 2 centimeters less than twice its width (w). What is its width if its perimeter is 50 centimeters?

5. The length of a rectangle is twice its width (w). What is its width if its perimeter is 120 centimeters?

6. The length of a rectangle is 2 centimeters more than twice its width (w). What is its width if its perimeter is 70 centimeters?

▶ **Make a drawing that pictures the facts. Then write an equation and solve the problem.**

7. The length of a rectangular table top is 30 centimeters more than its width (w). What is the width of the table top if its perimeter is 380 centimeters?

8. The length of a rectangular poster is 15 centimeters less than its width (w). What is the width of the poster if its perimeter is 230 centimeters?

9. The length of a rectangular garden is 3 times its width (w). What is the width of the garden if its perimeter is 240 meters?

10. The length of a rectangular field is 6 times its width (w). What is the width of the field if its perimeter is 280 meters?

11. The length of a rectangular mirror is 3 centimeters more than twice its width (w). What is the width of the mirror if its perimeter is 426 centimeters?

12. The length of a rectangular picture is 4 centimeters less than twice its width (w). What is the width of the picture if its perimeter is 436 centimeters?

★13. One side of a triangle is 3 centimeters longer than the shortest side (s), and the other side is 4 centimeters longer than the shortest side. How long is the shortest side if the perimeter is 67 centimeters?

★14. One side of a triangle is 5 centimeters longer than the shortest side (s), and the other side is 3 centimeters longer than the shortest side. How long is the shortest side if the perimeter is 59 centimeters?

Cumulative Skill Practice

▶ **Change to a fraction, whole number, or mixed number. Give each answer in simplest form.** *(page 256)*

1. 36% **2.** 85% **3.** 144% **4.** 5% **5.** 60% **6.** 1%

7. 300% **8.** 125% **9.** 250% **10.** $33\frac{1}{3}\%$ **11.** $37\frac{1}{2}\%$ **12.** $62\frac{1}{2}\%$

13. $87\frac{1}{2}\%$ **14.** $66\frac{2}{3}\%$ **15.** $162\frac{1}{2}\%$ **16.** $116\frac{2}{3}\%$ **17.** $233\frac{1}{3}\%$ **18.** $206\frac{1}{4}\%$

▶ **Change to a percent.** *(page 258)*

19. $\frac{1}{4}$ **20.** $\frac{3}{2}$ **21.** $\frac{1}{2}$ **22.** $\frac{3}{10}$ **23.** $\frac{3}{4}$ **24.** $\frac{9}{10}$

25. 1 **26.** 3 **27.** $\frac{3}{8}$ **28.** $\frac{4}{5}$ **29.** $\frac{5}{8}$ **30.** $\frac{5}{4}$

31. $\frac{13}{3}$ **32.** $\frac{15}{8}$ **33.** $\frac{11}{6}$ **34.** $\frac{4}{9}$ **35.** $\frac{7}{6}$ **36.** $\frac{8}{3}$

▶ **Solve.** *(page 262)*

37. 50% of 42 = n **38.** 30% of 20 = n **39.** 25% of 44 = n

40. 31% of 80 = n **41.** 52% of 127 = n **42.** 79% of 174 = n

43. 5.8% of 20 = n **44.** 9.2% of 235 = n **45.** 3.4% of 118 = n

46. 80% of 45 = n **47.** 120% of 90 = n **48.** 200% of 64 = n

▶ **Change each percent to a fraction or decimal and solve.** *(page 264)*

49. 50% of n = 16 **50.** 25% of n = 8 **51.** 75% of n = 42

52. 60% of n = 39 **53.** 150% of n = 48 **54.** 35% of n = 56

55. 12.5% of n = 12 **56.** 18% of n = 27 **57.** 37.5% of n = 51

58. 12.5% of n = 18.2 **59.** 275% of n = 88 **60.** 150% of n = 24.6

▶ **Solve.** *(page 266)*

61. n% of 5 = 4 **62.** n% of 16 = 4 **63.** n% of 8 = 16

64. $4\frac{1}{2}\%$ of 16 = n **65.** $8\frac{1}{3}\%$ of 48 = n **66.** $66\frac{2}{3}\%$ of n = 44

67. 20% of n = 11 **68.** 1% of n = 1.75 **69.** 62.5% of n = 75

70. n% of 42 = 28 **71.** n% of 6 = 10 **72.** 12.5% of n = 10

Problem Solving—Applications

▶ **Use a drawing to help solve each problem.**

1. How many feet of fencing are needed to enclose an 80-foot by 50-foot rectangular garden?
2. How many feet of fencing are needed to enclose a square garden that is 55 feet on a side?
3. How large a square can you fence in with 120 feet of fencing?
4. You use 240 feet of fencing to fence in a rectangular yard. If the length of the yard is 80 feet, how wide is the yard?

▶ **Use the weekend special prices. Find the total cost for each fencing project.**

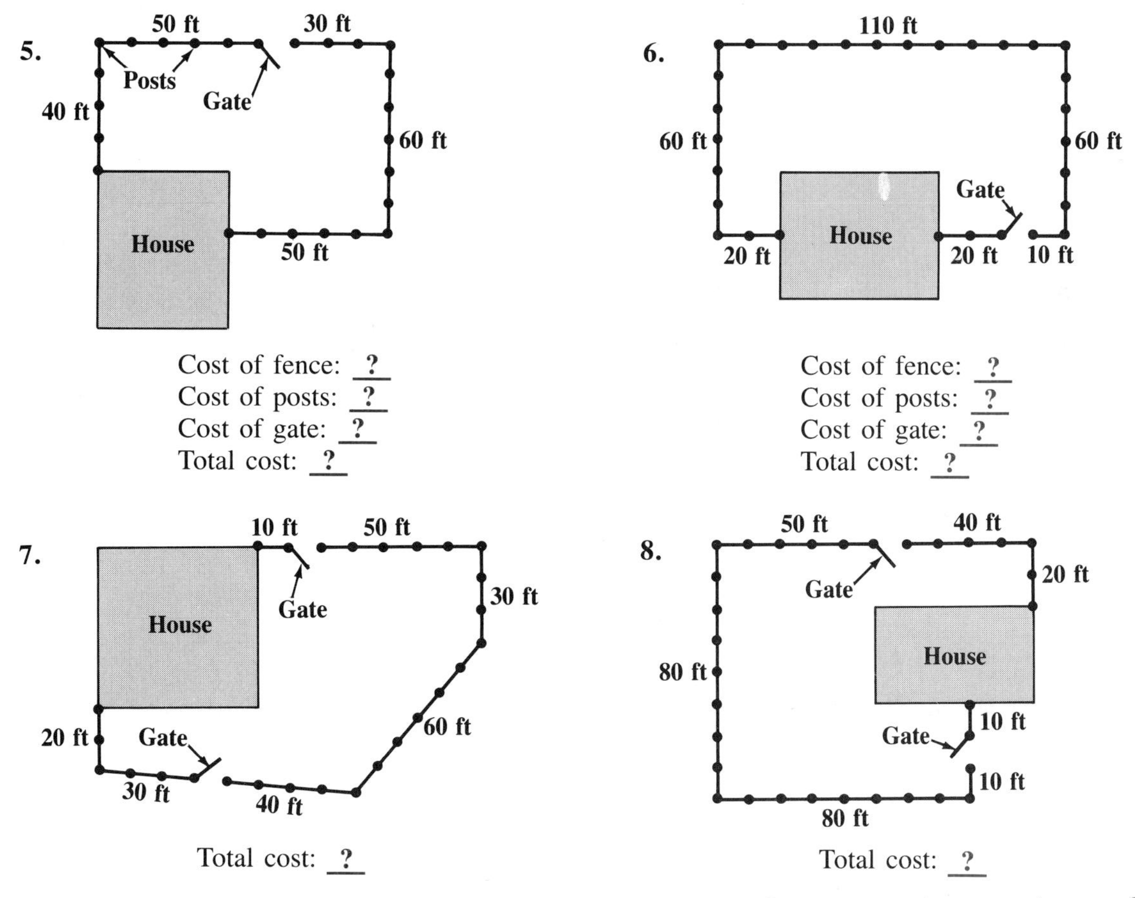

5. Cost of fence: ?
Cost of posts: ?
Cost of gate: ?
Total cost: ?

6. Cost of fence: ?
Cost of posts: ?
Cost of gate: ?
Total cost: ?

7. Total cost: ?

8. Total cost: ?

Chapter Review

Here are scrambled answers for the review exercises:

0.001	*1000*	*circumference*	*itself*	*parallel*	*rectangle*
5	*acute*	*decimal*	*kilometer*	*parallelogram*	*right*
6	*area*	*diameter*	*meter*	*perimeter*	*square*
112	*base*	*divide*	*millimeters*	*perpendicular*	*trapezoid*
113.04	*centimeters*	*height*	*obtuse*	*radius*	*width*

1. An ? angle measures between 0° and 90°. A ? angle measures 90°. An ? angle measures between 90° and 180°. *(page 278)*

2. In this drawing, line x is ? to line y, and line x is ? to line z. *(page 280)*

3. A rectangle is also a ? . A ? has exactly 1 pair of parallel sides. A pentagon has ? sides, and a hexagon has ? sides. *(page 282)*

4. In the metric system, the ? is the basic unit of length. *(page 284)*
1 kilometer = ? meters 1 millimeter = ? meter

5. To change units in the metric system, multiply or ? by 10, 100, or 1000. *(page 286)*
100 ? = 1 meter 1000 ? = 1 meter 1000 meters = 1 ?

6. The ? of a polygon is the distance around the polygon. Use the formula $P = 4s$ to find the perimeter of a ? . Use the formula $P = 2(l + w)$ to find the perimeter of a ? . *(page 288)*

7. In this drawing, the ? of the circle is 8 inches and the ? of the circle is 4 inches. The distance around a circle is called the ? . To find the circumference, use the formula $C = \pi d$. A ? approximation for π is 3.14. *(page 290)*

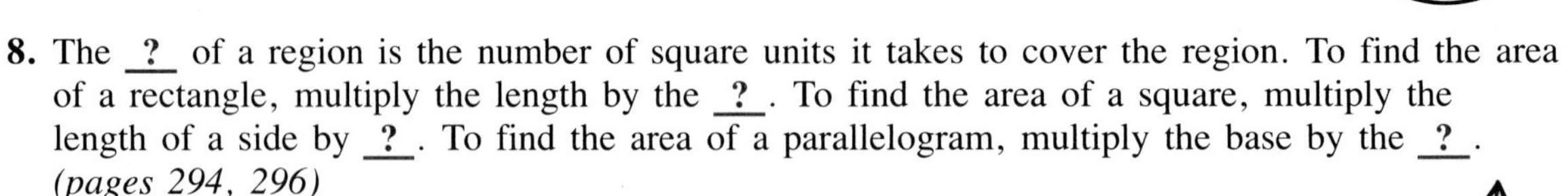

8. The ? of a region is the number of square units it takes to cover the region. To find the area of a rectangle, multiply the length by the ? . To find the area of a square, multiply the length of a side by ? . To find the area of a parallelogram, multiply the base by the ? . *(pages 294, 296)*

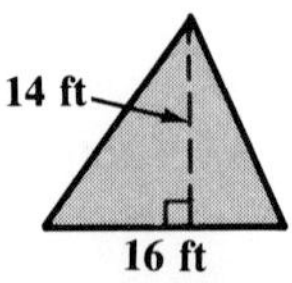

9. To find the area of a triangle, use the formula $A = \frac{1}{2}bh$, where b stands for the ? and h stands for the height. The area of this triangle is ? ft^2. *(page 298)*

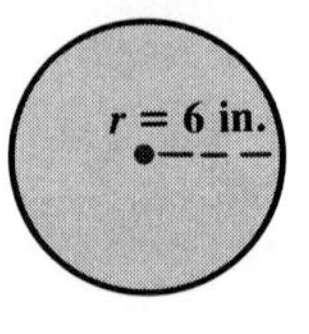

10. To find the area of a circle, use the formula $A = \pi r^2$, where r stands for the radius. The area of this circle is ? in.^{2} (Use 3.14 for π.) *(page 300)*

Chapter Test

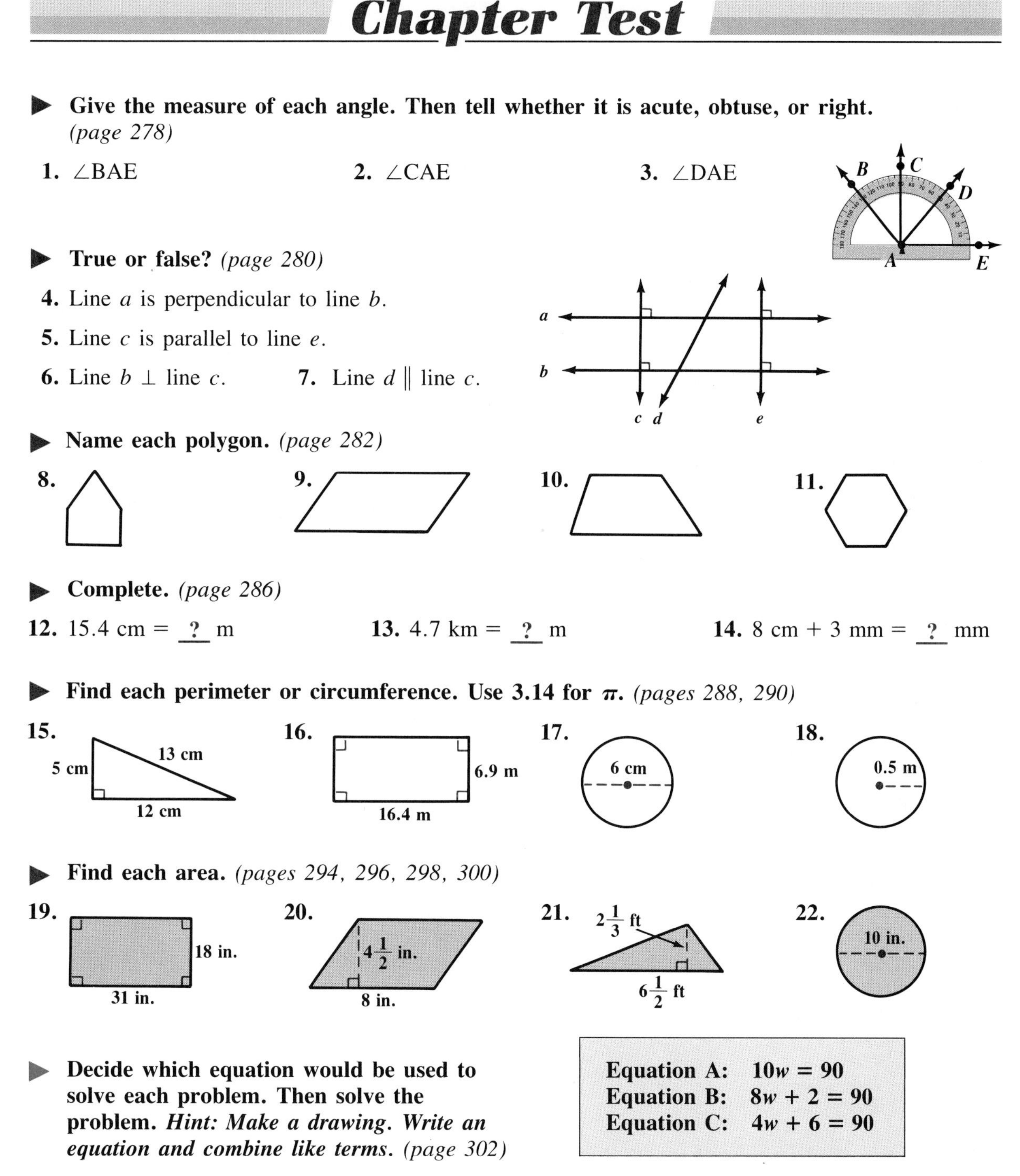

Give the measure of each angle. Then tell whether it is acute, obtuse, or right. *(page 278)*

1. ∠BAE
2. ∠CAE
3. ∠DAE

True or false? *(page 280)*

4. Line a is perpendicular to line b.
5. Line c is parallel to line e.
6. Line $b \perp$ line c.
7. Line $d \parallel$ line c.

Name each polygon. *(page 282)*

8. 9. 10. 11.

Complete. *(page 286)*

12. 15.4 cm = ? m
13. 4.7 km = ? m
14. 8 cm + 3 mm = ? mm

Find each perimeter or circumference. Use 3.14 for π. *(pages 288, 290)*

15. 5 cm, 13 cm, 12 cm
16. 6.9 m, 16.4 m
17. 6 cm
18. 0.5 m

Find each area. *(pages 294, 296, 298, 300)*

19. 18 in., 31 in.
20. $4\frac{1}{2}$ in., 8 in.
21. $2\frac{1}{3}$ ft, $6\frac{1}{2}$ ft
22. 10 in.

Decide which equation would be used to solve each problem. Then solve the problem. ***Hint: Make a drawing. Write an equation and combine like terms.*** *(page 302)*

Equation A: $10w = 90$
Equation B: $8w + 2 = 90$
Equation C: $4w + 6 = 90$

23. A rectangle has a length that is 3 feet more than its width. Its perimeter is 90 feet. What is its width?

24. A rectangle has a length that is 1 foot more than 3 times its width. Its perimeter is 90 feet. What is its width?

Cumulative Test

Standardized Format

▶ **Choose the correct letter.**

1. Simplify by combining like terms.

$5y - 8 - 3y + 1$

A. $8y - 7$
B. $2y - 9$
C. $2y - 7$
D. none of these

2. Solve.

$3w + 9 + 5w = {}^{-}11$

A. ${}^{-}\frac{1}{4}$ B. ${}^{-}2\frac{1}{2}$
C. $2\frac{1}{2}$ D. none of these

3. Solve.

$4n - 9 - n = {}^{-}7 + 15$

A. $\frac{{}^{-}1}{5}$ B. $5\frac{2}{3}$
C. $4\frac{1}{4}$ D. none of these

4. Complete.

$\frac{7a}{3b} = \frac{?}{12ab^2}$

A. $28a^2b$
B. $28a^2$
C. $4ab$
D. none of these

5. Solve.

$\frac{n}{5} = \frac{7}{1\frac{1}{2}}$

A. $52\frac{1}{2}$ B. $1\frac{1}{14}$
C. $23\frac{1}{3}$ D. none of these

6. Change to a fraction.

$62\frac{1}{2}\% = \underline{\ ?\ }$

A. $\frac{3}{8}$ B. $\frac{1}{2}$
C. $\frac{7}{8}$ D. none of these

7. Change to a percent.

$\frac{11}{6} = \underline{\ ?\ }$

A. $87\frac{1}{2}\%$ B. $83\frac{1}{3}\%$
C. $62\frac{1}{2}\%$ D. none of these

8. Solve.

7.5% of $72 = \underline{\ ?\ }$

A. 1.8
B. 3.6
C. 4.8
D. none of these

9. Solve.

125% of $n = 38.5$

A. 30.8
B. 38.5
C. 48.125
D. none of these

10. Solve.

$n\%$ of $45 = 60$

A. 75
B. 115
C. $133\frac{1}{3}$
D. none of these

11. Solve.

$8\frac{1}{3}\%$ of $n = 12$

A. 36
B. 72
C. 144
D. none of these

12. Choose the equation.

Six more than the sum of 5 times a number and 3 times a number is 62. What is the number?

A. $5n + 3n + 6 = 62$
B. $5n - 3n + 6 = 62$
C. $5n - 3n - 6 = 62$
D. $5n + 3n - 6 = 62$

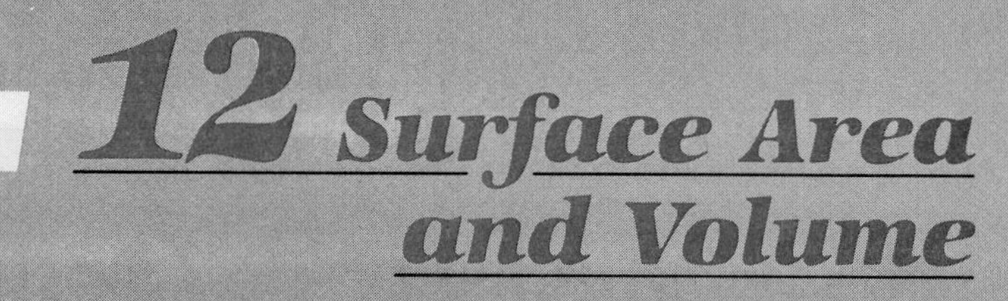

12 Surface Area and Volume

$$V = \frac{1}{3}Bh$$

The volume of a pyramid equals one third times the area of the base times the height of the pyramid.
(page 322)

The picture shows the pyramids of the Muttart Conservatory in Edmonton, Alberta, Canada. The volume of these pyramids can be found by using the above formula.

Space Figures

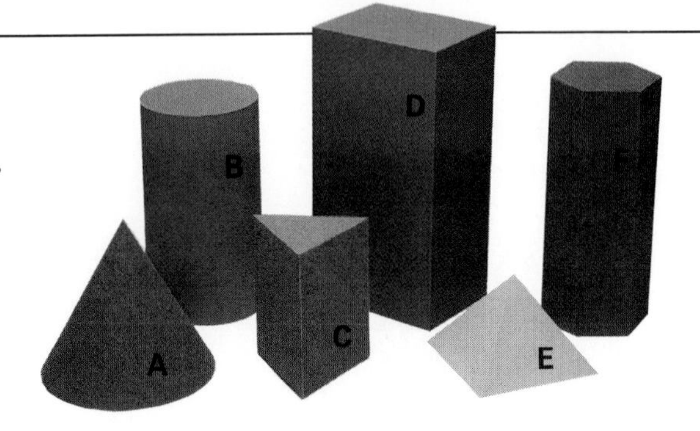

The models at the right are three-dimensional. Three-dimensional shapes are called **space figures.**

1. Which model has 9 edges, 6 vertices (corners), and 5 faces (sides)?
2. Which model has 4 triangular faces and 1 square face?

Here's how space figures are named.

In the drawings below, the shaded faces are the **bases.** Prisms and pyramids are named according to the shapes of their bases. Notice that a cube is a rectangular prism whose faces are square, all the same size.

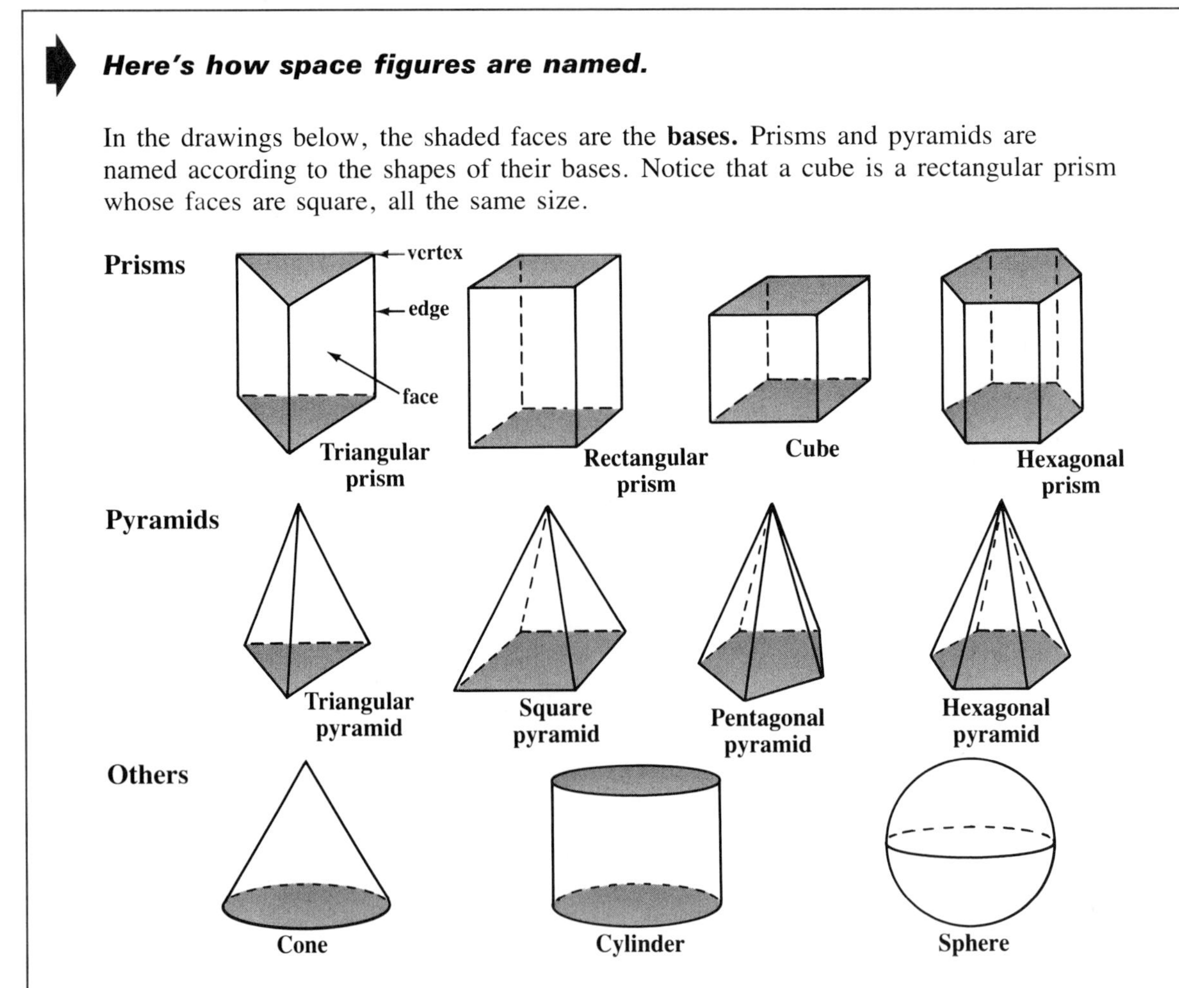

3. Use the models and the drawings above to answer these questions.
   a. Which model is a square pyramid?
   b. Which model is a cylinder?
   c. Which model is a cone?
   d. Which 3 models are prisms?

EXERCISES

► **Name the space figure in each exercise. A top view and a side view are given for each figure.**

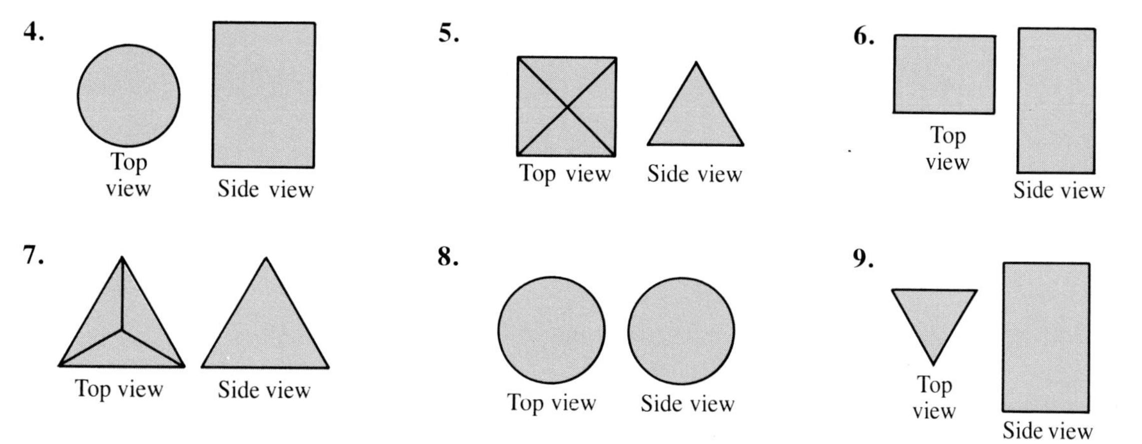

Problem Solving

► **Use the clues and the drawings on page 310. Name each space figure.**

10. *Clues:*
- This space figure is a pyramid.
- It has 6 vertices.

11. *Clues:*
- This space figure is a prism.
- All its faces are squares.

12. *Clues:*
- This space figure has 8 edges.
- It has 5 faces.

13. *Clues:*
- This space figure has 2 bases.
- It has 12 vertices.

14. *Clues:*
- Cut this space figure one way and the shape that is formed is a rectangle.
- Cut it another way and the shape that is formed is a circle.

15. *Clues:*
- Cut this space figure one way and the shape that is formed is a circle.
- Cut it another way and the shape that is formed is a triangle.

Challenge

► **Use graph paper and copy each drawing.** ***Hint: Count the squares carefully.***

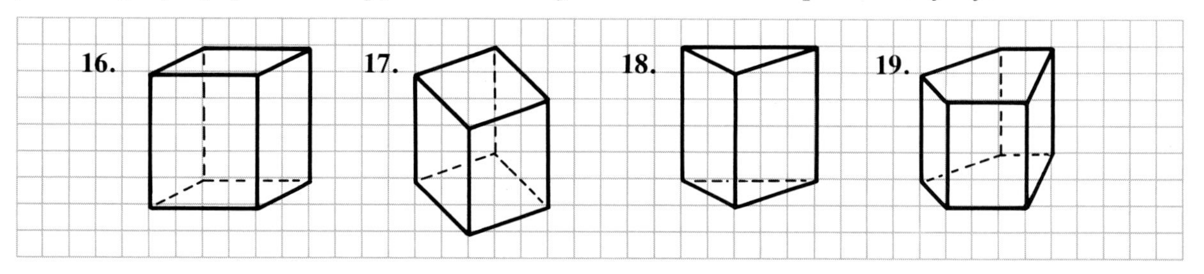

More on Space Figures

The pattern below was made from some of the pieces that are shown at the right. When the pattern is folded, it forms a triangular prism.

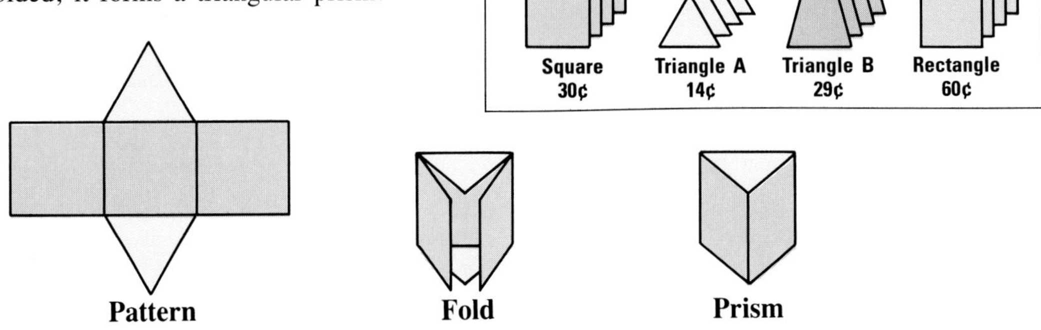

1. Look at the pattern.
   a. How many pieces were used to make the pattern?
   b. Which shape was used for the bases (top and bottom)? What is the total cost of the bases?
   c. Which shape was used for the other faces? What is their total cost?
2. What is the total cost of the triangular prism?

EXERCISES

▶ **Find the total cost of each pattern.**

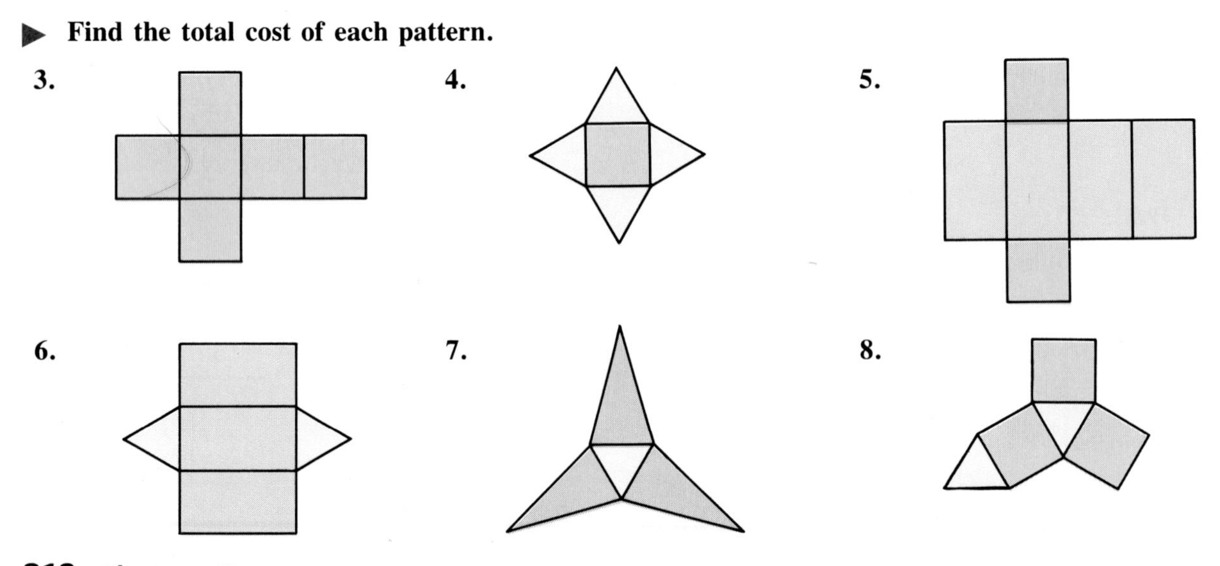

▶ **Find the total cost of each space figure.**

9.

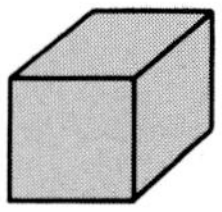

10.

11.

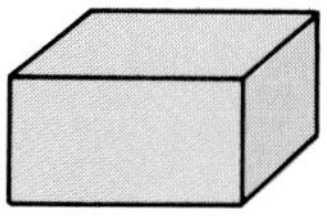

12.

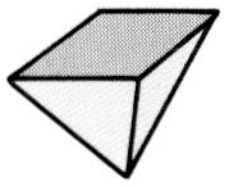

13.

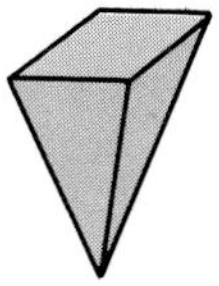

14.

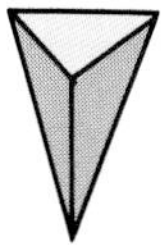

15.

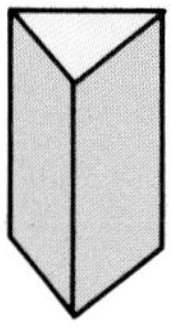

16.

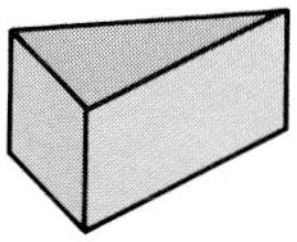

17.

18.

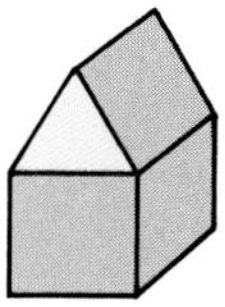

19.

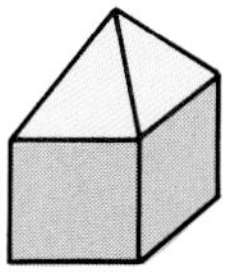

20.

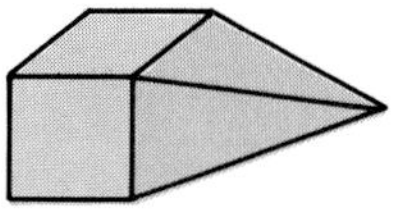

21.

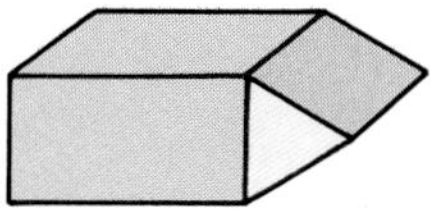

22.

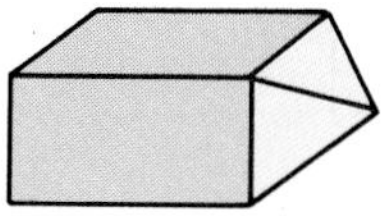

23.

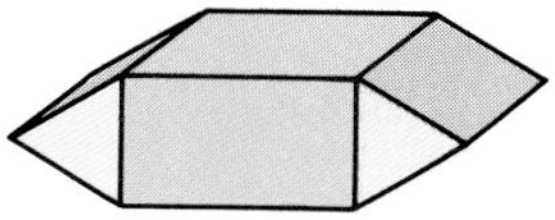

Challenge

▶ **Imagine each pattern folded to make a cube.**

24. Which face is opposite

a. face A?
b. face B?
c. face D?

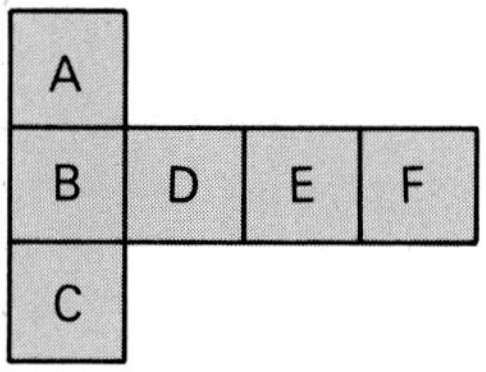

A			
B	D	E	F
C			

25. Which face is opposite

a. face A?
b. face B?
c. face F?

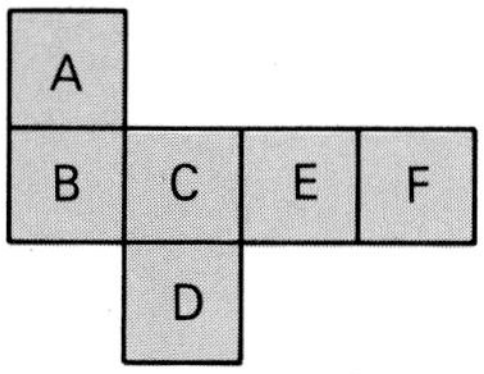

A			
B	C	E	F
	D		

26. Which face is opposite

a. face A?
b. face B?
c. face C?

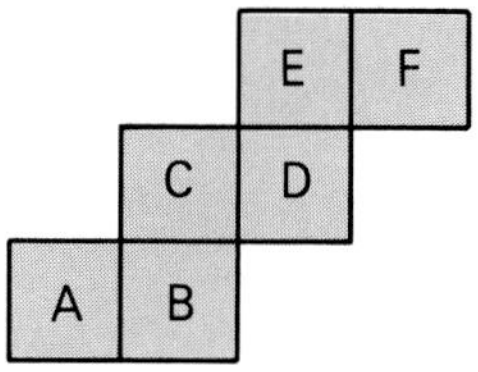

		E	F
	C	D	
A	B		

Surface Area—Rectangular Prisms and Cubes

Karen and Jill used 1-inch-square pictures to cover the 6 faces of their photo boxes.

1. Which girl used 52 pictures to cover all 6 faces of her photo box?

The sum of the areas of the 6 faces of a rectangular prism or cube is called the **surface area.**

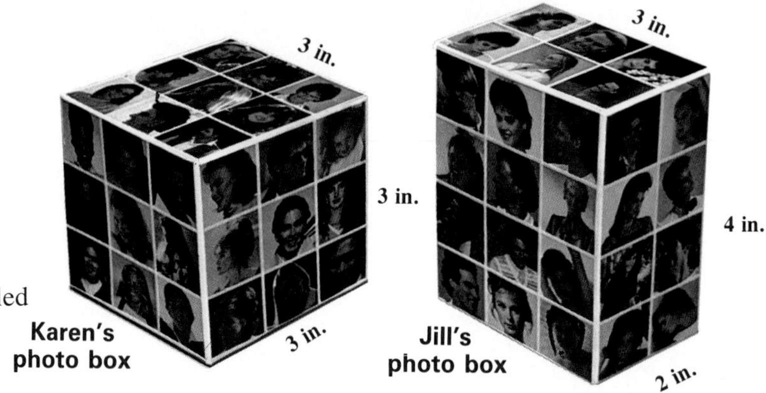

Here's how to find the surface area of a rectangular prism.

Think about unfolding Jill's photo box. To find the surface area, compute the area of each face by multiplying its length by its width. Then add all six areas.

	Top (2″ × 3″)		
Left face (2″ × 4″)	Front (3″ × 4″)	Right face (2″ × 4″)	Back (3″ × 4″)
	Bottom (2″ × 3″)		

Area of front	12 in.^{2}
back	12 in.^{2}
top	6 in.^{2}
bottom	6 in.^{2}
left face	8 in.^{2}
right face	8 in.^{2}
Surface area =	52 in.^{2}

2. Look at the example above. The area of the front is the same as the area of the __?__. The area of the top is the same as the area of the __?__. The area of the left face is the same as the area of the __?__ face.

3. To find the surface area of a rectangular prism, you could first find the total area of its front, top, and left faces and then multiply by __?__.

4. Look at Karen's photo box. If the area of each face is 9 square inches, then the surface area of the cube is __?__ square inches.

5. To find the surface area of a cube, you could first find the area of one face and then multiply by __?__.

▶ **Find the surface area of each rectangular prism.**
Here are scrambled answers for the next row of exercises: *162 in.*^{2} *216 in.*^{2} *158 in.*^{2}

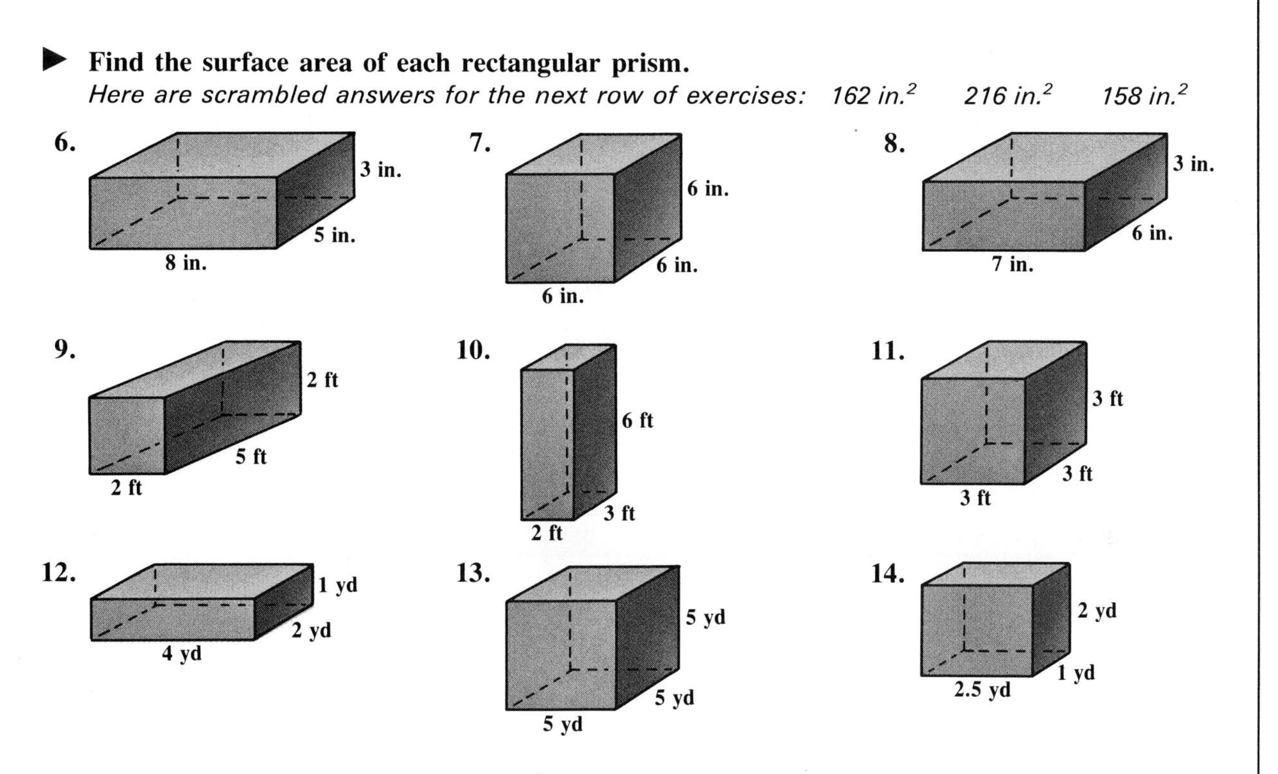

Problem Solving

▶ **Solve.**

15. How many 1-inch-square pictures are needed to cover a photo box 4 inches long, 3 inches wide, and 5 inches high?

16. How many 1-inch-square pictures are needed to cover a photo cube that is 4 inches on an edge?

Challenge

▶ **Use the area clues to find the missing length *(l)*, width *(w)*, and height *(h)*.**
Hint: Guess and check.

17.

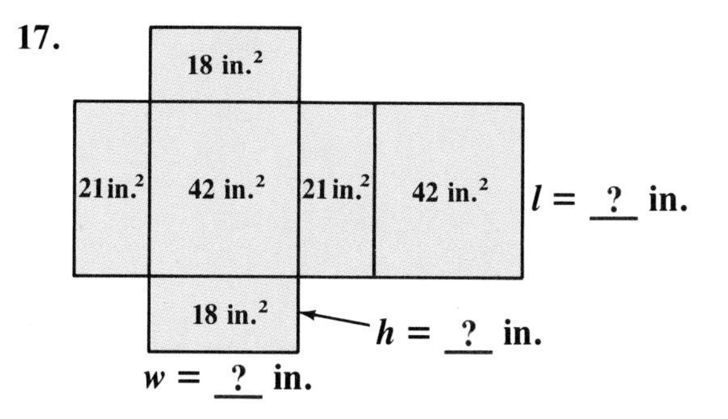

18.

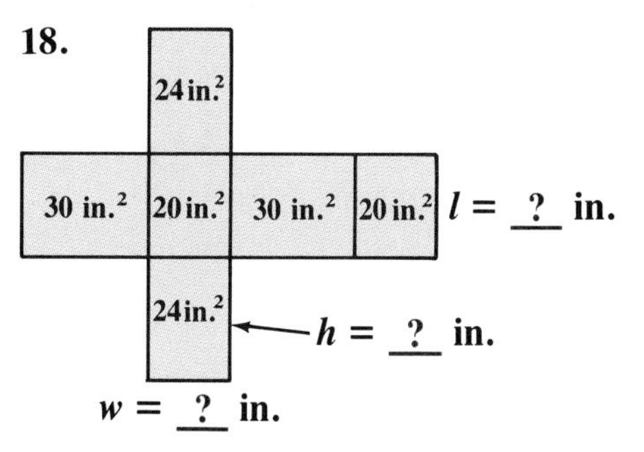

Cumulative Skill Practice

Write in simplest form. *(page 150)*

1. $\frac{10}{15}$ **2.** $\frac{26}{4}$ **3.** $\frac{18}{3}$ **4.** $\frac{2a}{6b}$ **5.** $\frac{12x}{18x}$ **6.** $\frac{9b^2}{2b}$

7. $\frac{10f}{6g}$ **8.** $\frac{4x}{3xy}$ **9.** $\frac{6r}{r^2s}$ **10.** $\frac{10pq}{3pq^2}$ **11.** $\frac{8xy^2}{16xy}$ **12.** $\frac{16cd^2}{24c^2d}$

Give each sum or difference in simplest form. *(pages 156, 158)*

13. $\frac{1}{8} + \frac{7}{8}$ **14.** $\frac{1}{2} + \frac{5}{6}$ **15.** $\frac{5}{8} + \frac{1}{6}$ **16.** $\frac{7}{8} - \frac{3}{8}$ **17.** $\frac{5}{6} - \frac{3}{10}$

18. $\frac{a}{2} + \frac{b}{6}$ **19.** $\frac{r}{2} + \frac{s}{3}$ **20.** $\frac{x}{6} + \frac{2y}{3}$ **21.** $\frac{3m}{4} + \frac{n}{3}$ **22.** $\frac{2r}{3} + \frac{6s}{5}$

23. $\frac{p}{4} - \frac{q}{6}$ **24.** $\frac{t}{3} - \frac{u}{12}$ **25.** $\frac{5a}{4} - \frac{b}{8}$ **26.** $\frac{3x}{5} - \frac{2y}{7}$ **27.** $\frac{5m}{6} - \frac{5n}{6}$

Give each product in simplest form. *(page 172)*

28. $\frac{4}{5} \cdot \frac{1}{4}$ **29.** $3 \cdot \frac{5}{6}$ **30.** $\frac{7}{12} \cdot \frac{4}{5}$ **31.** $\frac{5}{6} \cdot \frac{6}{5}$ **32.** $\frac{10}{3} \cdot \frac{18}{5}$

33. $\frac{x}{5} \cdot \frac{1}{x}$ **34.** $10 \cdot \frac{y}{2}$ **35.** $\frac{5}{6} \cdot \frac{3y}{10}$ **36.** $\frac{2}{3d} \cdot \frac{3}{9f}$ **37.** $\frac{a}{b} \cdot \frac{3b}{2a}$

38. $\frac{a}{b^2} \cdot \frac{3b}{a}$ **39.** $\frac{r}{s} \cdot \frac{s}{r}$ **40.** $\frac{n^2}{5} \cdot \frac{m}{n}$ **41.** $\frac{3y}{z} \cdot \frac{z}{3w}$ **42.** $\frac{5d}{e} \cdot \frac{4e}{15d^2}$

Give each quotient in simplest form. *(page 176)*

43. $\frac{5}{2} \div \frac{1}{2}$ **44.** $\frac{4}{5} \div \frac{2}{9}$ **45.** $\frac{7}{8} \div \frac{7}{2}$ **46.** $\frac{5}{8} \div 2$ **47.** $4 \div \frac{3}{2}$

48. $\frac{3}{a} \div \frac{4}{a}$ **49.** $\frac{6}{b} \div \frac{2}{c}$ **50.** $\frac{j}{6} \div \frac{k}{4}$ **51.** $\frac{3y}{z} \div \frac{y}{6}$ **52.** $\frac{a}{b} \div \frac{3b}{4}$

53. $\frac{3y}{z} \div \frac{9y}{z}$ **54.** $\frac{m}{p} \div \frac{5m}{3q}$ **55.** $\frac{2d^2}{e} \div \frac{d}{e}$ **56.** $\frac{x}{12y} \div \frac{x^2}{8y}$ **57.** $\frac{9a}{2b} \div \frac{3a}{4b^2}$

Solve. Give answers in simplest form. *(page 182)*

58. $\frac{1}{3}$ of $27 = n$ **59.** $\frac{3}{4}$ of $40 = n$ **60.** $\frac{7}{8}$ of $72 = n$ **61.** $\frac{3}{2}$ of $28 = n$

62. $\frac{3}{8}$ of $56 = n$ **63.** $\frac{5}{6}$ of $60 = n$ **64.** $\frac{9}{4}$ of $15 = n$ **65.** $\frac{2}{5}$ of $27 = n$

66. $\frac{5}{9}$ of $38 = n$ **67.** $\frac{5}{3}$ of $41 = n$ **68.** $\frac{4}{5}$ of $49 = n$ **69.** $\frac{3}{8}$ of $2 = n$

Problem Solving—Applications

Use the grocery ad to solve each problem. Round answers to the nearest cent.

1. What is the cost of 3.5 pounds of grapes?

2. What is the cost of $\frac{1}{2}$ dozen apples?

3. How much would 2.2 pounds of cherries cost?
   Hint: $\frac{0.59}{1} = \frac{n}{2.2}$

4. How much would 5 oranges cost?
   Hint: $\frac{0.95}{6} = \frac{n}{5}$

5. How much would 5 apples cost?

6. How much would 18 apples cost?

7. If you gave the cashier \$5 for 2.4 pounds of grapes, how much change should you receive?

8. If you gave the cashier \$5 for some cantaloupes and received \$1.05 in change, how many cantaloupes did you buy?

Write an equation and solve the problem.

9. Joel bought a cantaloupe and some bananas. He spent a total of \$1.09. How many pounds of bananas did he buy? (Let j = the number of pounds of bananas Joel bought.)

10. Beth paid \$4.43 for 3 pounds of grapes and some cherries. How many pounds of cherries did she buy? (Let b = the number of pounds of cherries Beth bought.)

11. Susan bought 3 times as many cantaloupes as Phil did. Together they bought 12 cantaloupes. How many cantaloupes did Phil buy? (Let p = the cantaloupes Phil bought.)

12. Marty bought twice as many pounds of grapes as Chuck did. Together they bought 7.5 pounds of grapes. How many pounds of grapes did Chuck buy? (Let c = the pounds of grapes Chuck bought.)

Volume—Rectangular Prisms and Cubes

The **volume** of a space figure is the number of cubic units that it takes to fill it.

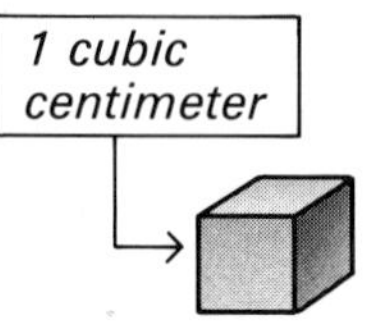

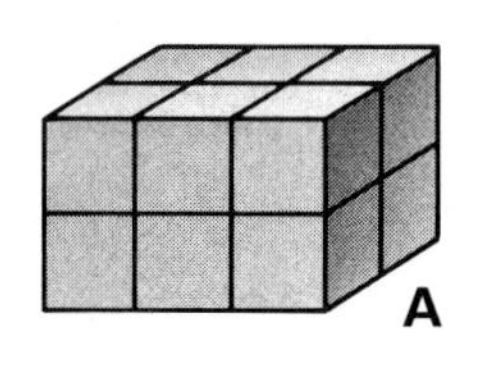

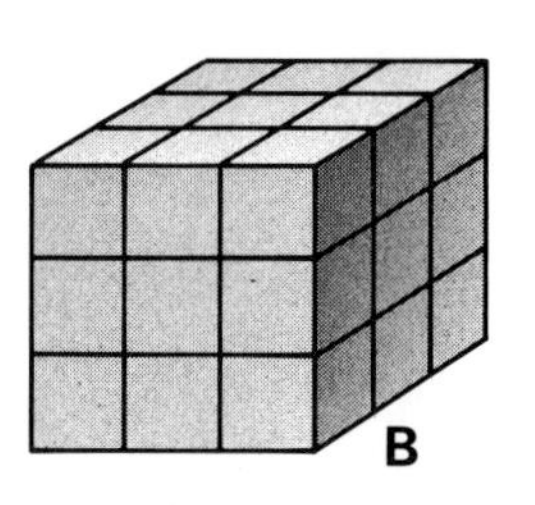

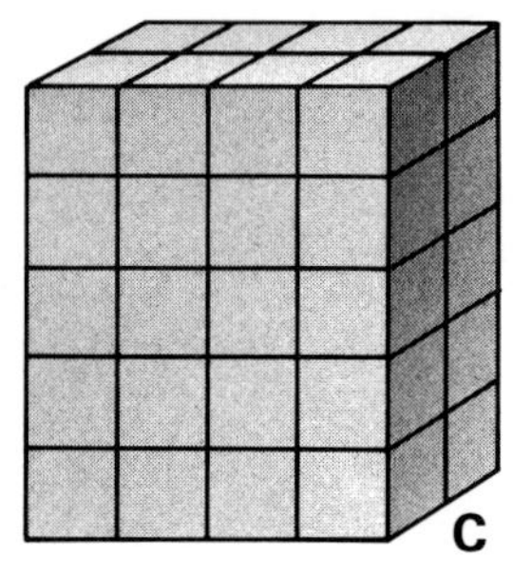

1. Count the cubes. Which prism has a volume of 12 cubic centimeters?
2. Which prism has a volume of 27 cubic centimeters?
3. What is the volume of prism C?

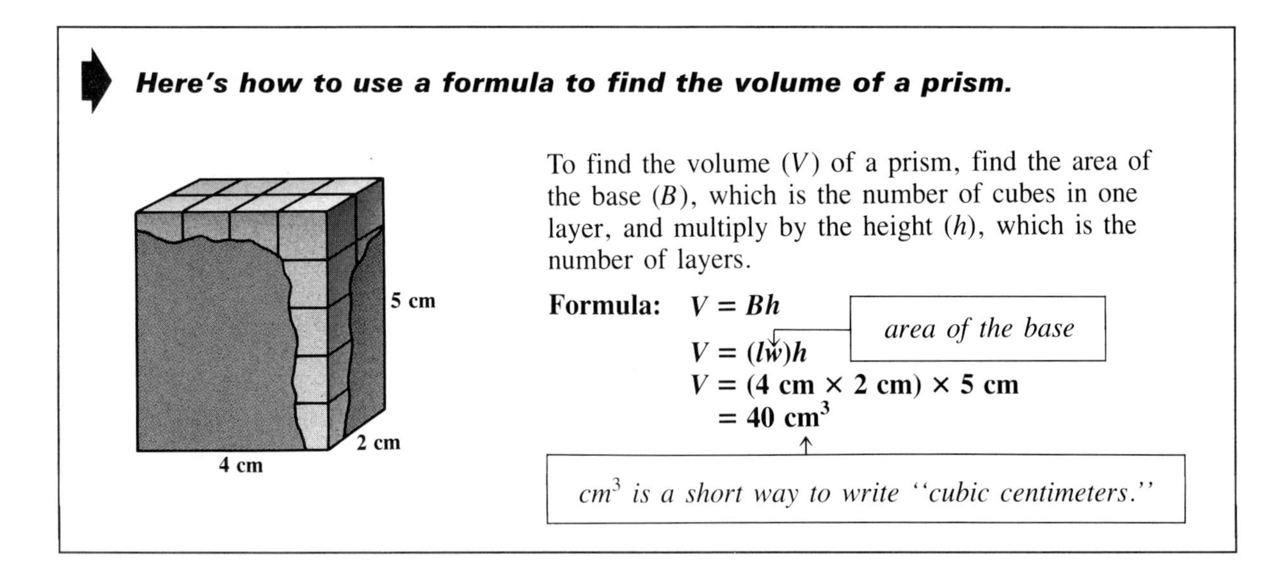

Here's how to use a formula to find the volume of a prism.

To find the volume (V) of a prism, find the area of the base (B), which is the number of cubes in one layer, and multiply by the height (h), which is the number of layers.

Formula: $V = Bh$

$V = (lw)h$ ← *area of the base*

$V = (4 \text{ cm} \times 2 \text{ cm}) \times 5 \text{ cm}$

$= 40 \text{ cm}^3$

cm^3 is a short way to write "cubic centimeters."

4. Look at the example above. What is the formula for the volume of a rectangular prism? What do the letters V, l, w, and h represent?
5. Complete these examples.

a.

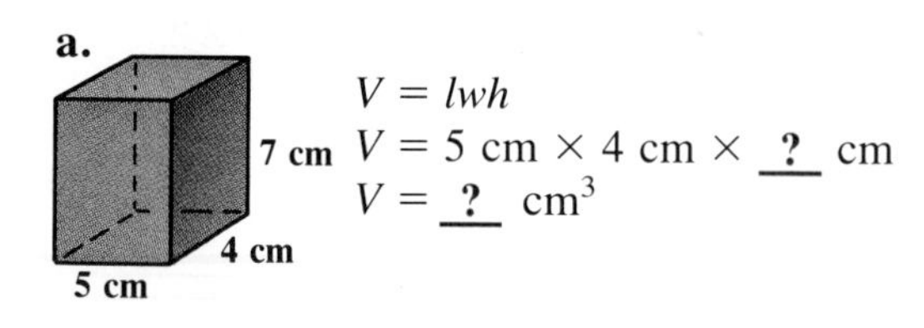

$V = lwh$

$V = 5 \text{ cm} \times 4 \text{ cm} \times \underline{\ ?\ } \text{ cm}$

$V = \underline{\ ?\ } \text{ cm}^3$

b.

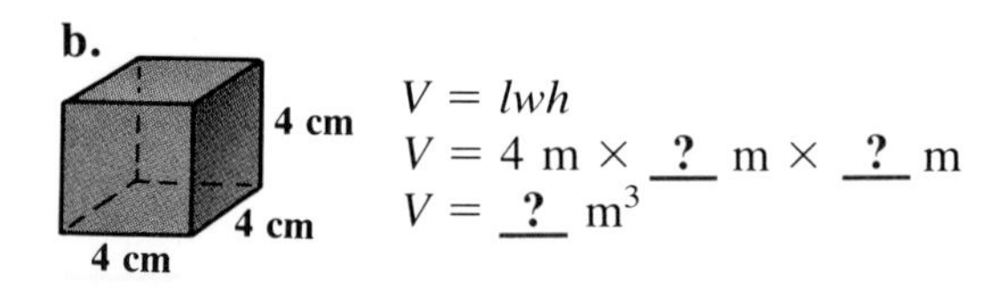

$V = lwh$

$V = 4 \text{ m} \times \underline{\ ?\ } \text{ m} \times \underline{\ ?\ } \text{ m}$

$V = \underline{\ ?\ } \text{ m}^3$

▶ **Find the volume.**

6. **7.** **8.**

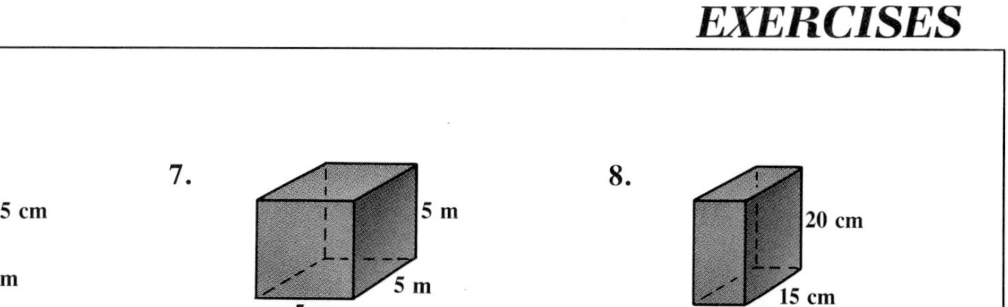

9. 4 cm, 10 cm, 31.5 cm

10. 5.2 m, 2.5 m, 1 m

11. 6.2 m, 6.2 m, 6.2 m

▶ **Substitute in the formula $V = lwh$ to find the missing measure.**

12. $l = 6$ m
$w = 7$ m
$h = 10$ m
$V =$?

13. $l = 12$ cm
$w = 6$ cm
$h = 20$ cm
$V =$?

14. $l = 8$ m
$w = 8$ m
$h = 8$ m
$V =$?

15. $l = 13$ cm
$w = 5$ cm
$h = 12$ cm
$V =$?

16. $l = 2.5$ m
$w = 6$ m
$h = 4$ m
$V =$?

17. $l = 12.4$ cm
$w = 8$ cm
$h = 20$ cm
$V =$?

18. $l = 7.5$ cm
$w = 6.2$ cm
$h = 8$ cm
$V =$?

19. $l = 2.1$ m
$w = 3.2$ m
$h = 4$ m
$V =$?

Problem Solving

▶ **Tell whether the question involves perimeter, area, or volume.**

20. How much sand is needed to fill a sandbox?

21. How much fence is needed to fence a garden?

22. How much sod is needed to cover a lawn?

23. How much paper is needed to wrap a box?

24. How much water is needed for a swimming pool?

25. How many flowers are needed to border a patio?

Challenge

▶ **Each space figure is made from 1-centimeter cubes. Find each volume.**

26.

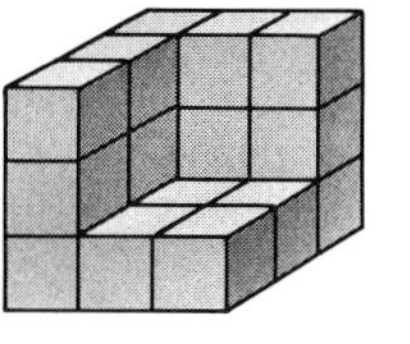

27.

28.

Volume—Cylinders

The volume of the rectangular container is 96 cubic inches. Is the volume of the cylindrical container more or less than 96 cubic inches?

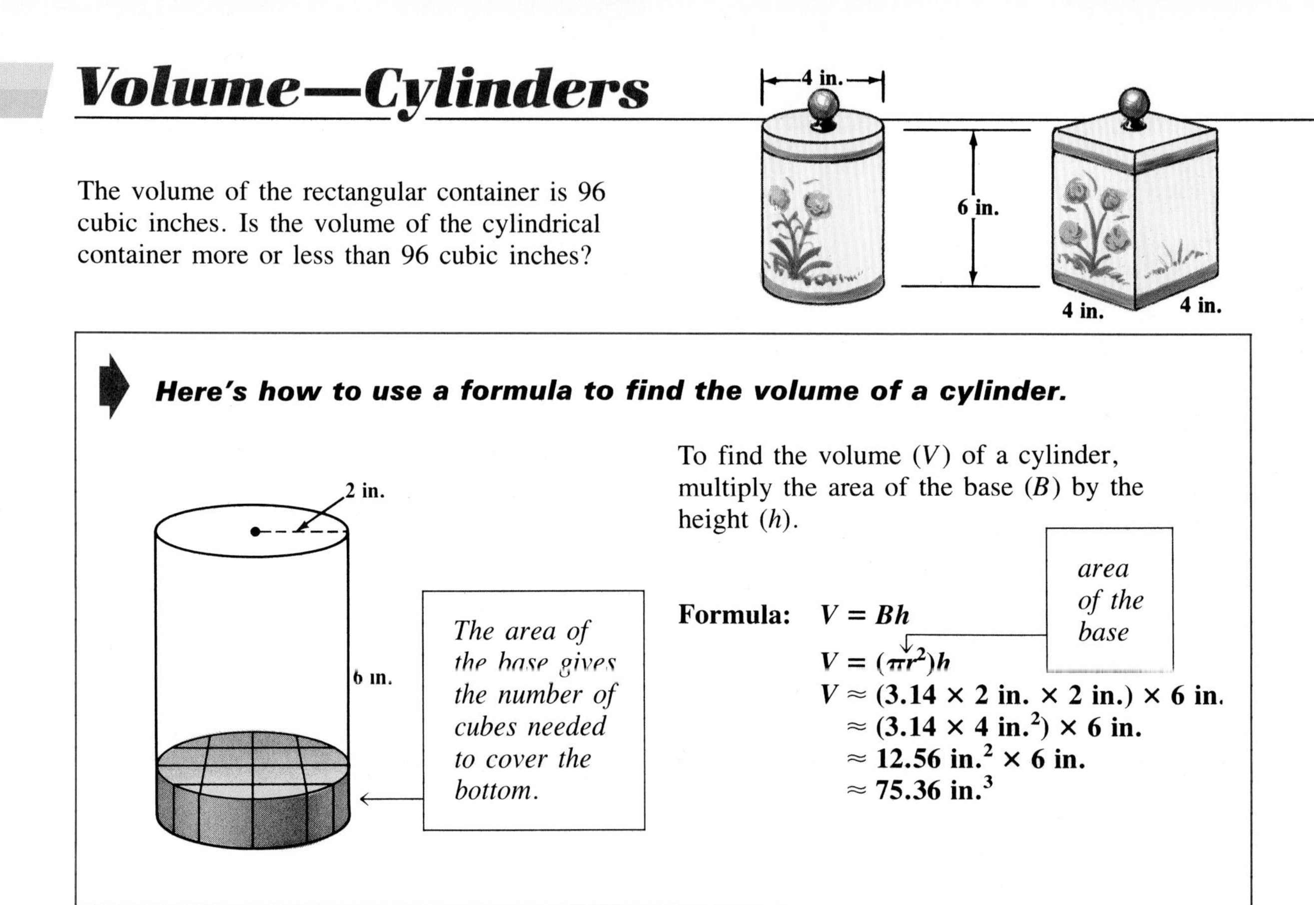

Here's how to use a formula to find the volume of a cylinder.

The area of the base gives the number of cubes needed to cover the bottom.

To find the volume (V) of a cylinder, multiply the area of the base (B) by the height (h).

Formula: $V = Bh$ (*area of the base*)

$V = (\pi r^2)h$

$V \approx (3.14 \times 2 \text{ in.} \times 2 \text{ in.}) \times 6 \text{ in.}$

$\approx (3.14 \times 4 \text{ in.}^2) \times 6 \text{ in.}$

$\approx 12.56 \text{ in.}^2 \times 6 \text{ in.}$

$\approx 75.36 \text{ in.}^3$

1. Look at the example above. What is the formula for the volume of a cylinder? What do the letters V, π, r, and h represent?

2. In the formula $V = \pi r^2 h$, the r^2 means __?__ times __?__.

3. Complete these examples.

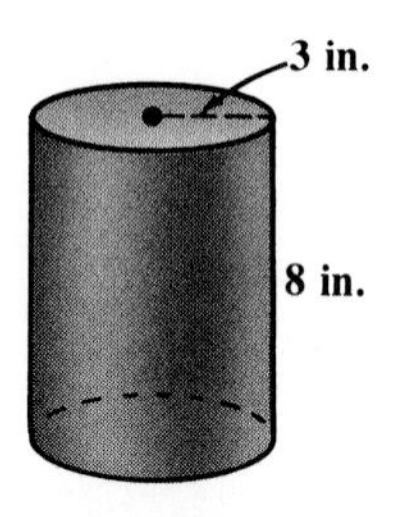

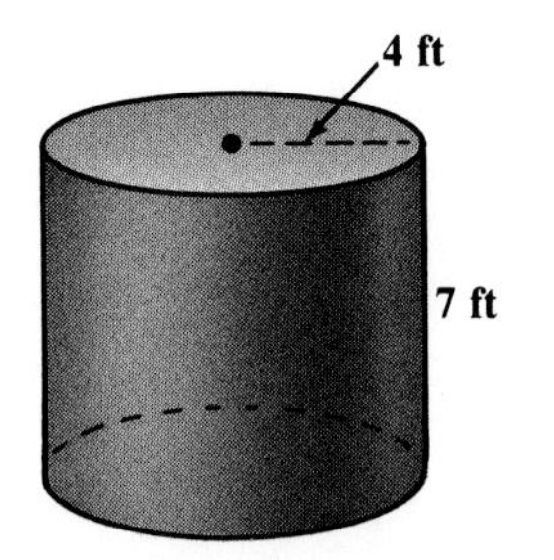

a. $V = \pi r^2 h$

$V \approx (3.14 \times 3 \text{ in.} \times 3 \text{ in.}) \times 8 \text{ in.}$

$\approx (3.14 \times \underline{?} \text{ in.}^2) \times 8 \text{ in.}$

$\approx 28.26 \text{ in.}^2 \times 8 \text{ in.}$

$\approx \underline{?} \text{ in.}^3$

b. $V = \pi r^2 h$

$V \approx (3.14 \times 4 \text{ ft} \times \underline{?} \text{ ft}) \times 7 \text{ ft}$

$\approx (3.14 \times \underline{?} \text{ ft}^2) \times 7 \text{ ft}$

$\approx 50.24 \text{ ft}^2 \times \underline{?} \text{ ft}$

$\approx \underline{?} \text{ ft}^3$

EXERCISES

▶ **Find the volume. Use 3.14 as an approximation for π.**

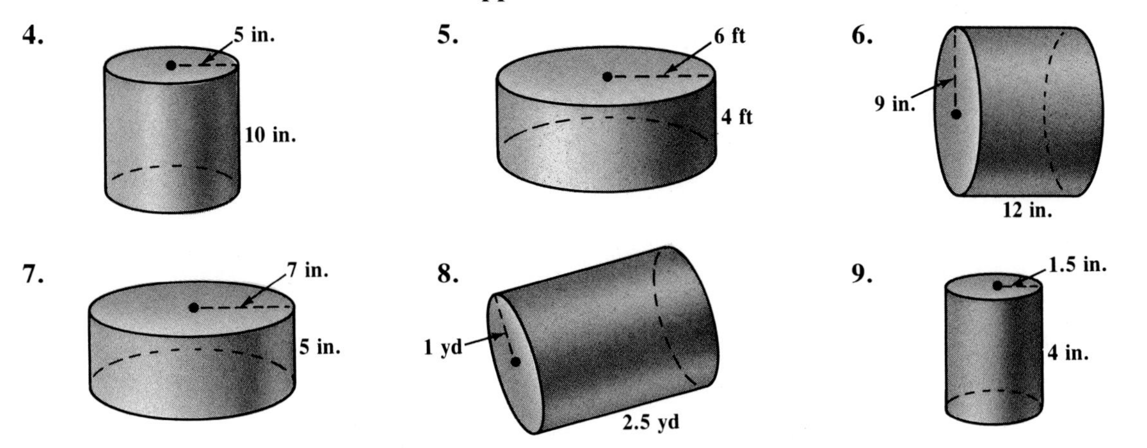

▶ **Substitute in the formula $V = \pi r^2 h$ to find the missing measure.**

10. $r = 4$ in.
$\pi \approx 3.14$
$h = 9$ in.
$V \approx$ __?__

11. $r = 6$ in.
$\pi \approx 3.14$
$h = 2$ in.
$V \approx$ __?__

12. $r = 2$ yd
$\pi \approx 3.14$
$h = 3$ yd
$V \approx$ __?__

13. $r = 5$ ft
$\pi \approx 3.14$
$h = 2$ ft
$V \approx$ __?__

14. $r = 8$ in.
$\pi \approx 3.14$
$h = 2.5$ in.
$V \approx$ __?__

15. $r = 10$ in.
$\pi \approx 3.14$
$h = 20.5$ in.
$V \approx$ __?__

16. $r = 9$ ft
$\pi \approx 3.14$
$h = 3.25$ ft
$V \approx$ __?__

17. $r = 0.5$ yd
$\pi \approx 3.14$
$h = 4$ yd
$V \approx$ __?__

18. $r = 1$ yd
$\pi \approx 3.14$
$h =$ __?__
$V \approx 6.28$ yd^3

19. $r = 3$ in.
$\pi \approx 3.14$
$h =$ __?__
$V \approx 56.52$ in.^{3}

20. $r = 20$ in.
$\pi \approx 3.14$
$h =$ __?__
$V \approx 12{,}560$ in.^{3}

21. $r = 5$ ft
$\pi \approx 3.14$
$h =$ __?__
$V \approx 549.5$ ft^3

Challenge

22. Here are two ways to roll a sheet of paper to make a cylinder. Do you think the two cylinders have the same volume? Find a way to decide.

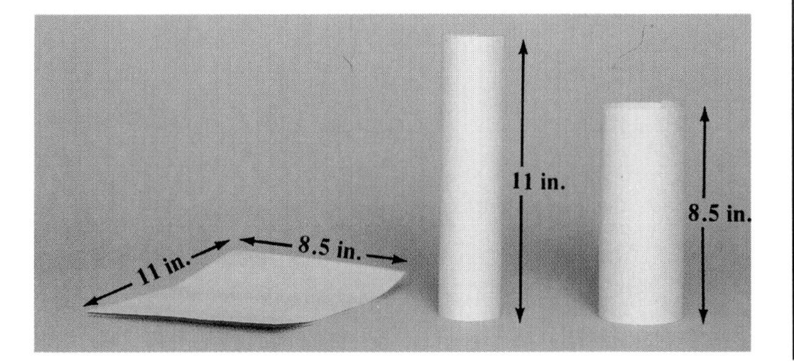

Volume—Pyramids and Cones

1. It takes 3 pyramids of sand to fill the prism. So, the volume of a pyramid is ___?___ the volume of a prism having the same base and height.

2. It takes 3 cones of sand to fill the cylinder. So, the volume of a cone is ___?___ the volume of a cylinder having the same base and height.

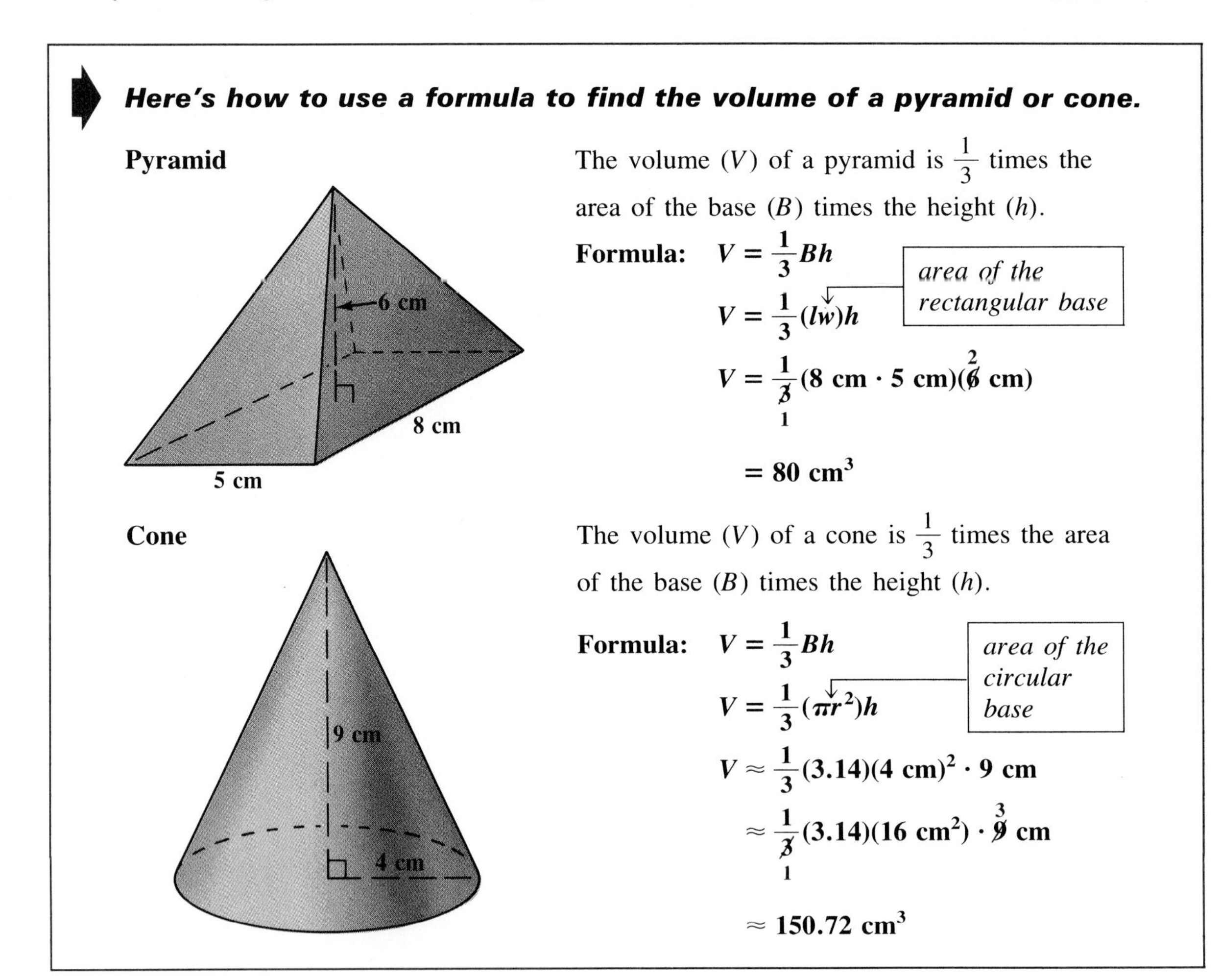

Here's how to use a formula to find the volume of a pyramid or cone.

Pyramid

The volume (V) of a pyramid is $\frac{1}{3}$ times the area of the base (B) times the height (h).

Formula: $V = \frac{1}{3}Bh$

$V = \frac{1}{3}(lw)h$ — *area of the rectangular base*

$V = \frac{1}{3}(8 \text{ cm} \cdot 5 \text{ cm})(6 \text{ cm})$ (3 and 6 cancelled: $\frac{1}{1}$, 2)

$= 80 \text{ cm}^3$

Cone

The volume (V) of a cone is $\frac{1}{3}$ times the area of the base (B) times the height (h).

Formula: $V = \frac{1}{3}Bh$

$V = \frac{1}{3}(\pi r^2)h$ — *area of the circular base*

$V \approx \frac{1}{3}(3.14)(4 \text{ cm})^2 \cdot 9 \text{ cm}$

$\approx \frac{1}{3}(3.14)(16 \text{ cm}^2) \cdot 9 \text{ cm}$ (3 and 9 cancelled: 1, 3)

$\approx 150.72 \text{ cm}^3$

3. Look at the examples above.

   a. If the area of the base of a pyramid is 40 square centimeters and the height is 6 centimeters, the volume is ___?___ cubic centimeters.

   b. What is the formula for the volume of a cone? What do the letters V, π, r, and h represent?

▶ **Find the volume of each pyramid or cone. Use 3.14 for π.**

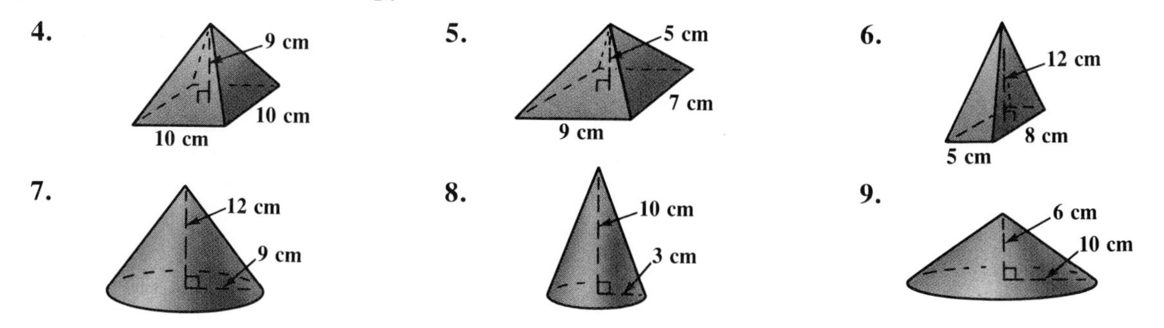

▶ **Each pyramid described below has a rectangular base. Find the volume.**

10. $l = 5$ m, $w = 6$ m, $h = 3$ m

11. $l = 12$ cm, $w = 7$ cm, $h = 4$ cm

12. $l = 1$ m, $w = 9$ m, $h = 5$ m

13. $l = 24$ cm, $w = 10$ cm, $h = 2$ cm

14. $l = 4$ cm, $w = 11$ cm, $h = 12$ cm

15. $l = 2.5$ m, $w = 4$ m, $h = 6$ m

16. $l = 10$ m, $w = 4.4$ m, $h = 3$ m

17. $l = 4.2$ cm, $w = 6.5$ cm, $h = 15$ cm

▶ **Find the volume of each cone. Use 3.14 for π. Round the answer to the nearest tenth.**

18. $r = 2$ m, $h = 6$ m

19. $r = 5$ m, $h = 9$ m

20. $r = 3$ m, $h = 10$ m

21. $r = 4$ m, $h = 3$ m

22. $r = 6$ m, $h = 20$ m

23. $r = 8$ m, $h = 12$ m

24. $r = 30$ m, $h = 8.5$ m

25. $r = 2.2$ m, $h = 3$ m

Challenge

The cone in the cup is 8 centimeters high and holds 80 cubic centimeters of juice when full. The graph shows the volume of juice in the cone at different heights.

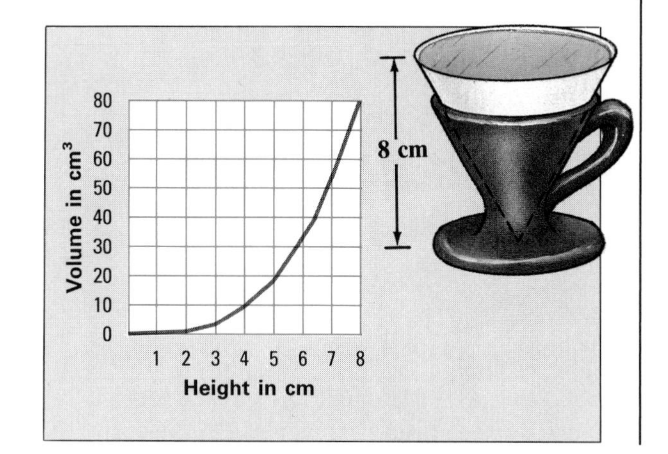

26. About how many centimeters high is the juice in the cone when the cone is

a. $\frac{3}{4}$ full? **b.** $\frac{1}{2}$ full?

27. About how many cubic centimeters of juice are in the cone when the height is

a. $\frac{3}{4}$ as high? **b.** $\frac{1}{2}$ as high?

Metric Units of Capacity and Weight

The **liter** (L) and **milliliter** (mL) are metric units of liquid measure or capacity.

1 L = 1000 mL

The **gram** (g) and **kilogram** (kg) are metric units of weight.

1 kg = 1000 g

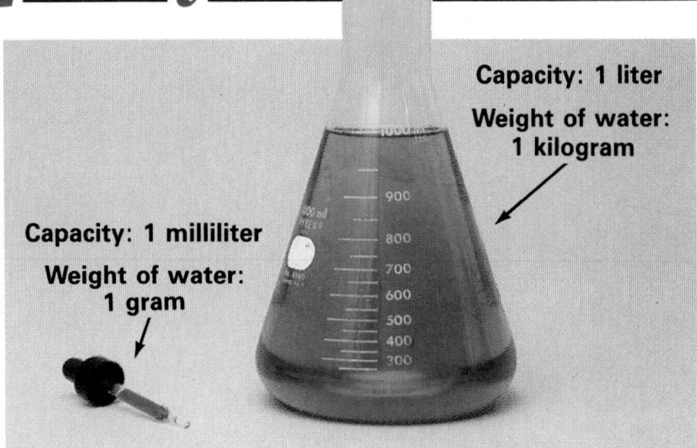

Here's how to change from one unit of capacity to another.

350 mL = ? L

Think: Changing from smaller units to larger units, so divide.

Remember: 1000 mL = 1 L

350 mL = 0.350 L (÷ 1000)

4.2 L = ? mL

Think: Changing from larger units to smaller units, so multiply.

Remember: 1 L = 1000 mL

4.2 L = 4200 mL (× 1000)

1. Look at the examples above. To change from milliliters to liters, divide by __?__. To change from liters to milliliters, multiply by __?__.

Here's how to change from one unit of weight to another.

8275 g = ? kg

Think: Changing from smaller units to larger units, so divide.

Remember: 1000 g = 1 kg

8275 g = 8.275 kg (÷1000)

0.625 kg = ? g

Think: Changing from larger units to smaller units, so multiply.

Remember: 1 kg = 1000 g

0.625 kg = 625 g (×1000)

2. Look at the examples above. To change from grams to kilograms, divide by __?__. To change from kilograms to grams, multiply by __?__.

EXERCISES

▶ **Which capacity seems reasonable?**

3. A tablespoon:
a. 15 mL **b.** 150 mL

4. A bathtub:
a. 3 L **b.** 300 L

5. A soft-drink can:
a. 4 mL **b.** 400 mL

6. A thermos bottle:
a. 800 mL **b.** 8000 mL

7. A fruit-juice pitcher:
a. 0.1 L **b.** 1 L

8. A car's gas tank:
a. 6 L **b.** 60 L

▶ **Which weight seems reasonable?**

9. A dime:
a. 3 g **b.** 300 g

10. An orange:
a. 4 g **b.** 400 g

11. A can of peaches:
a. 46.4 g **b.** 464 g

12. A bicycle:
a. 1.2 kg **b.** 12 kg

13. A straight pin:
a. 0.13 g **b.** 13 g

14. An automobile:
a. 200 kg **b.** 2000 kg

▶ **Copy and complete.**

15. 9 L = ? mL
16. 25 L = ? mL
17. 125 L = ? mL
18. 7000 mL = ? L
19. 2875 mL = ? L
20. 1400 mL = ? L
21. 6.4 L = ? mL
22. 0.65 L = ? mL
23. 25.75 L = ? mL
24. 17,000 mL = ? L
25. 870 mL = ? L
26. 25 mL = ? L
27. 7 kg = ? g
28. 13 kg = ? g
29. 28 kg = ? g
30. 8000 g = ? kg
31. 1250 g = ? kg
32. 14,288 g = ? kg
33. 4.6 kg = ? g
34. 12.75 kg = ? g
35. 0.33 kg = ? g

Problem Solving

▶ **Solve.**

36. A recipe calls for 0.25 liter of cream. How many milliliters is that?

37. A bag of peanuts weighs 575 grams. How many kilograms is that?

38. A marshmallow weighs about 5 grams. How many marshmallows are there in a 0.45-kilogram bag of marshmallows?

39. How many 240-milliliter glasses can be filled from a 1.2-liter bottle of orange juice?

40. A teaspoon has a capacity of 5 milliliters. How many teaspoons of vanilla are there in a liter bottle?

41. When empty, a jelly jar weighs 85 grams. When full, it weighs 0.35 kilogram. How many grams of jelly does the jar hold?

Relating Metric Units of Volume, Capacity, and Weight

The metric units of volume, capacity, and weight have a special relationship.

Look at the small container. It holds 1 cubic centimeter of water. Its capacity is 1 milliliter. The weight of the water is 1 gram.

The large container holds 1000 cubic centimeters of water. Its capacity is 1 liter (1000 milliliters). The weight of the water is 1 kilogram (1000 grams).

$1\ cm^3$ of water

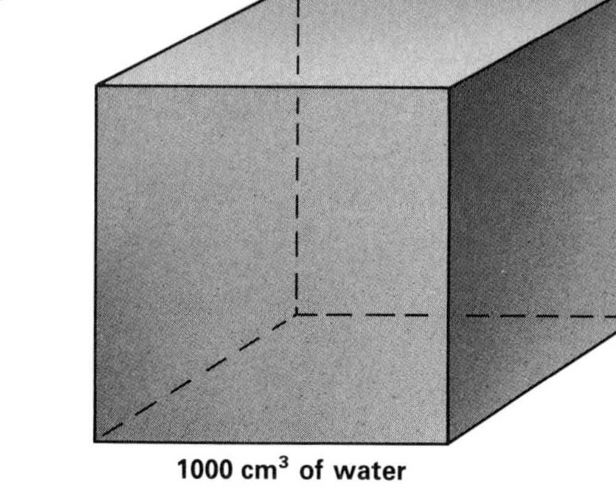

$1000\ cm^3$ of water

1. A container that has a volume of 75 cubic centimeters can hold ? milliliters of water. The weight of the water is ? grams.
2. A container that has a volume of 3000 cubic centimeters can hold ? liters of water. The weight of the water is ? kilograms.

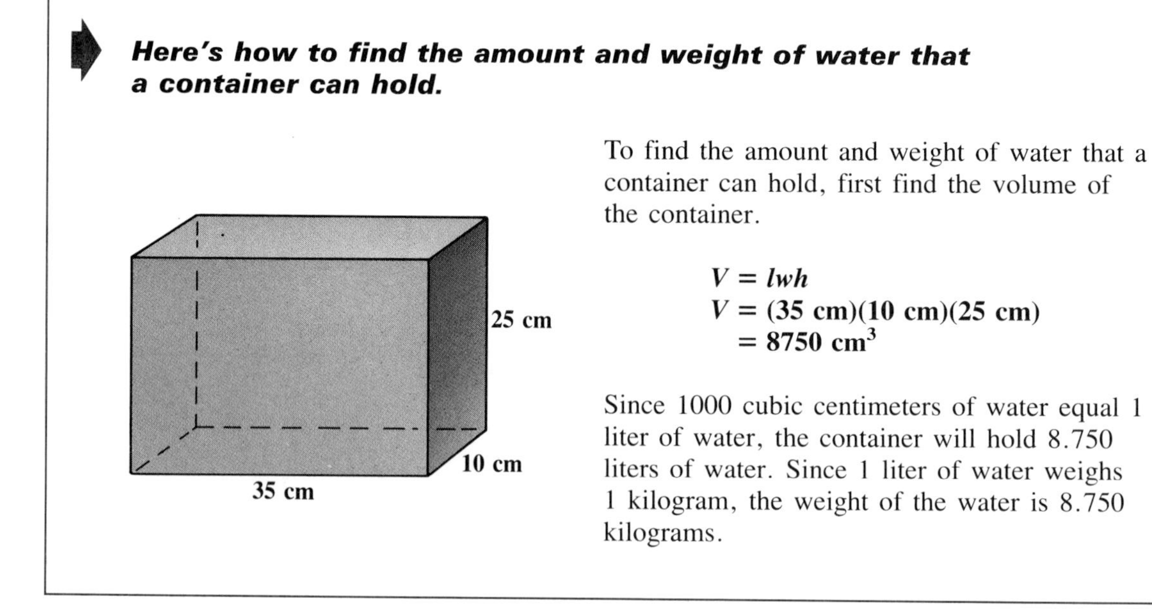

Here's how to find the amount and weight of water that a container can hold.

To find the amount and weight of water that a container can hold, first find the volume of the container.

$$V = lwh$$
$$V = (35 \text{ cm})(10 \text{ cm})(25 \text{ cm})$$
$$= 8750 \text{ cm}^3$$

Since 1000 cubic centimeters of water equal 1 liter of water, the container will hold 8.750 liters of water. Since 1 liter of water weighs 1 kilogram, the weight of the water is 8.750 kilograms.

3. Look at the example above. A container that has a volume of 8750 cubic centimeters will hold ? liters of water. The weight of the water is ? kilograms.

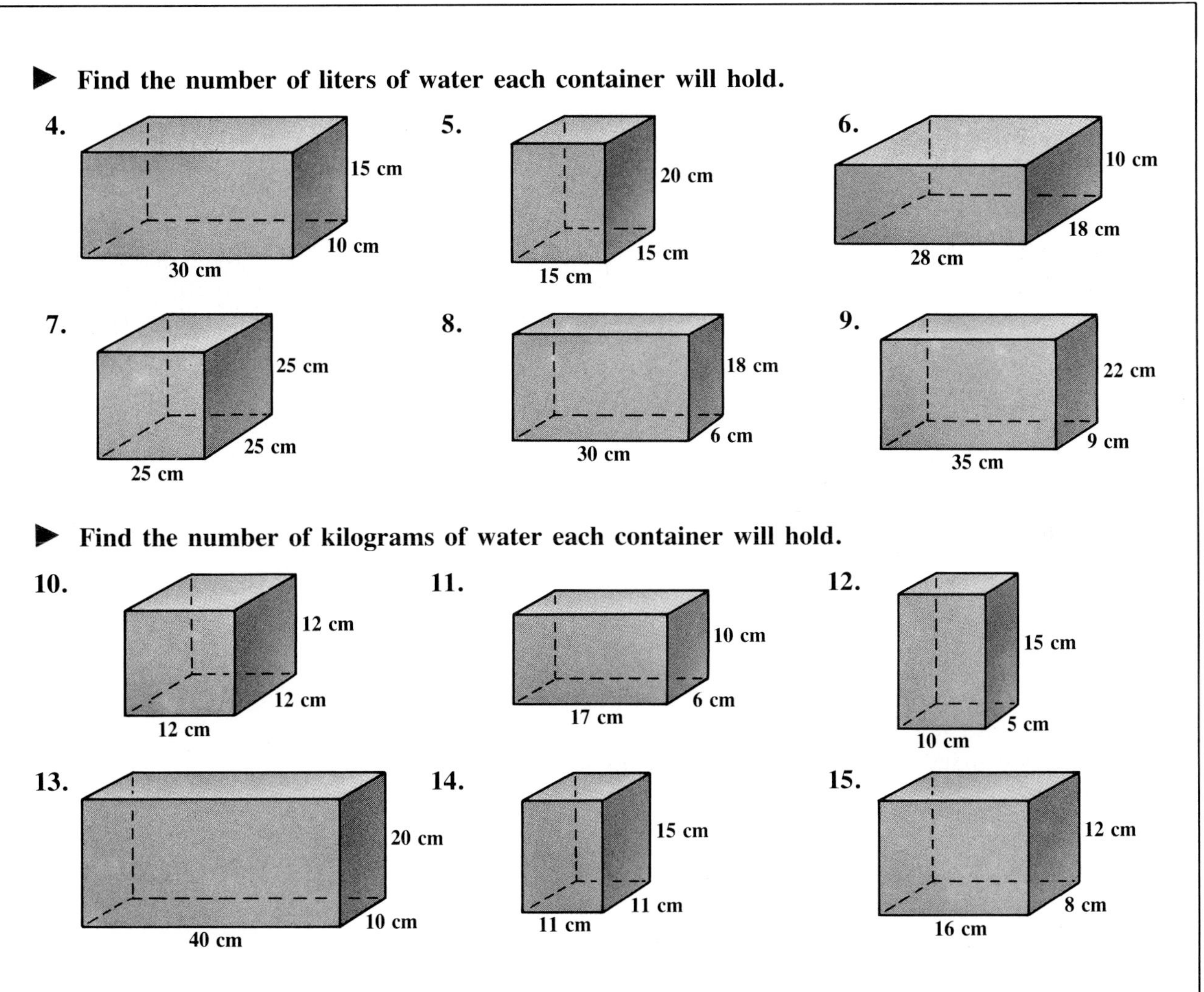

CALCULATOR

▶ **Find the length of a side of each cube.** ***Hint: Estimate. Compute the volume using a calculator. Repeat until you get the answer.***

16.

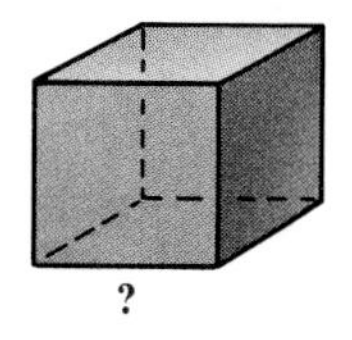

This cube holds 2197 milliliters of water.

17.

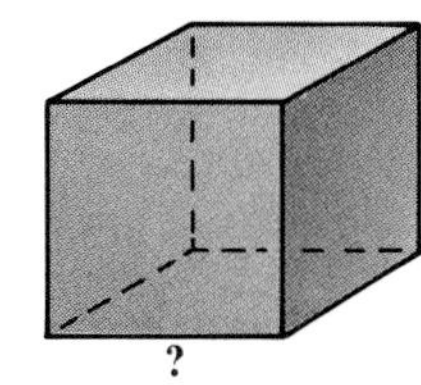

This cube holds 13,824 milliliters of water.

18.

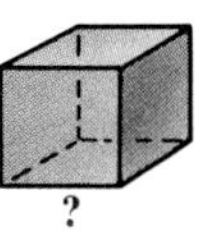

This cube holds 3.375 milliliters of water.

Problem Solving—Using Formulas

Earlier you used formulas to solve area and volume problems. In this lesson you will solve problems by combining formulas.

Area Formulas	Volume Formulas
Rectangle: $A = lw$ Square: $A = s^2$ Circle: $A = \pi r^2$	Rectangular prism: $V = lwh$ Cylinder: $V = \pi r^2 h$ Cone: $V = \frac{1}{3}\pi r^2 h$

Here's how to combine formulas to solve problems.

Area problem: Find the area of the lawn.

Notice that the lawn has the shape of a rectangle with a circle removed. To find the grass area, you need to subtract the area of the circle from the area of the rectangle.

10 ft
40 ft
30 ft

Write a formula. $\quad A = lw - \pi r^2$

Substitute and simplify.

$$\begin{aligned} A &\approx 40\text{ ft}(30\text{ ft}) - 3.14(10\text{ ft})^2 \\ &\approx 1200\text{ ft}^2 - 314\text{ ft}^2 \\ &\approx 886\text{ ft}^2 \end{aligned}$$

The area of the lawn is about 886 ft^2.

Volume problem: Find the volume of the water tower.

Notice that the tower is shaped like a cylinder with a cone on top. To find the total volume, you need to add the volume of the cylinder to the volume of the cone.

3 ft
9 ft
6 ft

Write a formula. $\quad V = \pi r^2 h + \frac{1}{3}\pi r^2 h$

Substitute and simplify.

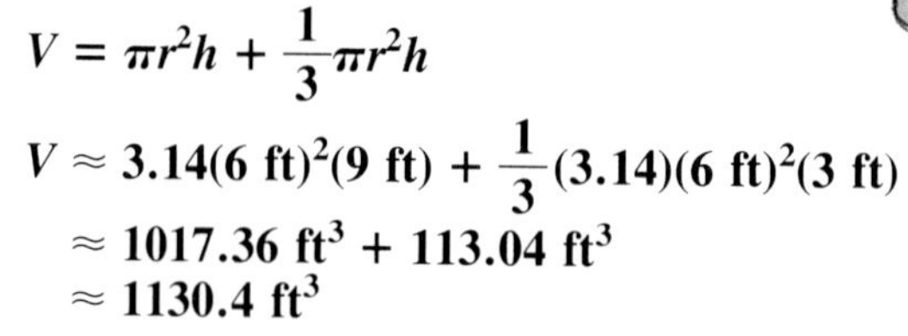

$$\begin{aligned} V &\approx 3.14(6\text{ ft})^2(9\text{ ft}) + \frac{1}{3}(3.14)(6\text{ ft})^2(3\text{ ft}) \\ &\approx 1017.36\text{ ft}^3 + 113.04\text{ ft}^3 \\ &\approx 1130.4\text{ ft}^3 \end{aligned}$$

The volume of the water tower is about 1130.4 ft^3.

▶ **Find the area of each shaded region. Use 3.14 for π.**

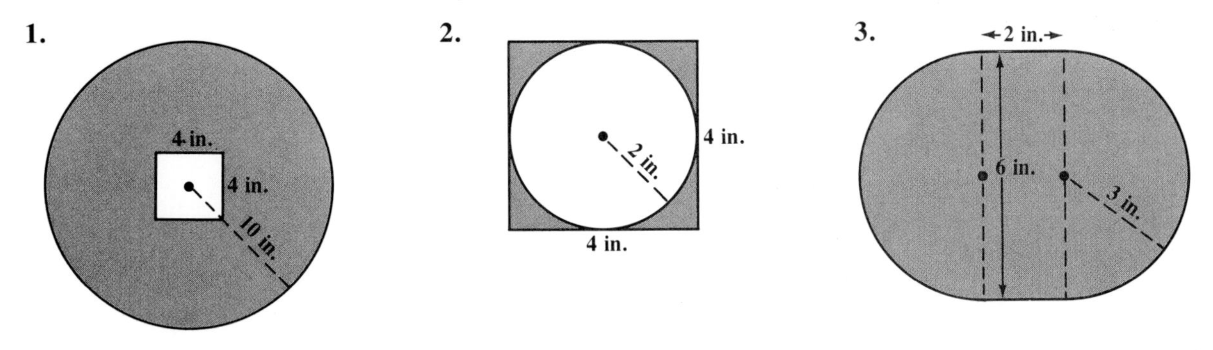

▶ **Find the volume of each shaded space figure. Use 3.14 for π.**

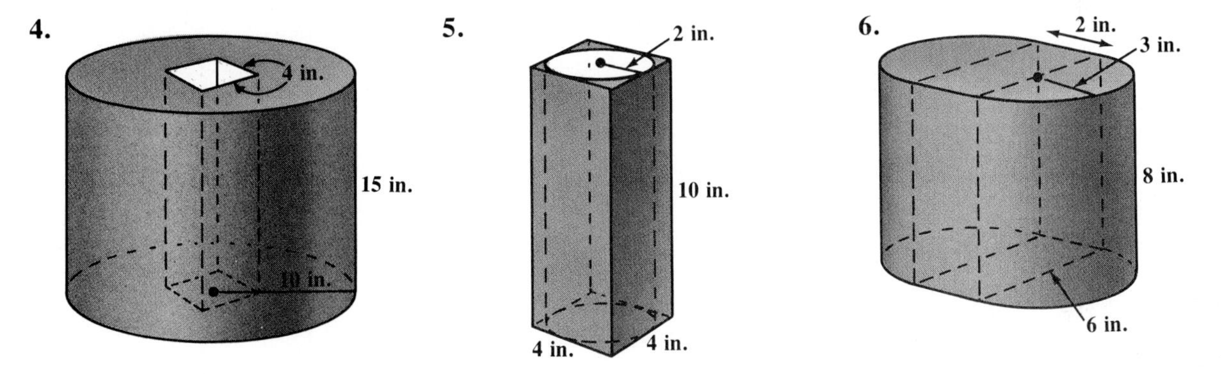

▶ **Make a drawing to picture the facts. Then write a formula and solve the problem. Use 3.14 for π.**

7. A rectangular room is 12 feet by 15 feet. A circular rug is in the center of the floor. The radius of the rug is 4 feet. What is the area of the uncovered portion of the floor?

8. A table top is shaped like a rectangle with half circles at each of the two longer sides of the rectangle. The rectangular part of the table top is 40 inches by 30 inches. The radius of each half circle is 20 inches. What is the area of the table top?

9. A storage bin is shaped like a cylinder attached to a cone. The height of the cylindrical part is 12 feet. The height of the conical part is 4 feet. The radius is 5 feet. What is the volume of the storage bin?

10. A cylindrical can is packed in a box 6 inches by 6 inches by 8 inches. The height of the can is 8 inches, and its radius is 3 inches. What is the volume of the space remaining in the box?

Cumulative Skill Practice

Solve. Give answers in simplest form. *(page 186)*

1. $\frac{1}{3}n = 11$ **2.** $\frac{1}{4}n = 15$ **3.** $\frac{2}{3}n = 22$ **4.** $\frac{3}{4}n = 21$ **5.** $\frac{5}{8}n = 35$

6. $\frac{5}{6}n = 40$ **7.** $\frac{3}{2}n = 39$ **8.** $\frac{5}{2}n = 41$ **9.** $\frac{2}{3}n = 19$ **10.** $\frac{5}{4}n = 32$

11. $\frac{7}{8}n = 40$ **12.** $\frac{9}{4}n = 20$ **13.** $\frac{4}{9}n = 20$ **14.** $\frac{5}{9}n = 37$ **15.** $\frac{9}{5}n = 37$

Solve and check. *(page 240)*

16. $3y + 5y = 9 - 4$ **17.** $9x - x = {}^-8 + 19$ **18.** $w - 6w = 10 - 18$

19. $5n - 8n - 7 = 13 + 11$ **20.** $5n - 8 - 7n = 13 + 11$ **21.** $5 - 8n - 7n = 13 + 11$

22. $9y + 13 - 4y - 11 = {}^-6 - 12$ **23.** $9y + 13 - 4 - 11y = {}^-6 - 12$

24. ${}^-7t + 8 + t - 5 = {}^-14 + 20$ **25.** ${}^-7 + 8t + t - 5 = {}^-14 + 20$

Solve each proportion *(page 252)*

26. $\frac{n}{3} = \frac{5}{6}$ **27.** $\frac{7}{n} = \frac{5}{9}$ **28.** $\frac{9}{12} = \frac{n}{6}$ **29.** $\frac{8}{5} = \frac{5}{n}$ **30.** $\frac{n}{10} = \frac{12}{5}$

31. $\frac{5}{8} = \frac{n}{13}$ **32.** $\frac{16}{12} = \frac{4}{n}$ **33.** $\frac{n}{6} = \frac{14}{9}$ **34.** $\frac{13}{n} = \frac{5}{9}$ **35.** $\frac{11}{4} = \frac{n}{5}$

36. $\frac{n}{31} = \frac{5}{8}$ **37.** $\frac{17}{n} = \frac{3}{8}$ **38.** $\frac{9}{10} = \frac{n}{30}$ **39.** $\frac{3}{1\frac{1}{4}} = \frac{5}{n}$ **40.** $\frac{n}{2\frac{2}{3}} = \frac{7}{4}$

Solve. *(page 266)*

41. $n\%$ of $8 = 6$ **42.** $n\%$ of $20 = 5$ **43.** $n\%$ of $8 = 20$ **44.** $3\frac{1}{2}\%$ of $15 = n$

45. $8\frac{1}{3}\%$ of $56 = n$ **46.** $33\frac{1}{3}\%$ of $n = 17$ **47.** 25% of $n = 13$ **48.** 1% of $n = 2.5$

49. $87\frac{1}{2}\%$ of $n = 63$ **50.** $n\%$ of $48 = 32$ **51.** $n\%$ of $8 = 30$ **52.** $37\frac{1}{2}\%$ of $n = 30$

Find the percent of increase or decrease. Use *i* to indicate increase and *d* to indicate decrease. Give answers to the nearest tenth of a percent. *(page 268)*

53. from 24 to 30 **54.** from 60 to 30 **55.** from 30 to 60

56. from 50 to 20 **57.** from 112 to 138 **58.** from 138 to 112

59. from 16 to 56 **60.** from 39 to 91 **61.** from 91 to 39

Problem Solving—Applications

Computers are used to draw "blueprints" of an architect's design. The computer can be programmed to display a floor plan on a screen or printout.

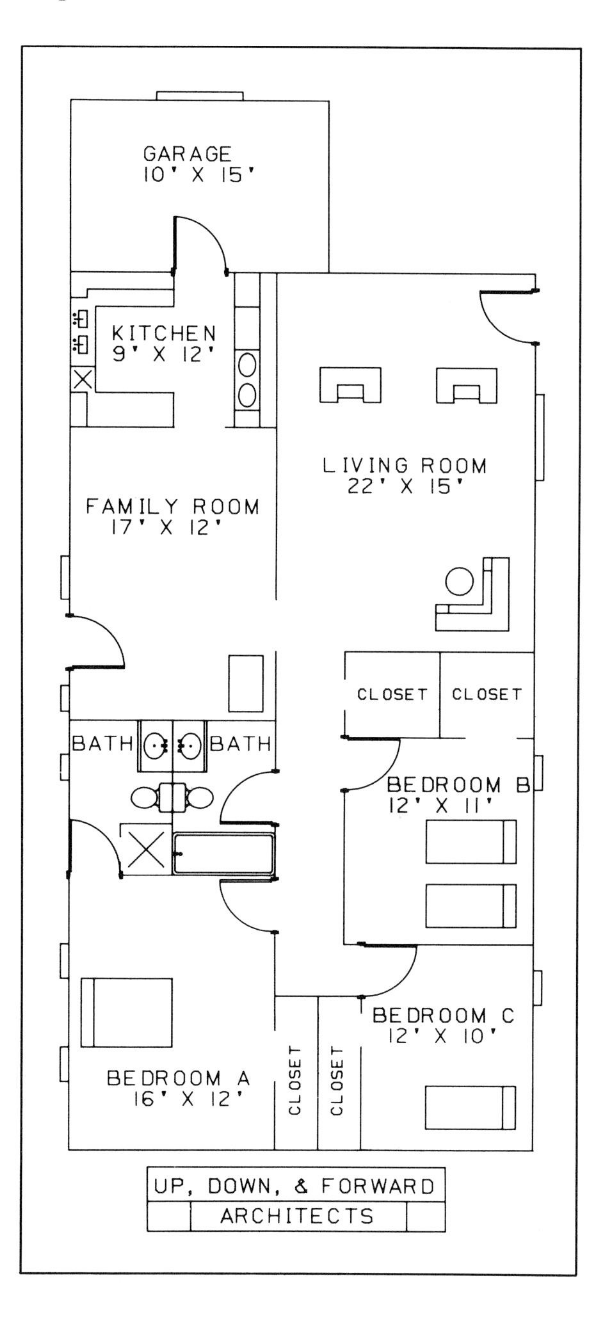

Use the floor plan to solve each problem.

1. Which room is 17 feet by 12 feet?
2. Which room is 16 feet by 12 feet?
3. What are the length and width of the living room?
4. What are the dimensions of the kitchen?
5. Which room has an area of 132 square feet?
6. What is the area of the smallest bedroom?
7. What is the area of the largest bedroom?
8. Carpet costs $1.50 per square foot. How much will it cost to carpet Bedroom B?
9. At $1.75 per square foot, how much will it cost to carpet the living room?
10. A floor tile 1 foot by 1 foot costs $.49. How much will it cost to tile the family-room floor?
11. A gallon of paint covers 600 square feet. What fraction of a gallon of paint will it take to cover the garage floor?
12. A contractor said his house could be built for $50 per square foot. Would you expect the cost to be more or less than $60,000?

Chapter Review

Here are scrambled answers for the review exercises.

$\frac{1}{3}$	200	area	divide	milliliter	space	triangular
1	1000	bases	height	multiply	sphere	volume
13.5	2512	cone	kilogram	pyramid	square	weight
20	add	cylinder	liter	rectangular	surface	width

1. Three-dimensional shapes are called __?__ figures. Prisms and pyramids are named according to the shapes of their __?__ . *(page 310)*

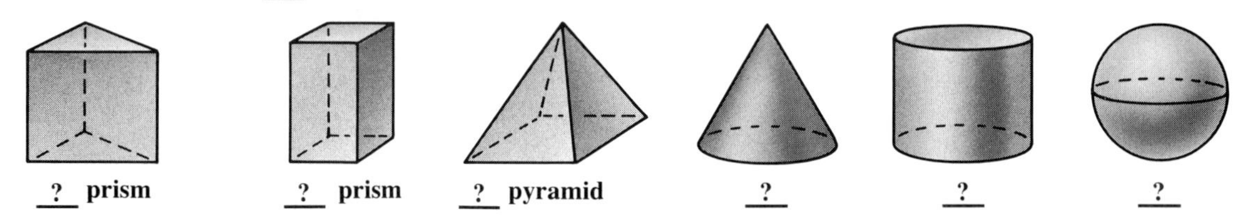

2. The sum of the areas of the 6 faces of a rectangular prism or cube is called the __?__ area. To find the surface area of this rectangular prism, you would compute the area of each face by multiplying its length by its __?__ . Then you would __?__ all six areas. *(pages 312, 314)*

3. The __?__ of a space figure is the number of cubic units that it takes to fill it. To find the volume of a prism, you can use the formula $V = Bh$, where B stands for the area of the base and h stands for the __?__ . The volume of this prism is __?__ ft³. *(page 318)*

10 ft
4 ft
5 ft

4. To find the volume of a cylinder, you can use the formula $V = Bh$, where B stands for the __?__ of the base and h stands for the height. The volume of this cylinder is __?__ in.³. Use 3.14 as an approximation for π. *(page 320)*

10 in.
8 in.

5. The volume of a __?__ or cone is __?__ times the area of the base times the height. The volume of this pyramid is __?__ ft³. *(page 322)*

4 ft
3 ft
5 ft

6. The __?__ and the milliliter are metric units of liquid measure or capacity. The gram and the __?__ are metric units of weight. 1 liter = __?__ milliliters
__?__ kilogram = 1000 grams To change from milliliters to liters, you would __?__ by 1000. To change from kilograms to grams, you would __?__ by 1000. *(page 324)*

7. The metric units of volume, capacity, and __?__ have a special relationship. A container that will hold 1 cm³ of water has a capacity of 1 __?__ . A container that will hold 1000 cm³ of water has a capacity of 1 liter. The weight of 1 liter of water is 1 kilogram. The container shown at the right holds __?__ liters of water, and the weight of the water would be 13.5 kilograms. *(page 326)*

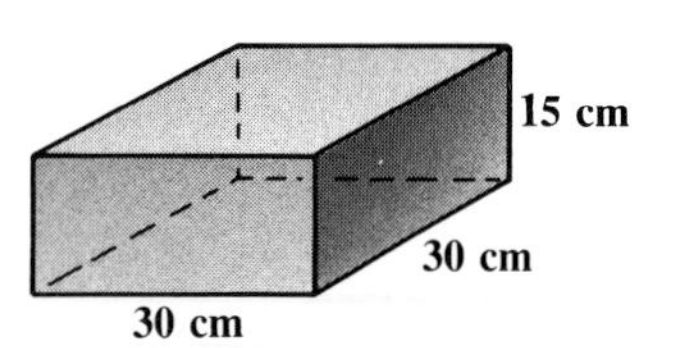

Chapter Test

▶ **Match each space figure with its name.** *(page 310)*

1. Cone
2. Cube
3. Cylinder
4. Pentagonal pyramid
5. Rectangular prism
6. Sphere
7. Square pyramid
8. Triangular prism
9. Triangular pyramid

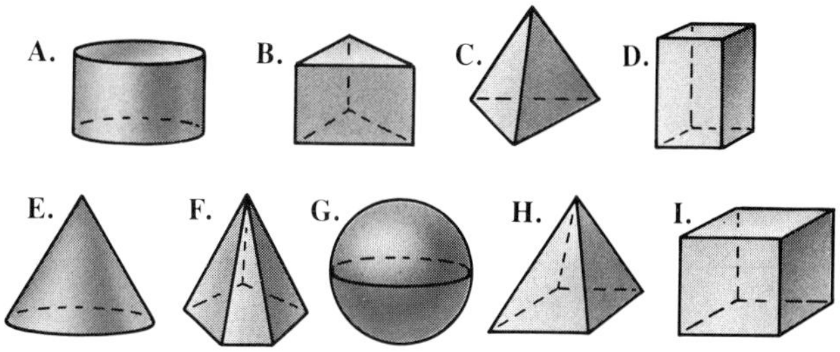

A. B. C. D. E. F. G. H. I.

▶ **Find the surface area.** *(pages 312, 314)*

10. 5 ft, 5 ft, 5 ft
11. 8 ft, 5 ft, 5 ft
12. 4 ft, 6 ft, 12 ft
13. 7 ft, 3 ft, 6 ft

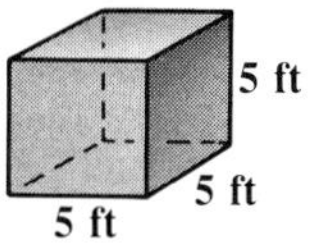

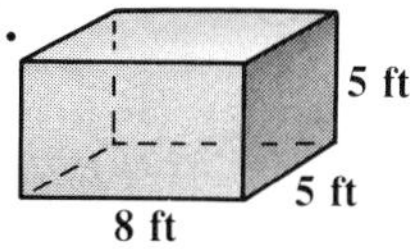

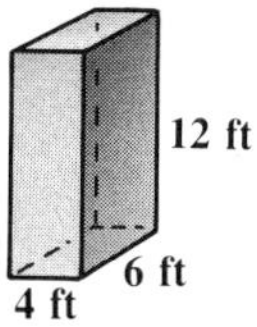

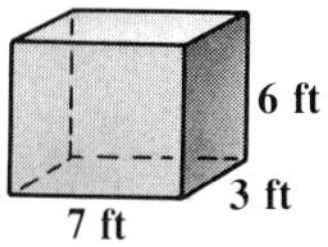

▶ **Find the volume. Use 3.14 as an approximation for π.** *(pages 318, 320, 322)*

14. 4 in., 4 in., 6 in.
15. 2 in., 8 in.
16. 6 in., 9 in., 8 in.
17. 10 in., 3 in.

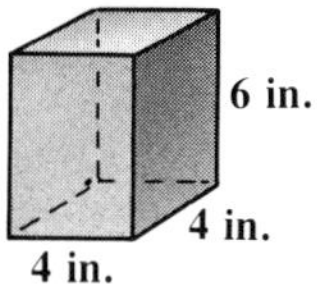

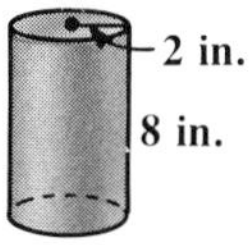

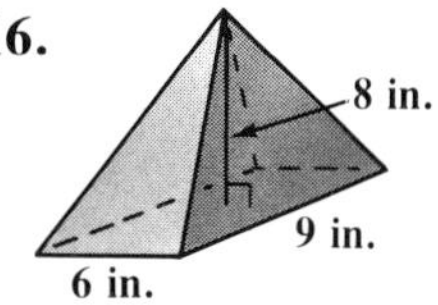

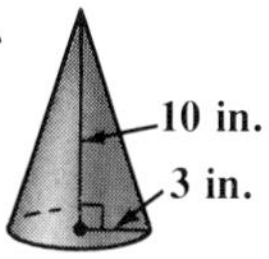

▶ **Complete.** *(page 324)*

18. 45 L = __?__ mL
19. 2500 mL = __?__ L
20. 0.65 L = __?__ mL
21. 856 mL = __?__ L
22. 25 kg = __?__ g
23. 1650 g = __?__ kg
24. 0.46 kg = __?__ g
25. 37 g = __?__ kg

▶ **Complete.** *(page 326)*

26. The container will hold __?__ liters of water.
27. The container will hold __?__ kilograms of water.

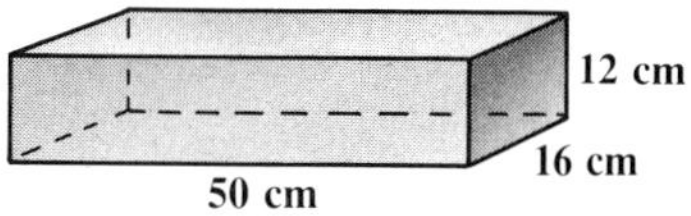

50 cm, 16 cm, 12 cm

▶ **Choose the formula and find the area of each shaded region. Use 3.14 for π.** *(page 328)*

$A = s^2 - \pi r^2$ $\quad A = S^2 - s^2$
$A = \pi r^2 - lw$ $\quad A = \pi R^2 - \pi r^2$

28. 2 in., 3 in., 3 in.
29. 3 in.
30. 8 in., 2 in.
31. 3 in., 3 in., 6 in., 6 in.

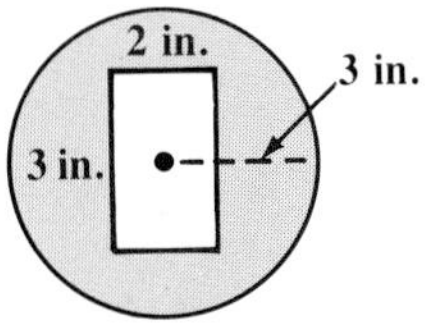

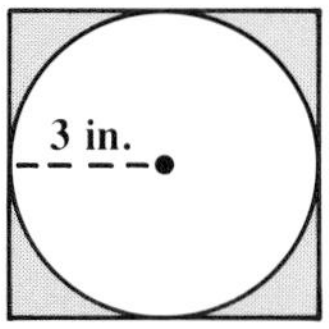

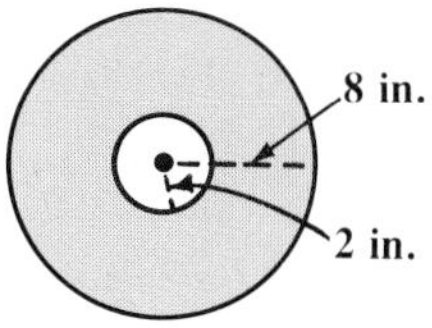

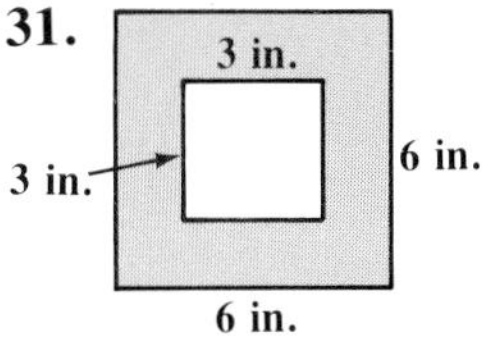

Cumulative Test
Standardized Format

▶ **Choose the correct letter.**

1. $\frac{4xy^2}{18x^2y}$ written in simplest form is

A. $\frac{2xy^2}{9x^2y}$
B. $\frac{4xy}{18x^2}$
C. $\frac{14xy}{18x^2}$
D. none of these

2. Give the sum.

$$\frac{2x}{3} + \frac{y}{4}$$

A. $\frac{2x + y}{12}$
B. $\frac{2x + y}{7}$
C. $\frac{8x + 3y}{12}$
D. none of these

3. Give the difference.

$$\frac{2r}{3} - \frac{s}{6}$$

A. $\frac{2r - 3s}{6}$
B. $\frac{2r - s}{6}$
C. $\frac{r - s}{3}$
D. none of these

4. Give the product.

$$\frac{5c}{6d} \cdot \frac{5d}{2c^2}$$

A. $\frac{25}{12c}$
B. $\frac{25c}{6c^2}$
C. $\frac{12c}{25}$
D. none of these

5. Give the quotient.

$$\frac{a}{b} \div \frac{7a}{4d}$$

A. $\frac{7a^2}{4bd}$
B. $\frac{7b}{4d}$
C. $\frac{4d}{7a}$
D. none of these

6. Solve.

$$\frac{5}{6} \text{ of } 33 = n$$

A. $39\frac{3}{5}$
B. $27\frac{1}{2}$
C. $5\frac{1}{2}$
D. none of these

7. Solve.

$$\frac{5}{8}n = 31$$

A. $49\frac{3}{5}$
B. $43\frac{3}{5}$
C. $19\frac{3}{8}$
D. none of these

8. Solve.

$$5k - 6 - 3k = {}^-9 - 6$$

A. ${}^-4\frac{1}{2}$
B. ${}^-1\frac{3}{8}$
C. $2\frac{1}{2}$
D. none of these

9. Solve.

$$\frac{n}{5} = \frac{3}{2\frac{2}{3}}$$

A. $4\frac{5}{9}$
B. $5\frac{5}{8}$
C. 40
D. none of these

10. Solve.

$$6\frac{1}{2}\% \text{ of } 108 = n$$

A. 6.50
B. 16.62
C. 7.02
D. none of these

11. The percent of increase from 21 to 28 is

A. $33\frac{1}{3}\%$
B. 25%
C. 7%
D. none of these

12. Choose the equation.

You sold 7 tickets on Monday and 5 tickets on Tuesday. After deducting \$6 for selling the tickets, you turned in \$36. What was the cost of each ticket?

A. $7n + 5n + 6 = 36$
B. $7n - 5n + 6 = 36$
C. $7n + 5n - 6 = 36$
D. $7n - 5n - 6 = 36$

13 Graphing Equations and Inequalities

$y = \frac{1}{4}x + 40$

This formula shows the relationship between the number of times a cricket chirps per minute (x) and the temperature in degrees Fahrenheit (y).

(page 347)

You can estimate the temperature by counting a cricket's chirps. If a cricket chirps 60 times per minute, the temperature is about 55°F.

Graphing Inequalities on the Number Line

Here are some examples of inequalities:

is less than	*is greater than*	*is less than or equal to*	*is greater than or equal to*
$x < 4$	$y > \frac{^{-}1}{2}$	$a \leq 1$	$c \geq \frac{2}{3}$

Look at the first inequality. There are many numbers that are solutions of $x < 4$. In fact, every number less than 4 is a solution.

1. Is 3 a solution of $x < 4$? Is $^{-}7$? Is $3\frac{5}{8}$?

2. Look at the second inequality. Is 0 a solution? Is 12? Is $\frac{^{-}1}{3}$?

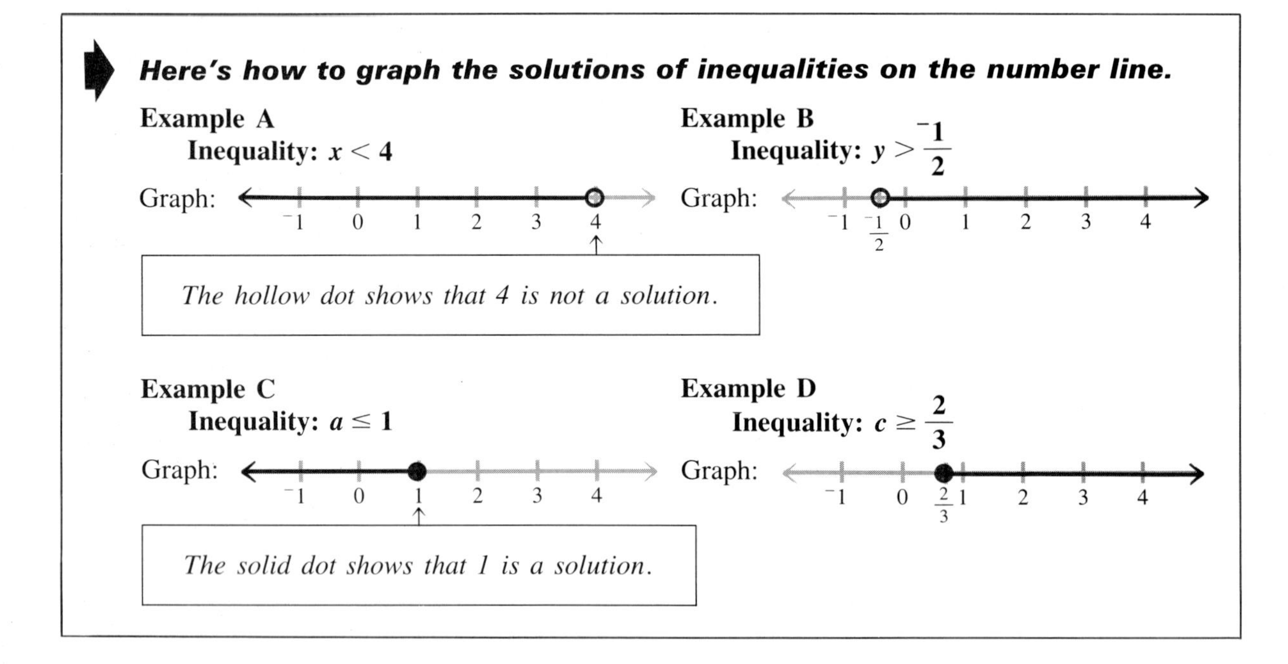

3. Look at the graph in Example A. Is 4 a solution?

4. Look at the graph in Example B. Is $\frac{^{-}1}{2}$ a solution?

5. Complete.

a. A hollow dot tells you that the number __?__ a solution.
is/is not

b. A solid dot tells you that the number __?__ a solution.
is/is not

EXERCISES

▶ **Match each inequality with its graph.**

6. $n < 2$ — **a.** $^{-}4 \quad ^{-}3 \quad ^{-}2 \quad ^{-}1 \quad 0 \quad 1 \quad 2 \quad 3 \quad 4$

7. $n > 2$ — **b.** $^{-}4 \quad ^{-}3 \quad ^{-}2 \quad ^{-}1 \quad 0 \quad 1 \quad 2 \quad 3 \quad 4$

8. $n \leq 2$ — **c.** $^{-}4 \quad ^{-}3 \quad ^{-}2 \quad ^{-}1 \quad 0 \quad 1 \quad 2 \quad 3 \quad 4$

9. $n \geq 2$ — **d.** $^{-}4 \quad ^{-}3 \quad ^{-}2 \quad ^{-}1 \quad 0 \quad 1 \quad 2 \quad 3 \quad 4$

10. $n < {}^{-}2$ — **e.** $^{-}4 \quad ^{-}3 \quad ^{-}2 \quad ^{-}1 \quad 0 \quad 1 \quad 2 \quad 3 \quad 4$

11. $n > {}^{-}2$ — **f.** $^{-}4 \quad ^{-}3 \quad ^{-}2 \quad ^{-}1 \quad 0 \quad 1 \quad 2 \quad 3 \quad 4$

12. $n \leq {}^{-}2$ — **g.** $^{-}4 \quad ^{-}3 \quad ^{-}2 \quad ^{-}1 \quad 0 \quad 1 \quad 2 \quad 3 \quad 4$

13. $n \geq {}^{-}2$ — **h.** $^{-}4 \quad ^{-}3 \quad ^{-}2 \quad ^{-}1 \quad 0 \quad 1 \quad 2 \quad 3 \quad 4$

▶ **Write an inequality for each graph.**

14. $^{-}2 \quad ^{-}1 \quad 0 \quad 1 \quad 2 \quad 3$

15. $^{-}6 \quad ^{-}5 \quad ^{-}4 \quad ^{-}3 \quad ^{-}2 \quad ^{-}1$

16. $4 \quad 5 \quad 6 \quad 7 \quad 8 \quad 9$

17. $^{-}3 \quad ^{-}2 \quad ^{-}1 \quad 0 \quad 1 \quad 2$

18. $^{-}2 \quad ^{-}1 \quad 0 \quad \frac{1}{2} \quad 1 \quad 2 \quad 3$

19. $^{-}3 \quad ^{-}2 \quad ^{-}1\frac{1}{2} \quad ^{-}1 \quad 0 \quad 1 \quad 2$

20. $0 \quad 1 \quad 2 \quad 2\frac{2}{3} \quad 3 \quad 4 \quad 5$

21. $^{-}4 \quad ^{-}3 \quad ^{-}2 \quad ^{-}1 \quad ^{-}\frac{3}{4} \quad 0 \quad 1$

22. $^{-}2 \quad ^{-}1 \quad 0 \quad \frac{5}{6} \quad 1 \quad 2 \quad 3$

23. $^{-}5 \quad ^{-}4 \quad ^{-}3\frac{3}{4} \quad ^{-}3 \quad ^{-}2 \quad ^{-}1 \quad 0$

▶ **Graph the solutions of each inequality.**

24. $x < 3$ **25.** $m \geq 4$ **26.** $a > {}^{-}3$ **27.** $f \leq {}^{-}1$

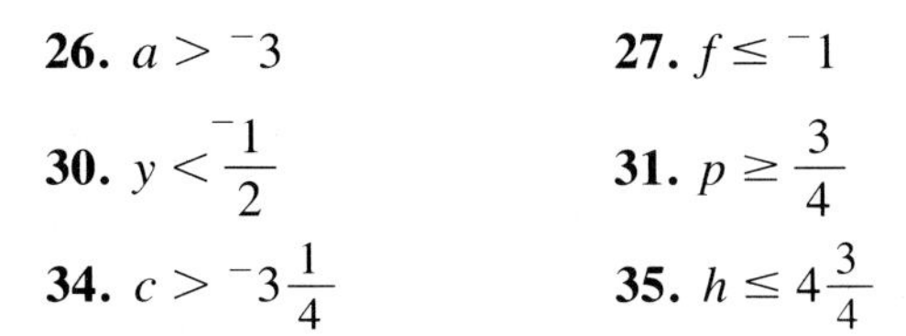

28. $b > 0$ **29.** $g \leq 5$ **30.** $y < \frac{^{-}1}{2}$ **31.** $p \geq \frac{3}{4}$

32. $n < 1\frac{1}{2}$ **33.** $q \geq {}^{-}3\frac{2}{3}$ **34.** $c > {}^{-}3\frac{1}{4}$ **35.** $h \leq 4\frac{3}{4}$

Solving Inequalities

Solving an inequality is much like solving an equation. In fact, the only difference is that **when you multiply or divide both sides of an inequality by a negative number, you must reverse the inequality sign.**

Here's how to solve inequalities.

Example A

Inequality:	$x - 3 < {}^-4$
Add 3 to both sides.	$x - 3 + 3 < {}^-4 + 3$
Simplify.	$x < {}^-1$

Example B

Inequality:	$y + 4 > {}^-5$
Subtract 4 from both sides.	$y + 4 - 4 > {}^-5 - 4$
Simplify.	$y > {}^-9$

Example C

Inequality:	$\frac{c}{6} \geq {}^-2$
Multiply both sides by 6.	$6 \cdot \frac{c}{6} \geq 6 \cdot {}^-2$
Simplify.	$c \geq {}^-12$

Notice that since we multiplied both sides by a **positive** number, the inequality sign was not reversed.

Example D

Inequality:	${}^-2n \leq {}^-11$
Divide both sides by ${}^-2$ and reverse the inequality sign.	$\frac{{}^-2n}{{}^-2} \geq \frac{{}^-11}{{}^-2}$
Simplify.	$n \geq 5\frac{1}{2}$

Notice that since we divided both sides by a **negative** number, the inequality sign was reversed.

1. In Example C, both sides of the inequality were __?__ by a **positive** number, so the inequality sign was not reversed.

2. In Example D, both sides of the inequality were __?__ by a **negative** number, so the inequality sign was reversed.

3. Complete.

a. $z - 8 < {}^-3$

$z - 8 + 8 < {}^-3 + 8$

$z <$ __?__

b. $\frac{h}{{}^-5} \geq 3$

${}^-5 \cdot \frac{h}{{}^-5} \leq$ __?__ $\cdot 3$

$h \leq {}^-15$

c. $4t \leq 18$

$\frac{4t}{4} \leq \frac{18}{4}$

$t \leq$ __?__

EXERCISES

▶ **Would you reverse the inequality sign when solving the inequality?**

4. $5a \leq 3$ **5.** $^{-}2z > 9$ **6.** $n + 6 \geq {}^{-}3$ **7.** $\frac{j}{^{-}4} \leq 3$

8. $\frac{n}{6} > {}^{-}7$ **9.** $y - 8 < {}^{-}5$ **10.** $^{-}8w \leq 5$ **11.** $\frac{t}{9} \geq {}^{-}10$

▶ **Solve.**

12. $^{-}4n > {}^{-}9$ **13.** $n + 9 \geq {}^{-}2$ **14.** $\frac{n}{^{-}2} < {}^{-}6$ **15.** $n - 4 \leq {}^{-}12$

16. $n - 9 < 16$ **17.** $6n \leq 15$ **18.** $n + 12 \geq 5$ **19.** $\frac{n}{^{-}5} > 3$

20. $n - 12 \geq {}^{-}5$ **21.** $\frac{n}{8} < {}^{-}10$ **22.** $^{-}9n > 30$ **23.** $n + 13 \leq {}^{-}5$

24. $n - 21 \leq {}^{-}6$ **25.** $^{-}12n > 34$ **26.** $\frac{n}{11} < {}^{-}9$ **27.** $n + 15 \geq 23$

28. $\frac{n}{^{-}12} > 0$ **29.** $n + 18 \geq {}^{-}6$ **30.** $^{-}10n \leq {}^{-}42$ **31.** $n - 12 < 11$

▶ **First solve the inequality. Then match the inequality with the graph of its solutions.**

32. $^{-}2y \leq 7$

33. $y - 6 > {}^{-}4$

34. $\frac{y}{2} \geq 1$

35. $y + 3 < 4$

36. $4y < 14$

37. $y - 4 \geq {}^{-}3$

38. $\frac{y}{^{-}3} \geq {}^{-}1$

39. $y + 2 < {}^{-}1$

a. $^{-}4$ $^{-}3$ $^{-}2$ $^{-}1$ 0 1 2 3 4

b. $^{-}4$ $^{-}3$ $^{-}2$ $^{-}1$ 0 1 2 3 4

c. $^{-}4$ $^{-}3$ $^{-}2$ $^{-}1$ 0 1 2 3 4

d. $^{-}4$ $^{-}3$ $^{-}2$ $^{-}1$ 0 1 2 3 $3\frac{1}{2}$ 4

e. $^{-}4$ $^{-}3$ $^{-}2$ $^{-}1$ 0 1 2 3 4

f. $^{-}4$ $^{-}3\frac{1}{2}$ $^{-}3$ $^{-}2$ $^{-}1$ 0 1 2 3 4

g. $^{-}4$ $^{-}3$ $^{-}2$ $^{-}1$ 0 1 2 3 4

h. $^{-}4$ $^{-}3$ $^{-}2$ $^{-}1$ 0 1 2 3 4

▶ **First solve the inequality. Then graph its solutions.**

40. $^{-}4n > {}^{-}3$ **41.** $n + 8 \geq 6$ **42.** $\frac{n}{^{-}3} < {}^{-}1$ **43.** $n - 6 \leq {}^{-}10$

44. $n - 7 < 11$ **45.** $5n \leq 7$ **46.** $n + 10 \geq 7$ **47.** $\frac{n}{^{-}3} > 2$

48. $n - 19 \geq {}^{-}15$ **49.** $\frac{n}{^{-}8} < 0$ **50.** $^{-}8n > 20$ **51.** $n + 12 \leq {}^{-}7$

Solving Two-Step Inequalities

In this lesson you will learn to solve two-step inequalities. Again, solving an inequality is much like solving an equation.

Here's how to solve two-step inequalities.

Example A

Inequality:	$4y - 3 \le {}^{-}8$
Add 3 to both sides.	$4y - 3 + 3 \le {}^{-}8 + 3$
Simplify.	$4y \le {}^{-}5$
Divide both sides by 4.	$\frac{4y}{4} \le \frac{^{-}5}{4}$
Simplify.	$y \le {}^{-}1\frac{1}{4}$

Example B

Inequality:	$\frac{z}{^{-}6} + 7 > 9$
Subtract 7 from both sides.	$\frac{z}{^{-}6} + 7 - 7 > 9 - 7$
Simplify.	$\frac{z}{^{-}6} > 2$
Multiply both sides by $^{-}6$ and reverse the inequality sign.	$^{-}6 \cdot \frac{z}{^{-}6} < {}^{-}6 \cdot 2$
Simplify.	$z < {}^{-}12$

1. Look at Example B. In the next to the last step, both sides of the equation were multiplied by __?__. Was the inequality sign reversed?

2. Complete.

a.
$$4a + 5 < {}^{-}1$$
$$4a + 5 - 5 < {}^{-}1 - \underline{\ ?\ }$$
$$4a < {}^{-}6$$
$$\frac{4a}{4} < \frac{^{-}6}{4}$$
$$a < {}^{-}1\frac{1}{2}$$

b.
$$^{-}3j - 8 \ge {}^{-}4$$
$$^{-}3j - 8 + 8 \ge {}^{-}4 + 8$$
$$^{-}3j \ge \underline{\ ?\ }$$
$$\frac{^{-}3j}{^{-}3}\ \underline{\ ?\ }\ \frac{4}{^{-}3}$$
$$j \le {}^{-}1\frac{1}{3}$$

c.
$$2n + 6 \le 7$$
$$2n + 6 - 6 \le 7 - 6$$
$$2n \le \underline{\ ?\ }$$
$$\frac{2n}{2}\ \underline{\ ?\ }\ \frac{1}{2}$$
$$n \le \frac{1}{2}$$

3. Would you reverse the inequality sign when solving the inequality?

a. $2y + 6 \le 4$ **b.** $\frac{r}{3} - 2 \ge {}^{-}4$ **c.** $^{-}3a - 5 > 2$ **d.** $\frac{t}{^{-}2} + 5 \le 0$

e. $\frac{j}{6} - 3 > {}^{-}1$ **f.** $^{-}7b + 6 < 5$ **g.** $\frac{c}{^{-}8} + 9 \le 11$ **h.** $5j - 4 \ge 6$

i. $4y + 8 \ge 16$ **j.** $\frac{m}{^{-}4} + 2 \le 5$ **k.** $^{-}4a + 1 \ge 5$ **l.** $\frac{t}{^{-}3} + 4 \ge 0$

EXERCISES

▶ **Solve.**

4. $5x + 3 < 3$ **5.** $\frac{x}{3} + 2 > 1$ **6.** $^-7x - 4 > 3$ **7.** $\frac{x}{^-5} - 3 < 2$

8. $\frac{x}{^-4} + 5 \leq {}^-3$ **9.** $^-3x + 5 \geq {}^-4$ **10.** $\frac{x}{6} - 4 \geq 14$ **11.** $9x - 3 \leq 5$

12. $^-6x + 5 \geq {}^-2$ **13.** $\frac{x}{2} - 7 > 6$ **14.** $\frac{x}{^-10} + 6 < 11$ **15.** $4x - 6 \leq 6$

16. $9x + 7 > {}^-5$ **17.** $\frac{x}{^-7} + 9 \leq 12$ **18.** $^-8x - 9 < 4$ **19.** $\frac{x}{9} - 8 \geq 7$

20. $\frac{x}{10} - 12 > {}^-12$ **21.** $10x + 3 \leq 8$ **22.** $\frac{x}{^-12} + 10 < 16$ **23.** $^-2x - 7 \geq {}^-3$

24. $^-12x + 5 \leq 6$ **25.** $\frac{x}{^-8} + 13 \leq 15$ **26.** $^-16x - 6 \geq 4$ **27.** $\frac{x}{16} - 15 \leq {}^-11$

▶ **First solve the inequality. Then match the inequality with the graph of its solution.**

28. $2n + 3 > 4$

29. $\frac{n}{2} - 6 \leq {}^-5$

30. $\frac{n}{^-4} + 9 < 8$

31. $4n - 3 \geq {}^-1$

32. $^-4n - 5 > {}^-1$

a. 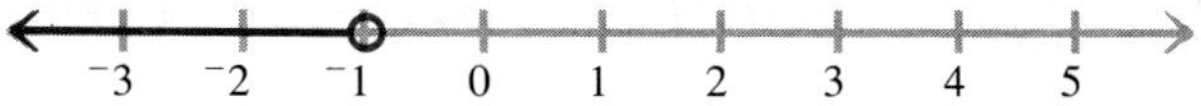 $^-3$ $^-2$ $^-1$ 0 1 2 3 4 5

b. 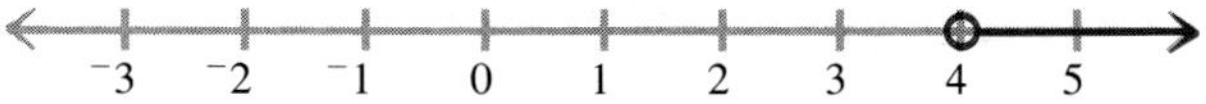 $^-3$ $^-2$ $^-1$ 0 1 2 3 4 5

c. 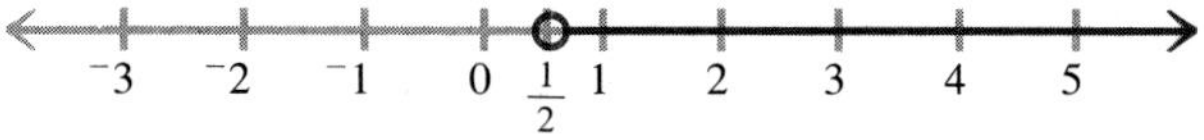 $^-3$ $^-2$ $^-1$ 0 $\frac{1}{2}$ 1 2 3 4 5

d. 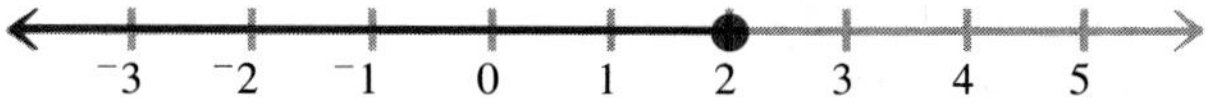 $^-3$ $^-2$ $^-1$ 0 1 2 3 4 5

e. 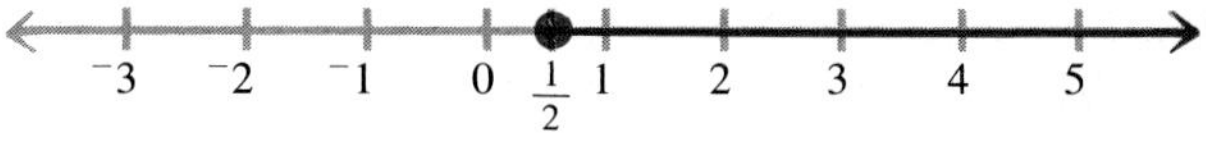 $^-3$ $^-2$ $^-1$ 0 $\frac{1}{2}$ 1 2 3 4 5

▶ **First solve the inequality. Then graph its solutions.**

33. $6a - 2 \leq 4$ **34.** $^-9c + 6 > {}^-21$ **35.** $\frac{r}{3} - 5 < {}^-6$ **36.** $\frac{t}{^-2} + 5 \geq 7$

37. $^-3y + 5 > 7$ **38.** $\frac{a}{5} - 8 < {}^-8$ **39.** $5j + 9 \geq 4$ **40.** $^-2k - 10 \leq {}^-13$

Challenge

▶ **Graph on a number line**

41. all numbers less than 2 *and* greater than $^-3$.

42. all numbers less than 4 *and* greater than or equal to $^-1$.

43. all numbers less than or equal to $^-1$ *and* greater than $^-4$.

44. all numbers less than or equal to 3 *and* greater than or equal to $^-1$.

45. all numbers not equal to $^-2$.

Cumulative Skill Practice

Give the prime factorization using exponents. *(page 124)*

1. 9 **2.** 4 **3.** 25 **4.** 20 **5.** 49 **6.** 28

7. 56 **8.** 98 **9.** 16 **10.** 72 **11.** 81 **12.** 32

13. 36 **14.** 64 **15.** 68 **16.** 128 **17.** 45 **18.** 225

Give the greatest common factor. *(page 126)*

19. 6, 24 **20.** 12, 18 **21.** 20, 10 **22.** 36, 24

23. 40, 30 **24.** 4, $8x$ **25.** $18y$, 27 **26.** f, $9f$

27. $6c$, $9c$ **28.** $32j$, $8j$ **29.** $3w^2$, $14w$ **30.** $18y$, $20y^2$

31. $6n^2$, $54n$ **32.** $12u^2v$, $18uv$ **33.** $18ab$, $21b^2$ **34.** $36c^2d^2$, $24cd^2$

Give each sum or difference in simplest form. *(page 158)*

35. $\frac{1}{6} + \frac{1}{3}$ **36.** $\frac{1}{2} + \frac{1}{3}$ **37.** $\frac{3}{4} + \frac{5}{6}$ **38.** $\frac{5}{6} - \frac{5}{8}$ **39.** $\frac{7}{8} - \frac{2}{3}$

40. $\frac{a}{4} + \frac{b}{8}$ **41.** $\frac{m}{16} + \frac{n}{8}$ **42.** $\frac{5x}{12} + \frac{y}{8}$ **43.** $\frac{w}{5} + \frac{4z}{15}$ **44.** $\frac{2x}{21} + \frac{3y}{7}$

45. $\frac{x}{3} - \frac{y}{6}$ **46.** $\frac{a}{4} - \frac{b}{5}$ **47.** $\frac{n}{12} - \frac{3m}{8}$ **48.** $\frac{2v}{9} - \frac{u}{12}$ **49.** $\frac{5p}{24} - \frac{3q}{16}$

Give each product in simplest form. *(page 172)*

50. $\frac{5}{8} \cdot \frac{8}{5}$ **51.** $\frac{1}{8} \cdot \frac{3}{4}$ **52.** $4 \cdot \frac{5}{8}$ **53.** $\frac{9}{10} \cdot \frac{5}{4}$ **54.** $\frac{12}{5} \cdot \frac{10}{3}$

55. $\frac{x}{3} \cdot \frac{1}{x}$ **56.** $8 \cdot \frac{y}{4}$ **57.** $\frac{5}{8} \cdot \frac{4y}{15}$ **58.** $\frac{2}{5d} \cdot \frac{5}{11e}$ **59.** $\frac{u}{v} \cdot \frac{3v}{2u}$

60. $\frac{n}{m^2} \cdot \frac{4m}{n}$ **61.** $\frac{f}{g} \cdot \frac{g}{f}$ **62.** $\frac{j^2}{4} \cdot \frac{k}{j}$ **63.** $\frac{6y}{z} \cdot \frac{z}{3w}$ **64.** $\frac{8d}{e} \cdot \frac{4e}{24d^2}$

Give each quotient in simplest form. *(page 176)*

65. $\frac{5}{8} \div \frac{1}{8}$ **66.** $\frac{7}{8} \div \frac{3}{2}$ **67.** $\frac{7}{8} \div \frac{3}{4}$ **68.** $\frac{3}{2} \div 2$ **69.** $8 \div \frac{5}{4}$

70. $\frac{5}{c} \div \frac{3}{d}$ **71.** $\frac{8}{n} \div \frac{2}{m}$ **72.** $\frac{d}{12} \div \frac{e}{8}$ **73.** $\frac{2y}{z} \div \frac{y}{6}$ **74.** $\frac{8}{q} \div \frac{4q}{5}$

75. $\frac{4z}{y} \div \frac{3x}{y}$ **76.** $\frac{a}{b} \div \frac{3a}{4b}$ **77.** $\frac{3d^2}{e} \div \frac{d}{e}$ **78.** $\frac{x}{12y} \div \frac{x^2}{9y}$ **79.** $\frac{12m}{5n} \div \frac{4m}{10n^2}$

Problem Solving—Applications

A **budget** is a plan for using one's money. Here is Kelly's weekly budget.

Rhonda uses a budget to keep track of her spending so that she won't run out of money between paychecks.

April keeps a budget to make sure she puts some money into savings each week.

Kelly
Earnings: $30/week

BUDGET	
Savings:	$6.00
Clothing:	4.50
Movies:	2.50
Records:	4.50
Lunches:	9.00
Other:	3.50

Rhonda
Earnings: $40/week

BUDGET	
Savings:	$ 4.00
Clothing:	10.00
Movies:	7.00
Records:	5.00
Lunches:	10.00
Other:	4.00

April
Earnings: $24/week

BUDGET	
Savings:	$3.00
Clothing:	6.50
Movies:	4.00
Records:	2.00
Lunches:	6.50
Other:	2.00

Use the budgets to solve each problem.

1. Which person budgets $\frac{1}{4}$ of her total earnings for clothing?

2. Who budgets $\frac{1}{8}$ of her total earnings for savings?

3. What fraction of Rhonda's total earnings does she save? Give the answer in lowest terms.

4. What fraction of her total earnings does April budget for movies? Give the answer in lowest terms.

5. Who spends 15% of total earnings for clothing?

6. Who spends 50% of her total earnings for clothing and lunches?

7. What percent of Kelly's total earnings does she budget for clothing?

8. What percent of April's total earnings does she budget for records?

Study the clues. Use the budgets to name each person.

9. *Clues:*
- This person budgets more than 20% of her total earnings for clothing.
- She budgets less than 20% of her total earnings for movies.

10. *Clues:*
- This person budgets more than 10% of her total earnings for records.
- She budgets less than 30% of her total earnings for lunches.

Graphing Ordered Pairs

Look at the picture at the right.

1. What is the horizontal number line called?
2. What is the vertical number line called?
3. Notice that the two axes intersect. What is the point of intersection called?

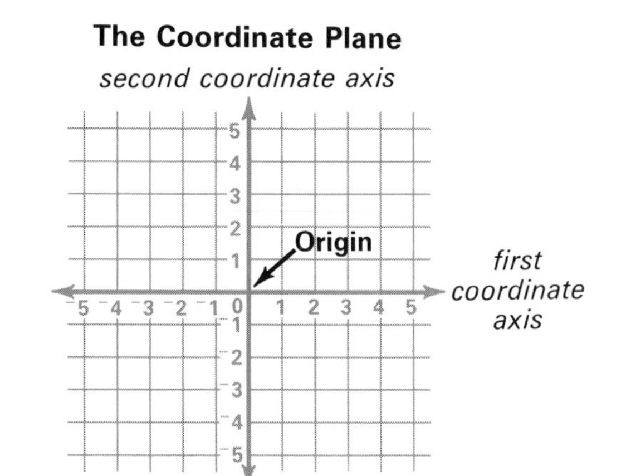

➧ *Here's how to graph ordered pairs on the coordinate plane.*

Example A

(3, 4) is read as "the ordered pair three four." 3 is called the first coordinate and 4 is called the second coordinate.

To graph (3, 4):

a. Start at the origin.

b. Move along the first coordinate axis to the first coordinate of the ordered pair, 3.

c. Move parallel to the second coordinate axis to the second coordinate of the ordered pair, 4.

Example B

To graph $\left(^-2, {}^-3\frac{1}{2}\right)$:

a. Start at the origin.

b. Move along the first coordinate axis to the first coordinate of the ordered pair, $^-2$.

c. Move parallel to the second coordinate axis to the second coordinate of the ordered pair, $^-3\frac{1}{2}$.

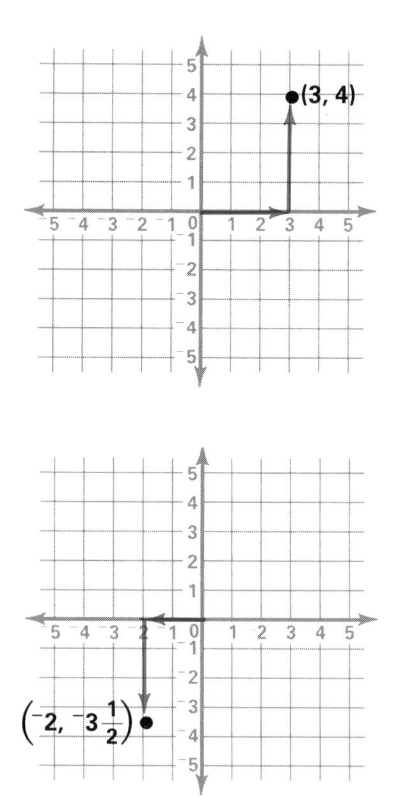

Give the ordered pair for each point.

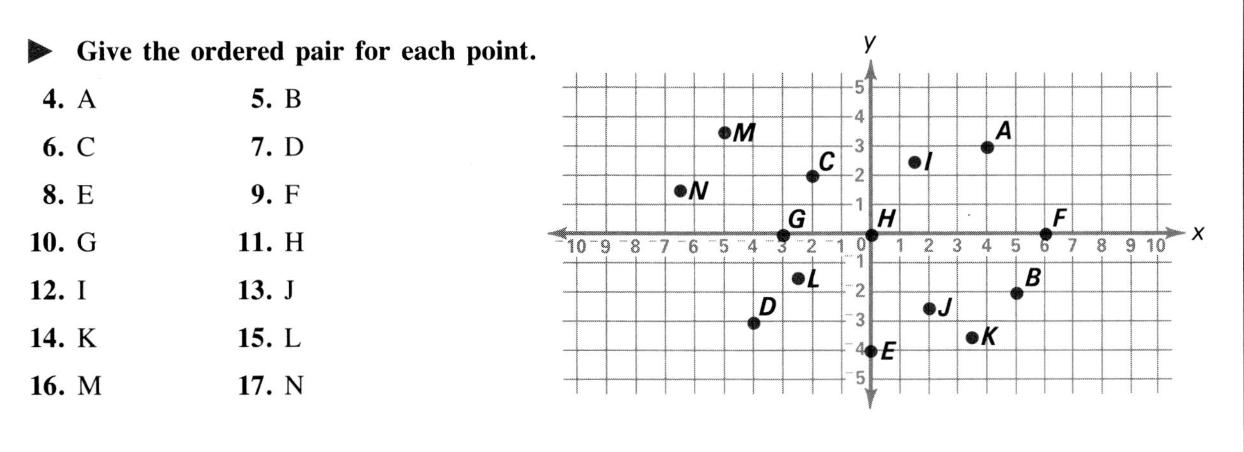

4. A **5.** B

6. C **7.** D

8. E **9.** F

10. G **11.** H

12. I **13.** J

14. K **15.** L

16. M **17.** N

Graph these ordered pairs. Label each point with its ordered pair.

18. $(2, 5)$ **19.** $({}^-4, 6)$ **20.** $(5, {}^-3)$ **21.** $(6, 0)$ **22.** $(0, 0)$

23. $(0, 8)$ **24.** $({}^-4, {}^-1)$ **25.** $\left({}^-4, 5\frac{1}{2}\right)$ **26.** $\left({}^-2\frac{1}{2}, {}^-5\frac{1}{2}\right)$ **27.** $\left(5\frac{1}{2}, {}^-1\frac{1}{2}\right)$

Solve.

28. Here are some ordered pairs in which the second coordinate is 3 more than the first coordinate.

$({}^-4, {}^-1), ({}^-3, 0), ({}^-2, 1)$

a. List 3 more such ordered pairs.

b. Graph all 6 ordered pairs.

c. Do the points "line up"?

29. Here are some ordered pairs in which the second coordinate is the square of the first coordinate.

$({}^-3, 9), ({}^-2, 4), ({}^-1, 1)$

a. List 3 more such ordered pairs.

b. Graph all 6 ordered pairs.

c. Do the points "line up"?

Challenge

30. Copy the triangle on graph paper. Now draw on the same graph paper the triangle that you get when you

a. multiply the first coordinate of each ordered pair by $^-1$ and keep the same second coordinate.

b. keep the first coordinate of each ordered pair the same and multiply the second coordinate by $^-1$.

c. multiply both coordinates of each ordered pair by $^-1$.

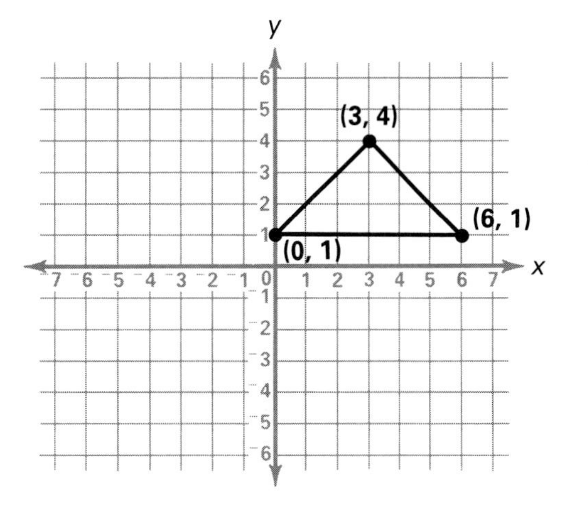

Equations with Two Variables

Thus far you have worked with equations that have only one variable. In this lesson you will work with equations that have two variables. Here is an example:

$$y = 2x + 3$$

Notice that for $x = 0$ and $y = 3$ you get a true equation. Therefore, the ordered pair

(0, 3) ← *Notice that the value of x is written first and the value of y is written second.*

is one solution of the equation. Actually such equations have an infinite number of solutions.

1. Substitute 3 for x and 0 for y. Is (3, 0) a solution?

2. Is ($^-1$, 1) a solution?

3. Is $\left(\frac{^-1}{2}, 2\right)$ a solution?

Here's how to find solutions of equations with two variables.

To find an ordered pair that is a solution of an equation, choose a value for x and solve the equation to find the value for y.

Example: $y = 3x - 5$

If you choose 2 for x, then

$$y = 3 \cdot 2 - 5$$
$$= 1$$

So (2, 1) is a solution.

If you choose $^-3$ for x, then

$$y = 3 \cdot {}^-3 - 5$$
$$= {}^-14$$

So ($^-3$, $^-14$) is a solution.

If you choose $\frac{2}{3}$ for x, then

$$y = 3 \cdot \frac{2}{3} - 5$$
$$= 2 - 5$$
$$= {}^-3$$

So $\left(\frac{2}{3}, {}^-3\right)$ is a solution.

4. Look at the example in the box. If you choose 2 for x and solve the equation for y, you get the solution (2, __?__).

5. What two other ordered pairs were found to be solutions of the equation?

6. Often a table of values is used to show solutions of an equation with two variables. Complete this table of values for the solutions found above.

$y = 3x - 5$	
x	y
2	1
$^-3$	$^-14$
$\frac{2}{3}$	?

Copy and complete each table of values.

7.

$y = 2x$	
x	y
$^-2$	?
$^-1$	?
0	?
1	?
2	?

8.

$y = {}^-3x$	
x	y
$^-3$	?
$^-2$	?
$^-1$	?
0	?
1	?

9.

$y = 5x + 1$	
x	y
$^-1$	?
0	?
1	?
2	?
3	?

10.

$y = \frac{1}{2}x - 1$	
x	y
$^-2$	?
0	?
2	?
4	?
6	?

Copy the equation and make a table of values showing four solutions.

11. $y = {}^-2x$ **12.** $y = 5x$ **13.** $y = 5x - 8$ **14.** $y = 3x + 7$

15. $y = 4x + 3$ **16.** $y = {}^-2x - 6$ **17.** $y = \frac{1}{4}x + 2$ **18.** $y = \frac{^-3}{4}x - 1$

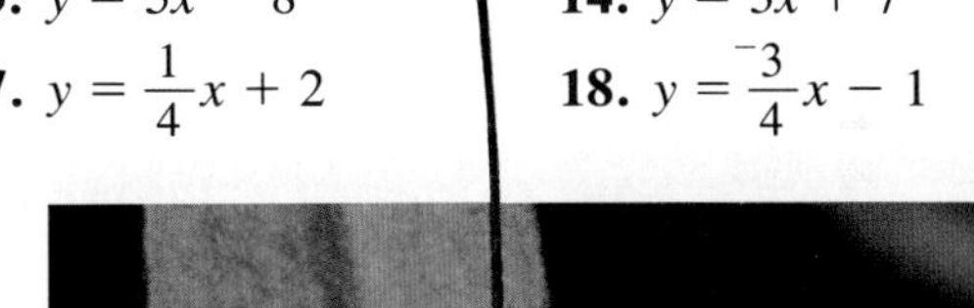

Problem Solving

Use the equation below to solve the problems.

Nature provides us with many interesting number relationships. For example, the number of times a cricket chirps per minute depends on the temperature.

$$y = \frac{1}{4}x + 40$$

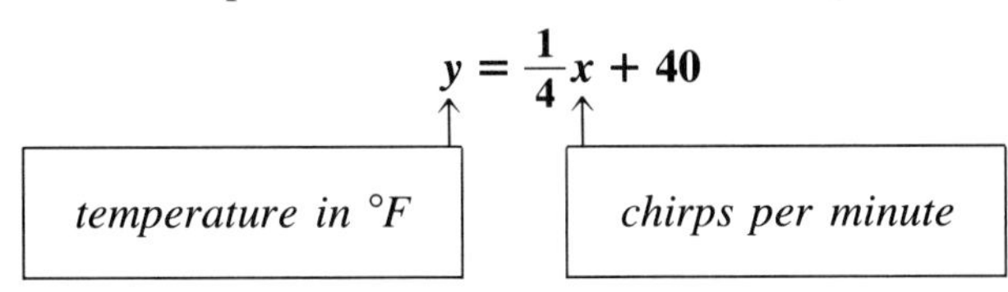

19. What is the temperature when a cricket chirps 20 times per minute?

20. How many chirps per minute should a cricket make when the temperature is 60°F?

Challenge

Write an equation for the table of values.
Hint: Study the ordered pairs and look for a pattern.

21.

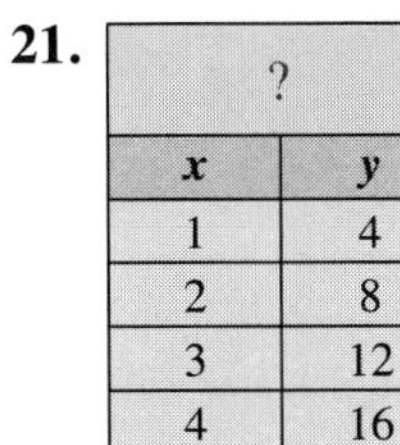

?	
x	y
1	4
2	8
3	12
4	16

22.

?	
x	y
$^-2$	$^-3$
$^-1$	$^-1$
0	1
1	3

23.

?	
x	y
$^-1$	2
0	0
1	$^-2$
2	$^-4$

24.

?	
x	y
0	4
1	2
2	0
3	$^-2$

Graphing Linear Equations

An equation of the form of

$$y = 2x + 1$$

is called a **linear equation,** because if you graph the solutions on the coordinate plane, the points all lie on a straight line.

Since the graph slopes upward (looking from left to right), we say that it has a **positive slope.** If a graph slopes downward, we say that it has a **negative slope.** Since the graph crosses the y-axis at (0, 1), (0, 1) is called the ***y*-intercept.**

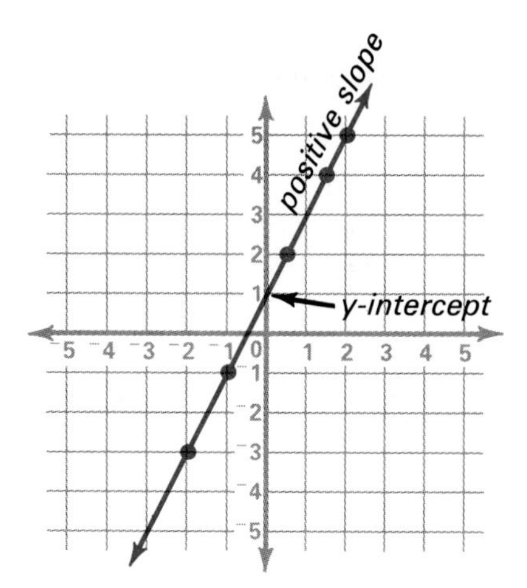

Here's how to graph a linear equation.

Step 1. Make a table of values.

$y = {}^-3x + 2$	
x	y
$^-1$	5
0	2
1	$^-1$
2	$^-4$

Step 2. Label the first coordinate axis x and the second coordinate axis y.

Step 3. Graph the ordered pairs given in the table of values.

Step 4. Draw a line through the points.

Step 5. Label the graph with the equation.

1. Look at the example above. When a linear equation is graphed, the first coordinate axis is labeled x and the second coordinate axis is labeled __?__.

2. How many points were graphed before the line was drawn?

3. Every ordered pair on the line is a solution of the equation $y = {}^-3x + 2$. By looking at the graph, do you think that $\left(\frac{^-1}{3}, 3\right)$ could be a solution? Is it a solution?

▶ **First copy and complete the table of values. Then graph the equation.**

4.

$y = x$	
x	**y**
$^-2$	?
$^-1$	?
0	?
1	?

5.

$y = x - 4$	
x	**y**
$^-1$	?
0	?
1	?
2	?

6.

$y = {}^-2x$	
x	**y**
$^-2$	?
$^-1$	?
0	?
1	?

7.

$y = 2x - 3$	
x	**y**
0	?
1	?
2	?
3	?

8.

$y = {}^-3x + 1$	
x	**y**
$^-1$	?
0	?
1	?
2	?

9.

$y = 3x + 2$	
x	**y**
$^-2$	?
$^-1$	?
0	?
1	?

10.

$y = \frac{1}{2}x + 2$	
x	**y**
$^-4$	?
$^-2$	?
0	?
2	?

11.

$y = \frac{2}{3}x - 3$	
x	**y**
$^-3$	?
0	?
3	?
6	?

▶ **First make a table of values showing three solutions. Then graph the equation.**

12. $y = 3x$ **13.** $y = 4x$ **14.** $y = 2x + 3$ **15.** $y = 3x - 2$

16. $y = {}^-2x + 1$ **17.** $y = 3x + 1$ **18.** $y = \frac{1}{3}x - 2$ **19.** $y = \frac{^-1}{3}x - 2$

20. Refer to your graphs for exercises 16 through 19. Tell whether each slope is positive or negative and give the y-intercepts.

Challenge

▶ **Find the equation for each graph.**
Hint: List some ordered pairs and look for a pattern.

21.

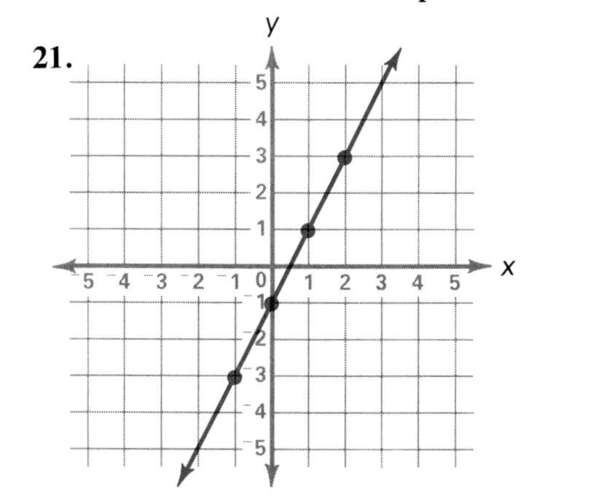

22.

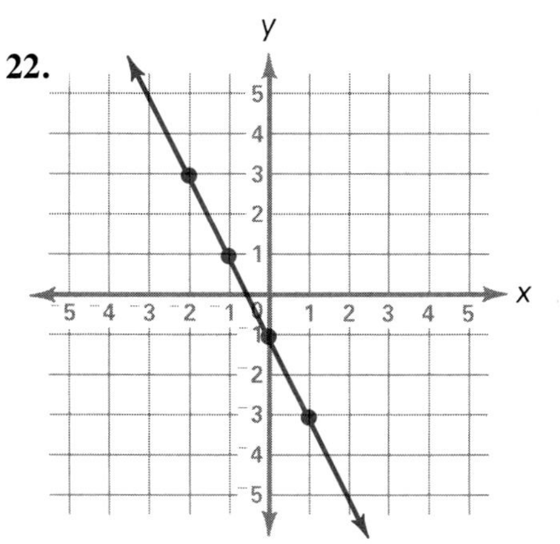

Graphing Linear Inequalities

The graph of a linear equation separates the coordinate plane into two regions. The **region above** the graph of $y = \frac{1}{2}x + 1$ is the graph of the linear inequality $y > \frac{1}{2}x + 1$.

1. Are the following ordered pairs solutions of the linear inequality $y > \frac{1}{2}x + 1$?
   Hint: Substitute and simplify.

   a. (1, 2) **b.** (⁻2, 1) **c.** (⁻4, 0) **d.** (0, 3)

2. Do the graphs of the ordered pairs lie in the green region?

   The **region below** the graph of $y = \frac{1}{2}x + 1$ is the graph of the linear inequality $y < \frac{1}{2}x + 1$.

3. Are the following ordered pairs solutions of the linear inequality $y < \frac{1}{2}x + 1$?
   a. (2, 0) **b.** (3, 2) **c.** (1, 0) **d.** (4, 3)

4. Do the graphs of the ordered pairs lie in the yellow region?

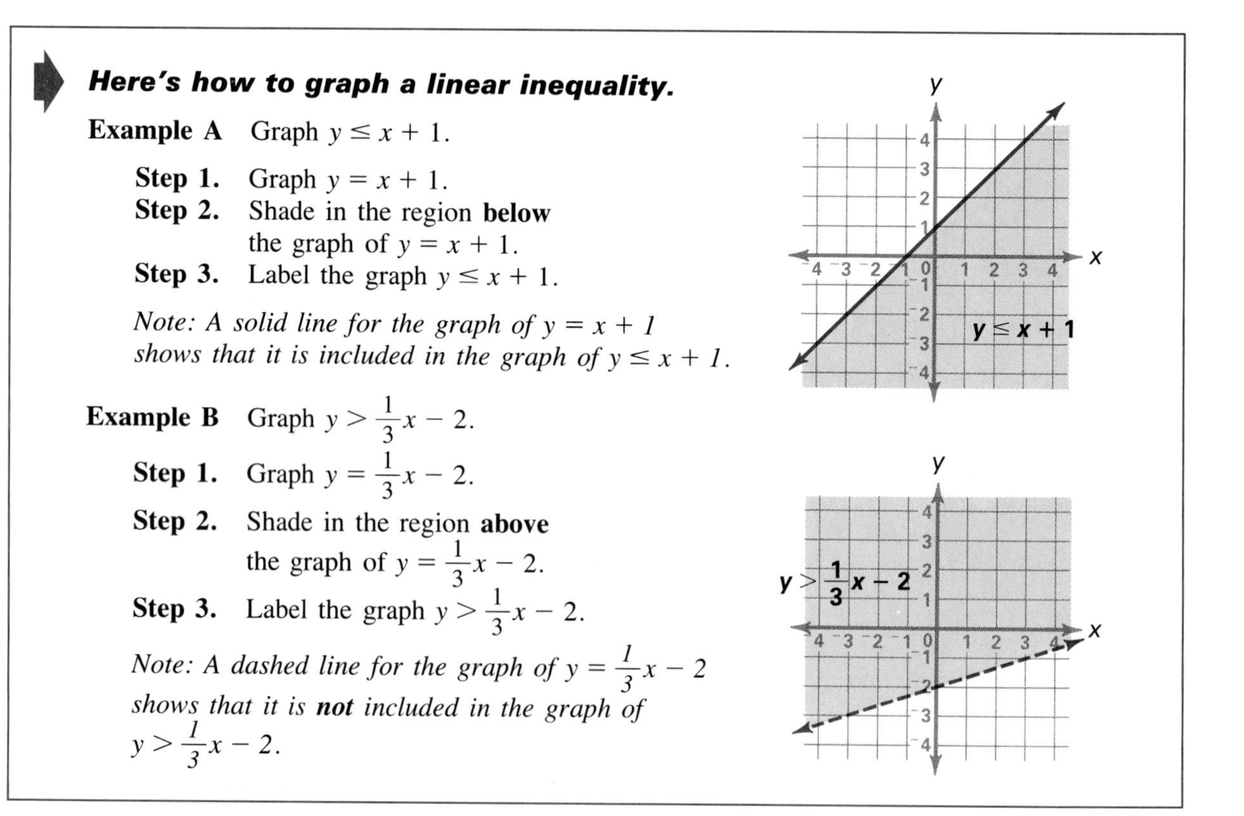

Here's how to graph a linear inequality.

Example A Graph $y \leq x + 1$.

Step 1. Graph $y = x + 1$.
Step 2. Shade in the region **below** the graph of $y = x + 1$.
Step 3. Label the graph $y \leq x + 1$.

Note: A solid line for the graph of $y = x + 1$ shows that it is included in the graph of $y \leq x + 1$.

Example B Graph $y > \frac{1}{3}x - 2$.

Step 1. Graph $y = \frac{1}{3}x - 2$.
Step 2. Shade in the region **above** the graph of $y = \frac{1}{3}x - 2$.
Step 3. Label the graph $y > \frac{1}{3}x - 2$.

*Note: A dashed line for the graph of $y = \frac{1}{3}x - 2$ shows that it is **not** included in the graph of $y > \frac{1}{3}x - 2$.*

5. Look at Example A. The graph of $y \leq x + 1$ includes the graph of $y = x + 1$ and the region __?__ the graph of $y = x + 1$.

6. Look at Example B. The graph of $y > \frac{1}{3}x - 2$ is the region __?__ the graph of $y = \frac{1}{3}x - 2$.

EXERCISES

▶ **In each exercise you are given the graph of a linear inequality. First study the equation of the line. Then give the inequality.**

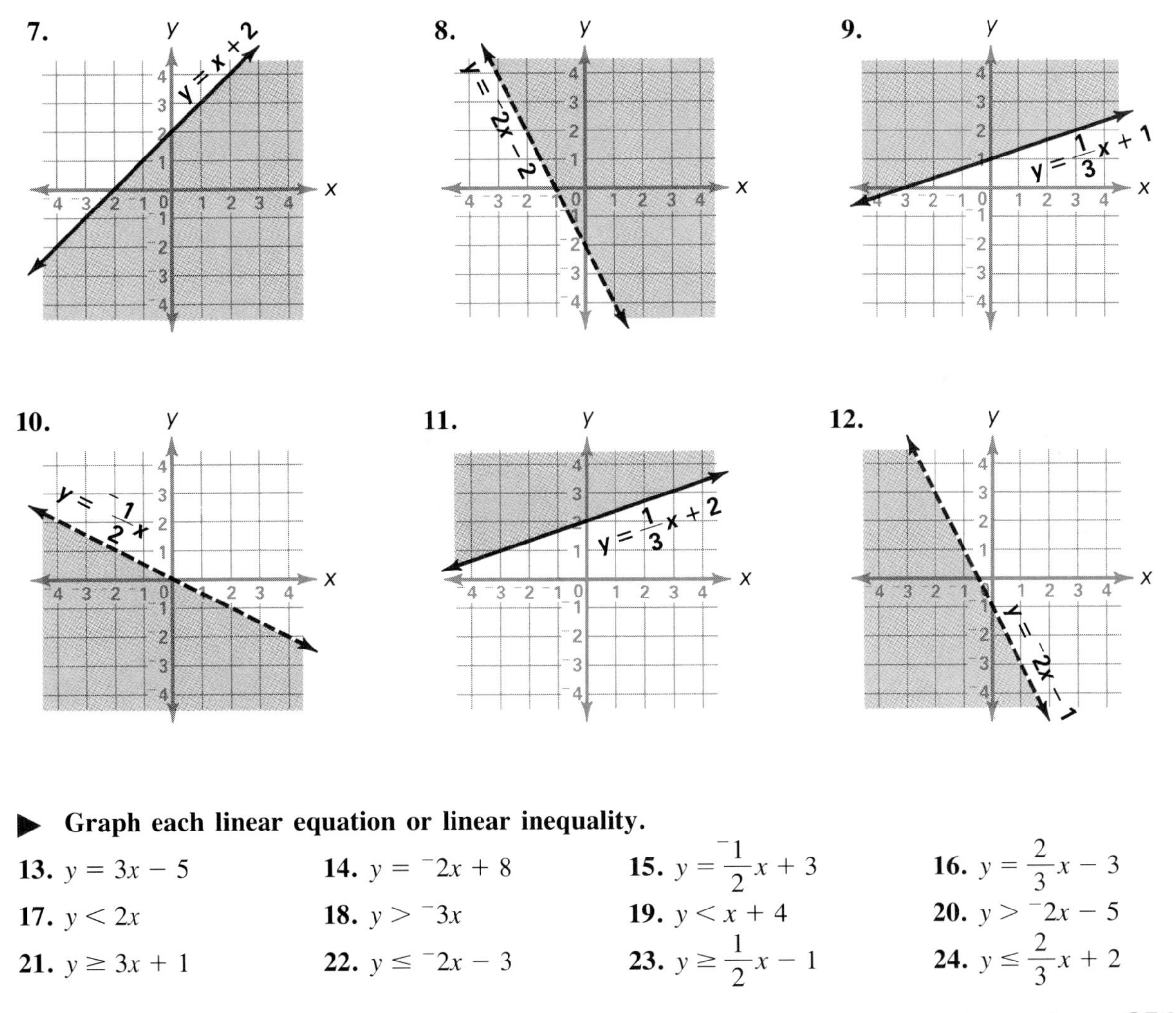

▶ **Graph each linear equation or linear inequality.**

13. $y = 3x - 5$	**14.** $y = {}^{-}2x + 8$	**15.** $y = \frac{{}^{-}1}{2}x + 3$	**16.** $y = \frac{2}{3}x - 3$
17. $y < 2x$	**18.** $y > {}^{-}3x$	**19.** $y < x + 4$	**20.** $y > {}^{-}2x - 5$
21. $y \geq 3x + 1$	**22.** $y \leq {}^{-}2x - 3$	**23.** $y \geq \frac{1}{2}x - 1$	**24.** $y \leq \frac{2}{3}x + 2$

Systems of Linear Equations

Notice that the graphs of $y = {}^{-}2x - 6$ and $y = \frac{1}{2}x - 1$ are shown on the same coordinate plane.

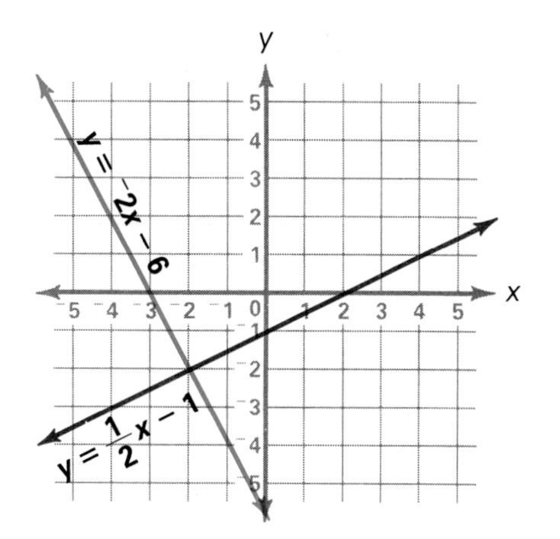

1. The ordered pair $({}^{-}3, 0)$ is a solution of which equation?
2. The ordered pair $({}^{-}4, {}^{-}3)$ is a solution of which equation?
3. What ordered pair appears to be a solution of both equations? *Hint: Where do the graphs intersect?*

The ordered pair that is a solution of both equations is the solution of the **system of equations**

$$y = {}^{-}2x - 6$$
$$y = \frac{1}{2}x - 1$$

Here's how to solve a system of equations by graphing.

Example. Solve the system of equations

$$y = {}^{-}2x + 5$$
$$y = 3x$$

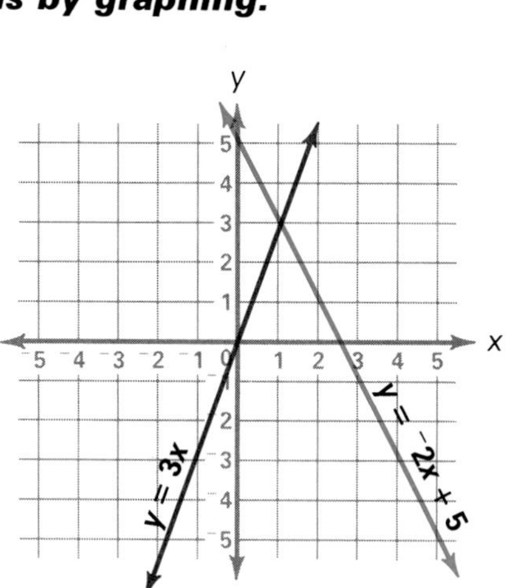

Step 1. Graph both equations on the same coordinate plane.

Step 2. It appears that (1, 3) is a solution of both equations. To be sure that (1, 3) is a solution of the system of equations, we check to see whether (1, 3) is a solution of both equations.

$y = {}^{-}2x + 5$	$y = 3x$
$3 \stackrel{?}{=} {}^{-}2 \cdot 1 + 5$	$3 \stackrel{?}{=} 3 \cdot 1$
$3 \stackrel{?}{=} {}^{-}2 + 5$	
$3 = 3$	$3 = 3$

So (1, 3) is the solution of the system of equations.

▶ **Determine whether the ordered pair is the solution of the system of equations by substituting in both equations.**

4. (1, 2)
$y = {}^-3x + 5$
$y = 2x$

5. (2, ⁻1)
$y = x - 3$
$y = 3x - 7$

6. (0, 1)
$y = 2x + 1$
$y = 3x - 1$

7. (⁻1, ⁻1)
$y = x$
$y = {}^-2x - 3$

8. (⁻2, 6)
$y = \frac{^-1}{3}x$
$y = 4x + 2$

▶ **First study the graphs and list the ordered pair that appears to be the solution of the system of equations. Then check to see if the ordered pair is a solution by substituting in both equations.**

9.

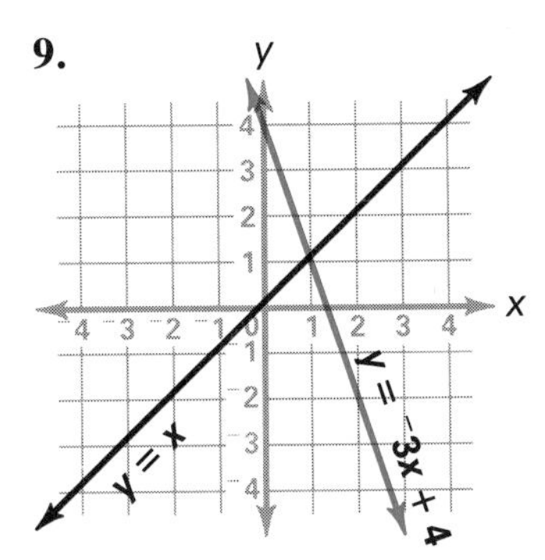

10.

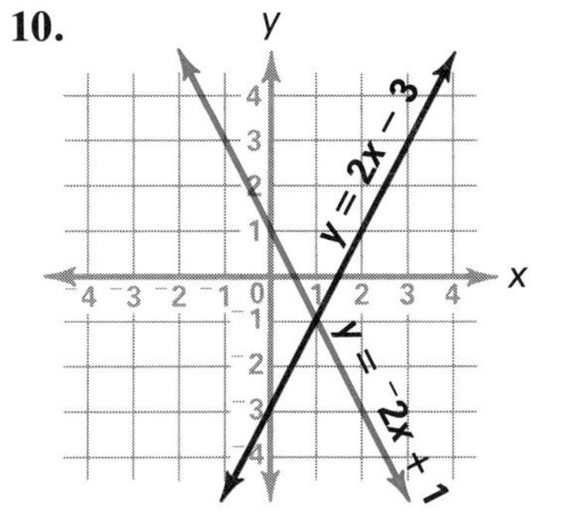

11.

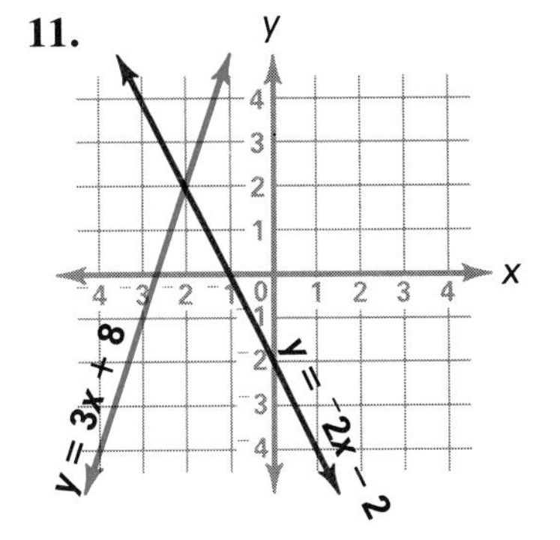

12.

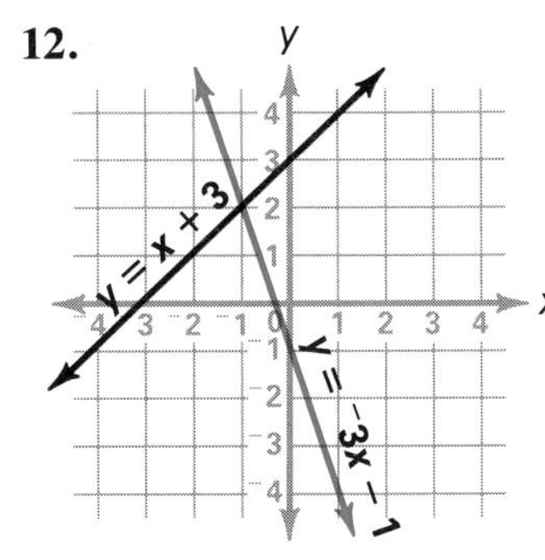

13.

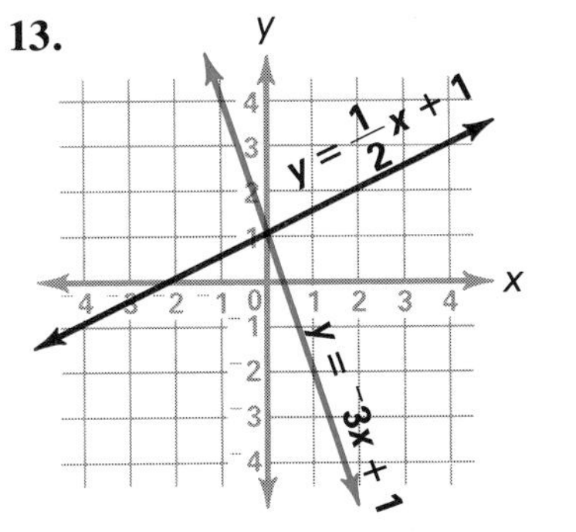

14.

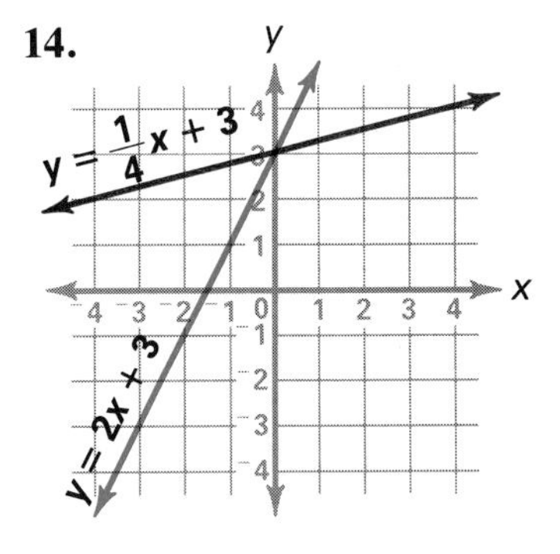

▶ **Solve each system of equations by graphing.**

15. $y = x$
$y = 3x - 4$

16. $y = 2x$
$y = x - 1$

17. $y = x + 3$
$y = 2x + 1$

18. $y = 3x - 2$
$y = {}^-4x - 2$

19. $y = 2x + 3$
$y = \frac{1}{2}x + 2$

20. $y = {}^-3x - 3$
$y = \frac{^-1}{2}x + 2$

Problem Solving—Using Systems of Linear Equations

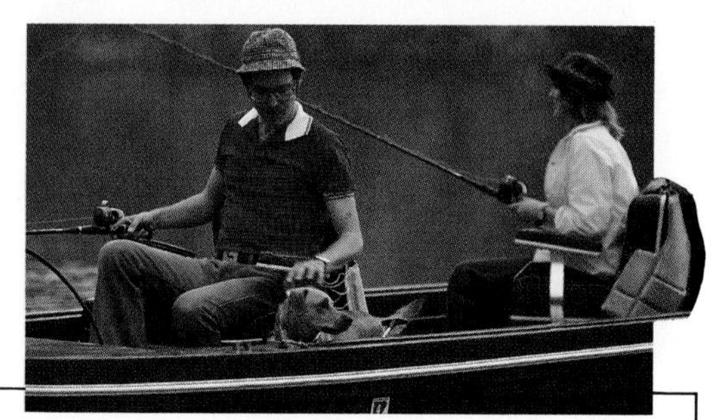

In this lesson you will use what you learned about systems of linear equations to solve problems.

Here's how to use systems of linear equations to solve problems.

Problem: Carla and David caught a total of 12 fish. Carla caught 3 times as many fish as David. How many fish did each person catch?

Step 1. Choose variables. Use them and the facts to write two equations.

Let c = the number of fish Carla caught. Let d = the number of fish David caught.

Together they caught 12 fish.	*Carla caught 3 times as many fish as David.*
$c + d = 12$	$c = 3d$

Step 2. Solve the system of equations.

It appears that (9, 3) is the solution to both equations.
So Carla caught 9 fish and David caught 3.

1. Look at the example above.

a. In Step 1, we let c equal the number of fish ___?___ caught and ___?___ equal the number of fish David caught. The two equations for the problem are ___?___ and ___?___.

b. In Step 2, the ordered pair (___?___, ___?___) is the solution to both equations. So Carla caught ___?___ fish and David caught ___?___ fish.

2. To check the solution, ask yourself whether the answer fits the facts in the problem. Does 9 plus 3 equal 12? Does 3 times 3 equal 9?

▶ **Read the facts. Then complete the steps to answer the question.**

3. *Facts:* Martha and Nancy earned a total of \$20. Martha earned \$8 more than Nancy.

Question: How many dollars did each earn?

a. If you let m equal the number of dollars Martha earned and let n equal the number of dollars Nancy earned, then two equations for the problem are $m + n =$ __?__ and $n +$ __?__ $= m$.

b. Look at the graph. The ordered pair (__?__, __?__) is the solution to both equations. So Martha earned __?__ dollars and Nancy earned __?__ dollars.

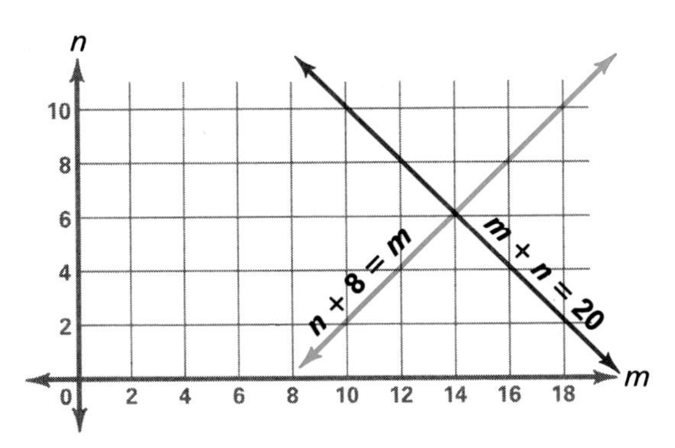

4. *Facts:* Steve and Ted scored a total of 17 points. Ted scored 7 fewer points than Steve.

Question: How many points did each score?

a. If you let s equal the number of points Steve scored and let t equal the number of points Ted scored, then two equations for the problem are $s + t =$ __?__ and $s -$ __?__ $= t$.

b. Look at the graph. The ordered pair (__?__, __?__) is the solution to both equations. So Steve scored __?__ points and Ted scored __?__ points.

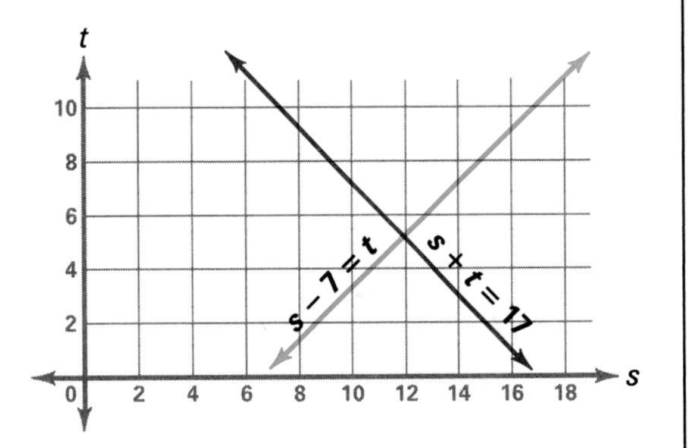

▶ **Solve each problem.**
First write two equations.
Then solve the system of equations by graphing.

5. The sum of two numbers is 22. The first number (f) is 8 more than the second number (s). What are the two numbers?

6. The sum of two numbers is 23. The first number (f) is 5 less than the second number (s). What are the two numbers?

7. The sum of two numbers is 25. The first number (f) is 4 times the second number (s). What are the two numbers?

8. The sum of two numbers is 36. The first number (f) is 8 times the second number (s). What are the two numbers?

9. Jim and Kelly sold a total of 26 tickets. Jim (j) sold 12 more tickets than Kelly (k). How many tickets did each sell?

10. Fran and Greg spent a total of \$30. Fran (f) spent 7 times as much money as Greg (g). How many dollars did each spend?

Cumulative Skill Practice

▶ **Change to a fraction, whole number, or mixed number. Give each answer in simplest form.** *(page 256)*

1. 40%	**2.** 75%	**3.** 5%	**4.** 80%	**5.** 1%	**6.** 50%
7. 18%	**8.** 65%	**9.** 132%	**10.** 100%	**11.** 64%	**12.** 150%
13. 400%	**14.** 175%	**15.** 350%	**16.** $12\frac{1}{2}\%$	**17.** $33\frac{1}{3}\%$	**18.** $208\frac{1}{3}\%$

▶ **Change to a percent.** *(page 258)*

19. $\frac{1}{2}$	**20.** $\frac{1}{3}$	**21.** $\frac{1}{4}$	**22.** $\frac{1}{5}$	**23.** $\frac{1}{6}$	**24.** $\frac{1}{8}$
25. $\frac{3}{4}$	**26.** $\frac{2}{5}$	**27.** $\frac{3}{2}$	**28.** $\frac{9}{4}$	**29.** $\frac{4}{3}$	**30.** $\frac{3}{5}$
31. $\frac{7}{4}$	**32.** $\frac{3}{8}$	**33.** $\frac{13}{8}$	**34.** $\frac{5}{3}$	**35.** $\frac{5}{12}$	**36.** $\frac{11}{16}$

▶ **Solve.** *(page 262)*

37. 25% of 64 = n	**38.** 60% of 80 = n	**39.** 120% of 65 = n
40. 43% of 75 = n	**41.** 89% of 27 = n	**42.** 61% of 98 = n
43. 6.2% of 30 = n	**44.** 5.9% of 45 = n	**45.** 0.5% of 82 = n
46. 0.9% of 46 = n	**47.** 125.8% of 100 = n	**48.** 87.5% of 120 = n

▶ **Change each percent to a fraction or decimal and solve.** *(page 264)*

49. 20% of n = 17	**50.** 50% of n = 23	**51.** 75% of n = 42
52. 80% of n = 36	**53.** 150% of n = 48	**54.** 125% of n = 65
55. 37.5% of n = 18	**56.** 1% of n = 2.25	**57.** 87.5% of n = 84
58. 17.5% of n = 50.75	**59.** 225% of n = 96.75	**60.** 275% of n = 49.5

▶ **Solve.** *(page 266)*

61. n% of 20 = 13	**62.** n% of 57 = 19	**63.** n% of 16 = 40
64. $5\frac{1}{4}\%$ of 58 = n	**65.** $16\frac{2}{3}\%$ of 66 = n	**66.** $33\frac{1}{3}\%$ of 51 = n
67. 30% of n = 15	**68.** 1% of n = 2.42	**69.** 62.5% of n = 95
70. n% of 44 = 33	**71.** n% of 9 = 20	**72.** 87.5% of n = 126

Problem Solving—Applications

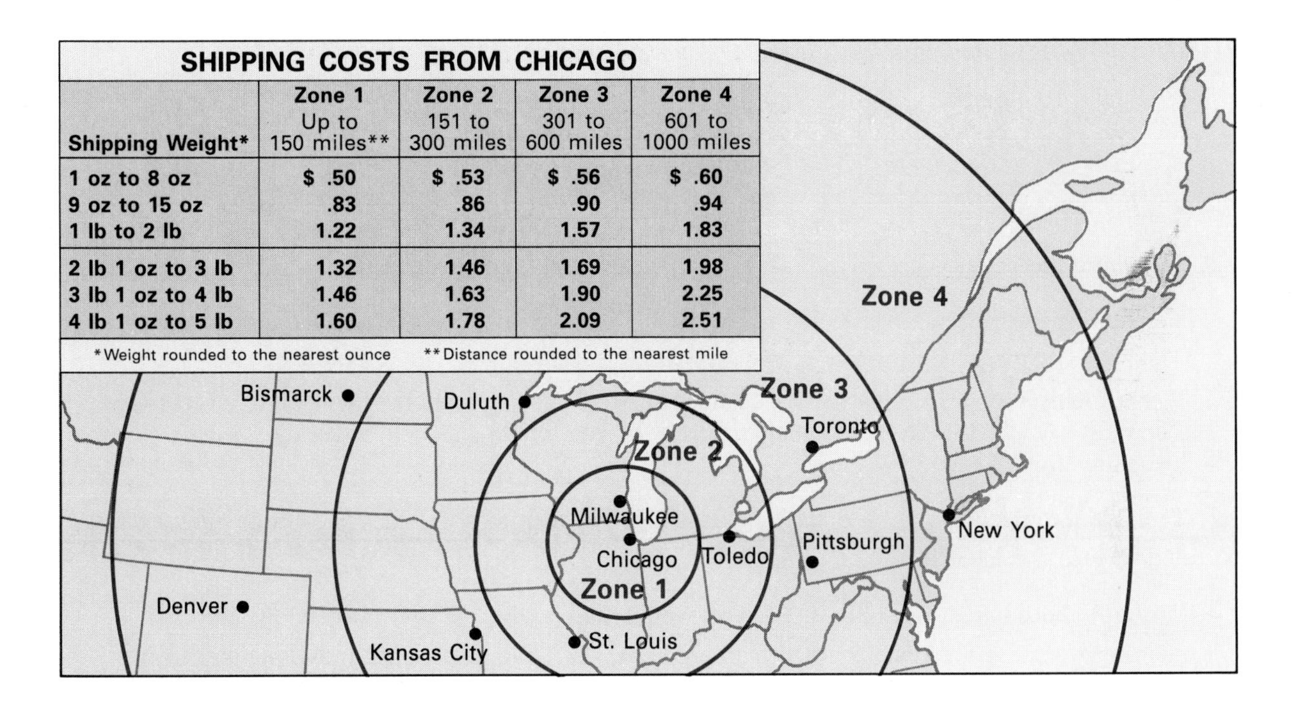

SHIPPING COSTS FROM CHICAGO				
Shipping Weight*	Zone 1 Up to 150 miles**	Zone 2 151 to 300 miles	Zone 3 301 to 600 miles	Zone 4 601 to 1000 miles
1 oz to 8 oz	$ .50	$ .53	$ .56	$ .60
9 oz to 15 oz	.83	.86	.90	.94
1 lb to 2 lb	1.22	1.34	1.57	1.83
2 lb 1 oz to 3 lb	1.32	1.46	1.69	1.98
3 lb 1 oz to 4 lb	1.46	1.63	1.90	2.25
4 lb 1 oz to 5 lb	1.60	1.78	2.09	2.51

*Weight rounded to the nearest ounce **Distance rounded to the nearest mile

Use the map and the shipping information to solve these problems.

1. How much does it cost to ship a 20-ounce package to Zone 4?

2. What is the cost to ship a 4-pound package 500 miles?

3. Can you ship a 40-ounce package from Chicago to Pittsburgh for less than $1.50?

4. How much does it cost to ship a 30-ounce package 800 miles?

5. It cost Danny $1.90 to ship a 3.5-pound box to his sister. Does his sister live in Kansas City or Toledo?

6. How much more does it cost to ship two 20-ounce packages to St. Louis than it costs to ship one 40-ounce package to St. Louis?

7. How much more does it cost to ship a 5-pound package from Chicago to New York than from Chicago to Kansas City?

8. What is the total cost to ship a 2-pound 6-ounce package and a 1-pound 4-ounce package from Chicago to Milwaukee?

Write an equation and solve the problem.

9. The weight of a box is 20 ounces more than the weight of a package. If the box weighs 60 ounces, what is the weight of the package?
(Let p = the weight of the package.)

10. A package weighs 14 ounces. It weighs 2 ounces less than 4 times the weight of a letter. What is the weight of the letter?
(Let w = the weight of the letter.)

Chapter Review

Here are scrambled answers for the review exercises:

$^-7$	below	equation	linear	ordered	second
0	both	graphing	multiply	origin	sign
1	coordinate	inequality	negative	plane	subtract
above	divide	line	not	reverse	

1. Inequality: $x < \frac{^-1}{2}$

Graph: 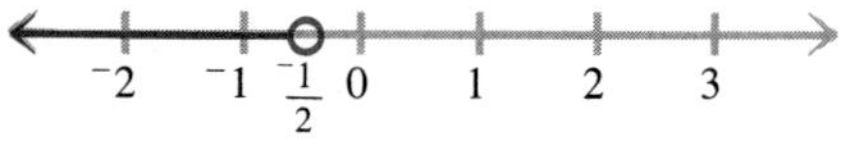

The graph shows that $\frac{^-1}{2}$ is _?_ a solution. *(page 336)*

2. If you multiply or divide both sides of an inequality by a _?_ number, you must reverse the inequality sign. To solve the inequality $^-3n < 8$, you would _?_ both sides by $^-3$ and _?_ the inequality sign. *(page 338)*

3. To solve the inequality $\frac{y}{^-2} + 8 \geq {^-5}$, you would _?_ 8 from both sides, _?_ both sides by $^-2$, and reverse the inequality _?_. *(page 340)*

4. To graph the ordered pair $\left(2, {^-1}\frac{1}{2}\right)$, you would start at the _?_ and move along the first coordinate axis to the first _?_ of the ordered pair, 2. Then you would move parallel to the _?_ coordinate axis to the second coordinate, $^-1\frac{1}{2}$. *(page 344)*

5. To find an _?_ pair that is a solution of $y = 2x - 7$, choose a value for x and solve the equation for y. For example, if you choose 0 for x, then y would equal _?_. The ordered pair (_?_, $^-7$) is a solution of the equation. *(page 346)*

6. An equation of the form $y = 3x + 4$ is called a _?_ equation. If you graph the equation, you will get a straight _?_. *(page 348)*

7. To graph the linear _?_ $y \geq x + 1$, you would first graph the linear _?_ $y = x + 1$. Then you would shade in the region _?_ the graph of $y = x + 1$. To graph the linear inequality $y \leq x + 1$, you would shade in the region _?_ the graph of $y = x + 1$. *(page 350)*

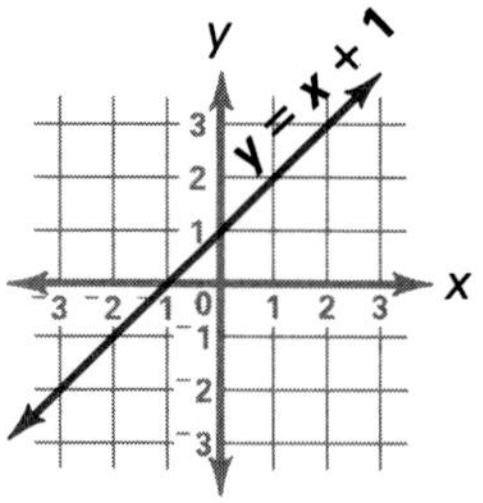

8. To solve a system of equations by _?_, you would first graph both equations on the same coordinate _?_. In the example, it appears that (_?_, 0) is a solution of both equations. The last step would be to check to see whether (1, 0) is a solution of _?_ equations. *(page 352)*

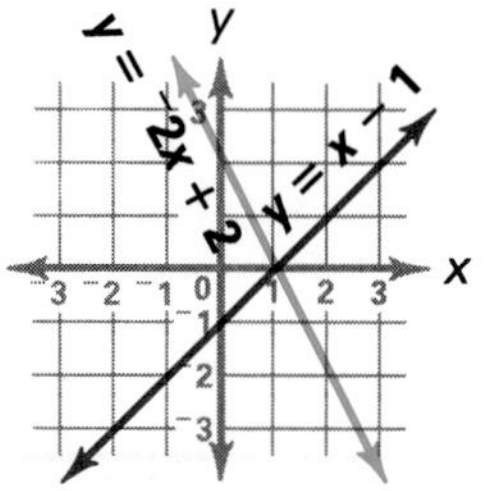

Chapter Test

Write an inequality for each graph. *(page 336)*

1.

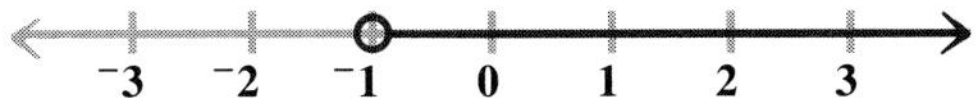

2.

Solve. *(pages 338, 340)*

3. $n + 8 \leq {}^-3$ **4.** $n - 6 > 11$ **5.** $6n < {}^-20$ **6.** $\frac{n}{^-3} \geq 8$

7. $3n - 2 > 5$ **8.** ${}^-5n + 8 \leq {}^-6$ **9.** $\frac{n}{4} - 10 < 3$ **10.** $\frac{n}{^-6} + 2 \geq 0$

Give the ordered pair of each point. *(page 344)*

11. A **12.** B **13.** C

14. D **15.** E **16.** F

17. G **18.** H **19.** I

20. J **21.** K **22.** L

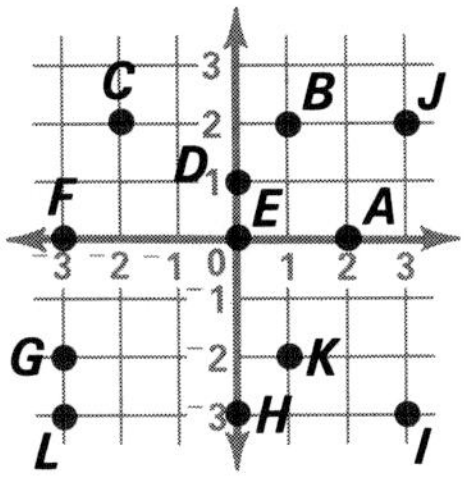

First copy and complete each table of values. Then graph the equation. *(pages 346, 348)*

23. $y = {}^-2x$

x	y
0	?
1	?
2	?

24. $y = x + 8$

x	y
$^-3$	?
$^-2$	?
$^-1$	?

25. $y = 3x - 7$

x	y
$^-1$	?
0	?
1	?

26. $y = \frac{1}{2}x + 2$

x	y
$^-2$	?
0	?
2	?

Graph each linear inequality. *(page 350)*

27. $y \geq 2x - 3$ **28.** $y \leq {}^-3x + 6$ **29.** $y > \frac{1}{3}x - 5$ **30.** $y < \frac{^-3}{4}x + 7$

Solve each system of equations by graphing. *(page 352)*

31. $y = x$, $y = 2x - 1$

32. $y = 2x$, $y = x - 3$

33. $y = x + 5$, $y = 2x - 1$

34. $y = {}^-3x + 1$, $y = \frac{1}{2}x + 1$

Write two equations for each problem. Then solve each system of equations by graphing. *(page 354)*

35. The sum of two numbers is 10. The first number (f) is 6 more than the second number (s). What are the two numbers?

36. The sum of two numbers is 12. The first number (f) is 2 less than the second number (s). What are the two numbers?

Cumulative Test

Standardized Format

Choose the correct letter.

1. The prime factorization of 72 is

A. $8 \cdot 9$
B. $2 \cdot 3 \cdot 2 \cdot 6$
C. $2^3 \cdot 3^2$
D. none of these

2. The greatest common factor of

$12x^2y$ and $20xy^2$ is

A. $4x$
B. $4y$
C. $4x^2y^2$
D. none of these

3. Give the sum.

$\frac{2u}{3} + \frac{v}{4}$

A. $\frac{2u + v}{7}$
B. $\frac{8u + 3v}{12}$
C. $\frac{4y + 3v}{12}$
D. none of these

4. Give the difference.

$\frac{c}{6} - \frac{3d}{4}$

A. $\frac{2c - 9d}{12}$
B. $\frac{c - 3d}{2}$
C. $\frac{3c - 2d}{12}$
D. none of these

5. Give the product.

$\frac{2a}{b} \cdot \frac{b^2}{4a}$

A. $\frac{2ab}{4}$
B. $\frac{2b}{4u}$
C. $\frac{b}{2}$
D. none of these

6. Give the quotient.

$\frac{m}{3n} \div \frac{4m}{n^2}$

A. $\frac{n}{12}$
B. $\frac{12}{n}$
C. $\frac{n^2}{12}$
D. none of these

7. Change to a fraction.

$87\frac{1}{2}\% = ?$

A. $\frac{1}{8}$
B. $\frac{5}{6}$
C. $\frac{7}{8}$
D. none of these

8. Change to a percent.

$\frac{7}{6} = ?$

A. $16\frac{2}{3}\%$
B. $83\frac{1}{3}\%$
C. $133\frac{1}{3}\%$
D. none of these

9. Solve.

4.5% of $30 = n$

A. 1.35
B. 13.5
C. 6.67
D. none of these

10. Solve.

1% of $n = 4.75$

A. 0.0475
B. 47.5
C. 475
D. none of these

11. Solve.

$66\frac{2}{3}\%$ of $40 = n$

A. $13\frac{1}{3}$
B. $26\frac{2}{3}$
C. 60
D. none of these

12. Choose the equation.

In a bike-a-thon, Jill took 3 hours to reach the first checkpoint and 2 hours to reach the second checkpoint. She was then 6 miles from finishing the 50-mile course. How many miles per hour had she averaged?

A. $3n + 2n + 6 = 50$
B. $3n + 2n - 6 = 50$
C. $3n - 2n + 6 = 50$
D. $3n - 2n - 6 = 50$

14 Probability and Statistics

$P(4, 6 \text{ or } 6, 4) = \frac{1}{18}$

The probability of rolling a 4 and a 6 or a 6 and a 4 is $\frac{1}{18}$.

(page 369)

When you roll two dice, there are 36 possible outcomes. Therefore, the probability of rolling a *4* and a *6* or a *6* and a *4* is $\frac{2}{36}$, or $\frac{1}{18}$.

A Basic Counting Principle

To make a baseball T-shirt, you need a T-shirt and a baseball decal. A store has red and green T-shirts and 3 kinds of decals.

1. How many different baseball T-shirts can be made with the red T-shirt?
2. How many different baseball T-shirts can be made with the green T-shirt?
3. How many different baseball T-shirts can be made in all?

Here's how to find the total number of baseball T-shirts that can be made.

You can find how many different baseball T-shirts can be made by drawing a **tree diagram.**

red — **Tigers**, **Orioles**, **Padres**

green — **Tigers**, **Orioles**, **Padres**

The blue "branch" represents a red T-shirt and a Tigers decal.

You can compute how many different baseball T-shirts can be made by using a **basic counting principle:**

If there are **2** ways to choose a T-shirt and **3** ways to choose a baseball decal, then the total number of ways to make a baseball T-shirt is **2 × 3,** or **6.**

4. Look at the tree diagram. What baseball T-shirt is represented by the top branch? The bottom branch?
5. How many different branches are there in the tree diagram?
6. Does the number of branches in the tree diagram equal the number of ways to make a baseball T-shirt?

▶ **Solve.**

7. Suppose you have a supply of blue T-shirts and yellow T-shirts and a supply of the baseball decals shown at the right.

a. How many choices of T-shirts do you have? How many choices of baseball decals do you have?

b. Draw a tree diagram to show all possible baseball T-shirts you could make.

c. How many different baseball T-shirts could you make?

d. How many different baseball T-shirts could you make with the yellow T-shirt?

e. How many different baseball T-shirts could you make if you did not use a Cardinals decal?

f. Suppose instead that you have 5 colors of T-shirts and the 4 baseball decals. How many different baseball T-shirts could you make?

8. A snack bar serves 6 kinds of sandwiches and 4 kinds of juice. How many different orders of 1 sandwich and 1 juice could you place?

★9. How many different outfits could you make from 3 pairs of pants, 5 shirts, and 2 sweaters if each outfit consists of pants, a shirt, and a sweater?

★10. In an election of class officers, 3 students were running for president, 2 for vice president, and 2 for secretary. How many different ways could you vote?

★11. You decide to buy a stereo system. You can choose from 5 amplifiers, 4 speakers, and 3 turntables. How many different systems could you buy?

★12. Suppose you decide to buy a car and can choose any of the options shown on the list. How many choices would you still have if you decided that you wanted only

a. a red car?

b. a white interior?

c. a blue car with a black interior?

d. a yellow car with manual transmission?

e. a brown interior with automatic transmission?

CAR OPTIONS		
6 Paint colors	**3 Interior colors**	**2 Transmissions**
red yellow blue brown black white	brown black white	manual automatic

Permutations

Carol, David, and Alice are seated on a toboggan.

1. Who is in the front? The middle? The back?

2. The letters *CDA* may be used to describe the order in which they are seated. Use the three letters to list all possible orders in which they can be seated.

3. How many ways can the three people be seated on the toboggan?

A **permutation** is a possible arrangement of things in a definite order.

Here's how to compute the number of permutations.

Number of people to choose from for first position		*Number left to choose from for second position*		*Number left to choose from for third position*		*Number of possible arrangements*
↓		↓		↓		↓
3	×	2	×	1	=	6

4. Look at the example above. To compute the number of permutations (possible arrangements) of 3 things, you would multiply what three numbers?

5. Think about 4 people on a toboggan.

   a. How many people would there be to choose from for the front position?

   b. How many people would there be left to choose from for the second position? The third position? The back position?

   c. What four numbers would you multiply to compute the number of permutations of 4 things?

   d. How many ways can the 4 people be seated on a toboggan?

EXERCISES

Solve.

6. Carol, David, and Alice decided to go skiing. How many ways could they line up to purchase their lift tickets?

7. The sign shows the different lifts available at the ski area.

a. How many lifts are there?

b. In how many different orders could Carol take the 5 lifts?

LIFTS
DOUBLE-CHAIR LIFT
TRIPLE-CHAIR LIFT
GONDOLA
T-BAR
ROPE TOW

8. Each gondola car seats 4 people. In how many ways can 4 people be seated in a gondola car?

9. Each seat on the triple-chair holds 3 people. In how many ways can 6 people be seated in 2 chairs?

10. There were 8 skiers in a race. In how many different orders could the 8 skiers finish?

★11. Each gondola car seats 4 people. If Carol, David, and Alice were the only people in the gondola car, in how many ways could they be seated?

12. David decided to buy a sandwich and a drink for lunch. He could choose from 8 sandwiches and 5 drinks. How many different lunches could he buy?

13. Carol decided to buy some soup and a sandwich for lunch. She could choose from 6 soups and 8 sandwiches. How many different lunches could she buy?

14. There were 6 soups, 5 drinks, and 3 desserts. How many soup-drink-dessert lunches could be ordered?

15. How many soup-sandwich-drink-dessert lunches could be ordered?
Hint: See exercises 13 and 14.

CALCULATOR

Solve. Use a calculator.

16. Each table in the lodge seats 10 people. Suppose that you and 9 of your friends were at one of the tables.

a. How many ways could the group be seated?

b. Suppose that the group could change the seating order every 5 seconds. How many seconds would it take for the group to sit in all possible orders?

c. How many minutes would it take? How many hours? How many days?

Probability

1. Suppose that you rolled the die. How many different outcomes would be possible? (How many different numbers could possibly land facing up?)
2. Would the possible outcomes be equally likely? (Would all numbers have the same chance of landing facing up?)

Here's how to find the probability (the chance) of a particular event when all the outcomes are equally likely.

$$\textbf{Probability} \text{ of a particular event} = \frac{\text{number of ways that the particular event can occur}}{\text{number of possible outcomes}}$$

Probability of rolling a 2

$$P(2) = \frac{\textbf{number of ways of rolling a 2}}{\textbf{number of possible outcomes}}$$

$$P(2) = \frac{1}{6}$$

Probability of rolling either a 3 or a 4

$$P(3 \text{ or } 4) = \frac{2}{6}$$

There are two ways to get either a 3 or a 4.

$$P(3 \text{ or } 4) = \frac{1}{3}$$

3. Look at the examples above. What is the probability of rolling a 2?
4. What is the probability of rolling a 3 or a 4?

EXERCISES

Give each probability in simplest form. Think about rolling a die.

5. $P(4)$
6. $P(1 \text{ or } 3)$
7. $P(\text{odd number})$
8. $P(4, 5, \text{ or } 6)$
9. $P(4 \text{ or less})$
10. $P(\text{not } 6)$
11. $P(\text{prime number})$
12. $P(\text{factor of } 12)$
13. $P(8) = \frac{0}{6}$ — *There are no, or 0, ways that an outcome of 8 can occur.*
14. Rolling an 8 is an example of an impossible event. Look at your answer to exercise 13. What is the probability of an impossible event?
15. $P(\text{a number less than } 9) = \frac{6}{6}$ — *All six outcomes are less than 9.*
16. Rolling a number less than 9 is an example of an event that is certain to occur. Look at your answer to exercise 15. What is the probability of an event that is certain to occur?

▶ **Give each probability in simplest form.**

Think about spinning this spinner.

17. P(green)
18. P(not red)
19. P(blue)
20. P(not blue)
21. P(yellow)
22. P(not yellow)
23. P(red)
24. P(not green)
25. P(black)
26. P(not black)
27. P(brown or red)
28. P(yellow or blue)
29. P(yellow or green)
30. P(red or green)
31. P(blue or green)
32. P(black or yellow)
33. P(yellow, blue, or green)
34. P(brown, blue, or red)
35. P(red, blue or yellow)

Think about shuffling these cards and then turning one of the cards faceup.

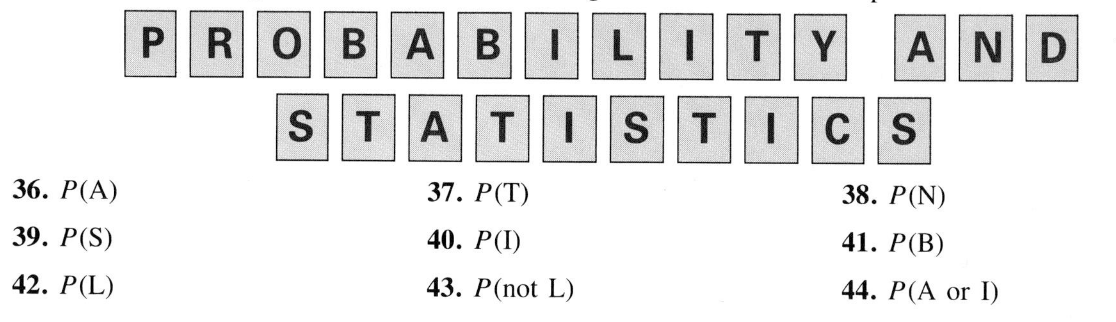

36. P(A)
37. P(T)
38. P(N)
39. P(S)
40. P(I)
41. P(B)
42. P(L)
43. P(not L)
44. P(A or I)

Challenge

45. When you toss a thumbtack, there are these two possible outcomes:

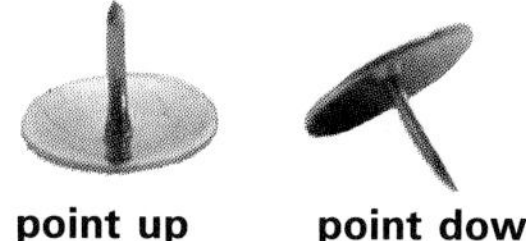

a. Do you think that the outcomes are equally likely?

b. Toss a thumbtack 60 times and keep a record of the outcomes.

c. From the results of your experiments, do you think a thumbtack has a greater chance of landing point up or point down?

46. When you toss a paper cup, there are these three possible outcomes:

a. Do you think that the outcomes are equally likely?

b. Toss a paper cup 60 times and keep a record of the outcomes.

c. From the results of your experiments, predict which outcome is most likely. Predict which outcome is least likely.

Sample Space

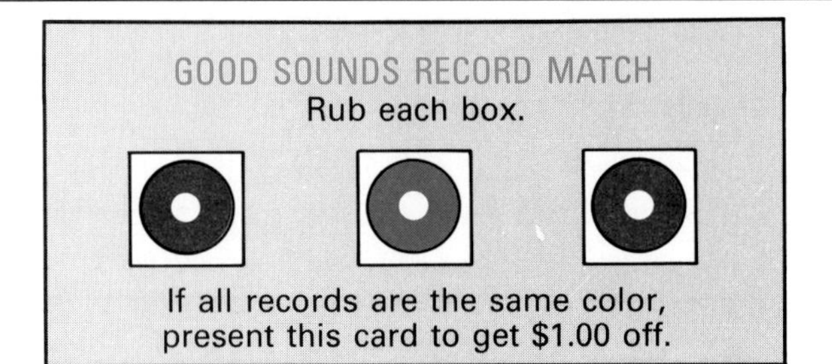

Every customer who buys a record at the Good Sounds store gets a Record Match card. When you rub each box, a picture of a red or blue record is equally likely to appear.

1. What is the prize for the winning card?
2. Is the card shown above a winning card?

To find the probability of getting a winning card, it is helpful to first list the **sample space.** The sample space is the set of all possible outcomes.

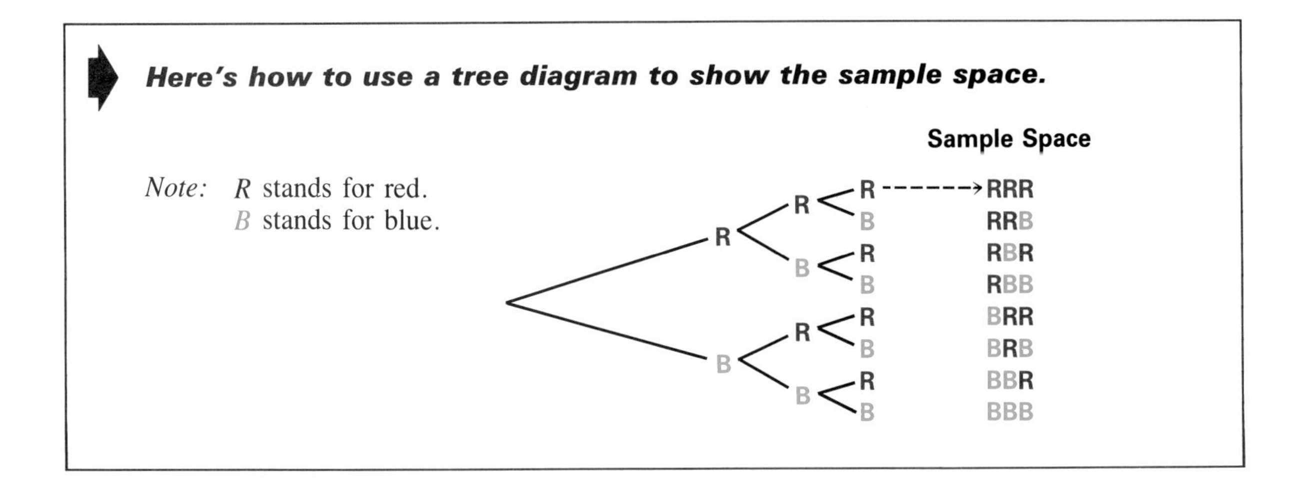

3. Look at the example. How many outcomes are in the sample space?
4. How many of the outcomes are winners (that is, have all pictures the same color)?
5. What is the probability (in simplest form) of getting a winning card?

EXERCISES

▶ **Use the sample space above. Give each probability in simplest form.**

What is the probability of getting

6. a card having exactly 1 red record?
7. a card having exactly 2 blue records?
8. a card having a blue record in the first box?
9. a card having a red record in the middle box?
10. a card having a blue record in the first two boxes?
11. a losing card?

▶ **Solve.**

12. Think about tossing this coin 3 times. Make a tree diagram to show the sample space.

13. Refer to your sample space in exercise 12 to find the following probabilities:

a. P(all heads)

b. P(no heads)

c. P(1 head and 2 tails)

d. P(2 heads and 1 tail)

e. P(less than 3 heads)

f. P(more than 3 tails)

14. Think about rolling these dice. Copy and complete the table to show the sample space. The outcome shown on the dice is entered in the table.

Number on green die

Number on red die	1	2	3	4	5	6
1						
2						
3				(3, 4)		
4						
5						
6						

15. Refer to your sample space in exercise 14 to find the following probabilities:

a. P(sum of 12)

b. P(not sum of 12)

c. P(sum of 3)

d. P(sum of 7)

e. P(sum less than 7)

f. P(sum greater than 7)

g. P(doubles)

h. P(not doubles)

i. P(sum of 1)

Challenge

▶ **Solve.**

16. Think about putting these four marbles in a bag. Then imagine taking two marbles out of the bag one after the other without looking.

a. Make a tree diagram of the sample space.

b. What is the probability that the red marble will be picked?

c. What is the probability that the blue marble will not be picked?

d. What is the probability that at least 1 marble will be green?

Probability—Independent Events

Think about first rolling a die and then tossing a coin. Since the outcome on the die in no way affects the outcome on the coin, two events such as rolling a 1 and tossing heads are called **independent events.**

The tree diagram shows all possible outcomes of first rolling a die and then tossing a coin.

1. First think about rolling a die. What is the probability of rolling a 1?
2. Next think about tossing a coin. What is the probability of tossing heads (H)?
3. Now look at the tree diagram. What is the probability of first rolling a 1 and then tossing heads (H)?

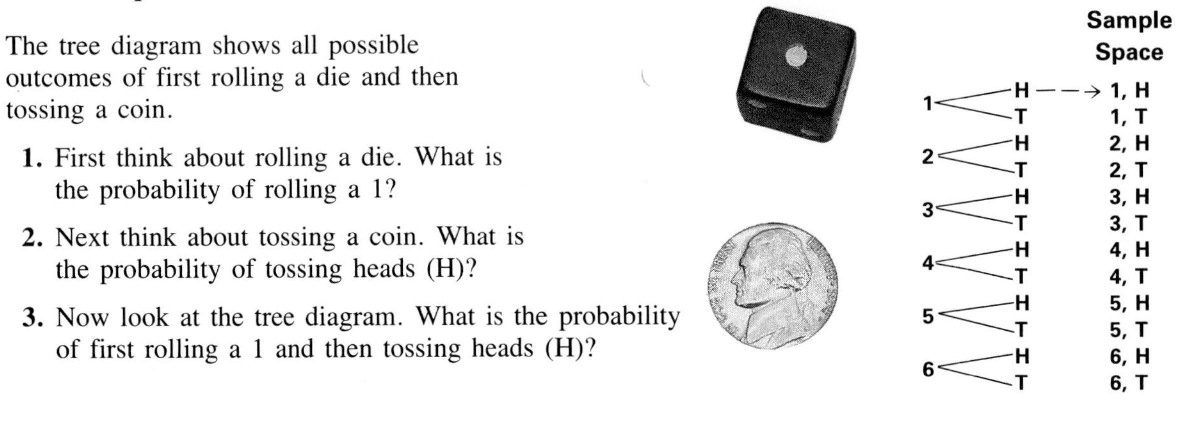

Here's how to compute the probability of two or more independent events.

The probability of the first event followed by the second event is the product of the probabilities of the individual events.

the probability of rolling a 1 and then tossing heads → $P(1, H) = \underset{P(1)}{\frac{1}{6}} \times \underset{P(H)}{\frac{1}{2}} = \frac{1}{12}$

4. Look at the example. What is $P(1)$? What is $P(H)$? What is $P(1, H)$?
5. What is $P(4, T)$?

EXERCISES

▶ **Give each probability as a fraction in simplest form.**

Think about first rolling a die and then tossing a coin.

6. **a.** $P(5)$
   b. $P(T)$
   c. $P(5, T)$
7. **a.** $P(\text{odd number})$
   b. $P(H)$
   c. $P(\text{odd number}, H)$
8. $P(\text{number less than } 4, T)$
9. $P(\text{not } 6, T)$

Give each probability as a fraction in simplest form.

Think about first rolling the die and then spinning the spinner.

10. $P(1, \text{green})$

11. $P(5, \text{red})$

12. $P(\text{odd number, yellow})$

13. $P(\text{not } 4, \text{blue})$

14. $P(6, \text{not yellow})$

15. $P(\text{not } 3, \text{not red})$

16. $P(\text{number greater than } 3, \text{green})$

Think about spinning the above spinner once and then spinning it again.

17. $P(\text{red, red})$

18. $P(\text{yellow, yellow})$

19. $P(\text{brown, blue})$

20. $P(\text{red, yellow})$

21. $P(\text{yellow, green})$

22. $P(\text{not red, green})$

23. $P(\text{yellow, not yellow})$

24. $P(\text{not green, not blue})$

25. $P(\text{not green, not yellow})$

Think about placing the 6 marbles in a bag and thoroughly mixing them up. Suppose that, without looking, you picked out a first marble, **put it back into the bag,** and then picked out a second marble.

26. $P(\text{green, blue})$

27. $P(\text{yellow, green})$

28. $P(\text{blue, red})$

29. $P(\text{green, not yellow})$

30. $P(\text{not yellow, green})$

31. $P(\text{blue, not blue})$

Problem Solving

Solve.

32. If you toss a coin 3 times, what is the probability that you will get 3 heads?

33. If you toss a coin 3 times, what is the probability in simplest form that you will get either all heads or all tails?

Challenge

Solve.

34. If you toss a coin 4 times, what is the probability that you will not get all heads?

35. If you toss a coin 6 times, what is the probability in simplest form that all outcomes will be alike?

Probability—Dependent Events

Suppose that these cards were thoroughly shuffled and spread out facedown in front of you.

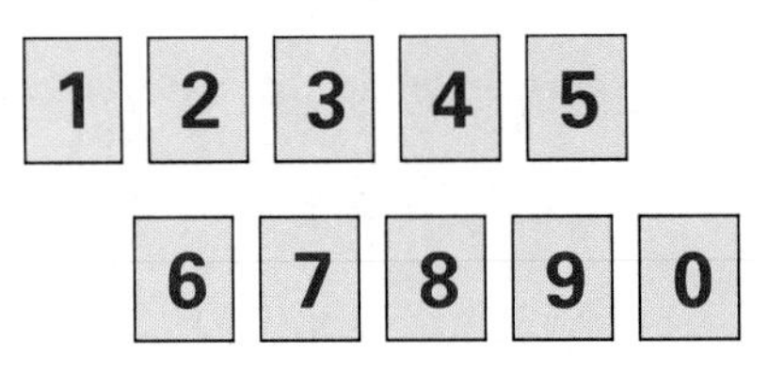

1. If you picked a card, what is the probability of picking the 3?
2. Suppose that you picked the 3 on your first draw, **did not replace the card,** and drew a second card. What is the probability that your second card would be the 8?

Since the outcome of picking the first card affects the outcome of picking the second card from the remaining cards, two events such as drawing a 3 and then drawing an 8 are called **dependent events.**

Here's how to compute the probability of two or more dependent events.

The probability of the first event followed by the second event is the product of the probabilities of the individual events.

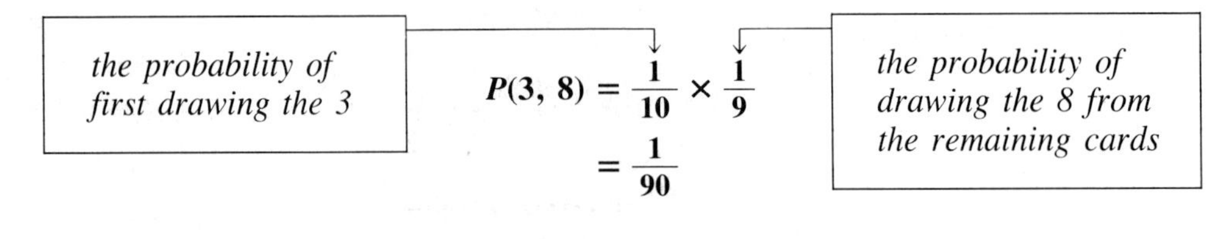

$$P(3, 8) = \frac{1}{10} \times \frac{1}{9}$$
$$= \frac{1}{90}$$

3. Look at the example. To find $P(3, 8)$, __?__ the probability of first drawing the 3 by the probability of drawing the 8 from the remaining cards.
4. What is $P(3, 8)$?

EXERCISES

▶ **Give each probability as a fraction in simplest form.**

Think about drawing a card from the cards shown above, then without replacement drawing a second card.

5. $P(6, 1)$
6. $P(\text{even}, 5)$
7. $P(8, \text{odd})$
8. $P(\text{odd}, \text{even})$
9. $P(3, \text{prime})$
10. $P(\text{prime}, \text{composite})$

Suppose that these cards were thoroughly shuffled and spread out facedown in front of you. Think about drawing cards without replacement.

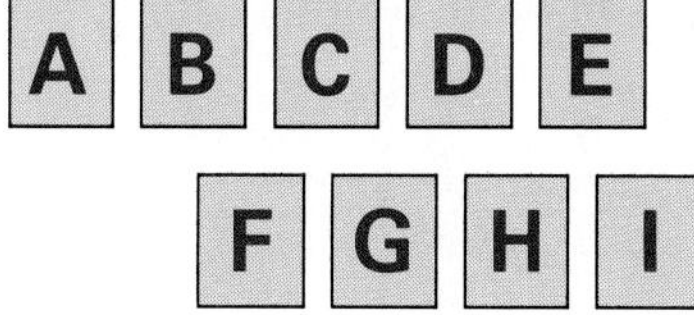

▶ **Give each probability as a fraction in simplest form.**

11. P(A, H)

12. P(B, not A)

13. P(not I, I)

14. P(vowel, H)

15. P(E, consonant)

16. P(not E, not E)

17. P(not vowel, E)

18. P(consonant, vowel)

19. P(not vowel, vowel)

20. P(consonant, consonant)

21. P(A, I, D)

22. P(vowel, vowel, vowel)

★**23.** P(H, I, D, E)

★**24.** P(not E, not E, not E, E)

★**25.** P(consonant, consonant, consonant, consonant)

CALCULATOR

A container has 36 Ping-Pong balls numbered 1–36. Look at the rules for these two games:

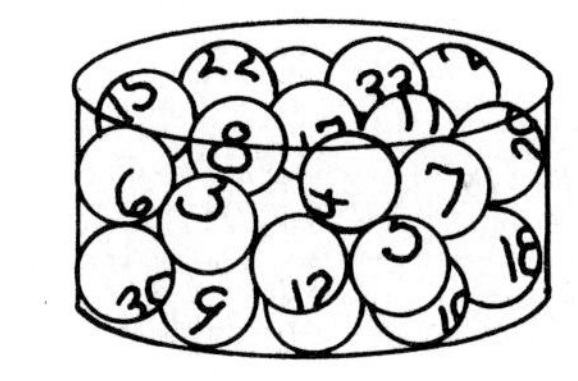

Game 1

- Guess six numbers. (You can choose the same number more than once.)
- Mix the balls and draw one without looking.
- Replace the ball, mix, and draw another ball.
- Repeat until six balls have been drawn.

Game 2

- Guess six different numbers.
- Mix the balls.
- Without looking, draw six balls *without* replacement.

You win if you guessed all six numbers that were drawn.

26. Which game has P(winning) equal to

a. $\frac{1}{36} \times \frac{1}{36} \times \frac{1}{36} \times \frac{1}{36} \times \frac{1}{36} \times \frac{1}{36}$?

b. $\frac{6}{36} \times \frac{5}{35} \times \frac{4}{34} \times \frac{3}{33} \times \frac{2}{32} \times \frac{1}{31}$?

27. What is P(winning)

a. Game 1?

b. Game 2?

28. Which game would you be more likely to win?

Cumulative Skill Practice

Solve. Give answers in simplest form. *(page 182)*

1. $\frac{1}{2}$ of $42 = n$ **2.** $\frac{1}{4}$ of $44 = n$ **3.** $\frac{3}{4}$ of $36 = n$ **4.** $\frac{2}{3}$ of $51 = n$

5. $\frac{7}{8}$ of $32 = n$ **6.** $\frac{5}{2}$ of $50 = n$ **7.** $\frac{2}{5}$ of $21 = n$ **8.** $\frac{5}{3}$ of $35 = n$

9. $\frac{9}{4}$ of $41 = n$ **10.** $\frac{3}{5}$ of $43 = n$ **11.** $\frac{4}{9}$ of $35 = n$ **12.** $\frac{7}{4}$ of $110 = n$

Complete. *(page 184)*

13. $1\frac{1}{2}$ ft = ___?___ in. **14.** $2\frac{2}{3}$ ft = ___?___ in. **15.** $3\frac{2}{3}$ yd = ___?___ ft **16.** $1\frac{1}{4}$ days = ___?___ h

17. $2\frac{1}{2}$ days = ___?___ h **18.** $2\frac{3}{4}$ h = ___?___ min **19.** $2\frac{2}{3}$ h = ___?___ min **20.** $1\frac{1}{5}$ min = ___?___ s

21. $2\frac{5}{6}$ min = ___?___ s **22.** $1\frac{1}{4}$ gal = ___?___ qt **23.** $3\frac{1}{2}$ qt = ___?___ pt **24.** $1\frac{3}{4}$ gal = ___?___ pt

Solve. Give answers in simplest form. *(page 186)*

25. $\frac{1}{2}n = 17$ **26.** $\frac{1}{4}n = 37$ **27.** $\frac{2}{3}n = 48$ **28.** $\frac{3}{4}n = 51$

29. $\frac{5}{2}n = 75$ **30.** $\frac{7}{3}n = 63$ **31.** $\frac{7}{12}n = 19$ **32.** $\frac{5}{6}n = 28$

33. $\frac{6}{5}n = 35$ **34.** $\frac{4}{5}n = 43$ **35.** $\frac{5}{4}n = 51$ **36.** $\frac{7}{8}n = 47$

Solve and check. *(page 214)*

37. $5x + 8 = {}^-22$ **38.** $3y - 2 = {}^-23$ **39.** $\frac{w}{2} + 4 = {}^-1$ **40.** $\frac{z}{3} - 5 = {}^-9$

41. $1 = {}^-8w + 17$ **42.** ${}^-12 = {}^-3z - 9$ **43.** ${}^-6 = \frac{k}{2} + 10$ **44.** ${}^-14 = \frac{h}{{}^-3} - 9$

45. ${}^-32 = \frac{c}{8} - 36$ **46.** ${}^-5r - 9 = 26$ **47.** ${}^-8t + 7 = 63$ **48.** $\frac{y}{{}^-10} - 16 = {}^-21$

Simplify by combining like terms. *(page 236)*

49. $8x + x$ **50.** $7z - z$ **51.** $5y - 5y$

52. ${}^-3w + 5w - 3$ **53.** ${}^-3w + 5 - 3w$ **54.** ${}^-3 + 5w - 3w$

55. ${}^-9n - n - 9$ **56.** ${}^-9n + n - 8$ **57.** ${}^-9n + 1 - 8$

58. $12y + 10 + 3y - 5$ **59.** $12 + 10y + 3y - 5$ **60.** $12 + 10y + 3 - 5y$

Problem Solving—Applications

FIRST-CLASS STAMP FACTS

Before 1885, the first-class letter rate (cost for the first ounce) depended on distance traveled. On July 1, 1885, the national rate became 2 cents. Since then the rate has been changed several times. The following list shows these changes.

Date	Rate
November 3, 1917	3 cents
July 1, 1919	2 cents
July 6, 1932	3 cents
August 1, 1958	4 cents
January 7, 1963	5 cents
May 16, 1971	8 cents
March 2, 1974	10 cents
December 11, 1975	13 cents
May 29, 1978	15 cents
March 22, 1981	18 cents
November 1, 1981	20 cents
February 17, 1985	22 cents

Use the information in the article to solve each problem.

1. What was the total cost of postage for mailing 15 one-ounce letters on July 5, 1971?

2. On July 6, 1932, a roll of 50 stamps cost $1.50. How much did a similar roll of 50 stamps cost 40 years later?

3. How much more did it cost to mail a Father's Day card in 1975 than it did in 1950? *Hint: Father's Day is always in June.*

4. How much more did it cost to mail 24 Valentine cards in 1980 than it did in 1950? *Hint: Valentine's Day is February 14.*

5. What was the percent of decrease in the first-class letter rate from November 10, 1917, to November 10, 1919?

6. What was the percent of increase in the first-class letter rate from March 15, 1974, to March 15, 1976?

Write an equation and solve the problem.

7. The cost to mail a 7.5-ounce letter first class is $1.39. That is $.51 less than twice the cost to mail the same letter third class. How much does it cost to mail the letter third class?
(Let c = the cost to mail the letter third class.)

★8. The cost to mail a 10.5 ounce package third class is $1.15. That is $.20 more than half the cost to mail the same package first class. How much does it cost to mail the package first class?
(Let p = the cost to mail the package first class.)

Odds

The table shows the contents of the gum-ball machine.

Color	Number of Gum Balls
Green	80
Blue	90
White	70
Yellow	140
Red	100
Orange	120

1. Suppose that the gum balls have been thoroughly mixed. Which color do you have the best chance of getting? The worst chance of getting?
2. How many gum balls are red?
3. How many gum balls are not red?

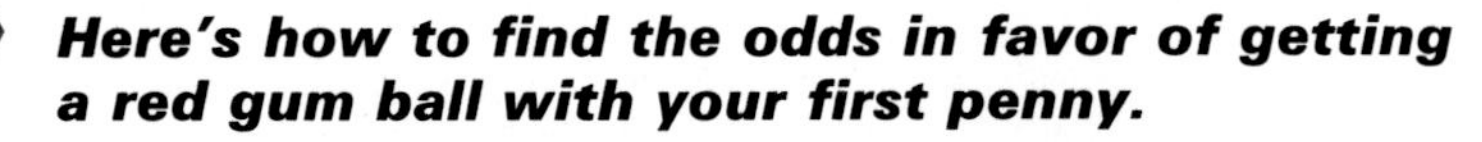

Here's how to find the odds in favor of getting a red gum ball with your first penny.

To find the **odds in favor of an event,** write the ratio of the number of ways the event can occur to the number of ways that the event cannot occur.

number of ways event ***can occur*** → 100

number of ways event ***cannot occur*** → 500

$$\frac{100}{500} = \frac{1}{5}$$

The odds in favor of getting a red gum ball are 1 to 5.

4. Look at the example above. What is the number of ways the event can occur? Cannot occur?
5. What are the odds in favor of getting a red gum ball?

Here's how to find the odds against getting a red gum ball with your first penny.

To find the **odds against an event,** write the ratio of the number of ways that the outcome cannot occur to the number of ways that the outcome can occur.

number of ways event ***cannot occur*** → 500

number of ways event ***can occur*** → 100

$$\frac{500}{100} = \frac{5}{1}$$

The odds against getting a red gum ball are 5 to 1.

Notice that if the odds in favor of an event are $\frac{a}{b}$, then the odds against the event are $\frac{b}{a}$.

6. Look at the second example. What is the number of ways that the event cannot occur? Can occur?

7. What are the odds against getting a red gum ball with your first penny?

EXERCISES

▶ **Give the odds as a fraction in lowest terms.**
Think about putting the first penny into the gum-ball machine.

8. Odds in favor of getting a yellow

9. Odds in favor of getting an orange

10. Odds in favor of getting a blue

11. Odds in favor of getting a white

12. Odds in favor of getting either a green or an orange

13. Odds in favor of getting either an orange or a yellow

14. Odds against getting a blue

15. Odds against getting an orange

16. Odds against getting a yellow

17. Odds against getting a white

18. Odds against getting either a red or a white

19. Odds against getting either a yellow or a green

Problem Solving

▶ **Solve.**

20. Suppose that in another gum-ball machine the odds in favor of your getting your favorite color are 1 to 7. What would be the odds against your getting your favorite color?

21. If the odds against getting a black gum ball are 10 to 3, what are the odds in favor of getting a black gum ball?

22. Suppose that you bought 5 of 160 tickets for a door prize. What are the odds in lowest terms in favor of your winning the door prize? The odds against?

23. Suppose that the probability of your name's being chosen in a drawing is $\frac{1}{30}$. What are the odds in favor of your name's being chosen? The odds against?

Challenge

▶ **Solve.**

24. What are the odds in favor of getting 3 heads when you toss a coin 3 times?

25. What are the odds against getting the same number twice when you roll a die twice?

Expectation

Here is a game that was played at a school carnival.

1. How much did it cost to spin the wheel?

2. What is the probability that the wheel will stop on green?

3. What is the value of the prize?

Here's how to compute the expectation for a game of Spin-the-Wheel.

To find the expectation, multiply the probability of winning the prize by the value of the prize.

		P(winning)		Value of Prize		
Expectation	=	$\mathbf{\frac{1}{8}}$	×	**\$6**	=	**\$.75**

The expectation for a game of Spin-the-Wheel is \$.75.

4. Look at the example. What is the expectation for a game of Spin-the-Wheel?

5. To decide whether such a game is a good deal for the player, you compare the cost of playing with the expectation. Is the expectation less than or greater than the cost of playing?

6. If the expectation is less than the cost of playing, then such a game is a "bad deal" for the player. Is the game Spin-the-Wheel a "bad deal" for the player?

7. How much would the expectation have to be for the game to be considered a "good deal" for the player?

▶ **Solve.**

A merchant donated this guitar to the school carnival. The carnival committee decided to sell 180 chances on it, at $.75 each.

8. What is the cost of a chance?

9. If you bought one chance, what would be your probability of winning?

10. What is the value of the guitar?

11. What is the expectation rounded to the nearest cent?

12. Is the expectation greater than or less than the cost of a chance?

13. Is buying a chance a good deal or a bad deal?

Suppose that the same wheel pictured on page 378 was used for the following games.

14. Pay $2; if the wheel stops on green, you win a $17 camera.

a. What is the probability of winning?

b. What is the expectation rounded to the nearest cent?

c. Is the game a good deal?

15. Pay $3; if the wheel stops on yellow, you win a school sweatshirt worth $6.25.

a. What is the probability of winning?

b. What is the expectation rounded to the nearest cent?

c. Is the game a good deal?

16. Pay $2; if the wheel stops on blue, you win a school T-shirt worth $5. Is the game a good deal?

17. Pay $3; if the wheel stops on yellow or green, you win a $6 gift certificate to a record store. Is the game a good deal?

Challenge

▶ **Solve.**

18. Alice bought a chance on a camera and a chance on a radio. She spent $2.25. The chance on the radio cost $.25 more than the chance on the camera. How much did she pay for each chance?

19. John bought 2 chances on a watch and 1 chance on a radio. He spent $4.00. Sue bought 1 chance on the watch and 2 chances on the radio. She spent $3.50. How much would one chance on each have cost?

Analyzing Data—Finding the Mean

Nine students in a psychology class conducted an experiment on hand-eye coordination. Each student was asked to stack 50 pennies as quickly as possible.

The results (the data) are shown in the chart.

The study of collecting, organizing, and interpreting data is called **statistics.**

Student	Time (seconds)
Alice	41.4
Bill	45.5
Don	43.2
Gayle	38.4
Heidi	52.7
Mike	43.1
Nan	54.5
Paul	50.8
Roger	39.0

1. What was Alice's time?

2. Which student stacked the coins in 43.1 seconds?

3. Who had the shortest time? The longest time?

4. The average of a set of numbers is called the **mean.** Whose time do you think is closer to the mean, Bill's or Roger's?

Here's how to find the mean.

Find the sum of all the times.

$$\begin{array}{r} 41.4 \\ 45.5 \\ 43.2 \\ 38.4 \\ 52.7 \\ 43.1 \\ 54.5 \\ 50.8 \\ +39.0 \\ \hline 408.6 \end{array}$$

Divide the sum by the number of students.

$$\begin{array}{r} 45.4 \\ 9\overline{)408.6} \\ -36 \\ \hline 48 \\ -45 \\ \hline 36 \\ -36 \\ \hline 0 \end{array}$$

5. Look at the example. Did any student have the same time as the mean time?

6. How many students had a better (shorter) time than the mean time?

7. Which students took longer than the mean time?

EXERCISES

Find the mean. Round each answer to the nearest tenth.
Here are scrambled answers for the next two rows of exercises: 182.6 32.3 9.8 264.6

8. 12, 4, 14, 9

9. 35, 39, 27, 28

10. 195, 176, 183, 178, 181

11. 253, 276, 248, 281, 265

12. 361, 375, 392, 386, 379

13. 432, 481, 467, 429, 450

14. 18.6, 19.4, 21.6

15. 13.5, 14.8, 14.2

16. 29.6, 32.7, 31.9, 28.7

17. 46.8, 48.9, 43.7, 41.2

18. 112.2, 114.7, 116.3

19. 129.6, 128.7, 126.3

20. 18, 28, 16, 32, 14, 26, 10

21. 15, 21, 18, 24, 31, 27, 19

22. 28, 31, 19, 42, 37, 16, 12

23. 19, 29, 17, 33, 15, 27, 11

24. 51.4, 50.5, 38.9, 47.6, 48.4, 53.7

25. 19.4, 23.8, 15.6, 20.7, 28.3

26. 8.1, 3.7, 9.4, 6.5, 6.6, 4.2

27. 17.5, 13.8, 12.4, 11.7, 12.4, 17.0

Problem Solving

Solve. Use the chart on page 380.

28. Who stacked the coins in a shorter time, Alice or Mike?

29. Which student had a time that was 0.1 second slower than the mean time?

30. Who stacked the coins 6.4 seconds faster than the mean time?

31. Who stacked the coins 5.4 seconds slower than the mean time?

32. To the nearest tenth, what was the mean time of the 4 best times?

33. To the nearest tenth, what was the mean time of the 3 worst times?

34. Suppose that Gayle had not done the experiment. Would the mean time have been less or greater?

35. Suppose that Nan had not done the experiment. Would the mean time have been less or greater?

Challenge

Solve.

36. Ask several classmates how many minutes they spent watching television last night.

a. Find the mean time.

b. Did you watch television more or less than the mean time?

37. Ask several classmates how many minutes they spent doing homework last night.

a. Find the mean time.

b. How did the time you spent doing homework compare with the mean time?

Median, Mode, and Range

The table shows the pulse rates (heartbeats per minute) of some physical education students.

1. What was Carlin's pulse rate?

2. Who had a pulse rate of 71?

3. Who had the lowest pulse rate? The highest pulse rate?

Name	Pulse Rate
Allen, C.	72
Andrews, D.	70
Berry, J.	66
Carlin, N.	75
Cole, M.	78
Davis, A.	73
Dori, T.	70
Fallons, K.	74
Jackson, B.	81
Kerry, C.	70
Lopez, D.	79
Manning, A.	64
Napes, R.	74
Porter, M.	70
Rogers, L.	71
Weaver, S.	69
Wong, D.	78

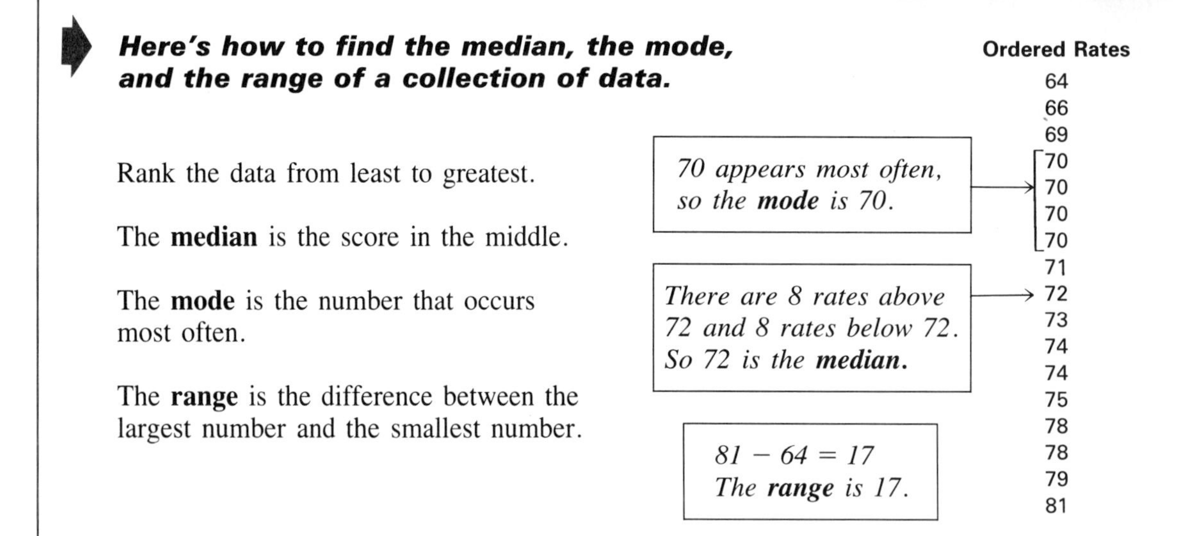

Here's how to find the median, the mode, and the range of a collection of data.

Rank the data from least to greatest.

The **median** is the score in the middle.

The **mode** is the number that occurs most often.

The **range** is the difference between the largest number and the smallest number.

*70 appears most often, so the **mode** is 70.*

*There are 8 rates above 72 and 8 rates below 72. So 72 is the **median**.*

$81 - 64 = 17$
*The **range** is 17.*

Ordered Rates

64
66
69
70
70
70
70
71
72
73
74
74
75
78
78
79
81

4. Look at the example above. What is the median? The mode? The range?

5. How many students had higher pulse rates than the median rate? Had lower pulse rates than the median rate?

6. Is the mode less than or greater than the median?

7. Find the mean pulse rate rounded to the nearest tenth.

8. Is the mean less than or greater than the mode?

▶ **Find the median.**

> *Hint: Average the two middle numbers 10 and 11.*

9. 13, 12, 11, 6, 7, 12, 9

10. 12, 9, 8, 14, 10, 11

11. 14, 7, 12, 7, 7, 10, 13

12. 13, 14, 9, 11, 13, 10, 9

13. 183, 182, 183, 180, 187, 182

14. 12, 15, 13, 19, 13, 15, 13

15. 6797, 6785, 6897, 6579, 6057, 6896, 6570, 6075, 6597, 6895, 6579, 6719, 6852

▶ **Find the mode and range. (It is possible for a list to have more than one mode.)**

16. 5, 7, 9, 7, 5, 9, 7

17. 11, 15, 12, 15, 10, 14, 15

18. 20, 27, 22, 23, 21, 24, 22

19. 66, 82, 69, 73, 68, 66, 76, 66

20. 506, 511, 508, 503, 500, 503, 505, 508, 505, 503, 514, 501, 505, 509

Problem Solving

Each member of a physical education class recorded his/her best high jump. The data are shown in the table.

21. Compute the mean score rounded to the nearest tenth.

22. Rank the data and find the median and mode.

23. Find the range.

24. How many students fell below the median?

25. Which students jumped higher than the mean jump?

High Jump Records

Name	Height in inches
Allen, C.	31
Andrews, D.	40
Berry, J.	28
Carlin, N.	43
Cole, M.	39
Davis, A.	48
Dori, T.	43
Fallons, K.	54
Jackson, B.	29
Kerry, C.	36
Lopez, D.	51
Manning, A.	41
Napes, R.	50
Porter, M.	37
Rogers, L.	34
Weaver, S.	43
Wong, D.	42

Challenge

▶ **Study the clues to find what numbers are on the cards that are facedown.**

26.

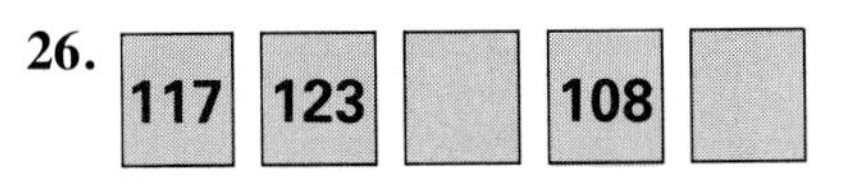

Clues:
- The mean is 116.
- The mode is 117.

27. [ ] [ ] [60] [ ] [ ]

Clues:
- The mean is 56.
- The median is 55.
- The mode is 54.

Interpreting Data—Graphs

A **frequency table** shows the number of times different events or responses occur.

Use the frequency table to answer each question.

Number of Movies Attended Last Month

Number of Movies	Number of Students	
	Tally	Frequency
4	III	3
3	~~IIII~~ I	6
2	~~IIII~~ ~~IIII~~	10
1	II	2
0	III	3

1. How many students attended four movies last month?
2. How many didn't attend a movie?
3. How many attended 2 or fewer movies?
4. How many attended 3 or more movies?
5. How many students were in the survey?
6. What percent of the students attended only 1 movie?
7. What percent of the students attended fewer than 3 movies?
8. What percent attended at least 1 movie?

Use the bar graph to answer each question.

9. How many hours did Gayle spend doing homework?
10. Who spent the most time doing homework?
11. How many more hours did Kim spend doing homework than David?
12. By what percent would David have to increase his homework time to spend as much time as Gayle?
13. Who spent 10% less time on homework than Kim?

Use the broken-line graph to answer each question.

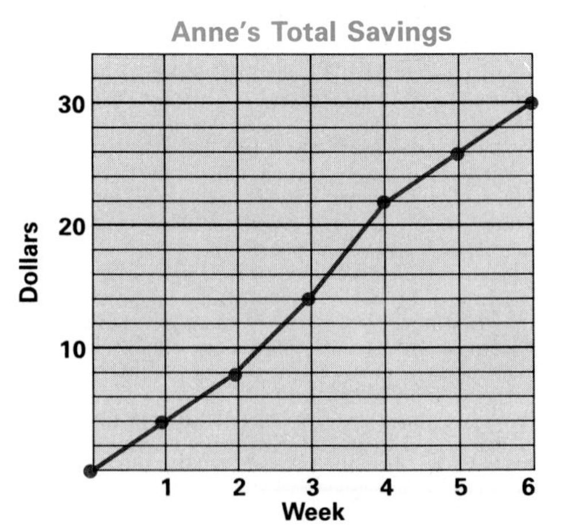

14. By the end of the second week, Anne had saved \$8. How much had she saved by the end of the third week?
15. During which week did Anne save the most?
16. How much did Anne save during the six weeks?
17. Anne is saving to buy a \$90 radio-tape player. What percent of the money will she have by the end of the sixth week?
18. If Anne continues to save at the rate of her first six weeks, how many weeks must she save for the \$90 radio-tape player?

▶ Use the picture graph to answer each question.

19. Who has the most records? The fewest?

20. How many records does Bob have?

21. How many records does Loni have?

22. Bob has how many more records than Carl?

23. Who has 40% more records than Randy?

24. Who has about 36% fewer records than Bob?

▶ Use the circle graph to answer the following questions.

25. For which category does Mike allow the most money? The least money?

26. How much does Mike spend on food each week?

27. How much more does he spend a week on clothes than on hobbies?

28. On which two categories does he spend half his budget?

29. How much would Mike spend on movies during a year (52 weeks)?

▶ Use the broken-line graphs to answer the following questions.

30. What percent took French in 1981? In 1985?

31. In what year did the percent of students taking algebra decrease?

32. In what year were there more students taking biology than algebra?

33. What was the first year that more students were enrolled in French than in Spanish?

34. Suppose that there were 300 ninth-grade students in 1984. Estimate how many students took each elective.

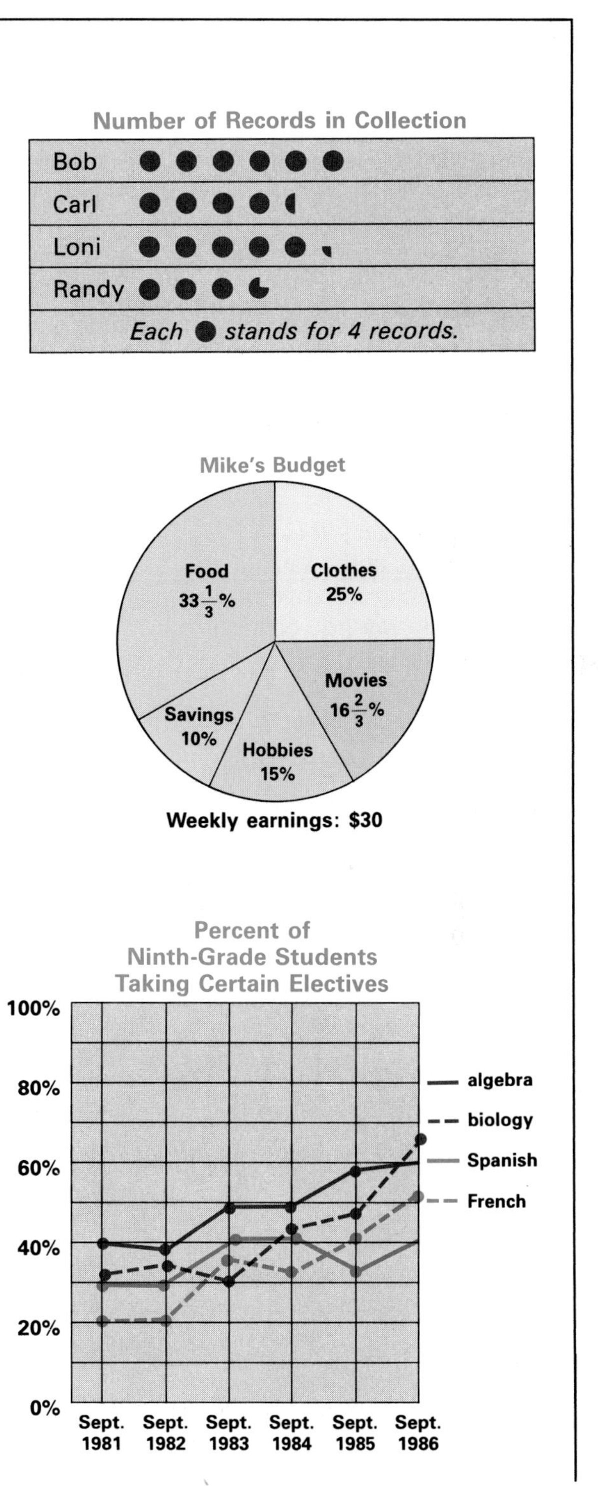

Misleading Statistics

These six students were asked if they lived more than three blocks from school. The results of this "sample" were printed in the school newspaper:

"Five Out of Six Students Live More Than Three Blocks from School."

1. How many students were in the sample?
2. Do you think that the students in the sample were representative of the **population** (the entire student body)? Why or why not?
3. Do you think that the statement in the school newspaper could be misleading?

A sample that is *not representative* of the population being sampled is called a **biased sample.** The sample above is likely to be biased because students who ride in a car to school probably live farther than three blocks from the school.

4. Suppose instead that you asked the first 40 students in a lunch line if they lived more than 3 blocks from school. Would the sample be biased if all students must eat lunch at school?

Often, misleading statements result from the wrong interpretation of facts. Explain why each statement could be misleading.

5. *Fact:* Fifty-seven percent of the automobile accidents in Lake City involved male drivers.

   "Male drivers are worse drivers than female drivers!"

6. *Fact:* Sixty-four percent of the people in Lake City that had an accident did so within 25 miles of their homes.

   "The most unsafe place to drive is within 25 miles of where you live!"

If not studied carefully, some graphs can be misleading.

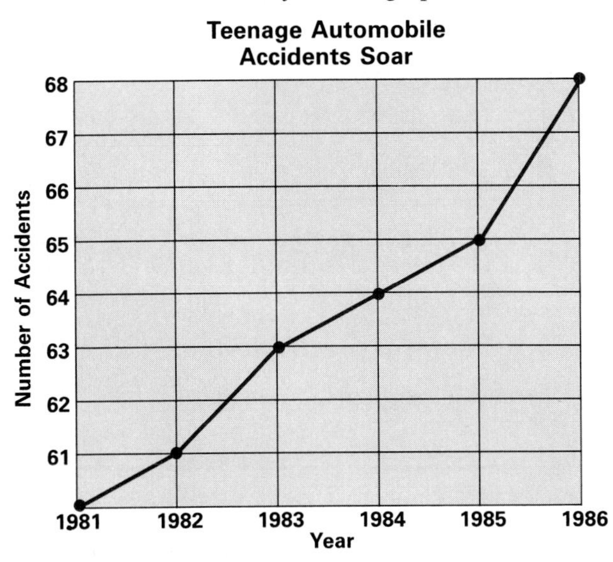

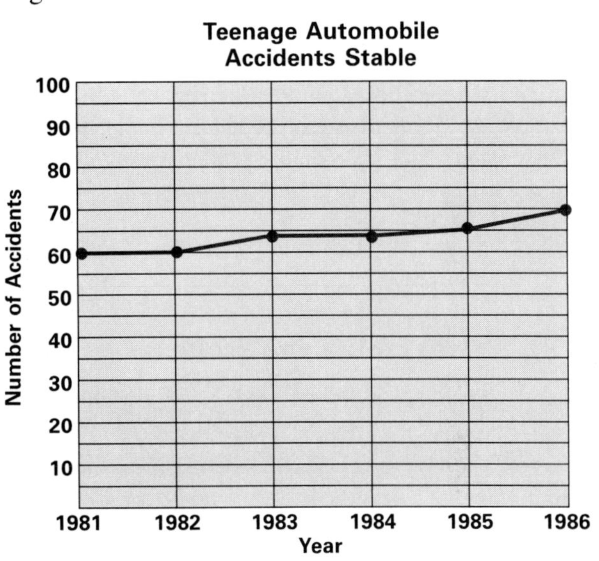

▶ **Solve.**

7. Look at the first graph. How many accidents occurred in each of the years?

8. Does the second graph appear to show the same information?

9. Which graph would you use if you were trying to raise auto-insurance rates for teenagers?

10. Which graph would you use if you were trying to lower auto-insurance rates for teenagers?

11. Look at the first graph. What was the percent of increase in accidents from 1981 to 1986? Round your answer to the nearest tenth percent.

12. Look at the first graph. What was the percent of increase in accidents from 1985 to 1986? Round your answer to the nearest tenth percent.

Challenge

13. **a.** Take a sample of 20 classmates to find what fraction ate a candy bar yesterday.
    b. Find out how many students go to your school.
    c. Use the information you gathered and solve a proportion to predict how many students in your school ate a candy bar yesterday.

14. From a sample, predict how many students in your school slept less than 8 hours last night.

15. From a sample, predict how many students in your school watched more than 2 hours of television last night.

Problem Solving—Using a Sample to Make Predictions

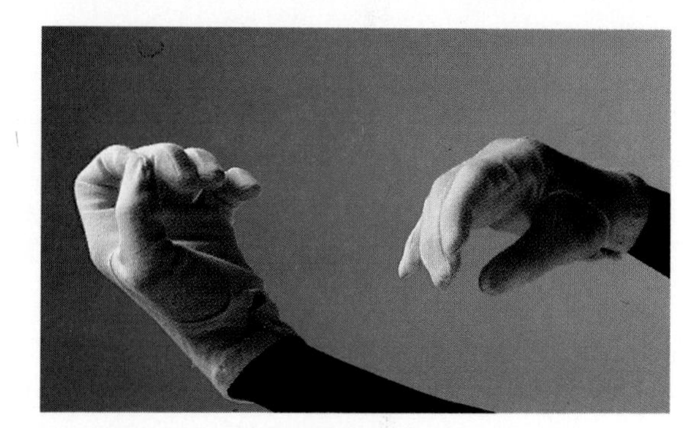

Some students were asked to find what percent of the student body could identify what these hands are doing. Instead of asking each student, they asked a sample of the student population and estimated the percent from their sample.

Here's how the students used a sample to make a prediction.

Step 1. For their sample, they chose the first 40 students to enter the school. The results were:

Students who knew the hands are playing a violin	𝍸 𝍸 𝍸 𝍸 𝍸 I
Students who did not know the hands are playing a violin	𝍸 𝍸 IIII

Step 2. From their sample they predicted the percent of the student body that would know what the hands are doing. To do this, they solved a proportion.

number who knew the hands are playing a violin → 26

number in the sample → 40

$$\frac{26}{40} = \frac{n}{100}$$

$$40n = 2600$$

$$n = 65$$

From the sample of 40, they could predict that 65% of the student body would know that the hands are playing a violin.

1. Look at the example above.

a. How many students were in the sample?
b. How many students in the sample could identify what the hands are doing?
c. What percent of the students sampled knew that the hands are playing a violin?

2. On the basis of the sample, how many students of a student population of 1000 would know what the hands are doing?

Use the sample to solve.

3. *Sample question:* What are these hands doing?

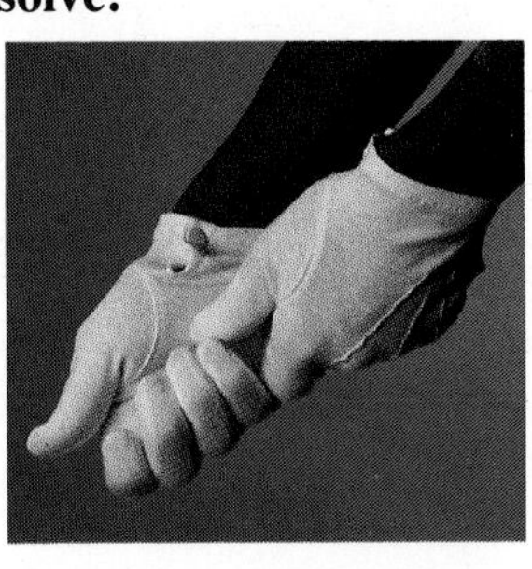

Sample results:

Number who know what the hands are doing	卌 卌 卌 III
Number who do not know	卌 II

a. How many people in the sample know that the hands are holding a golf club?
b. How many people are in the sample?
c. What percent of the sample know what the hands are doing?
d. On the basis of the sample, how many people out of 600 would you predict would know that the hands are holding a golf club?

4. *Sample question:* What are these hands doing?

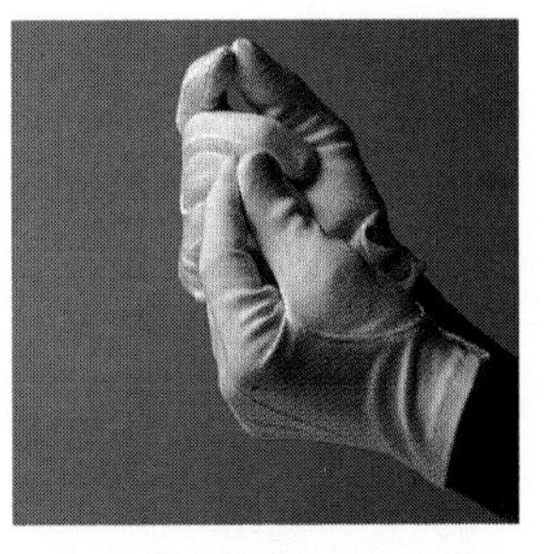

Sample results:

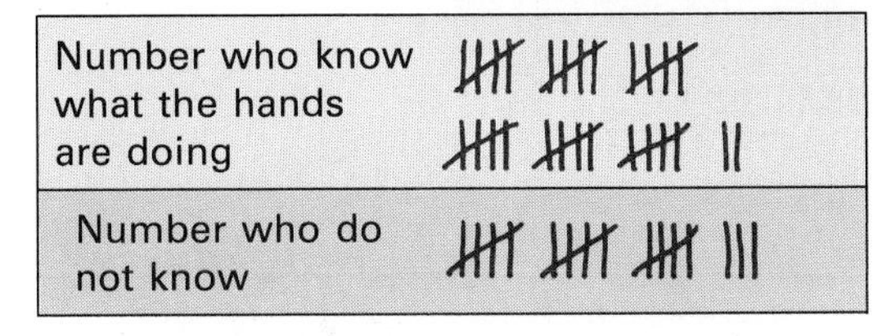

Number who know what the hands are doing	卌 卌 卌 卌 卌 卌 II
Number who do not know	卌 卌 卌 III

a. How many people in the sample know that the hands are threading a needle?
b. How many people are in the sample?
c. What percent of the sample know what the hands are doing?
d. On the basis of the sample, how many people out of 800 would you predict would know that the hands are threading a needle?

Use a proportion to solve each problem. Round each answer to the nearest whole number.

5. In a sample, 15 out of 40 people said their favorite color is red. Based on the sample, how many people out of 1000 would you predict would pick red as their favorite color?

6. In a sample, 45 out of 80 people said that they sleep at least 8 hours a night. Based on the sample, how many people out of 500 would you predict sleep at least 8 hours a night?

7. In a sample, 38 out of 60 people said vanilla is their favorite ice cream. Based on the sample, how many people out of 1500 would pick vanilla as their favorite ice cream?

8. In a sample, 24 out of 30 people see at least one movie a year. Based on the sample, how many people out of 200 see at least one movie a year?

9. In a sample, 38 out of 70 families have 2 cars. Suppose 200 families are sampled. How many do you predict would have 2 cars?

10. In a sample, 22 out of 30 families take a vacation each year. Suppose 100 families are sampled. How many do you predict take a vacation each year?

Cumulative Skill Practice

Solve and check. *(page 238)*

1. $3x + x = 32$
2. $7n - n = 15$
3. $5e + 2e = 18$
4. $5y + y - 2 = 17$
5. $5y + 1 - 2y = 17$
6. $5 + y - 2y = 17$
7. $8z - 2z + 7 = {}^-11$
8. $8z - 2 + 7z = {}^-11$
9. $8 - 2z + 7z = {}^-11$
10. ${}^-6y - 10y - 13 = {}^-19$
11. ${}^-6y - 10 - 13y = {}^-19$
12. ${}^-6 - 10y - 13y = {}^-19$

Solve and check. *(page 240)*

13. $6c - 3c + 9 = {}^-3 + 12$
14. $6c - 3 + 9c = {}^-3 + 12$
15. ${}^-8d + 12 - 3d = 16 - 21$
16. ${}^-8d + 12d - 3 = 16 - 21$
17. $15y - 3y + 9 - 6 = {}^-5 + 23$
18. $15 - 3y + 9y - 6 = {}^-5 + 23$

Solve each proportion. *(page 252)*

19. $\frac{8}{n} = \frac{24}{30}$
20. $\frac{3}{5} = \frac{n}{8}$
21. $\frac{16}{11} = \frac{8}{n}$
22. $\frac{n}{12} = \frac{13}{7}$
23. $\frac{19}{n} = \frac{15}{8}$
24. $\frac{6}{5} = \frac{n}{12}$
25. $\frac{16}{20} = \frac{32}{n}$
26. $\frac{n}{10} = \frac{3}{7}$
27. $\frac{16}{n} = \frac{5}{4}$
28. $\frac{12}{21} = \frac{n}{30}$
29. $\frac{4}{3\frac{1}{2}} = \frac{8}{n}$
30. $\frac{n}{3\frac{1}{2}} = \frac{8}{5}$
31. $\frac{9}{n} = \frac{4}{2\frac{2}{3}}$
32. $\frac{3}{1\frac{1}{4}} = \frac{n}{6}$
33. $\frac{2\frac{3}{4}}{4} = \frac{9}{n}$

Solve. *(page 266)*

34. $n\%$ of $8 = 6$
35. $n\%$ of $20 = 4$
36. $n\%$ of $9 = 36$
37. $3\frac{1}{2}\%$ of $18 = n$
38. $8\frac{1}{3}\%$ of $64 = n$
39. $33\frac{1}{3}\%$ of $n = 38$
40. 25% of $n = 13$
41. 1% of $n = 16.5$
42. 12.5% of $n = 42$
43. $n\%$ of $40 = 25$
44. $n\%$ of $9 = 27$
45. $37\frac{1}{2}\%$ of $n = 57$

Find the percent of increase or decrease. Use *i* to indicate increase and *d* to indicate decrease. Give answers to the nearest tenth of a percent. *(page 268)*

46. from 20 to 30
47. from 30 to 20
48. from 18 to 36
49. from 36 to 18
50. from 68 to 92
51. from 75 to 108
52. from 92 to 67
53. from 49 to 65
54. from 118 to 83

Problem Solving—Applications

Lori Adriano is the Fine Arts Coordinator for Lincoln High School. She uses a personal computer to store data about students who participate in school-sponsored fine-arts activities. A special **software** package helped her produce these graphs.

GRAPH 1

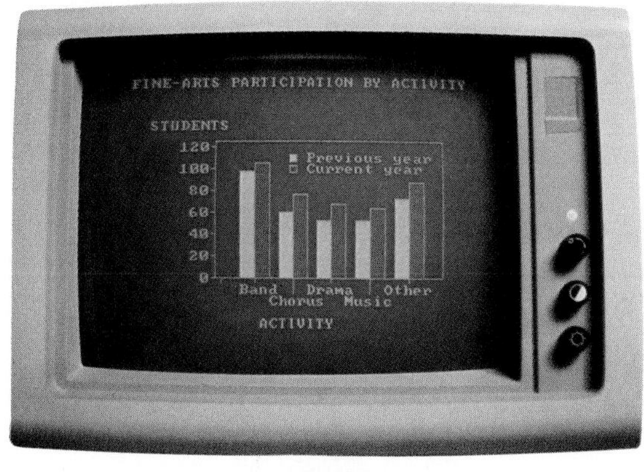

GRAPH 2

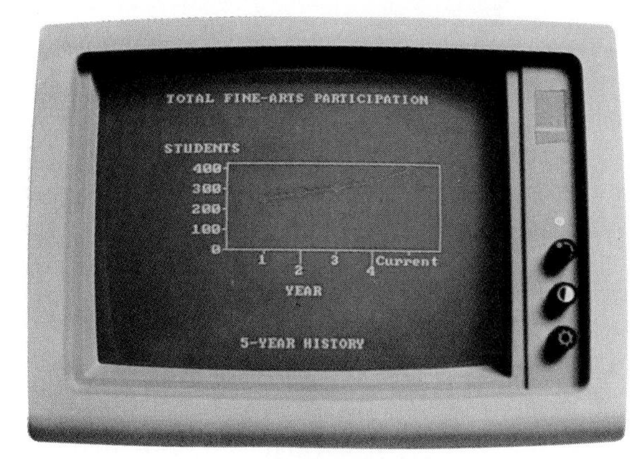

GRAPH 3

▶ **Solve.**

1. Look at Graph 1. Which grade has the largest enrollment in fine-arts activities?
2. Look at Graph 2. Are more students enrolled in Band or Drama this year?

▶ **Decide which graph or graphs Ms. Adriano could use to answer the question. Then write a reasonable answer.**

3. Parent: "Which fine-arts activity is the most popular?"
4. School Board Member: "Are the school's fine-arts activities as popular with seniors as they are with freshmen?"
5. Taxpayer: "How many students are enrolled in fine-arts activities anyway?"
6. Parent: "Is participation in fine-arts activities increasing or decreasing?"
7. School Board Member: "Our costs have gone up nearly 25% over the past 5 years. How do you account for this?"
8. Taxpayer: "I read in the paper that 50 players tried out for football this year. Why doesn't the school do more for non-athletes?"

Chapter Review

Here are scrambled answers for the review exercises:

5	*48*	*independent*	*multiply*	*probability*
8	*120*	*mean*	*odds*	*range*
12	*cannot*	*median*	*outcomes*	*sample*
15	*dependent*	*mode*	*permutation*	*value*

1. To compute the total number of ways that several decisions can be made, ? the number of choices for each of the decisions. If you have 6 pairs of slacks and 8 sweaters, you would have ? slacks-sweater combinations. *(page 362)*

2. An arrangement of things in a definite order is called a ? . When 5 students line up for lunch, they can line up in ? different ways. *(page 364)*

3. If you roll a die,

$$P(3 \text{ or less}) = \frac{\textbf{number of ways to roll a 3 or less}}{\textbf{number of possible ?}}$$

A ? space is the set of all possible outcomes. If you list the sample space for tossing a coin 3 times, the sample space will have ? outcomes. *(pages 366, 368)*

4. Since an event such as rolling a 2 does not affect an event such as tossing heads, the two events are called ? events.

$$P(2, \text{H}) = \frac{1}{?}$$

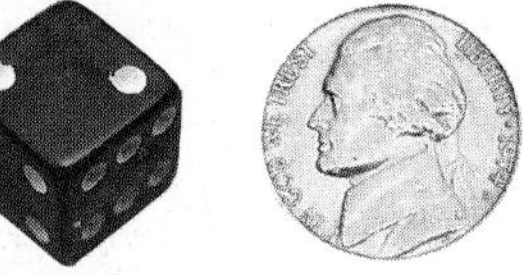

If the outcome of a first event can affect the outcome of a second event, the events are called ? events. If you draw two cards without replacement,

$$P(\text{B, vowel}) = \frac{1}{?}$$

A B C D E F

(pages 370, 372)

5. The ? in favor of an event are the ratio of the number of ways the event can occur to the number of ways that the event ? occur. If you roll a die, the odds that you will roll a 4 are 1 to ? . *(page 376)*.

6. To find the expectation, multiply the ? of winning by the ? of the prize. *(page 378)*

7. The average of a set of data is called the ? . The ? is the score in the middle. The ? is the number that occurs most often. The ? is the difference between the largest number and the least number. *(pages 380, 382)*

Chapter Test

Solve. *(pages 362, 364)*

1. How many different outfits can you make with 6 blouses and 5 skirts?

2. In how many ways can 6 people line up at a ticket booth?

Give each probability in simplest form. *(page 366)*

Think about drawing a card, without looking, from the five cards shown at the right.

1 2 3 4 5

3. $P(3)$

4. $P(\text{odd})$

5. $P(\text{even})$

6. $P(\text{not } 4)$

Solve. *(page 368)*

Think about drawing a card without looking from the five cards shown above, replacing it, and drawing a second card without looking.

7. List the sample space.

8. What is the probability that each card will have an even number?

Give each probability in simplest form. *(pages 370, 372)*

Think about drawing a card without looking from the five cards shown above, then tossing a coin.

9. $P(4, \text{heads})$

10. $P(\text{even}, \text{tails})$

11. $P(\text{not } 2, \text{heads})$

Think about drawing a card without looking from the five cards shown above, then without replacement drawing a second card without looking.

12. $P(5, 4)$

13. $P(\text{even}, 1)$

14. $P(\text{odd}, \text{even})$

Give the odds as a fraction in lowest terms. *(page 376)*

Think about drawing a card without looking from the five cards shown above.

15. Odds in favor of drawing an even number

16. Odds against drawing a number greater than 3

Solve. *(page 378)*

17. a. Eighty chances were sold on binoculars worth $120. Each chance cost $2 each. If you bought one chance, what would be your expectation?

b. Is buying a chance a good deal?

Solve using the scores. *(pages 380, 382)*

Scores: 35, 43, 31, 43, 45, 52, 50, 43, 36

18. Find the mean.

19. Find the median.

20. Find the mode.

21. Find the range.

Cumulative Test
Standardized Format

▶ **Choose the correct letter.**

1. Solve.

$\frac{5}{6}$ of $60 = n$

A. 72
B. 50
C. 60
D. none of these

2. $2\frac{2}{3}$ yd = ? in.

A. 8
B. 32
C. 96
D. none of these

3. Solve.

$\frac{9}{4}n = 45$

A. 20
B. 72
C. $101\frac{1}{4}$
D. none of these

4. Solve.

$^{-}8 = \frac{t}{^{-}2} - 11$

A. 6
B. $^{-}38$
C. 38
D. none of these

5. Simplify by combining like terms.

$6 + 9y - 9 - y$

A. $8y - 3$
B. $10y - 3$
C. $8y + 3$
D. none of these

6. Solve.

$^{-}5x - 4 + 7x = {}^{-}11$

A. $^{-}3\frac{1}{2}$
B. $^{-}7\frac{1}{2}$
C. $3\frac{1}{2}$
D. none of these

7. Solve.

$13n - 5 - n + 16 = {}^{-}9 + 21$

A. $\frac{1}{14}$
B. $1\frac{11}{12}$
C. $^{-}1\frac{11}{12}$
D. none of these

8. Solve.

$\frac{n}{2\frac{1}{2}} = \frac{4}{7}$

A. $1\frac{3}{7}$
B. $4\frac{3}{8}$
C. $11\frac{1}{5}$
D. none of these

9. Solve.

$n\%$ of $48 = 32$

A. $33\frac{1}{3}$
B. $66\frac{2}{3}$
C. 75
D. none of these

10. Solve.

6.5% of $43 = n$

A. 2.795
B. 27.95
C. 66.15
D. none of these

11. The percent of decrease from 48 to 40 is

A. 25%
B. 20%
C. $16\frac{2}{3}\%$
D. none of these

12. Choose the equation.

Twelve less than the sum of a number multiplied by 6 and the number multiplied by 3 is 51. What is the number?

A. $6n + 3n + 12 = 51$
B. $6n + 3n - 12 = 51$
C. $6n - 3n + 12 = 51$
D. $6n - 3n - 12 = 51$

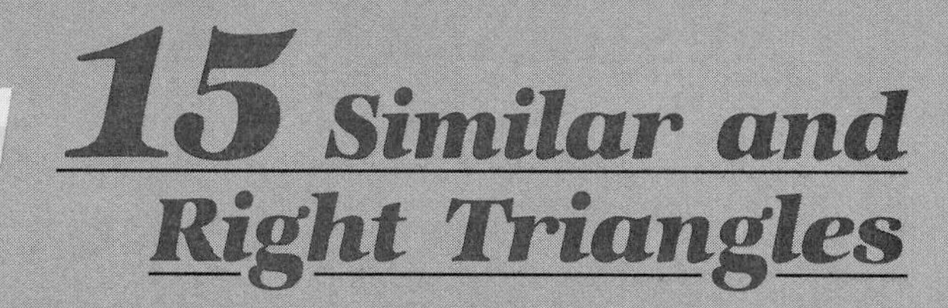

15 Similar and Right Triangles

$c^2 = a^2 + b^2$

In a right triangle, the square of the length of the hypotenuse is equal to the sum of the squares of the lengths of the legs. This is known as the Pythagorean theorem.

(page 412)

The Pythagorean theorem can be used to calculate the length of the rope if we know the height of the pole and the distance from the pole to the stake.

Similar Figures

The sails in the photographs are the same shape. Two figures that have the same shape are called **similar figures.**

Look at these two similar triangles.

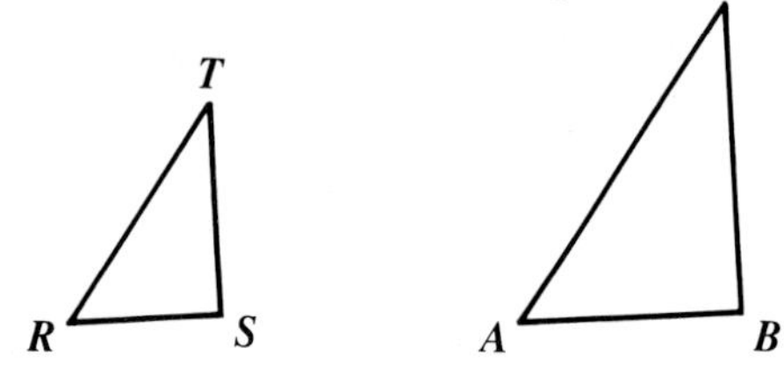

Side AB corresponds to side RS.

1. What side corresponds to side BC? To side AC?

$\angle A$ corresponds to $\angle R$.

2. What angle corresponds to $\angle B$? To $\angle C$?

In similar figures, the corresponding angles are **congruent** (have the same measure), and the ratios of the lengths of corresponding sides are equal.

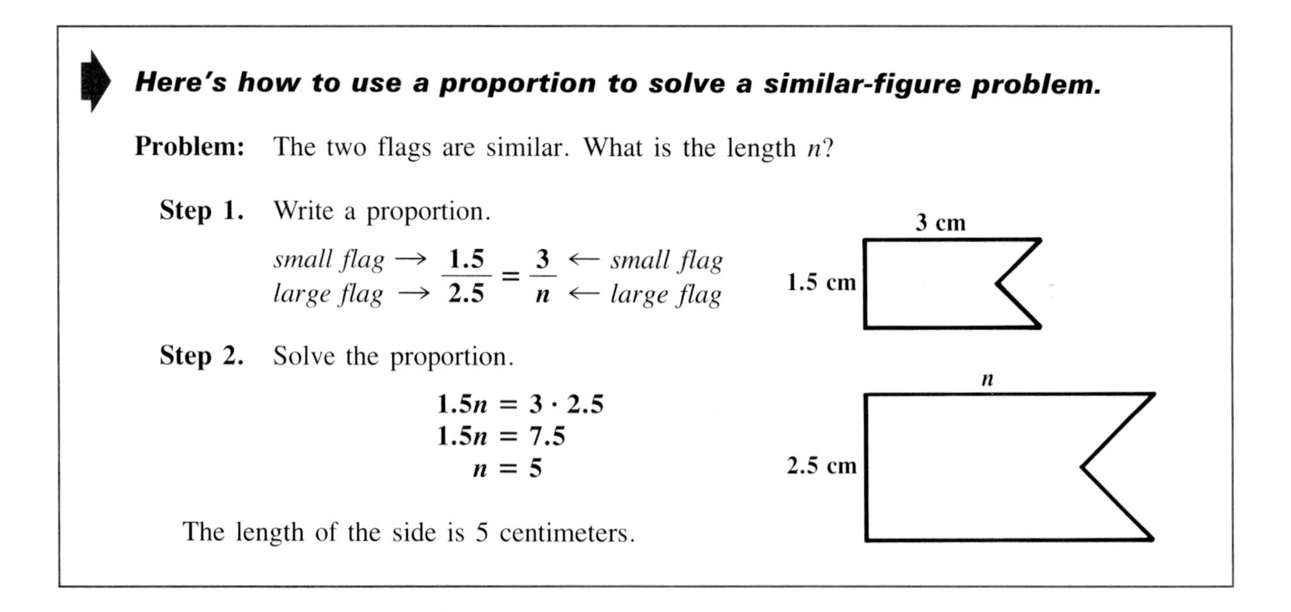

Here's how to use a proportion to solve a similar-figure problem.

Problem: The two flags are similar. What is the length n?

Step 1. Write a proportion.

$$\begin{matrix} \textit{small flag} \rightarrow \\ \textit{large flag} \rightarrow \end{matrix} \frac{1.5}{2.5} = \frac{3}{n} \begin{matrix} \leftarrow \textit{small flag} \\ \leftarrow \textit{large flag} \end{matrix}$$

Step 2. Solve the proportion.

$$1.5n = 3 \cdot 2.5$$
$$1.5n = 7.5$$
$$n = 5$$

The length of the side is 5 centimeters.

3. Look at the example. What is the length n?

EXERCISES

▶ **The two figures are similar. Solve a proportion to find the length n.**

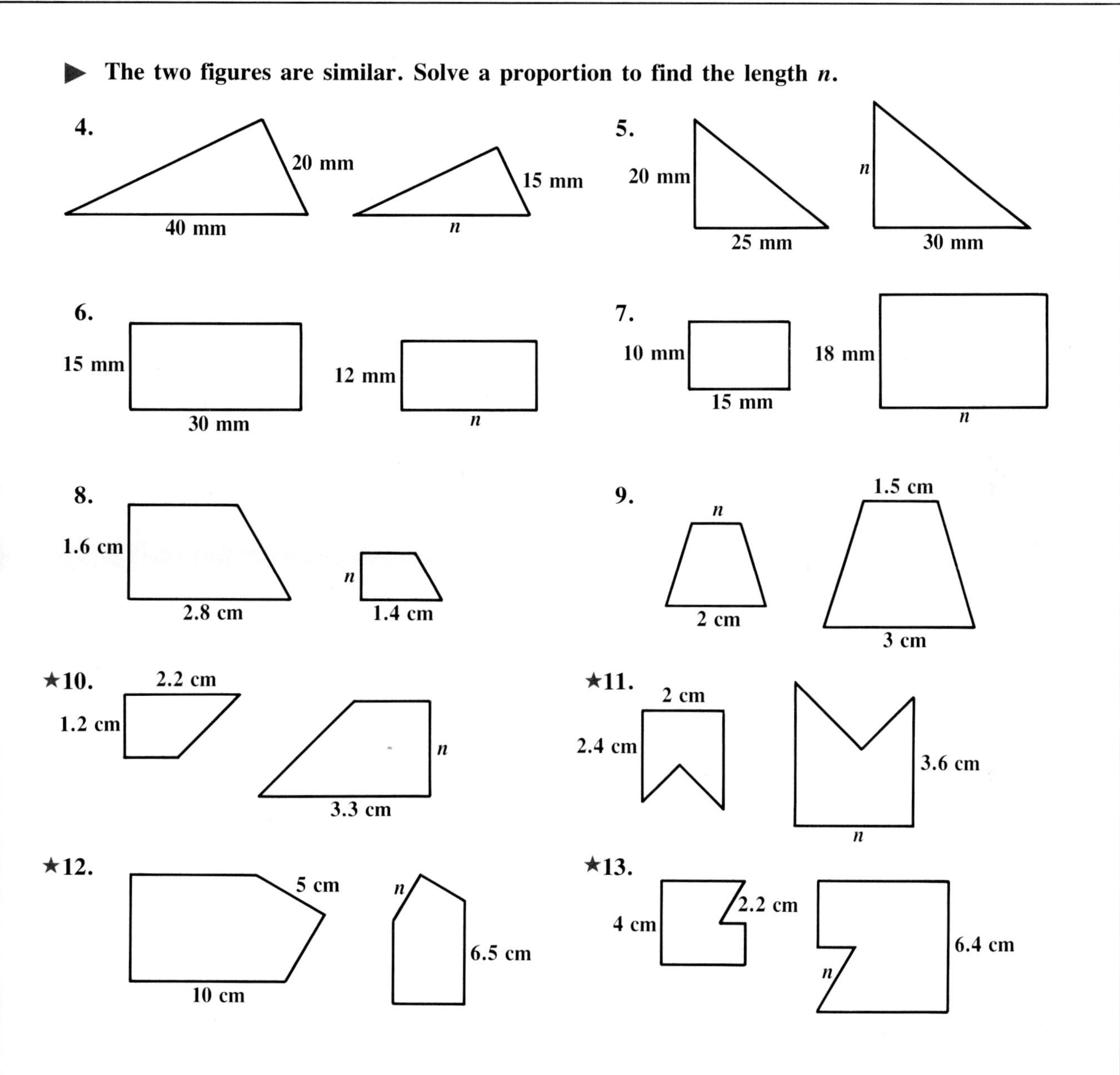

Problem Solving

▶ **Solve by solving a proportion. Refer to the triangles on page 396.**

14. Suppose that the length of side AB is 8 meters and the length of side BC is 12 meters. If the length of side ST is 7.5 meters, what is the length of side RS?

15. Use the information in exercise 14 and the fact that the length of side AC is 13 meters to find the length of side RT.

Similar Right Triangles

A **right triangle** is a triangle that has a right angle.

The right triangle made by the stop sign and its shadow is similar to the right triangle made by the flagpole and its shadow.

1. What is the height of the stop sign?
2. What is the length of the shadow of the stop sign?
3. What is the length of the shadow of the flagpole?

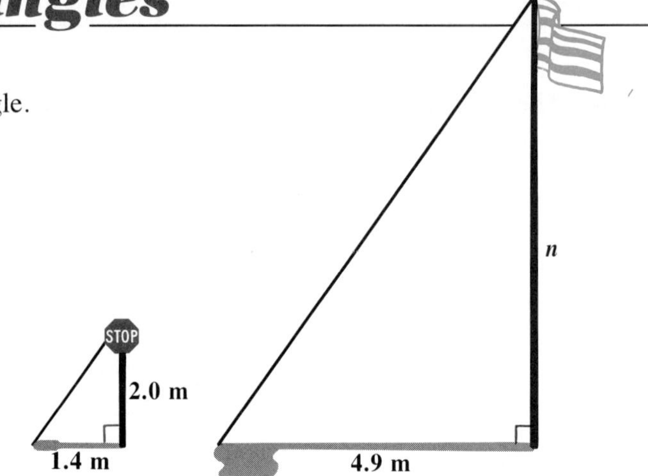

Here's how to find the height of the flagpole by solving a proportion.

$$\begin{matrix} \textit{flagpole} \rightarrow \\ \textit{stop sign} \rightarrow \end{matrix} \frac{n}{2} = \frac{4.9}{1.4} \begin{matrix} \leftarrow \textit{shadow of flagpole} \\ \leftarrow \textit{shadow of stop sign} \end{matrix}$$

$$1.4n = 2 \cdot 4.9$$

$$1.4n = 9.8$$

$$n = 7$$

The height of the flagpole is 7 meters.

4. Look at the example. What is the height of the flagpole?

EXERCISES

The two right triangles are similar. Solve a proportion to find the length n.

5.

6.

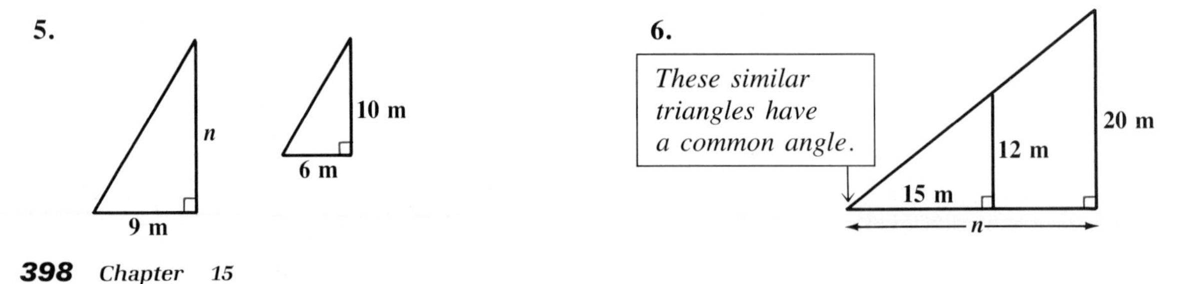

▶ The triangles in each exercise are similar. Find the length n rounded to the nearest tenth of a meter.

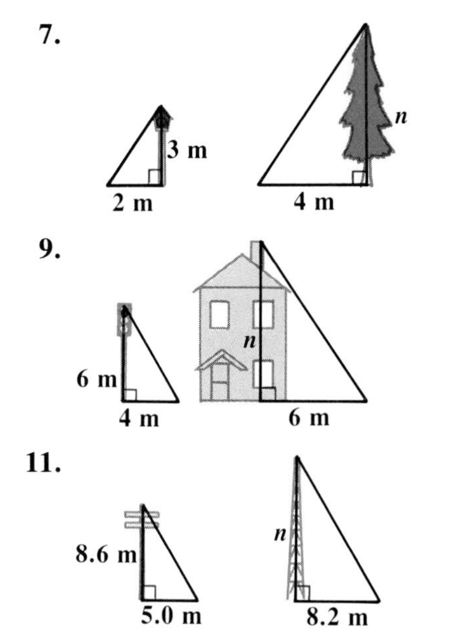

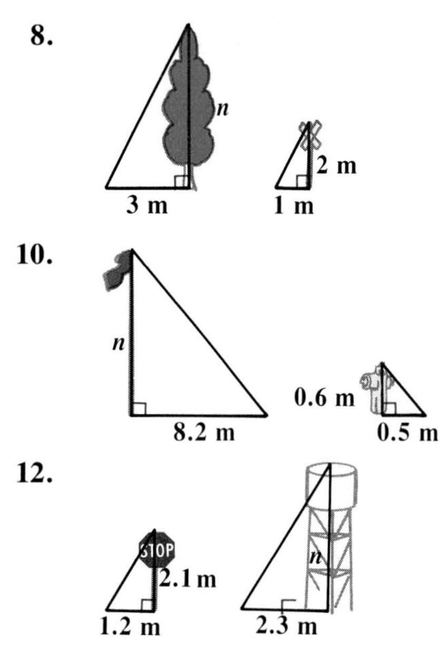

Problem Solving

▶ First make a drawing. Then solve the problem. Round answers to the nearest hundredth of a meter.

13. When an elephant casts a 2.5-meter shadow, a man 2 meters tall casts a 1.5-meter shadow. How tall is the elephant?

14. When a Ferris wheel casts a 20-meter shadow, a man 1.9 meters tall casts a 2.4-meter shadow. How tall is the Ferris wheel?

15. When a high-diving pole casts a 25-meter shadow, a man 2 meters tall casts a 1-meter shadow. How tall is the high-diving pole?

16. When a woman 1.6 meters tall casts a 0.75-meter shadow, a diving tank casts a 1.2-meter shadow. How high is the diving tank?

17. When an animal trainer 1.8 meters tall casts a 2.2-meter shadow, a black bear casts a 3.3-meter shadow. How tall is the black bear?

18. When a 2-meter sign casts a 3.4-meter shadow, a flagpole casts a 45-meter shadow. How tall is the flagpole?

19. A TV tower is 31.6 meters high and casts a 10-meter shadow. How tall is a nearby tree that casts a 6-meter shadow at the same time?

20. A fence around a water tower is 2.5 meters high and casts a 4-meter shadow. How tall is the water tower that casts a 46.4-meter shadow at the same time?

Tangent of an Angle

Pictured at the right are three similar right triangles.

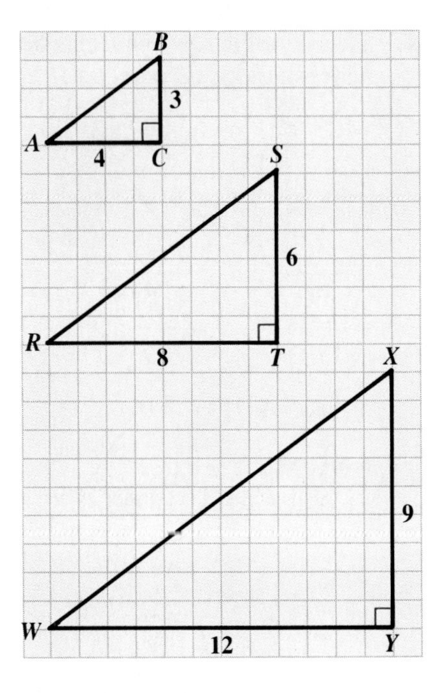

Look at $\triangle ABC$. ← *Read as "triangle ABC."*

The two sides that form the right angle (side AC and side BC) are called the **legs** of the right triangle.

1. Which two sides are the legs of $\triangle RST$? of $\triangle WXY$?

The length of the leg **opposite** $\angle A$ is 3 units.

2. What is the length of the leg opposite $\angle R$? $\angle W$?

3. What is the length of the leg opposite $\angle B$? $\angle S$? $\angle X$?

The length of the leg **adjacent** to $\angle A$ is 4 units.

4. What is the length of the leg adjacent to $\angle R$? $\angle W$?

5. What is the length of the leg adjacent to $\angle B$? $\angle S$? $\angle X$?

In a **right** triangle, the ratio of the length of the leg opposite an acute angle to the length of the leg adjacent to the acute angle is called the **tangent** of the angle.

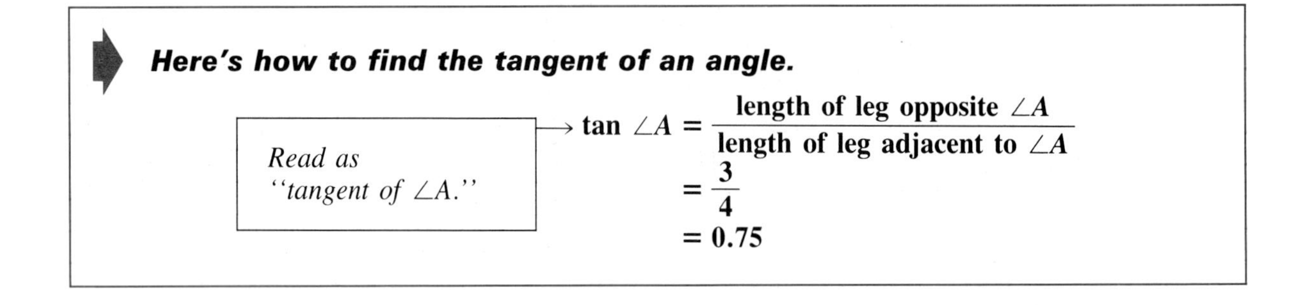

Here's how to find the tangent of an angle.

Read as "tangent of $\angle A$." →

$$\tan \angle A = \frac{\text{length of leg opposite } \angle A}{\text{length of leg adjacent to } \angle A}$$

$$= \frac{3}{4}$$

$$= 0.75$$

6. Look at the example above. What is the tan $\angle A$?

7. Complete these examples.

a. $\tan \angle R = \frac{6}{?}$
$= 0.75$

b. $\tan \angle W = \frac{9}{?}$
$= \underline{?}$

c. $\tan \angle B = \frac{4}{3}$
$= \underline{?}$

d. $\tan \angle X = \frac{12}{?}$
$= \underline{?}$

8. Remember that $\triangle RST$ and $\triangle WXY$ are similar triangles. Look at your answers to 7a and 7b. Are they equal? Does the tangent of an angle depend on the measure of the angle or the size of the triangle?

EXERCISES

▶ **Give the tan $\angle X$ as a decimal rounded to the nearest hundredth.**

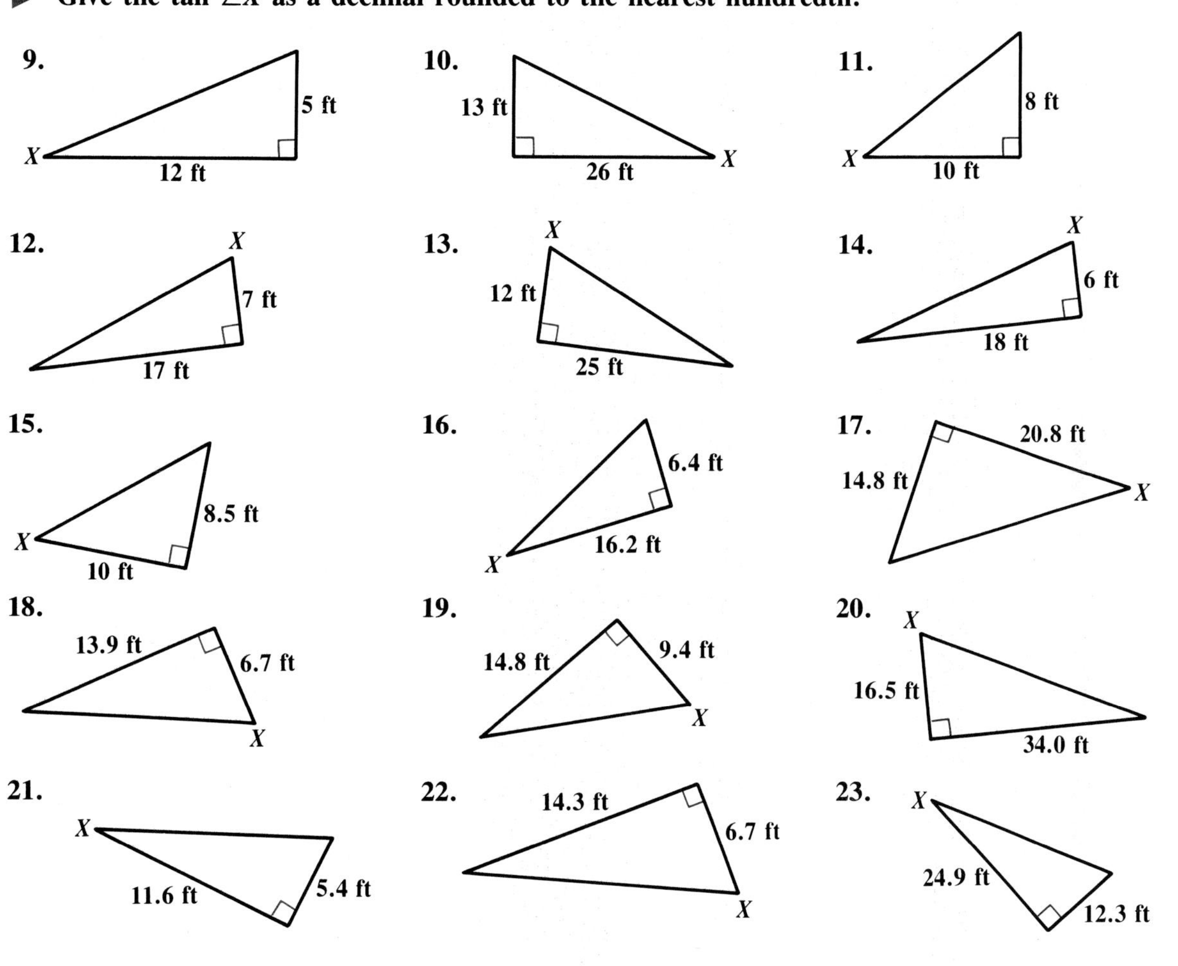

CALCULATOR

The slope, or grade, of a road is the ratio of the "rise" to the "run."

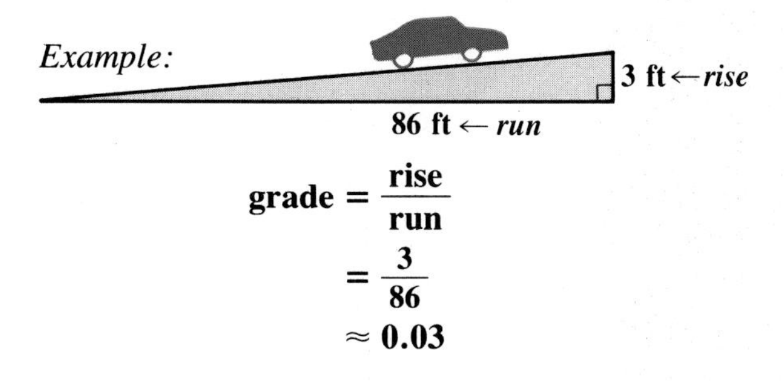

$$\text{grade} = \frac{\text{rise}}{\text{run}} = \frac{3}{86} \approx 0.03$$

24. Copy and complete this table. Round answers to the nearest hundredth.

	Rise (ft)	Run (ft)	Grade
a.	3	74	?
b.	9	318	?
c.	7	109	?

Sine and Cosine of an Angle

Remember that the sides that form the right angle in a right triangle are called the legs of the right triangle. The side opposite the right angle of a right triangle is called the **hypotenuse.**

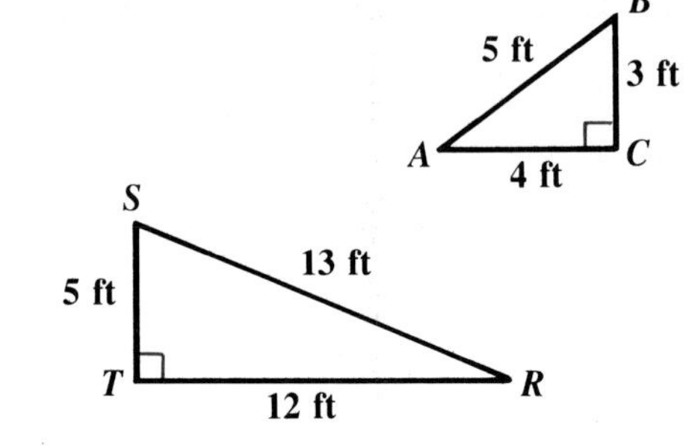

1. Which side of $\triangle ABC$ is the hypotenuse?

2. Which side of $\triangle RST$ is the hypotenuse?

3. What is the length of the hypotenuse of $\triangle ABC$? of $\triangle RST$?

In a right triangle, the ratio of the length of the leg opposite an acute angle to the length of the hypotenuse is called the **sine** of the angle.

In a right triangle, the ratio of the length of the leg adjacent to an acute angle to the length of the hypotenuse is called the **cosine** of the angle.

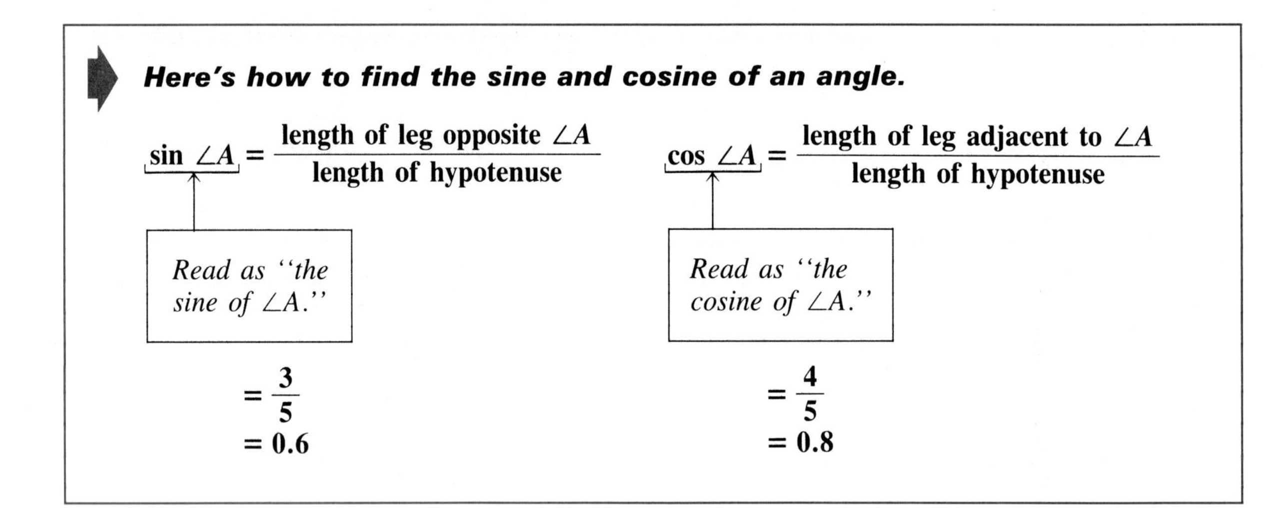

Here's how to find the sine and cosine of an angle.

$$\sin \angle A = \frac{\text{length of leg opposite } \angle A}{\text{length of hypotenuse}} = \frac{3}{5} = 0.6$$

Read as "the sine of $\angle A$."

$$\cos \angle A = \frac{\text{length of leg adjacent to } \angle A}{\text{length of hypotenuse}} = \frac{4}{5} = 0.8$$

Read as "the cosine of $\angle A$."

4. Look at the examples. What is the $\sin \angle A$? What is the $\cos \angle A$?

5. Complete these examples. Give answers as decimals rounded to the nearest hundredth.

a. $\sin \angle B = \frac{4}{5} = \underline{?}$

b. $\sin \angle R = \frac{5}{?} = \underline{?}$

c. $\sin \angle S = \frac{?}{13} = \underline{?}$

d. $\cos \angle B = \frac{3}{5} = \underline{?}$

e. $\cos \angle R = \frac{12}{?} = \underline{?}$

f. $\cos \angle S = \frac{?}{13} = \underline{?}$

EXERCISES

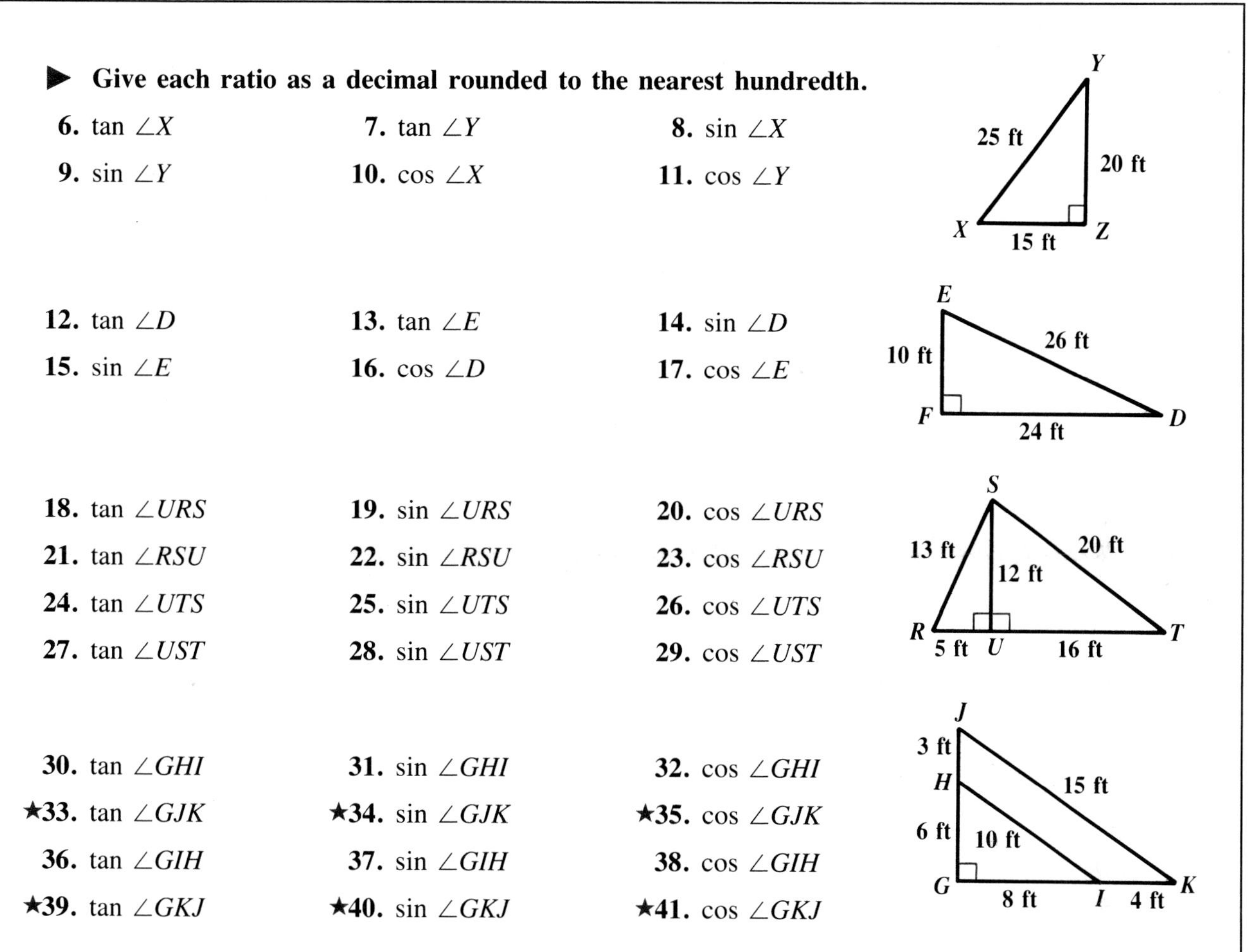

▶ **Give each ratio as a decimal rounded to the nearest hundredth.**

6. tan $\angle X$ **7.** tan $\angle Y$ **8.** sin $\angle X$

9. sin $\angle Y$ **10.** cos $\angle X$ **11.** cos $\angle Y$

12. tan $\angle D$ **13.** tan $\angle E$ **14.** sin $\angle D$

15. sin $\angle E$ **16.** cos $\angle D$ **17.** cos $\angle E$

18. tan $\angle URS$ **19.** sin $\angle URS$ **20.** cos $\angle URS$

21. tan $\angle RSU$ **22.** sin $\angle RSU$ **23.** cos $\angle RSU$

24. tan $\angle UTS$ **25.** sin $\angle UTS$ **26.** cos $\angle UTS$

27. tan $\angle UST$ **28.** sin $\angle UST$ **29.** cos $\angle UST$

30. tan $\angle GHI$ **31.** sin $\angle GHI$ **32.** cos $\angle GHI$

★33. tan $\angle GJK$ **★34.** sin $\angle GJK$ **★35.** cos $\angle GJK$

36. tan $\angle GIH$ **37.** sin $\angle GIH$ **38.** cos $\angle GIH$

★39. tan $\angle GKJ$ **★40.** sin $\angle GKJ$ **★41.** cos $\angle GKJ$

Challenge

▶ **First make a drawing. Then answer the question.**

42. If sin $\angle A = \frac{3}{5}$ and cos $\angle A = \frac{4}{5}$, what is the tan $\angle A$?

43. If sin $\angle A = \frac{5}{13}$ and tan $\angle A = \frac{5}{12}$, what is the cos $\angle A$?

44. If the tangent of one acute angle of a right triangle is $\frac{12}{19}$, what is the tangent of the other acute angle?

45. If the sine of one acute angle of a right triangle is $\frac{9}{16}$, what is the cosine of the other acute angle?

46. If the cosine of one acute angle of a right triangle is $\frac{7}{12}$, what is the sine of the other acute angle?

47. If an acute angle of a right triangle has a sine of $\frac{12}{13}$ and a cosine of $\frac{5}{13}$, what is the tangent of the acute angle?

Cumulative Skill Practice

Give the greatest common factor. *(page 126)*

1. 5, 10 **2.** 16, 24 **3.** 28, 21 **4.** 72, 24 **5.** 84, 63

6. $3, 6c$ **7.** $18, 12y$ **8.** $5w, 13w$ **9.** $9j, 4j^2$ **10.** $35g, 7g^2$

11. $21xy, 18y^2$ **12.** $14a^2b, 21ab^2$ **13.** $56cd^2, 42c^2$ **14.** $48r^2s^2, 32rs^2$ **15.** $50x^2y^3, 15xy^3$

Write in lowest terms. *(page 132)*

16. $\frac{8}{24}$ **17.** $\frac{42}{36}$ **18.** $\frac{21}{42}$ **19.** $\frac{60}{45}$ **20.** $\frac{27}{45}$ **21.** $\frac{35}{50}$

22. $\frac{n}{n^2}$ **23.** $\frac{12}{9x}$ **24.** $\frac{6x}{18y}$ **25.** $\frac{rs}{3s}$ **26.** $\frac{32ab}{8a^2}$ **27.** $\frac{40}{56c^2}$

28. $\frac{36j}{9k}$ **29.** $\frac{c^2d}{9d^2}$ **30.** $\frac{45s}{72st}$ **31.** $\frac{19k^3}{4k^2}$ **32.** $\frac{45pq^2}{25p^2}$ **33.** $\frac{16y^2z}{40y^2z^2}$

Give each sum or difference in simplest form. *(page 158)*

34. $\frac{1}{2} + \frac{1}{8}$ **35.** $\frac{1}{4} + \frac{1}{5}$ **36.** $\frac{2}{3} + \frac{3}{4}$ **37.** $\frac{7}{8} + \frac{5}{6}$ **38.** $\frac{5}{9} + \frac{4}{5}$

39. $\frac{a}{3} + \frac{b}{6}$ **40.** $\frac{j}{24} + \frac{k}{8}$ **41.** $\frac{5y}{12} + \frac{z}{8}$ **42.** $\frac{j}{6} + \frac{5k}{18}$ **43.** $\frac{3a}{35} + \frac{2b}{7}$

44. $\frac{5}{6} - \frac{1}{3}$ **45.** $\frac{3}{4} - \frac{1}{2}$ **46.** $\frac{5}{6} - \frac{4}{5}$ **47.** $\frac{8}{9} - \frac{3}{4}$ **48.** $\frac{13}{6} - \frac{5}{8}$

49. $\frac{c}{5} - \frac{d}{10}$ **50.** $\frac{m}{3} - \frac{n}{4}$ **51.** $\frac{j}{8} - \frac{k}{12}$ **52.** $\frac{y}{15} - \frac{3z}{10}$ **53.** $\frac{5q}{18} - \frac{5r}{12}$

Give each product in simplest form. *(page 172)*

54. $\frac{1}{6} \cdot \frac{1}{5}$ **55.** $\frac{3}{4} \cdot \frac{1}{3}$ **56.** $5 \cdot \frac{7}{10}$ **57.** $\frac{7}{8} \cdot \frac{8}{7}$ **58.** $\frac{5}{6} \cdot \frac{3}{10}$

59. $\frac{y}{4} \cdot \frac{1}{y}$ **60.** $9 \cdot \frac{c}{3}$ **61.** $\frac{5}{6} \cdot \frac{4k}{15}$ **62.** $\frac{3}{4d} \cdot \frac{4}{13e}$ **63.** $\frac{a}{b} \cdot \frac{7b}{3a}$

64. $\frac{r}{s^2} \cdot \frac{6s}{r}$ **65.** $\frac{m}{n} \cdot \frac{n}{m}$ **66.** $\frac{t^2}{5} \cdot \frac{s}{t}$ **67.** $\frac{9x}{y} \cdot \frac{y}{6x}$ **68.** $\frac{12c}{d} \cdot \frac{3d}{30c^2}$

Give each quotient in simplest form. *(page 176)*

69. $\frac{5}{6} \div \frac{1}{6}$ **70.** $\frac{6}{7} \div \frac{2}{7}$ **71.** $\frac{9}{8} \div \frac{3}{4}$ **72.** $\frac{4}{5} \div 5$ **73.** $8 \div \frac{3}{5}$

74. $\frac{7}{n} \div \frac{3}{n}$ **75.** $\frac{10}{a} \div \frac{5}{b}$ **76.** $\frac{r}{16} \div \frac{s}{12}$ **77.** $\frac{3s}{t} \div \frac{5s}{t}$ **78.** $\frac{2j^2}{k} \div \frac{j}{k}$

Problem Solving—Applications

Triangles can be classified according to the types of angles they contain.

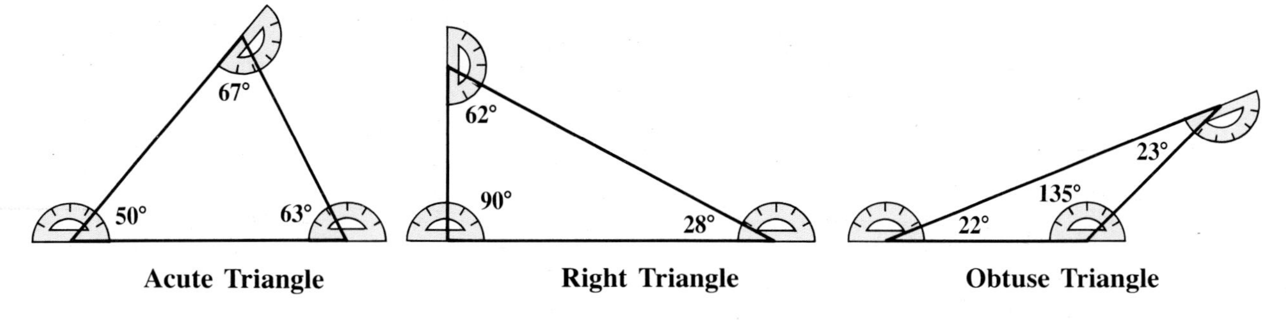

Use the triangles above. Complete each sentence.

1. An acute triangle has __?__ acute angle(s). The sum of its three angles is __?__ degrees.
2. A right triangle has __?__ right angle(s). The sum of its three angles is __?__ degrees.
3. An obtuse triangle has __?__ obtuse angle(s). The sum of its three angles is __?__ degrees.
4. The sum of the measures of the angles of any triangle is __?__ degrees.

Write and solve an equation to find the measures of the missing angles.
Remember: The sum of the measures of the angles of any triangle is 180°.

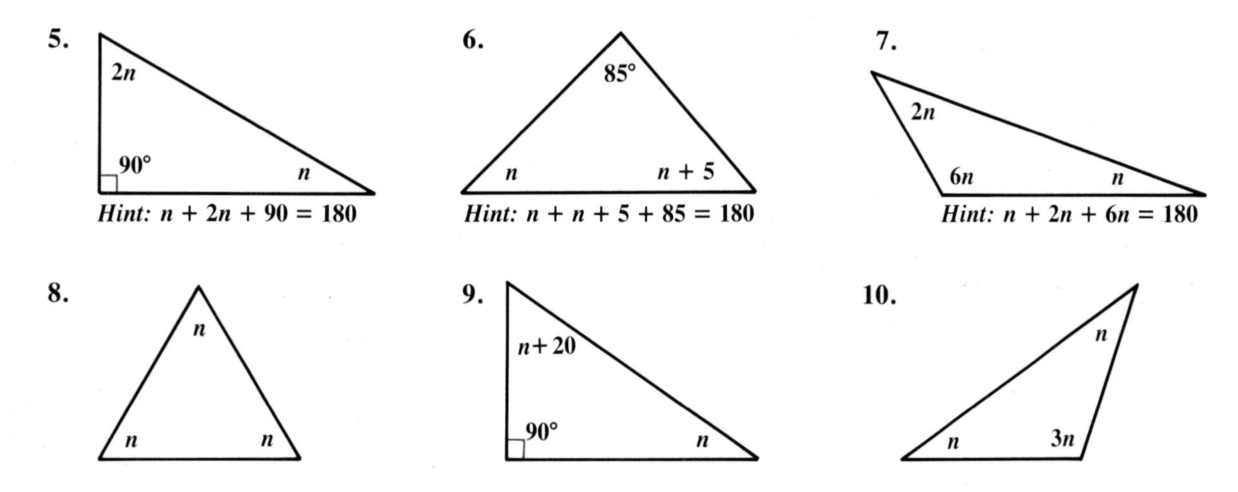

11. In a right triangle the measure of one of the acute angles is 4 times the measure of the other acute angle. Find the measure of each angle.
12. Find the measure of each angle in a triangle if the measure of the second angle is 3 times that of the first angle, and the measure of the third angle is 5 times that of the first angle.

Using a Trigonometry Table to Find a Side

In this lesson you will use a table of sine, cosine, and tangent ratios to find the length of a side of a right triangle.

Each ratio in the table has been expressed as a decimal rounded to the nearest ten-thousandth. A more complete table of trigonometric ratios can be found on page 498.

Table of Trigonometric Ratios			
Angle	**Sine**	**Cosine**	**Tangent**
35°	0.5736	0.8192	0.7002
40°	0.6428	0.7660	0.8391
45°	0.7071	0.7071	1.0000
50°	0.7660	0.6428	1.1918
55°	0.8192	0.5736	1.4281
60°	0.8660	0.5000	1.7321
65°	0.9063	0.4226	2.1445
70°	0.9397	0.3420	2.7475

1. What is the sine 40°?

2. What is the cos 50°?

3. What is the tan 45°?

Here's how to use the table of trigonometric ratios to find the length of a side of a right triangle.

35° | 18 feet | n

Step 1. Since we have to find the length of the side opposite the given angle and we know the length of the side adjacent to the given angle, we use the tangent ratio.

$$\tan 35° = \frac{n}{18}$$

Step 2. Look up the tan 35° and substitute it in the equation.

$$0.7002 = \frac{n}{18}$$

Step 3. Solve the equation.

$$18 \times 0.7002 = 18 \times \frac{n}{18}$$

$$12.6036 = n$$

Rounded to the nearest tenth, the length of the side is 12.6 feet.

4. Look at the example. What value was substituted for tan 35°? What was n rounded to the nearest tenth?

5. Complete these examples.

a.

$$\sin 60° = \frac{n}{20}$$

$$\underline{\ ?\ } = \frac{n}{20}$$

$$20 \times 0.8660 = n$$

$$\underline{\ ?\ } = n$$

20 ft | 60° | n

b.

$$\cos 45° = \frac{n}{27}$$

$$\underline{\ ?\ } = \frac{n}{27}$$

$$27 \times 0.7071 = n$$

$$\underline{\ ?\ } = n$$

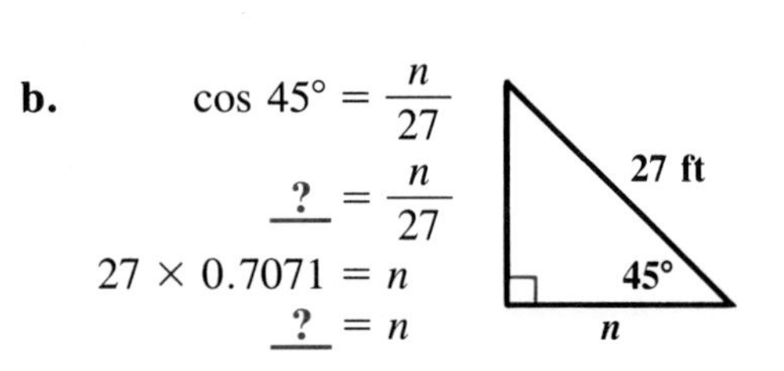

EXERCISES

▶ **Find n rounded to the nearest tenth of a foot.**

Use the tangent ratios in the table on page 406.

Use the sine ratios in the table on page 406.

Use the cosine ratios in the table on page 406.

▶ **Find n rounded to the nearest tenth of a foot. Use the table on page 498.**

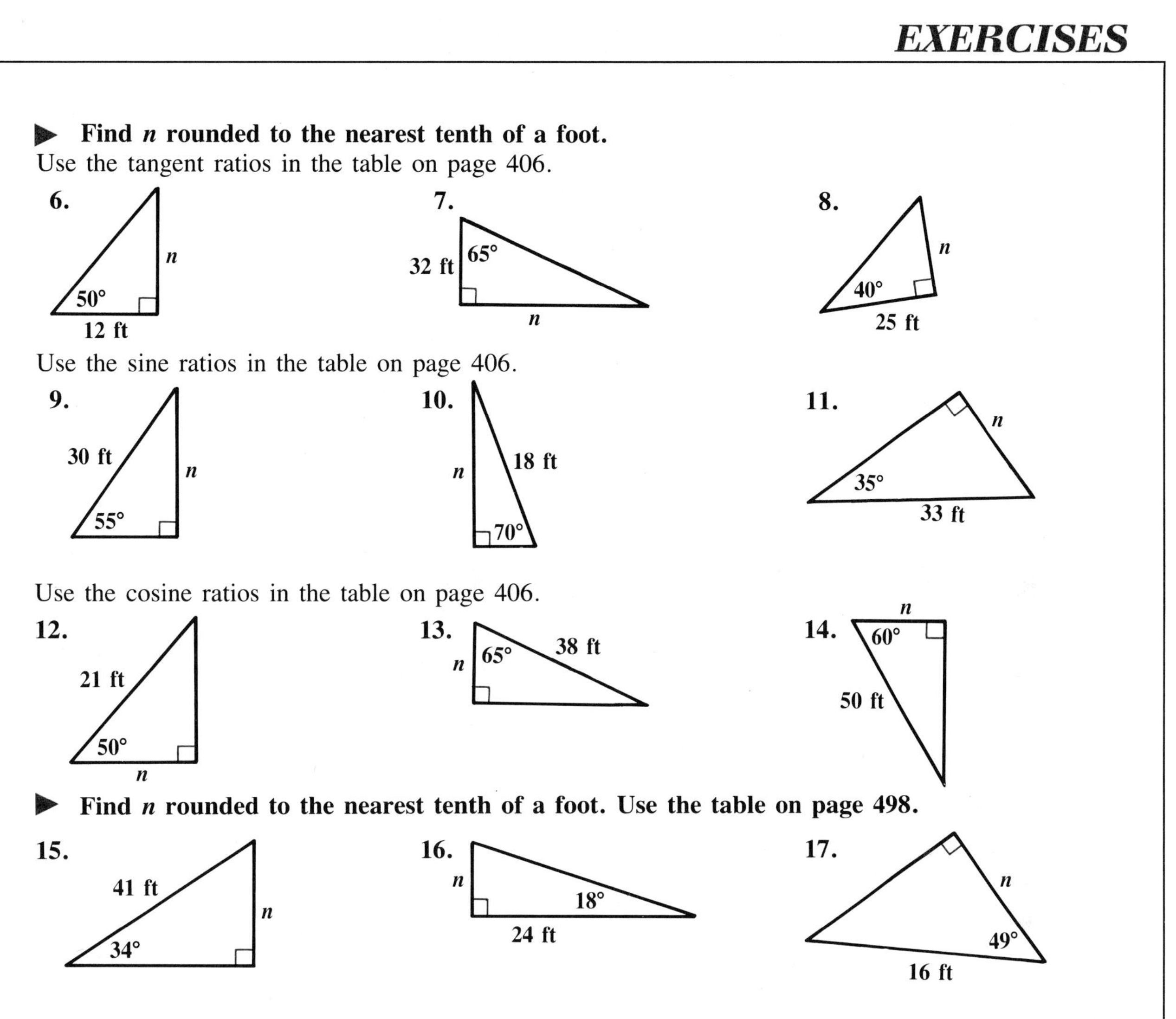

Problem Solving

▶ **First make a drawing. Then solve the problem. Round answers to the nearest tenth. Use the table on page 498.**

18. A hot-air balloon is directly over a small town. A man 10 miles away can look directly at the balloon by sighting 32° above horizontal. How high is the balloon?

19. How tall is a television tower if someone standing 800 feet away can look directly at the top by sighting 23° above horizontal?

20. When a kite flier had let out 240 feet of string, she noticed that the kite was 58° above horizontal. How high was the kite? Disregard any sag in the kite string.

21. When a 500-foot cable is attached to a sunken treasure, the cable forms a 37° angle with the surface of the ocean. How deep is the treasure? Disregard any sag in the cable.

Using a Trigonometry Table to Find an Angle

Angle	Sine	Cosine	Tangent
31°	0.5150	0.8572	0.6009
32°	0.5299	0.8480	0.6249
33°	0.5446	0.8387	0.6494
34°	0.5592	0.8290	0.6745
35°	0.5736	0.8192	0.7002
36°	0.5878	0.8090	0.7265
37°	0.6018	0.7986	0.7536
38°	0.6157	0.7880	0.7813
39°	0.6293	0.7771	0.8098
40°	0.6428	0.7660	0.8391

Table of Trigonometric Ratios

Use the table to answer the following questions.

1. What is the measure of an angle that has
   a. a sine of 0.5446?
   b. a cosine of 0.7771?
   c. a tangent of 0.7265?

An angle that has a sine of 0.5162 has a measure between 31° and 32°. Since 0.5162 is closer to 0.5150 (sin 31°) than to 0.5299 (sin 32°), the measure of the angle to the nearest degree is 31°.

2. What is the measure of an angle (to the nearest degree) that has a cosine of 0.8000?

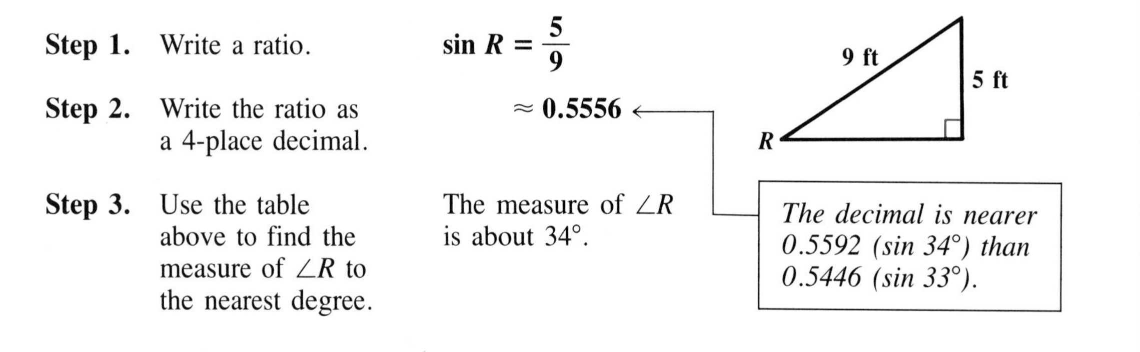

Here's how to use the table of trigonometric ratios to approximate an angle of a right triangle.

Step 1. Write a ratio. $\sin R = \frac{5}{9}$

Step 2. Write the ratio as a 4-place decimal. ≈ 0.5556

Step 3. Use the table above to find the measure of $\angle R$ to the nearest degree. The measure of $\angle R$ is about 34°.

The decimal is nearer 0.5592 (sin 34°) than 0.5446 (sin 33°).

3. Look at the example. Between what two values in the table is 0.5556? Which of the two values is it closer to?

4. What is the approximate measure of $\angle R$?

5. Complete these examples. Use the table above.

a. $\cos \angle X = \frac{30}{38}$
≈ 0.7895

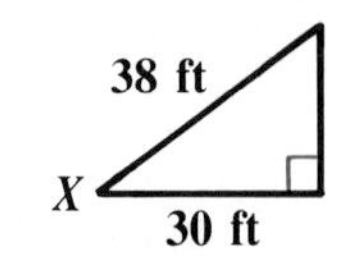

What is the measure of $\angle X$ to the nearest degree?

b. $\tan \angle Y = \frac{21}{30}$
$= 0.7000$

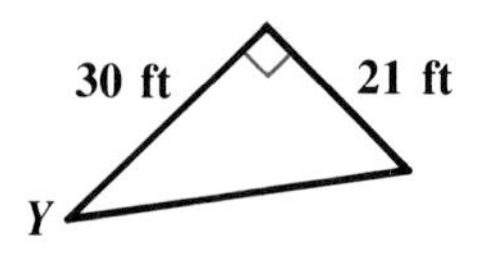

What is the measure of $\angle Y$ to the nearest degree?

▶ **Find the measure of the labeled angle to the nearest degree. Use the trigonometric table on page 498. You may wish to use a calculator to express each ratio as a 4-place decimal.**

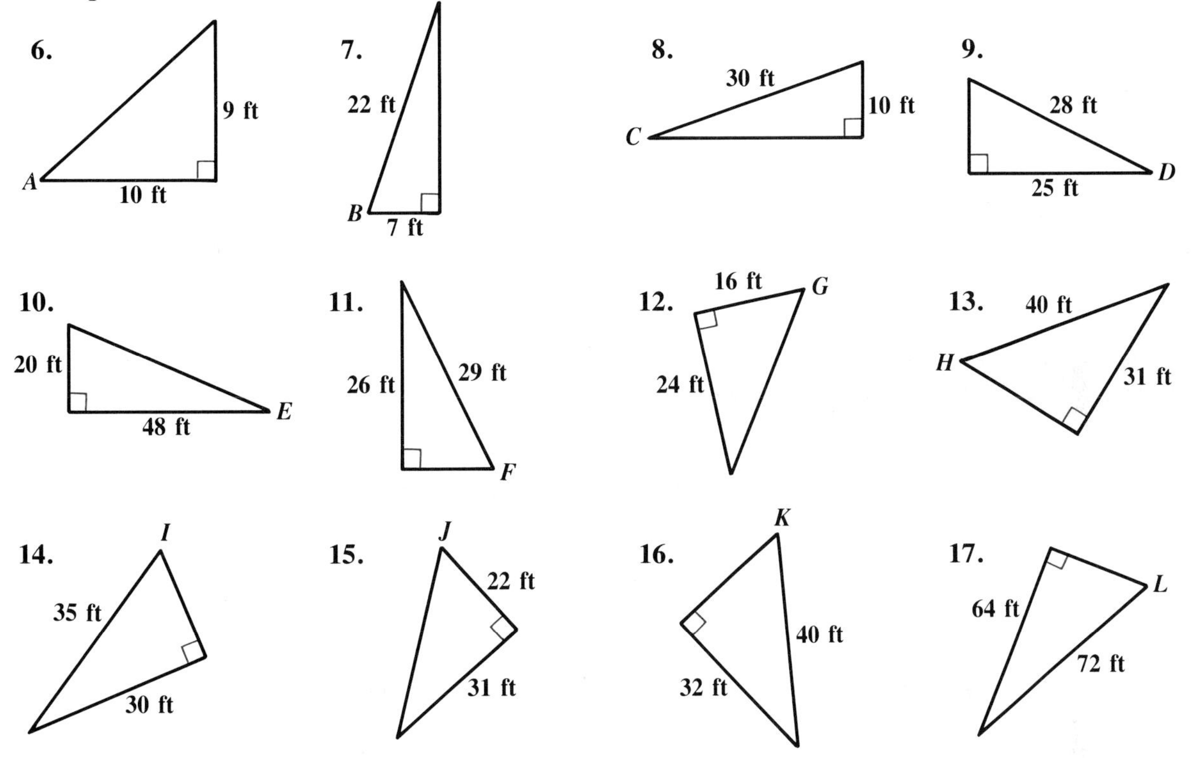

Problem Solving

▶ **First make a drawing. Then solve the problem. Give angles to the nearest degree and lengths to the nearest tenth of a foot. Use the table on page 498.**

18. When a submarine was ordered to dive, it traveled 240 feet to get to 100 feet below the surface of the water. What angle did the submarine's course make with the surface of the water?

★19. From the top of a 185-foot radio tower a construction worker observed a stop sign. If his line of sight made a 60° angle with the tower, how far from the tower was the stop sign?

20. A 40-foot inclined ramp is used to load freight on an airplane. The bottom of the cargo door is 18 feet above the ground. What angle does the ramp make with the runway?

★21. A 60-foot pine tree was struck by lightning. At a point 20 feet above the ground, the tree bent over, allowing the top of the tree to touch the ground. What angle did the upper part of the tree make with the ground?

Square Roots

Ancient mathematicians often thought about numbers in geometric terms. For example, if they multiplied a number by itself, they thought about finding the area of a square. That is the reason we still talk about squaring numbers.

From the figure we have

$$4^2 = 16$$

Read as "4 squared is 16."

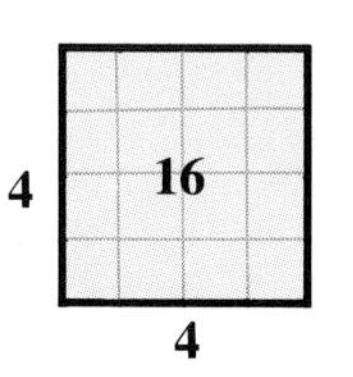

To find the **square root** of a number, we can first think about a square having the number as its area. Then we find the square root by finding the length of a side.

Table of Square Roots			
n	$\sqrt{n}$	n	$\sqrt{n}$
1	1	**11**	3.317
2	1.414	**12**	3.464
3	1.732	**13**	3.606
4	2	**14**	3.742
5	2.236	**15**	3.873
6	2.449	**16**	4
7	2.646	**17**	4.123
8	2.828	**18**	4.243
9	3	**19**	4.359
10	3.162	**20**	4.472

From the same figure we also have

$$\sqrt{16} = 4$$

Read as "the square root of 16 is 4."

You will generally be working with a decimal approximation of the square root of a number. From the table above we have

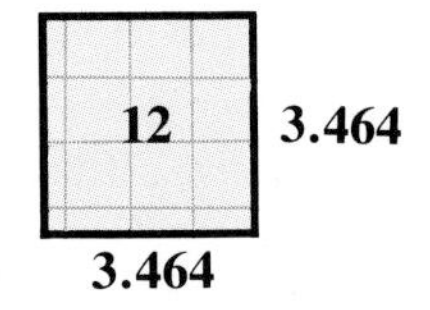

$$\sqrt{12} \approx 3.464$$

1. Multiply 3.464 by itself. Is the product near 12?

Sometimes you may need to find the square root of a number when you do not have a table of square roots or a calculator with a $\sqrt{}$ key.

Here's how to find the square root of a number by using the divide-and-average method.

Example: Find $\sqrt{46}$ to the nearest tenth.

Step 1.
Estimate $\sqrt{46}$.

$\sqrt{36} = 6$

$\sqrt{46} = ?$

$\sqrt{49} = 7$

$\sqrt{46}$ is between 6 and 7. We will try 6.5.

Step 2.
Divide 46 by 6.5.

$46.000 \div 6.5 = 7.07 \approx 7.1$

$\sqrt{46}$ is between 6.5 and 7.1

Step 3.
Average 6.5 and 7.1.

$$\frac{6.5 + 7.1}{2} = 6.8$$

Step 4.
Divide 46 by 6.8.

$46.000 \div 6.8 = 6.76 \approx 6.8$

$\sqrt{46}$ is between 6.8 and 6.8. When rounded to the nearest tenth, $\sqrt{46} = 6.8$.

2. Look at the example in the box on page 410. We first found that $\sqrt{46}$ was between what two whole numbers?

3. In Step 2 we found that $\sqrt{46}$ was between what two numbers?

4. In Step 4 we found that $\sqrt{46}$ was between what two numbers?

5. When rounded to the nearest tenth, $\sqrt{46} = \underline{\ ?\ }$.

EXERCISES

▶ **Simplify.**
Here are scrambled answers for the next row of exercises: *5 3 1 4 2 8*

6. $\sqrt{4}$ **7.** $\sqrt{1}$ **8.** $\sqrt{16}$ **9.** $\sqrt{25}$ **10.** $\sqrt{9}$ **11.** $\sqrt{64}$

12. $\sqrt{144}$ **13.** $\sqrt{256}$ **14.** $\sqrt{121}$ **15.** $\sqrt{1.44}$ **16.** $\sqrt{2.56}$ **17.** $\sqrt{1.21}$

▶ **Give the approximate square root found in the tables on pages 496 and 497.**

18. $\sqrt{29}$ **19.** $\sqrt{47}$ **20.** $\sqrt{71}$ **21.** $\sqrt{87}$ **22.** $\sqrt{98}$ **23.** $\sqrt{127}$

▶ **True or false?**

24. $\sqrt{11}$ is between 3 and 4.

25. $\sqrt{31}$ is between 5 and 6.

26. $\sqrt{150}$ is between 13 and 14.

27. $\sqrt{200}$ is between 14 and 15.

▶ **Use the divide-and-average method to give an approximation to the nearest tenth.**

28. $\sqrt{300}$ **29.** $\sqrt{421}$ **30.** $\sqrt{506}$ **31.** $\sqrt{766}$ **32.** $\sqrt{919}$

Challenge

33. a. Use a protractor and carefully draw a right triangle.
b. Measure each side to the nearest millimeter.
c. Square the length of each leg.
d. Add the squares of the lengths of the legs.
e. Square the length of the hypotenuse.
f. Compare the sum of the squares of the lengths of the legs (part **d**) and the square of the length of the hypotenuse (part **e**). Are they the same or ''close'' to being the same?
g. Draw another right triangle and repeat steps **a** through **f**.

The Pythagorean Theorem

Look at the figure at the right.

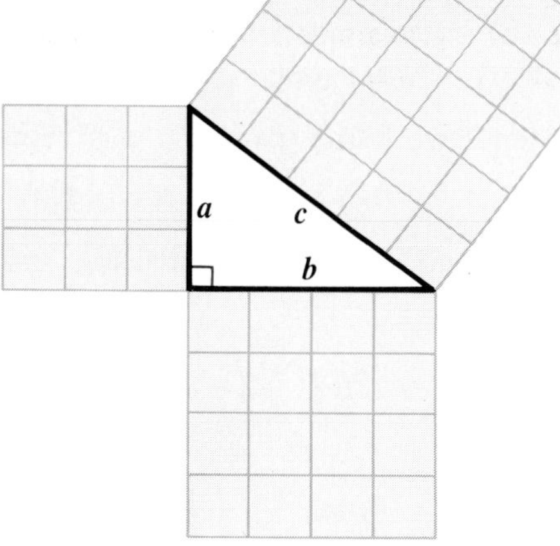

1. The area of the square on leg a is 9 square units. What is the area of the square on leg b? What is the sum of the two areas?
2. What is the area of the square on the hypotenuse?
3. Is the sum of the areas of the squares on the legs the same as the area of the square on the hypotenuse?

The Pythagorean Theorem

In a right triangle, the sum of the squares of the lengths of the legs is equal to the square of the length of the hypotenuse.

The Pythagorean theorem can be written as $a^2 + b^2 = c^2$, where a and b are the lengths of the legs and c is the length of the hypotenuse of a right triangle.

Here's how to use the Pythagorean theorem to find the length of a side of a right triangle when the lengths of the other two sides are known.

Example A

$$a^2 + b^2 = c^2$$
$$7^2 + 9^2 = c^2$$
$$49 + 81 = c^2$$
$$130 = c^2$$
$$\sqrt{130} = c$$
$$11.4 \approx c$$

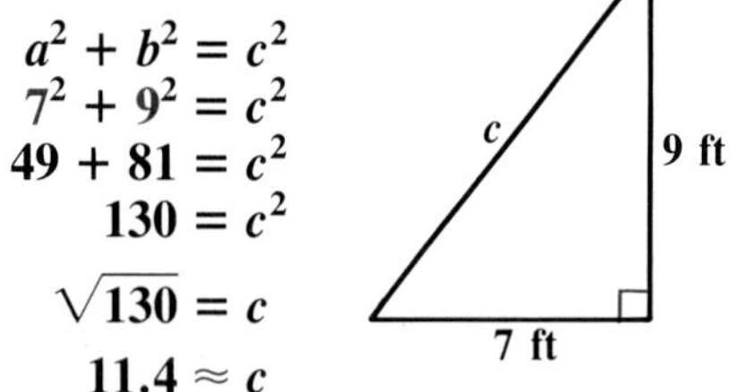

The approximate length c of the side is 11.4 feet.

Example B

$$a^2 + b^2 = c^2$$
$$15^2 + b^2 = 20^2$$
$$225 + b^2 = 400$$
$$b^2 = 175$$
$$b = \sqrt{175}$$
$$b \approx 13.2$$

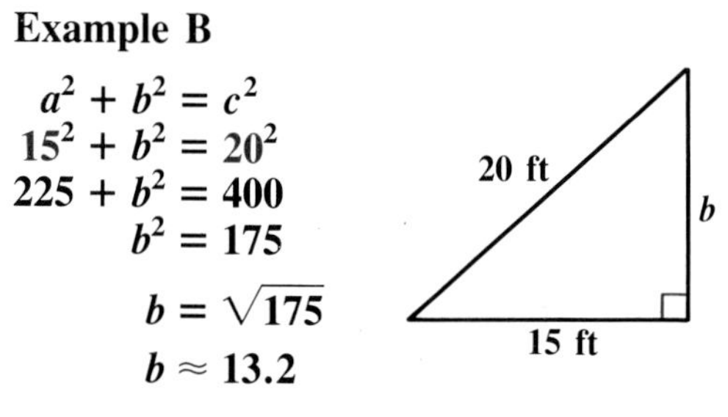

The approximate length b of the side is 13.2 feet.

4. Look at the example. In which example was the length of the hypotenuse found? The length of a leg found?
5. What was the approximate length c of the side in Example A?
6. What was the approximate length b of the side in Example B?

▶ **Use the Pythagorean theorem to find the length *n* rounded to the nearest tenth of a foot. Use the square-root tables on pages 496 and 497.**

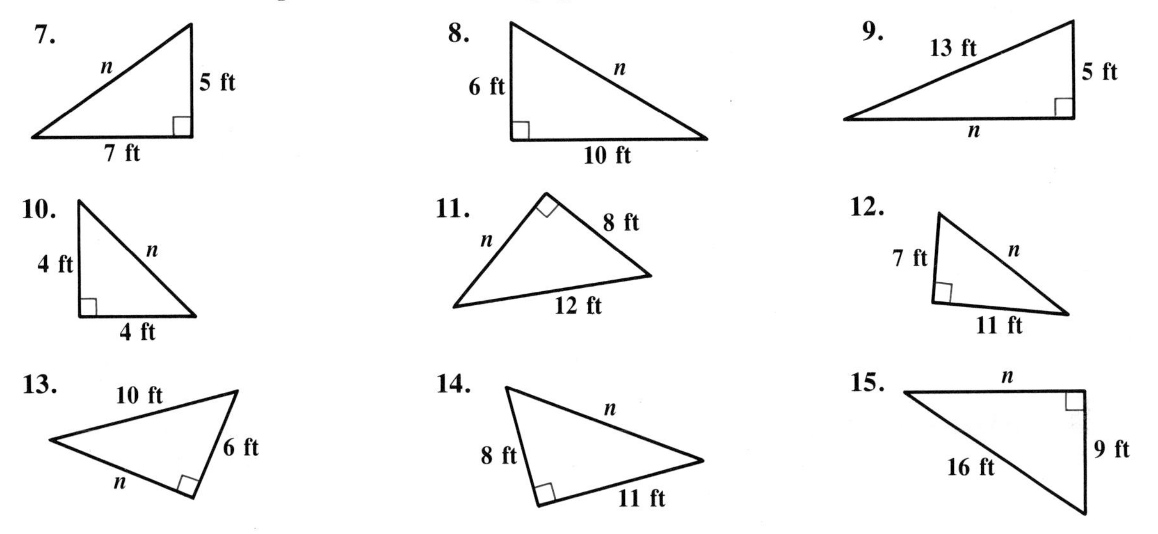

Problem Solving

▶ **Use the Pythagorean theorem to solve each problem. Round answers to the nearest tenth. Use the square-root tables on pages 496 and 497.**

16. Find the length of the diagonal of the rectangle.

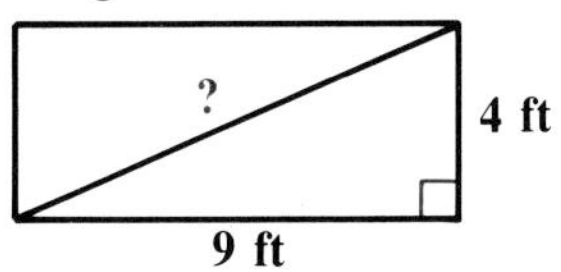

17. Find the width of the rectangle.

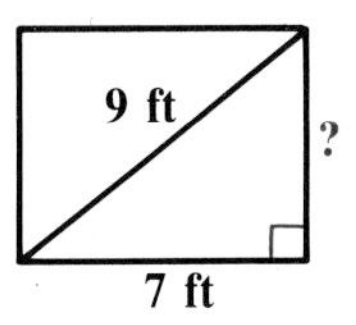

18. Find the diameter of the circle.

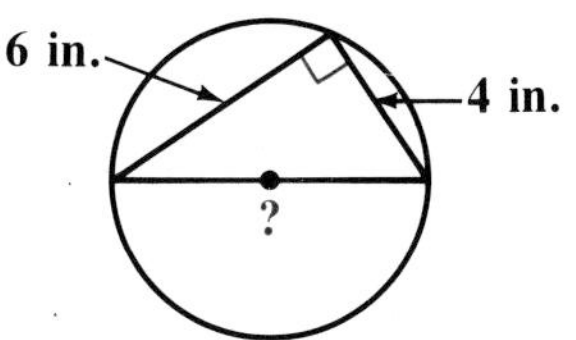

19. Find the height of the cone.

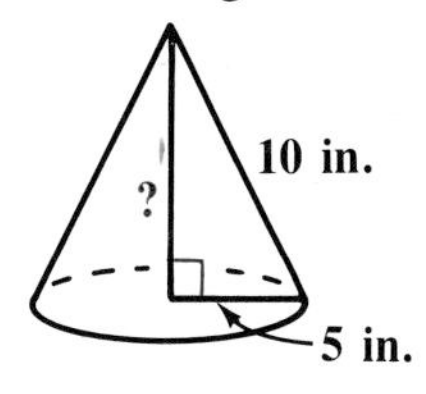

Challenge

▶ **Is the triangle with the given lengths a right triangle? Write *Yes* or *No*.**

20. 5, 12, 13 **21.** 1, 2, 3 **22.** 8, 15, 16 **23.** 4, 4, 6

24. 20, 21, 29 **25.** 16, 30, 34 **26.** 15, 20, 25 **27.** 8, 9, 15

Problem Solving—Using the Pythagorean Theorem

In this lesson you will solve problems by using the Pythagorean theorem. In solving these problems, it will be helpful to use drawings that picture the facts in the problem.

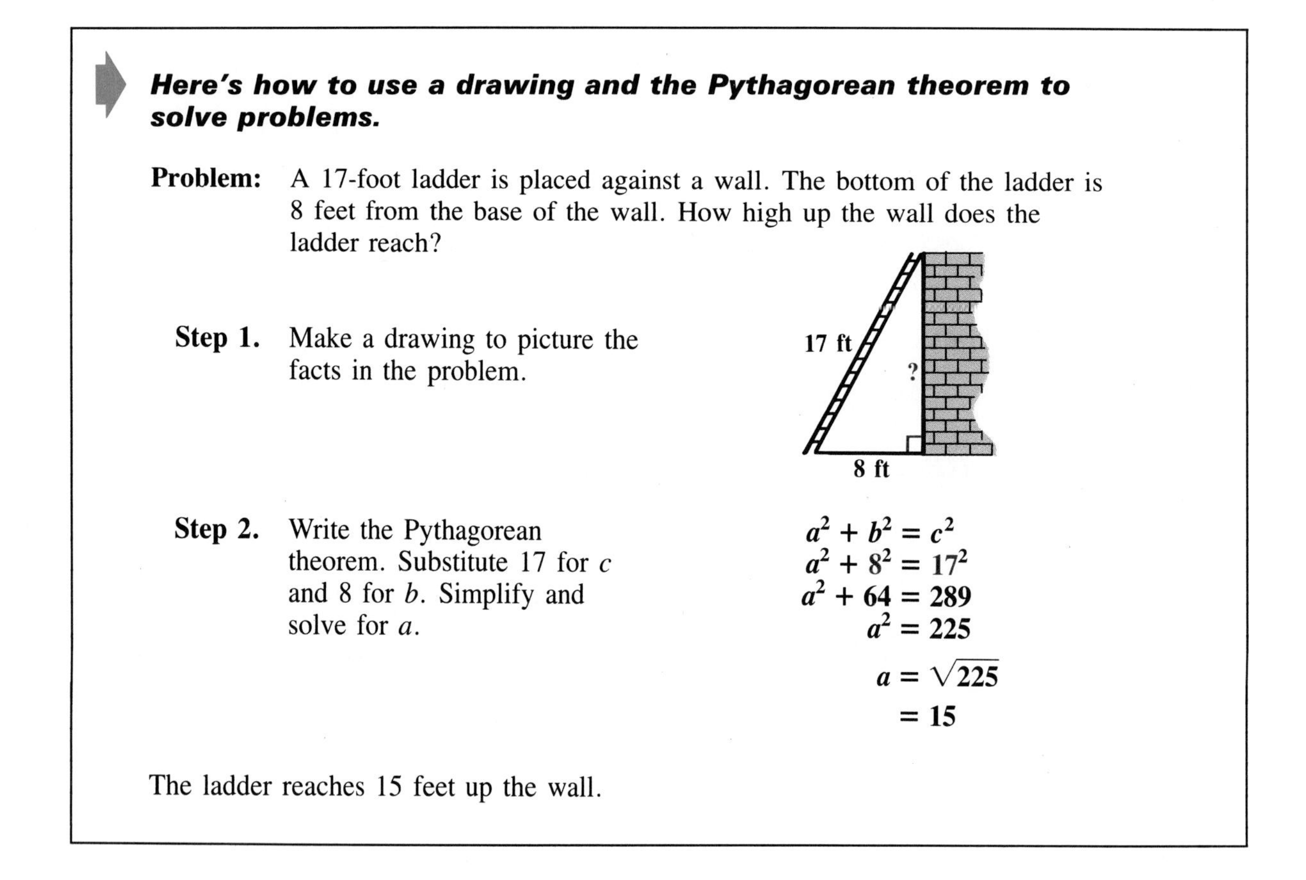

Here's how to use a drawing and the Pythagorean theorem to solve problems.

Problem: A 17-foot ladder is placed against a wall. The bottom of the ladder is 8 feet from the base of the wall. How high up the wall does the ladder reach?

Step 1. Make a drawing to picture the facts in the problem.

Step 2. Write the Pythagorean theorem. Substitute 17 for c and 8 for b. Simplify and solve for a.

$$a^2 + b^2 = c^2$$
$$a^2 + 8^2 = 17^2$$
$$a^2 + 64 = 289$$
$$a^2 = 225$$
$$a = \sqrt{225}$$
$$= 15$$

The ladder reaches 15 feet up the wall.

1. Look at the example above.

a. In Step 1, the ladder forms a right triangle with the wall and the ground. The hypotenuse of the right triangle is _?_ feet. The shorter leg is _?_ feet.

b. In Step 2, we substituted _?_ for c and 8 for _?_.

c. An equation for the problem is $a^2 + 64 =$ _?_.

2. To check the solution, ask yourself if the answer fits the facts in the problem. Does $8^2 + 15^2 = 17^2$?

▶ **Decide which drawing would be used to picture the facts in each problem. Then use the drawing and the Pythagorean theorem to solve the problem. Round your answers to the nearest tenth. The tables of square roots are on pages 496 and 497.**

Drawing A

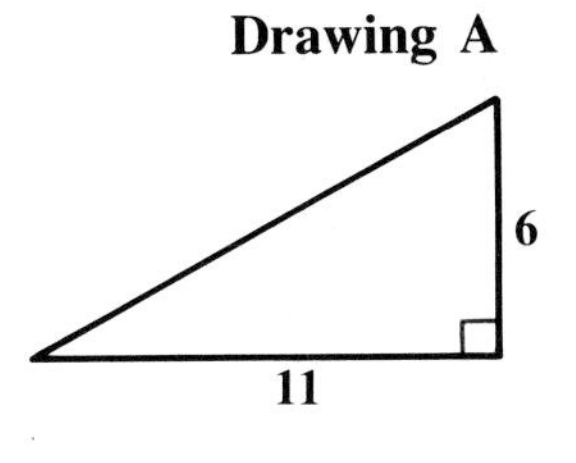

Drawing B

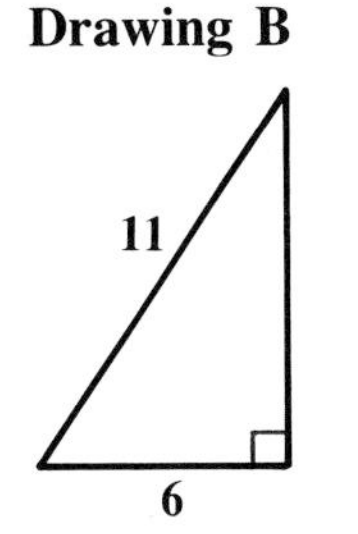

3. An airplane is 6 miles directly above a control tower. An observer on the ground is 11 miles from the control tower. How far is the observer from the airplane?

4. An 11-foot rope is fastened to the top of a flagpole. The rope reaches a point on the ground 6 feet from the base of the flagpole. What is the height of the flagpole?

5. An 11-foot ladder is placed so that it reaches the top of a wall. The bottom of the ladder is 6 feet from the wall. How high is the wall?

6. Arlo and Janie biked 11 miles east and then 6 miles north. How far are they from their starting point?

▶ **First make a drawing. Then solve the problem. Use the divide-and-average method to find the square root. Round your answers to the nearest tenth.**

7. A boat traveled 15 miles west and then 10 miles south. How far is the boat from its starting point?

8. A 27-foot rope is attached to the top of a 17-foot pole. If the rope is stretched to the ground and fastened, how far from the base of the pole is it fastened?

CALCULATOR

▶ **Solve using a calculator. Round your answers to the nearest tenth.**

9. The bases on a baseball diamond are 90 feet apart. How long a throw is it from second base to home plate?

10. A square empty lot that is often used as a shortcut is 50 feet on a side. How much shorter is the diagonal across the lot than the walk along two of its sides?

11. A 100-foot cable is fastened to the top of a television tower and to a stake that is 25 feet from the base of the tower. How tall is the tower?

12. A cable is fastened to the top of a 100-foot television tower and to a stake that is 25 feet from the base of the tower. How long is the cable?

Cumulative Skill Practice

▶ **Solve. Give each answer in simplest form.** *(page 182)*

1. $\frac{1}{3}$ of $39 = n$ **2.** $\frac{1}{5}$ of $55 = n$ **3.** $\frac{2}{3}$ of $48 = n$ **4.** $\frac{3}{4}$ of $52 = n$

5. $\frac{5}{8}$ of $64 = n$ **6.** $\frac{4}{5}$ of $65 = n$ **7.** $\frac{5}{6}$ of $42 = n$ **8.** $\frac{3}{2}$ of $80 = n$

9. $\frac{3}{5}$ of $27 = n$ **10.** $\frac{7}{3}$ of $41 = n$ **11.** $\frac{5}{4}$ of $42 = n$ **12.** $\frac{4}{5}$ of $51 = n$

▶ **Complete.** *(page 184)*

13. $1\frac{1}{3}$ ft = ___?___ in. **14.** $2\frac{3}{4}$ ft = ___?___ in. **15.** $2\frac{1}{3}$ yd = ___?___ ft

16. $1\frac{1}{2}$ days = ___?___ h **17.** $2\frac{2}{3}$ h = ___?___ min **18.** $1\frac{1}{3}$ min = ___?___ s

19. $1\frac{1}{3}$ yd = ___?___ in. **20.** $2\frac{1}{4}$ yd = ___?___ in. **21.** $1\frac{1}{2}$ gal = ___?___ qt

22. $2\frac{1}{2}$ qt = ___?___ pt **23.** $2\frac{3}{4}$ gal = ___?___ pt **24.** $3\frac{1}{2}$ pt = ___?___ c

▶ **Solve. Give answers in simplest form.** *(page 186)*

25. $\frac{1}{3}n = 14$ **26.** $\frac{1}{2}n = 21$ **27.** $\frac{1}{5}n = 33$ **28.** $\frac{2}{3}n = 36$

29. $\frac{3}{4}n = 42$ **30.** $\frac{5}{8}n = 50$ **31.** $\frac{5}{3}n = 65$ **32.** $\frac{7}{4}n = 56$

33. $\frac{5}{8}n = 18$ **34.** $\frac{4}{5}n = 41$ **35.** $\frac{7}{5}n = 60$ **36.** $\frac{5}{6}n = 62$

▶ **Simplify by combining like terms.** *(page 236)*

37. $9y + y$ **38.** $5z - z$ **39.** $7j - 7j$

40. $^{-}4n + 7n - 11$ **41.** $^{-}4n + 7 - 11n$ **42.** $^{-}4 + 7n - 11n$

43. $^{-}12t - t - 15$ **44.** $^{-}12t + t - 15$ **45.** $^{-}12t + 1 - 15$

▶ **Solve and check.** *(page 240)*

46. $3n + 2n = 5 - 17$ **47.** $13y - y = {}^{-}7 + 23$ **48.** $z - 9z = 15 - 26$

49. $5j - 4j - 6 = 11 + 27$ **50.** $5j - 4 - 6j = 11 + 27$ **51.** $5 - 4j - 6j = 11 + 27$

52. $11t + 13 - 7t - 8 = {}^{-}4 - 18$ **53.** $11t + 13 - 7 - 8t = {}^{-}4 - 18$

Problem Solving—Applications

The higher you go, the farther you see. The chart shows how far you can see on a clear day at different heights.

Height (miles)	Distance (miles)
0.1	28.3
0.2	40.0
0.3	48.9
0.4	56.5
0.5	63.2
0.6	69.2

1. On a clear day, how many miles can you see from a hang glider at a height of 0.1 mile?
2. How far can you see at a height of 0.2 mile?
3. How far can you see at a height of 0.4 mile?
4. Can you see twice as far at a height of 0.4 mile as you can see at a height of 0.2 mile?
5. Can you see more or less than 50 miles at a height of 2640 feet? *Hint: 5280 feet = 1 mile.*
6. Are you above or below 500 feet if you can see a distance of 30 miles?

Solve. Use the formula at the right. The tables of square roots are on pages 496 and 497.

$$d = 89.4\sqrt{h}$$

d: *distance seen in miles*; *h*: *height in miles*

7. On a clear day, how many miles can you see from an airplane at a height of 4 miles?
8. How far can you see at a height of 1 mile?
9. How far can you see at a height of 9 miles?
10. Can you see a distance of 150 miles at a height of 2 miles?
11. To the nearest mile, how much farther can you see at a height of 2 miles than you can see at a height of 1 mile?

Chapter Review

Here are scrambled answers for the review exercises:

0.8480	*6.2*	*10*	*26*	*congruent*	*hypotenuse*	*sum*
5	*6.4*	*12*	*31*	*cosine*	*legs*	*tangent*
6	*9*	*13*	*average*	*equal*	*square*	

1. In similar figures, corresponding angles are __?__ and the ratios of the lengths of corresponding sides are __?__. *(page 396)*

2. The two right triangles are similar. To find the length n of the side, you can solve this proportion:

$$\frac{n}{25} = \frac{?}{?} \quad \textit{(page 398)}$$

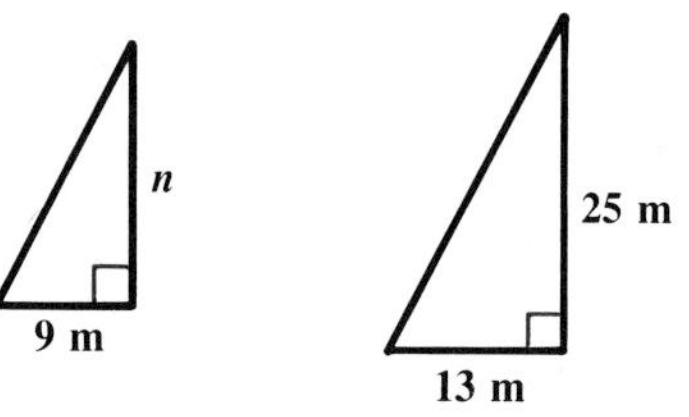

3. In a right triangle, the two sides that form the right angle are called the __?__. In a right triangle, the ratio of the length of the leg opposite an acute angle to the length of the leg adjacent to the acute angle is called the __?__ of the angle. *(page 400)*

4. The side opposite the right angle in a right triangle is called the __?__. In the triangle at the right, the sin $\angle R = \frac{?}{13}$; the cos $\angle R = \frac{?}{13}$. *(page 402)*

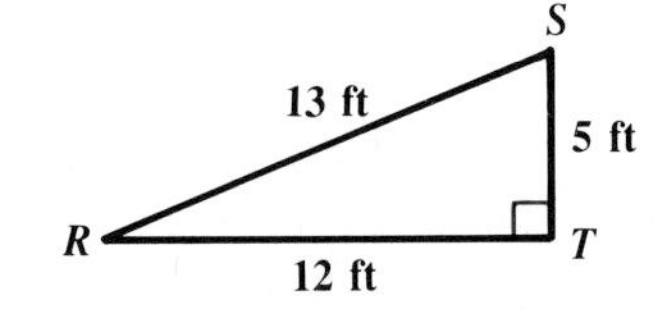

5. To find the length n, you would first write $\cos 32° = \frac{n}{?}$.

Then you would look up the __?__ of 32° in the table. The last step would be to solve $\underline{?} = \frac{n}{10}$. *(page 406)*

Table of Trigonometric Ratios			
Angle	**Sine**	**Cosine**	**Tangent**
31°	0.5150	0.8572	0.6009
32°	0.5299	0.8480	0.6249
33°	0.5446	0.8387	0.6494

6. To approximate $\angle X$, you would first write $\sin \angle X = \frac{?}{50}$
$= 0.5200$

Then you would use the table to approximate $\angle X$ to the nearest degree. The measure of $\angle X$ to the nearest degree is __?__°. *(page 408)*

7. You can use the divide-and-__?__ method to find the square root of a number. The $\sqrt{39}$ is between __?__ and 7. Try 6.1.

$$6.1\overline{)39.00}\ \ 6.39$$

From the division, you know that the $\sqrt{39}$ is between 6.1 and __?__. Next, you would divide 39 by the average of 6.1 and 6.4. When rounded to the nearest tenth, $\sqrt{39} =$ __?__. *(page 410)*

8. In a right triangle, the __?__ of the squares of the lengths of the legs is equal to the __?__ of the length of the hypotenuse. *(page 412)*

Chapter Test

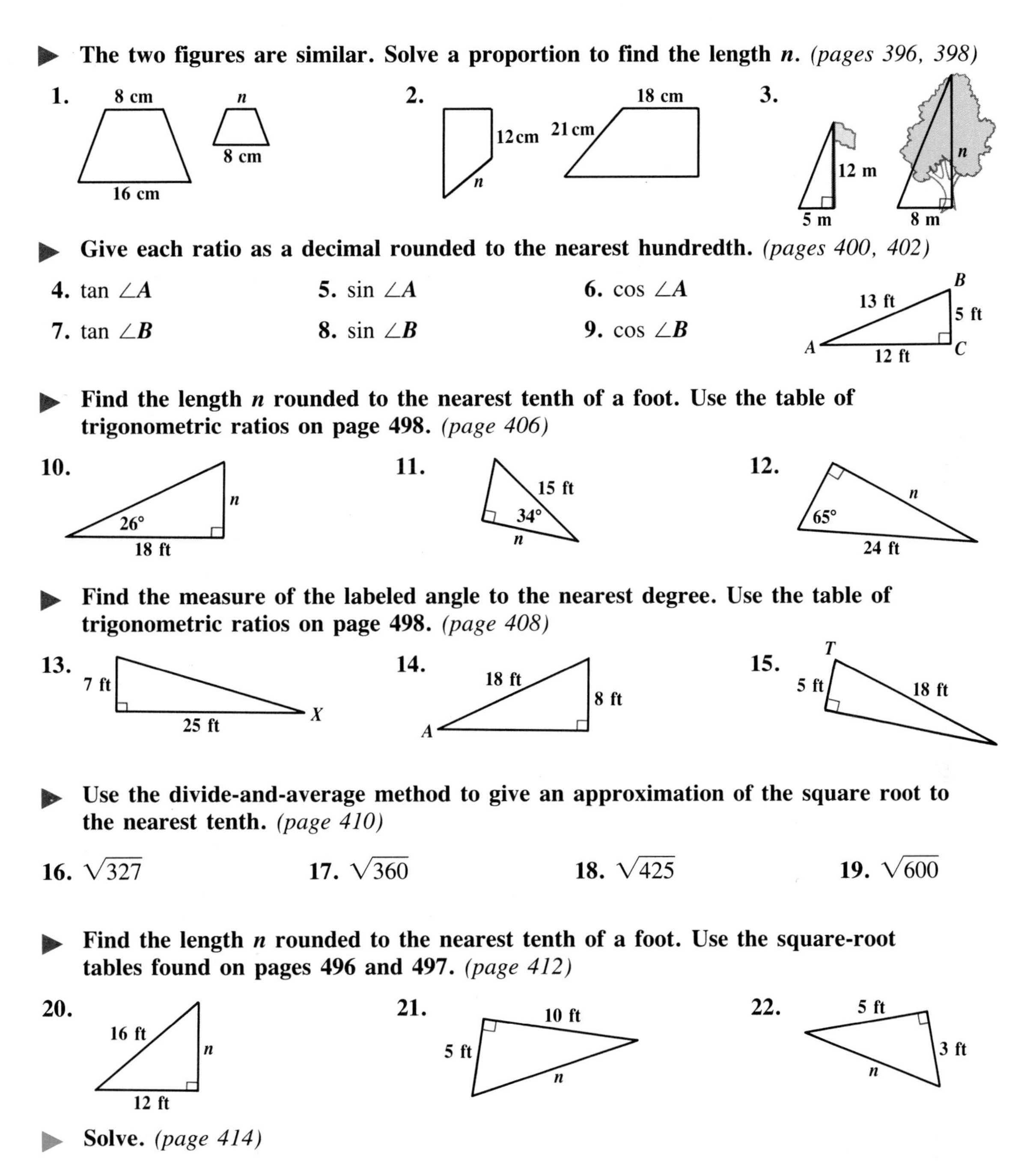

▶ **The two figures are similar. Solve a proportion to find the length n.** *(pages 396, 398)*

1.

2.

3.

▶ **Give each ratio as a decimal rounded to the nearest hundredth.** *(pages 400, 402)*

4. tan $\angle A$

5. sin $\angle A$

6. cos $\angle A$

7. tan $\angle B$

8. sin $\angle B$

9. cos $\angle B$

▶ **Find the length n rounded to the nearest tenth of a foot. Use the table of trigonometric ratios on page 498.** *(page 406)*

10.

11.

12.

▶ **Find the measure of the labeled angle to the nearest degree. Use the table of trigonometric ratios on page 498.** *(page 408)*

13.

14.

15.

▶ **Use the divide-and-average method to give an approximation of the square root to the nearest tenth.** *(page 410)*

16. $\sqrt{327}$

17. $\sqrt{360}$

18. $\sqrt{425}$

19. $\sqrt{600}$

▶ **Find the length n rounded to the nearest tenth of a foot. Use the square-root tables found on pages 496 and 497.** *(page 412)*

20.

21.

22.

▶ **Solve.** *(page 414)*

23. A ladder is 10 feet long. The bottom is 6 feet from a wall. How high up the wall does the ladder reach?

24. A family traveled 6 miles north from their home and then 8 miles west. How far from their home were they then?

Cumulative Test

Standardized Format

▶ **Choose the correct letter.**

1. The greatest common factor of $16ab^2$ and $20a^2b$ is

A. $4a$
B. $4b$
C. $4a^2b^2$
D. none of these

2. $\frac{21u^2v}{15uv^2}$ written in lowest terms is

A. $\frac{7u^2}{5uv}$ B. $\frac{7uv}{5v^2}$
C. $\frac{7u}{5v}$ D. none of these

3. Give the sum.

$\frac{3c}{4} + \frac{d}{5}$

A. $\frac{15c + 4d}{20}$ B. $\frac{15c + d}{20}$
C. $\frac{3c + d}{20}$ D. none of these

4. Give the product.

$\frac{7x}{y^2} \cdot \frac{y}{14x}$

A. $\frac{7}{2xy}$ B. $\frac{1}{2y}$
C. $\frac{7y}{2}$ D. none of these

5. Give the quotient.

$\frac{a}{4b} \div \frac{5a}{b^2}$

A. $\frac{b}{20}$ B. $\frac{20}{b}$
C. $\frac{b^2}{20}$ D. none of these

6. Solve.

$\frac{4}{3}$ of $72 = n$

A. 54
B. 72
C. 96
D. none of these

7. $2\frac{1}{3}$ yd = __?__ in.

A. 7
B. 28
C. 48
D. none of these

8. Solve.

$\frac{5}{3}n = 33$

A. 55 B. 33
C. $19\frac{4}{5}$ D. none of these

9. Simplify by combining like terms.

$9x + 7 - x - 17$

A. $10x - 10$
B. $8x + 10$
C. $8x - 10$
D. none of these

10. Solve.

$^-4 + 3t + 7 + t = 3 - 19$

A. $^-3\frac{1}{4}$
B. $^-4\frac{3}{4}$
C. $3\frac{1}{4}$
D. none of these

11. Find the volume. Use 3.14 for π.

10 in.
3 in.

A. 62.8 in.^{3}
B. 286.6 in.^{3}
C. 94.2 in.^{3}
D. none of these

12. Choose the equation.

Jill worked 5 hours yesterday and 3 hours today. She earned a total of $52. How much did she earn per hour?

A. $5n + 3n = 52$
B. $5n - 3n = 52$
C. $3n + 52 = 5n$
D. $5n - 52 = 3n$

16 BASIC Programming

30 F = 9 / 5 * C + 32

This line is part of a BASIC program that converts degrees Celsius to degrees Fahrenheit.

(page 431)

The photo shows the Juneau Icefield in the Coast Mountains of Alaska. The temperature at the time the photo was taken was $^{-}20$°C. You can use the computer program on page 431 to convert this temperature to degrees Fahrenheit.

Computing with BASIC Programs

To communicate with a computer, you have to use a language that the computer understands. A commonly used language is **B**eginner's **A**ll-purpose **S**ymbolic **I**nstruction **C**ode, or **BASIC.** In BASIC, these symbols are used:

+	Add	*	Multiply	↑	Raise to a power
−	Subtract	/	Divide	( )	Grouping symbols

Here's how to compute the output for an expression written in BASIC.

```
PRINT (36 + 12) / 2 ↑ 3
      48 / 2 ↑ 3
      48 / 8
      6
```

2 ↑ 3 means 2^3.

```
PRINT 13 * 5 − (2 + 5)
      13 * 5 − 7
      65 − 7
      58
```

Note: To simplify a BASIC expression, a computer will do the operation in the grouping symbols first and the powers second; then it will follow the order-of-operation rules you learned in Chapter 4.

A **program** is a set of statements that tells the computer what to do. Each line in a program is numbered. (Any number between 0 and 9999 may be used.) The line numbers tell the order in which the statements are to be done.

In the program below, **PRINT statements** are used to tell the computer to do the computations and print the results.

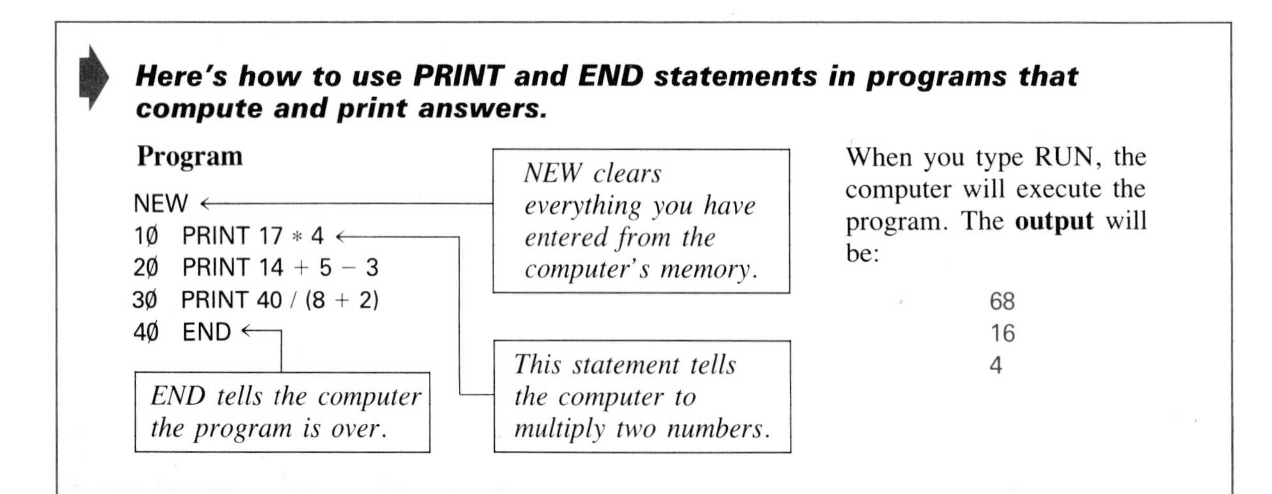

Here's how to use PRINT and END statements in programs that compute and print answers.

Program

```
NEW
10  PRINT 17 * 4
20  PRINT 14 + 5 − 3
30  PRINT 40 / (8 + 2)
40  END
```

NEW clears everything you have entered from the computer's memory.

This statement tells the computer to multiply two numbers.

END tells the computer the program is over.

When you type RUN, the computer will execute the program. The **output** will be:

```
68
16
4
```

EXERCISES

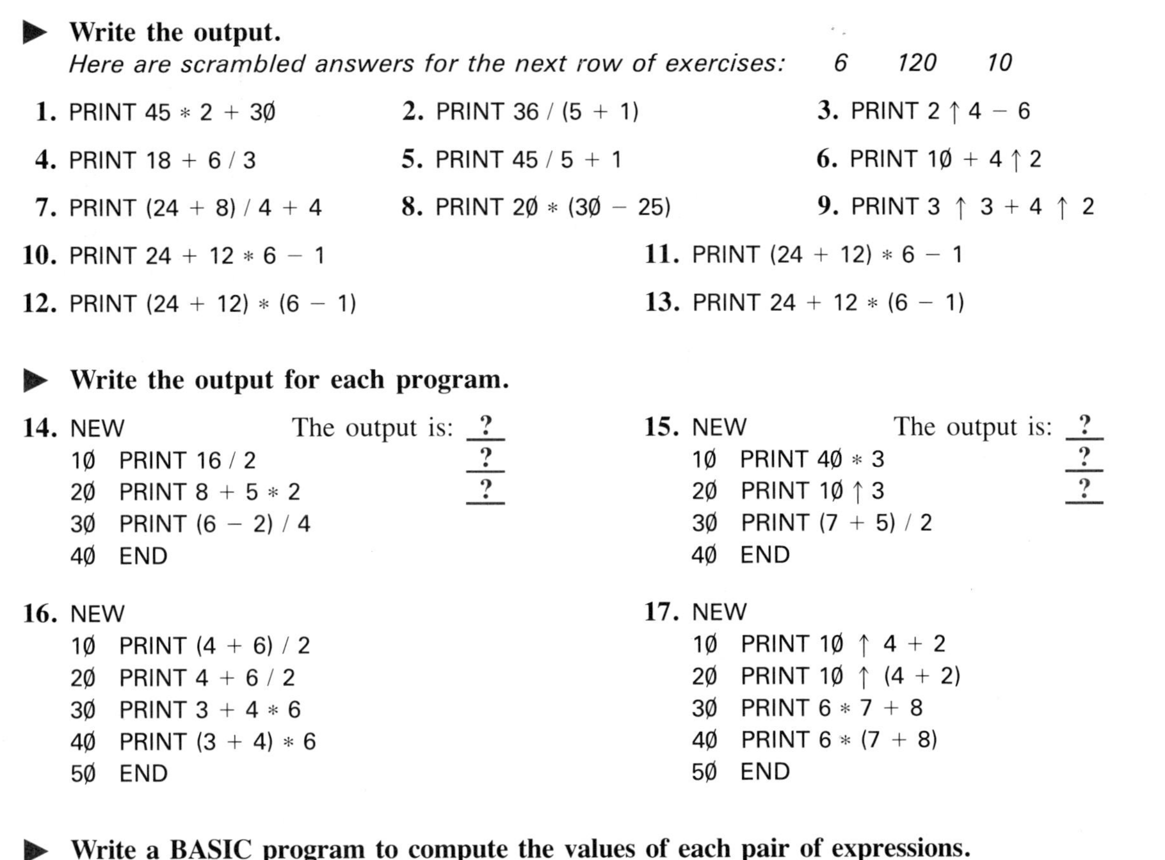

▶ **Write the output.**
Here are scrambled answers for the next row of exercises: 6 120 10

1. PRINT 45 * 2 + 3Ø
2. PRINT 36 / (5 + 1)
3. PRINT 2 ↑ 4 − 6
4. PRINT 18 + 6 / 3
5. PRINT 45 / 5 + 1
6. PRINT 1Ø + 4 ↑ 2
7. PRINT (24 + 8) / 4 + 4
8. PRINT 2Ø * (3Ø − 25)
9. PRINT 3 ↑ 3 + 4 ↑ 2
10. PRINT 24 + 12 * 6 − 1
11. PRINT (24 + 12) * 6 − 1
12. PRINT (24 + 12) * (6 − 1)
13. PRINT 24 + 12 * (6 − 1)

▶ **Write the output for each program.**

14.
```
NEW
1Ø  PRINT 16 / 2
2Ø  PRINT 8 + 5 * 2
3Ø  PRINT (6 − 2) / 4
4Ø  END
```
The output is: ? ? ?

15.
```
NEW
1Ø  PRINT 4Ø * 3
2Ø  PRINT 1Ø ↑ 3
3Ø  PRINT (7 + 5) / 2
4Ø  END
```
The output is: ? ? ?

16.
```
NEW
1Ø  PRINT (4 + 6) / 2
2Ø  PRINT 4 + 6 / 2
3Ø  PRINT 3 + 4 * 6
4Ø  PRINT (3 + 4) * 6
5Ø  END
```

17.
```
NEW
1Ø  PRINT 1Ø ↑ 4 + 2
2Ø  PRINT 1Ø ↑ (4 + 2)
3Ø  PRINT 6 * 7 + 8
4Ø  PRINT 6 * (7 + 8)
5Ø  END
```

▶ **Write a BASIC program to compute the values of each pair of expressions.**
Hint: Use PRINT statements.

18. $6 \times 7 \times 10$
$7 - (3 + 2)$

19. $47 + 53 + 9$
$4 \times 9 + 6$

20. $125 - 86$
$(32 + 8) \div 4$

21. $27 \div 5$
$7^2 + 10$

Challenge

▶ **Complete each program to get the output shown on the computer screen.**
Hint: Look for a pattern.

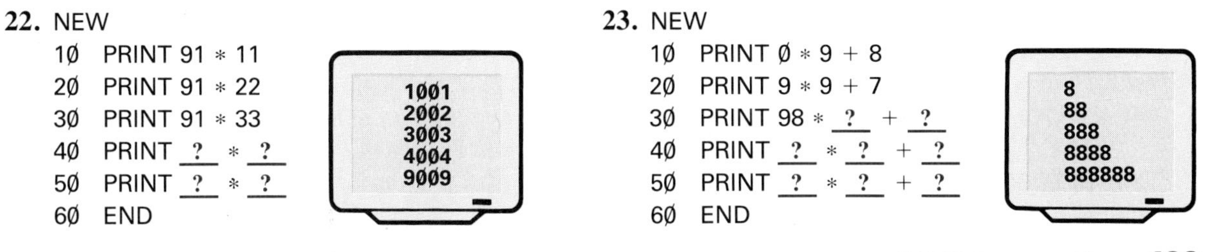

22.
```
NEW
1Ø  PRINT 91 * 11
2Ø  PRINT 91 * 22
3Ø  PRINT 91 * 33
4Ø  PRINT _?_ * _?_
5Ø  PRINT _?_ * _?_
6Ø  END
```

23.
```
NEW
1Ø  PRINT Ø * 9 + 8
2Ø  PRINT 9 * 9 + 7
3Ø  PRINT 98 * _?_ + _?_
4Ø  PRINT _?_ * _?_ + _?_
5Ø  PRINT _?_ * _?_ + _?_
6Ø  END
```

Using Variables

Architects use a blueprint and the formula below to make an estimate of the cost of construction.

Estimated cost of construction →	$E = C \times A$ ↑ *cost per square foot of construction*	← *square feet of floor space*

1. Look at the formula. What does the letter *C* represent? What does the letter A represent?
2. An architect estimates that a house having 1900 square feet of floor space can be built for \$45 per square foot. To find the estimated cost, you could compute 45 × _?_.

Letters can be used to name numbers in BASIC programs. These letters are called **variables.**

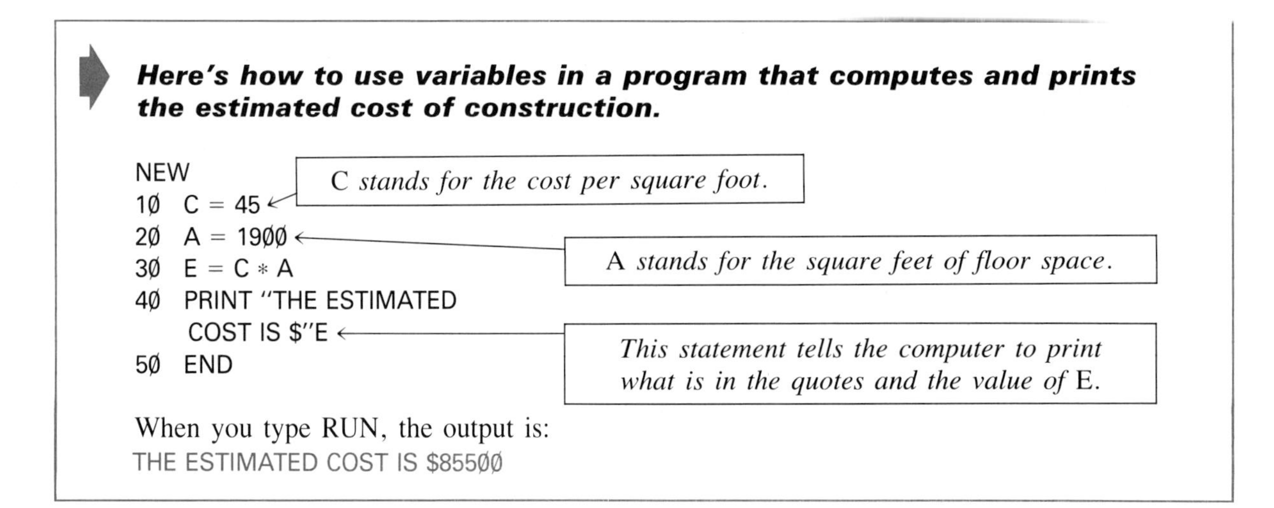

Here's how to use variables in a program that computes and prints the estimated cost of construction.

```
NEW
1Ø  C = 45
2Ø  A = 19ØØ
3Ø  E = C * A
4Ø  PRINT "THE ESTIMATED
     COST IS $"E
5Ø  END
```

C *stands for the cost per square foot.*

A *stands for the square feet of floor space.*

This statement tells the computer to print what is in the quotes and the value of E.

When you type RUN, the output is:

```
THE ESTIMATED COST IS $855ØØ
```

3. Look at the program above.
   a. The statement C = 45 (line 10) tells the computer that the variable C has the value _?_.
   b. The statement A = 19ØØ tells the computer that the variable A has the value _?_.
   c. The statement E = C * A tells the computer that the value of the variable _?_ is the product of the values of C and A.
4. Give the output of the program.

```
NEW
1Ø E = 35Ø
2Ø F = 5
3Ø PRINT E + F,  E - F,  E * F,  E / F
4Ø END
```

Commas tell the computer to print answers on the same line.

▶ **Write the output for each program.**

5.
```
NEW
10  B = 680
20  C = 20
30  Q = B / C
40  PRINT "THE QUOTIENT IS "Q
50  END
```

6.
```
NEW
10  R = 3750
20  S = 825
30  D = R - S
40  PRINT "THE DIFFERENCE IS "D
50  END
```

7.
```
NEW
10  L = 25.4
20  W = 2.6
30  A = L * W
40  PRINT "THE AREA IS "A" SQUARE
    UNITS"
50  END
```

8.
```
NEW
10  B = 40
20  H = 15
30  A = 0.5 * B * H
40  PRINT "THE AREA IS "A" SQUARE
    UNITS"
50  END
```

9.
```
NEW
10  R = 30
20  A = 3.14 * R ↑ 2
30  PRINT "THE AREA IS "A" SQUARE
    UNITS"
40  END
```

10.
```
NEW
10  D = 20
20  C = 3.14 * D
30  PRINT "THE CIRCUMFERENCE IS"
    C" UNITS"
40  END
```

11.
```
NEW
10  E = 24
20  F = 6
30  PRINT E * F, E / F, F / E,
    (E + F) / 2
40  END
```

12.
```
NEW
10  S = 25
20  T = 5
30  PRINT (S + T), S ↑ 2, T ↑ 3,
    (S - T) / T
40  END
```

13. What will be the output if line 10 in exercise 5 is changed to 10 B = 4800?

14. What will be the output if lines 10 and 20 in exercise 11 are changed to 10 E = 40 and 20 F = 4?

Challenge

15. The program at the right computes and prints the volume of a cylinder.

a. Write the output for the program.

b. Change the program so that it computes and prints the volume of a cone. (Use the same values for R and H.) Write the output.

```
NEW
10  R = 8
20  B = 3.14 * R ↑ 2
30  H = 30
40  V = B * H
50  PRINT "THE VOLUME IS "V" CUBIC
    UNITS"
60  END
```

Using INPUT Statements

Suppose you are a statistician for a baseball team. You could use the formula below to compute a player's batting average.

$$\text{batting average} \longrightarrow A = \frac{H \leftarrow \text{number of hits}}{(B - W)}$$

B: number of times at bat
W: number of walks

1. What information do you need to know to compute a player's batting average?

To make a computer ask for information, you can use an **INPUT** statement. When a computer comes to an INPUT statement in a program, it stops and waits for data to be entered. Then the computer will store the information in its memory and continue to the next step in the program.

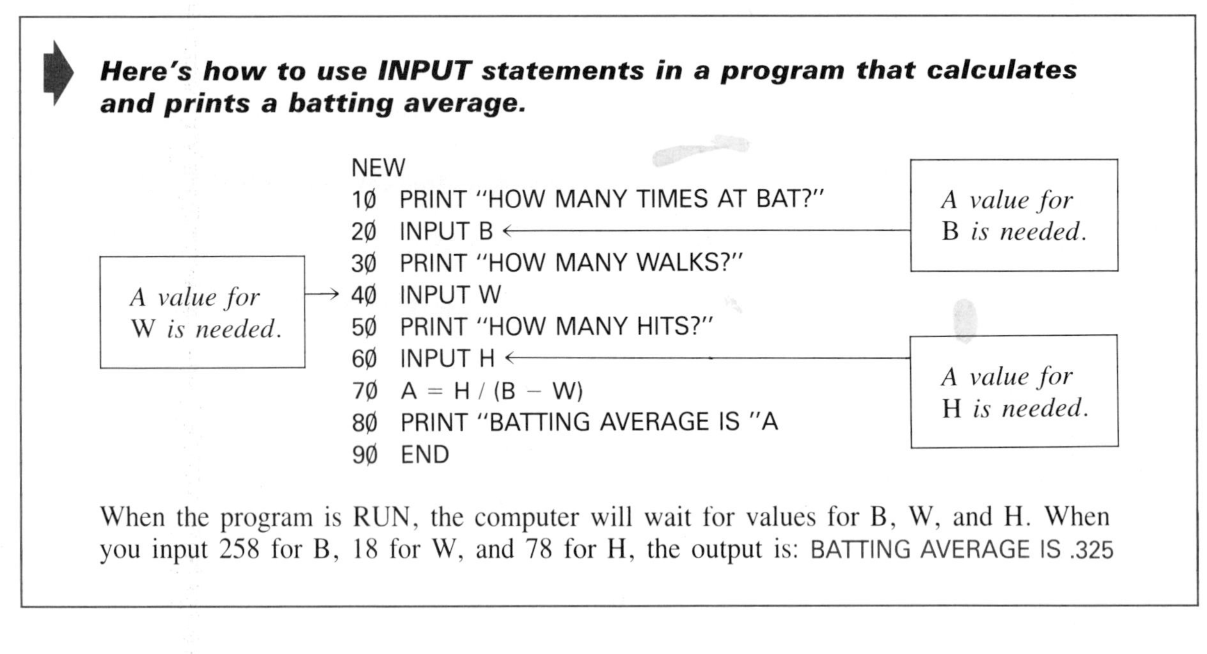

Here's how to use INPUT statements in a program that calculates and prints a batting average.

```
NEW
10 PRINT "HOW MANY TIMES AT BAT?"
20 INPUT B
30 PRINT "HOW MANY WALKS?"
40 INPUT W
50 PRINT "HOW MANY HITS?"
60 INPUT H
70 A = H / (B - W)
80 PRINT "BATTING AVERAGE IS "A
90 END
```


When the program is RUN, the computer will wait for values for B, W, and H. When you input 258 for B, 18 for W, and 78 for H, the output is: BATTING AVERAGE IS .325

2. Use the program above. What will the output be if B = 166, W = 16, and H = 42?

3. What will the output be if B = 325, W = 25, and H = 100?

EXERCISES

Program A

```
NEW
10  PRINT "INPUT WHAT VALUE?"
20  INPUT N
30  M = N ↑ 2
40  PRINT M
50  END
```

Program B

```
NEW
10  PRINT "INPUT WHAT 2 VALUES?"
20  INPUT X, Y
30  R = 4 * X + Y
40  S = 4 * (X + Y)
50  PRINT R, S
60  END
```

Program C

```
NEW
10  PRINT "ENTER FOUR NUMBERS"
20  INPUT C, D, E, F
30  A = (C + D + E + F) / 4
40  PRINT "THE AVERAGE IS "A
50  END
```

Program D

```
NEW
10  PRINT "ENTER LENGTH AND WIDTH"
20  INPUT L, W
30  P = 2 * L + 2 * W
40  PRINT "THE PERIMETER IS "P" UNITS"
50  END
```

▶ **Write the output.**

4. Input these values into Program A.

a. 10 **b.** 20
c. 9 **d.** 25
e. ⁻6 **f.** ⁻100

5. Input these values into Program B.

a. 2, 7 **b.** 4, 5
c. 8, 8 **d.** 6, 9
e. ⁻3, 10 **f.** 12, ⁻20

6. Input these values into Program C.

a. 7, 2, 14, 5 **b.** 44, 37, 19, 24
c. 82, 95, 63, 84 **d.** 110, 106, 90, 88
e. ⁻5, ⁻4, ⁻9, ⁻6 **f.** 33, ⁻56, 29, ⁻14

7. Input these values into Program D.

a. 25, 15 **b.** 60, 20
c. 17, 25 **d.** 120, 82
e. 25.4, 18.2 **f.** 17.5, 8.25

8. Use the program on page 426. Input the values given in the chart.

	Player	Times at Bat (*B*)	Number of Walks (*W*)	Number of Hits (*H*)
a.	Robinson	186	15	57
b.	Kelly	265	21	66
c.	Adams	107	7	31

Challenge

9. Write a program to input four numbers, compute their sum, and print the sum. Use these values in your program and write the output.

a. 17, 8, 25, 69 **b.** ⁻7, 6, ⁻13, ⁻9

Using FOR . . . NEXT Statements

The oranges are stacked in a square pyramid for display.

1. How many oranges are in the first (top) layer?
   How many oranges are in the second layer?
   To find the number of oranges that are in the bottom layer, you could compute 4 × ___?___.

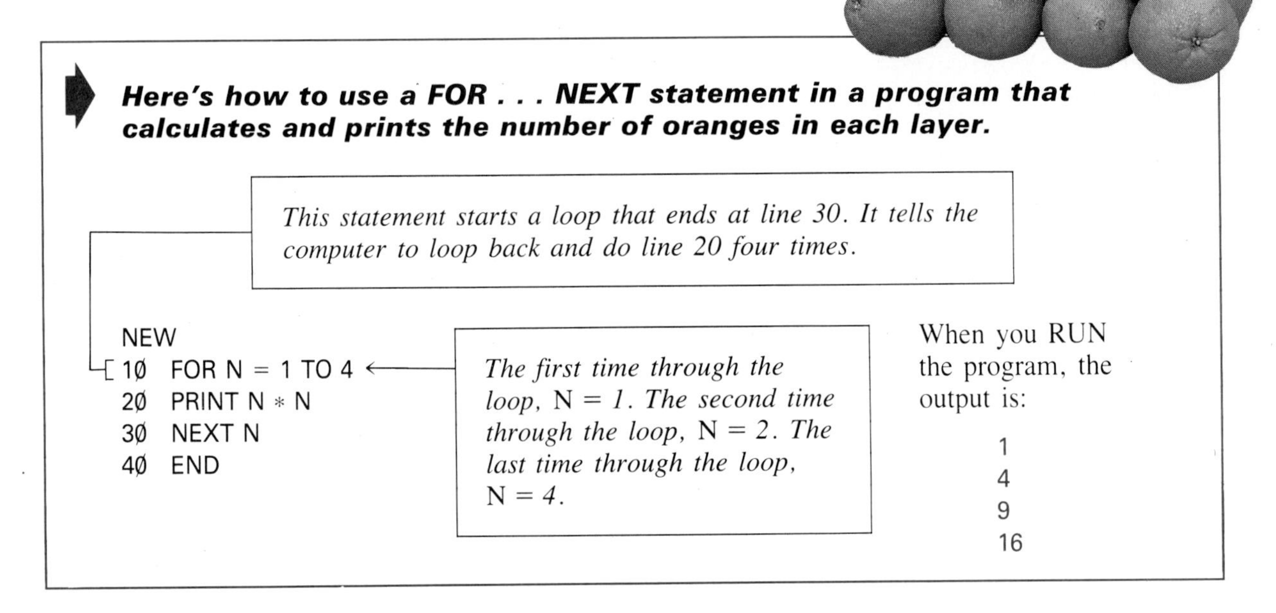

Here's how to use a FOR . . . NEXT statement in a program that calculates and prints the number of oranges in each layer.

This statement starts a loop that ends at line 30. It tells the computer to loop back and do line 20 four times.

```
NEW
1Ø  FOR N = 1 TO 4
2Ø  PRINT N * N
3Ø  NEXT N
4Ø  END
```

The first time through the loop, N = *1. The second time through the loop,* N = *2. The last time through the loop,* N = *4.*

When you RUN the program, the output is:

```
1
4
9
16
```

2. Look at the program above. The first time through the loop, the computer prints *1*. The second time through the loop, the computer prints ___?___. The last time through the loop, the computer prints ___?___.
3. What will be the output if line 10 is changed to 1Ø FOR N = 1 TO 8?

Here's how to use a STEP command to count by numbers other than 1.

```
NEW
1Ø  FOR N = 2Ø TO 26 STEP 2
2Ø  PRINT N
3Ø  NEXT N
4Ø  END
```

STEP 2 increases the value of N *by 2 each time through the loop. The first time through the loop,* N = *20. The second time through the loop,* N = *22.*

When you RUN the program, the output is:

```
2Ø
22
24
26
```

▶ **Write the output for each program.**

4.
```
NEW
10  FOR N = 1 TO 5
20  PRINT N
30  NEXT N
40  END
```

5.
```
NEW
10  FOR N = 1 TO 5
20  PRINT N + 2
30  NEXT N
40  END
```

6.
```
NEW
10  FOR N = 10 TO 15
20  PRINT N * 2
30  NEXT N
40  END
```

7.
```
NEW
10  FOR N = 0 TO 10
20  PRINT 10 - N
30  NEXT N
40  END
```

8.
```
NEW
10  FOR G = 1 TO 19 STEP 2
20  PRINT G
30  NEXT G
40  END
```

9.
```
NEW
10  FOR H = 0 TO 20 STEP 5
20  PRINT H
30  NEXT H
40  END
```

10.
```
NEW
10  FOR T = 0 TO 16 STEP 4
20  PRINT T / 2
30  NEXT T
40  END
```

11.
```
NEW
10  FOR W = 100 TO 150 STEP 10
20  PRINT (W / 5) * 3
30  NEXT W
40  END
```

12.
```
NEW
10  FOR L = 2 TO 5
20  W = 12
30  A = L * W
40  PRINT "AREA IS "A" SQUARE UNITS"
50  NEXT L
60  END
```

13.
```
NEW
10  FOR R = 1 TO 4
20  P = 3.14
30  A = P * R ↑ 2
40  PRINT "AREA IS "A" SQUARE UNITS"
50  NEXT R
60  END
```

14. What will be the output if line 10 in exercise 4 is changed to
`10 FOR N = 100 TO 105`?

15. What will be the output if line 10 in exercise 8 is changed to
`10 FOR G = 1 TO 17 STEP 4`?

16. What will be the output if line 10 in exercise 12 is changed to
`10 FOR L = 10 TO 14 STEP 2`?

17. What will be the output if line 10 in exercise 13 is changed to
`10 FOR R = 10 TO 30 STEP 10`?

Challenge

18. Write a program to print out the multiples of 8 from 8 to 88.

19. Write a program to print out the cubes of the whole numbers from 1 to 10.

Cumulative Skill Practice

▶ **Write each decimal in simplest fractional form.** *(page 226)*

1. 0.4	**2.** ${}^{-}0.20$	**3.** ${}^{-}0.6$	**4.** 0.25	**5.** ${}^{-}0.375$
6. ${}^{-}0.24$	**7.** 0.72	**8.** ${}^{-}0.16$	**9.** 0.150	**10.** ${}^{-}0.875$
11. 2.25	**12.** ${}^{-}1.8$	**13.** 2.40	**14.** ${}^{-}9.6$	**15.** 4.55
16. ${}^{-}7.2$	**17.** 3.08	**18.** ${}^{-}5.125$	**19.** 6.40	**20.** ${}^{-}1.625$

▶ **Give each sum or difference in simplest form.** *(page 228)*

21. $\frac{2}{3} + \frac{{}^{-}1}{3}$	**22.** $\frac{3}{8} + \frac{1}{2}$	**23.** $\frac{{}^{-}5}{16} + \frac{3}{8}$	**24.** $\frac{{}^{-}3}{5} + \frac{{}^{-}1}{4}$
25. $2\frac{5}{8} + {}^{-}4\frac{1}{4}$	**26.** ${}^{-}9\frac{5}{8} + 4\frac{2}{3}$	**27.** $\frac{3}{5} - \frac{1}{10}$	**28.** $\frac{{}^{-}3}{8} - \frac{1}{2}$
29. $\frac{1}{3} - \frac{3}{5}$	**30.** $\frac{5}{6} - \frac{{}^{-}7}{8}$	**31.** $\frac{{}^{-}9}{10} - \frac{{}^{-}3}{4}$	**32.** $4\,{}^{3}_{5} \quad {}^{-}2\,{}^{1}_{10}$
33. ${}^{-}6 - 3\frac{7}{8}$	**34.** $5\frac{1}{2} - {}^{-}1\frac{3}{4}$	**35.** ${}^{-}6\frac{7}{8} - {}^{-}7\frac{2}{3}$	**36.** ${}^{-}9 - 5\frac{5}{6}$

▶ **Give each product or quotient in simplest form.** *(page 230)*

37. $\frac{{}^{-}2}{3} \cdot \frac{1}{5}$	**38.** $\frac{{}^{-}1}{4} \cdot \frac{{}^{-}1}{3}$	**39.** $\frac{1}{8} \cdot 8$	**40.** $\frac{{}^{-}5}{3} \cdot \frac{3}{10}$
41. $\frac{{}^{-}4}{5} \cdot \frac{{}^{-}5}{4}$	**42.** $3 \cdot {}^{-}1\frac{1}{2}$	**43.** ${}^{-}2\frac{7}{8} \cdot {}^{-}3$	**44.** ${}^{-}2\frac{1}{2} \cdot 2\frac{1}{2}$
45. ${}^{-}6 \div \frac{3}{4}$	**46.** $\frac{9}{5} \div \frac{3}{10}$	**47.** $\frac{{}^{-}5}{12} \div \frac{15}{4}$	**48.** ${}^{-}10 \div 2\frac{1}{2}$
49. ${}^{-}1\frac{1}{4} \div {}^{-}2\frac{1}{3}$	**50.** $2\frac{5}{6} \div 1\frac{3}{4}$	**51.** $4\frac{2}{5} \div {}^{-}1\frac{3}{10}$	**52.** ${}^{-}4\frac{2}{3} \div 2\frac{5}{6}$

▶ **Solve and check.** *(page 234)*

53. $6n + 7 = 19$	**54.** ${}^{-}5j - 14 = 31$	**55.** ${}^{-}6 - 12n = 9$
56. $14k - 13 = 23$	**57.** $8 - 7q = 0$	**58.** $12d + 8 = 8$
59. $20m - 24 = 26$	**60.** ${}^{-}11 + 11j = 31$	**61.** ${}^{-}20 - 14p = {}^{-}6$

▶ **Simplify by combining like terms.** *(page 236)*

62. $12j + j$	**63.** $15y - y$	**64.** $16x - 16x$
65. $3v + v + 12$	**66.** $10n - 6 + 3n$	**67.** ${}^{-}12j + 9 + 5j$
68. $15v - 11v - 3 + 5$	**69.** $15v - 11 - 3v + 5$	**70.** $15 - 11v - 3 + 5v$

Problem Solving—Applications

When the wind is blowing, the temperature feels colder than it actually is. The wind-chill chart shows, for example, that when the thermometer reading is 10° Fahrenheit (F) and the wind speed is 20 miles per hour (mph), the wind chill is $^{-}$24°F. In other words, the wind makes 10°F feel like $^{-}$24°F.

Wind-Chill Chart							
Wind Speed (mph)	Thermometer Reading in Degrees Fahrenheit						
	30°	20°	10°	0°	$^{-}$10°	$^{-}$20°	$^{-}$30°
5	27°	19°	7°	$^{-}$5°	$^{-}$15°	$^{-}$26°	$^{-}$36°
10	16°	3°	$^{-}$9°	$^{-}$22°	$^{-}$34°	$^{-}$46°	$^{-}$58°
15	9°	$^{-}$5°	$^{-}$18°	$^{-}$31°	$^{-}$45°	$^{-}$58°	$^{-}$72°
20	4°	$^{-}$10°	$^{-}$24°	$^{-}$39°	$^{-}$53°	$^{-}$67°	$^{-}$81°
25	1°	$^{-}$15°	$^{-}$29°	$^{-}$44°	$^{-}$59°	$^{-}$74°	$^{-}$88°
30	$^{-}$2°	$^{-}$18°	$^{-}$33°	$^{-}$49°	$^{-}$64°	$^{-}$79°	$^{-}$93°
35	$^{-}$4°	$^{-}$20°	$^{-}$35°	$^{-}$52°	$^{-}$67°	$^{-}$82°	$^{-}$97°

Use the wind-chill chart to complete each statement.

1. A 20°F temperature with a 15-mph wind feels the same as __?__ °F with no wind.
2. A $^{-}$10°F temperature with a 20-mph wind feels the same as __?__ °F with no wind.
3. A 30°F temperature with a __?__ -mph wind feels the same as $^{-}$2°F with no wind.
4. A $^{-}$30°F temperature with a __?__ -mph wind feels the same as $^{-}$81°F with no wind.
5. A __?__ °F temperature with a 25-mph wind feels the same as $^{-}$29°F with no wind.
6. A __?__ °F temperature with a 30-mph wind feels the same as $^{-}$79°F with no wind.

The program at the right converts degrees Celsius (°C) to degrees Fahrenheit (°F). Use the program to solve these problems.

```
NEW
1Ø  PRINT "ENTER DEGREES CELSIUS"
2Ø  INPUT C
3Ø  F = (9 / 5) * C + 32
4Ø  PRINT "TEMP. IS "F" DEGREES F"
5Ø  END
```

7. The lowest temperature recorded in Nova Scotia, Canada, is $^{-}$41°C. How many degrees Fahrenheit is that?

8. The lowest temperature recorded in Yukon Territory is $^{-}$63°C. How many degrees Fahrenheit is that?

9. The highest temperature recorded in Alberta, Canada, is 42°C. How many degrees Fahrenheit is that?

10. When the temperature in Montreal is $^{-}$5°C and the wind speed is 10 mph, is the wind chill above or below 0°F? *(Hint: Use the program to change to degrees Fahrenheit. Then use the wind-chill chart.)*

11. When the temperature in Edmonton is $^{-}$25°C and the wind speed is 20 mph, is the wind chill above or below $^{-}$50°F?

Using READ and DATA Statements

Read the data in the scores chart.

1. What was Robin's score in Game 1?
2. Who had a score of 140 in Game 2?
3. To find Robin's average (mean) score, you would add 134 + 142 + 129 and then divide by _?_ .

You can use **READ** and **DATA** statements to tell a computer to find data in a program. When a program says READ K, it tells the computer to go and find what K equals in a DATA statement.

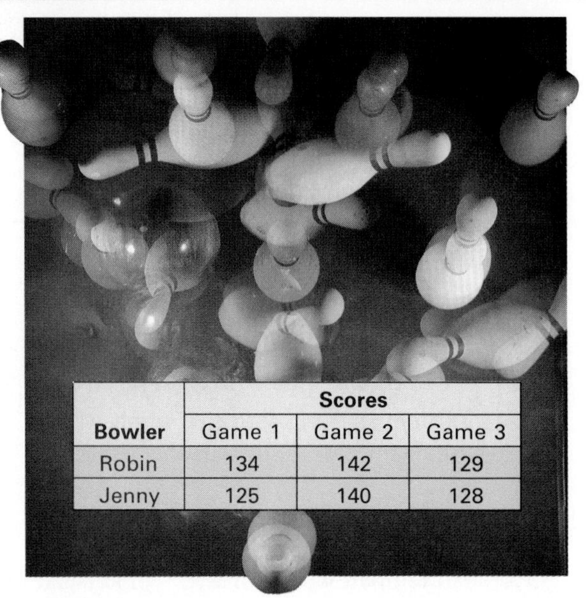

Bowler	Scores		
	Game 1	Game 2	Game 3
Robin	134	142	129
Jenny	125	140	128

Here's how to use READ and DATA statements in a program that calculates and prints the average of three bowling scores.

```
NEW
1Ø  READ K, L, M
2Ø  A = (K + L + M) / 3
3Ø  PRINT "THE AVERAGE SCORE IS "A
4Ø  DATA 134, 142, 129
5Ø  END
```

This statement tells the computer to look in a DATA statement for the values of the variables. The computer assigns 134 to K, *142 to* L, *and 129 to* M.

When you type RUN, the output is THE AVERAGE SCORE IS 135.

4. Use the program above. What will be the output if line 40 is changed to 4Ø DATA 125, 14Ø, 128? Who had the higher average score, Robin or Jenny?

5. Write the output for each program.

a.

```
NEW
1Ø  READ B, C, D
2Ø  P = B * C * D
3Ø  PRINT "THE PRODUCT IS "P
4Ø  DATA 2Ø, 3Ø, 1Ø
5Ø  END
```

b.

```
NEW
1Ø  READ R, S
2Ø  Q = R / S
3Ø  PRINT "THE QUOTIENT IS "Q
4Ø  DATA 15ØØ, 3Ø
5Ø  END
```

Write the output for each program.

6.
```
NEW
1Ø  READ W, Y
2Ø  PRINT W − Y, W + Y
3Ø  DATA 132, 1Ø2
4Ø  END
```

7.
```
NEW
1Ø  READ R, S
2Ø  PRINT R * S, R / S
3Ø  DATA 14Ø, 2
4Ø  END
```

8.
```
NEW
1Ø  READ C, D, E
2Ø  PRINT C * (D − E)
3Ø  DATA 7, 1Ø, 2
4Ø  END
```

9.
```
NEW
1Ø  READ J, K, L
2Ø  PRINT (J + K) / L
3Ø  DATA −6, 1Ø, 2
4Ø  END
```

10.
```
NEW
1Ø  READ L, W
2Ø  A = L * W
3Ø  PRINT "AREA IS "A" SQUARE UNITS"
4Ø  DATA 1Ø.2, 6.5
5Ø  END
```

11.
```
NEW
1Ø  READ L, W, H
2Ø  V = L * W * H
3Ø  PRINT "VOLUME IS "V" CUBIC UNITS"
4Ø  DATA 12, 6.6, 3.2
5Ø  END
```

12.
```
NEW
1Ø  READ P, D
2Ø  C = P * D
3Ø  PRINT "CIRCUMFERENCE IS "C" UNITS"
4Ø  DATA 3.14, 8
5Ø  END
```

13.
```
NEW
1Ø  READ L, W
2Ø  P = 2 * (L + W)
3Ø  PRINT "PERIMETER IS "P" UNITS"
4Ø  DATA 2.5, 1.6
5Ø  END
```

14. Use the bowling-average program on page 432. Write the output for the program if the data in line 40 are replaced by the data for each bowler in the chart at the right.

	Scores		
Bowler	**Game 1**	**Game 2**	**Game 3**
Evans	142	138	152
Akers	166	154	175
Norman	122	141	138
DeBower	189	175	182

Challenge

15. The program at the right computes and prints a bowler's handicap, which is 80% of the difference between a bowler's average and 200.

a. Write the output for the program.

b. Change the program so that it uses READ and DATA to assign values to A, T, and P.

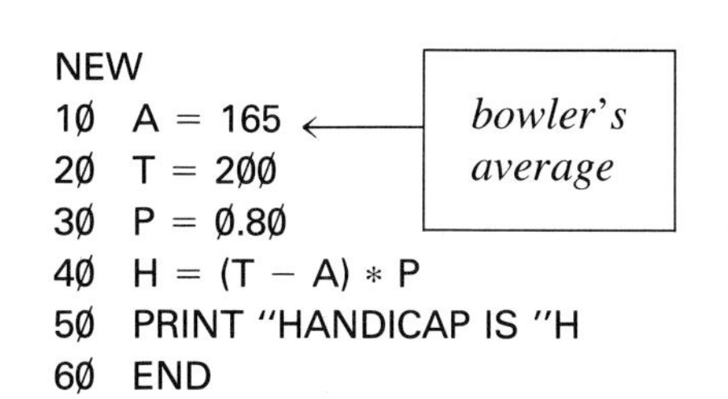


```
NEW
1Ø  A = 165
2Ø  T = 2ØØ
3Ø  P = Ø.8Ø
4Ø  H = (T − A) * P
5Ø  PRINT "HANDICAP IS "H
6Ø  END
```

Using READ . . . DATA and GOTO Statements

A salesperson at Collier's Furniture is paid a base pay of $4 per hour plus 2% of his/her sales.

Salesperson	Hours (*H*)	Sales (*S*) in dollars
Robinson	24	3000
McNally	30	5200
Donovan	40	4300

You can use a **GOTO** statement to form a loop and have the computer do the same calculations on more than one set of data.

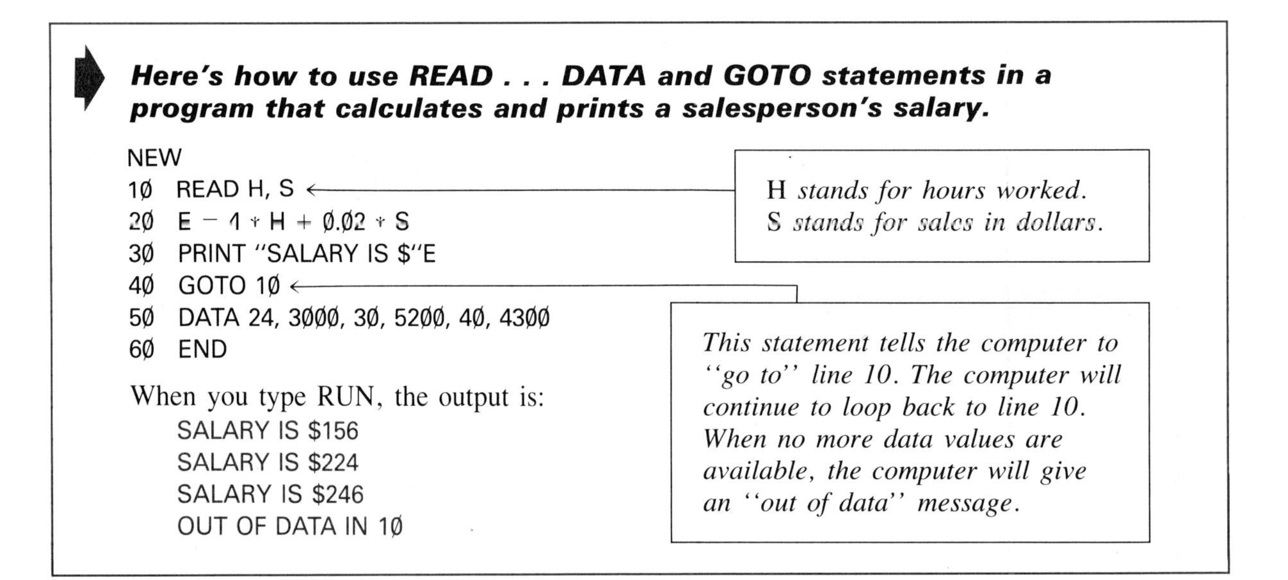

Here's how to use READ . . . DATA and GOTO statements in a program that calculates and prints a salesperson's salary.

```
NEW
1Ø  READ H, S
2Ø  E = 4 * H + Ø.Ø2 * S
3Ø  PRINT "SALARY IS $"E
4Ø  GOTO 1Ø
5Ø  DATA 24, 3ØØØ, 3Ø, 52ØØ, 4Ø, 43ØØ
6Ø  END
```

H *stands for hours worked.*
S *stands for sales in dollars.*

When you type RUN, the output is:

```
SALARY IS $156
SALARY IS $224
SALARY IS $246
OUT OF DATA IN 1Ø
```

This statement tells the computer to "go to" line 10. The computer will continue to loop back to line 10. When no more data values are available, the computer will give an "out of data" message.

1. Look at the program above.

a. The first time through the loop, H = 24 and S = 3000. The second time through the loop, H = __?__ and S = __?__.

b. The first time through the loop, the statement E = 4 * H + Ø.Ø2 * S tells the computer that the variable E has the value __?__. The second time through the loop, E has the value __?__.

c. What will be the output if line 50 is changed to 5Ø DATA 15, 5ØØ, 2Ø, 7ØØ?

2. Write the output for each program.

a.

```
NEW
1Ø  READ N
2Ø  PRINT N ↑ 2
3Ø  GOTO 1Ø
4Ø  DATA 5, 6, 7
5Ø  END
```

b.

```
NEW
1Ø  READ R, S
2Ø  PRINT R / S
3Ø  GOTO 1Ø
4Ø  DATA 3Ø, 1Ø, 45, 5, 12, 5
5Ø  END
```

▶ **Write the output for each program.**

3.
```
NEW
1Ø   READ E, F
2Ø   PRINT E + F
3Ø   GOTO 1Ø
4Ø   DATA 13, 42, 36, 98
5Ø   END
```

4.
```
NEW
1Ø   READ R, S
2Ø   PRINT R ↑ 2 − S ↑ 2
3Ø   GOTO 1Ø
4Ø   DATA 3, 4, 6, 2, 9, 1Ø
5Ø   END
```

5.
```
NEW
1Ø   READ N
2Ø   PRINT N, N ↑ 2
3Ø   GOTO 1Ø
4Ø   DATA 1Ø, 11, 12, 13, 14
5Ø   END
```

6.

SQR(N) *tells the computer to find the square root of* N.

```
NEW
1Ø   READ N
2Ø   PRINT SQR(N)
3Ø   GOTO 1Ø
4Ø   DATA 196, 484, 2Ø25
5Ø   END
```

7. A used-car salesperson receives 4% of the selling price of the car as commission. Program A at the right computes and prints the commission for each sale. Write the output for the program.

Program A

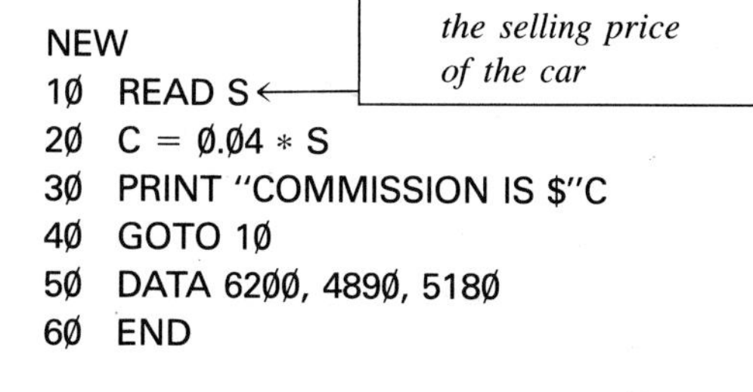


```
NEW
1Ø   READ S
2Ø   C = Ø.Ø4 * S
3Ø   PRINT "COMMISSION IS $"C
4Ø   GOTO 1Ø
5Ø   DATA 62ØØ, 489Ø, 518Ø
6Ø   END
```

8. A carpet store has four employees. Each receives $150 per week plus 5% of his/her weekly sales. Program B computes and prints each employee's weekly earnings. Write the output for the program.

Program B

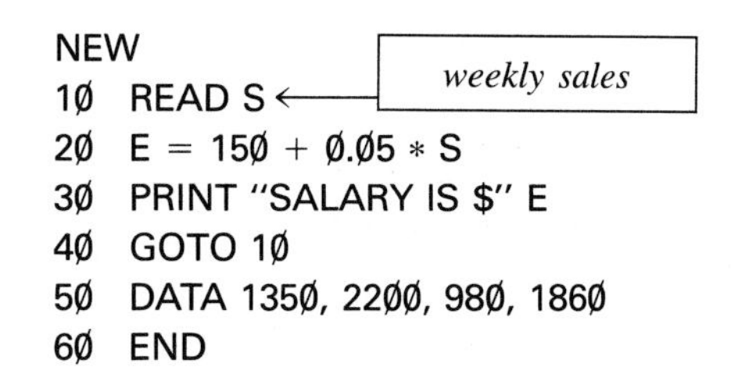


```
NEW
1Ø   READ S
2Ø   E = 15Ø + Ø.Ø5 * S
3Ø   PRINT "SALARY IS $" E
4Ø   GOTO 1Ø
5Ø   DATA 135Ø, 22ØØ, 98Ø, 186Ø
6Ø   END
```

Challenge

9. An assembly plant pays its employees $5.50 per hour plus $.03 for each item produced. Write a program to read hours worked and items produced; then have your program compute and print an employee's earnings. Use your program and complete the chart at the right.

Name	Hours worked	Items produced	Earnings
Kilgore	35	2700	?
Novak	40	3070	?
Wiseman	43	3320	?

Using IF . . . THEN Statements

A station-to-station call from Chicago to Los Angeles costs $1.52 for the first 3 minutes and $.44 for each additional minute.

1. When the calling time (T) is 3 minutes or less, the cost of the call is __?__.
2. When the calling time (T) is more than 3 minutes, you can find the cost by computing $1.52 + (T - 3) \times$ __?__.

To calculate the cost of a station-to-station call, a computer must decide whether the calling time is 3 minutes or less, or more than 3 minutes. In a BASIC program, a decision is made by using an **IF . . . THEN** statement.

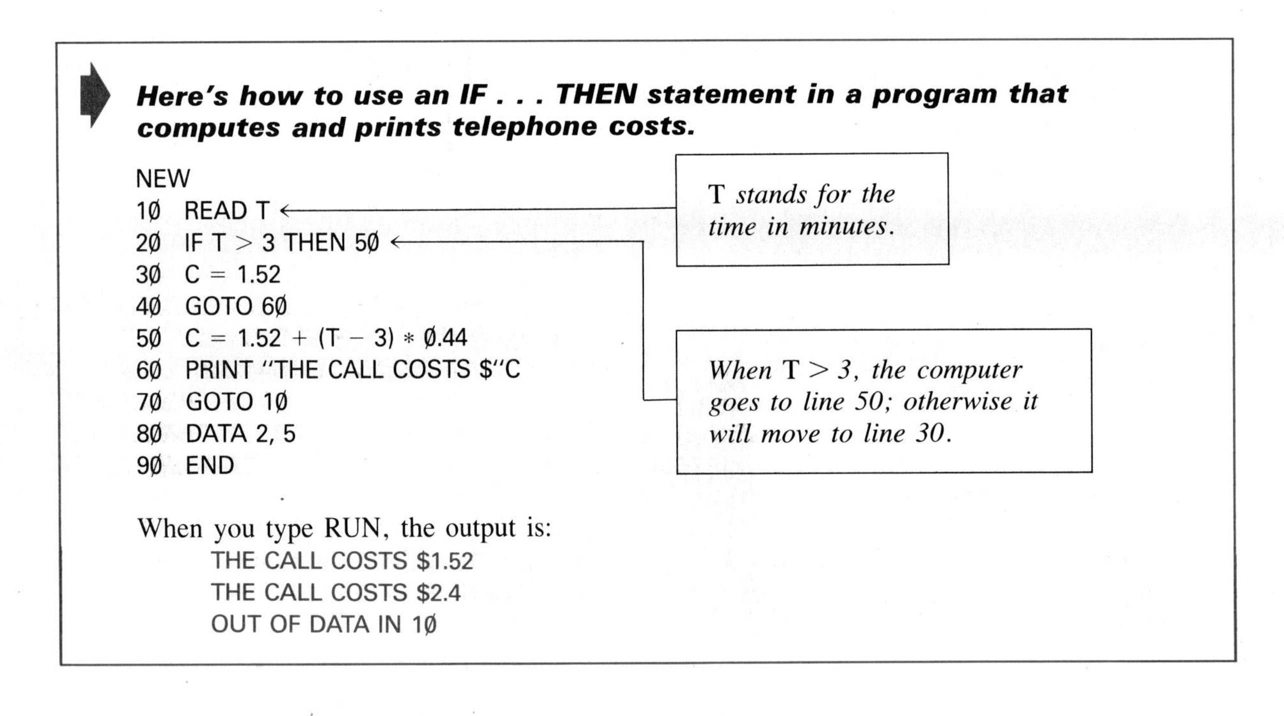

Here's how to use an IF . . . THEN statement in a program that computes and prints telephone costs.

```
NEW
1Ø  READ T
2Ø  IF T > 3 THEN 5Ø
3Ø  C = 1.52
4Ø  GOTO 6Ø
5Ø  C = 1.52 + (T - 3) * Ø.44
6Ø  PRINT "THE CALL COSTS $"C
7Ø  GOTO 1Ø
8Ø  DATA 2, 5
9Ø  END
```


When you type RUN, the output is:

```
THE CALL COSTS $1.52
THE CALL COSTS $2.4
OUT OF DATA IN 1Ø
```

3. Use the program above. What will be the output if line 80 is changed to 8Ø DATA 1, 4?
4. Write the output for the program.

```
NEW
1Ø  READ N
2Ø  IF N <= 1Ø THEN 4Ø
3Ø  PRINT N
4Ø  GOTO 1Ø
5Ø  DATA 4, 15, 36, 2, 1Ø
6Ø  END
```

<= means less than or equal to.

▶ **Write the output for each program.**

5.
```
NEW
1Ø  READ T
2Ø  IF T > Ø THEN 1Ø
3Ø  PRINT T
4Ø  GOTO 1Ø
5Ø  DATA 6, −3, −4, Ø, 1.2, 75
6Ø  END
```

6.
```
NEW
1Ø  READ S
2Ø  IF S <=1Ø THEN 1Ø
3Ø  PRINT S ↑ 2
4Ø  GOTO 1Ø
5Ø  DATA 5, 11, 2Ø, 15, 1Ø, 2
6Ø  END
```

7.
```
NEW
 1Ø  READ M, N
 2Ø  IF M = N THEN 6Ø
 3Ø  IF M < N THEN 8Ø
 4Ø  PRINT M" > "N
 5Ø  GOTO 1Ø
 6Ø  PRINT M" = "N
 7Ø  GOTO 1Ø
 8Ø  PRINT M" < "N
 9Ø  GOTO 1Ø
1ØØ  DATA 6, 3, −2, 7, −7, −1Ø, 7, 7
11Ø  END
```

8.
```
NEW
 1Ø  READ A, B
 2Ø  C = A / B
 3Ø  IF C = 1 THEN 7Ø
 4Ø  IF C > 1 THEN 9Ø
 5Ø  PRINT A" / "B" < "1
 6Ø  GOTO 1Ø
 7Ø  PRINT A" / "B" = "1
 8Ø  GOTO 1Ø
 9Ø  PRINT A" / "B" > "1
1ØØ  GOTO 1Ø
11Ø  DATA 3, 4, 7, 5, −8, −3, 9, 9
12Ø  END
```

9. Change the program in exercise 5 to print the numbers greater than zero. What will the output be?

10. Change the program in exercise 6 to print S^3 instead of S^2. What will the output be?

11. What will the output be if line 100 in exercise 7 is changed to
1ØØ DATA 4, −6, 9, 1Ø, 2.1, 2.Ø9?

12. What will the output be if line 110 in exercise 8 is changed to
11Ø DATA 8, 6, −4, 5, Ø, 12?

Challenge

13. A federal excise tax of 2% is added to all station-to-station telephone calls.

a. Change the telephone-cost program on page 436 so that it computes and prints the amount (cost plus tax) of a station-to-station call.

b. Use your program to find the cost (plus tax) for each call shown on the bill at the right.

State Telephone Company PAGE 2
Chicago, Illinois

DETAILS OF ITEMIZED CALLS

Date	Place Called	Area	Tel No.	Min	Amount
07/14	LOS ANGELES	213	555-1214	4	?
07/17	LOS ANGELES	213	555-4813	7	?
07/23	LOS ANGELES	213	555-4045	12	?

Problem Solving—Using Flowcharts

Before writing a program, a programmer may write a plan called a **flowchart.** A flowchart shows the steps in a problem, the choices there are, and the order in which the steps must be done.

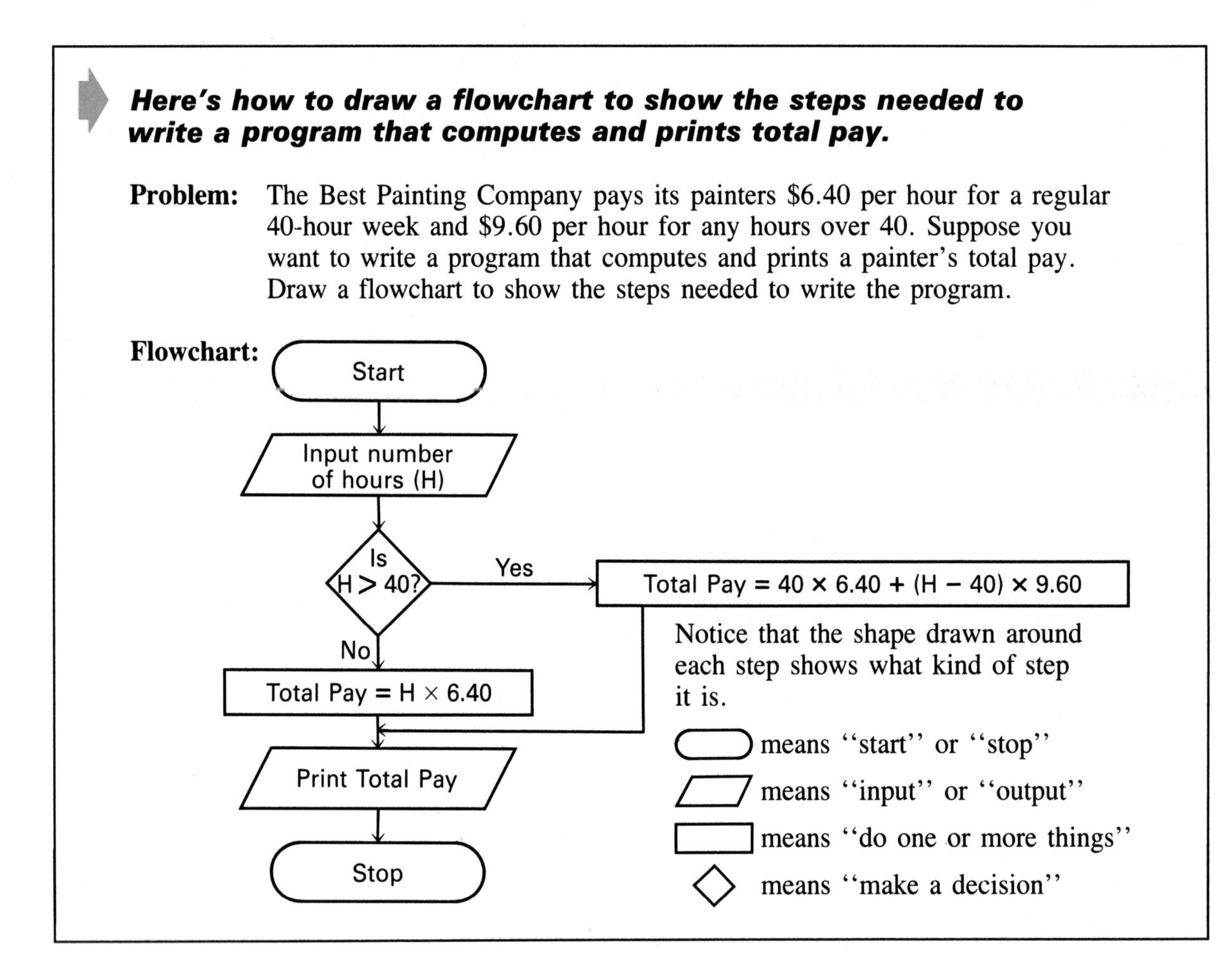

Here's how to draw a flowchart to show the steps needed to write a program that computes and prints total pay.

Problem: The Best Painting Company pays its painters \$6.40 per hour for a regular 40-hour week and \$9.60 per hour for any hours over 40. Suppose you want to write a program that computes and prints a painter's total pay. Draw a flowchart to show the steps needed to write the program.

Flowchart:

Notice that the shape drawn around each step shows what kind of step it is.

- (rounded shape) means "start" or "stop"
- (parallelogram) means "input" or "output"
- (rectangle) means "do one or more things"
- (diamond) means "make a decision"

1. Look at the flowchart above.

a. What does the letter H represent?

b. If your answer to the question in the decision diamond is *No*, you compute H × __?__ to get total pay. If your answer is *Yes*, you compute 40 × 6.40 + (H − __?__) × 9.60 to get total pay.

2. Use the flowchart to compute total pay for each number of hours.

a. 35 hours **b.** 50 hours **c.** 40 hours **d.** 62 hours

▶ **Solve.**

3. Below is a flowchart for computing and printing multiples of 4.

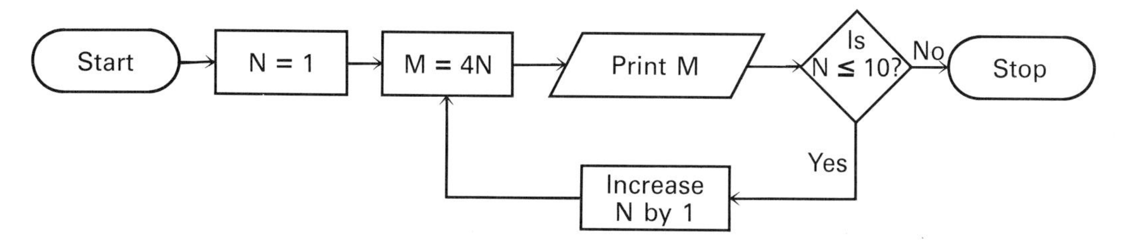

a. Notice the loop in the flowchart. If your answer to the question is *Yes*, you increase N by __?__ and go back to the statement __?__.

b. If your answer is *No*, you __?__.

c. Work through the flowchart and write the output.

▶ **Write the output when you work through each flowchart.**

4.

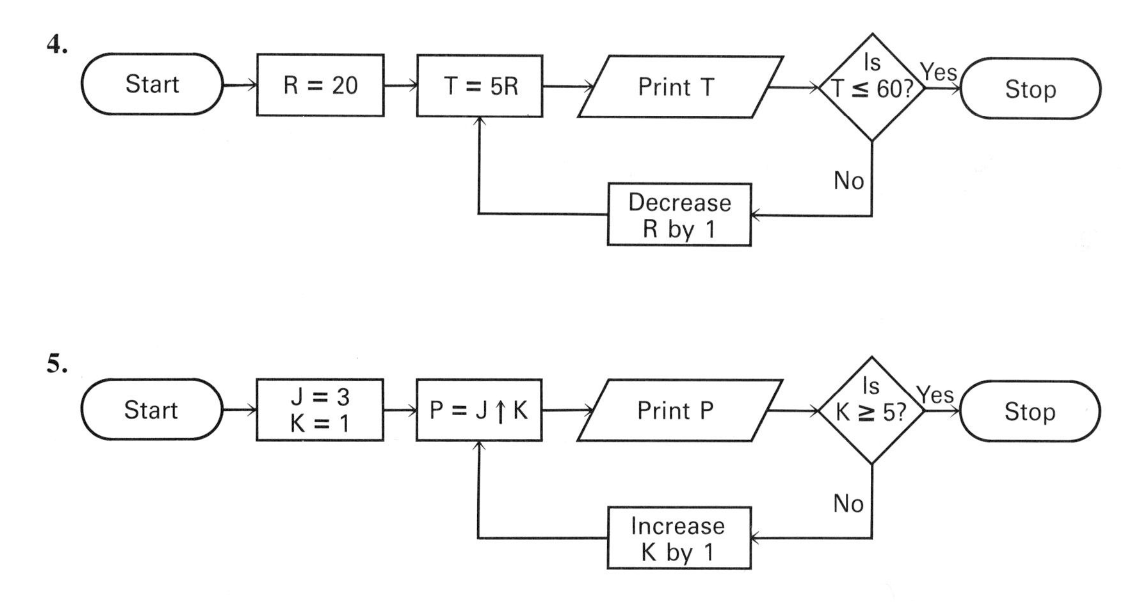

▶ **Make a flowchart for**

6. computing and printing the first ten multiples of 6.

7. computing and printing the first power through the tenth power of 2.

Cumulative Skill Practice

▶ **Solve and check.** *(page 238)*

1. $5y + 2y = 35$
2. $7c - c = 21$
3. $4j - 3j = {}^-23$
4. $6n + n - 3 = 18$
5. $6d + 3 - 5d = {}^-23$
6. $8 + m - 3m = 15$
7. $12z - 2z + 6 = {}^-34$
8. $9t - 3 + 3t = {}^-15$
9. $6 - 4z + 10z = 30$
10. ${}^-5r - 12r - 15 = {}^-18$
11. ${}^-4a - 10 - 11a = 0$
12. ${}^-9 + 3b - 17b = {}^-9$

▶ **Solve and check.** *(page 240)*

13. $7c - 4c + 10 = {}^-4 + 13$
14. $7c - 4 + 10c = {}^-4 + 13$
15. $7 - 4c + 10c = {}^-4 + 13$
16. ${}^-9d + 13d - 4 = 17 - 22$
17. ${}^-9d + 13 - 4d = 17 - 22$
18. ${}^-9 + 13d - 4d = 17 - 22$
19. $16y - 4y + 10 - 7 = {}^-6 + 24$
20. $16 - 4y + 10y - 7 = {}^-6 + 24$
21. $16 - 4 + 10y - 7y = {}^-6 + 24$
22. $12n - n - 9 - 20 = {}^-7 - 15$

▶ **Solve each proportion.** *(page 252)*

23. $\frac{n}{8} = \frac{4}{7}$
24. $\frac{3}{n} = \frac{5}{11}$
25. $\frac{20}{16} = \frac{n}{8}$
26. $\frac{16}{7} = \frac{9}{n}$
27. $\frac{n}{11} = \frac{4}{5}$
28. $\frac{9}{8} = \frac{n}{12}$
29. $\frac{11}{20} = \frac{33}{n}$
30. $\frac{n}{15} = \frac{4}{10}$
31. $\frac{20}{n} = \frac{4}{5}$
32. $\frac{15}{25} = \frac{n}{10}$
33. $\frac{3}{1\frac{1}{2}} = \frac{17}{n}$
34. $\frac{n}{2\frac{1}{4}} = \frac{8}{3}$
35. $\frac{9}{n} = \frac{4}{5\frac{2}{3}}$
36. $\frac{6}{2\frac{3}{4}} = \frac{n}{11}$
37. $\frac{3\frac{5}{6}}{9} = \frac{4}{n}$

▶ **Solve.** *(page 266)*

38. $n\%$ of $10 = 3$
39. $n\%$ of $32 = 4$
40. $n\%$ of $7 = 21$
41. $2\frac{1}{2}\%$ of $16 = n$
42. $8\frac{1}{3}\%$ of $72 = n$
43. $66\frac{2}{3}\%$ of $n = 34$
44. $n\%$ of $40 = 35$
45. $n\%$ of $16 = 40$
46. 12.5% of $n = 29$

▶ **Find the percent of increase or decrease. Use *i* to indicate increase and *d* to indicate decrease. Give answers to the nearest tenth of a percent.** *(page 268)*

47. From 30 to 45
48. From 45 to 30
49. From 32 to 64
50. From 64 to 32
51. From 100 to 150
52. From 150 to 100
53. From 56 to 80
54. From 94 to 57
55. From 92 to 106

Problem Solving—Applications

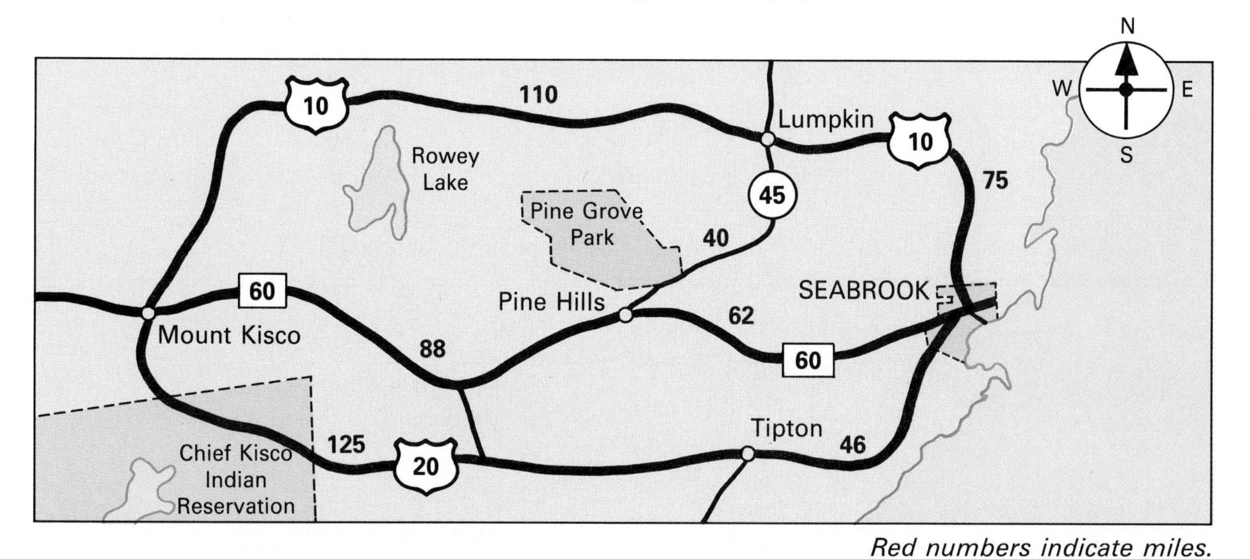

Red numbers indicate miles.

▶ **Use the map to solve the problems.**

1. Which city is 150 miles from Seabrook?

2. Highway 60 goes through which three cities?

3. Which highway from Seabrook to Mount Kisco is 14 miles shorter than Highway 10?

4. At a speed of 50 miles per hour, how many hours would it take to get from Tipton to Mount Kisco on Highway 20?

5. How fast (miles per hour) should a driver travel on Highway 10 to get from Lumpkin to Seabrook in 1 hour 30 minutes?

6. You are traveling east on Highway 60. How far are you from Pine Hills if you have traveled 50% of the distance from Mount Kisco to Seabrook?

7. You are traveling east on Highway 60. Your speed is 50 miles per hour. How many hours is the trip from Mount Kisco to Seabrook?

8. If gasoline costs $1.39 per gallon and your car averages 30 miles per gallon, how much will the gasoline cost for your trip on Highway 60 from Mount Kisco to Seabrook?

▶ **Write the output for each program.**

9.

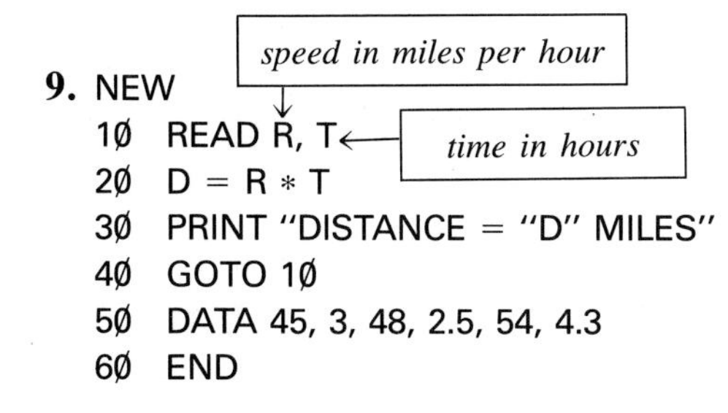


```
NEW
10  READ R, T
20  D = R * T
30  PRINT "DISTANCE = "D" MILES"
40  GOTO 10
50  DATA 45, 3, 48, 2.5, 54, 4.3
60  END
```

10.

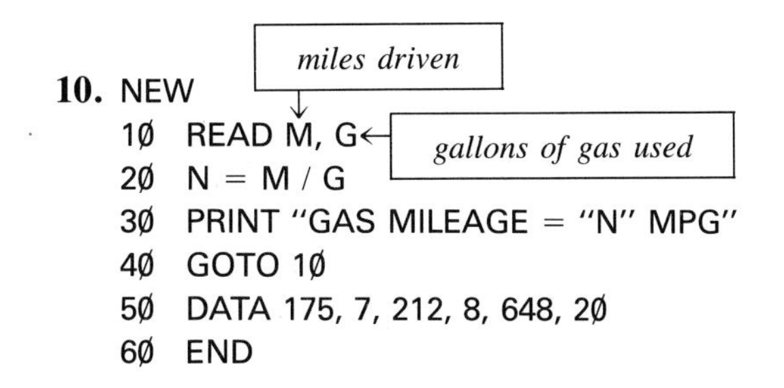


```
NEW
10  READ M, G
20  N = M / G
30  PRINT "GAS MILEAGE = "N" MPG"
40  GOTO 10
50  DATA 175, 7, 212, 8, 648, 20
60  END
```

Chapter Review

Here are scrambled answers for the review exercises:

0	*80*	*H*	*flowchart*	*loop*	*powers*
4	*125*	*N*	*IF . . . THEN*	*multiply*	*READ*
45	*400*	*divide*	*INPUT*	*output*	*subtract*

1. In BASIC language, the symbol * means __?__. To simplify the expression 15 / (16 − 4), a computer would first __?__ and then __?__. *(page 422)*

2. In this program, 17 is assigned to the variable __?__. When the program is RUN, the __?__ will be 68. *(page 424)*

```
NEW
1Ø  N = 17
2Ø  T = 4 * N
3Ø  PRINT T
4Ø  END
```

3. In this program, the __?__ statement accepts information for the variables A and B. When you enter 5 for A and 3 for B, the output will be __?__. *(page 426)*

```
NEW
1Ø  PRINT "WHAT VALUES FOR A, B?"
2Ø  INPUT A, B
3Ø  PRINT A ↑ B
4Ø  END
```

4. In this program, STEP 4 increases the value of N by __?__ each time through the loop. When the program is RUN, the output will be the multiples of 4 from __?__ to __?__. *(page 428)*

```
NEW
1Ø  FOR N = Ø TO 8Ø STEP 4
2Ø  PRINT N
3Ø  NEXT N
4Ø  END
```

5. The __?__ statement gets information from the DATA statement. In this program, 1 will be assigned to the variable __?__. Line 40 tells the computer to __?__ back to line 10 as long as DATA values are available. When the program is RUN, the output will be __?__ of 2. *(pages 432, 434)*

```
NEW
1Ø  READ G, H
2Ø  I = G ↑ H
3Ø  PRINT I
4Ø  GOTO 1Ø
5Ø  DATA 2, 1, 2, 2, 2, 3, 2, 4
6Ø  END
```

6. In this program, an __?__ statement is used to tell the computer to make a decision. When the program is RUN, the computer will print the number __?__. *(page 436)*

```
NEW
1Ø  READ N
2Ø  IF N < 2Ø THEN 1Ø
3Ø  PRINT N
4Ø  GOTO 1Ø
5Ø  DATA 17, 45, 12, −5Ø
6Ø  END
```

7. A programmer may write a plan called a __?__. When you work through this flowchart, the output will be __?__. *(page 438)*

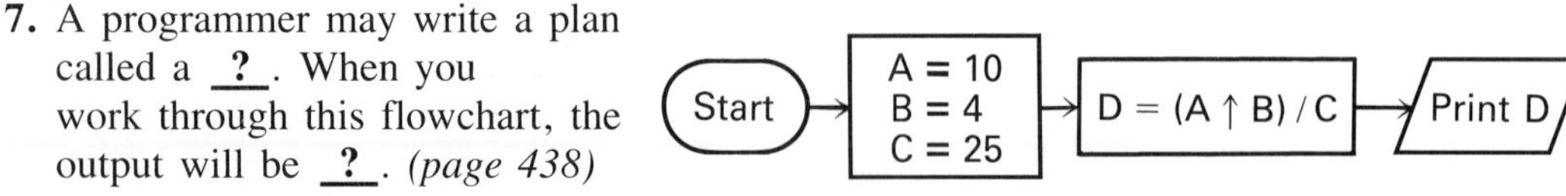

Chapter Test

▶ **Write the output.** *(page 422)*

1. PRINT 15 * 4 + 25

2. PRINT 64 / (12 − 4)

3. PRINT (75 − 14) * 5

4. PRINT 25 + 5 ↑ 2

5. PRINT 7 ↑ 2 − 6 ↑ 2

6. PRINT 36 + 12 * (7 − 5)

▶ **Write the output for each program.** *(pages 424, 428, 432, 434, and 436)*

7.
```
NEW
1Ø  E = 64Ø
2Ø  F = 32Ø
3Ø  PRINT E + F, E − F, E / F
4Ø  END
```

8.
```
NEW
1Ø  FOR D = 2 TO 5
2Ø  C = 3.14 * D
3Ø  PRINT "CIRCUMFERENCE
    IS "C" UNITS"
4Ø  NEXT D
5Ø  END
```

9.
```
NEW
1Ø  FOR N = Ø TO 8Ø STEP 1Ø
2Ø  PRINT N
3Ø  NEXT N
4Ø  END
```

10.
```
NEW
1Ø  READ L, W
2Ø  P = 2 * L + 2 * W
3Ø  PRINT "PERIMETER IS "P" UNITS"
4Ø  DATA 25, 6
5Ø  END
```

11.
```
NEW
1Ø  READ J, K, L
2Ø  PRINT J / K + L
3Ø  GOTO 1Ø
4Ø  DATA 12, 4, 2, −2Ø, 6, 4
5Ø  END
```

12.
```
NEW
1Ø  READ A
2Ø  IF A >= 1Ø THEN 1Ø
3Ø  PRINT A ↑ 2
4Ø  GOTO 1Ø
5Ø  DATA 6, 15, 8, 1Ø, Ø, −2
6Ø  END
```

▶ **Solve. Use the programs above.** *(pages 424, 432, 434, and 436)*

13. Change lines 20 and 30 in program 10 so that the computer will compute and print the area of the rectangle. What will the output be?

14. Change line 30 in program 12 so that the computer will compute and print the cubes of integers less than 10. What will the output be?

▶ **Solve.** *(page 438)*

15. Work through the flowchart at the right. What is the output?

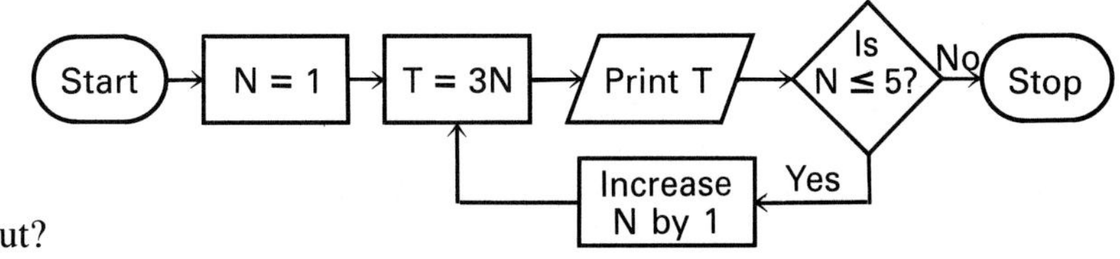

Cumulative Test

Standardized Format

Choose the correct letter.

1. $^-1.375$ written in simplest fractional form is

A. $^-1\frac{3}{8}$ B. $^-1\frac{5}{8}$ C. $1\frac{3}{8}$ D. none of these

2. Give the difference.

$\frac{^-3}{4} - \frac{5}{6}$

A. $\frac{^-1}{12}$ B. $\frac{1}{12}$ C. $^-1\frac{7}{12}$ D. none of these

3. Give the quotient.

$\frac{^-5}{8} \div \frac{15}{32}$

A. $1\frac{1}{3}$ B. $\frac{3}{4}$ C. $\frac{^-3}{4}$ D. none of these

4. Solve.

$^-20 - 12y = {}^-35$

A. $4\frac{7}{12}$ B. $^-1\frac{1}{4}$ C. $1\frac{1}{4}$ D. none of these

5. Simplify

$19t + 8 - t - 20$

by combining like terms.

A. $20t - 12$
B. $18t + 20$
C. $18t - 12$
D. none of these

6. Solve.

$18 - 3t + 8t = {}^-30$

A. $^-4\frac{4}{11}$ B. $^-2\frac{2}{5}$ C. $9\frac{3}{5}$ D. none of these

7. Solve.

$15x - 6 + x + 13 = {}^-6 + 29$

A. 1
B. $1\frac{7}{8}$
C. $1\frac{1}{15}$
D. none of these

8. Solve.

$\frac{n}{2\frac{1}{3}} = \frac{6}{11}$

A. $4\frac{5}{18}$ B. $1\frac{3}{11}$ C. $2\frac{4}{7}$ D. none of these

9. Solve.

$5.4\% \text{ of } 33 = n$

A. 1.782
B. 17.82
C. 6.11
D. none of these

10. The percent of increase from 60 to 72 is

A. 20%
B. $16\frac{2}{3}\%$
C. 25%
D. none of these

11. Find the area of this circle. Use 3.14 for π.

6 cm

A. 18.84 cm^2
B. 28.26 cm^2
C. 113.04 cm^2
D. none of these

12. Choose the equation.

Ten more than the sum of 5 times a number and the number itself is $^-60$.

A. $5n + n + 10 = {}^-60$
B. $5n - n + 10 = {}^-60$
C. $5n + n - 10 = {}^-60$
D. $5n - n - 10 = {}^-60$

Skill Test

Pages 446–455

This test will help you find out which skills you know well and which skills you need to practice more.

Skill Practice

Pages 456–495

These practice sets cover the skills tested on the Skill Test. Each set practices one skill. The skills are presented in the same order as they are in the book. Page references will help you and your teacher decide when to use them.

Skill Test

Skill	Test Items				Skill Practice
1 Evaluating expressions ***page 4***	Evaluate for $x = 12$, $y = 7$, and $z = 9$.				***page 456***
	$x + y + z$		$x + z - y$		
	$x + z + z$		$y - y + x + z$		
	$14 - z + x - y$		$23 - z - z + y$		
2 Rounding whole numbers ***page 6***	Round to the nearest hundred.				***page 456***
	63	1250	6829	5983	
	Round to the nearest thousand.				
	4460	9672	28,095	65,817	
3 Adding whole numbers ***page 10***	$7549 + 4261$		$80{,}665 + 24{,}364$		***page 457***
	$496 + 3081 + 2566$		$26{,}245 + 6518 + 276$		
4 Subtracting whole numbers ***page 12***	$882 - 378$		$608 - 374$		***page 457***
	$4500 - 3492$		$7554 - 1429$		
	$81{,}365 - 62{,}471$		$53{,}800 - 14{,}529$		
5 Solving addition equations ***page 14***	$c + 17 = 24$		$y + 21 = 46$		***page 458***
	$x + 16 = 57$		$w + 31 = 53$		
	$n + 87 = 87$		$d + 58 = 141$		
6 Solving subtraction equations ***page 16***	$z - 19 = 28$		$d - 26 = 35$		***page 458***
	$n - 48 = 48$		$r - 33 = 47$		
	$j - 42 = 50$		$y - 74 = 33$		
7 Solving equations with the variable on the right side ***page 18***	$93 = y + 37$		$46 = w - 35$		***page 459***
	$81 = z + 81$		$106 = k + 61$		
	$132 = j - 56$		$200 = n - 118$		
8 Evaluating expressions ***page 30***	Evaluate for $a = 24$, $b = 12$, and $c = 8$.				***page 459***
	$bc - a$	$\frac{a}{c} + b$	$\frac{b}{b} + c$		
	$5b + a$	$\frac{420}{b} - c$	$10a - b$		

Skill Test

	Skill	Test Items			Skill Practice
9	**Multiplying by multiples of 10, 100, or 1000** *page 32*	35×100	40×60	324×10	*page 460*
		78×1000	70×500	500×600	
		92×1000	90×6000	300×400	
10	**Multiplying by a 1-digit number** *page 34*	527×5	984×7		*page 460*
		3168×4	5907×9		
		4190×3	6105×6		
11	**Multiplying by 2- and 3-digit numbers** *page 36*	59×47	6035×81		*page 461*
		261×103	7448×517		
		212×112	3410×203		
12	**Dividing by a 1-digit number** *page 40*	$474 \div 6$	$3224 \div 4$		*page 461*
		$7182 \div 3$	$78{,}408 \div 9$		
		$4582 \div 2$	$63{,}240 \div 5$		
13	**Dividing by 2- and 3-digit numbers** *page 42*	$5362 \div 19$	$6877 \div 37$		*page 462*
		$6135 \div 24$	$7506 \div 25$		
		$8096 \div 120$	$53{,}162 \div 415$		
14	**Solving multiplication equations** *page 44*	$7x = 84$	$9y = 99$	$6c = 192$	*page 462*
		$12b = 0$	$25n = 275$	$10w = 350$	
		$4x = 12$	$10n = 920$	$5m = 150$	
15	**Solving division equations** *page 46*	$\frac{y}{3} = 21$	$\frac{x}{7} = 17$	$\frac{k}{4} = 48$	*page 463*
		$\frac{a}{12} = 10$	$\frac{c}{16} = 31$	$\frac{r}{15} = 29$	
		$\frac{m}{14} = 8$	$\frac{n}{25} = 6$	$\frac{s}{10} = 16$	
16	**Solving equations with the variable on the right side** *page 48*	$62 = w + 17$	$53 = m - 35$		*page 463*
		$75 = j + 37$	$280 = 20f$		
		$15 = \frac{c}{12}$	$480 = 16m$		

Skill Test

	Skill	Test Items				Skill Practice
17	**Rounding decimals** *page 60*	Round to the nearest tenth.				*page 464*
		1.38	2.50	63.056	36.9521	
		Round to the nearest hundredth.				
		18.342	0.375	0.4968	8.6402	
18	**Comparing decimals** *page 62*	< or >?				*page 464*
		3.57 ◆ 3.75	4.2 ◆ 3.21	0.2 ◆ 0.19		
		0.345 ◆ 0.3366	0.4 ◆ 4.0	0.031 ◆ 0.13		
19	**Adding decimals** *page 64*	2.34 + 1.7	5.62 + 2.94			*page 465*
		8.04 + 7 + 9.6	0.483 + 1.56 + 4.4			
20	**Subtracting decimals** *page 66*	5 − 2.7	7 − 2.4	25.3 − 6		*page 465*
		4.23 − 2.849	13 − 6.7	16.2 − 3.571		
21	**Solving equations with decimals** *page 68*	$r + 3.8 = 17.2$	$25.3 = t + 19.5$			*page 466*
		$j - 14.3 = 38$	$8.52 = m - 14.7$			
22	**Multiplying decimals** *page 72*	5.4 × 0.36	6.3 × 1.2	34 × 0.88		*page 466*
		6.05 × 0.39	2.04 × 1.6	8.25 × 2.06		
23	**Multiplying decimals by 10, 100, or 1000** *page 74*	0.93 × 100	0.3 × 10	4.7 × 10		*page 467*
		5.28 × 1000	4.1 × 1000	0.004 × 100		
		3.8 × 10	5.22 × 100	0.03 × 1000		
24	**Dividing a decimal by a whole number** *page 76*	Round each quotient to the nearest hundredth.				*page 467*
		12.17 ÷ 8	6.34 ÷ 8	27.62 ÷ 9		
		6.335 ÷ 24	7.873 ÷ 25	1.6238 ÷ 44		

Skill Test

Skill	Test Items			Skill Practice
25 Dividing by a decimal *page 78*	$2.04 \div 0.6$ $0.0644 \div 0.04$ $4.221 \div 0.21$		$1.64 \div 0.4$ $0.1206 \div 0.18$ $0.3233 \div 5.3$	*page 468*
26 Dividing decimals by 10, 100, or 1000 *page 80*	$9.45 \div 10$ $450.5 \div 100$ $6.94 \div 1000$		$8.3 \div 10$ $53.5 \div 1000$ $0.84 \div 100$	*page 468*
27 Solving equations with decimals *page 82*	$3r = 1.95$ $16.7 = d + 9.3$ $\frac{w}{2.7} = 1.6$		$4.08 = 2y$ $25.23 = t - 14.7$ $5.21 = \frac{c}{0.8}$	*page 469*
28 Simplifying expressions *page 92*	$12 - 8 + 4$ $24 \times (12 - 2)$ $36 + 4 \times 7 - 3$		$18 \div 6 \times 2$ $16 + 3 \times 4 \div 2$ $(36 + 4) \times 7 - 3$	*page 469*
29 Solving equations using the commutative properties *page 98*	$56 = 33 + b$ $1.68 = d(21)$ $59 = 10 + r$	$69 = 27 + j$ $7.9 = 4 + x$ $6.4 = 3 + s$	$132 = n(12)$ $2.4 = m(3)$ $4.8 = m(4)$	*page 470*
30 Solving two-step equations *page 102*	$4n + 9 = 37$ $39 = 10x + 9$ $12c - 5.1 = 18.9$		$2w - 6 = 52$ $15.8 = 5j - 4.2$ $9.6 = 7k + 6.1$	*page 470*
31 Solving two-step equations *page 104*	$\frac{n}{6} + 3 = 12$ $125 = 22r - 51$ $15 = \frac{d}{8} + 3$		$8k - 8 = 88$ $16r + 37 = 37$ $\frac{f}{10} - 21 = 0$	*page 471*
32 Combining like terms *page 108*	$8c + 3c$ $3n + 4n + 2n$ $5x + 3 + 4 + 2x$		$11t + t$ $11g + g + 5g$ $9y + 8 + y + 5$	*page 471*

Skill Test

Skill	Test Items	Skill Practice
33 **Solving equations by first combining like terms** *page 110*	$6a + 3a = 72$; $5j + j = 96$; $9n + 6n = 165$; $0 = 8w + 3w$; $17.4 = 2t + t$; $5n + 11n = 3.68$	*page 472*
34 **Writing expressions using exponents** *page 120*	Simplify using exponents for the variables. $a \cdot b \cdot a \cdot b \cdot a$; $9 \cdot a \cdot a \cdot 2 \cdot a$; $3 \cdot 2 \cdot b \cdot b \cdot 4 \cdot b$; $7 \cdot a \cdot b \cdot 5 \cdot a \cdot b \cdot b \cdot b$	*page 472*
35 **Writing the prime or algebraic factorization** *page 124*	Give the prime factorization. 15; 18; 36; 48. Give the algebraic factorization. $21x^2$; $30x^3$; $42x^2y$; $45x^2y^3$	*page 473*
36 **Writing the GCF and the LCM** *page 126*	Give the greatest common factor. 25, 20; 15, 24; 32, 48; $6, 9w$; $8w, 12w^2$; $36wz, 45w^2z$. Give the least common multiple. 3, 4; 9, 6; 12, 8; $8, 12u$; $5u, 7u^2$; $10u^2v, 25uv^2$	*page 473*
37 **Writing an equivalent fraction** *page 130*	$\frac{5}{2} = \frac{?}{6}$; $\frac{7}{8} = \frac{?}{40}$; $\frac{7}{12} = \frac{?}{24}$; $\frac{3}{c} = \frac{?}{4c}$; $\frac{9c}{d} = \frac{?}{4cd}$; $\frac{4c}{3d} = \frac{?}{12cd^2}$	*page 474*
38 **Writing fractions in lowest terms** *page 132*	$\frac{8}{12}$; $\frac{16}{40}$; $\frac{30}{20}$; $\frac{35}{50}$; $\frac{3}{6j}$; $\frac{j}{jk}$; $\frac{14j}{21j^2}$; $\frac{11jk^2}{33k}$	*page 474*
39 **Finding the least common denominator** *page 134*	Find the least common denominator. $\frac{1}{3}, \frac{1}{2}$; $\frac{1}{4}, \frac{3}{4}$; $\frac{3}{4}, \frac{5}{6}$; $\frac{5}{6}, \frac{5}{8}$; $\frac{4}{m}, \frac{1}{3m}$; $\frac{6}{m}, \frac{5}{n}$; $\frac{1}{mn^2}, \frac{3}{m^2n^2}$; $\frac{m}{4mn}, \frac{6}{3m^2n}$	*page 475*
40 **Comparing fractions** *page 136*	$<$ or $>$? $\frac{4}{5}$ ◆ $\frac{3}{5}$; $\frac{1}{4}$ ◆ $\frac{3}{8}$; $\frac{3}{4}$ ◆ $\frac{2}{3}$; $\frac{5}{6}$ ◆ $\frac{7}{8}$	*page 475*

Skill Test

	Skill	Test Items				Skill Practice
41	**Writing whole and mixed numbers as fractions** *page 146*	Change to fourths.				*page 476*
		2	4	6	3	
		Change to a fraction.				
		$1\frac{1}{4}$	$1\frac{2}{3}$	$2\frac{3}{4}$	$3\frac{5}{6}$	
42	**Writing fractions as whole numbers or mixed numbers** *page 148*	Change to a whole number or mixed number.				*page 476*
		$\frac{8}{2}$	$\frac{9}{3}$	$\frac{16}{4}$	$\frac{18}{6}$	
		$\frac{4}{3}$	$\frac{5}{2}$	$\frac{13}{5}$	$\frac{11}{4}$	
43	**Writing fractions and mixed numbers in simplest form** *page 150*	Write in simplest form.				*page 477*
		$\frac{6}{9}$	$3\frac{2}{4}$	$\frac{15}{3}$	$\frac{14}{6}$	
44	**Writing quotients as mixed numbers** *page 152*	Write each quotient as a mixed number in simplest form.				*page 477*
		$28 \div 5$	$58 \div 4$	$142 \div 12$	$200 \div 16$	
45	**Adding and subtracting fractions with common denominators** *page 156*	Give each sum or difference in simplest form.				*page 478*
		$\frac{1}{8} + \frac{5}{8}$	$\frac{5}{6} + \frac{1}{6}$	$\frac{r}{s} + \frac{t}{s}$	$\frac{19}{t^2} + \frac{4}{t^2}$	
		$\frac{7}{12} - \frac{1}{12}$	$\frac{5}{9} - \frac{2}{9}$	$\frac{r}{t} - \frac{s}{t}$	$\frac{16}{rs} - \frac{9}{rs}$	
46	**Adding and subtracting fractions with different denominators** *page 158*	Give each sum or difference in simplest form.				*page 478*
		$\frac{1}{3} + \frac{1}{2}$	$\frac{5}{6} + \frac{5}{8}$	$\frac{m}{8} + \frac{3}{4}$	$\frac{3m}{5} + \frac{4n}{7}$	
		$\frac{5}{6} - \frac{1}{2}$	$\frac{11}{12} - \frac{2}{3}$	$\frac{m}{3} - \frac{n}{9}$	$\frac{5m}{6} - \frac{2n}{5}$	
47	**Adding and subtracting mixed numbers without regrouping** *page 160*	Give each sum or difference in simplest form.				*page 479*
		$3\frac{1}{2} + 2\frac{1}{4}$	$5\frac{2}{3} + 3\frac{1}{8}$	$6 + 9\frac{5}{12}$		
		$5\frac{2}{3} - 2\frac{1}{2}$	$8\frac{5}{6} - 6\frac{1}{4}$	$11\frac{7}{8} - 9\frac{2}{3}$		

Skill Test

	Skill	Test Items	Skill Practice
48	**Adding and subtracting mixed numbers with regrouping** *page 162*	Give each sum or difference in simplest form. $6\frac{2}{3} + 4\frac{3}{4}$ $8\frac{7}{8} + 7\frac{5}{12}$ $9\frac{7}{10} + 7\frac{5}{6}$ $8\frac{1}{3} - 3\frac{1}{2}$ $12\frac{1}{4} - 9\frac{5}{6}$ $11\frac{3}{5} - 4\frac{7}{8}$	*page 479*
49	**Multiplying fractions** *page 172*	Give each product in simplest form. $\frac{1}{2} \cdot \frac{1}{3}$ $\frac{2}{3} \cdot \frac{3}{4}$ $3 \cdot \frac{3}{4}$ $\frac{6}{5} \cdot \frac{5}{6}$ $r \cdot \frac{5}{t}$ $\frac{5}{6} \cdot \frac{3s}{4t}$ $\frac{s^2}{14} \cdot \frac{1}{s}$ $\frac{3s}{t} \cdot \frac{t^2}{8}$	*page 480*
50	**Multiplying mixed numbers** *page 174*	Give each product in simplest form. $1\frac{1}{4} \cdot 1\frac{1}{2}$ $2 \cdot 2\frac{1}{2}$ $1\frac{2}{3} \cdot 1\frac{3}{4}$ $3\frac{1}{5} \cdot 2\frac{3}{8}$	*page 480*
51	**Dividing fractions** *page 176*	Give each quotient in simplest form. $\frac{2}{3} \div 5$ $\frac{3}{8} \div \frac{3}{2}$ $\frac{9}{4} \div \frac{5}{6}$ $\frac{0}{8} \div \frac{5}{12}$ $\frac{a}{b} \div \frac{c}{d}$ $\frac{3a}{b} \div \frac{b}{c}$ $\frac{a^2}{b} \div \frac{a}{c}$ $\frac{a}{6b} \div \frac{c}{3b}$	*page 481*
52	**Dividing mixed numbers** *page 178*	Give each quotient in simplest form. $3 \div 2\frac{1}{3}$ $3\frac{2}{3} \div 1\frac{1}{2}$ $4\frac{3}{4} \div 2$ $4\frac{1}{5} \div 2\frac{5}{8}$	*page 481*
53	**Finding a fraction of a number** *page 182*	$\frac{1}{2}$ of $24 = n$ $\frac{1}{3}$ of $18 = n$ $\frac{2}{3}$ of $42 = n$ $\frac{3}{5}$ of $60 = n$ $\frac{2}{7}$ of $21 = n$ $\frac{3}{4}$ of $72 = n$	*page 482*
54	**Multiplying a whole number by a mixed number** *page 184*	$1\frac{2}{3}$ h = ? min $2\frac{1}{2}$ ft = ? in. $2\frac{2}{3}$ yd = ? ft $1\frac{3}{4}$ gal = ? qt	*page 482*
55	**Finding a number when a fraction of it is known** *page 186*	Give answers in simplest form. $\frac{1}{3}n = 8$ $\frac{5}{6}n = 55$ $\frac{3}{4}n = 51$ $\frac{5}{2}n = 42$ $\frac{7}{8}n = 20$ $\frac{11}{12}n = 34$	*page 483*

Skill Test

	Skill	Test Items			Skill Practice
56	**Comparing integers** ***page 196***	$<$ or $>$? $^{-}3 ◆ ^{-}2$ $^{+}12 ◆ ^{+}11$	 $^{+}9 ◆ 0$ $^{+}10 ◆ ^{-}13$		***page 483***
57	**Adding integers** ***page 198***	$^{+}4 + ^{+}7$ $^{-}18 + ^{+}18$	$^{+}9 + ^{-}3$ $^{-}22 + ^{-}15$		***page 484***
58	**Subtracting integers** ***page 200***	$^{-}7 - ^{+}3$ $^{+}34 - ^{+}34$	$^{+}8 - ^{-}9$ $^{-}46 - ^{-}20$		***page 484***
59	**Multiplying integers** ***page 202***	$^{+}6 \cdot ^{-}7$ $^{-}5 \cdot ^{+}19$	$^{+}8 \cdot ^{+}10$ $^{-}23 \cdot 0$		***page 485***
60	**Dividing integers** ***page 204***	$^{-}24 \div ^{+}8$ $^{-}45 \div ^{-}5$	$^{+}54 \div ^{-}9$ $^{+}72 \div ^{-}18$		***page 485***
61	**Writing numbers in scientific notation** ***page 208***	42,000 0.084	345,000 0.0091	1,960,000 0.000675	***page 486***
62	**Solving addition and subtraction equations involving integers** ***page 210***	$c + 18 = ^{-}4$ $11 = c + 19$ $c - 11 = ^{-}23$ $c + 10 = ^{-}15$	$c + ^{-}6 = ^{-}5$ $c - 5 = 9$ $27 = c - 32$ $c - 8 = ^{-}12$		***page 486***
63	**Solving multiplication and division equations involving integers** ***page 212***	$^{-}3d = 15$ $^{-}42 = 14d$ $\frac{d}{^{-}5} = ^{-}8$	$^{-}12d = 0$ $\frac{d}{6} = ^{-}4$ $15 = \frac{d}{^{-}7}$		***page 487***
64	**Solving two-step equations involving integers** ***page 214***	$3n + 9 = 0$ $^{-}12n + 15 = ^{-}45$ $\frac{n}{^{-}7} - 3 = ^{-}9$	$^{-}6n - 7 = 23$ $\frac{n}{8} + 2 = 6$ $\frac{n}{^{-}9} + 12 = 12$		***page 487***

Skill Test

	Skill	Test Items	Skill Practice
65	**Comparing rational numbers** *page 224*	$<$ or $>$? $\frac{2}{3} \blacklozenge \frac{3}{4}$ $\frac{^-5}{6} \blacklozenge \frac{^-7}{8}$ $^-3\frac{1}{4} \blacklozenge 3$ $^-2\frac{3}{4} \blacklozenge {^-2}\frac{5}{6}$	***page 488***
66	**Writing a rational number in decimal form** *page 226*	Write each rational number in decimal form. $\frac{2}{5}$ $\frac{^-7}{4}$ $\frac{1}{3}$ $^-3\frac{5}{6}$	***page 488***
67	**Writing a decimal in simplest fractional form** *page 226*	Write each decimal in simplest fractional form. 0.8 $^-0.75$ 2.375 $^-6.125$ 0.25 3.6 $^-1.5$ 2.4	***page 489***
68	**Adding and subtracting rational numbers** *page 228*	Give each sum or difference in simplest form. $\frac{2}{3} + \frac{^-1}{4}$ $\frac{^-5}{9} + \frac{^-1}{6}$ $4\frac{1}{3} + 3\frac{7}{8}$ $^-5\frac{3}{4} + 2\frac{1}{2}$ $\frac{^-3}{4} - \frac{1}{2}$ $\frac{^-2}{3} - \frac{^-7}{12}$ $10\frac{1}{4} - 8\frac{5}{8}$ $^-6\frac{9}{10} - {^-4}\frac{5}{6}$	***page 489***
69	**Multiplying and dividing rational numbers** *page 230*	Give each product or quotient in simplest form. $\frac{^-2}{3} \cdot \frac{4}{5}$ $\frac{^-3}{8} \cdot {^-8}$ $2\frac{1}{2} \cdot 3\frac{1}{4}$ $^-4\frac{2}{3} \cdot {^-1}\frac{1}{5}$ $\frac{^-3}{4} \div \frac{^-1}{4}$ $\frac{5}{6} \div \frac{^-5}{8}$ $4\frac{1}{4} \div 2\frac{1}{8}$ $10\frac{3}{5} \div 3\frac{3}{10}$	***page 490***
70	**Solving equations having rational solutions** *page 234*	$5x - 3 = {^-2}$ $^-4x + 17 = {^-12}$ $^-12x - 6 = 11$ $18 + 15x = 19$ $^-10 - 8x = {^-30}$ $16 - 20x = {^-43}$	***page 490***
71	**Simplifying expressions by combining like terms** *page 236*	Simplify. $8j + j$ $^-8j + 15j - 2$ $11j + 14 - 7j$ $11j + 4 - 9 - 6j$ $11 + 4j - 9 - 6j$ $11 + 4j - 9j - 6$	***page 491***
72	**Solving equations by first combining like terms** *pages 238, 240*	$5n - n = {^-13}$ $11n + n - 18 = 6$ $20n - 23 - 14n = 36$ $4n + 3n = {^-8} + 17$ $^-3n + 9 - 7n = {^-22} + 8$ $15 + 2n - 6n + 3 = {^-18} - 32$	***page 491***

Skill Test

Skill	Test Items	Skill Practice
73 Writing equal ratios *page 250*	Complete to get an equal ratio. $\frac{14}{21} = \frac{?}{3}$ $\frac{3}{2} = \frac{?}{10}$ $\frac{7}{8} = \frac{?}{32}$ $\frac{12}{5} = \frac{?}{30}$ $\frac{a}{b} = \frac{?}{3b}$ $\frac{6}{a} = \frac{?}{5ab}$ $\frac{a^2}{b} = \frac{?}{8b^2}$ $\frac{7a}{4b} = \frac{?}{16ab^2}$	*page 492*
74 Solving a proportion *page 252*	$\frac{4}{n} = \frac{5}{8}$ $\frac{n}{15} = \frac{10}{9}$ $\frac{4}{13} = \frac{n}{6\frac{1}{2}}$ $\frac{2\frac{3}{8}}{5} = \frac{17}{n}$	*page 492*
75 Changing a percent to a fraction or mixed number *page 256*	Change to a fraction or mixed number in simplest form. 25% 150% $33\frac{1}{3}\%$ $62\frac{1}{2}\%$	*page 493*
76 Changing a fraction to a percent *page 258*	Change to a percent. $\frac{3}{5}$ $\frac{3}{2}$ $\frac{1}{6}$ $\frac{8}{3}$	*page 493*
77 Finding a percent of a number *page 262*	25% of 44 = n 9% of 37 = n 6.5% of 38 = n 0.5% of 60 = n	*page 494*
78 Finding the number when a percent is known *page 264*	Round each answer to the nearest tenth. 20% of n = 16 75% of n = 48 8.5% of n = 12.5 32.2% of n = 34.6	*page 494*
79 Solving a percent problem by solving a proportion *page 266*	Solve by solving a proportion. n% of 8 = 6 n% of 15 = 10 $4\frac{1}{2}\%$ of 12 = n $83\frac{1}{3}\%$ of 42 = n $8\frac{1}{4}\%$ of n = 33 5% of n = 15.4	*page 495*
80 Finding the percent of increase or decrease *page 268*	Find the percent of increase or decrease. Use i to indicate increase and d to indicate decrease. Give answers to the nearest tenth of a percent. 18 to 27 60 to 80 80 to 60 56 to 40 81 to 100 125 to 95	*page 495*

Skill Practice

Skill 1 (Use after page 4.)

Example

Evaluate the expression

$a + b - c$

for $a = 9$, $b = 6$, and $c = 7$.

Substitute.

$9 + 6 - 7$

Simplify.

8

Evaluate each expression for $x = 10$, $y = 5$, and $z = 8$.

1. $x + 3$	**2.** $x - 7$	**3.** $x + 9$
4. $y - 5$	**5.** $y + 8$	**6.** $y - 2$
7. $z + 6$	**8.** $z - 8$	**9.** $z + 5$
10. $x + y$	**11.** $y + x$	**12.** $y + z$
13. $x + z$	**14.** $x - y$	**15.** $z - y$
▲ **16.** $y + x + z$	▲ **17.** $y + z - 4$	▲ **18.** $z + x - 9$
■ **19.** $y + y - 4$	■ **20.** $z + z - 9$	■ **21.** $x + x - 5$
● **22.** $x + y + z$	● **23.** $x - y + 4$	● **24.** $x + z - 5$
25. $16 - y + x$	**26.** $15 + y - x$	**27.** $20 - y - y$
28. $18 + x - y$	**29.** $24 + y + z$	**30.** $30 + z - z$

Skill 2 (Use after page 6.)

Example

Round 45,359 to the nearest hundred.

Rounding to this place
↓
45,359
↑
When the next digit to the right is 5 or greater, round up.

45,359 rounds to 45,400.

Round to the nearest ten.

1. 74	**2.** 37	**3.** 42	**4.** 75
5. 183	**6.** 366	**7.** 805	**8.** 411
9. 4336	**10.** 3721	**11.** 3605	**12.** 2398

Round to the nearest hundred.

▲ **13.** 276	▲ **14.** 550	▲ **15.** 743	▲ **16.** 849
17. 3408	**18.** 3423	**19.** 6660	**20.** 8050
21. 20,305	**22.** 32,780	**23.** 42,912	**24.** 62,950

Round to the nearest thousand.

■ **25.** 4841	■ **26.** 6851	■ **27.** 9310	■ **28.** 6500
29. 35,431	**30.** 42,573	**31.** 719,527	**32.** 273,500

Round to the nearest ten thousand.

● **33.** 24,146	● **34.** 52,700	● **35.** 56,913	● **36.** 49,430
37. 92,604	**38.** 28,911	**39.** 249,300	**40.** 613,812

Skill 3 (Use after page 10.)

Example

245 + 92 + 3916 = ?

Line up the digits vertically.

```
  245
   92
+3916
```

Add.

```
 11
  245
 1 92
+3916
 4253
```

Give the sum.

1. 6438 + 8310
2. 5832 + 694
3. 966 + 2947
4. 3370 + 1938
5. 34,006 + 8825
6. 4721 + 76,082
7. 12,500 + 38,926
8. 38,842 + 27,111
9. 493 + 3493 + 977
10. 8218 + 739 + 1005
11. 182 + 4200 + 3628
12. 7467 + 941 + 604
13. 593 + 444 + 1660
14. 2741 + 8009 + 476
15. 4850 + 1188 + 2055
16. 1748 + 2966 + 1826
17. 54,388 + 2112 + 599
18. 4368 + 829 + 12,477
19. 29,006 + 2704 + 1822
20. 2864 + 31,000 + 8002

▲21. 4589 + 3594 + 1642

▲22. 563 + 2516 + 9292

■23. 374 + 209 + 5618

■24. 721 + 4441 + 356

●25. 2843 + 78 + 197

●26. 5381 + 927 + 58

Skill 4 (Use after page 12.)

Example

8305 − 4078 = ?

Line up the digits vertically and subtract in columns.

```
   2
 8 3̸ ¹0 5
−4 0  7 8
```

```
   2  9
 8 3̸ ¹0̸ ¹5
−4 0  7  8
```

```
   2  9
 8 3̸ ¹0̸ ¹5
−4 0  7  8
 4 2  2  7
```

Give the difference.

1. 828 − 411
2. 594 − 221
3. 710 − 463
4. 824 − 258
5. 504 − 356
6. 701 − 588
7. 806 − 529
8. 903 − 165
9. 800 − 361
10. 400 − 249
11. 700 − 318
12. 600 − 233
13. 800 − 444
14. 500 − 381
15. 4916 − 2854
16. 5874 − 2222

▲17. 3406 − 2153

▲18. 7112 − 4338

■19. 2502 − 458

■20. 3701 − 229

●21. 5205 − 1286

●22. 6101 − 2255

23. 53,621 − 47,950
24. 64,206 − 39,178
25. 48,000 − 21,462
26. 72,003 − 19,740

Skill 5 (Use after page 14.)

Example

Solve.

$$x + 14 = 23$$

Subtract 14 from both sides.

$$x + 14 - 14 = 23 - 14$$

Simplify.

$$x = 9$$

Check:

$$9 + 14 \stackrel{?}{=} 23$$
$$23 = 23$$

Solve and check.

1. $w + 5 = 9$ **2.** $h + 8 = 15$ **3.** $e + 10 = 12$

4. $b + 9 = 15$ **5.** $t + 5 = 20$ **6.** $p + 7 = 18$

7. $r + 11 = 20$ **8.** $a + 13 = 13$ **9.** $k + 18 = 29$

10. $x + 17 = 34$ **11.** $z + 19 = 42$ **12.** $v + 22 = 47$

13. $c + 21 = 30$ **14.** $m + 23 = 53$ **15.** $g + 34 = 58$

▲ **16.** $r + 42 = 75$ ▲ **17.** $y + 46 = 48$ ▲ **18.** $d + 43 = 43$

■ **19.** $t + 36 = 55$ ■ **20.** $d + 29 = 35$ ■ **21.** $f + 37 = 60$

● **22.** $i + 51 = 54$ ● **23.** $u + 42 = 56$ ● **24.** $c + 48 = 92$

25. $s + 73 = 93$ **26.** $g + 65 = 65$ **27.** $v + 59 = 87$

28. $j + 60 = 100$ **29.** $n + 78 = 116$ **30.** $s + 83 = 133$

Skill 6 (Use after page 16.)

Example

Solve.

$$y - 26 = 34$$

Add 26 to both sides.

$$y - 26 + 26 = 34 + 26$$

Simplify.

$$y = 60$$

Check:

$$60 - 26 \stackrel{?}{=} 34$$
$$34 = 34$$

Solve and check.

1. $v - 9 = 8$ **2.** $r - 7 = 10$ **3.** $f - 6 = 9$

4. $c - 8 = 7$ **5.** $a - 11 = 0$ **6.** $q - 15 = 12$

7. $n - 19 = 15$ **8.** $j - 12 = 23$ **9.** $a - 20 = 19$

10. $w - 24 = 21$ **11.** $b - 32 = 50$ **12.** $f - 41 = 27$

13. $b - 37 = 40$ **14.** $d - 48 = 16$ **15.** $k - 55 = 24$

▲ **16.** $s - 43 = 46$ ▲ **17.** $c - 30 = 35$ ▲ **18.** $v - 29 = 43$

■ **19.** $x - 62 = 17$ ■ **20.** $p - 52 = 26$ ■ **21.** $e - 43 = 20$

● **22.** $t - 40 = 33$ ● **23.** $e - 56 = 37$ ● **24.** $z - 30 = 42$

25. $g - 62 = 22$ **26.** $d - 65 = 18$ **27.** $m - 44 = 44$

28. $t - 57 = 45$ **29.** $h - 71 = 25$ **30.** $y - 66 = 34$

31. $a - 46 = 50$ **32.** $b - 83 = 0$ **33.** $c - 1 = 59$

34. $d - 0 = 87$ **35.** $e - 62 = 62$ **36.** $f - 74 = 47$

Skill 7 (Use after page 18.)

Example

Solve.

$$28 = y + 11$$

Use the symmetric property of equality.

$$y + 11 = 28$$

Subtract 11 from both sides.

$$y + 11 - 11 = 28 - 11$$

Simplify.

$$y = 17$$

Check:

$$28 \stackrel{?}{=} 17 + 11$$
$$28 = 28$$

Solve and check.

1. $19 = f + 8$
2. $f - 6 = 6$
3. $20 = f - 19$
4. $a + 9 = 15$
5. $45 = t + 35$
6. $e + 12 = 56$
7. $18 = b - 16$
8. $p - 17 = 35$
9. $60 = y + 23$
10. $q + 20 = 42$
11. $18 = j - 16$
12. $49 = g + 37$
13. $45 = h - 30$
14. $b - 44 = 27$
15. $k + 42 = 42$
16. ▲ $h - 31 = 53$
17. ▲ $60 = w + 42$
18. ▲ $m + 25 = 100$
19. ■ $58 = x - 23$
20. ■ $52 = c + 52$
21. ■ $35 = u - 25$
22. ● $92 = a + 61$
23. ● $g - 17 = 60$
24. ● $d + 23 = 84$
25. $c - 42 = 23$
26. $30 = d - 56$
27. $101 = z + 74$
28. $58 = v - 35$
29. $r - 35 = 76$
30. $j + 53 = 112$

Skill 8 (Use after page 30.)

Example

Evaluate the expression

$$\frac{r}{t} + s$$

for $r = 12$, $s = 4$, and $t = 2$.

Substitute.

$$\frac{12}{2} + 4$$

Simplify.

$$10$$

Evaluate each expression for $x = 12$, $y = 6$, and $z = 3$.

1. $5x$
2. $9y$
3. $\frac{x}{4}$
4. $\frac{y}{2}$
5. $3 + z$
6. $15 - y$
7. $3x + 4$
8. $8y - 3$
9. $10z + 6$
10. $12y + z$
11. $2x - y$
12. $3x + z$
13. $\frac{x}{3} + z$
14. $\frac{y}{2} - z$
15. $\frac{x}{6} + y$
16. ▲ $xy - z$
17. ▲ $xz + y$
18. ▲ $yz - x$
19. ■ $5x + x$
20. ■ $7y - y$
21. ■ $8z - z$
22. ● $10x - z$
23. ● $4y + x$
24. ● $2x + x$
25. $\frac{42}{y} + z$
26. $\frac{30}{z} - y$
27. $\frac{24}{x} + x$
28. $\frac{x}{z} - z$
29. $\frac{x}{y} + z$
30. $\frac{y}{z} + x$

Skill 9 (Use after page 32.)

Example

30 × 200 = ?

Multiply 3 × 2 and annex 3 zeros.

30 × 200 = 6000

Give the product.

1. 9 × 10	**2.** 6 × 100	**3.** 5 × 1000
4. 3 × 100	**5.** 8 × 20	**6.** 8 × 200
7. 12 × 10	**8.** 15 × 1000	**9.** 20 × 50
10. 80 × 300	**11.** 3 × 800	**12.** 20 × 40
13. 30 × 2000	**14.** 40 × 400	**15.** 50 × 100
▲**16.** 50 × 1000	▲**17.** 40 × 200	▲**18.** 20 × 3000
■**19.** 30 × 20	■**20.** 40 × 300	■**21.** 400 × 30
●**22.** 145 × 100	●**23.** 256 × 1000	●**24.** 228 × 10
25. 400 × 60	**26.** 300 × 300	**27.** 600 × 5000
28. 300 × 200	**29.** 800 × 40	**30.** 700 × 6000

Skill 10 (Use after page 34.)

Example

527 × 4 = ?

Line up the digits vertically.

```
 527
  ×4
```

Multiply.

```
 12
 527
  ×4
2108
```

Give the product.

1. 23 × 3	**2.** 12 × 4	**3.** 44 × 2
4. 11 × 6	**5.** 56 × 5	**6.** 78 × 7
7. 39 × 9	**8.** 82 × 4	**9.** 143 × 3
10. 481 × 6	**11.** 330 × 2	**12.** 513 × 5
13. 307 × 8	**14.** 632 × 7	**15.** 812 × 4
▲**16.** 961 × 9	▲**17.** 748 × 6	▲**18.** 853 × 7
■**19.** 571 × 4	■**20.** 660 × 8	■**21.** 493 × 3
●**22.** 3218 × 3	●**23.** 5175 × 5	●**24.** 4069 × 8
25. 3506 × 6	**26.** 7153 × 4	**27.** 9188 × 5
28. 2009 × 9	**29.** 6021 × 7	**30.** 5228 × 3
31. 4837 × 6	**32.** 2740 × 8	**33.** 6050 × 7
34. 8162 × 5	**35.** 3908 × 4	**36.** 3625 × 8

Skill 11 (Use after page 36.)

Example

145 × 23 = ?

Multiply by 3.

$$\begin{array}{r} 145 \\ \times 23 \\ \hline 435 \end{array}$$

Multiply by 20.

$$\begin{array}{r} 145 \\ \times 23 \\ \hline 435 \\ 2900 \end{array}$$

Add.

$$\begin{array}{r} 145 \\ \times 23 \\ \hline 435 \\ 2900 \\ \hline 3335 \end{array}$$

Give the product.

1. 34 × 12	**2.** 26 × 20	**3.** 40 × 41
4. 51 × 33	**5.** 75 × 18	**6.** 84 × 25
7. 59 × 36	**8.** 47 × 29	**9.** 43 × 55
10. 50 × 62	**11.** 78 × 18	**12.** 95 × 77
▲**13.** 125 × 31	▲**14.** 236 × 22	▲**15.** 304 × 58
■**16.** 411 × 70	■**17.** 638 × 63	■**18.** 905 × 85
●**19.** 731 × 108	●**20.** 592 × 604	●**21.** 521 × 461
22. 940 × 218	**23.** 3015 × 226	**24.** 4628 × 314
25. 4708 × 316	**26.** 8162 × 407	**27.** 3047 × 902
28. 6005 × 584	**29.** 3714 × 215	**30.** 1010 × 101

Skill 12 (Use after page 40.)

Example

4016 ÷ 8 = ?

Not enough thousands. Think 40 hundreds. Divide hundreds.

$$\begin{array}{r} 5 \\ 8\overline{)4016} \\ -40 \end{array}$$

Not enough tens.
Think 16 ones.

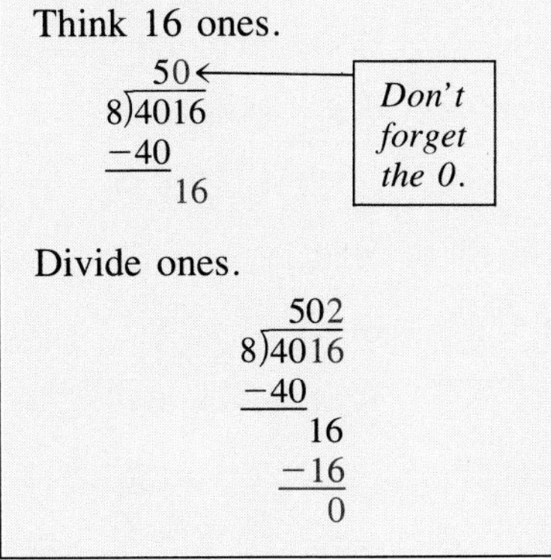

Give the quotient.

1. 464 ÷ 8	**2.** 207 ÷ 3	**3.** 635 ÷ 5
4. 934 ÷ 2	**5.** 513 ÷ 9	**6.** 812 ÷ 7
7. 584 ÷ 4	**8.** 366 ÷ 6	**9.** 728 ÷ 2
10. 428 ÷ 4	**11.** 198 ÷ 9	**12.** 624 ÷ 6
13. 635 ÷ 5	**14.** 582 ÷ 6	**15.** 498 ÷ 6
▲**16.** 808 ÷ 2	▲**17.** 588 ÷ 7	▲**18.** 729 ÷ 9
■**19.** 508 ÷ 4	■**20.** 695 ÷ 5	■**21.** 728 ÷ 8
●**22.** 2016 ÷ 4	●**23.** 5688 ÷ 8	●**24.** 9396 ÷ 9
25. 8330 ÷ 7	**26.** 4656 ÷ 6	**27.** 4000 ÷ 8
28. 2945 ÷ 5	**29.** 3804 ÷ 4	**30.** 6210 ÷ 9
31. 8091 ÷ 3	**32.** 1908 ÷ 6	**33.** 7624 ÷ 8
34. 1572 ÷ 4	**35.** 8113 ÷ 7	**36.** 7155 ÷ 9

Skill 13 (Use after page 42.)

Example

3999 ÷ 48 = ?

Think about dividing 39 by 4. So try 9.

48 ×9 = 432 48)3999

432 is too big!

Try 8.

48 ×8 = 384

```
     8
48)3999
  -384
    15
```

Think about dividing 15 by 4. So try 3.

48 ×3 = 144

```
     83 R15
48)3999
  -384
    159
   -144
     15
```

Divide.

1. 2946 ÷ 12
2. 9375 ÷ 32
3. 8611 ÷ 25
4. 2589 ÷ 43
5. 8526 ÷ 50
6. 6351 ÷ 81
7. 4490 ÷ 70
8. 8555 ÷ 49
9. 5773 ÷ 64
10. 6310 ÷ 38
11. 7008 ÷ 60
12. 9362 ÷ 75
13. 8610 ÷ 35
14. 6235 ÷ 91
15. ▲ 6192 ÷ 32
16. ▲ 7815 ÷ 15
17. ■ 38,500 ÷ 125
18. ■ 67,800 ÷ 150
19. ● 91,372 ÷ 212
20. ● 57,988 ÷ 436
21. 81,088 ÷ 516
22. 73,849 ÷ 406
23. 47,321 ÷ 616
24. 91,156 ÷ 688
25. 183,405 ÷ 361
26. 162,261 ÷ 219

Skill 14 (Use after page 44.)

Example

Solve.

$$4c = 36$$

Divide both sides by 4.

$$\frac{4c}{4} = \frac{36}{4}$$

Simplify.

$$c = 9$$

✔ *Check:*

$$4(9) \stackrel{?}{=} 36$$
$$36 = 36$$

Solve and check.

1. $8c = 16$
2. $9x = 36$
3. $5n = 15$
4. $6y = 54$
5. $7p = 49$
6. $3v = 0$
7. $9s = 63$
8. $4a = 80$
9. $2n = 42$
10. $8m = 88$
11. $5v = 65$
12. $6h = 0$
13. $3z = 81$
14. $4b = 96$
15. $8s = 104$
16. ▲ $10e = 50$
17. ▲ $15u = 135$
18. ▲ $12m = 48$
19. ■ $15q = 0$
20. ■ $12d = 60$
21. ■ $10g = 80$
22. ● $11t = 77$
23. ● $18r = 36$
24. ● $11q = 99$
25. $20f = 160$
26. $25p = 175$
27. $30j = 150$
28. $40n = 200$
29. $16r = 320$
30. $25t = 225$

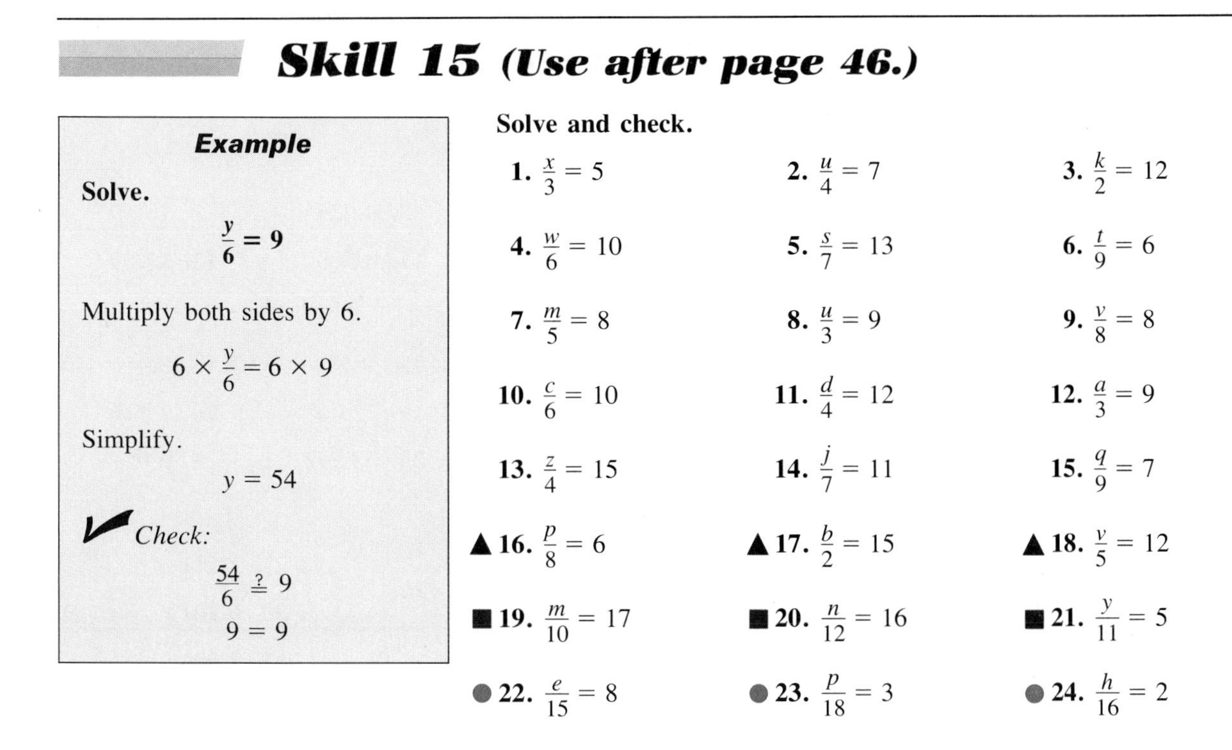

Skill 15 (Use after page 46.)

Example

Solve.

$$\frac{y}{6} = 9$$

Multiply both sides by 6.

$$6 \times \frac{y}{6} = 6 \times 9$$

Simplify.

$$y = 54$$

✔ *Check:*

$$\frac{54}{6} \stackrel{?}{=} 9$$

$$9 = 9$$

Solve and check.

1. $\frac{x}{3} = 5$ **2.** $\frac{u}{4} = 7$ **3.** $\frac{k}{2} = 12$

4. $\frac{w}{6} = 10$ **5.** $\frac{s}{7} = 13$ **6.** $\frac{t}{9} = 6$

7. $\frac{m}{5} = 8$ **8.** $\frac{u}{3} = 9$ **9.** $\frac{v}{8} = 8$

10. $\frac{c}{6} = 10$ **11.** $\frac{d}{4} = 12$ **12.** $\frac{a}{3} = 9$

13. $\frac{z}{4} = 15$ **14.** $\frac{j}{7} = 11$ **15.** $\frac{q}{9} = 7$

▲ **16.** $\frac{p}{8} = 6$ ▲ **17.** $\frac{b}{2} = 15$ ▲ **18.** $\frac{v}{5} = 12$

■ **19.** $\frac{m}{10} = 17$ ■ **20.** $\frac{n}{12} = 16$ ■ **21.** $\frac{y}{11} = 5$

● **22.** $\frac{e}{15} = 8$ ● **23.** $\frac{p}{18} = 3$ ● **24.** $\frac{h}{16} = 2$

Skill 16 (Use after page 48.)

Example

Solve.

$$63 = 9x$$

Use the symmetric property of equality.

$$9x = 63$$

Divide both sides by 9.

$$\frac{9x}{9} = \frac{63}{9}$$

Simplify.

$$x = 7$$

✔ *Check:*

$$63 \stackrel{?}{=} 9(7)$$

$$63 = 63$$

Solve and check.

1. $8 = \frac{r}{2}$ **2.** $5p = 15$ **3.** $\frac{h}{9} = 3$

4. $16 = 2q$ **5.** $4 = \frac{j}{5}$ **6.** $40 = 4b$

7. $0 = \frac{y}{9}$ **8.** $\frac{d}{3} = 11$ **9.** $4c = 20$

10. $60 = 3j$ **11.** $85 = 5k$ **12.** $6 = \frac{t}{7}$

13. $\frac{e}{5} = 15$ **14.** $30 = 10t$ **15.** $81 = 9c$

▲ **16.** $8n = 72$ ▲ **17.** $14 = \frac{k}{3}$ ▲ **18.** $0 = 6g$

■ **19.** $10 = \frac{x}{11}$ ■ **20.** $6v = 60$ ■ **21.** $\frac{b}{9} = 11$

● **22.** $88 = 11k$ ● **23.** $\frac{a}{15} = 0$ ● **24.** $13u = 52$

25. $\frac{f}{12} = 10$ **26.** $7m = 84$ **27.** $12 = \frac{a}{8}$

Skill 17 (Use after page 60.)

Example

Round 36.487 to the nearest tenth.

Rounding to this place
↓
36.487
↑
Since the next digit to the right is 5 or greater, round up.

36.487 rounds to 36.5.

Round to the nearest whole number.

▲ **1.** 16.6 ▲ **2.** 38.3 ▲ **3.** 92.4 ▲ **4.** 35.5
5. 51.27 **6.** 38.93 **7.** 0.025 **8.** 20.19
9. 327.04 **10.** 118.40 **11.** 0.500 **12.** 12.099

Round to the nearest tenth.

■ **13.** 403.38 ■ **14.** 26.10 ■ **15.** 5.25 ■ **16.** 3.95
17. 21.39 **18.** 24.188 **19.** 22.06 **20.** 7.472
21. 204.29 **22.** 444.484 **23.** 0.0592 **24.** 0.95

Round to the nearest hundredth.

● **25.** 22.317 ● **26.** 56.208 ● **27.** 5.531
28. 54.325 **29.** 71.594 **30.** 6.30196
31. 0.0518 **32.** 1.065 **33.** 0.0946
34. 11.269 **35.** 3.9421 **36.** 0.097
37. 42.3381 **38.** 28.095 **39.** 0.6422

Skill 18 (Use after page 62.)

Example

< or >?

82.64 ◆ 82.39

Start at the left and compare digits that are in the same place.

82.64 *is greater than* 82.39

So

82.64 > 82.39

< or >?

1. 0.3 ◆ 0.8 **2.** 0.6 ◆ 0.1
3. 0.04 ◆ 0.03 **4.** 0.06 ◆ 0.07
5. 0.004 ◆ 0.002 **6.** 0.008 ◆ 0.009
7. 15.5 ◆ 15.0 **8.** 8.43 ◆ 8.34
9. 0.57 ◆ 0.5 **10.** 0.007 ◆ 0.06
11. 0.6 ◆ 0.07 **12.** 9.73 ◆ 9.37
▲ **13.** 42.89 ◆ 42.9 ▲ **14.** 5.1 ◆ 4.99
■ **15.** 4.352 ◆ 43.52 ■ **16.** 0.625 ◆ 1.2
● **17.** 3.08 ◆ 3.008 ● **18.** 0.715 ◆ 0.72
19. 51.86 ◆ 51.87 **20.** 33.78 ◆ 31.88

Skill 19 (Use after page 64.)

Example

3 + 2.51 + 8.6 = ?

Line up the decimal points.

```
   3
   2.51
  +8.6
```

Add.

```
   1
   3
   2.51
  +8.6
  14.11
```

Give the sum.

1. 4.64 + 3.08

2. 7.564 + 3.806

3. 6.3521 + 0.5821

4. 721.6 + 38.4

5. 2.35 + 4.829

6. 5.008 + 3.62

7. 43.6 + 27.48

8. 10.88 + 9.3

9. 5.6 + 3.04 + 2.7

10. 2.64 + 5.7 + 8.8

11. 4.20 + 9.2 + 3.65

12. 6.1 + 2.22 + 6.83

13. 2.641 + 0.75 + 3.58

14. 5.34 + 0.756 + 2.84

▲**15.** 9.3645 + 2.055 + 0.221

▲**16.** 8.471 + 0.4911 + 3.300

■**17.** 7.4 + 4.611 + 8.5

■**18.** 15.966 + 8.4 + 4.8

●**19.** 32 + 3.4 + 2.08

●**20.** 5.7 + 41 + 6.63

21. 5 + 3.741 + 2.68

22. 18 + 5.77 + 6.411

23. 3.216 + 2.84 + 0.95

24. 0.8 + 9.142 + 5.33

Skill 20 (Use after page 66.)

Example

20 − 14.38 = ?

Line up the decimal points.
Write the zeros.

```
  2 0 . 0 0
 −1 4 . 3 8
```

Subtract.

```
  1 9    9
  2̸ ¹0̸ . ¹0̸ ¹0
 −1 4 .  3  8
    5 .  6  2
```

Give the difference.

1. 9 − 3.2

2. 8 − 4.6

3. 15 − 7.2

4. 23 − 8.6

5. 18.01 − 9.45

6. 14.05 − 7.75

7. 9.4 − 6.73

8. 8.5 − 4.55

9. 8.3 − 6

10. 7.4 − 2

11. 10.3 − 8.4

12. 30.1 − 9.7

13. 7 − 3.44

14. 8 − 6.45

▲**15.** 8.23 − 0.749

▲**16.** 6.729 − 0.88

■**17.** 8.5 − 3.692

■**18.** 5.1 − 0.651

●**19.** 42 − 8.2

●**20.** 34 − 9.5

21. 81.64 − 33

22. 63.89 − 18

23. 100 − 44.63

24. 200 − 53.87

25. 102 − 9.4

26. 105 − 49.7

Skill 21 (Use after page 68.)

Example

Solve.

$$n + 4.6 = 13$$

Subtract 4.6 from both sides.

$$n + 4.6 - 4.6 = 13 - 4.6$$

Simplify.

$$n = 8.4$$

✔ *Check:*

$$8.4 + 4.6 \stackrel{?}{=} 13$$
$$13 = 13$$

Solve and check.

1. $8 = z + 3.4$
2. $a + 6.2 = 15$
3. $h - 3.7 = 18$
4. $15 = x + 7.5$
5. $27 = v + 16.3$
6. $14 = z - 8.5$
7. $j - 15.6 = 18$
8. $f - 4.6 = 3.7$
9. $19.6 = p - 12.5$
10. $h + 16.2 = 18.4$
11. $20.6 = u + 16.5$
12. $d + 3.7 = 9.4$
13. $q - 19.8 = 20$
14. $34.6 = z + 34.6$
15. $18.3 = n - 0$
16. $s - 15.6 = 0$
▲**17.** $q + 6.5 = 13$
▲**18.** $0 = z - 5.8$
■**19.** $31 = t + 16.4$
■**20.** $40 = n + 26.3$
●**21.** $t + 35.3 = 40$
●**22.** $h + 8 = 12.7$
23. $c - 4.8 = 100$
24. $93 = s + 14.3$

Skill 22 (Use after page 72.)

Example

$3.08 \times 4.2 = ?$

Multiply as whole numbers.

```
    3.0 8
    ×4.2
    6 1 6
 1 2 3 2
 1 2 9 3 6
```

Count the digits to the right of the decimal points.

```
   3.0 8   [3]
   ×4.2
   6 1 6
1 2 3 2
1 2.9 3 6
```

Count off the same number of digits in the product.

Give the product.

1. 4.2×12
2. 3.8×10
3. 2.6×2.6
4. 5.9×8.7
5. 4.06×0.8
6. 2.05×5.5
7. 0.94×0.34
8. 0.95×0.55
9. 58×0.25
10. 74×0.78
11. 221×4.6
12. 360×8.2
13. 3.62×0.95
14. 2.88×0.47
▲**15.** 6.16×7.5
▲**16.** 2.09×0.8
■**17.** 5.4×0.06
■**18.** 8.8×0.07
●**19.** 6.25×0.56
●**20.** 8.65×0.44
21. 30.5×20.2
22. 56.7×18.4
23. 55.5×21.6
24. 63.2×8.94
25. 300×4.8
26. 600×0.52
27. 2.54×2.54
28. 3.08×3.08

Skill 23 *(Use after page 74.)*

Examples

2.47 × 10 = ?

When multiplying by 10, move the decimal point 1 place to the right.

$2.47 \times 10 = 24.7$

2.47 × 100 = ?

When multiplying by 100, move the decimal point 2 places to the right.

$2.47 \times 100 = 247$

Give the product.

1. 4.2×10
2. 0.38×100
3. 16×1000
4. 6.5×100
5. 1.25×100
6. 113×1000
7. 8.2×10
8. 0.05×1000
9. 6.8×100
10. 4.7×100
11. 2.95×10
12. 9.44×1000
13. 220×1000
14. 300×10
15. 6.5×100
16. 9.55×100
17. 8.74×1000
18. 0.75×10
▲**19.** 0.005×10
▲**20.** 0.002×100
▲**21.** 0.008×1000
■**22.** 8.4×1000
■**23.** 7.2×100
■**24.** 9.6×10
●**25.** 6.9×10
●**26.** 3.74×100
●**27.** 5.34×1000
28. 3.96×1000
29. 6.66×10
30. 8.51×1000
31. 4.798×100
32. 4.798×10
33. 4.798×1000

Skill 24 *(Use after page 76.)*

Example

12.99 ÷ 23 = ?

Divide.

```
     0.56
23)12.99
  -11 5
    1 49
   -1 38
      11
```

To round quotient to nearest hundredth, write a zero and carry out the division another place.

```
     0.564
23)12.990
  -11 5
    1 49
   -1 38
      110
      -92
       18
```

Give the quotient.

1. $8.1 \div 5$
2. $25.9 \div 7$
3. $4.32 \div 8$
4. $0.938 \div 2$
5. $6.75 \div 9$
6. $0.847 \div 7$
7. $1.44 \div 12$
8. $7.13 \div 23$
9. $1.008 \div 36$
10. $0.2491 \div 47$

Divide. Round the quotient to the nearest hundredth.

11. $2.5 \div 3$
12. $0.32 \div 6$
▲**13.** $0.53 \div 9$
▲**14.** $56.92 \div 6$
■**15.** $7.34 \div 14$
■**16.** $8.91 \div 49$
●**17.** $3.114 \div 42$
●**18.** $0.8113 \div 29$
19. $89.1 \div 94$
20. $5.347 \div 85$

Skill 25 *(Use after page 78.)*

Example

$0.42\overline{)0.5670}$

Move both decimal points two places to the right.

$0.42.\overline{)0.56.70}$

Divide.

```
          1.35
0.42.)0.56.70
       -42
        14 7
       -12 6
         2 10
        -2 10
            0
```

Give the quotient.

1. 38.36 ÷ 0.7
2. 2.634 ÷ 0.6
3. 4.584 ÷ 0.08
4. 2.076 ÷ 0.03
5. 1.473 ÷ 0.03
6. 3.605 ÷ 0.005
7. 0.2656 ÷ 0.004
8. 96.3 ÷ 0.3
9. 6.4 ÷ 0.04
10. 350.4 ÷ 0.6
11. 0.0644 ÷ 0.07
12. 0.963 ÷ 0.9
13. ▲ 8.6055 ÷ 0.005
14. ▲ 0.0152 ÷ 0.08
15. ■ 5.2 ÷ 1.3
16. ■ 0.144 ÷ 1.2
17. ● 0.6075 ÷ 0.15
18. ● 28.52 ÷ 2.3
19. 1.3995 ÷ 0.45
20. 1.2912 ÷ 2.4
21. 0.22274 ÷ 0.37
22. 29.011 ÷ 6.7
23. 19.292 ÷ 5.3
24. 0.38442 ÷ 0.86

Skill 26 *(Use after page 80.)*

Examples

5.2 ÷ 10 = ?

When dividing by 10, move the decimal point 1 place to the left.

5.2 ÷ 10 = 0.52

5.2 ÷ 100 = ?

When dividing by 100, move the decimal point 2 places to the left.

5.2 ÷ 100 = 0.052

Give the quotient.

1. 34.2 ÷ 10
2. 34.2 ÷ 100
3. 34.2 ÷ 1000
4. 45.8 ÷ 100
5. 45.8 ÷ 1000
6. 45.8 ÷ 10
7. 252.5 ÷ 100
8. 252.5 ÷ 10
9. 252.5 ÷ 1000
10. 80 ÷ 10
11. 80 ÷ 100
12. 80 ÷ 1000
13. 23.94 ÷ 10
14. 23.94 ÷ 100
15. 23.94 ÷ 1000
16. 2.8 ÷ 10
17. 2.8 ÷ 100
18. 2.8 ÷ 1000
19. ▲ 2.84 ÷ 1000
20. ▲ 9.05 ÷ 10
21. ■ 0.96 ÷ 100
22. ■ 9.05 ÷ 100
23. ● 9.05 ÷ 1000
24. ● 90.5 ÷ 10
25. 3.25 ÷ 100
26. 3.25 ÷ 10
27. 3.25 ÷ 1000
28. 82.5 ÷ 1000

Skill 27 (Use after page 82.)

Example

Solve.

$$4 = \frac{t}{2.3}$$

Use the symmetric property of equality.

$$\frac{t}{2.3} = 4$$

Multiply both sides by 2.3.

$$2.3 \times \frac{t}{2.3} = 2.3 \times 4$$

Simplify.

$$t = 9.2$$

Check:

$$4 \stackrel{?}{=} \frac{9.2}{2.3}$$

$$4 = 4$$

Solve and check.

1. $4 = \frac{s}{2.1}$ **2.** $4p = 9.6$ **3.** $\frac{h}{6} = 0.12$

4. $4.8 = 3q$ **5.** $8 = \frac{j}{0.6}$ **6.** $1.44 = 6d$

7. $0 = \frac{y}{5.8}$ **8.** $\frac{n}{2.5} = 4$ **9.** $6c = 0.96$

10. $0.35 = 5k$ **11.** $0.72 = 9j$ **12.** $4 = \frac{m}{6.4}$

13. $\frac{e}{3.8} = 10$ **14.** $15.6 = 10t$ **15.** $1.25 = 5c$

▲ **16.** $7f = 1.47$ ▲ **17.** $11 = \frac{k}{6.2}$ ▲ **18.** $1.32 = 4g$

■ **19.** $14.5 = \frac{x}{0.1}$ ■ **20.** $12v = 0.96$ ■ **21.** $\frac{b}{3.5} = 3.5$

● **22.** $3.81 = 3k$ ● **23.** $\frac{a}{1.7} = 0$ ● **24.** $1.3u = 10.4$

25. $\frac{f}{5.7} = 3.4$ **26.** $7m = 35.14$ **27.** $15.8 = \frac{a}{9.2}$

28. $1.8 = \frac{w}{10.4}$ **29.** $18z = 86.04$ **30.** $\frac{g}{2.45} = 6.4$

Skill 28 (Use after page 92.)

Example

$$6 + 8 \times (4 - 2) = ?$$

First, work within the grouping symbols.

$$6 + 8 \times 2$$

Next, do the multiplication and division.

$$6 + 16$$

Last, do the addition and subtraction.

$$22$$

Simplify.

1. $6 \div 3 \times 2$ **2.** $12 - 8 + 4$

3. $5 + 2 \times 5 - 1$ **4.** $5 \times 2 + 10 \div 2$

5. $5 + (3 + 9) \div 6$ **6.** $(4 + 5) \times 2 - 8$

7. $12 \div 4 - 1$ **8.** $8 \times 5 - 3$

9. $24 - 4 \div 4$ **10.** $30 - 12 - 6$

11. $10 + 16 \div 4$ **12.** $18 + 6 \div 3$

▲ **13.** $48 \div 8 \times 2$ ▲ **14.** $35 + 12 - 10$

■ **15.** $18 - 6 + 6$ ■ **16.** $20 - 9 + 5$

● **17.** $(12 + 18) \div 6$ ● **18.** $34 \times (8 - 3)$

19. $16 + 8 \div 4 + 4$ **20.** $(16 + 8) \div 4 + 4$

21. $16 + 8 \div (4 + 4)$ **22.** $20 + 12 \times 4 - 1$

Skill 29 (Use after page 98.)

Example

Solve.

$$19 + j = 63$$

Use the commutative property of addition.

$$j + 19 = 63$$
$$j + 19 - 19 = 63 - 19$$
$$j = 44$$

Check:

$$19 + 44 \stackrel{?}{=} 63$$
$$63 = 63$$

Solve and check.

1. $15 + g = 36$ **2.** $j(12) = 120$ **3.** $100 = y(20)$

4. $37 = 21 + b$ **5.** $110 = x(11)$ **6.** $27 + h = 91$

7. $50 = 33 + c$ **8.** $n(25) = 225$ **9.** $74 = 43 + y$

10. $8k = 128$ **11.** $p(6) = 144$ **12.** $56 = u - 19$

13. $220 = t(20)$ **14.** $6 = \frac{g}{12}$ **15.** $64 = w + 23$

▲ **16.** $\frac{h}{5} = 13$ ▲ **17.** $56 = k(2)$ ▲ **18.** $17 = \frac{m}{4}$

■ **19.** $c + 3.4 = 6$ ■ **20.** $5.1 = \frac{j}{10}$ ■ **21.** $d - 9.4 = 19$

● **22.** $18.5 = 4.6 + d$ ● **23.** $12.3 = n - 7.7$ ● **24.** $23.2 = 23.2 + p$

25. $20.4 = t(5)$ **26.** $12 = \frac{r}{0.1}$ **27.** $12.6 = u(4)$

Skill 30 (Use after page 102.)

Example

Solve.

$$8n + 3 = 59$$

Subtract 3 from both sides. Then simplify.

$$8n + 3 - 3 = 59 - 3$$
$$8n = 56$$

Divide both sides by 8. Then simplify.

$$\frac{8n}{8} = \frac{56}{8}$$
$$n = 7$$

Check:

$$8(7) + 3 \stackrel{?}{=} 59$$
$$59 = 59$$

Solve and check.

1. $3b + 9 = 27$ **2.** $5c - 4 = 31$

3. $7f + 4 = 60$ **4.** $4h - 8 = 16$

5. $9g + 10 = 100$ **6.** $6d - 16 = 50$

7. $39 = 2y + 5$ **8.** $0 = 4z - 16$

9. $57 = 8x + 17$ **10.** $20 = 7t - 15$

11. $93 = 6u + 21$ **12.** $29 = 3r - 13$

13. $12s + 8 = 116$ **14.** $15n - 23 = 127$

15. $20q + 30 = 250$ **16.** $18x + 17 = 17$

▲ **17.** $12w - 50 = 82$ ▲ **18.** $25z + 33 = 283$

■ **19.** $2c + 4.4 = 9$ ■ **20.** $5a - 6.7 = 18$

● **21.** $4b + 8 = 15.4$ ● **22.** $12 = 3m - 3.6$

23. $20 = 9p + 1.1$ **24.** $27 = 6r - 9.6$

25. $5z - 4.3 = 10.9$ **26.** $2y + 8.4 = 8.4$

27. $8v - 6.3 = 27.3$ **28.** $7.5 = 2n + 3.6$

29. $8.2 = 10k - 15.9$ **30.** $28.6 = 4f + 12.4$

Skill 31 (Use after page 104.)

Example

Solve.

$$\frac{n}{5} - 3 = 6$$

Add 3 to both sides. Then simplify.

$$\frac{n}{5} - 3 + 3 = 6 + 3$$
$$\frac{n}{5} = 9$$

Multiply both sides by 5. Then simplify.

$$5 \times \frac{n}{5} = 5 \times 9$$
$$n = 45$$

Check:

$$\frac{45}{5} - 3 \stackrel{?}{=} 6$$
$$6 = 6$$

Solve and check.

1. $\frac{n}{4} + 3 = 7$
2. $\frac{r}{6} - 4 = 1$
3. $12 = \frac{d}{2} + 8$
4. $6 + \frac{t}{3} = 6$
5. $4n + 6 = 30$
6. $3j - 5 = 43$
7. $15 = 7w - 13$
8. $6m + 7 = 67$
9. $\frac{r}{9} - 23 = 27$
10. $\frac{m}{6} + 8 = 9$
11. $\frac{c}{3} - 4 = 7$
12. $24 = \frac{f}{5} + 9$
13. $9p - 4 = 41$
14. $68 = 5v + 13$
15. $15h - 22 = 38$
16. ▲ $7y + 14 = 56$
17. ▲ $\frac{n}{3} - 12 = 8$
18. ▲ $126 = 10j + 16$
19. ■ $23 = \frac{d}{8} + 19$
20. ■ $102 = 12f - 18$
21. ■ $3 = \frac{g}{2} - 21$
22. ● $\frac{n}{6} + 1 = 20$
23. ● $5j - 31 = 34$
24. ● $\frac{t}{16} + 37 = 37$
25. $2t - 8.4 = 0$
26. $9.6 = 4y + 2.4$
27. $10j - 3.9 = 7.4$
28. $\frac{f}{3} + 2.6 = 13.4$
29. $\frac{n}{8} - 1.4 = 8.7$
30. $19.7 = 8t + 4.5$

Skill 32 (Use after page 108.)

Example

Simplify.

$$4x + 3 + x + 4$$

Combine like terms.

like terms ($4x$ and x)

$$4x + 3 + x + 4 = 5x + 7$$

like terms (3 and 4)

Simplify by combining like terms.

1. $5x + 3x$
2. $9y + 6y$
3. $7w + w$
4. $n + 12n$
5. $3t + 2t + 5t$
6. $6v + 3v + 8v$
7. $m + m + 3m$
8. $j + j + j$
9. $5y + 2y + 7$
10. $5y + 2 + 7y$
11. $8c + 5 + 3c$
12. $8 + 5c + 3c$
13. $16f + 3f + 16$
14. $16 + 3f + 16f$
15. ▲ $18d + d + 13$
16. ▲ $18 + d + 13d$
17. ■ $15x + 3x + 6 + 8$
18. ■ $15x + 3 + 6x + 8$
19. ● $10z + 11 + 4 + 9z$
20. ● $10 + 11z + 4 + 9z$
21. $22 + 11j + 9 + 15j$
22. $22j + 11 + 9j + 15$

Skill 33 (Use after page 110.)

Example

Solve.

$$8v + 2v = 19.6$$

Simplify by combining like terms.

$$10v = 19.6$$

$$\frac{10v}{10} = \frac{19.6}{10}$$

$$v = 1.96$$

✔ *Check:*

$$8(1.96) + 2(1.96) \stackrel{?}{=} 19.6$$

$$19.6 = 19.6$$

Solve and check.

1. $3a + 2a = 55$ **2.** $49 = 4n + 3n$ **3.** $63 = 8r + r$

4. $5c + 7c = 96$ **5.** $114 = 11f + 8f$ **6.** $y + 10y = 132$

7. $m + m = 78$ **8.** $15 = 9f + 6f$ **9.** $0 = 13e + e$

10. $12c + 8c = 180$ **11.** $144 = n + 11n$ **12.** $156 = 2k + k$

13. $16j + 6j = 88$ **14.** $162 = 9x + 9x$ **15.** $13y + 3y = 0$

▲**16.** $21d + 4d = 275$ ▲**17.** $300 = g + 9g$ ▲**18.** $168 = 2n + 10n$

■**19.** $3k + k = 18$ ■**20.** $37 = v + v$ ■**21.** $6y + 2y = 118$

●**22.** $y + 9y = 6.8$ ●**23.** $3y + 9y = 19.2$ ●**24.** $c + c = 38.6$

25. $17.6 = 2n + 2n$ **26.** $36.12 = t + 3t$ **27.** $4m + 4m = 1.92$

28. $2a + 5a = 4.9$ **29.** $37.8 = n + 2n$ **30.** $27 = 2c + 4c$

31. $8 = 6b + 4b$ **32.** $3f + f = 0.24$ **33.** $5d + 3d = 8.4$

Skill 34 (Use after page 120.)

Examples

Write using exponents.

$$4 \cdot 4 \cdot 4 = 4^3$$

Write using exponents for the variables.

$$a \cdot a \cdot a \cdot b \cdot b = a^3b^2$$

$$2 \cdot c \cdot d \cdot 3 \cdot c \cdot d \cdot d = 6c^2d^3$$

Write using exponents.

1. $2 \cdot 2 \cdot 2$ **2.** $5 \cdot 5 \cdot 5 \cdot 5$

3. $3 \cdot 3 \cdot 4 \cdot 4 \cdot 4$ **4.** $6 \cdot 6 \cdot 6 \cdot 6 \cdot 10 \cdot 10 \cdot 10$

5. $2 \cdot 7 \cdot 7 \cdot 7 \cdot 7 \cdot 7 \cdot 7$ **6.** $3 \cdot 3 \cdot 3 \cdot 3 \cdot 3 \cdot 8 \cdot 8 \cdot 8 \cdot 8$

Write using exponents for the variables.

7. $x \cdot x \cdot y$ **8.** $m \cdot m \cdot n \cdot n \cdot n$

9. $a \cdot a \cdot b \cdot b \cdot b$ **10.** $r \cdot s \cdot s \cdot s \cdot s$

11. $4 \cdot d \cdot 3 \cdot d$ **12.** $2 \cdot j \cdot j \cdot 7 \cdot j$

13. $9 \cdot 3 \cdot m \cdot n \cdot n$ **14.** $x \cdot 4 \cdot x \cdot 3 \cdot x \cdot 2$

▲**15.** $3 \cdot a \cdot a \cdot c \cdot c$ ▲**16.** $3 \cdot a \cdot c \cdot c \cdot c$

■**17.** $8 \cdot x \cdot x \cdot 2 \cdot y$ ■**18.** $8 \cdot x \cdot x \cdot 2 \cdot y \cdot y$

●**19.** $p \cdot q \cdot 3 \cdot p \cdot 7 \cdot q$ ●**20.** $y \cdot z \cdot z \cdot 5 \cdot y \cdot 3$

21. $c \cdot d \cdot 4 \cdot d \cdot c \cdot d$ **22.** $m \cdot 3 \cdot n \cdot 2 \cdot m \cdot n \cdot n$

23. $9 \cdot y \cdot z \cdot 3 \cdot y \cdot z \cdot y$ **24.** $j \cdot k \cdot 3 \cdot k \cdot k \cdot 4 \cdot j \cdot k$

Skill 35 (Use after page 124.)

Examples

Give the prime factorization.

$20 = 4 \cdot 5$

Not prime! Factor again.

$= 2 \cdot 2 \cdot 5$

Give the algebraic factorization.

$12a^2b^3 = 2 \cdot 2 \cdot 3 \cdot a \cdot a \cdot b \cdot b \cdot b$

Give the prime factorization.

1. 10	**2.** 15	**3.** 9	**4.** 18
5. 8	**6.** 21	**7.** 30	**8.** 25
9. 39	**10.** 45	**11.** 48	**12.** 56
13. 72	**14.** 64	**15.** 100	**16.** 120

Give the algebraic factorization.

17. $3a^2$	**18.** $4y^2$	**19.** $11t^3$	**20.** $10r^4$
▲**21.** $16x^2$	▲**22.** $20z^3$	▲**23.** $18n^4$	▲**24.** $32t^3$
■**25.** $10ab^2$	■**26.** $27rs^2$	■**27.** $30st^2$	■**28.** $15mn^3$
●**29.** $35y^2z^2$	●**30.** $42x^3y^2$	●**31.** $65m^4n^2$	●**32.** $84c^2d^3$

Skill 36 (Use after page 126.)

Examples

GCF of 12, 18 = ?

$12 = 2 \cdot 2 \cdot 3$
$18 = 2 \cdot 3 \cdot 3$
$\text{GCF} = 2 \cdot 3$
$= 6$

GCF of $4r^2s^3$, $10rs^2$ = ?

$4r^2s^3 = 2 \cdot 2 \cdot r \cdot r \cdot s \cdot s \cdot s$
$10rs^2 = 2 \cdot 5 \cdot r \cdot s \cdot s$
$\text{GCF} = 2 \cdot r \cdot s \cdot s$
$= 2rs^2$

LCM of 12, 18 = ?

$12 = 2 \cdot 2 \cdot 3$
$18 = 2 \cdot 3 \cdot 3$
$\text{LCM} = 2 \cdot 2 \cdot 3 \cdot 3$
$= 36$

LCM of $4r^2s^3$, $10rs^2$ = ?

$4r^2s^3 = 2 \cdot 2 \cdot r \cdot r \cdot s \cdot s \cdot s$
$10rs^2 = 2 \cdot 5 \cdot r \cdot s \cdot s$
$\text{LCM} = 2 \cdot 2 \cdot 5 \cdot r \cdot r \cdot s \cdot s \cdot s$
$= 20r^2s^3$

Give the greatest common factor (GCF).

1. 6, 18	**2.** 4, 28	**3.** 16, 30
4. 20, 35	**5.** 27, 45	**6.** 40, 30
7. 27, 64	**8.** 54, 90	**9.** 45, 75
▲**10.** 3, $6a$	▲**11.** 12, $9d$	▲**12.** $5d$, 15
■**13.** j, $7j$	■**14.** $12e$, $15e$	■**15.** $15w$, $11w$
●**16.** $5x$, $10x^2$	●**17.** $3yz$, z^2	●**18.** $10a^2b$, $15ab^2$

Give the least common multiple (LCM).

19. 9, 12	**20.** 8, 12	**21.** 16, 24
22. 20, 30	**23.** 25, 20	**24.** 36, 24
25. 21, 15	**26.** 30, 24	**27.** 25, 30
▲**28.** 10, $5x$	▲**29.** $6k$, 9	▲**30.** 15, $20t$
■**31.** $7j$, j	■**32.** m, $9m$	■**33.** $8r$, r
●**34.** j^2, $3j$	●**35.** $8c$, $4c^2$	●**36.** $5m^2n$, mn

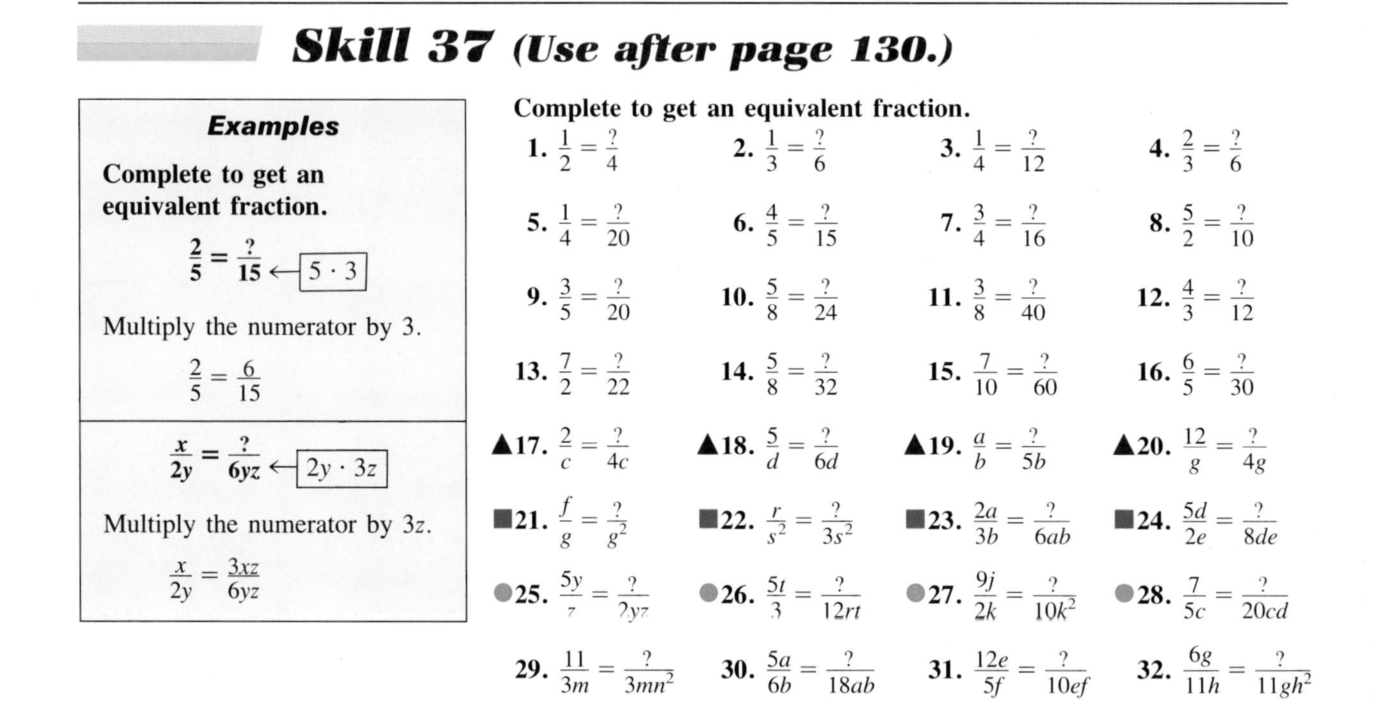

Skill 37 (Use after page 130.)

Examples

Complete to get an equivalent fraction.

$\frac{2}{5} = \frac{?}{15} \leftarrow \boxed{5 \cdot 3}$

Multiply the numerator by 3.

$\frac{2}{5} = \frac{6}{15}$

$\frac{x}{2y} = \frac{?}{6yz} \leftarrow \boxed{2y \cdot 3z}$

Multiply the numerator by $3z$.

$\frac{x}{2y} = \frac{3xz}{6yz}$

Complete to get an equivalent fraction.

1. $\frac{1}{2} = \frac{?}{4}$ **2.** $\frac{1}{3} = \frac{?}{6}$ **3.** $\frac{1}{4} = \frac{?}{12}$ **4.** $\frac{2}{3} = \frac{?}{6}$

5. $\frac{1}{4} = \frac{?}{20}$ **6.** $\frac{4}{5} = \frac{?}{15}$ **7.** $\frac{3}{4} = \frac{?}{16}$ **8.** $\frac{5}{2} = \frac{?}{10}$

9. $\frac{3}{5} = \frac{?}{20}$ **10.** $\frac{5}{8} = \frac{?}{24}$ **11.** $\frac{3}{8} = \frac{?}{40}$ **12.** $\frac{4}{3} = \frac{?}{12}$

13. $\frac{7}{2} = \frac{?}{22}$ **14.** $\frac{5}{8} = \frac{?}{32}$ **15.** $\frac{7}{10} = \frac{?}{60}$ **16.** $\frac{6}{5} = \frac{?}{30}$

▲**17.** $\frac{2}{c} = \frac{?}{4c}$ ▲**18.** $\frac{5}{d} = \frac{?}{6d}$ ▲**19.** $\frac{a}{b} = \frac{?}{5b}$ ▲**20.** $\frac{12}{g} = \frac{?}{4g}$

■**21.** $\frac{f}{g} = \frac{?}{g^2}$ ■**22.** $\frac{r}{s^2} = \frac{?}{3s^2}$ ■**23.** $\frac{2a}{3b} = \frac{?}{6ab}$ ■**24.** $\frac{5d}{2e} = \frac{?}{8de}$

●**25.** $\frac{5y}{z} = \frac{?}{2yz}$ ●**26.** $\frac{5t}{3} = \frac{?}{12rt}$ ●**27.** $\frac{9j}{2k} = \frac{?}{10k^2}$ ●**28.** $\frac{7}{5c} = \frac{?}{20cd}$

29. $\frac{11}{3m} = \frac{?}{3mn^2}$ **30.** $\frac{5a}{6b} = \frac{?}{18ab}$ **31.** $\frac{12e}{5f} = \frac{?}{10ef}$ **32.** $\frac{6g}{11h} = \frac{?}{11gh^2}$

Skill 38 (Use after page 132.)

Examples

Write in lowest terms.

$\frac{18}{24} = \frac{\overset{1}{\cancel{2}} \cdot \overset{1}{\cancel{3}} \cdot 3}{\underset{1}{\cancel{2}} \cdot 2 \cdot 2 \cdot \underset{1}{\cancel{3}}}$

$= \frac{3}{4}$

$\frac{9x^2}{6xy} = \frac{\overset{1}{\cancel{3}} \cdot 3 \cdot \overset{1}{\cancel{x}} \cdot x}{2 \cdot \underset{1}{\cancel{3}} \cdot \underset{1}{\cancel{x}} \cdot y}$

$= \frac{3x}{2y}$

Write in lowest terms.

1. $\frac{3}{6}$ **2.** $\frac{3}{9}$ **3.** $\frac{2}{8}$ **4.** $\frac{6}{9}$

5. $\frac{9}{6}$ **6.** $\frac{14}{16}$ **7.** $\frac{9}{12}$ **8.** $\frac{10}{12}$

9. $\frac{8}{10}$ **10.** $\frac{5}{15}$ **11.** $\frac{6}{4}$ **12.** $\frac{7}{14}$

13. $\frac{8}{16a}$ **14.** $\frac{15}{6b}$ **15.** $\frac{2d}{10}$ **16.** $\frac{16f}{12}$

▲ **17.** $\frac{cd}{6d}$ ▲ **18.** $\frac{x}{xy}$ ▲ **19.** $\frac{6a}{16b}$ ▲ **20.** $\frac{4m}{12n}$

■ **21.** $\frac{3y}{12xy}$ ■ **22.** $\frac{4m}{6n}$ ■ **23.** $\frac{3r^2}{18r}$ ■ **24.** $\frac{15uv}{18u^2}$

● **25.** $\frac{10r}{6s^2}$ ● **26.** $\frac{15e^2}{20de}$ ● **27.** $\frac{5yz^2}{10z}$ ● **28.** $\frac{m^2n}{15n^2}$

29. $\frac{6pq^2}{13q}$ **30.** $\frac{4ab}{21ab}$ **31.** $\frac{18st^2}{24s^2}$ **32.** $\frac{9c^2d}{16c^2d^2}$

Skill 39 (Use after page 134.)

Examples

The least common denominator (LCD) is the least common multiple of the denominators.

LCD of $\frac{3}{4}, \frac{5}{6}$ = ?

$$4 = 2 \cdot 2$$
$$6 = 2 \cdot 3$$
$$\text{LCM} = 2 \cdot 2 \cdot 3 = 12$$

So the LCD of $\frac{3}{4}$ and $\frac{5}{6}$ is 12.

LCD of $\frac{8}{3x}, \frac{1}{4x}$ = ?

$$3x = 3 \cdot x$$
$$4x = 2 \cdot 2 \cdot x$$
$$\text{LCM} = 2 \cdot 2 \cdot 3 \cdot x = 12x$$

So the LCD of $\frac{8}{3x}$ and $\frac{1}{4x}$ is $12x$.

Find the least common denominator.

1. $\frac{1}{6}, \frac{1}{5}$
2. $\frac{3}{4}, \frac{1}{2}$
3. $\frac{1}{5}, \frac{2}{9}$
4. $\frac{1}{10}, \frac{2}{5}$
5. $\frac{3}{20}, \frac{1}{10}$
6. $\frac{1}{4}, \frac{1}{6}$
7. $\frac{5}{6}, \frac{3}{8}$
8. $\frac{1}{6}, \frac{1}{8}$
9. $\frac{1}{8}, \frac{4}{3}$

▲10. $\frac{7}{8}, \frac{1}{12}$
▲11. $\frac{1}{6}, \frac{3}{4}$
▲12. $\frac{1}{5}, \frac{3}{7}$

■13. $\frac{2}{5a}, \frac{1}{4a}$
■14. $\frac{1}{10b}, \frac{4}{5b^2}$
■15. $\frac{5}{9c}, \frac{1}{2c}$

●16. $\frac{3}{10}, \frac{1}{4e}$
●17. $\frac{1}{6f}, \frac{4}{5g}$
●18. $\frac{7}{6h}, \frac{5}{9hi}$

19. $\frac{5}{6k^2}, \frac{1}{15k^3}$
20. $\frac{1}{7m}, \frac{1}{3m^2}$
21. $\frac{2}{5np}, \frac{1}{8n}$
22. $\frac{1}{4st}, \frac{1}{7st^2}$
23. $\frac{1}{9u^2v}, \frac{2}{3v^2}$
24. $\frac{1}{3w^3}, \frac{2}{9wx}$

Skill 40 (Use after page 136.)

Example

<, >, or = ?

$\frac{2}{3} ◆ \frac{3}{4}$

Find the LCD.

$\frac{2}{3} ◆ \frac{3}{4}$ → 12

Write equivalent fractions and compare.

$\frac{8}{12} ◆ \frac{9}{12}$

$\frac{2}{3} < \frac{3}{4}$

<, >, or = ?

1. $\frac{1}{4} ◆ \frac{3}{4}$
2. $\frac{3}{5} ◆ \frac{2}{5}$
3. $\frac{3}{7} ◆ \frac{4}{7}$
4. $\frac{0}{8} ◆ \frac{5}{8}$
5. $\frac{5}{4} ◆ \frac{4}{4}$
6. $\frac{7}{5} ◆ \frac{9}{5}$
7. $\frac{5}{8} ◆ \frac{7}{8}$
8. $\frac{7}{3} ◆ \frac{5}{3}$

▲9. $\frac{2}{3} ◆ \frac{4}{6}$
▲10. $\frac{5}{4} ◆ \frac{3}{2}$
▲11. $\frac{2}{7} ◆ \frac{1}{3}$
▲12. $\frac{3}{4} ◆ \frac{6}{8}$

■13. $\frac{1}{8} ◆ \frac{1}{6}$
■14. $\frac{3}{8} ◆ \frac{1}{4}$
■15. $\frac{3}{10} ◆ \frac{1}{3}$
■16. $\frac{1}{4} ◆ \frac{2}{5}$

●17. $\frac{1}{4} ◆ \frac{1}{3}$
●18. $\frac{2}{9} ◆ \frac{3}{4}$
●19. $\frac{2}{3} ◆ \frac{3}{4}$
●20. $\frac{5}{8} ◆ \frac{4}{7}$

21. $\frac{3}{5} ◆ \frac{9}{15}$
22. $\frac{3}{4} ◆ \frac{5}{6}$
23. $\frac{8}{9} ◆ \frac{7}{8}$
24. $\frac{1}{3} ◆ \frac{5}{12}$
25. $\frac{7}{8} ◆ \frac{5}{6}$
26. $\frac{2}{3} ◆ \frac{7}{10}$
27. $\frac{8}{12} ◆ \frac{2}{3}$
28. $\frac{9}{2} ◆ \frac{9}{4}$

Skill 41 (Use after page 146.)

Examples

$4 = \frac{?}{3}$

Write the whole number over 1 and multiply both numerator and denominator by 3.

$\frac{4}{1} = \frac{12}{3}$

$2\frac{3}{4} = ?$

To change a mixed number to a fraction, multiply the denominator by the whole number and add the numerator.

$2\frac{3}{4} = \frac{11}{4}$

Change to thirds.

1. 2
2. 1
3. 4
4. 5

▲ 5. 3
▲ 6. 8
▲ 7. 10
▲ 8. 6

Change to fourths.

■ 9. 3
■ 10. 1
■ 11. 4
■ 12. 2

● 13. 7
● 14. 9
● 15. 10
● 16. 8

Change to a fraction.

17. $1\frac{1}{3}$
18. $2\frac{1}{4}$
19. $2\frac{1}{2}$
20. $1\frac{1}{5}$

▲ 21. $1\frac{2}{3}$
▲ 22. $2\frac{1}{3}$
▲ 23. $1\frac{1}{4}$
▲ 24. $3\frac{1}{4}$

■ 25. $1\frac{1}{2}$
■ 26. $2\frac{7}{8}$
■ 27. $3\frac{3}{8}$
■ 28. $2\frac{5}{6}$

● 29. $5\frac{1}{4}$
● 30. $2\frac{2}{3}$
● 31. $3\frac{1}{2}$
● 32. $4\frac{5}{8}$

33. $4\frac{4}{5}$
34. $3\frac{1}{3}$
35. $5\frac{3}{10}$
36. $4\frac{1}{5}$

Skill 42 (Use after page 148.)

Examples

To change a fraction to a whole number or mixed number, divide the numerator by the denominator.

$\frac{18}{3} = 6$

$\frac{19}{4} = 4\frac{3}{4}$

$$\begin{array}{r} 4 \\ 4\overline{)19} \\ -16 \\ \hline 3 \end{array}$$

There are 3 fourths left over.

Change to a whole number.

▲ 1. $\frac{4}{2}$
▲ 2. $\frac{40}{5}$
▲ 3. $\frac{10}{2}$
▲ 4. $\frac{9}{3}$

■ 5. $\frac{25}{5}$
■ 6. $\frac{8}{2}$
■ 7. $\frac{32}{4}$
■ 8. $\frac{30}{3}$

● 9. $\frac{18}{3}$
● 10. $\frac{35}{5}$
● 11. $\frac{16}{4}$
● 12. $\frac{50}{5}$

Change to a mixed number.

▲ 13. $\frac{3}{2}$
▲ 14. $\frac{5}{4}$
▲ 15. $\frac{5}{3}$
▲ 16. $\frac{9}{2}$

■ 17. $\frac{11}{4}$
■ 18. $\frac{4}{3}$
■ 19. $\frac{13}{5}$
■ 20. $\frac{7}{6}$

● 21. $\frac{16}{3}$
● 22. $\frac{13}{10}$
● 23. $\frac{5}{2}$
● 24. $\frac{8}{3}$

25. $\frac{23}{10}$
26. $\frac{9}{5}$
27. $\frac{13}{12}$
28. $\frac{19}{6}$

Skill 43 (Use after page 150.)

Examples

Write in simplest form.

$\frac{6}{9} = \frac{2}{3}$

$3\frac{4}{6} = 3\frac{2}{3}$

$\frac{18}{3} = 6$

$\frac{14}{4} = 3\frac{2}{4} = 3\frac{1}{2}$

$\frac{5a^2}{15ab} = \frac{a}{3b}$

$\frac{12cd}{8c^2d} = \frac{3}{2c}$

Write in simplest form.

1. $\frac{10}{12}$	**2.** $\frac{6}{15}$	**3.** $\frac{4}{3}$	**4.** $\frac{15}{5}$
▲ **5.** $\frac{9}{2}$	▲ **6.** $1\frac{8}{10}$	▲ **7.** $1\frac{3}{6}$	▲ **8.** $2\frac{4}{6}$
■ **9.** $1\frac{2}{4}$	■ **10.** $\frac{10}{2}$	■ **11.** $\frac{11}{3}$	■ **12.** $3\frac{6}{16}$
● **13.** $\frac{23}{4}$	● **14.** $4\frac{4}{10}$	● **15.** $5\frac{9}{24}$	● **16.** $\frac{20}{24}$
▲ **17.** $\frac{36x}{6}$	▲ **18.** $\frac{17y^2}{2y}$	▲ **19.** $\frac{25z}{5z^2}$	▲ **20.** $\frac{13r}{3r^2}$
■ **21.** $\frac{18m^2}{5m}$	■ **22.** $\frac{24r^2}{3rs}$	■ **23.** $\frac{12y^2}{15y^2}$	■ **24.** $\frac{9ab}{12b}$
● **25.** $\frac{10st}{12t^2}$	● **26.** $\frac{19c^2d}{4cd}$	● **27.** $\frac{12a^2b}{16b^2}$	● **28.** $\frac{17jk}{5j^2k^2}$

Skill 44 (Use after page 152.)

Example

$124 \div 6 = ?$

Divide.

$$6\overline{)124} = 20 \text{ R } 4$$

$$\begin{array}{r} 20 \\ 6\overline{)124} \\ \underline{12} \\ 4 \end{array}$$

Write the quotient as a mixed number.

$$\begin{array}{r} 20\frac{4}{6} \\ 6\overline{)124} \\ \underline{12} \\ 4 \end{array}$$

Write the number in simplest form.

$$20\frac{4}{6} = 20\frac{2}{3}$$

Divide. Write each quotient as a mixed number in simplest form.

1. $27 \div 2$	**2.** $22 \div 4$	**3.** $46 \div 8$
4. $20 \div 6$	**5.** $30 \div 8$	**6.** $53 \div 7$
7. $48 \div 9$	**8.** $43 \div 5$	**9.** $39 \div 2$
10. $62 \div 3$	**11.** $82 \div 4$	**12.** $57 \div 6$
13. $80 \div 6$	**14.** $71 \div 3$	**15.** $86 \div 7$
▲ **16.** $86 \div 8$	▲ **17.** $57 \div 2$	▲ **18.** $90 \div 4$
■ **19.** $117 \div 4$	■ **20.** $69 \div 9$	■ **21.** $100 \div 8$
● **22.** $125 \div 10$	● **23.** $134 \div 12$	● **24.** $60 \div 16$
25. $150 \div 12$	**26.** $100 \div 24$	**27.** $168 \div 10$
28. $175 \div 20$	**29.** $200 \div 32$	**30.** $235 \div 25$

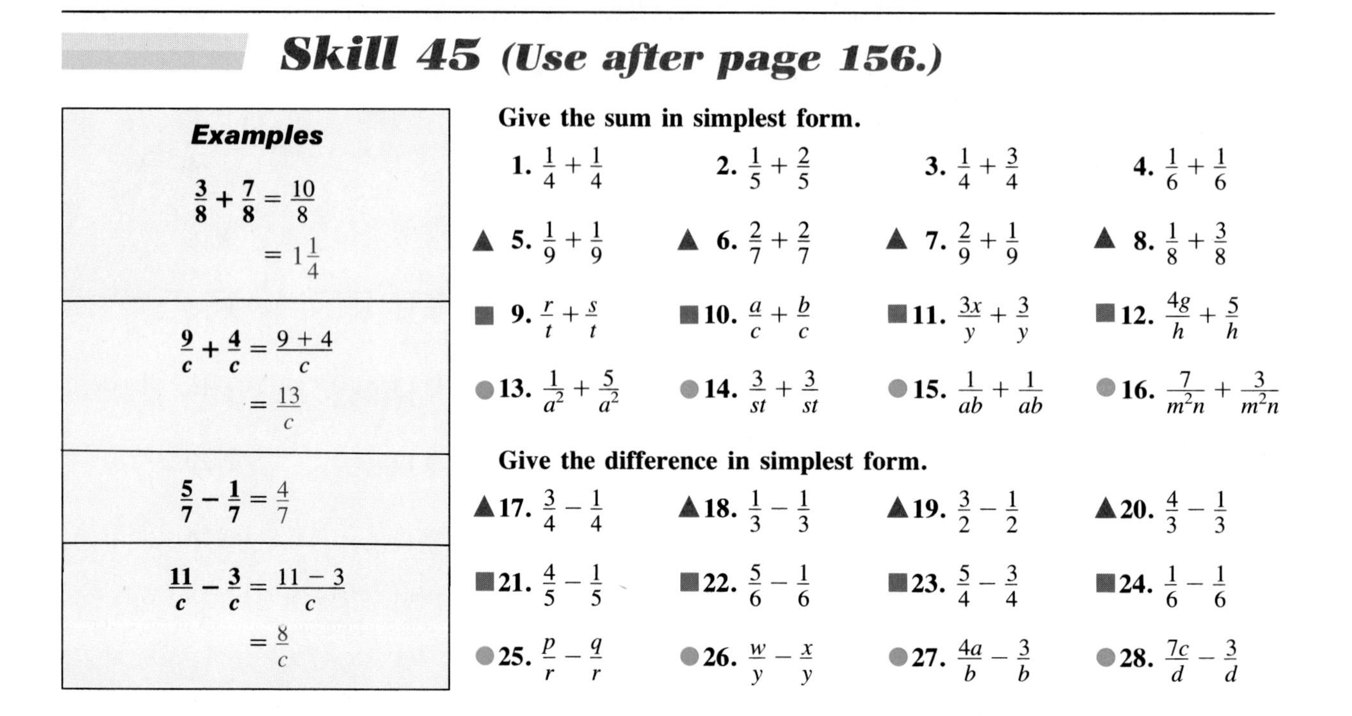

Skill 45 (Use after page 156.)

Examples

$\frac{3}{8} + \frac{7}{8} = \frac{10}{8}$
$= 1\frac{1}{4}$

$\frac{9}{c} + \frac{4}{c} = \frac{9 + 4}{c}$
$= \frac{13}{c}$

$\frac{5}{7} - \frac{1}{7} = \frac{4}{7}$

$\frac{11}{c} - \frac{3}{c} = \frac{11 - 3}{c}$
$= \frac{8}{c}$

Give the sum in simplest form.

1. $\frac{1}{4} + \frac{1}{4}$ 2. $\frac{1}{5} + \frac{2}{5}$ 3. $\frac{1}{4} + \frac{3}{4}$ 4. $\frac{1}{6} + \frac{1}{6}$

▲ 5. $\frac{1}{9} + \frac{1}{9}$ ▲ 6. $\frac{2}{7} + \frac{2}{7}$ ▲ 7. $\frac{2}{9} + \frac{1}{9}$ ▲ 8. $\frac{1}{8} + \frac{3}{8}$

■ 9. $\frac{r}{t} + \frac{s}{t}$ ■ 10. $\frac{a}{c} + \frac{b}{c}$ ■ 11. $\frac{3x}{y} + \frac{3}{y}$ ■ 12. $\frac{4g}{h} + \frac{5}{h}$

● 13. $\frac{1}{a^2} + \frac{5}{a^2}$ ● 14. $\frac{3}{st} + \frac{3}{st}$ ● 15. $\frac{1}{ab} + \frac{1}{ab}$ ● 16. $\frac{7}{m^2n} + \frac{3}{m^2n}$

Give the difference in simplest form.

▲ 17. $\frac{3}{4} - \frac{1}{4}$ ▲ 18. $\frac{1}{3} - \frac{1}{3}$ ▲ 19. $\frac{3}{2} - \frac{1}{2}$ ▲ 20. $\frac{4}{3} - \frac{1}{3}$

■ 21. $\frac{4}{5} - \frac{1}{5}$ ■ 22. $\frac{5}{6} - \frac{1}{6}$ ■ 23. $\frac{5}{4} - \frac{3}{4}$ ■ 24. $\frac{1}{6} - \frac{1}{6}$

● 25. $\frac{p}{r} - \frac{q}{r}$ ● 26. $\frac{w}{y} - \frac{x}{y}$ ● 27. $\frac{4a}{b} - \frac{3}{b}$ ● 28. $\frac{7c}{d} - \frac{3}{d}$

Skill 46 (Use after page 158.)

Examples

$\frac{3}{8} + \frac{1}{6} = \frac{9}{24} + \frac{4}{24}$
$= \frac{13}{24}$

$\frac{x}{3} + \frac{y}{4} = \frac{4x}{12} + \frac{3y}{12}$
$= \frac{4x + 3y}{12}$

$\frac{3}{8} - \frac{1}{3} = \frac{9}{24} - \frac{8}{24}$
$= \frac{1}{24}$

$\frac{a}{6} - \frac{b}{9} = \frac{3a}{18} - \frac{2b}{18}$
$= \frac{3a - 2b}{18}$

Give the sum in simplest form.

1. $\frac{1}{2} + \frac{1}{4}$ 2. $\frac{1}{6} + \frac{2}{3}$ 3. $\frac{3}{8} + \frac{1}{4}$ 4. $\frac{1}{2} + \frac{5}{8}$

▲ 5. $\frac{1}{3} + \frac{1}{6}$ ▲ 6. $\frac{4}{5} + \frac{3}{10}$ ▲ 7. $\frac{1}{5} + \frac{3}{10}$ ▲ 8. $\frac{2}{3} + \frac{3}{4}$

■ 9. $\frac{d}{3} + \frac{3}{7}$ ■ 10. $\frac{a}{9} + \frac{1}{6}$ ■ 11. $\frac{3k}{8} + \frac{3}{4}$ ■ 12. $\frac{s}{5} + \frac{t}{4}$

● 13. $\frac{2a}{3} + \frac{b}{9}$ ● 14. $\frac{4c}{3} + \frac{d}{2}$ ● 15. $\frac{2r}{3} + \frac{3s}{8}$ ● 16. $\frac{5j}{2} + \frac{7k}{6}$

Give the difference in simplest form.

17. $\frac{1}{3} - \frac{1}{4}$ 18. $\frac{1}{2} - \frac{1}{4}$ 19. $\frac{3}{4} - \frac{1}{2}$ 20. $\frac{5}{8} - \frac{1}{4}$

▲ 21. $\frac{3}{4} - \frac{0}{2}$ ▲ 22. $\frac{2}{3} - \frac{1}{2}$ ▲ 23. $\frac{1}{4} - \frac{1}{8}$ ▲ 24. $\frac{1}{3} - \frac{1}{8}$

■ 25. $\frac{t}{4} - \frac{3}{8}$ ■ 26. $\frac{a}{8} - \frac{2}{3}$ ■ 27. $\frac{3k}{2} - \frac{1}{3}$ ■ 28. $\frac{s}{3} - \frac{t}{8}$

● 29. $\frac{5c}{9} - \frac{d}{6}$ ● 30. $\frac{2a}{3} - \frac{b}{6}$ ● 31. $\frac{5j}{8} - \frac{2k}{5}$ ● 32. $\frac{7m}{10} - \frac{2n}{5}$

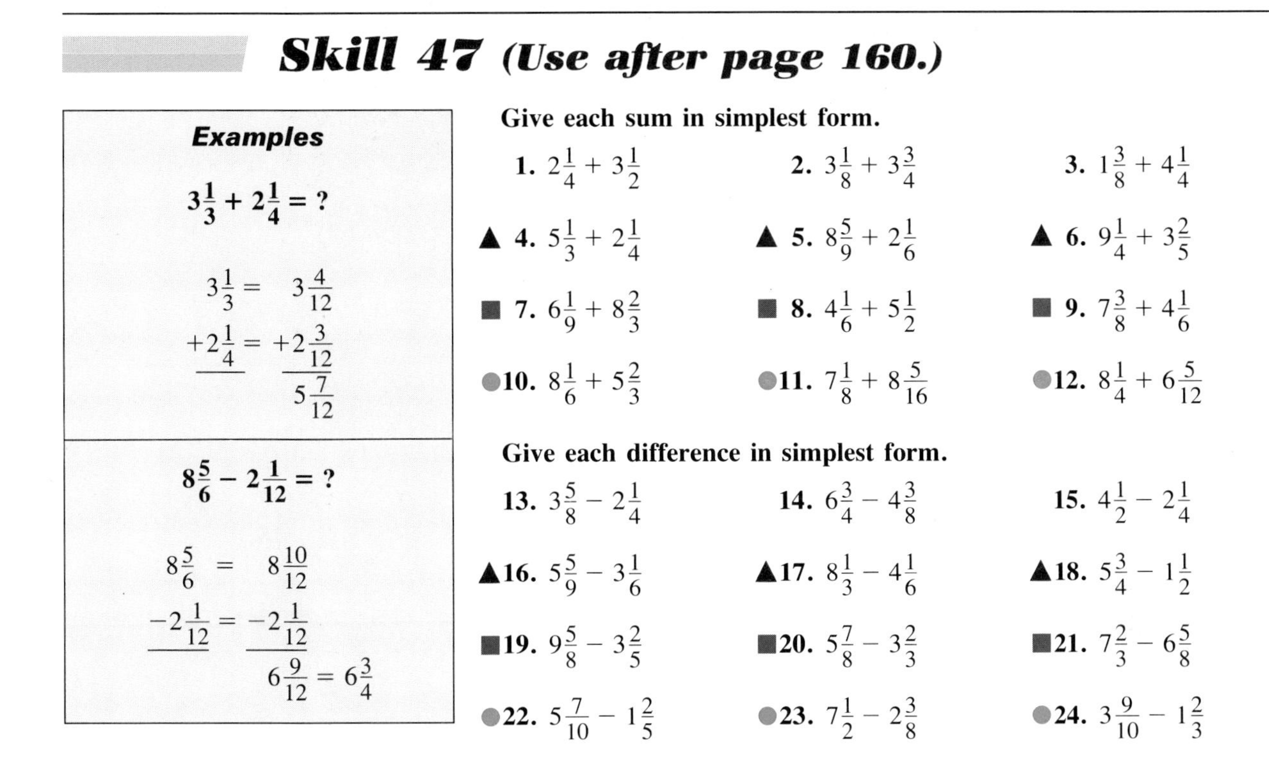

Skill 47 (Use after page 160.)

Examples

$3\frac{1}{3} + 2\frac{1}{4} = ?$

$$\begin{array}{rcr} 3\frac{1}{3} & = & 3\frac{4}{12} \\ +2\frac{1}{4} & = & +2\frac{3}{12} \\ \hline & & 5\frac{7}{12} \end{array}$$

$8\frac{5}{6} - 2\frac{1}{12} = ?$

$$\begin{array}{rcr} 8\frac{5}{6} & = & 8\frac{10}{12} \\ -2\frac{1}{12} & = & -2\frac{1}{12} \\ \hline & & 6\frac{9}{12} = 6\frac{3}{4} \end{array}$$

Give each sum in simplest form.

1. $2\frac{1}{4} + 3\frac{1}{2}$	**2.** $3\frac{1}{8} + 3\frac{3}{4}$	**3.** $1\frac{3}{8} + 4\frac{1}{4}$
▲ **4.** $5\frac{1}{3} + 2\frac{1}{4}$	▲ **5.** $8\frac{5}{9} + 2\frac{1}{6}$	▲ **6.** $9\frac{1}{4} + 3\frac{2}{5}$
■ **7.** $6\frac{1}{9} + 8\frac{2}{3}$	■ **8.** $4\frac{1}{6} + 5\frac{1}{2}$	■ **9.** $7\frac{3}{8} + 4\frac{1}{6}$
● **10.** $8\frac{1}{6} + 5\frac{2}{3}$	● **11.** $7\frac{1}{8} + 8\frac{5}{16}$	● **12.** $8\frac{1}{4} + 6\frac{5}{12}$

Give each difference in simplest form.

13. $3\frac{5}{8} - 2\frac{1}{4}$	**14.** $6\frac{3}{4} - 4\frac{3}{8}$	**15.** $4\frac{1}{2} - 2\frac{1}{4}$
▲ **16.** $5\frac{5}{9} - 3\frac{1}{6}$	▲ **17.** $8\frac{1}{3} - 4\frac{1}{6}$	▲ **18.** $5\frac{3}{4} - 1\frac{1}{2}$
■ **19.** $9\frac{5}{8} - 3\frac{2}{5}$	■ **20.** $5\frac{7}{8} - 3\frac{2}{3}$	■ **21.** $7\frac{2}{3} - 6\frac{5}{8}$
● **22.** $5\frac{7}{10} - 1\frac{2}{5}$	● **23.** $7\frac{1}{2} - 2\frac{3}{8}$	● **24.** $3\frac{9}{10} - 1\frac{2}{3}$

Skill 48 (Use after page 162.)

Examples

$2\frac{5}{8} + 1\frac{2}{3} = ?$

$$\begin{array}{rcr} 2\frac{5}{8} & = & 2\frac{15}{24} \\ +1\frac{2}{3} & = & +1\frac{16}{24} \\ \hline & & 3\frac{31}{24} = 4\frac{7}{24} \end{array}$$

$6\frac{1}{4} - 2\frac{2}{3} = ?$

$$\begin{array}{rcr} 6\frac{1}{4} & = & \overset{5}{\cancel{6}}\,\frac{\overset{15}{\cancel{3}}}{12} \\ -2\frac{2}{3} & = & -2\frac{8}{12} \\ \hline & & 3\frac{7}{12} \end{array}$$

Give each sum in simplest form.

1. $4\frac{3}{4} + 3\frac{1}{2}$	**2.** $5\frac{3}{8} + 1\frac{3}{4}$	**3.** $8\frac{2}{3} + 3\frac{5}{6}$
▲ **4.** $6\frac{7}{8} + 6\frac{1}{4}$	▲ **5.** $9\frac{2}{5} + 4\frac{1}{2}$	▲ **6.** $7\frac{5}{8} + 2\frac{2}{3}$
■ **7.** $8\frac{3}{4} + 7\frac{2}{3}$	■ **8.** $6\frac{1}{8} + 9\frac{2}{5}$	■ **9.** $5\frac{2}{3} + 5\frac{3}{8}$
● **10.** $4\frac{5}{6} + 8\frac{5}{8}$	● **11.** $3\frac{3}{4} + 7\frac{4}{5}$	● **12.** $9\frac{2}{3} + 8\frac{7}{10}$

Give each difference in simplest form.

13. $4\frac{1}{2} - 3\frac{3}{4}$	**14.** $5\frac{5}{8} - 1\frac{3}{4}$	**15.** $7\frac{3}{4} - 4\frac{1}{2}$
▲ **16.** $8\frac{2}{5} - 2\frac{1}{2}$	▲ **17.** $9\frac{1}{3} - 6\frac{3}{4}$	▲ **18.** $6\frac{1}{4} - 1\frac{3}{8}$
■ **19.** $8\frac{1}{8} - 3\frac{1}{3}$	■ **20.** $5\frac{2}{3} - 4\frac{7}{8}$	■ **21.** $4\frac{1}{5} - 3\frac{2}{3}$
● **22.** $9\frac{5}{9} - 3\frac{5}{6}$	● **23.** $6\frac{2}{3} - 5\frac{3}{4}$	● **24.** $7\frac{5}{16} - 2\frac{7}{8}$

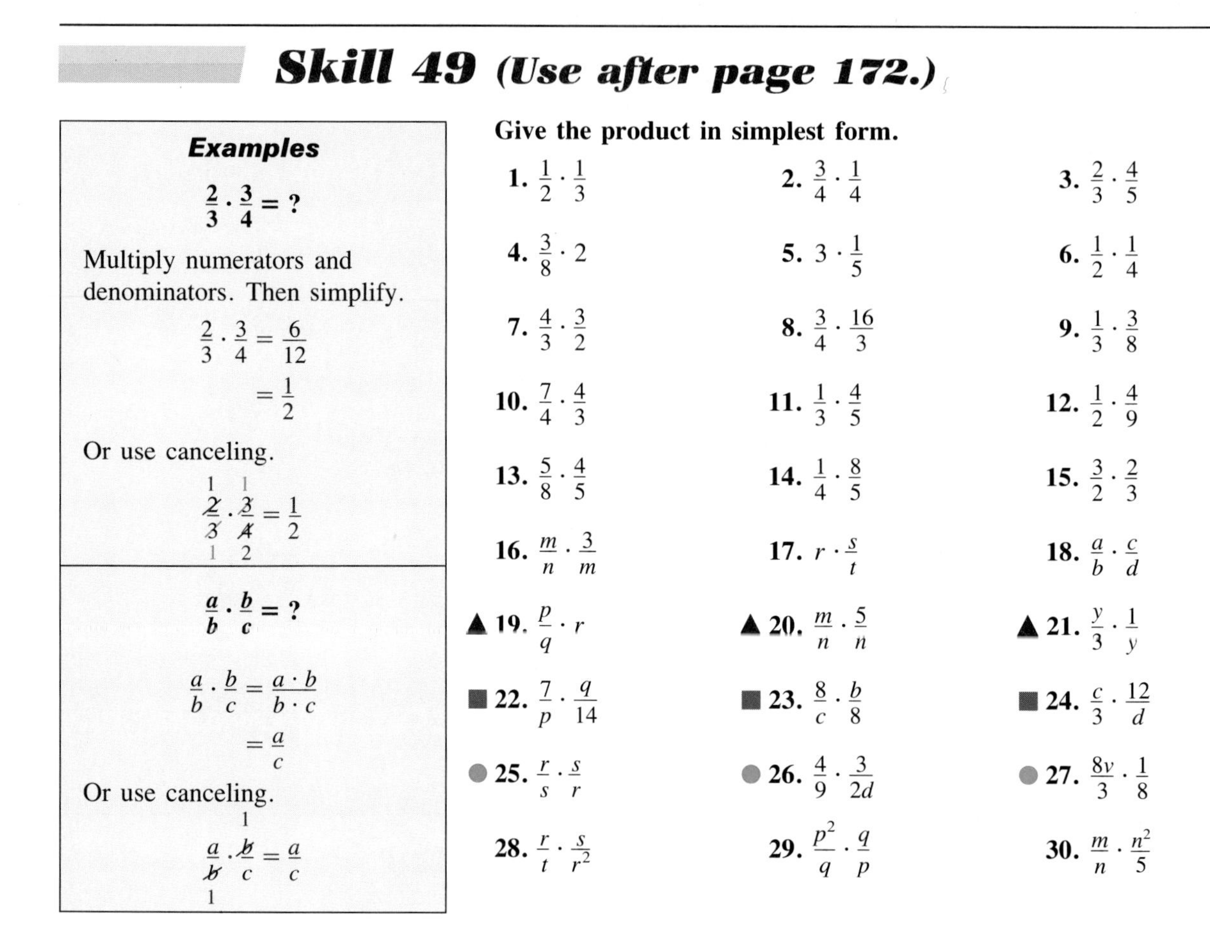

Skill 49 (Use after page 172.)

Examples

$\frac{2}{3} \cdot \frac{3}{4} = ?$

Multiply numerators and denominators. Then simplify.

$$\frac{2}{3} \cdot \frac{3}{4} = \frac{6}{12}$$
$$= \frac{1}{2}$$

Or use canceling.

$$\frac{\overset{1}{\cancel{2}}}{\underset{1}{\cancel{3}}} \cdot \frac{\overset{1}{\cancel{3}}}{\underset{2}{\cancel{4}}} = \frac{1}{2}$$

$\frac{a}{b} \cdot \frac{b}{c} = ?$

$$\frac{a}{b} \cdot \frac{b}{c} = \frac{a \cdot b}{b \cdot c}$$
$$= \frac{a}{c}$$

Or use canceling.

$$\frac{a}{\underset{1}{\cancel{b}}} \cdot \frac{\overset{1}{\cancel{b}}}{c} = \frac{a}{c}$$

Give the product in simplest form.

1. $\frac{1}{2} \cdot \frac{1}{3}$
2. $\frac{3}{4} \cdot \frac{1}{4}$
3. $\frac{2}{3} \cdot \frac{4}{5}$
4. $\frac{3}{8} \cdot 2$
5. $3 \cdot \frac{1}{5}$
6. $\frac{1}{2} \cdot \frac{1}{4}$
7. $\frac{4}{3} \cdot \frac{3}{2}$
8. $\frac{3}{4} \cdot \frac{16}{3}$
9. $\frac{1}{3} \cdot \frac{3}{8}$
10. $\frac{7}{4} \cdot \frac{4}{3}$
11. $\frac{1}{3} \cdot \frac{4}{5}$
12. $\frac{1}{2} \cdot \frac{4}{9}$
13. $\frac{5}{8} \cdot \frac{4}{5}$
14. $\frac{1}{4} \cdot \frac{8}{5}$
15. $\frac{3}{2} \cdot \frac{2}{3}$
16. $\frac{m}{n} \cdot \frac{3}{m}$
17. $r \cdot \frac{s}{t}$
18. $\frac{a}{b} \cdot \frac{c}{d}$

▲ 19. $\frac{p}{q} \cdot r$
▲ 20. $\frac{m}{n} \cdot \frac{5}{n}$
▲ 21. $\frac{y}{3} \cdot \frac{1}{y}$

■ 22. $\frac{7}{p} \cdot \frac{q}{14}$
■ 23. $\frac{8}{c} \cdot \frac{b}{8}$
■ 24. $\frac{c}{3} \cdot \frac{12}{d}$

● 25. $\frac{r}{s} \cdot \frac{s}{r}$
● 26. $\frac{4}{9} \cdot \frac{3}{2d}$
● 27. $\frac{8v}{3} \cdot \frac{1}{8}$

28. $\frac{r}{t} \cdot \frac{s}{r^2}$
29. $\frac{p^2}{q} \cdot \frac{q}{p}$
30. $\frac{m}{n} \cdot \frac{n^2}{5}$

Skill 50 (Use after page 174.)

Example

$2\frac{1}{2} \cdot 1\frac{2}{3} = ?$

Change to fractions.

$$2\frac{1}{2} \cdot 1\frac{2}{3} = \frac{5}{2} \cdot \frac{5}{3}$$

Multiply.

$$2\frac{1}{2} \cdot 1\frac{2}{3} = \frac{5}{2} \cdot \frac{5}{3}$$
$$= \frac{25}{6}$$
$$= 4\frac{1}{6}$$

Give the product in simplest form.

1. $2 \cdot 1\frac{1}{2}$
2. $1\frac{1}{2} \cdot 1\frac{1}{3}$
3. $2\frac{2}{3} \cdot 1\frac{1}{4}$
4. $1\frac{3}{4} \cdot 1\frac{3}{4}$
5. $3 \cdot 2\frac{1}{3}$
6. $2\frac{1}{3} \cdot 2$
7. $2\frac{2}{5} \cdot 3$
8. $1\frac{5}{6} \cdot 2\frac{1}{3}$
9. $3\frac{1}{4} \cdot 3\frac{1}{4}$

▲ 10. $4\frac{1}{6} \cdot 2\frac{1}{3}$
▲ 11. $2\frac{2}{3} \cdot 2\frac{1}{2}$
▲ 12. $3 \cdot 4\frac{1}{2}$

■ 13. $2 \cdot 1\frac{2}{3}$
■ 14. $1\frac{1}{2} \cdot 2\frac{1}{2}$
■ 15. $3\frac{3}{4} \cdot 2$

● 16. $1\frac{3}{8} \cdot 2\frac{1}{2}$
● 17. $3\frac{3}{4} \cdot 3\frac{1}{8}$
● 18. $1\frac{5}{8} \cdot 1\frac{5}{8}$

Skill 51 (Use after page 176.)

Examples

To divide by a fraction, multiply by its reciprocal.

$\mathbf{\frac{3}{4} \div \frac{9}{2} = ?}$

$\frac{3}{4} \div \frac{9}{2} = \frac{3}{4} \cdot \frac{2}{9}$

Cancel. $= \frac{\overset{1}{\cancel{3}}}{\underset{2}{\cancel{4}}} \cdot \frac{\overset{1}{\cancel{2}}}{\underset{3}{\cancel{9}}}$

$= \frac{1}{6}$

$\mathbf{\frac{5a}{b} \div \frac{3}{b^2} = ?}$

$\frac{5a}{b} \div \frac{3}{b^2} = \frac{5a}{b} \cdot \frac{b^2}{3}$

Cancel. $= \frac{5a}{\underset{1}{\cancel{b}}} \cdot \frac{\overset{b}{\cancel{b^2}}}{3}$

$= \frac{5ab}{3}$

Give the quotient in lowest terms.

1. $\frac{3}{4} \div \frac{1}{4}$
2. $\frac{2}{3} \div \frac{1}{3}$
3. $\frac{1}{2} \div \frac{1}{3}$
4. $\frac{3}{5} \div \frac{1}{5}$
5. $\frac{4}{5} \div 3$
6. $\frac{7}{8} \div \frac{7}{8}$
7. $\frac{5}{6} \div \frac{2}{3}$
8. $\frac{2}{3} \div \frac{1}{2}$
9. $\frac{3}{10} \div \frac{4}{5}$
10. $\frac{3}{4} \div \frac{3}{2}$
11. $6 \div \frac{3}{4}$
12. $\frac{5}{8} \div 3$
13. $\frac{5}{6} \div \frac{5}{8}$
14. $\frac{5}{8} \div \frac{2}{3}$
15. $\frac{2}{3} \div \frac{4}{5}$

▲16. $\frac{r}{s} \div \frac{t}{u}$
▲17. $\frac{a}{b} \div c$
▲18. $\frac{1}{j} \div \frac{3}{k}$

■19. $\frac{m}{n} \div p$
■20. $\frac{a}{c} \div \frac{d}{e}$
■21. $\frac{2a}{b} \div \frac{3}{c}$

●22. $\frac{r}{s} \div \frac{2t}{3u}$
●23. $\frac{6a}{b} \div \frac{3c}{5d}$
●24. $\frac{4}{m} \div \frac{6}{n}$

25. $\frac{5r}{3} \div \frac{7s}{12}$
26. $\frac{x}{y} \div \frac{z}{y}$
27. $\frac{m^2}{n} \div \frac{m}{p}$
28. $\frac{3r}{t} \div \frac{6r}{5}$
29. $\frac{y^2}{z} \div \frac{y}{z}$
30. $\frac{a}{6b} \div \frac{c}{3b}$

Skill 52 (Use after page 178.)

Example

$\mathbf{2\frac{1}{4} \div 4\frac{1}{2} = ?}$

Change to fractions.

$2\frac{1}{4} \div 4\frac{1}{2} = \frac{9}{4} \div \frac{9}{2}$

Divide. Write in simplest form.

$2\frac{1}{4} \div 4\frac{1}{2} = \frac{9}{4} \div \frac{9}{2}$

$= \frac{\overset{1}{\cancel{9}}}{\underset{2}{\cancel{4}}} \cdot \frac{\overset{1}{\cancel{2}}}{\underset{1}{\cancel{9}}}$

$= \frac{1}{2}$

Give the quotient in simplest form.

1. $5 \div 2\frac{1}{2}$
2. $2\frac{1}{2} \div 1\frac{1}{4}$
3. $5 \div 1\frac{1}{4}$
4. $3\frac{1}{2} \div 2$
5. $10 \div 3\frac{1}{3}$
6. $5\frac{1}{4} \div 3$
7. $4\frac{1}{6} \div 5$
8. $4\frac{3}{4} \div 2$
9. $2\frac{1}{3} \div 1\frac{1}{4}$
10. $2\frac{1}{2} \div 2\frac{1}{2}$
11. $7\frac{1}{2} \div 2\frac{1}{2}$
12. $6\frac{3}{4} \div 3\frac{1}{2}$

▲13. $3\frac{1}{2} \div 1\frac{3}{4}$
▲14. $2\frac{7}{8} \div 3\frac{1}{4}$
▲15. $4\frac{5}{8} \div 2\frac{2}{3}$

■16. $3\frac{5}{6} \div 2\frac{1}{3}$
■17. $5 \div 1\frac{1}{4}$
■18. $5\frac{3}{4} \div 2\frac{2}{3}$

●19. $6\frac{2}{3} \div 5\frac{1}{3}$
●20. $4\frac{7}{8} \div 6\frac{1}{4}$
●21. $2\frac{3}{4} \div 5\frac{2}{3}$

Skill 53 (Use after page 182.)

Example

Solve.

$\frac{5}{6}$ of $26 = n$

$\frac{5}{6} \cdot 26 = n$

$\frac{5}{\not{6}_3} \cdot \not{26}^{13} = n$

$\frac{65}{3} = n$

$21\frac{2}{3} = n$

Solve. Give answers in simplest form.

1. $\frac{1}{4}$ of $12 = n$ **2.** $\frac{1}{2}$ of $18 = n$ **3.** $\frac{1}{3}$ of $24 = n$

4. $\frac{1}{5}$ of $30 = n$ **5.** $\frac{1}{8}$ of $72 = n$ **6.** $\frac{1}{6}$ of $42 = n$

7. $\frac{2}{3}$ of $18 = n$ **8.** $\frac{3}{4}$ of $20 = n$ **9.** $\frac{2}{5}$ of $10 = n$

10. $\frac{3}{8}$ of $32 = n$ **11.** $\frac{2}{3}$ of $24 = n$ **12.** $\frac{5}{6}$ of $30 = n$

▲**13.** $\frac{3}{4}$ of $32 = n$ ▲**14.** $\frac{5}{8}$ of $40 = n$ ▲**15.** $\frac{2}{5}$ of $40 = n$

■**16.** $\frac{3}{5}$ of $22 = n$ ■**17.** $\frac{5}{6}$ of $40 = n$ ■**18.** $\frac{2}{3}$ of $38 = n$

●**19.** $\frac{9}{10}$ of $96 = n$ ●**20.** $\frac{2}{3}$ of $28 = n$ ●**21.** $\frac{4}{5}$ of $46 = n$

22. $\frac{3}{4}$ of $38 = n$ **23.** $\frac{7}{10}$ of $45 = n$ **24.** $\frac{7}{8}$ of $58 = n$

Skill 54 (Use after page 184.)

Example

$2\frac{3}{4}$ days = ___?___ h

Find the hours in 2 days and $\frac{3}{4}$ of a day.

$2\frac{3}{4}$ days = 48 h + 18 h

Add.

$2\frac{3}{4}$ days = 48 h + 18 h
= 66 h

Complete.

1. $1\frac{1}{2}$ days = ___?___ h **2.** $1\frac{1}{4}$ h = ___?___ min

3. $1\frac{3}{4}$ h = ___?___ min **4.** $2\frac{1}{2}$ min = ___?___ s

5. $2\frac{1}{4}$ min = ___?___ s **6.** $2\frac{1}{3}$ days = ___?___ h

7. $1\frac{2}{3}$ yd = ___?___ ft **8.** $1\frac{3}{4}$ ft = ___?___ in.

▲ **9.** $1\frac{1}{2}$ yd = ___?___ in. ▲**10.** $2\frac{2}{3}$ ft = ___?___ in.

■**11.** $4\frac{1}{3}$ yd = ___?___ ft ■**12.** $1\frac{3}{4}$ yd = ___?___ in.

●**13.** $1\frac{1}{4}$ gal = ___?___ qt ●**14.** $2\frac{1}{2}$ qt = ___?___ pt

15. $3\frac{1}{2}$ pt = ___?___ c **16.** $3\frac{1}{2}$ qt = ___?___ pt

Skill 55 (Use after page 186.)

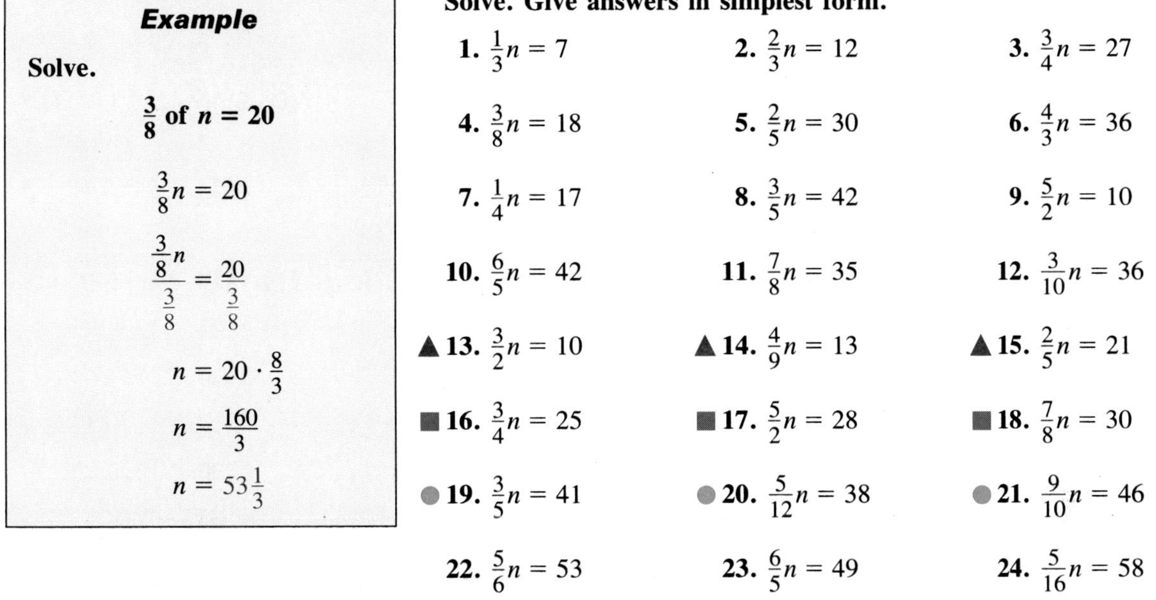

Example

Solve.

$\frac{3}{8}$ **of** $n = 20$

$\frac{3}{8}n = 20$

$\dfrac{\frac{3}{8}n}{\frac{3}{8}} = \dfrac{20}{\frac{3}{8}}$

$n = 20 \cdot \frac{8}{3}$

$n = \frac{160}{3}$

$n = 53\frac{1}{3}$

Solve. Give answers in simplest form.

1. $\frac{1}{3}n = 7$ **2.** $\frac{2}{3}n = 12$ **3.** $\frac{3}{4}n = 27$

4. $\frac{3}{8}n = 18$ **5.** $\frac{2}{5}n = 30$ **6.** $\frac{4}{3}n = 36$

7. $\frac{1}{4}n = 17$ **8.** $\frac{3}{5}n = 42$ **9.** $\frac{5}{2}n = 10$

10. $\frac{6}{5}n = 42$ **11.** $\frac{7}{8}n = 35$ **12.** $\frac{3}{10}n = 36$

▲ **13.** $\frac{3}{2}n = 10$ ▲ **14.** $\frac{4}{9}n = 13$ ▲ **15.** $\frac{2}{5}n = 21$

■ **16.** $\frac{3}{4}n = 25$ ■ **17.** $\frac{5}{2}n = 28$ ■ **18.** $\frac{7}{8}n = 30$

● **19.** $\frac{3}{5}n = 41$ ● **20.** $\frac{5}{12}n = 38$ ● **21.** $\frac{9}{10}n = 46$

22. $\frac{5}{6}n = 53$ **23.** $\frac{6}{5}n = 49$ **24.** $\frac{5}{16}n = 58$

Skill 56 (Use after page 196.)

Examples

< or >?

0 ◆ $^{+}2$

$^{-}2$ ◆ $^{-}1$

$^{-}2$ $^{-}1$ 0 $^{+}1$ $^{+}2$

← *smaller* *larger* →

$0 < {}^{+}2$

${}^{-}2 < {}^{-}1$

< or >?

1. $^{+}5$ ◆ $^{+}8$ **2.** $^{+}5$ ◆ $^{-}8$ **3.** $^{-}5$ ◆ $^{-}8$

4. $^{-}6$ ◆ $^{+}1$ **5.** $^{+}6$ ◆ $^{-}1$ **6.** $^{+}6$ ◆ $^{+}1$

7. 0 ◆ $^{-}5$ **8.** 0 ◆ $^{+}5$ **9.** $^{-}7$ ◆ 0

10. $^{+}9$ ◆ $^{-}4$ **11.** $^{-}9$ ◆ $^{+}4$ **12.** $^{+}9$ ◆ $^{+}4$

13. $^{-}7$ ◆ $^{-}2$ **14.** $^{-}8$ ◆ $^{+}3$ **15.** 0 ◆ $^{+}6$

16. $^{+}9$ ◆ $^{+}4$ **17.** $^{-}6$ ◆ $^{+}6$ **18.** $^{-}3$ ◆ $^{-}5$

19. $^{-}11$ ◆ $^{+}10$ **20.** $^{+}16$ ◆ $^{-}17$ **21.** $^{+}15$ ◆ $^{+}17$

▲ **22.** 0 ◆ $^{-}12$ ▲ **23.** $^{+}15$ ◆ $^{-}15$ ▲ **24.** $^{-}19$ ◆ $^{-}13$

■ **25.** $^{-}16$ ◆ $^{+}11$ ■ **26.** $^{-}19$ ◆ $^{-}18$ ■ **27.** $^{+}14$ ◆ $^{+}17$

● **28.** $^{-}22$ ◆ $^{+}22$ ● **29.** $^{-}26$ ◆ $^{-}21$ ● **30.** $^{+}23$ ◆ $^{+}24$

31. $^{+}27$ ◆ $^{-}20$ **32.** $^{-}29$ ◆ $^{+}23$ **33.** $^{-}28$ ◆ $^{-}26$

34. 0 ◆ $^{+}32$ **35.** $^{-}36$ ◆ 0 **36.** $^{+}37$ ◆ $^{-}31$

Skill 57 (Use after page 198.)

Examples

To add integers, think about combining charges.

$^{+}2 + ^{-}3 = ^{-}1$

$^{-}1 + ^{+}2 = ^{+}1$

Give the sum.

1. $^{+}3 + ^{+}2$ **2.** $^{+}3 + ^{-}2$ **3.** $^{-}3 + ^{-}2$

4. $^{-}1 + ^{+}5$ **5.** $^{-}1 + ^{-}5$ **6.** $^{+}1 + ^{-}5$

7. $0 + ^{-}8$ **8.** $0 + ^{+}8$ **9.** $^{-}6 + 0$

10. $^{+}4 + ^{-}4$ **11.** $^{-}4 + ^{+}4$ **12.** $^{+}4 + ^{+}4$

13. $^{+}7 + ^{-}3$ **14.** $^{-}7 + ^{+}3$ **15.** $^{-}7 + ^{-}3$

16. $^{-}6 + ^{+}9$ **17.** $^{+}6 + ^{-}9$ **18.** $^{-}6 + ^{-}9$

19. $^{+}10 + ^{+}12$ **20.** $^{+}11 + ^{-}11$ **21.** $^{-}17 + ^{+}14$

▲ **22.** $^{-}19 + ^{-}13$ ▲ **23.** $^{+}18 + ^{-}19$ ▲ **24.** $^{-}16 + ^{+}11$

■ **25.** $^{+}15 + ^{+}14$ ■ **26.** $^{-}18 + ^{-}12$ ■ **27.** $^{-}11 + ^{+}19$

● **28.** $^{+}17 + ^{-}17$ ● **29.** $^{-}19 + ^{+}14$ ● **30.** $^{+}12 + ^{+}15$

31. $^{-}20 + ^{-}20$ **32.** $^{-}21 + ^{+}25$ **33.** $^{+}27 + ^{-}22$

34. $^{-}31 + ^{+}31$ **35.** $0 + ^{+}34$ **36.** $^{-}32 + ^{-}36$

Skill 58 (Use after page 200.)

Examples

To subtract an integer, add the opposite of the integer.

$^{+}5 - ^{+}2 = ^{+}5 + ^{-}2 = ^{+}3$

$^{-}5 - ^{+}2 = ^{-}5 + ^{-}2 = ^{-}7$

$^{+}5 - ^{-}2 = ^{+}5 + ^{+}2 = ^{+}7$

$^{-}5 - ^{-}2 = ^{-}5 + ^{+}2 = ^{-}3$

Give the difference.

1. $^{+}4 - ^{-}6$ **2.** $^{-}4 - ^{+}6$ **3.** $^{+}4 - ^{+}6$

4. $^{-}7 - ^{-}3$ **5.** $^{+}7 - ^{-}3$ **6.** $^{-}7 - ^{+}3$

7. $^{+}8 - ^{+}1$ **8.** $^{-}8 - ^{+}1$ **9.** $^{+}8 - ^{-}1$

10. $^{-}7 - 0$ **11.** $0 - ^{+}7$ **12.** $0 - ^{-}7$

13. $^{+}5 - ^{+}9$ **14.** $^{+}5 - ^{-}9$ **15.** $^{-}5 - ^{+}9$

16. $^{-}5 - ^{-}5$ **17.** $^{+}5 - ^{+}5$ **18.** $^{-}5 - ^{+}5$

19. $^{+}12 - ^{-}11$ **20.** $^{-}13 - ^{+}16$ **21.** $^{-}14 - ^{-}14$

▲ **22.** $^{-}16 - ^{+}19$ ▲ **23.** $^{+}18 - ^{+}11$ ▲ **24.** $^{+}19 - ^{+}14$

■ **25.** $^{+}17 - ^{-}10$ ■ **26.** $^{-}10 - ^{+}17$ ■ **27.** $^{-}16 - ^{-}16$

● **28.** $^{+}11 - ^{+}15$ ● **29.** $^{-}15 - ^{+}18$ ● **30.** $^{+}17 - ^{-}14$

31. $^{-}23 - ^{-}27$ **32.** $^{+}25 - ^{+}25$ **33.** $^{-}28 - ^{+}24$

34. $0 - ^{-}34$ **35.** $^{-}36 - ^{+}32$ **36.** $^{+}33 - ^{-}38$

Skill 59 (Use after page 202.)

Examples

The product of two integers with the same signs is positive.

$^{+}2 \times {}^{+}3 = {}^{+}6$

$^{-}4 \times {}^{-}5 = {}^{+}20$

The product of two integers with different signs is negative.

$^{+}6 \times {}^{-}3 = {}^{-}18$

$^{-}5 \times {}^{+}6 = {}^{-}30$

The product of any integer and 0 is 0.

$^{+}7 \times 0 = 0$

$0 \times {}^{-}4 = 0$

Give the product.

1. $^{+}3 \times {}^{+}4$	**2.** $^{+}3 \times {}^{-}4$	**3.** $^{-}3 \times {}^{-}4$
4. $^{-}6 \times {}^{+}5$	**5.** $^{+}6 \times {}^{+}5$	**6.** $^{+}6 \times {}^{-}5$
7. $^{-}5 \times {}^{+}7$	**8.** $^{-}5 \times {}^{-}7$	**9.** $^{+}5 \times {}^{+}7$
10. $^{+}2 \times {}^{-}6$	**11.** $^{-}6 \times {}^{+}2$	**12.** $^{-}6 \times {}^{-}2$
13. $^{+}7 \times 0$	**14.** $^{-}7 \times 0$	**15.** 0×0
16. $^{-}9 \times {}^{-}8$	**17.** $^{+}8 \times {}^{-}8$	**18.** $^{-}6 \times {}^{+}5$
19. $^{+}4 \times {}^{+}6$	**20.** $^{-}5 \times {}^{+}5$	**21.** $^{+}6 \times {}^{-}6$
▲**22.** $^{-}5 \times {}^{-}9$	▲**23.** $^{+}7 \times {}^{-}8$	▲**24.** $^{-}8 \times {}^{+}7$
■**25.** $^{+}9 \times {}^{+}7$	■**26.** $^{-}7 \times {}^{-}7$	■**27.** $0 \times {}^{+}8$
●**28.** $^{+}10 \times {}^{-}6$	●**29.** $^{-}10 \times {}^{+}6$	●**30.** $^{+}10 \times {}^{+}6$
31. $^{-}11 \times {}^{-}11$	**32.** $^{+}11 \times {}^{-}11$	**33.** $^{+}11 \times {}^{+}11$
34. $^{-}13 \times {}^{+}14$	**35.** $^{+}18 \times {}^{+}15$	**36.** $^{-}19 \times {}^{-}13$

Skill 60 (Use after page 204.)

Examples

The quotient of two integers with the same signs is positive.

$^{+}12 \div {}^{+}6 = {}^{+}2$

$^{-}21 \div {}^{-}7 = {}^{+}3$

The quotient of two integers with different signs is negative.

$^{+}20 \div {}^{-}4 = {}^{-}5$

$^{-}32 \div {}^{+}8 = {}^{-}4$

The quotient of 0 divided by any nonzero integer is 0.

$0 \div {}^{-}6 = 0$

$0 \div {}^{+}7 = 0$

Give the quotient.

1. $^{+}12 \div {}^{+}3$	**2.** $^{+}12 \div {}^{-}3$	**3.** $^{-}12 \div {}^{-}3$
4. $^{-}8 \div {}^{+}2$	**5.** $^{+}8 \div {}^{+}2$	**6.** $^{+}8 \div {}^{-}2$
7. $^{-}16 \div {}^{+}4$	**8.** $^{-}16 \div {}^{-}4$	**9.** $^{+}16 \div {}^{-}4$
10. $^{-}18 \div {}^{+}6$	**11.** $^{+}18 \div {}^{+}6$	**12.** $^{+}18 \div {}^{-}6$
13. $^{-}25 \div {}^{+}5$	**14.** $^{-}25 \div {}^{-}5$	**15.** $^{+}25 \div {}^{-}5$
16. $0 \div {}^{+}4$	**17.** $0 \div {}^{-}4$	**18.** $0 \div {}^{-}9$
19. $^{+}49 \div {}^{-}7$	**20.** $^{-}42 \div {}^{+}6$	**21.** $^{-}45 \div {}^{-}5$
▲**22.** $^{+}36 \div {}^{+}6$	▲**23.** $^{-}32 \div {}^{+}8$	▲**24.** $^{+}35 \div {}^{-}7$
■**25.** $^{-}36 \div {}^{-}9$	■**26.** $^{+}54 \div {}^{+}6$	■**27.** $^{-}64 \div {}^{+}8$
●**28.** $^{+}72 \div {}^{-}9$	●**29.** $^{-}81 \div {}^{-}9$	●**30.** $^{+}63 \div {}^{-}7$
31. $^{-}70 \div {}^{+}10$	**32.** $^{+}90 \div {}^{+}10$	**33.** $^{-}60 \div {}^{-}10$
34. $^{-}132 \div {}^{+}12$	**35.** $^{+}182 \div {}^{-}13$	**36.** $^{+}224 \div {}^{+}16$

Skill 61 (Use after page 208.)

Examples

Large number	Small number
830,000	**0.000381**

Locate the decimal point to get a number between 1 and 10.

830000 ↑	0.000381 ↑

Count the number of places the decimal point was moved to get a number between 1 and 10.

830000	0.000381
5 places to left	*4 places to right*

Write the number as a product of a number between 1 and 10 and a power of 10.

8.3×10^5	3.81×10^{-4}

Write in scientific notation.

1. 4100   **2.** 600   **3.** 57,000

4. 9300   **5.** 94,000   **6.** 536,000

7. 7,420,000   **8.** 390,000   **9.** 8000

10. 91,000   **11.** 6,800,000   **12.** 43,200,000

13. 596,000   **14.** 8,160,000   **15.** 16,000,000

16. 420   **17.** 40,200   **18.** 4,200,000

▲ **19.** 0.0035   ▲ **20.** 0.057   ▲ **21.** 0.82

■ **22.** 0.00017   ■ **23.** 0.0039   ■ **24.** 0.00006

● **25.** 0.0534   ● **26.** 0.000174   ● **27.** 0.00018

28. 0.000039   **29.** 0.000751   **30.** 0.0000048

31. 0.000023   **32.** 0.0135   **33.** 0.0000712

34. 0.000042   **35.** 0.42   **36.** 0.00402

Skill 62 (Use after page 210.)

Examples

$$\mathbf{x + 13 = {}^-6}$$

$$x + 13 - 13 = {}^-6 - 13$$

$$x = {}^-19$$

✔ *Check:*

$${}^-19 + 13 \stackrel{?}{=} {}^-6$$

$${}^-6 = {}^-6$$

$$\mathbf{y - 17 = {}^-4}$$

$$y - 17 + 17 = {}^-4 + 17$$

$$y = 13$$

✔ *Check:*

$$13 - 17 \stackrel{?}{=} {}^-4$$

$${}^-4 = {}^-4$$

Solve and check.

1. $x + 8 = {}^-4$ **2.** $g - 9 = 7$ **3.** $d + {}^-6 = 9$

4. $e - 10 = 6$ **5.** $y + {}^-12 = 13$ **6.** $m - 18 = {}^-5$

7. $h - {}^-20 = 11$ **8.** $f - 11 = 18$ **9.** $z + {}^-5 = {}^-16$

10. $j - 13 = {}^-15$ **11.** $w + {}^-19 = 20$ **12.** $k + 23 = 23$

13. $a + {}^-16 = 15$ **14.** $n - 12 = {}^-12$ **15.** $q + {}^-26 = 35$

▲ **16.** $c - 25 = 11$ ▲ **17.** $p - {}^-32 = 22$ ▲ **18.** $b + 42 = 50$

■ **19.** ${}^-3 = r + {}^-13$ ■ **20.** $18 = y - 11$ ■ **21.** $12 = u + 9$

● **22.** ${}^-21 = x - 23$ ● **23.** $24 = s - {}^-17$ ● **24.** ${}^-26 = z + {}^-18$

25. ${}^-15 = w + {}^-15$ **26.** $11 = m - 36$ **27.** ${}^-30 = t + 33$

28. $40 = k + {}^-41$ **29.** ${}^-36 = v - 52$ **30.** $40 = j - {}^-49$

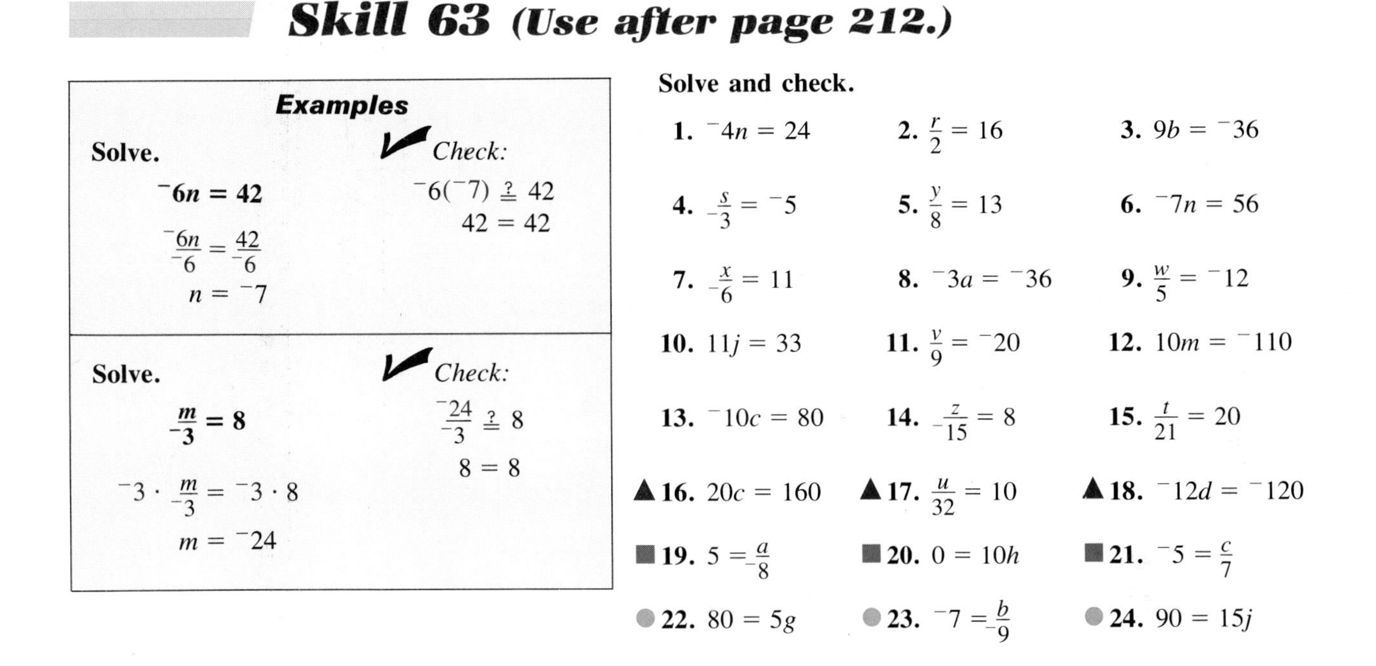

Skill 63 (Use after page 212.)

Examples

Solve.

$$^-6n = 42$$

$$\frac{^-6n}{^-6} = \frac{42}{^-6}$$

$$n = {}^-7$$

Check:

$$^-6(^-7) \stackrel{?}{=} 42$$

$$42 = 42$$

Solve.

$$\frac{m}{^-3} = 8$$

$$^-3 \cdot \frac{m}{^-3} = {}^-3 \cdot 8$$

$$m = {}^-24$$

Check:

$$\frac{^-24}{^-3} \stackrel{?}{=} 8$$

$$8 = 8$$

Solve and check.

1. $^-4n = 24$
2. $\frac{r}{2} = 16$
3. $9b = {}^-36$
4. $\frac{s}{^-3} = {}^-5$
5. $\frac{y}{8} = 13$
6. $^-7n = 56$
7. $\frac{x}{^-6} = 11$
8. $^-3a = {}^-36$
9. $\frac{w}{5} = {}^-12$
10. $11j = 33$
11. $\frac{v}{9} = {}^-20$
12. $10m = {}^-110$
13. $^-10c = 80$
14. $\frac{z}{^-15} = 8$
15. $\frac{t}{21} = 20$

▲16. $20c = 160$ ▲17. $\frac{u}{32} = 10$ ▲18. $^-12d = {}^-120$

■19. $5 = \frac{a}{^-8}$ ■20. $0 = 10h$ ■21. $^-5 = \frac{c}{7}$

●22. $80 = 5g$ ●23. $^-7 = \frac{b}{^-9}$ ●24. $90 = 15j$

Skill 64 (Use after page 214.)

Examples

Solve.

$$3n + {}^-6 = 6$$

$$3n + {}^-6 - {}^-6 = 6 - {}^-6$$

$$3n = 12$$

$$\frac{3n}{3} = \frac{12}{3}$$

$$n = 4$$

Check:

$$3(4) + {}^-6 \stackrel{?}{=} 6$$

$$6 = 6$$

Solve.

$$\frac{m}{^-2} + 8 = 3$$

$$\frac{m}{^-2} + 8 - 8 = 3 - 8$$

$$\frac{m}{^-2} = {}^-5$$

$$^-2 \cdot \frac{m}{^-2} = {}^-2 \cdot {}^-5$$

$$m = 10$$

Check:

$$\frac{10}{^-2} + 8 \stackrel{?}{=} 3$$

$$3 = 3$$

Solve and check.

1. $^-5a + 4 = 19$
2. $\frac{j}{3} + 4 = {}^-10$
3. $\frac{p}{6} - 11 = {}^-9$
4. $7q + 15 = 36$
5. $4s - {}^-12 = 0$
6. $^-9c + 15 = {}^-12$
7. $\frac{g}{^-10} + {}^-7 = {}^-3$
8. $\frac{f}{7} - 14 = {}^-14$
9. $20d + 10 = 70$
10. $^-12t - {}^-3 = 15$

▲11. $\frac{n}{9} + {}^-8 = {}^-11$ ▲12. $\frac{h}{16} - {}^-6 = {}^-7$

■13. $2 = 3y + 8$ ■14. $^-4 = \frac{s}{^-3} - 2$

●15. $0 = \frac{t}{9} + {}^-7$ ●16. $^-15 = {}^-5r + 10$

17. $1 = \frac{w}{^-4} + {}^-8$
18. $5 = {}^-3h - 4$
19. $0 = {}^-4j + 8$
20. $2 = \frac{m}{4} + 6$

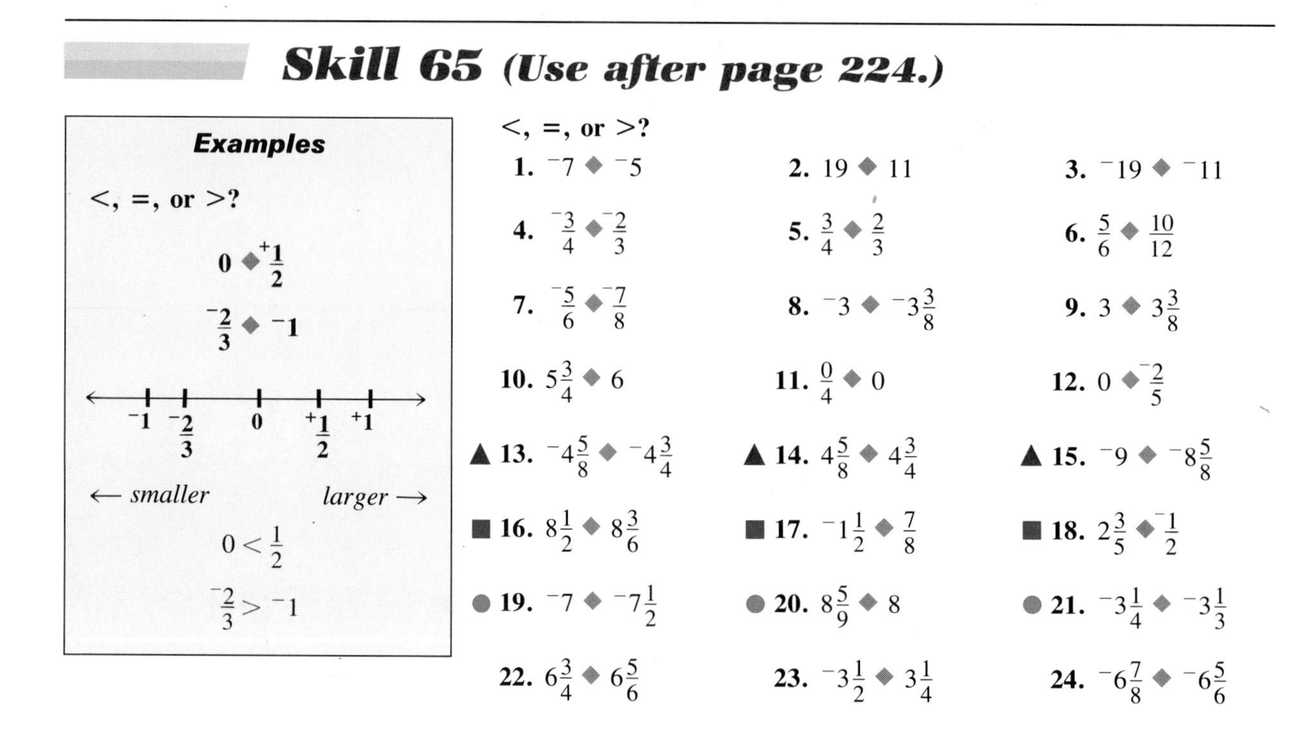

Skill 65 (Use after page 224.)

Examples

<, =, or >?

$0 \blacklozenge {}^{+}\frac{1}{2}$

$^{-}\frac{2}{3} \blacklozenge {}^{-}1$

$0 < \frac{1}{2}$

$^{-}\frac{2}{3} > {}^{-}1$

<, =, or >?

1. $^{-}7 \blacklozenge {}^{-}5$
2. $19 \blacklozenge 11$
3. $^{-}19 \blacklozenge {}^{-}11$
4. $^{-}\frac{3}{4} \blacklozenge {}^{-}\frac{2}{3}$
5. $\frac{3}{4} \blacklozenge \frac{2}{3}$
6. $\frac{5}{6} \blacklozenge \frac{10}{12}$
7. $^{-}\frac{5}{6} \blacklozenge {}^{-}\frac{7}{8}$
8. $^{-}3 \blacklozenge {}^{-}3\frac{3}{8}$
9. $3 \blacklozenge 3\frac{3}{8}$
10. $5\frac{3}{4} \blacklozenge 6$
11. $\frac{0}{4} \blacklozenge 0$
12. $0 \blacklozenge {}^{-}\frac{2}{5}$

▲ 13. $^{-}4\frac{5}{8} \blacklozenge {}^{-}4\frac{3}{4}$

▲ 14. $4\frac{5}{8} \blacklozenge 4\frac{3}{4}$

▲ 15. $^{-}9 \blacklozenge {}^{-}8\frac{5}{8}$

■ 16. $8\frac{1}{2} \blacklozenge 8\frac{3}{6}$

■ 17. $^{-}1\frac{1}{2} \blacklozenge \frac{7}{8}$

■ 18. $2\frac{3}{5} \blacklozenge {}^{-}\frac{1}{2}$

● 19. $^{-}7 \blacklozenge {}^{-}7\frac{1}{2}$

● 20. $8\frac{5}{9} \blacklozenge 8$

● 21. $^{-}3\frac{1}{4} \blacklozenge {}^{-}3\frac{1}{3}$

22. $6\frac{3}{4} \blacklozenge 6\frac{5}{6}$

23. $^{-}3\frac{1}{2} \blacklozenge 3\frac{1}{4}$

24. $^{-}6\frac{7}{8} \blacklozenge {}^{-}6\frac{5}{6}$

Skill 66 (Use after page 226.)

Example

$\frac{5}{6} = ?$

To write a rational number in decimal form, divide the numerator by the denominator.

$$\begin{array}{r} 0.833 \\ 6\overline{)5.000} \\ -4\,8 \\ \hline 20 \\ -18 \\ \hline 20 \\ -18 \\ \hline 2 \end{array}$$

$\frac{5}{6} = 0.8\overline{3}$

Write each rational number in decimal form.

1. $\frac{1}{4}$
2. $\frac{3}{4}$
3. $^{-}\frac{1}{5}$
4. $^{-}\frac{2}{3}$
5. $\frac{9}{10}$
6. $^{-}\frac{2}{5}$
7. $\frac{7}{10}$
8. $^{-}\frac{4}{5}$
9. $^{-}\frac{1}{8}$
10. $\frac{3}{10}$
11. $^{-}\frac{7}{4}$
12. $\frac{9}{8}$
13. $\frac{9}{2}$
14. $^{-}\frac{3}{8}$
15. $\frac{3}{5}$
16. $^{-}\frac{7}{8}$
17. $^{-}\frac{9}{4}$
18. $\frac{11}{3}$
19. $^{-}\frac{1}{16}$
20. $\frac{11}{8}$

▲ 21. $\frac{5}{16}$

▲ 22. $^{-}\frac{3}{2}$

▲ 23. $\frac{8}{5}$

▲ 24. $^{-}\frac{13}{5}$

■ 25. $^{-}2\frac{1}{2}$

■ 26. $3\frac{3}{4}$

■ 27. $^{-}3\frac{4}{5}$

■ 28. $2\frac{7}{8}$

● 29. $1\frac{2}{5}$

● 30. $^{-}4\frac{3}{8}$

● 31. $6\frac{4}{5}$

● 32. $^{-}3\frac{1}{3}$

33. $^{-}18\frac{7}{8}$

34. $10\frac{1}{16}$

35. $^{-}12\frac{5}{16}$

36. $24\frac{4}{5}$

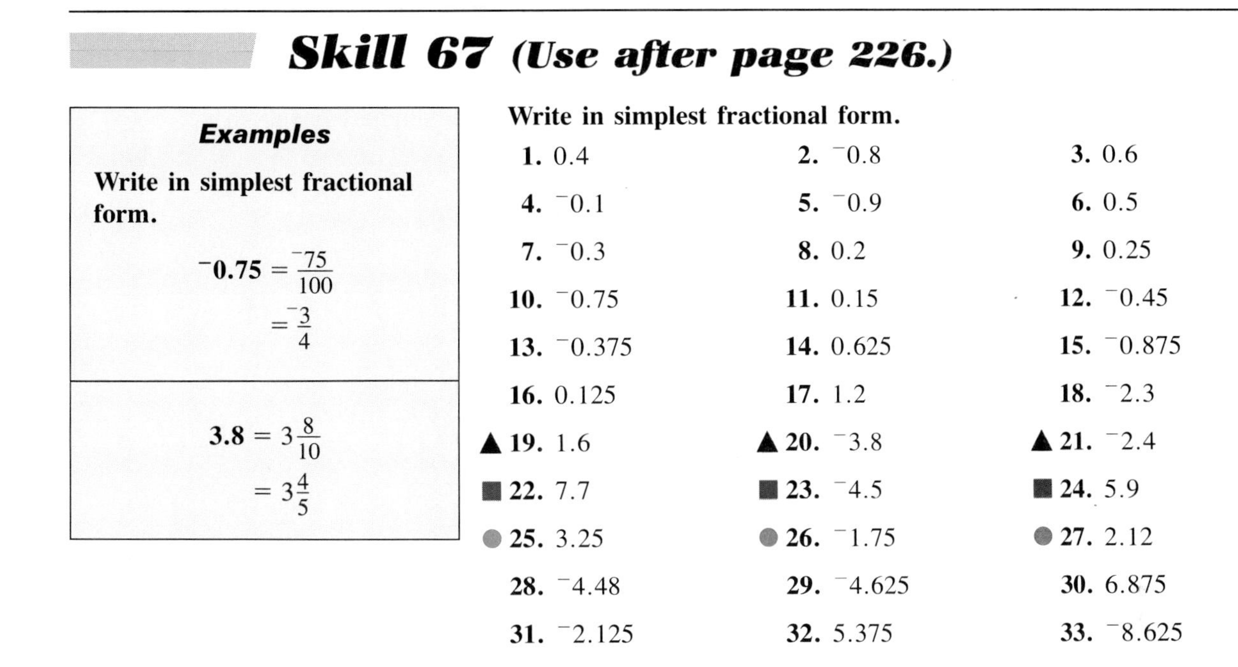

Skill 67 (Use after page 226.)

Examples

Write in simplest fractional form.

$$^{-}0.75 = \frac{^{-}75}{100} = \frac{^{-}3}{4}$$

$$3.8 = 3\frac{8}{10} = 3\frac{4}{5}$$

Write in simplest fractional form.

1. 0.4	**2.** $^{-}0.8$	**3.** 0.6
4. $^{-}0.1$	**5.** $^{-}0.9$	**6.** 0.5
7. $^{-}0.3$	**8.** 0.2	**9.** 0.25
10. $^{-}0.75$	**11.** 0.15	**12.** $^{-}0.45$
13. $^{-}0.375$	**14.** 0.625	**15.** $^{-}0.875$
16. 0.125	**17.** 1.2	**18.** $^{-}2.3$
▲ **19.** 1.6	▲ **20.** $^{-}3.8$	▲ **21.** $^{-}2.4$
■ **22.** 7.7	■ **23.** $^{-}4.5$	■ **24.** 5.9
● **25.** 3.25	● **26.** $^{-}1.75$	● **27.** 2.12
28. $^{-}4.48$	**29.** $^{-}4.625$	**30.** 6.875
31. $^{-}2.125$	**32.** 5.375	**33.** $^{-}8.625$

Skill 68 (Use after page 228.)

Examples

Give the sum in simplest form.

$$\frac{^{-}3}{8} + \frac{1}{4} = \frac{^{-}3}{8} + \frac{2}{8} = \frac{^{-}1}{8}$$

Give the difference in simplest form.

$$^{-}2\frac{1}{3} - 3\frac{1}{4} = \frac{^{-}7}{3} - \frac{13}{4} = \frac{^{-}7}{3} + \frac{^{-}13}{4} = \frac{^{-}28}{12} + \frac{^{-}39}{12} = \frac{^{-}67}{12} = {^{-}5}\frac{7}{12}$$

Give each sum in simplest form.

1. $\frac{3}{8} + \frac{5}{8}$	**2.** $\frac{^{-}2}{9} + \frac{^{-}4}{9}$	**3.** $\frac{7}{3} + \frac{^{-}5}{3}$
▲ **4.** $\frac{5}{12} + \frac{^{-}7}{8}$	▲ **5.** $\frac{^{-}4}{5} + \frac{3}{4}$	▲ **6.** $\frac{5}{6} + \frac{0}{8}$
■ **7.** $\frac{^{-}3}{5} + \frac{^{-}5}{8}$	■ **8.** $\frac{5}{6} + \frac{7}{8}$	■ **9.** $\frac{7}{12} + \frac{^{-}2}{3}$
● **10.** $3\frac{1}{2} + {^{-}2}\frac{1}{4}$	● **11.** $^{-}1\frac{2}{3} + 2\frac{3}{4}$	● **12.** $^{-}4\frac{3}{8} + {^{-}2}\frac{5}{6}$

Give each difference in simplest form.

13. $\frac{5}{6} - \frac{1}{6}$	**14.** $\frac{^{-}7}{8} - \frac{3}{8}$	**15.** $\frac{^{-}5}{9} - \frac{^{-}2}{9}$
▲ **16.** $\frac{3}{5} - \frac{^{-}9}{10}$	▲ **17.** $\frac{^{-}5}{12} - \frac{3}{4}$	▲ **18.** $\frac{^{-}7}{8} - \frac{^{-}5}{6}$
■ **19.** $\frac{9}{16} - \frac{4}{5}$	■ **20.** $\frac{^{-}3}{8} - \frac{^{-}4}{5}$	■ **21.** $\frac{^{-}5}{12} - \frac{0}{4}$
● **22.** $2\frac{1}{2} - 4\frac{1}{3}$	● **23.** $^{-}2\frac{3}{4} - 1\frac{5}{6}$	● **24.** $^{-}4\frac{2}{5} - {^{-}2}\frac{3}{10}$

Skill 69 (Use after page 230.)

Examples

Give the product in simplest form.

$\frac{^-12}{5} \cdot \frac{10}{9} =$

$\frac{\overset{^-4}{\cancel{^-12}}}{\underset{1}{\cancel{5}}} \cdot \frac{\overset{2}{\cancel{10}}}{\underset{3}{\cancel{9}}} = \frac{^-8}{3}$

$= {^-2}\frac{2}{3}$

Give the quotient in simplest form.

${^-3}\frac{1}{4} \div 1\frac{1}{3} = \frac{^-13}{4} \div \frac{4}{3}$

$= \frac{^-13}{4} \cdot \frac{3}{4}$

$= \frac{^-39}{16}$

$= {^-2}\frac{7}{16}$

Give each product in simplest form.

▲ **1.** $\frac{6}{5} \cdot \frac{5}{6}$ ▲ **2.** $\frac{^-2}{3} \cdot \frac{^-2}{3}$ ▲ **3.** $\frac{^-4}{5} \cdot \frac{3}{4}$

■ **4.** $\frac{7}{8} \cdot \frac{0}{3}$ ■ **5.** $\frac{^-5}{6} \cdot \frac{3}{10}$ ■ **6.** $\frac{^-7}{8} \cdot \frac{^-8}{7}$

● **7.** $2\frac{5}{6} \cdot {^-1}\frac{1}{3}$ ● **8.** $3\frac{1}{10} \cdot 2\frac{2}{5}$ ● **9.** ${^-4}\frac{1}{8} \cdot {^-2}\frac{3}{4}$

Give each quotient in simplest form.

▲ **10.** $\frac{^-3}{4} \div \frac{^-2}{3}$ ▲ **11.** $\frac{^-7}{8} \div \frac{5}{4}$ ▲ **12.** $\frac{^-9}{10} \div \frac{3}{5}$

■ **13.** $\frac{2}{3} \div {^-6}$ ■ **14.** $\frac{5}{12} \div \frac{^-10}{3}$ ■ **15.** $\frac{^-7}{8} \div \frac{^-21}{2}$

● **16.** ${^-2}\frac{1}{2} \div 1\frac{1}{4}$ ● **17.** $3\frac{1}{5} \div 1\frac{3}{10}$ ● **18.** $4\frac{7}{8} \div {^-2}\frac{3}{4}$

Skill 70 (Use after page 234.)

Examples

Solve.

$^-4x + 7 = {^-18}$

$^-4x + 7 - 7 = {^-18} - 7$

$^-4x = {^-25}$

$\frac{^-4x}{^-4} = \frac{^-25}{^-4}$

$x = 6\frac{1}{4}$

Check:

$^-4 \cdot 6\frac{1}{4} + 7 \stackrel{?}{=} {^-18}$

$^-25 + 7 \stackrel{?}{=} {^-18}$

$^-18 = {^-18}$

Solve.

$6 - 3y = {^-8}$

$6 + {^-3y} = {^-8}$

$^-3y + 6 = {^-8}$

$^-3y + 6 - 6 = {^-8} - 6$

$^-3y = {^-14}$

$\frac{^-3y}{^-3} = \frac{^-14}{^-3}$

$y = 4\frac{2}{3}$

Check:

$6 - 3 \cdot 4\frac{2}{3} \stackrel{?}{=} {^-8}$

$6 - 14 \stackrel{?}{=} {^-8}$

$^-8 = {^-8}$

Solve and check.

1. $4m + 6 = 17$ **2.** $7b - 6 = {^-4}$

3. $^-3 - 2n = 9$ **4.** $5 + 3y = {^-4}$

5. $^-5c - 10 = 9$ **6.** $^-12 + 5c = 9$

7. $^-3a + 12 = 13$ **8.** $^-15 - 4t = 16$

9. $6k + 9 = {^-17}$ **10.** $5 - 6p = 0$

11. $12q - 4 = 2$ **12.** $^-16 + 10r = {^-7}$

13. $16g - 8 = 11$ **14.** $^-13 - 9q = {^-16}$

15. $14 + 12d = 22$ **16.** $18j + 9 = {^-11}$

17. $^-8z - 14 = 0$ **18.** $^-12t + 30 = 6$

▲ **19.** $^-10 + 6f = {^-6}$ ▲ **20.** $20v + 13 = {^-7}$

■ **21.** $19 + 24g = {^-13}$ ■ **22.** $11j - 10 = {^-10}$

● **23.** $24 - 2t = {^-18}$ ● **24.** $^-30 + 10j = 30$

25. $^-15n - 12 = 24$ **26.** $20z + 34 = 4$

27. $9c - 16 = 30$ **28.** $^-30n + 18 = 3$

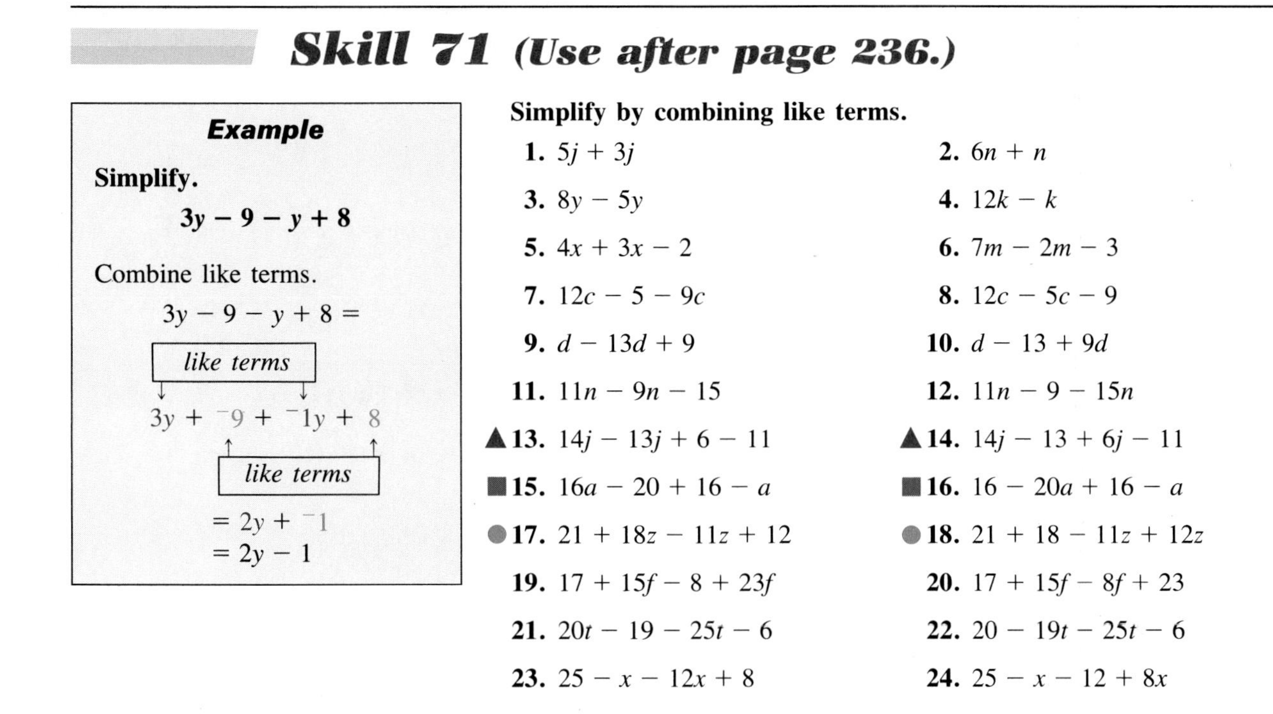

Skill 71 (Use after page 236.)

Example

Simplify.

$$3y - 9 - y + 8$$

Combine like terms.

$$3y - 9 - y + 8 =$$

$$3y + {}^{-}9 + {}^{-}1y + 8$$

$$= 2y + {}^{-}1$$
$$= 2y - 1$$

Simplify by combining like terms.

1. $5j + 3j$
2. $6n + n$
3. $8y - 5y$
4. $12k - k$
5. $4x + 3x - 2$
6. $7m - 2m - 3$
7. $12c - 5 - 9c$
8. $12c - 5c - 9$
9. $d - 13d + 9$
10. $d - 13 + 9d$
11. $11n - 9n - 15$
12. $11n - 9 - 15n$

▲13. $14j - 13j + 6 - 11$

▲14. $14j - 13 + 6j - 11$

■15. $16a - 20 + 16 - a$

■16. $16 - 20a + 16 - a$

●17. $21 + 18z - 11z + 12$

●18. $21 + 18 - 11z + 12z$

19. $17 + 15f - 8 + 23f$
20. $17 + 15f - 8f + 23$
21. $20t - 19 - 25t - 6$
22. $20 - 19t - 25t - 6$
23. $25 - x - 12x + 8$
24. $25 - x - 12 + 8x$

Skill 72 (Use after page 240.)

Example

Solve.

$$3x + 8 + x - 12 = 13 - 5$$

Combine like terms.

$$4x - 4 = 8$$
$$4x - 4 + 4 = 8 + 4$$
$$4x = 12$$
$$\frac{4x}{4} = \frac{12}{4}$$
$$x = 3$$

✔ *Check:*

$$3 \cdot 3 + 8 + 3 - 12 \stackrel{?}{=} 13 - 5$$
$$9 + 8 + 3 - 12 \stackrel{?}{=} 13 - 5$$
$$8 = 8$$

Solve and check.

1. $8y - y = 35$
2. $9j + j = {}^{-}25$
3. $8n + 6 - 5 = 7$
4. $6c - 18 + 10 = {}^{-}14$
5. $10d + 2d + 4 = 0$
6. ${}^{-}3z - z + 15 = 27$
7. ${}^{-}15j + 19 - j = {}^{-}1$
8. $20m - 19 - 12m = 32$
9. $3r + 4r = {}^{-}6 + 19$
10. $19t - t = {}^{-}7 - 1$
11. $5w + 3w - 6 = 11 - 5$
12. $11s + s + 6 = {}^{-}18 + 6$

▲13. $12y - 3y - 9 = 21 - 3$

▲14. $5c - c + 6 = {}^{-}13 + 19$

■15. $3d - 5d - 11 = 13 - 20$

■16. $3 - 5d - 11d = 13 - 20$

●17. $8n + 2n + 16 = {}^{-}18 - 12$

●18. $8n + 2 + 16n = {}^{-}18 - 12$

19. ${}^{-}7t + 3t - 8 + 9 = 6 + 29$
20. ${}^{-}7t - 8t + 9 = 6 + 29$
21. $6m - 3 + 7 - m = {}^{-}3 + 18$
22. $6m - 3 + 7m - 1 = {}^{-}3 + 18$
23. $25 - 10 - w - w = 9 - 23$
24. $25 - 10w - w - 1 = 9 - 23$

Skill 73 (Use after page 250.)

Examples

$$\frac{5}{3} = \frac{?}{12}$$

To get an equal ratio, multiply both terms by the same number (not 0) or expression.

$$\frac{5}{3} = \frac{5 \cdot 4}{3 \cdot 4}$$
$$= \frac{20}{12}$$

$$\frac{3}{2x} = \frac{?}{4xy}$$
$$\frac{3}{2x} = \frac{3 \cdot 2y}{2x \cdot 2y}$$
$$= \frac{6y}{4xy}$$

Complete to get an equal ratio.

1. $\frac{2}{3} = \frac{?}{12}$ 2. $\frac{1}{5} = \frac{?}{15}$ 3. $\frac{3}{8} = \frac{?}{16}$ 4. $\frac{9}{2} = \frac{?}{20}$

5. $\frac{4}{5} = \frac{?}{25}$ 6. $\frac{7}{8} = \frac{?}{48}$ 7. $\frac{7}{4} = \frac{?}{36}$ 8. $\frac{5}{6} = \frac{?}{66}$

9. $\frac{4}{3} = \frac{?}{36}$ 10. $\frac{2}{5} = \frac{?}{45}$ 11. $\frac{4}{5} = \frac{?}{100}$ 12. $\frac{9}{4} = \frac{?}{80}$

13. $\frac{5}{12} = \frac{?}{72}$ 14. $\frac{7}{2} = \frac{?}{30}$ 15. $\frac{3}{10} = \frac{?}{80}$ 16. $\frac{5}{16} = \frac{?}{48}$

▲17. $\frac{5}{c} = \frac{?}{3c}$ ▲18. $\frac{3}{r} = \frac{?}{rs}$ ▲19. $\frac{n}{6} = \frac{?}{6m}$ ▲20. $\frac{11}{d} = \frac{?}{d^2}$

■21. $\frac{u}{v} = \frac{?}{2v^2}$ ■22. $\frac{a}{b} = \frac{?}{3b^2}$ ■23. $\frac{t^2}{v} = \frac{?}{3v^2}$ ■24. $\frac{4c}{3d} = \frac{?}{18cd}$

●25. $\frac{3y}{2z} = \frac{?}{10z^2}$ ●26. $\frac{5j}{12k} = \frac{?}{12jk}$ ●27. $\frac{4s^2t}{3s} = \frac{?}{18s}$ ●28. $\frac{11mn}{m^2n} = \frac{?}{m^2n^2}$

29. $\frac{5ab^2}{6ab} = \frac{?}{12a^2b}$ 30. $\frac{10}{3a} = \frac{?}{9a^2b}$ 31. $\frac{5c}{6d} = \frac{?}{24cd^2}$ 32. $\frac{9y^2z}{8} = \frac{?}{24z}$

Skill 74 (Use after page 252.)

Example

Solve.

$$\frac{n}{6} = \frac{5}{9}$$

Cross-multiply.

$$\frac{n}{6} \times \frac{5}{9}$$
$$9n = 6 \cdot 5$$
$$9n = 30$$
$$\frac{9n}{9} = \frac{30}{9}$$
$$n = 3\frac{1}{3}$$

Solve each proportion.

1. $\frac{n}{6} = \frac{11}{4}$ 2. $\frac{8}{n} = \frac{2}{9}$ 3. $\frac{9}{8} = \frac{n}{7}$ 4. $\frac{10}{7} = \frac{4}{n}$

5. $\frac{5}{n} = \frac{2}{9}$ 6. $\frac{n}{13} = \frac{6}{5}$ 7. $\frac{7}{4} = \frac{n}{6}$ 8. $\frac{5}{8} = \frac{3}{n}$

9. $\frac{3}{7} = \frac{9}{n}$ 10. $\frac{18}{n} = \frac{6}{5}$ 11. $\frac{n}{21} = \frac{6}{7}$ 12. $\frac{n}{6} = \frac{15}{8}$

13. $\frac{9}{n} = \frac{3}{13}$ 14. $\frac{18}{n} = \frac{9}{16}$ 15. $\frac{6}{11} = \frac{24}{n}$ 16. $\frac{5}{7} = \frac{9}{n}$

▲17. $\frac{n}{7} = \frac{11}{4}$ ▲18. $\frac{6}{n} = \frac{8}{3}$ ▲19. $\frac{19}{2} = \frac{n}{5}$ ▲20. $\frac{10}{13} = \frac{16}{n}$

■21. $\frac{9}{n} = \frac{2}{15}$ ■22. $\frac{n}{9} = \frac{4}{3}$ ■23. $\frac{6}{15} = \frac{30}{n}$ ■24. $\frac{11}{4} = \frac{n}{8}$

●25. $\frac{n}{4} = \frac{6}{8}$ ●26. $\frac{1}{n} = \frac{7}{21}$ ●27. $\frac{6}{9} = \frac{n}{3}$ ●28. $\frac{6}{10} = \frac{18}{n}$

29. $\frac{1\frac{1}{2}}{15} = \frac{3}{n}$ 30. $\frac{10}{3} = \frac{n}{2\frac{1}{4}}$ 31. $\frac{7}{n} = \frac{2\frac{2}{3}}{9}$ 32. $\frac{n}{8} = \frac{1\frac{3}{4}}{4}$

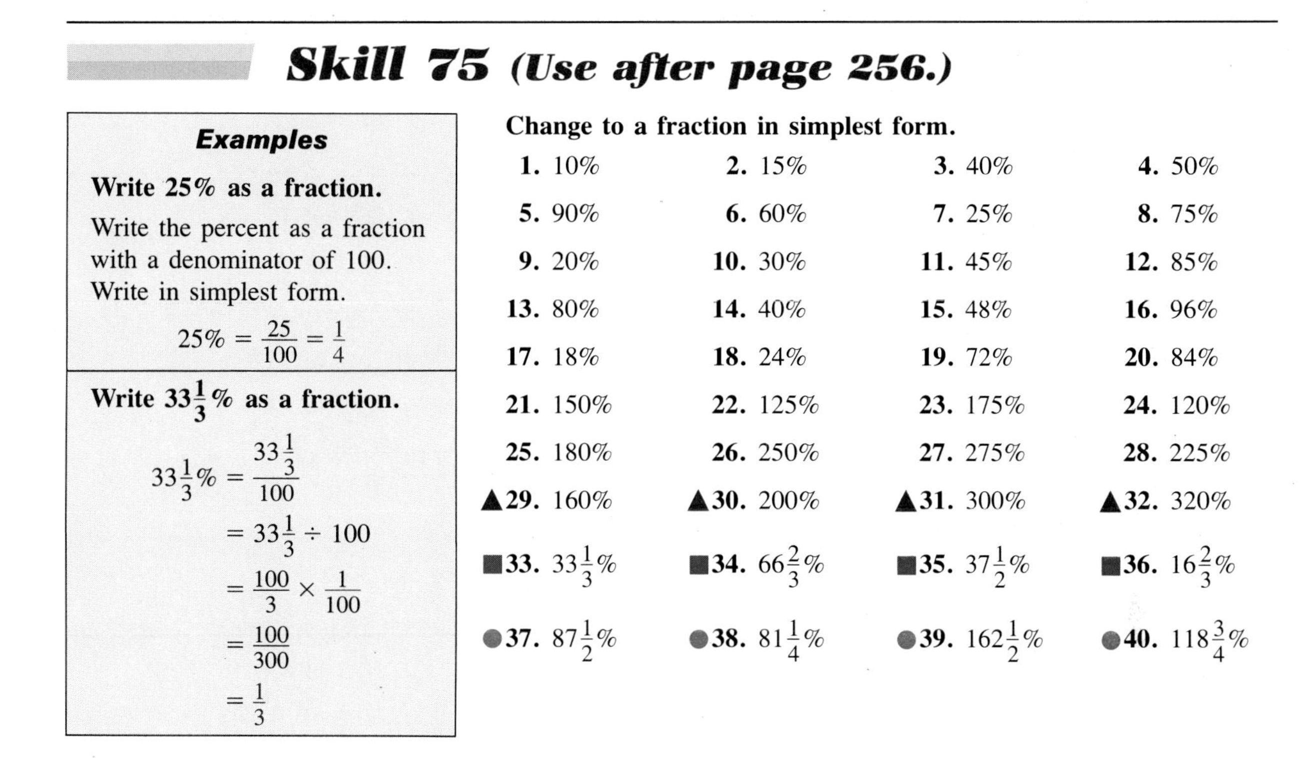

Skill 75 (Use after page 256.)

Examples

Write 25% as a fraction.

Write the percent as a fraction with a denominator of 100. Write in simplest form.

$25\% = \frac{25}{100} = \frac{1}{4}$

Write $33\frac{1}{3}\%$ as a fraction.

$$33\frac{1}{3}\% = \frac{33\frac{1}{3}}{100}$$
$$= 33\frac{1}{3} \div 100$$
$$= \frac{100}{3} \times \frac{1}{100}$$
$$= \frac{100}{300}$$
$$= \frac{1}{3}$$

Change to a fraction in simplest form.

1. 10%	**2.** 15%	**3.** 40%	**4.** 50%
5. 90%	**6.** 60%	**7.** 25%	**8.** 75%
9. 20%	**10.** 30%	**11.** 45%	**12.** 85%
13. 80%	**14.** 40%	**15.** 48%	**16.** 96%
17. 18%	**18.** 24%	**19.** 72%	**20.** 84%
21. 150%	**22.** 125%	**23.** 175%	**24.** 120%
25. 180%	**26.** 250%	**27.** 275%	**28.** 225%
▲**29.** 160%	▲**30.** 200%	▲**31.** 300%	▲**32.** 320%
■**33.** $33\frac{1}{3}\%$	■**34.** $66\frac{2}{3}\%$	■**35.** $37\frac{1}{2}\%$	■**36.** $16\frac{2}{3}\%$
●**37.** $87\frac{1}{2}\%$	●**38.** $81\frac{1}{4}\%$	●**39.** $162\frac{1}{2}\%$	●**40.** $118\frac{3}{4}\%$

Skill 76 (Use after page 258.)

Examples

Write $\frac{1}{2}$ as a percent.

Change to an equivalent fraction with a denominator of 100. Write as a percent.

$\frac{1}{2} = \frac{50}{100} = 50\%$

Write $\frac{1}{6}$ as a percent.

If necessary, solve a proportion.

$$\frac{1}{6} = \frac{n}{100}$$
$$6n = 100$$
$$n = 16\frac{2}{3}$$

So $\frac{1}{6} = \frac{16\frac{2}{3}}{100} = 16\frac{2}{3}\%$

Change to a percent.

1. $\frac{1}{5}$	**2.** $\frac{1}{4}$	**3.** $\frac{1}{2}$	**4.** $\frac{4}{5}$
5. $\frac{3}{4}$	**6.** $\frac{1}{3}$	**7.** $\frac{2}{5}$	**8.** $\frac{2}{3}$
9. $\frac{1}{8}$	**10.** $\frac{3}{5}$	**11.** $\frac{3}{8}$	**12.** $\frac{3}{2}$
13. $\frac{6}{5}$	**14.** $\frac{1}{6}$	**15.** $\frac{5}{4}$	**16.** $\frac{7}{5}$
17. $\frac{1}{10}$	**18.** $\frac{8}{5}$	**19.** $\frac{3}{10}$	**20.** $\frac{1}{12}$
▲**21.** $\frac{5}{2}$	▲**22.** 3	▲**23.** $\frac{7}{4}$	▲**24.** $\frac{1}{20}$
■**25.** $\frac{5}{8}$	■**26.** $\frac{7}{10}$	■**27.** $\frac{11}{8}$	■**28.** $\frac{7}{3}$
●**29.** $\frac{5}{12}$	●**30.** $\frac{5}{3}$	●**31.** 2	●**32.** $\frac{7}{12}$

Skill 77 (Use after page 262.)

Examples

75% of 36 = n

75% of $36 = \frac{3}{4} \times 36$
$= 27$

6.5% of 9 = n

6.5% of $9 = 0.065 \times 9$
$= 0.585$

Solve.

1. 50% of 28 = n
2. 25% of 24 = n
3. 40% of 60 = n
4. 20% of 45 = n
5. 80% of 40 = n
6. 10% of 50 = n
7. 125% of 40 = n
8. 250% of 72 = n
9. ▲ 14% of 26 = n
10. ▲ 23% of 75 = n
11. ■ 56% of 29 = n
12. ■ 41% of 83 = n
13. ● 5.4% of 60 = n
14. ● 6.5% of 47 = n

Skill 78 (Use after page 264.)

Examples

60% of n = 50

First change the percent to a fraction. Then solve the equation.

$$\frac{3}{5}n = 50$$

$$\frac{\frac{3}{5}n}{\frac{3}{5}} = \frac{50}{\frac{3}{5}}$$

$$n = 50 \cdot \frac{5}{3}$$

$$= \frac{250}{3}$$

$$= 83\frac{1}{3}$$

6.5% of n = 10

First change the percent to a decimal. Then solve the equation.

$$0.065n = 10$$

$$\frac{0.065n}{0.065} = \frac{10}{0.065}$$

$$n \approx 153.8$$

Solve.

1. 25% of n = 14
2. 50% of n = 19
3. 75% of n = 33
4. 60% of n = 48
5. ▲ 80% of n = 64
6. ▲ 40% of n = 46
7. ■ 10% of n = 16
8. ■ 5% of n = 120
9. ● 30% of n = 57
10. ● 20% of n = 65
11. 45% of n = 27
12. 90% of n = 216
13. 8% of n = 6
14. 1% of n = 3

Solve. Round each answer to the nearest tenth.

15. 8.5% of n = 6
16. 7.5% of n = 11
17. ▲ 20.5% of n = 16.2
18. ▲ 14.2% of n = 37
19. ■ 34.6% of n = 18.5
20. ■ 42.8% of n = 10.3
21. ● 1.8% of n = 2.4
22. ● 4.7% of n = 2.9
23. 125% of n = 17.6
24. 250% of n = 31.3
25. 45% of n = 70.8
26. 90% of n = 145
27. 9% of n = 35
28. 3% of n = 64.7

Skill 79 (Use after page 266.)

Examples

$n\%$ of 60 = 45

$$\text{part} \rightarrow \frac{n}{100} = \frac{45}{60} \leftarrow \text{part}, \quad \text{whole} \rightarrow 100,\ 60 \leftarrow \text{whole}$$

$$60n = 4500$$
$$n = 75$$

$33\frac{1}{3}\%$ of 36 = n

$$\text{part} \rightarrow \frac{33\frac{1}{3}}{100} = \frac{n}{36} \leftarrow \text{part}, \quad \text{whole} \rightarrow 100,\ 36 \leftarrow \text{whole}$$

$$100n = 33\tfrac{1}{3} \cdot 36$$
$$100n = 1200$$
$$n = 12$$

$12\frac{1}{2}\%$ of n = 20

$$\text{part} \rightarrow \frac{12\frac{1}{2}}{100} = \frac{20}{n} \leftarrow \text{part}, \quad \text{whole} \rightarrow 100,\ n \leftarrow \text{whole}$$

$$12\tfrac{1}{2}n = 2000$$
$$\frac{12\frac{1}{2}n}{12\frac{1}{2}} = \frac{2000}{12\frac{1}{2}}$$
$$n = 160$$

Solve.

1. $n\%$ of 8 = 2
2. $n\%$ of 20 = 15
3. $n\%$ of 16 = 6
4. $n\%$ of 24 = 15
5. $n\%$ of 30 = 10
6. $n\%$ of 30 = 5
7. $n\%$ of 40 = 60
8. $n\%$ of 60 = 40
9. $n\%$ of 80 = 48
10. $n\%$ of 160 = 72
11. 20% of 95 = n
12. 75% of 92 = n
13. ▲ $87\frac{1}{2}\%$ of 48 = n
14. ▲ $66\frac{2}{3}\%$ of 96 = n
15. ■ $33\frac{1}{3}\%$ of 72 = n
16. ■ $8\frac{1}{3}\%$ of 60 = n
17. ● $2\frac{1}{2}\%$ of 50 = n
18. ● $112\frac{1}{2}\%$ of 50 = n
19. 20% of n = 16
20. 25% of n = 18
21. 1% of n = 3.82
22. 4% of n = 2.5
23. $16\frac{2}{3}\%$ of n = 23
24. $37\frac{1}{2}\%$ of n = 21
25. $133\frac{1}{3}\%$ of n = 64
26. 250% of n = 36
27. $66\frac{2}{3}\%$ of n = 54
28. $58\frac{1}{3}\%$ of n = 42

Skill 80 (Use after page 268.)

Examples

Find the percent of increase from 40 to 50.

$$\frac{10}{40} = \frac{x}{100}$$

increase → 10; *number before increase* → 40

$$40x = 1000$$

Increase of 25%

Find the percent of decrease from 50 to 40.

$$\frac{10}{50} = \frac{x}{100}$$

decrease → 10; *number before decrease* → 50

$$50x = 1000$$
$$x = 20$$

Decrease of 20%

Find the percent of increase or decrease.
Use i to indicate increase and d to indicate decrease.
Give answers to the nearest tenth of a percent.

1. From 10 to 20
2. From 20 to 10
3. From 16 to 20
4. From 20 to 16
5. From 36 to 48
6. From 48 to 36
7. From 60 to 72
8. From 72 to 60
9. ▲ From 75 to 100
10. ▲ From 100 to 75
11. ■ From 120 to 150
12. ■ From 150 to 120
13. ● From 160 to 200
14. ● From 200 to 160

Table of Square Roots of Integers from 1 to 320

Number	Positive Square Root	Number	Positive Square Root	Number	Positive Square Root	Number	Positive Square Root
N	$\sqrt{N}$	N	$\sqrt{N}$	N	$\sqrt{N}$	N	$\sqrt{N}$
1	1	**41**	6.403	**81**	9	**121**	11
2	1.414	**42**	6.481	**82**	9.055	**122**	11.045
3	1.732	**43**	6.557	**83**	9.110	**123**	11.091
4	2	**44**	6.633	**84**	9.165	**124**	11.136
5	2.236	**45**	6.708	**85**	9.220	**125**	11.180
6	2.449	**46**	6.782	**86**	9.274	**126**	11.225
7	2.646	**47**	6.856	**87**	9.327	**127**	11.269
8	2.828	**48**	6.928	**88**	9.381	**128**	11.314
9	3	**49**	7	**89**	9.434	**129**	11.358
10	3.162	**50**	7.071	**90**	9.487	**130**	11.402
11	3.317	**51**	7.141	**91**	9.539	**131**	11.446
12	3.464	**52**	7.211	**92**	9.592	**132**	11.489
13	3.606	**53**	7.280	**93**	9.644	**133**	11.533
14	3.742	**54**	7.348	**94**	9.695	**134**	11.576
15	3.873	**55**	7.416	**95**	9.747	**135**	11.619
16	4	**56**	7.483	**96**	9.798	**136**	11.662
17	4.123	**57**	7.550	**97**	9.849	**137**	11.705
18	4.243	**58**	7.616	**98**	9.899	**138**	11.747
19	4.359	**59**	7.681	**99**	9.950	**139**	11.790
20	4.472	**60**	7.746	**100**	10	**140**	11.832
21	4.583	**61**	7.810	**101**	10.050	**141**	11.874
22	4.690	**62**	7.874	**102**	10.100	**142**	11.916
23	4.796	**63**	7.937	**103**	10.149	**143**	11.958
24	4.899	**64**	8	**104**	10.198	**144**	12
25	5	**65**	8.062	**105**	10.247	**145**	12.042
26	5.099	**66**	8.124	**106**	10.296	**146**	12.083
27	5.196	**67**	8.185	**107**	10.344	**147**	12.124
28	5.292	**68**	8.246	**108**	10.392	**148**	12.166
29	5.385	**69**	8.307	**109**	10.440	**149**	12.207
30	5.477	**70**	8.367	**110**	10.488	**150**	12.247
31	5.568	**71**	8.426	**111**	10.536	**151**	12.288
32	5.657	**72**	8.485	**112**	10.583	**152**	12.329
33	5.745	**73**	8.544	**113**	10.630	**153**	12.369
34	5.831	**74**	8.602	**114**	10.677	**154**	12.410
35	5.916	**75**	8.660	**115**	10.724	**155**	12.450
36	6	**76**	8.718	**116**	10.770	**156**	12.490
37	6.083	**77**	8.775	**117**	10.817	**157**	12.530
38	6.164	**78**	8.832	**118**	10.863	**158**	12.570
39	6.245	**79**	8.888	**119**	10.909	**159**	12.610
40	6.325	**80**	8.944	**120**	10.954	**160**	12.649

Exact square roots are shown in red. For the others, rational approximations are given correct to three decimal places.

Number	Positive Square Root	Number	Positive Square Root	Number	Positive Square Root	Number	Positive Square Root
N	$\sqrt{N}$	N	$\sqrt{N}$	N	$\sqrt{N}$	N	$\sqrt{N}$
161	12.689	**201**	14.177	**241**	15.524	**281**	16.763
162	12.728	**202**	14.213	**242**	15.556	**282**	16.793
163	12.767	**203**	14.248	**243**	15.588	**283**	16.823
164	12.806	**204**	14.283	**244**	15.620	**284**	16.852
165	12.845	**205**	14.318	**245**	15.652	**285**	16.882
166	12.884	**206**	14.353	**246**	15.684	**286**	16.912
167	12.923	**207**	14.387	**247**	15.716	**287**	16.941
168	12.961	**208**	14.422	**248**	15.748	**288**	16.971
169	13	**209**	14.457	**249**	15.780	**289**	17
170	13.038	**210**	14.491	**250**	15.811	**290**	17.029
171	13.077	**211**	14.526	**251**	15.843	**291**	17.059
172	13.115	**212**	14.560	**252**	15.875	**292**	17.088
173	13.153	**213**	14.595	**253**	15.906	**293**	17.117
174	13.191	**214**	14.629	**254**	15.937	**294**	17.146
175	13.229	**215**	14.663	**255**	15.969	**295**	17.176
176	13.266	**216**	14.697	**256**	16	**296**	17.205
177	13.304	**217**	14.731	**257**	16.031	**297**	17.234
178	13.342	**218**	14.765	**258**	16.062	**298**	17.263
179	13.379	**219**	14.799	**259**	16.093	**299**	17.292
180	13.416	**220**	14.832	**260**	16.125	**300**	17.321
181	13.454	**221**	14.866	**261**	16.155	**301**	17.349
182	13.491	**222**	14.900	**262**	16.186	**302**	17.378
183	13.528	**223**	14.933	**263**	16.217	**303**	17.407
184	13.565	**224**	14.967	**264**	16.248	**304**	17.436
185	13.601	**225**	15	**265**	16.279	**305**	17.464
186	13.638	**226**	15.033	**266**	16.310	**306**	17.493
187	13.675	**227**	15.067	**267**	16.340	**307**	17.521
188	13.711	**228**	15.100	**268**	16.371	**308**	17.550
189	13.748	**229**	15.133	**269**	16.401	**309**	17.578
190	13.784	**230**	15.166	**270**	16.432	**310**	17.607
191	13.820	**231**	15.199	**271**	16.462	**311**	17.635
192	13.856	**232**	15.232	**272**	16.492	**312**	17.664
193	13.892	**233**	15.264	**273**	16.523	**313**	17.692
194	13.928	**234**	15.297	**274**	16.553	**314**	17.720
195	13.964	**235**	15.330	**275**	16.583	**315**	17.748
196	14	**236**	15.362	**276**	16.613	**316**	17.776
197	14.036	**237**	15.395	**277**	16.643	**317**	17.804
198	14.071	**238**	15.427	**278**	16.673	**318**	17.833
199	14.107	**239**	15.460	**279**	16.703	**319**	17.861
200	14.142	**240**	15.492	**280**	16.733	**320**	17.889

Table of Trigonometric Ratios

Angle	Sine	Cosine	Tangent	Angle	Sine	Cosine	Tangent
1°	0.0175	0.9998	0.0175	**46°**	0.7193	0.6947	1.0355
2°	0.0349	0.9994	0.0349	**47°**	0.7314	0.6820	1.0724
3°	0.0523	0.9986	0.0524	**48°**	0.7431	0.6691	1.1106
4°	0.0698	0.9976	0.0699	**49°**	0.7547	0.6561	1.1504
5°	0.0872	0.9962	0.0875	**50°**	0.7660	0.6428	1.1918
6°	0.1045	0.9945	0.1051	**51°**	0.7771	0.6293	1.2349
7°	0.1219	0.9925	0.1228	**52°**	0.7880	0.6157	1.2799
8°	0.1392	0.9903	0.1405	**53°**	0.7986	0.6018	1.3270
9°	0.1564	0.9877	0.1584	**54°**	0.8090	0.5878	1.3764
10°	0.1736	0.9848	0.1763	**55°**	0.8192	0.5736	1.4281
11°	0.1908	0.9816	0.1944	**56°**	0.8290	0.5592	1.4826
12°	0.2079	0.9781	0.2126	**57°**	0.8387	0.5446	1.5399
13°	0.2250	0.9744	0.2309	**58°**	0.8480	0.5299	1.6003
14°	0.2419	0.9703	0.2493	**59°**	0.8572	0.5150	1.6643
15°	0.2588	0.9659	0.2679	**60°**	0.8660	0.5000	1.7321
16°	0.2756	0.9613	0.2867	**61°**	0.8746	0.4848	1.8040
17°	0.2924	0.9563	0.3057	**62°**	0.8829	0.4695	1.8807
18°	0.3090	0.9511	0.3249	**63°**	0.8910	0.4540	1.9626
19°	0.3256	0.9455	0.3443	**64°**	0.8988	0.4384	2.0503
20°	0.3420	0.9397	0.3640	**65°**	0.9063	0.4226	2.1445
21°	0.3584	0.9336	0.3839	**66°**	0.9135	0.4067	2.2460
22°	0.3746	0.9272	0.4040	**67°**	0.9205	0.3907	2.3559
23°	0.3907	0.9205	0.4245	**68°**	0.9272	0.3746	2.4751
24°	0.4067	0.9135	0.4452	**69°**	0.9336	0.3584	2.6051
25°	0.4226	0.9063	0.4663	**70°**	0.9397	0.3420	2.7475
26°	0.4384	0.8988	0.4877	**71°**	0.9455	0.3256	2.9042
27°	0.4540	0.8910	0.5095	**72°**	0.9511	0.3090	3.0777
28°	0.4695	0.8829	0.5317	**73°**	0.9563	0.2924	3.2709
29°	0.4848	0.8746	0.5543	**74°**	0.9613	0.2756	3.4874
30°	0.5000	0.8660	0.5774	**75°**	0.9659	0.2588	3.7321
31°	0.5150	0.8572	0.6009	**76°**	0.9703	0.2419	4.0108
32°	0.5299	0.8480	0.6249	**77°**	0.9744	0.2250	4.3315
33°	0.5446	0.8387	0.6494	**78°**	0.9781	0.2079	4.7046
34°	0.5592	0.8290	0.6745	**79°**	0.9816	0.1908	5.1446
35°	0.5736	0.8192	0.7002	**80°**	0.9848	0.1736	5.6713
36°	0.5878	0.8090	0.7265	**81°**	0.9877	0.1564	6.3138
37°	0.6018	0.7986	0.7536	**82°**	0.9903	0.1392	7.1154
38°	0.6157	0.7880	0.7813	**83°**	0.9925	0.1219	8.1443
39°	0.6293	0.7771	0.8098	**84°**	0.9945	0.1045	9.5144
40°	0.6428	0.7660	0.8391	**85°**	0.9962	0.0872	11.4301
41°	0.6561	0.7547	0.8693	**86°**	0.9976	0.0698	14.3007
42°	0.6691	0.7431	0.9004	**87°**	0.9986	0.0523	19.0811
43°	0.6820	0.7314	0.9325	**88°**	0.9994	0.0349	28.6363
44°	0.6947	0.7193	0.9657	**89°**	0.9998	0.0175	57.2900
45°	0.7071	0.7071	1.0000	**90°**	1.0000	0.0000	.....

Glossary

acute angle (p. 278) An angle that measures between 0° and 90°.

acute triangle (p. 405) A triangle with three acute angles.

adding 0 property (p. 94) The sum of any number and 0 is the number. $a + 0 = a$

algebraic factorization (p. 124) An algebraic expression written as the product of its factors.

angle (p. 278) A figure formed by two rays with the same endpoint.

area (p. 294) The number of unit squares that it takes to cover a region.

associative property of addition (p. 94) Changing the grouping of the addends does not change the sum.
$(a + b) + c = a + (b + c)$

associative property of multiplication (p. 96) Changing the grouping of the factors does not change the product. $(ab)c = a(bc)$

average (p. 380) The sum of the numbers divided by the number of numbers.

axes (p. 344) Two perpendicular lines used as a reference for graphing ordered pairs.

base (of an exponent) (p. 120) The number that is raised to a power.

base $\rightarrow 2^3 \leftarrow$ *power*

BASIC (p. 422) A commonly used computer language. The complete name is *B*eginner's *A*ll-purpose *S*ymbolic *I*nstruction *C*ode.

basic counting principle (p. 362) If a first event has m outcomes and a second event has n outcomes, then the first event followed by the second event has $m \times n$ outcomes.

canceling (p. 172) Dividing both the numerator and the denominator by a common factor before multiplying fractions.

centimeter (p. 284) A metric unit of length.
1 centimeter = 0.01 meter

circle (p. 290) A curved plane figure with all points a given distance from the center.

circumference (p. 290) The distance around a circle.

common factor (p. 126) 2 is a common factor of 4 and 6, because 2 is a factor of both 4 and 6.

common multiple (p. 126) 30 is a common multiple of 5 and 6 because it is a multiple of both 5 and 6.

commutative property of addition (p. 94) Changing the order of the addends does not change the sum. $a + b = b + a$

commutative property of multiplication (p. 96) Changing the order of the factors does not change the product. $ab = ba$

composite number (p. 124) A whole number other than 0 that has more than two factors.

computer language (p. 422) A set of symbols and terms used to tell a computer what to do.

computer program (p. 422) A list of instructions to a computer telling it what to do and when to do it.

cone (p. 310) A space figure with one flat face (known as the base) that is a circle and with one other face that is curved.

congruent angles (p. 396) Angles having the same measure.

coordinates (p. 344) An ordered pair of numbers that locates a point on a grid.

cosine of an angle (p. 402) In a right triangle, the ratio of the length of the leg adjacent to an acute angle to the length of the hypotenuse.

cross products (p. 252) The cross products for the ratios below are 2×10 and 5×4. Two ratios are equal if their cross products are equal.

$$\frac{2}{5} = \frac{4}{10} \text{ because } 2 \times 10 = 5 \times 4$$

cube (p. 310) A rectangular prism whose six faces are squares.

cylinder (p. 310) A space figure that has two circular bases that are the same size and are in parallel planes. It has one curved face.

data (p. 380) Pieces of information.

decimal (p. 58) A number such as 3.86 or 0.4 that is written with a decimal point and has place value.

denominator (p. 130) In the fraction $\frac{2}{3}$, the denominator is 3.

dependent events (p. 372) Two events such that the outcome of the first affects the outcome of the second—for instance, drawing a first and a second card without replacing the first card.

diameter (p. 290) The distance across a circle through its center. The length of the diameter is twice the length of the radius.

difference (p. 12) The answer to a subtraction problem.

digits (p. 6) The basic symbols used to write numerals. In our system, the digits are 0, 1, 2, 3, 4, 5, 6, 7, 8, and 9.

distributive property of multiplication (p. 106) A product can be written as the sum of two products. $a(b + c) = ab + ac$

divisible (p. 122) One number is divisible by another number if there is no remainder after division. 84 is divisible by 2, since $84 \div 2$ leaves no remainder.

equation (p. 14) A sentence with an equal sign such as $3 \times 9 = 27$ or $8 + x = 10$.

equivalent fractions (p. 130) Fractions that name the same number. $\frac{1}{2}$, $\frac{2}{4}$, $\frac{3}{6}$ are equivalent fractions.

estimate (p. 10) To use rounded numbers to check whether an answer is correct. To estimate 47 + 32, you would add 50 + 30. The sum should be about 80.

evaluate an expression (p. 4) To replace a variable in an expression with one of its values and then complete the indicated arithmetic.

even number (p. 122) A whole number that is divisible by 2.

event (p. 366) A set of one or more outcomes.

expectation (p. 378) The probability of winning times the value of the prize.

exponent (p. 120) An exponent tells how many times a number is used as a factor.

exponent (points to the 3 in 2^3)

$$2^3 = \underbrace{2 \times 2 \times 2}_{3\ factors}$$

expression (p. 2) An expression represents a number. $n + 3$ and $5n - 2$ are expressions.

factors (p. 34) Numbers used in a multiplication problem.

$$\begin{array}{rl} 8 & \leftarrow \textit{factor} \\ \times 6 & \leftarrow \textit{factor} \\ \hline 48 & \leftarrow \textit{product} \end{array}$$

flowchart (p. 438) A general plan written before writing a program that gives step-by-step directions.

formula (p. 19) A general way of expressing a relationship using variables.

fraction (p. 146) A numeral for part of a group or for part of a region.

frequency table (p. 384) A table showing the number of times different events or responses occur.

gram (p. 324) A metric unit of weight (mass). 1 gram = 0.001 kilogram

greatest common factor (GCF) (p. 126) The greatest number that is a factor of each of two or more numbers. 4 is the GCF of 8 and 12.

hexagon (p. 282) A polygon with six sides.

hypotenuse (p. 402) The side of a right triangle that is opposite the right angle. It is the longest side of a right triangle.

independent events (p. 370) Events such that the outcome of the first does not affect the outcome of the second—for example, tossing *heads* and rolling a *1*.

inequality (p. 336) A mathematical sentence that contains a symbol such as $\neq$, $<$, $>$, $\geq$, or $\leq$.

$$3 + 6 < 11; \; 2r + 5 \geq 6$$

integers (p. 196) The numbers . . . $^-5$, $^-4$, $^-3$, $^-2$, $^-1$, 0, $^+1$, $^+2$, $^+3$, $^+4$, $^+5$, . . .

inverse operations (p. 14) Operations that undo each other. Addition and subtraction are inverse operations. Multiplication and division are inverse operations.

kilogram (p. 324) A metric unit of weight. 1 kilogram = 1000 grams

kilometer (p. 284) A metric unit of length. 1 kilometer = 1000 meters

least common denominator (p. 134) The least common denominator of two fractions is the least common multiple of the denominators.

least common multiple (p. 126) The least (smallest) common multiple of two or more numbers. The least common multiple of 6 and 15 is 30.

leg of a right triangle (p. 400) Either of the two shorter sides of a right triangle.

like terms (p. 108) Expressions that contain the same variables, such as $2ay$ and $5ay$; and expressions that contain no variables, such as 6 and $^-3$.

linear equation (p. 348) An equation for which the graph is a straight line.

linear inequality (p. 350) An inequality for which the graph is a region above or below a straight line.

liter (p. 324) A metric unit of liquid volume.

lowest terms (p. 132) A fraction is in lowest terms if the greatest common factor of the numerator and denominator is 1.

mean (p. 380) The average of all the numbers.

median (p. 382) If an odd number of numbers are ranked from least to greatest, the median is the middle number. For an even number of numbers, the median is the average of the two middle numbers.

meter (p. 284) A metric unit of length. 1 meter = 100 centimeters

metric system (p. 284) An international system of measurement that uses meter, liter, gram, and Celsius temperature.

milliliter (p. 324) A metric unit of liquid volume. 1 milliliter = 0.001 liter

millimeter (p. 284) A metric unit of length. 1 millimeter = 0.001 meter

mixed number (p. 146) A number that has a whole-number part and a fraction part. $2\frac{3}{4}$ is a mixed number.

mode (p. 382) The number that occurs most often.

multiple (p. 32) The product. 4, 8, 12, 16, 20, and so on, are multiples of 4.

multiplying by 1 property (p. 96) The product of any number and 1 is the number.
$x \times 1 = x$

negative number (p. 196) A number that is less than 0.

numerator (p. 130) In the fraction $\frac{2}{3}$, the numerator is 2.

obtuse angle (p. 278) An angle that measures between 90° and 180°.

obtuse triangle (p. 405) A triangle with an obtuse angle.

odd number (p. 122) A whole number that is not divisible by 2. The numbers 1, 3, 5, 7, 9, 11, and so on, are odd.

odds (p. 376) The ratio of the number of ways that an outcome can occur to the number of ways that the outcome cannot occur.

operation (p. 92) Addition, subtraction, multiplication, and division are examples of operations.

opposites (p. 198) Two numbers are opposites if their sum is 0.

$$^{-}3 + {}^{+}3 = 0$$
↑ ↑
opposites

ordered pair (p. 344) A pair of numbers that gives the location of a point on a grid.

origin (p. 344) The point where axes intersect.

outcome (p. 366) A possible result.

parallel lines (p. 280) Lines in a plane that do not intersect.

parallelogram (p. 282) A polygon with four sides and two pairs of parallel sides.

pentagon (p. 282) A polygon with five sides.

percent (%) (p. 256) *Percent* means "per hundred." 5% (5 percent) equals $\frac{5}{100}$.

perimeter (p. 288) The distance around a figure; the sum of the lengths of the sides.

permutation (p. 364) An ordered arrangement of a set of objects.

perpendicular lines (p. 280) Two lines that intersect to form right angles.

pi (p. 290) The number that is the ratio of the circumference of a circle to its diameter. It is represented by the Greek letter π and is approximately equal to 3.14.

plane (p. 280) A flat surface that extends endlessly in all directions.

polygon (p. 282) A closed plane figure made up of segments.

positive number (p. 196) A number greater than 0.

power (p. 120) An exponent. The number that tells how many times a number is used as a factor.

$2^3 \leftarrow$ *power*

prime factorization (p. 124) Expression of a composite number as a product of prime numbers. The prime factorization of 18 is $2 \cdot 3 \cdot 3$.

prime number (p. 124) A whole number that has exactly two factors. 2, 3, 5, 7, 11, 13, and so on, are prime numbers.

prism (p. 310) A space figure that has two bases that are the same size and shape and are in parallel planes. The other faces are all rectangles.

probability (p. 366) The ratio of the number of favorable outcomes to the total number of outcomes.

product (p. 34) The answer to a multiplication problem.

proportion (p. 252) An equation stating that two ratios are equal. $\frac{5}{8} = \frac{30}{48}$

protractor (p. 278) An instrument used to measure angles.

pyramid (p. 310) A solid figure with a face (known as the base) that is any polygon and with all other faces (which are triangles) sharing a common vertex.

Pythagorean theorem (p. 412) In a right triangle, the sum of the squares of the lengths of the two legs (*a* and *b*) is equal to the square of the length of the hypotenuse (*c*); $a^2 + b^2 = c^2$.

quotient (p. 40) The answer to a division problem.

radius (p. 290) The distance from the center of a circle to the circle. The radius is equal to one half the diameter.

range (p. 382) The difference between the least and greatest numbers.

rate (p. 254) A comparison by division of two quantities. $\frac{\text{87 kilometers}}{\text{2 hours}}$

ratio (p. 250) A comparison of two numbers by division.

rational number (p. 224) A number that can be written as the quotient of two integers (denominator not 0).

reciprocal (p. 176) Two numbers are reciprocals when their product is 1.

$$\frac{3}{4} \times \frac{4}{3} = 1$$

↑ ↑
reciprocals

rectangle (p. 282) A polygon with four sides and four right angles.

rectangular prism (p. 310) A prism whose bases are rectangles.

remainder (p. 42) In a division problem, the number that is "left over." When it is added to the product of the divisor and quotient, the sum is the dividend.

$$\begin{array}{r} 3 \\ 8\overline{)29} \\ -24 \\ \hline 5 \end{array} \leftarrow \textit{remainder}$$

repeating decimal (p. 226) A decimal in which a digit or a group of digits repeats forever.

0.3333 . . .   1.47474747 . . .

right angle (p. 278) An angle whose measure is 90°.

right triangle (p. 398) A triangle with a right angle.

round a number (p. 6) To replace a number by another one that is easier to use. You round a number to the nearest ten by choosing the nearest multiple of 10. (5 is rounded up.)

$13 \rightarrow 10$ $27 \rightarrow 30$
$45 \rightarrow 50$

You round a number to the nearest hundred by choosing the nearest multiple of 100.

$487 \rightarrow 500$ $1238 \rightarrow 1200$
$550 \rightarrow 600$

sample (p. 386) A small group, chosen from a larger group, that is examined carefully in order to make predictions about the larger group.

sample space (p. 368) The set of all possible outcomes of an event.

scale drawing (p. 261) A drawing of an object such that the ratio of a unit of length on the drawing to a unit of length on the object is fixed.

scientific notation (p. 208) A notation for writing a number as the product of a number between 1 and 10 and a power of 10.

$$186.3 = 1.863 \cdot 10^2$$

side of an angle (p. 278) One of the rays that make up an angle.

side of a plane figure (p. 282) One of the segments that make up a figure.

similar figures (p. 396) Two figures that have the same shape.

simplest form (p. 150) A fraction or mixed number is in simplest form if the fraction or fraction-part of the mixed number is less than 1 and in lowest terms.

sine of an angle (p. 402) In a right triangle, the ratio of the length of the leg opposite an acute angle to the length of the hypotenuse.

solve (p. 14) To find all the numbers that make an equation true.

sphere (p. 310) A round space figure shaped like a basketball. All points on a sphere are the same distance from the center.

square (p. 282) A polygon with 4 sides the same length and 4 right angles.

square root (p. 410) The number that can be squared to get a given number.

$$\sqrt{49} = 7$$

statistics (p. 380) A branch of mathematics that studies numerical facts as a basis for drawing general conclusions and making predictions.

substitute (p. 14) To replace a variable with a numeral.

$$7a + 3$$
$$7 \cdot 6 + 3$$

sum (p. 10) The answer to an addition problem.

surface area (p. 314) The sum of the areas of all the surfaces of a solid figure.

symmetric property of equality (p. 18) Exchanging the left and right sides of an equation does not affect the solution.
If $76 = x + 53$, then $x + 53 = 76$.

system of equations (p. 352) Two or more equations with the same variables.

tangent of an angle (p. 400) In a right triangle, the ratio of the length of the leg opposite an acute angle to the length of the leg adjacent to the acute angle.

term (p. 108) An expression using numerals or variables or both to indicate a product or quotient.

terminating decimal (p. 226) A decimal fraction, such as 0.5 or 1.47, that is not a repeating decimal.

trapezoid (p. 282) A polygon with 4 sides and exactly 1 pair of parallel sides.

tree diagram (p. 362) A diagram that shows all the possible outcomes of an event.

triangular prism (p. 310) A prism whose bases are triangles.

variable (p. 2) A symbol—usually a letter—that holds the place for a number.
$8x + 19 = 23$

vertex (p. 278) The point at the ''corner'' of an angle, plane figure, or solid figure.

volume (p. 318) The amount that a space figure holds.

whole number (p. 146) Any of the numbers 0, 1, 2, 3, 4, and so on.

Index

Selected Answers

Chapter 1 Addition and Subtraction Equations

Pages 2–3
1. Belafonte's **2.** Starr's **3.** Elvis Costello **4.** more **5.** decreased **7.** $w - 7$ **9.** $r - 7$ **11.** $m - 2$ **13.** $e + 10$ **15.** $d + 6$ **17.** $v - 7$ **19.** $u - 10$ **21.** $n - m$ **23.** $c - c$ **25.** $n - 4$ **27.** $n - 3$ **29.** $n - 2$ **31.** $n + 2$ **33.** B **35.** B **37.** A **39.** B

Pages 4–5
1. McHale **2.** Parish **3.** McHale **4.** Kite **5.** 20 points **6.** Johnson **7.** 12 **9.** 11 **11.** 4 **13.** 3 **15.** 14 **17.** 4 **19.** 11 **21.** 9 **23.** 14 **25.** 1 **27.** 12 **29.** 15 **31.** 6 **33.** 1 **35.** 10 **37.** 8 **39.** 11 **41.** 0 **43.** 1 **45.** 10 **47.** 4 **49.** 0 **51.** 1 **53.** 5 **55.** 6 **57.** 5 points **59.** McHale **61.** 18 points **63.** McHale **65.** McHale

Pages 6–7
1. 19,852 **2.** 20,000 **3.** 1; yes **4.** 20,000 **5.** 90 **7.** 10 **9.** 520 **11.** 3650 **13.** 6330 **15.** 300 **17.** 100 **19.** 500 **21.** 5600 **23.** 24,000 **25.** 6000 **27.** 1000 **29.** 0 **31.** 42,000 **33.** 50,000 **35.** 536,000 **37.** 880,000 **39.** 800,000 **41.** 30,000 **43.** 10,000 **45.** 290,000 **47.** 520,000 **49.** 100,000 **51.** Hundreds **53.** Ten thousands

Page 8
1. $y - 5$ **3.** $7 + d$ **5.** $b + 4$ **7.** $12 - s$ **9.** $x + 10$ **11.** $z - 18$ **13.** $r + 17$ **15.** $x - y$ **17.** $k - k$ **19.** 6 **21.** 0 **23.** 2 **25.** 18 **27.** 18 **29.** 4 **31.** 8 **33.** 16 **35.** 12 **37.** 8 **39.** 8 **41.** 4 **43.** 8 **45.** 13 **47.** 3 **49.** 17 **51.** 4000 **53.** 1000 **55.** 8000 **57.** 0 **59.** 36,000 **61.** 78,000 **63.** 53,000 **65.** 73,000 **67.** 45,000 **69.** 60,000 **71.** 521,000 **73.** 410,000 **75.** 821,000 **77.** 375,000 **79.** 322,000 **81.** 380,000

Page 9
1. 15 miles **3.** Pawnee **5.** Highways 70 and 23 **7.** 12 miles **9.** A **11.** C

Pages 10–11
1. 1511 **2.** Yes **3.** hundred **4.** Yes **7.** 1428

Pages 10–11 *(continued)*
9. 1748 **11.** 2348 **13.** 7604 **15.** 10,398 **17.** 10,437 **19.** 80,351 **21.** $103 **23.** $25 **25.** $96 **27.** $120 **29.** $42 **31.** $49 **33.** $104 **35.** $18 **37.** $109

Pages 12–13
1. hundred **2.** Yes **5.** 283 **7.** 83 **9.** 2997 **11.** 5185 **13.** 27,317 **15.** 40,155 **17.** 2100 **19.** 100 **21.** 1800 **23.** 3400 **25.** 1600 **27.** 1600 **29.** 3400 **31.** 1000 **33.** A **35.** C **37.** B **39.** 13

Pages 14–15
1. 5; 15 **2a.** 6 **2b.** 10 **2c.** 15 **2d.** 23 **2e.** 55 **2f.** 21 **3a.** 8 **3b.** 9 **3c.** 63 **3d.** 3 **3e.** 16 **3f.** 76 **5.** 25 **7.** 10 **9.** 23 **11.** 2 **13.** 33 **15.** 58 **17.** 18 **19.** 2 **21.** 33 **23.** 46 **25.** 19 **27.** 0 **29.** 11 **31.** 33 **33.** 1 **35.** 11 **37.** 9 **39.** 49 **41.** 9 **43.** 9 **45.** $t + 14 = 32$; 18 **47.** $r + 5 = 17$; 12 **49.** $m + 42 = 60$; 18 **51.** $s + 19 = 28$; 9 **53.** 57 grams

Pages 16–17
1a. 23; 39 **1b.** 39 **2a.** 7 **2b.** 46 **2c.** 23 **2d.** 23 **2e.** 26 **2f.** 40 **2g.** 5 **2h.** 3 **2i.** 33 **3a.** 4 **3b.** 34 **3c.** 71 **3d.** 7 **3e.** 43 **3f.** 113 **5.** 51 **7.** 40 **9.** 25 **11.** 32 **13.** 20 **15.** 24 **17.** 0 **19.** 16 **21.** 21 **23.** 80 **25.** 121 **27.** 49 **29.** 44 **31.** 70 **33.** 134 **35.** 146 **37.** 201 **39.** 170 **41.** 80 **43.** 155 **45.** A; 44 **47.** B; 68 **49.** A; $44 **51.** A; $44 **53.** 12

Pages 18–19
1a. right **1b.** left **2a.** 32 **2b.** 36 **2c.** 29 **2d.** 80 **2e.** 29 **2f.** 181 **3.** 29 **5.** 58 **7.** 7 **9.** 75 **11.** 99 **13.** 82 **15.** 0 **17.** 38 **19.** 36 **21.** 41 **23.** 40 **25.** 25 **27.** 54 **29.** 66 **31.** 53 **33.** 73 **35.** 91 **37.** 57 **39.** 167 **41.** 138 **43.** 146 **45.** 72 **47.** 66 **49.** 11 **51.** 100 **53.** 114 **55.** More **56a.** 415 **56c.** 285 **56e.** 365

Pages 20–21
1. first **2a.** points **2b.** 31 **2c.** 17 **3.** Yes **5.** B; 42 **7.** B; 42 **9.** $40 = n - 17$; 57 **11.** $d - 28 = 9$; $37 **13.** $s + 8 = 55$; $47

Pages 20–21 *(continued)*
15. $t - 8 = 30$; 38 points **17.** $a + 7 = 60$; 53 inches

Page 22
3. 8 **5.** 8 **7.** 0 **9.** 14 **11.** 15 **13.** 27 **15.** 28 **17.** 0 **19.** 15 **21.** 17 **23.** 28 **25.** 34 **27.** 25 **29.** 71 **31.** 93 **33.** 114 **35.** 43 **37.** 93 **39.** 19 **41.** 0 **43.** 89 **45.** 11 **47.** 41 **49.** 111 **51.** 55 **53.** 32 **55.** 49 **57.** 59

Page 23
1. 29,689 miles **3.** $1335 **5.** B; $2375 **7.** A; $2125 **9.** $m + 3500 = 5895$; $2395

Chapter 2 Multiplication and Division Equations

Pages 28–29
1. Greg Louganis **2.** Joan Benoit **3.** Mary Lou Retton **4.** Carl Lewis **5.** times **6.** divided **7.** $9n$ **9.** $2m$ **11.** $r + 8$ **13.** $e - 9$ **15.** $\frac{6}{t}$ **17.** cd **19.** $4m + 6$ **21.** $\frac{s}{s} + 3$ **23.** $6p$ **25.** $p - 4$ **27.** $3p + 5$ **29.** $\frac{p}{3} - 4$ **31.** A **33.** D **35.** B

Pages 30–31
1. Photo 1 **2.** Photo 4 **3.** Photo 2 **4.** 24 children **5.** Photo 2 **7.** 2 **9.** 1 **11.** 4 **13.** 3 **15.** 1 **17.** 6 **19.** 51 **21.** 1 **23.** 48 **25.** 30 **27.** 20 **29.** 10 **31.** 18 **33.** 4 **35.** 4 **37.** 23 **39.** 2 **41.** 6 **43.** 20 **45.** 9 **47.** 1 **49.** 10 **51.** 6 **53.** 40 adults **55.** Photo 1 **57.** Photo 4 **59.** Photo 3

Pages 32–33
1. 10 **2.** 8 **3.** 2 **4.** 5 **5.** 3 **7.** 1200 **9.** 15,000 **11.** 4000 **13.** 35,000 **15.** 24,000 **17.** 1000 **19.** 4000 **21.** 18,000 **23.** 2400 **25.** 25,000 **27.** 3000 **29.** 120,000 **31.** 70,000 **33.** 450,000 **35.** 800,000 **37.** 240,000 **39.** 625,000 **41.** 426,000 **43.** 120,000 **45.** 400,000 **47.** 80,000 **49.** 250,000 **51.** 10 people **53.** Academy Awards **55.** Super Bowl and Emmy Awards

Pages 34–35
1. 5358 **2.** Yes **3.** hundred **4.** Yes **7.** 3090 **9.** 1180 **11.** 4347 **13.** 4720 **15.** 7192 **17.** 4767 **19.** 31,536 **21.** 37,233 **23.** 15,596 **25.** 41,370 **27.** 72,063 **29.** 45,325 **31.** 2000 **33.** 3000 **35.** 4500 **37.** 2800 **39.** 509 **41.** 704 **43.** 491 **45.** 200 **47.** 510 **49.** 685 **51.** 2700 **53.** 4200 **55.** 6800 **57.** 3700 **59.** $r = 1{,}234{,}567$; $s = 9$; $t = 8$

Pages 36–37
1. 24 **2.** 21 **3.** Yes **4.** 8760 **5.** 180,000; 183,960 **6.** No **9.** 1452 **11.** 2542 **13.** 2655 **15.** 1242 **17.** 20,792 **19.** 55,083 **21.** 574,640 **23.** 136,703 **25.** 188,484 **27.** 219,675 **29.** 562,848 **31.** 4,572,088 **33.** 608,912 **35.** 784,624 **37.** 367,302 **39.** 2,908,864 **41.** 1400 **43.** 7000 **45.** 32,000 **47.** 40,000 **49.** 480 **51.** 500 **53.** 330 **55.** 0 **57.** 500 **59.** 71 **61.** 62 **63.** 398 **65.** 250 **67.** 500 **69.** 370 **71.** 0 **73.** 1670 **75.** 7600 **77.** $7n$ **79.** $\frac{n}{24}$ **81.** $\frac{n}{60}$

Page 38
1. $x + 6$ **3.** $r - 8$ **5.** $8 - u$ **7.** $s - 4$ **9.** $y - 14$ **11.** $q + 12$ **13.** $x - y$ **15.** $z - z$ **17.** 400 **19.** 200 **21.** 5700 **23.** 6100 **25.** 8300 **27.** 4500 **29.** 7300 **31.** 3300 **33.** 37,200 **35.** 74,800 **37.** 61,500 **39.** 57,500 **41.** 69,500 **43.** 90,000 **45.** 6 **47.** 24 **49.** 26 **51.** 7 **53.** 25 **55.** 34 **57.** 18 **59.** 36 **61.** 20 **63.** 20 **65.** 29 **67.** 74 **69.** 95 **71.** 58 **73.** 81 **75.** 91

Page 39
1a. $.62 **1c.** $2.34 **3.** $2.28 **5.** $3.47 **7.** $59 + 42n$ **9.** $38 + 26n$

Pages 40–41
1. $1845 **2.** 9 **3.** 9 **4.** Yes; $205 **7.** 109 **9.** 604 **11.** 1471 **13.** 109 **15.** 423 **17.** 125 **19.** 400 **21.** 1853 **23.** 931 **25.** 8100 **27.** 6211 **29.** 6146 **31.** 100 **33.** 300 **35.** 2400 **37.** 4800 **39.** 2000 **41.** 502 **43.** 1204 **45.** 5300 **47.** 6 **49.** 5996 **51.** 509; 3; 7; 27; 2

Pages 42–43
1. 10,000 **2.** 206 **3.** Yes **5.** 421 **7.** 507 **9.** 21 **11.** 342 **13.** 44 **15.** 14 **17.** 155 **19.** 196 R50 **21.** 38 R120 **23.** 19 R144 **25.** 29 **27.** 106 R310 **29.** 56 R8 **31.** 42 R40 **33.** 236 R82 **35.** 10 R14 **37.** 3 **39.** 3 **41.** 24 **43.** 333

Pages 44–45
1. 14 golf balls **2.** 14 **3.** 2 **4a.** 5 **4b.** 9 **4c.** 8 **5a.** 7 **5b.** 10 **5c.** 11 **7.** 7 **9.** 6 **11.** 13 **13.** 12 **15.** 10 **17.** 11 **19.** 9 **21.** 17 **23.** 21 **25.** 43 **27.** 20 **29.** 40 **31.** 23 **33.** 34 **35.** 0 **37.** 5 **39.** 55 **41.** 65 **43.** 56 **45.** 83 **47.** 15 **49.** 43 **51.** 18 **53.** 32 **55.** C; 3 **57.** B; 64 **59.** C; 3

Pages 46–47
1a. 8; 96 **1b.** 96 **2a.** 3 **2b.** 7 **2c.** 5 **3a.** 9 **3b.** 4 **3c.** 99 **3d.** 36 **3e.** 50 **3f.** 300 **5.** 32

Pages 46–47 *(continued)*
7. 80 **9.** 70 **11.** 56 **13.** 80 **15.** 90 **17.** 105 **19.** 405 **21.** 64 **23.** 0 **25.** 450 **27.** 11 **29.** 21 **31.** 32 **33.** 0 **35.** 18 **37.** A; 64 **39.** C; 3 **41.** A; $64 **43.** D; $30.72

Pages 48–49
1a. right **1b.** left **2a.** 19 **2b.** 7 **2c.** 94 **2d.** 17 **2e.** 12 **2f.** 207 **3.** 36 **5.** 32 **7.** 0 **9.** 90 **11.** 54 **13.** 0 **15.** 28 **17.** 67 **19.** 6 **21.** 72 **23.** 200 **25.** 25 **27.** 74 **29.** 65 **31.** 13 **33.** 83 **35.** 110 **37.** 15 **39.** 145 **41.** 35 **43.** 18 **45.** 204 **47.** 360 **49.** 21 **51.** 18 **53.** 3 **55.** 0 **57.** 1 **59a.** 26 **59c.** 175

Pages 50–51
1. 1 **2a.** cost **2b.** 54 **2c.** 3 **3.** Yes **5.** A; 1125 **7.** D; 90 **9.** D; 90 records **11.** A; 1125 records **13.** $11k = 165$; 15 **15.** $m - 13 = 24$; 37 **17.** $4a = 36$; 9 **19.** $\frac{k}{6} = 7$; 42 **21.** $3e = 39$; 13

Page 52
1. $8s$ **3.** $\frac{y}{12}$ **5.** $7w + 5$ **7.** 4866 **9.** 3681 **11.** 16,476 **13.** 1596 **15.** 84,847 **17.** 911,064 **19.** 27 **21.** 79 **23.** 56 **25.** 40 **27.** 83 **29.** 118 **31.** 8 **33.** 20 **35.** 13 **37.** 10 **39.** 27 **41.** 31 **43.** 54 **45.** 0 **47.** 120 **49.** 108 **51.** 150 **53.** 572 **55.** 28 **57.** 69 **59.** 140 **61.** 12 **63.** 15 **65.** 552

Page 53
1. $2820 **3.** $4452 **5.** C; $13 **7.** B; $168 **9.** $3c = 417$; $139

Chapter 3 Equations with Decimals

Pages 58–59
1. Tenths place **2.** Hundredths place **3.** hundredths **4.** thousandths **5.** ten-thousandths **7.** hundredths **9.** hundredths **11.** hundredths **13.** ten-thousandths **15.** hundredths **17.** hundredths **19.** tenths **21.** thousandths **23.** thousandths **25.** tenths **27.** 15 and 82 hundredths **29.** 14 and 2 thousandths **31.** 54 thousandths **33.** 5 and 74 ten-thousandths **35.** 476 ten-thousandths **37.** 866 and 38 hundredths **39.** 765 thousandths **41.** 470 and 8 tenths **43.** 4936 and 2 tenths **45.** 38 and 5 ten-thousandths **47.** 37 and 4 thousandths **49.** 321 and 6 tenths **51.** 48 and 3 hundredths **53.** 204 and 84 hundredths **55.** 32.6 **57.** 9.06 **59.** 114.58 **61.** 62.250 **63.** 0.1456 **65.** 5.0360

Pages 60–61
1. $7.92 **2.** 7.625 **3a.** 8 **3b.** 7.6 **3c.** 7.63 **4.** $8 **5.** 26 **7.** 0 **9.** 1 **11.** 39 **13.** 54 **15.** 3.7 **17.** 8.4 **19.** 9.2 **21.** 49.2 **23.** 6.5 **25.** 605.4 **27.** 0.1 **29.** 64.4 **31.** 0.3 **33.** 3.1 **35.** 16.32 **37.** 2.56 **39.** 25.61 **41.** 4.31 **43.** 6.47 **45.** 8.45 **47.** 27.94 **49.** 17.05 **51.** 33.72 **53.** 287.28 **55.** $7 **57.** $147 **59.** $28 **61.** $55 **63.** $100 **65.** $247 **67.** $40 **69.** $200 **71.** $.86

Pages 62–63
1. Sling Shot **2.** Old Smokie **3.** 8.70 and 8.71 **4.** Sling Shot **5.** Yes **7.** > **9.** > **11.** > **13.** > **15.** < **17.** < **19.** > **21.** < **23.** < **25.** > **27.** > **29.** > **31.** > **33.** < **35.** > **37.** > **39.** > **41.** < **43.** < **45.** > **47.** > **49.** > **51.** > **53.** < **55.** > **57.** > **59.** < **61.** Blue Flame **63.** Austin **65.** Blue Flame, Lightning, Flash Bye, Sling Shot, Old Smokie, Jetaway **67.** No

Pages 64–65
1. 3.39 miles **2.** 3.39 and 1.87 **3.** whole **4.** Yes **7.** 32.1 **9.** 23.7 **11.** 26.22 **13.** 20.723 **15.** 19.52 **17.** 48 **19.** 25.557 **21.** 8.63 **23.** 18.117 **25.** $49.99 **27.** $62 **29.** $149.99 **31.** $111.99 **33.** $169.99 **35.** $99.99 **37.** $149.98 **39.** $199.99 **41.** $139.99 **43.** 8.31 miles **45.** 6 hours **47.** 9:45 A.M.

Pages 66–67
1. 54.29 **2.** 60 **3.** whole **4.** Yes **7.** 28.2 **9.** 2.45 **11.** 17.25 **13.** 51.45 **15.** 1.94 **17.** 4.95 **19.** 75.65 **21.** 4.13 **23.** 2.349 **25.** 57.25 **27.** 4.566 **29.** 33.48 **31.** 24.06 **33.** 5.25 **35.** 9.58 **37.** 57.2 **39.** 2.75 **41.** 22.75 **43.** 0 **45.** 18.25 **47.** 17.25 **49.** 17.25 **51.** 28.25 **53.** 8.25 **55.** 17.25 **57.** 20 **59.** 23.75 **61.** 12.75 **63.** 16.5 **65.** 12.75 **67.** −; + **69.** +; − **71.** −; + **73.** +; − **75.** −; − **77.** −; +

Pages 68–69
1a. 3.8 **1b.** 4.6 **2a.** 5.5 **2b.** 7.6 **2c.** 8.4; 4.2 **2d.** 20 **2e.** 17.2; 10.9; 28.1 **2f.** 36.4; 6.48; 6.48 **3.** 13.1 **5.** 25.6 **7.** 11.6 **9.** 33.2 **11.** 8.4 **13.** 14.4 **15.** 3.5 **17.** 0 **19.** 18.2 **21.** 6.3 **23.** 35.2 **25.** 16.7 **27.** 8.9 **29.** 68.3 **31.** 11.9 **33.** 18.3 **35.** 2.29 **37.** 93.42 **39.** 36.55 **41.** 145.8 **43.** 185.6 **45.** 0.84 **47.** 34.28 **49.** 2.748 **51.** Less **52a.** $6.29 **52c.** $6.62 **52e.** $4.95 **52g.** $6.60

Page 70
1. 54 **3.** 32 **5.** 11 **7.** 42 **9.** 146 **11.** 34
13. $6n$ **15.** $\frac{c}{20}$ **17.** $4t + 18$ **19.** $\frac{s}{8} - 12$
21. $\frac{p}{a} + 9$ **23.** 34 **25.** 10 **27.** 34 **29.** 86 **31.** 11
33. 16 **35.** 264 **37.** 936 **39.** 4212 **41.** 23,436
43. 40,180 **45.** 304,410 **47.** 26 R18 **49.** 32 R4
51. 43 R29 **53.** 77 R18 **55.** 167 R10
57. 137 R317 **59.** 14 **61.** 10 **63.** 12 **65.** 33

Page 71
1a. $20 **1c.** $30 **3.** $577.91 **5.** B; $400
7. B; $400 **9.** $n + 460 = 535$; $75

Pages 72–73
1. $.85 **2.** 0.85 **3.** $2.04; yes **4a.** 6; 9; 1; 8
4b. 7; 6; 0; 3 **4c.** 8; 59; 6; 5 **7.** 9 **9.** 2.604
11. 148 **13.** 12 **15.** 22.05 **17.** 22.776
19. 7.7964 **21.** 609.9 **23.** 0.24275 **25.** 107.8
27. 0.048 **29.** 5.4 **31.** 0.68 **33.** 0.88 **35.** 0.5
37. 5.2 **39.** $1.26 **41.** 1 half-dollar, 1 dime, 2 pennies

Pages 74–75
1. Swimming **2.** 2.5 and 1000 **3.** 2500 people
5. 7200 **7.** 856 **9.** 8560 **11.** 860 **13.** 296
15. 296 **17.** 51.3 **19.** 5130 **21.** 940,000
23. 94,000 **25.** 8300 **27.** 83,000 **29.** 76
31. 7600 **33.** 9 **35.** 9 **37.** 421,000 **39.** 4210
41. 64,200 **43.** 642 **45.** 47.6 **47.** 47,600
49. Golf **51.** 2100 people **53.** Swimming, golf, tennis **55.** 800 people

Pages 76–77
1. 8 students **2.** 94.08 seconds **3.** 8 **4.** 11.76 seconds **5a.** 48 **5b.** 241 **7.** 2.54 **9.** 4.2
11. 2.74 **13.** 6.4 **15.** 3.71 **17.** 8.05 **19.** 18.37
21. 102.7 **23.** 1.89 **25.** 0.68 **27.** 0.70 **29.** 1.24
31. 7.32 **33.** 0.51 **35.** 0.09 **37.** 2.31 **39.** 0.13
41. 1.26 **43.** 0.3 **45.** 1.2 **47.** 0.54 **49.** 2.9
51. 5.6 **53.** 0.3 **55.** 4.4 **57.** Bev **59.** 11.8625 seconds

Pages 78–79
1. 26.2188 miles **2.** 1.8 **3.** one **4.** 14.566 miles per hour **5a.** 162; 108; 0 **5b.** 24; 36; 0 **7.** 74
9. 15.6 **11.** 2.6 **13.** 0.5 **15.** 38 **17.** 12.7
19. 190 **21.** 640 **23.** 1.15 **25.** 0.045 **27.** 4.6
29. 4.5 **31.** B **33.** B

Pages 80–81
1. left **2.** 2 **3.** 3 **4a.** 3.65 **4b.** 0.063

Pages 80–81 *(continued)*
4c. 0.0172 **5.** 7.6 **7.** 0.076 **9.** 21.72 **11.** 0.2172
13. 0.681 **15.** 6.81 **17.** 8 **19.** 0.08 **21.** 4.123
23. 0.04123 **25.** 0.846 **27.** 84.6 **29.** 0.2147
31. 21.47 **33.** 0.242 **35.** 0.00242 **37.** 0.185
39. 1.85 **41.** 0.009 **43.** 0.9 **45.** 0.039 **47.** 0.39
49. 25 **51.** 38 **53.** 14 **55.** 21 **57.** '79 Chevy Caprice

Pages 82–83
1a. 0.2; 35 **1b.** 1.2; 9.6 **1c.** 9.6 **2a.** 5 **2b.** 2.5
2c. 18.6 **2d.** 1.26; 1.4; 1.4; 0.9 **3.** 0.4 **5.** 0.07
7. 8.4 **9.** 0.21 **11.** 0.9 **13.** 0.2 **15.** 21
17. 0.25 **19.** 1.2 **21.** 2.5 **23.** 1.2 **25.** 2.5
27. 5.3 **29.** 8.5 **31.** 0.4 **33.** 0.2 **35.** 4.5
37. 2.3 **39a.** 60 **39c.** 154 **39e.** 3.85

Pages 84–85
1a. 1.75 **1b.** $c + 1.75$ **1c.** 1.75; 14.5 **1d.** 1.75
2. Yes **3a.** 3.5 **3b.** 29 **3c.** 3.5 **3d.** 29 **3e.** 32.5
5. $c + 7.4 = 20.7$; 13.3 **7.** $4f = 26.4$; 6.6
9. $n + 8.2 = 17.6$; 9.4 **11.** $1.3p = 6.5$; 5
13. $c + 1.8 = 13.5$; 11.7 seconds

Page 86
1. 24 **3.** 88 **5.** 150 **7.** 80 **9.** 260 **11.** 216
13. 66 **15.** 0 **17.** 52 **19.** 9 **21.** 320 **23.** 39
25. 108 **27.** 67 **29.** 22 **31.** 300 **33.** 64
35. 217 **37.** 6.1 **39.** 1.6 **41.** 10.06 **43.** 37.37
45. 4.64 **47.** 13.06 **49.** 16.4 **51.** 5.72 **53.** 30.48
55. 24.18 **57.** 0.9558 **59.** 34.8692 **61.** 3
63. 8.1 **65.** 3.1 **67.** 6.11 **69.** 0.48 **71.** 4.83

Page 87
1. $4.49 **3.** $16 **5.** B; 72 exposures **7.** A; 48 flashbulbs **9.** $6n = 96$; 16 pages

Chapter 4 Number Properties and Equations

Pages 92–93
1. 15 decals **2a.** No **2b.** Yes **3.** Yes
4. grouping **5.** addition **6.** 17 **7.** 8 **9.** 24
11. 38 **13.** 140 **15.** 32 **17.** 99 **19.** 6 **21.** 24
23. 22 **25.** 81 **27.** 35 **29.** 192 **31.** 54 **33.** 25
35. 215 **37.** 10 **39.** 100 **41.** 0 **43.** 32 **45.** 20
47. 81 **49.** 5 **51.** 78 **53.** 5

Pages 94–95
1. Yes **2.** Yes **3.** Yes **4a.** x **4b.** s **4c.** z **4d.** d
4e. 0 **4f.** q **4g.** a **4h.** y **4i.** q **4j.** r **5.** 59

Pages 94–95 *(continued)*
7. 77 **9.** 168 **11.** 45 **13.** 122 **15.** 141 **17.** 134 **19.** 147 **21.** 164 **23.** 157 **25.** 171 **27.** 185 **29.** $160.25 **31.** $200 **33.** $25.75 **35.** $20.50 **37.** $210.25 **39.** $55.75 **41.** $95.50 **43.** $195.50 **45.** $350 **47.** $70.50 **49.** $181

Pages 96–97
1. Yes **2.** Yes **3.** Yes **4a.** n **4b.** a **4c.** t **4d.** n **4e.** 1 **4f.** b **4g.** j **4h.** d **4i.** r **4j.** x **5.** 160 **7.** 280 **9.** 1700 **11.** 720 **13.** 4800 **15.** 6300 **17.** 4900 **19.** 8100 **21.** 3600 **23.** d **25.** a **27.** f **29.** 18 **31.** 73 **33.** 92 **35.** 30 **37.** 27 **39.** 62

Pages 98–99
1a. 14 **1b.** 11 **1c.** 54 **1d.** 17 **1e.** 26 **1f.** 20 **3.** 11 **5.** 26 **7.** 49 **9.** 14 **11.** 12 **13.** 31 **15.** 128 **17.** 9.5 **19.** 4 **21.** 11 **23.** 28.7 **25.** 13.6 **27.** 9 **29.** 4.25 **31.** 8.4 **33.** 14.4 **35.** 36 **37.** 1.62 **39.** 1.5 **41.** 0.9 **43.** 6.25 **45.** 5.125 **47.** 4.32 **49.** 14.5 **58a.** 172 **58c.** 5 **58e.** 51

Page 100
1. 20 **3.** 33 **5.** 87 **7.** 66 **9.** 17 **11.** 260 **13.** 720 **15.** 696 **17.** 4.8 **19.** 9.5 **21.** 8.1 **23.** 29.2 **25.** 5.5 **27.** 406.3 **29.** 0.1 **31.** 34.3 **33.** $>$ **35.** $<$ **37.** $>$ **39.** $>$ **41.** $>$ **43.** $<$ **45.** 16.5 **47.** 9.8 **49.** 57.7 **51.** 64 **53.** 3.2 **55.** 11.58 **57.** 0 **59.** 96.8 **61.** 61.25 **63.** 27.69 **65.** 4.2 **67.** 0.567 **69.** 1.702 **71.** 10.2 **73.** 10.557 **75.** 0.28712 **77.** 1.19686 **79.** 38.77878

Page 101
1. b **3.** b **5.** $1.32d = 82.038$; 62.15 feet

Pages 102–103
1. $7 **2.** $2 **3.** Number of records **4.** 2; 7 **5.** 4 records **7.** 4; 30; 5; 6 **9.** 5 **11.** 9 **13.** 7 **15.** 11 **17.** 7 **19.** 1 **21.** 12 **23.** 15 **25.** 12 **27.** 3 **29.** 1 **31.** 3.1 **33.** 1.9 **35.** 4 **37.** 4.2 **39.** 15.1 **41a.** 25.65 **41c.** 6 **41e.** 4.50 **41g.** 76.50 **41i.** 5.00

Pages 104–105
1. 19; 7 **2.** 7 **3a.** 6 **3b.** 22 **3c.** 3 **5.** 27 **7.** 10 **9.** 6 **11.** 7 **13.** 9 **15.** 60 **17.** 5 **19.** 11 **21.** 45 **23.** 6 **25.** 4 **27.** 80 **29.** D; 3 **31.** B; 48 **33.** B; 48

Pages 106–107
1. Yes **2a.** 6 **2b.** 5 **2c.** 2 **2d.** 12 **3a.** 7; 6; 42

Pages 106–107 *(continued)*
3b. 8; 25; 100; 8 **5.** 9 **7.** 6 **9.** 6 **11.** 4 **13.** 5 **15.** 4 **17.** 4 **19.** 80 **21.** 248 **23.** 252 **25.** 102 **27.** 1414 **29.** 1836 **31.** 40 **33.** 50 **35.** 400 **37.** 700 **39.** 150 **41.** 190 **43.** $15 **45.** $14 **47.** $11 **49.** $8.25 **51.** $5.75

Pages 108–109
1a. $11n$ **1b.** 1 **1c.** t **1d.** 8 **1e.** 1 **1f.** 12 **3.** $14n$ **5.** $7n$ **7.** $4n$ **9.** $12b$ **11.** $16m$ **13.** $15c$ **15.** $10y + 12$ **17.** $28g + 4$ **19.** $54t$ **21.** $7a$ **23.** $14r + 1$ **25.** $24c + 3$ **27.** 300 **29.** 2000 **31.** 600 **33.** 660 **35.** 2400 **37.** 840 **39.** 420 **41.** 3400 **43.** 1600 **45.** Wichita **47.** $3n + 12$ miles

Pages 110–111
1. 10; 10 **2.** $1.25 **3a.** 11 **3b.** 3 **3c.** 4 **5.** 5 **7.** 16 **9.** 13 **11.** 8 **13.** 4 **15.** 2 **17.** 12.3 **19.** 3.01 **21.** 0.35 **23.** 0.45 **25.** 6 **27.** 2 **29.** 26 **31.** 25 **33.** 7 **35.** 25 **37.** 36 **39.** 3 **41.** 37.5 **43.** 15.3 **45.** 0.4375 **47.** 0.66 **49.** B; $.74 **51.** A; $.35

Pages 112–113
1a. 30 **1b.** $4h + 30$ **1c.** 30; 58 **2.** Yes **3a.** 9 **3b.** 269 **3c.** 9 **3d.** 269 **3e.** 65 **5.** $7n - 9 = 68$; 11 **7.** $\frac{m}{6} - 5 = 4$; 54 **9.** $7p + 2 = 44$; 6 **11.** $6r + 10 = 64$; 9 **13.** $3e + 2 = 17$; $5

Page 114
1. 80 **3.** 0.8 **5.** 3420 **7.** 13,600 **9.** 5670 **11.** 43.7 **13.** 830 **15.** 75.1 **17.** 5037 **19.** 503.7 **21.** 54.8 **23.** 5.63 **25.** 49.1 **27.** 66.4 **29.** 0.12 **31.** 12.4 **33.** 0.538 **35.** 4.33 **37.** 46 **39.** 12.7 **41.** 4.2 **43.** 0.086 **45.** 0.3851 **47.** 0.03851 **49.** 42.1 **51.** 0.01256 **53.** 0.4661 **55.** 0.749 **57.** 5.29 **59.** 5.692 **61.** 3.36 **63.** 8.25 **65.** 0.72 **67.** 0.563 **69.** 9.5 **71.** 88.66 **73.** 11.52 **75.** 1.666 **77.** 3.84 **79.** 50.9

Page 115
1. $150 **3.** $280 **5.** 80 miles **7.** 800 miles **9.** Plan A

Chapter 5 Number Theory and Equivalent Fractions

Pages 120–121
1a. 3 **1b.** x **1c.** 3 **1d.** b **1e.** 2 **1f.** 14 **1g.** y **1h.** y **1i.** 3 **3.** 4^3 **5.** $2^3 3^2$ **7.** $8^2 10^3$ **9.** ab^3

Pages 120–121 *(continued)*
11. x^3y **13.** x^3y^2 **15.** m^3n^3 **17.** $6a^2$ **19.** $21a^2$ **21.** $12ab^2$ **23.** ac^2d^2 **25.** ac^3d **27.** $18m^2n^2$ **29.** $12a^2b^2$ **31.** $24a^3b^2$ **33.** $24r^3s^2$ **35.** $6x^2y^2$ **37.** $20a^2b^2$ **38a.** 16 **38c.** 144 **38e.** 400

Page 123
1. Yes **3.** Yes **5.** Yes **7.** Yes **9.** Yes **11.** Yes **13.** Yes **15.** No **17.** Yes **19.** No **21.** Yes **23.** Yes **25.** No **27.** No **29.** Yes **31.** Yes **33.** Yes **35.** Yes **37.** Yes **39.** Yes **41.** Yes **43.** Yes **45.** No **47.** Yes **49.** True **51.** True **53.** 96

Pages 124–125
1. 3 **2a.** 13 **2b.** 2 **2c.** 5 **3.** 3 **4a.** c **4b.** 3 **4c.** r **5.** $5 \cdot 7$ **7.** $2 \cdot 5$ **9.** $3 \cdot 5$ **11.** $2 \cdot 2 \cdot 2 \cdot 3$ **13.** $2 \cdot 11$ **15.** $2 \cdot 2 \cdot 2$ **17.** $3 \cdot 7$ **19.** $2 \cdot 2 \cdot 3$ **21.** $2 \cdot 5 \cdot 5$ **23.** $2 \cdot 2 \cdot 11$ **25.** $2 \cdot 19$ **27.** $2 \cdot 2 \cdot 2 \cdot 2$ **29.** $2 \cdot 2 \cdot 2 \cdot 2 \cdot 3$ **31.** $3 \cdot 11$ **33.** $7 \cdot 7$ **35.** $3 \cdot 3 \cdot 5$ **37.** $2 \cdot 29$ **39.** $2 \cdot 17$ **41.** 5^2 **43.** $2^3 \cdot 5$ **45.** 2^6 **47.** $2 \cdot 3 \cdot 11$ **49.** $2 \cdot 3^3$ **51.** $2 \cdot 31$ **53.** $5 \cdot 13$ **55.** $3 \cdot 23$ **57.** $2 \cdot 5 \cdot 7$ **59.** $2 \cdot 2 \cdot x \cdot x \cdot x$ **61.** $2 \cdot 5 \cdot c \cdot c$ **63.** $2 \cdot 2 \cdot 3 \cdot d$ **65.** $3 \cdot 5 \cdot g \cdot g$ **67.** $2 \cdot 2 \cdot 3 \cdot 3 \cdot y$ **69.** $5 \cdot 7 \cdot t \cdot t \cdot t$ **71.** $2 \cdot 2 \cdot 2 \cdot 2 \cdot 2 \cdot u$ **73.** $3 \cdot 3 \cdot 5 \cdot d \cdot d \cdot d$ **75.** $11 \cdot g$ **77.** $2 \cdot 2 \cdot 2 \cdot 3 \cdot j \cdot j$ **79.** $2 \cdot 2 \cdot 2 \cdot 2 \cdot 2 \cdot a \cdot a \cdot b$ **81.** $7 \cdot a \cdot b \cdot b \cdot b$ **83.** $2 \cdot 3 \cdot 3 \cdot 3 \cdot a \cdot a \cdot b \cdot b$ **85a.** 0.05 **85c.** 0.8

Pages 126–127
1. 6 **2.** 72 **3.** 4 **5.** 6 **7.** 8 **9.** 12 **11.** 3 **13.** 2 **15.** 12 **17.** 5 **19.** 3 **21.** 1 **23.** 2 **25.** $3d$ **27.** $2x$ **29.** x **31.** $5u$ **33.** $3c^2$ **35.** yz **37.** $4a$ **39.** 6 **41.** 12 **43.** 28 **45.** 24 **47.** 35 **49.** 12 **51.** 33 **53.** 12 **55.** 60 **57.** 60 **59.** $10w$ **61.** $16x$ **63.** $45b^2$ **65.** $24d^2e$ **67.** $48x^2y$ **69.** $55x^2y$

Page 128
1. 2.2 **3.** 2.6 **5.** 9.9 **7.** 7.5 **9.** 0.6 **11.** 0.08 **13.** 6 **15.** 0.96 **17.** 2 **19.** 23 **21.** 14 **23.** 14 **25.** 7 **27.** 50 **29.** 22 **31.** 17 **33.** 56 **35.** c **37.** a **39.** b **41.** d **43.** 13 **45.** 151 **47.** 165 **49.** 17 **51.** 17 **53.** 176 **55.** 24 **57.** 10.4

Page 129
1. 1870 **3.** $14.75 **5a.** .80 **5b.** .80 **5c.** 8.80 **5d.** $2.00 **7.** $5n + 6.50 = 15.25$; $1.75

Pages 130–131
1. $\frac{1}{4}$ **2.** $\frac{2}{3}$ **3.** Agree **4.** $\frac{15}{24}$ **5.** $2b$ **6a.** 6

Pages 130–131 *(continued)*
6b. 3; 3 **6c.** $2c$ **6d.** $2t$; $2t$ **7.** 8 **9.** 21 **11.** 6 **13.** 10 **15.** 12 **17.** 9 **19.** 42 **21.** 30 **23.** 9 **25.** 3 **27.** 50 **29.** 10 **31.** 40 **33.** 15 **35.** 40 **37.** xy **39.** $9t$ **41.** $25m$ **43.** $4a$ **45.** $3z^2$ **47.** $10b$ **49.** $4cd$ **51.** $20wx$ **53.** 15 students **55.** Cartoonist; U.S. president

Pages 132–133
1. 3 **2.** $2x$ **3.** divided **4.** $2x$ **5.** 3 **6.** $2x$ **7.** $\frac{2}{3}$ **9.** $\frac{2}{5}$ **11.** $\frac{5}{12}$ **13.** $\frac{1}{3}$ **15.** $\frac{2}{3}$ **17.** $\frac{2}{3}$ **19.** $\frac{2}{3}$ **21.** $\frac{11}{5}$ **23.** $\frac{5}{3}$ **25.** $\frac{6}{7}$ **27.** $\frac{5}{4}$ **29.** $\frac{3}{2}$ **31.** $\frac{1}{2a}$ **33.** $\frac{2}{3a}$ **35.** $\frac{3}{2a}$ **37.** $\frac{1}{b}$ **39.** $\frac{1}{s}$ **41.** $\frac{1}{w}$ **43.** $\frac{3s}{7r}$ **45.** $\frac{13}{10}$ **47.** $\frac{4r^2}{5}$ **49.** $\frac{5}{6n}$ **51.** $\frac{16r}{9}$ **53.** $\frac{5}{4m}$ **55.** $\frac{8yz}{9}$ **57.** $\frac{xy}{3}$ **59.** $\frac{3k^2}{2j}$ **61.** California **63.** Colorado

Pages 134–135
1. 6; 12 **2.** b; $3b$; $3b$ **3a.** 24; 24 **3b.** $18n$; $18n$ **3c.** a^2b^2 **5.** 18 **7.** 8 **9.** 24 **11.** 24 **13.** 6 **15.** 72 **17.** 40 **19.** 20 **21.** 12 **23.** 60 **25.** 45 **27.** 50 **29.** 30 **31.** 30 **33.** 150 **35.** $5n$ **37.** $6n$ **39.** $3d$ **41.** $4r^2$ **43.** a^3 **45.** $6b$ **47.** $6a$ **49.** $24m$ **51.** r^3 **53.** z^4 **55.** $10n^2$ **57.** $12t^3$ **59.** a^2b^2 **61.** $12ab$ **63.** $12c^2d$

Pages 136–137
1. $\frac{4}{9}$ **2.** Hamilton's **3.** $\frac{4}{9}$ and $\frac{2}{9}$ **4.** Lincoln **5.** $>$ **7.** $>$ **9.** $<$ **11.** $<$ **13.** $>$ **15.** $<$ **17.** $>$ **19.** $>$ **21.** $<$ **23.** $<$ **25.** $>$ **27.** $>$ **29.** $<$ **31.** $<$ **33.** $>$ **35.** $=$ **37.** $<$ **39.** $=$ **41.** $>$ **43.** $<$ **45.** $<$ **47.** $>$ **49.** $>$ **51.** $>$ **53.** $>$ **55.** $>$ **57.** $<$ **59.** $>$ **61.** $=$ **63.** $<$

Pages 138–139
1a. 40; n **1b.** $n + n + 40$ **1c.** 2; 400 **3a.** 30; 30 **3b.** 124 **3c.** 77 **5.** $j + j + 9 = 77$; 34 points **7.** $p + p - 10 = 80$; 45¢ **9.** $v + v - 45 = 267$; 156 pounds **11.** $d + d - 6 = 128$; 67 pages

Page 140
1. 5 **3.** 11 **5.** 3 **7.** 0 **9.** 25 **11.** 12 **13.** 1.8 **15.** 2.9 **17.** 0.1 **19.** 1.7 **21.** 32 **23.** 22 **25.** 7 **27.** 150 **29.** 4 **31.** 8 **33.** 1 **35.** 0 **37.** 30.1 **39.** 0 **41.** $8a$ **43.** $4c$ **45.** $13x$ **47.** $17w + 6$ **49.** $2r + 11$ **51.** $6n + 17$ **53.** $11t$ **55.** $6n + 15$ **57.** 15 **59.** 13 **61.** 21 **63.** 5 **65.** 13 **67.** 5 **69.** 0.79 **71.** 0.11 **73.** 6.2 **75.** 2.49

Page 141

1. McCrory **3.** 8 points **5.** Miller **7.** 48 points **9.** 61 points **11.** 26 field goals **13.** 7 free throws

Chapter 6 Addition and Subtraction of Fractions

Pages 146–147

1. Yes **2.** Yes **3.** three **4.** multiply; add **5.** $\frac{8}{2}$ **7.** $\frac{12}{2}$ **9.** $\frac{10}{2}$ **11.** $\frac{14}{2}$ **13.** $\frac{32}{2}$ **15.** $\frac{40}{2}$ **17.** $\frac{15}{5}$ **19.** $\frac{5}{5}$ **21.** $\frac{35}{5}$ **23.** $\frac{60}{5}$ **25.** $\frac{55}{5}$ **27.** $\frac{45}{5}$ **29.** $\frac{3}{2}$ **31.** $\frac{4}{3}$ **33.** $\frac{5}{2}$ **35.** $\frac{7}{4}$ **37.** $\frac{14}{5}$ **39.** $\frac{10}{3}$ **41.** $\frac{27}{4}$ **43.** $\frac{23}{4}$ **45.** $\frac{31}{6}$ **47.** $\frac{27}{2}$ **49.** $\frac{33}{2}$ **51.** $\frac{58}{5}$ **53.** David Berg **55.** Kim Arnez and Marcia Sanchez

Pages 148–149

1. 1 **3.** 5 **5.** 6 **7.** 4 **9.** 8 **11.** 14 **13.** 15 **15.** 21 **17.** 10 **19.** 3 **21.** $1\frac{1}{4}$ **23.** $1\frac{5}{6}$ **25.** $2\frac{3}{5}$ **27.** $1\frac{2}{9}$ **29.** $2\frac{1}{2}$ **31.** 4 **33.** $5\frac{1}{2}$ **35.** $2\frac{7}{10}$ **37.** $3\frac{6}{7}$ **39.** 6 **41.** 7 **43.** $8\frac{1}{3}$ **45.** $17\frac{1}{2}$ **47.** $3\frac{7}{10}$ **49.** 12 **51.** $6\frac{17}{20}$ **53.** 15 **55.** Less **56a.** $1\frac{3}{8}$ **56c.** $5\frac{3}{8}$ **56e.** 56

Pages 150–151

1. Yes **2.** Yes **3.** $\frac{3}{4}$ **5.** $\frac{3}{5}$ **7.** $\frac{4}{5}$ **9.** $\frac{2}{3}$ **11.** $\frac{1}{3}$ **13.** $\frac{4}{7}$ **15.** $2\frac{2}{3}$ **17.** $5\frac{5}{6}$ **19.** $4\frac{1}{3}$ **21.** $6\frac{1}{2}$ **23.** $7\frac{2}{3}$ **25.** $8\frac{4}{5}$ **27.** $6\frac{2}{3}$ **29.** $2\frac{1}{2}$ **31.** $9\frac{1}{8}$ **33.** 2 **35.** $5\frac{2}{3}$ **37.** $5\frac{1}{2}$ **39.** 5 **41.** $3\frac{3}{4}$ **43.** 12 **45.** 3 **47.** $1\frac{3}{4}$ **49.** $\frac{2}{3}$ **51.** 5 **53.** $1\frac{1}{2}$ **55.** $3\frac{3}{5}$ **57.** $\frac{12a}{b}$ **59.** $\frac{4}{3y^2}$ **61.** $\frac{11r}{8s}$ **63.** $\frac{3a}{4b}$ **65.** $\frac{4x}{3y}$ **67.** 2 **69.** $\frac{4m}{5}$ **71.** $\frac{5}{n^2}$ **73.** $3y$ **75.** $\frac{25r}{35q^2}$ **77.** $\frac{15mt}{20mt^2}$

Pages 152–153

1. 100 **2.** 90 **3.** 6000 **4.** divisor **5.** $66\frac{2}{3}$ inches **6a.** 5 **6b.** 1 **6c.** $\frac{5}{6}$ **7.** $4\frac{3}{5}$ **9.** $6\frac{1}{2}$ **11.** $20\frac{1}{2}$ **13.** $6\frac{2}{3}$ **15.** $6\frac{1}{2}$ **17.** $9\frac{2}{7}$ **19.** $18\frac{1}{2}$ **21.** 16 **23.** $13\frac{2}{5}$ **25.** $21\frac{1}{3}$ **27.** $36\frac{1}{2}$ **29.** $22\frac{1}{2}$ **31.** $7\frac{1}{4}$ **33.** $15\frac{3}{5}$ **35.** $13\frac{1}{5}$ **37.** $15\frac{1}{6}$ **39.** $9\frac{3}{13}$ **41.** $14\frac{2}{3}$

Pages 152–153 *(continued)*

43. $68\frac{4}{47}$ inches **47.** Later **49.** 15-year-old boy **50a.** 110 **50c.** 143 **50e.** 176

Page 154

1. 7 **3.** 7 **5.** 7 **7.** 48 **9.** 18 **11.** 9 **13.** 1.48 **15.** 3.2 **17.** $12k$ **19.** $2r$ **21.** $9x$ **23.** $9y + 3$ **25.** $12y$ **27.** $12n$ **29.** 21 **31.** 18 **33.** 15 **35.** 18 **37.** 1.6 **39.** 1.05 **41.** 2.5 **43.** 29.2 **45.** 4^3 **47.** $6^2 \cdot 8^2$ **49.** x^3y^2 **51.** $2y^2z^2$ **53.** $6y^3z^2$ **55.** $2 \cdot 7$ **57.** 2^4 **59.** $2 \cdot 3 \cdot 7$ **61.** $3^2 \cdot 5$ **63.** $3 \cdot 3 \cdot x \cdot x$ **65.** $3 \cdot 5 \cdot d$ **67.** $2 \cdot 2 \cdot 2 \cdot n \cdot n \cdot n$ **69.** $5 \cdot 5 \cdot r \cdot r \cdot s \cdot s$ **71.** $3 \cdot 3 \cdot 3 \cdot y \cdot y \cdot y \cdot z \cdot z$

Page 155

1. Spiral notebook **3.** Spiral notebook **5.** Yes **7a.** 0.30 **7b.** 0.30 **7c.** 1.20 **7d.** \$.50 **9.** $1.5m + 0.05 = 2.00$; \$1.30

Pages 156–157

1. $\frac{3}{8}$ mile **2.** $\frac{5}{8}$ and $\frac{7}{8}$ **3.** $1\frac{1}{2}$ miles **4a.** 7; 2 **4b.** t **4c.** z; 15 **5.** $\frac{5}{8}$ and $\frac{3}{8}$ **6.** $\frac{1}{4}$ mile **7.** $\frac{2}{3}$ **9.** 1 **11.** $1\frac{1}{4}$ **13.** 1 **15.** $\frac{3}{4}$ **17.** $\frac{b+c}{d}$ **19.** $\frac{2a+3}{c}$ **21.** $\frac{3b+7}{d}$ **23.** $\frac{16}{xy}$ **25.** $\frac{24}{k^2}$ **27.** $\frac{1}{5}$ **29.** 0 **31.** 2 **33.** 1 **35.** $\frac{1}{3}$ **37.** $\frac{r-s}{t}$ **39.** $\frac{3x-w}{y}$ **41.** $\frac{4d-5}{e}$ **43.** $\frac{6}{mn}$ **45.** $\frac{14}{j^2}$ **47.** $\frac{1}{2}$ **49.** 2 **51.** $1\frac{2}{3}$ **53.** 1 **55.** $1\frac{3}{4}$ **57.** $\frac{3}{4}$ mile **59.** No

Pages 158–159

1. $\frac{5}{12}$ and $\frac{1}{8}$ **2.** $\frac{13}{24}$ **3.** $\frac{1}{8}$ **4.** $\frac{7}{8}$ **5.** $\frac{5}{6}$ **7.** $1\frac{1}{15}$ **9.** $1\frac{5}{24}$ **11.** $\frac{4}{5}$ **13.** $\frac{19}{24}$ **15.** $\frac{3a+2b}{6}$ **17.** $\frac{c+2d}{4}$ **19.** $\frac{5r+4s}{20}$ **21.** $\frac{8+15q}{10}$ **23.** $\frac{8u+25v}{40}$ **25.** $\frac{15b+14c}{18}$ **27.** $\frac{6q+7a}{10}$ **29.** $\frac{8x+21y}{36}$ **31.** $\frac{1}{4}$ **33.** $\frac{3}{10}$ **35.** $\frac{1}{12}$ **37.** $\frac{1}{2}$ **39.** $\frac{7}{8}$ **41.** $\frac{6m-5}{30}$ **43.** $\frac{2x-3y}{12}$ **45.** $\frac{8a-3b}{12}$ **47.** $\frac{15k-4}{10}$ **49.** $\frac{5n-2}{6}$ **51.** $\frac{15x-8y}{20}$ **53.** $\frac{16m-35n}{40}$ **55.** $\frac{5}{24}$ **57.** $\frac{23}{24}$

Pages 160–161

1. Add $145\frac{1}{2}$ and $23\frac{1}{4}$. **2.** Subtract $17\frac{3}{8}$ from $38\frac{3}{4}$. **3.** $168\frac{3}{4}$ pounds; $21\frac{3}{8}$ miles **4a.** $\frac{3}{5}$ **4b.** 6 **4c.** $\frac{2}{3}$

Pages 160–161 *(continued)*

4d. $\frac{3}{12}$ **5.** $4\frac{5}{6}$ **7.** $5\frac{7}{8}$ **9.** $7\frac{7}{10}$ **11.** $9\frac{13}{24}$ **13.** $16\frac{13}{24}$
15. $4\frac{1}{2}$ **17.** $4\frac{13}{20}$ **19.** $7\frac{11}{12}$ **21.** $2\frac{3}{8}$ **23.** $3\frac{1}{8}$ **25.** $3\frac{3}{8}$
27. $7\frac{1}{4}$ **29.** $9\frac{1}{8}$ **31.** $1\frac{1}{10}$ **33.** $1\frac{3}{8}$ **35.** $7\frac{11}{24}$
37. A; $1\frac{1}{4}$ miles **39.** B; $3\frac{3}{4}$ miles

Pages 162–163

1. $1\frac{2}{3}$ and $3\frac{1}{2}$ **2.** $6\frac{1}{3}$ and $4\frac{1}{2}$ **3a.** $5\frac{1}{6}$ cups
3b. $1\frac{5}{6}$ cups **4a.** $\frac{5}{24}$ **4b.** 10 **4c.** 12 **5.** $6\frac{1}{6}$ **7.** $9\frac{3}{8}$
9. $5\frac{1}{2}$ **11.** $9\frac{9}{10}$ **13.** $7\frac{9}{10}$ **15.** $5\frac{1}{24}$ **17.** $5\frac{1}{20}$
19. $8\frac{1}{12}$ **21.** $4\frac{3}{8}$ **23.** $2\frac{3}{4}$ **25.** $5\frac{5}{6}$ **27.** $6\frac{1}{8}$ **29.** $1\frac{1}{2}$
31. $2\frac{7}{8}$ **33.** $\frac{3}{5}$ **35.** $\frac{8}{9}$ **37.** $4\frac{3}{8}$ **39.** $4\frac{7}{12}$ **41.** 90¢

Pages 164–165

1a. Tina's; $4\frac{1}{2}$ **1b.** $t + 4\frac{1}{2}$; $67\frac{3}{4}$ **1c.** $t + 4\frac{1}{2} = 67\frac{3}{4}$
2. Yes **3.** A; $62\frac{3}{4}$ inches **5.** A; $62\frac{3}{4}$ **7.** A; $62\frac{3}{4}$
9. B; $74\frac{1}{4}$ **11.** $n - 3\frac{1}{8} = 14\frac{1}{2}$; $17\frac{5}{8}$
13. $6\frac{1}{2} + n = 20\frac{2}{3}$; $14\frac{1}{6}$ **15.** $s + 3\frac{1}{2} = 26\frac{1}{4}$; $22\frac{3}{4}$ hours
17. $2h + 5 = 43$; 19 hours

Page 166

1. 5 **3.** 1 **5.** 6 **7.** a **9.** $5w$ **11.** x **13.** $6cd$
15. $5e^2f$ **17.** 24 **19.** 20 **21.** 15 **23.** $12rs$
25. $9ab$ **27.** $16y^2$ **29.** $32f^2g^2$ **31.** $\frac{1}{4}$ **33.** $\frac{4}{3}$ **35.** $\frac{1}{3}$
37. $\frac{1}{y}$ **39.** $\frac{y}{3}$ **41.** $\frac{2cd}{9}$ **43.** $\frac{4}{5a^2b}$ **45.** $\frac{wx^2}{5}$ **47.** $\frac{36t^2}{29}$
49. 6 **51.** 18 **53.** 36 **55.** 60 **57.** x^2 **59.** a^2b
61. $12yz$ **63.** $18j^2k^2$ **65.** $<$ **67.** $>$ **69.** $<$
71. $<$ **73.** $>$ **75.** $<$ **77.** $>$

Page 167

1. \$213.19 **3.** \$106.80 **5.** \$751.24 **7.** \$111.34
9. \$462.45 **11.** \$47.09

Chapter 7 Multiplication and Division of Fractions

Pages 172–173

1. $\frac{6}{12}$ or $\frac{1}{2}$ **2.** $\frac{2}{3}$ **3a.** 1 **3b.** 1 **3c.** t **3d.** a
5. $\frac{1}{2}$ **7.** $2\frac{1}{4}$ **9.** 6 **11.** $\frac{1}{6}$ **13.** 2 **15.** $\frac{1}{16}$

Pages 172–173 *(continued)*

17. $\frac{5}{8}$ **19.** $\frac{1}{4}$ **21.** $\frac{1}{5}$ **23.** $\frac{7}{8}$ **25.** 3 **27.** $\frac{1}{3}$
29. $2\frac{1}{4}$ **31.** 1 **33.** $\frac{1}{4}$ **35.** $\frac{p}{q}$ **37.** $\frac{2m}{n^2}$ **39.** $\frac{1}{5}$
41. $\frac{24}{j}$ **43.** $\frac{k}{2j}$ **45.** $20x$ **47.** $\frac{uv}{y^2}$ **49.** $\frac{v}{wz}$ **51.** 1
53. $\frac{d}{6e}$ **55.** $\frac{8}{s}$ **57.** $\frac{b}{15}$ **59.** $\frac{2a}{3b}$ **61.** s **63.** $\frac{21}{e}$
65. Orioles, 4; Indians, 3

Pages 174–175

1. $4\frac{1}{2}$ cups **2.** $1\frac{1}{2}$ and $4\frac{1}{2}$ **3.** $6\frac{3}{4}$ cups; yes
4a. $3\frac{8}{9}$ **4b.** $\frac{46}{3}$ **4c.** 3 **5.** $4\frac{1}{6}$ **7.** $7\frac{7}{8}$ **9.** $6\frac{1}{4}$
11. 7 **13.** $22\frac{1}{2}$ **15.** $8\frac{17}{24}$ **17.** $8\frac{2}{5}$ **19.** $15\frac{8}{9}$
21. $26\frac{1}{8}$ **23.** $6\frac{3}{5}$ **25.** $9\frac{1}{2}$ **27.** $8\frac{3}{4}$ **29.** $7\frac{5}{16}$
31. $10\frac{1}{2}$ **33.** $3\frac{3}{10}$ **35.** $3\frac{1}{2}$ teaspoons
37. $11\frac{1}{4}$ cups **39.** No

Pages 176–177

1a. 10 **1b.** 10 **2.** 5 **3a.** $\frac{2}{3}$ **3b.** wy **3c.** $\frac{3r^2}{4}$
5. 8 **7.** $\frac{2}{3}$ **9.** $\frac{5}{3}$ **11.** $1\frac{1}{8}$ **13.** $\frac{9}{16}$ **15.** $1\frac{2}{3}$
17. $\frac{4}{5}$ **19.** $12\frac{1}{2}$ **21.** $1\frac{1}{2}$ **23.** $\frac{7}{12}$ **25.** $1\frac{1}{6}$
27. $6\frac{2}{5}$ **29.** 4 **31.** $2\frac{4}{5}$ **33.** $\frac{ad}{bc}$ **35.** $\frac{a}{cd}$ **37.** $\frac{r^2}{4s}$
39. $\frac{3mq}{2n}$ **41.** $\frac{6d}{ef}$ **43.** $\frac{2q}{p}$ **45.** $\frac{x}{3z}$

Pages 178–179

1. $3\frac{3}{4}$ miles **2.** $1\frac{1}{4}$ hours **3.** $1\frac{1}{4}$
4. 3 miles per hour **5a.** $\frac{1}{10}$ **5b.** $\frac{4}{9}$ **5c.** $\frac{7}{4}$
7. $4\frac{1}{8}$ **9.** $2\frac{1}{4}$ **11.** $2\frac{7}{16}$ **13.** $3\frac{5}{9}$ **15.** $\frac{7}{9}$ **17.** 3
19. $1\frac{1}{3}$ **21.** $1\frac{25}{32}$ **23.** $\frac{6}{25}$ **25.** 4 **27.** $3\frac{1}{3}$
29. $3\frac{1}{5}$ **31.** $1\frac{1}{3}$ **33.** 1 **35.** 1 **37.** 5 **39.** $4\frac{1}{2}$
41. $1\frac{1}{4}$ miles **43.** 5 hours **45.** $1\frac{1}{3}$ miles per hour
47a. $2\frac{2}{5}$ **47c.** $2\frac{8}{9}$ **47e.** $7\frac{4}{5}$

Page 180

1. 55 **3.** 161 **5.** 109 **7.** 43 **9.** 19 **11.** 400
13. 5.6 **15.** 23.1 **17.** 51 **19.** 21 **21.** 12 **23.** 7
25. 1.2 **27.** 90 **29.** 7 **31.** 12 **33.** 37 **35.** 34
37. 24 **39.** 10 **41.** 1.5 **43.** 2.6 **45.** $2 \cdot 5 \cdot a \cdot a$
47. $3 \cdot b \cdot b \cdot b$ **49.** $7 \cdot g \cdot g \cdot g$ **51.** $2 \cdot 2 \cdot 2 \cdot 3 \cdot w$
53. $5 \cdot 5 \cdot n \cdot n \cdot n$ **55.** $3 \cdot 3 \cdot 3 \cdot k$ **57.** $7 \cdot g \cdot g \cdot g \cdot g$

Page 180 *(continued)*
59. $7 \cdot r \cdot r \cdot s$ **61.** $2 \cdot 5 \cdot y \cdot z \cdot z$
63. $2 \cdot 2 \cdot 3 \cdot u \cdot u \cdot v \cdot v$ **65.** 24 **67.** 48 **69.** 100
71. $10x$ **73.** $10y$ **75.** $18w$ **77.** $7k$ **79.** $12n$
81. $3g^2$ **83.** $18b^2$ **85.** $18c^2$ **87.** $3m^2n$

Page 181
1. $12\frac{3}{4}$ books **3.** 11 months **5.** $\frac{3}{4}$ of a book
7. $2f + \frac{1}{2} = 5\frac{1}{2}$; $2\frac{1}{2}$ books **9.** $5s + 2\frac{1}{2} = 12\frac{1}{2}$;
2 books

Pages 182–183
1. \$15 **2.** $\frac{2}{3}$ **3.** \$15 **4.** \$10 **5a.** $3\frac{3}{4}$ **5b.** 30
5c. $\frac{77}{2}$ **7.** $6\frac{2}{3}$ **9.** 54 **11.** $3\frac{3}{5}$ **13.** 22 **15.** $7\frac{7}{8}$
17. 56 **19.** \$19 **21.** \$36 **23.** \$6 **25.** \$28
27. 12 **29.** $15\frac{1}{2}$ **31.** \$3.20 **33.** \$7.50
35. \$13.13 **37.** \$20.83 **39.** \$3 **41.** African violets
43a. 235.2 **43c.** 472.5 **43e.** 28.8

Pages 184–185
1. 24 inches **2.** 6 inches **3.** Add 24 and 6.
4a. 30 inches **4b.** Yes **5.** 18 **7.** 28 **9.** 16
11. 54 **13.** 81 **15.** 44 **17.** 60 **19.** 80 **21.** 138
23. 100 **25.** 10 **27.** 7 **29.** 7 **31.** 22 **33.** 15
35. $24d$ **37.** $\frac{s}{60}$ **39.** $12f$ **41.** $36y$ **43.** $2q$ **45.** $\frac{c}{2}$

Pages 186–187
1. \$18 **2.** $\frac{3}{4}$ **3.** More **4.** \$24 **5a.** 95 **5b.** $\frac{3}{2}$
5c. $\frac{3}{4}$; $7\frac{1}{2}$ **7.** 15 **9.** $10\frac{2}{3}$ **11.** 36 **13.** 25 **15.** 8
17. 36 **19.** $11\frac{3}{7}$ **21.** 34 **23.** 90 **25.** 72 **27.** $37\frac{1}{2}$
29. 25 **31.** \$36 **33.** \$12 **35.** C; \$64
37. B; 30 ski jackets

Pages 188–189
1. n; $\frac{2}{3}n$ **2.** $\frac{2}{3}n$; 54 **3.** $\frac{2}{3}n = 54$ **5a.** C; 13 people
5b. D; 23 people **7.** $\frac{2}{5}m = 40$; 100
9. $t - \frac{1}{3} = \frac{1}{2}$; $\frac{5}{6}$ **11.** $\frac{v}{3} - 6 = 1$; 21
13. $2k + 3 = 15$; \$6 **15.** $\frac{2}{3}b = \frac{4}{5}$; $1\frac{1}{5}$

Page 190
1. $\frac{1}{3}$ **3.** $\frac{5}{9}$ **5.** $\frac{2}{3}$ **7.** $\frac{1}{y}$ **9.** $\frac{2a}{3b}$ **11.** $\frac{3d}{c}$ **13.** $\frac{3r}{s}$
15. $\frac{4}{5d}$ **17.** $\frac{5n^2}{4m}$ **19.** 10 **21.** 6 **23.** 18 **25.** $8c$

Page 190 *(continued)*
27. $6m$ **29.** m^2n **31.** $6cd$ **33.** $20a^2b^2$ **35.** $\frac{2}{3}$
37. 3 **39.** $7\frac{2}{3}$ **41.** 6 **43.** $7\frac{3}{5}$ **45.** 7 **47.** $\frac{3x^2}{4y}$
49. 3 **51.** $\frac{8n^2}{3}$ **53.** $\frac{5}{6}$ **55.** $1\frac{5}{12}$ **57.** $\frac{2r + s}{4}$
59. $\frac{4p + 3q}{12}$ **61.** $\frac{3r + 10}{18}$ **63.** $\frac{12x + 5y}{30}$
65. $\frac{10m + 15n}{36}$ **67.** $\frac{1}{6}$ **69.** $\frac{1}{12}$ **71.** $\frac{25}{48}$
73. $\frac{5m - 2n}{10}$ **75.** $\frac{7a}{12}$

Page 191
1. 1771 miles **3.** 1402 miles **5.** 265 miles **7.** No
9. Yes **11.** 43.28 gallons

Chapter 8 Integers and Equations

Pages 196–197
1. $^+15^\circ$ **2.** $^-30^\circ$ **3a.** Less than **3b.** Greater than
4a. $^-3$ **4b.** $^+5$ **4c.** $^-4$ **4d.** $^+5$ **5.** $<$ **7.** $<$
9. $<$ **11.** $<$ **13.** $>$ **15.** $<$ **17.** $>$ **19.** $>$
21. $>$ **23.** $>$ **25.** $>$ **27.** $>$ **29.** $<$ **31.** $>$
33. $>$ **35.** positive **37.** Zero **39.** less
41. Phoenix **43.** Phoenix **45.** $^-30$, $^-24$, $^-23$, $^-8$ (2 cities), $^-4$, $^-1$, $^+5$, $^+12$, $^+15$ (3 cities), $^+25$, $^+31$, $^+32$, $^+35$ **47a.** 0 **47c.** 15 **47e.** 86

Pages 198–199
1. $^+3$ **2.** $^-1$ **3a.** $^-2$ **3b.** $^+1$ **4.** 0; yes **5.** $^-8$; $^+6$; 0 **7.** $^+4$ **9.** $^-9$ **11.** $^+7$ **13.** $^-8$ **15.** 0
17. $^+10$ **19.** $^+2$ **21.** $^-25$ **23.** $^+8$ **25.** $^-98$
27. $^-53$ **29.** 0 **31.** $^+2$ **33.** 0 **35.** $^-42$ **37.** $^+5$
39. $^+47$ **41.** $^-22$ **43.** $^+24$ **45.** $^-60$ **47.** False
49. True

Pages 200–201
1. $^+3$ **2a.** $^+2$ **2b.** $^+2$ **3a.** $^+5$ **3b.** $^+5$ **4a.** $^-7$
4b. $^+6$ **5a.** $^-13$ **5b.** $^+17$ **5c.** $^+5$ **7.** $^-3$ **9.** $^-5$
11. $^+4$ **13.** $^-13$ **15.** $^-6$ **17.** $^+9$ **19.** $^-10$
21. $^-11$ **23.** $^+7$ **25.** $^-12$ **27.** $^-9$ **29.** $^-7$
31. $^-12$ **33.** $^+9$ **35.** $^-16$ **37.** $^+26$ **39.** 0 **41.** 0
43. $^-30$ **45.** $^-34$ **47.** $^+27$ **49.** $^-6$ **51.** $^+14$
53. $^+22$ **55.** $^+36$ **57.** $^+54$ **59.** $^+13$ **61.** $^+11$
63. $^-15$ **65.** $^-17$ **67.** $^-4$ **69.** $^-36$ **71.** $t - {}^+11$
73. $k - {}^+8$ **75.** ${}^-10 - v$ **77.** $c + {}^-15$ **79.** $j + {}^+20$
81. $d - b$ **83.** $c - r$ **85.** $h - h$ **87.** ${}^-1 + t$

Pages 202–203
1. 0 **2.** $^+4$ **3.** $^+4$ **4.** positive **5.** negative
6. positive **7.** 0 **9.** $^-24$ **11.** $^-8$ **13.** $^-8$

Pages 202–203 *(continued)*
15. $^{+}64$ **17.** 0 **19.** $^{+}40$ **21.** $^{+}72$ **23.** $^{-}24$ **25.** 0 **27.** 0 **29.** $^{+}12$ **31.** $^{-}28$ **33.** $^{-}15$ **35.** $^{-}32$ **37.** $^{+}24$ **39.** $^{+}198$ **41.** $^{-}224$ **43.** $^{-}9$ **45.** $^{-}48$ **47.** 0 **49.** $^{+}11$ **51.** $^{-}3$ **53.** $^{+}5$ **55.** $^{+}18$ **57.** $^{+}18$ **59.** $^{-}9$ **61.** $^{-}11$ **63.** $^{+}9$ **65.** $^{+}1$ **67.** $^{-}27$ **69.** $^{+}16$ **71.** $^{+}27$ **73.** $^{-}32$ **75.** $^{-}1$ **77.** $^{-}1$

Pages 204–205
1. $^{+}5$ **2.** $^{+}9$ **3.** 0 **4.** positive **5.** positive **6.** negative **7.** negative **9.** $^{-}8$ **11.** $^{-}4$ **13.** $^{-}7$ **15.** $^{+}7$ **17.** $^{-}7$ **19.** $^{+}5$ **21.** $^{-}6$ **23.** $^{-}4$ **25.** $^{-}4$ **27.** 0 **29.** $^{+}9$ **31.** $^{+}8$ **33.** $^{-}7$ **35.** $^{-}6$ **37.** 21 **39.** $^{-}5$ **41.** $^{-}7$ **43.** 100 **45.** $^{-}24$ **47.** $^{-}25$ **49.** 78 **51.** $^{-}12$ **53.** 42 **55.** 8 **57.** 24 **59.** $^{-}90$ **61.** 54 **63.** $^{-}19$ **65.** 146 **67a.** $^{-}255$ **67c.** 510 **67e.** $^{-}149$ **67g.** $^{-}21$ **67i.** $^{-}87$

Page 206
1. 2^2 **3.** $2 \cdot 3^2$ **5.** 5^2 **7.** 3^3 **9.** $2^2 \cdot 11$ **11.** $2^3 \cdot 5$ **13.** $2^3 \cdot 3^2$ **15.** $2^2 \cdot 5^2$ **17.** $2^2 \cdot 3^2 \cdot 5$ **19.** 4 **21.** 12 **23.** 4 **25.** d **27.** x **29.** $7w$ **31.** $5uv$ **33.** $3cd^2$ **35.** 10 **37.** 6 **39.** $10x$ **41.** $24d$ **43.** $3s^2$ **45.** $15de$ **47.** 4 **49.** $6\frac{1}{2}$ **51.** $\frac{2}{3}$ **53.** $1\frac{2}{3}$ **55.** $\frac{3}{8d}$ **57.** $\frac{1}{3b}$ **59.** $\frac{7c}{12}$ **61.** 4 **63.** $\frac{7n^2}{4}$ **65.** $\frac{7}{8}$ **67.** $\frac{1}{12}$ **69.** $\frac{2a+b}{6}$ **71.** $\frac{9x+8}{30}$ **73.** $\frac{3x-2y}{12}$ **75.** $\frac{4j-3k}{18}$

Page 207
1. 3 pounds **3.** $4.40 **5a.** 1.20; 1.20 **5b.** 1.20 **5c.** 5.20 **5d.** 2.5 pounds **7.** $1.20p + 1.89 = 5.73$; 3.2 pounds

Pages 208–209
1. 1; 10 **2a.** 3.6 **2b.** 8.5 **2c.** 4.05 **2d.** 1.25 **2e.** 8 **2f.** 9 **3.** 7 **5.** 5 **7.** 4 **9.** 5 **11.** 8 **13.** $^{-}4$ **15.** $^{-}6$ **17.** $^{-}2$ **19.** $^{-}7$ **21.** $3.1 \cdot 10^4$ **23.** $5.46 \cdot 10^6$ **25.** $2.36 \cdot 10^5$ **27.** $5.1 \cdot 10^4$ **29.** $7 \cdot 10^8$ **31.** $1.11 \cdot 10^6$ **33.** $4 \cdot 10^2$ **35.** $6.06 \cdot 10^6$ **37.** $9.9 \cdot 10^5$ **39.** $1.4 \cdot 10^3$ **41.** $7.5 \cdot 10^{-4}$ **43.** $6 \cdot 10^{-5}$ **45.** $3.17 \cdot 10^{-2}$ **47.** $6.49 \cdot 10^{-3}$ **49.** $1.2 \cdot 10^{-3}$ **51.** $3.75 \cdot 10^{-2}$ **53.** $2.5 \cdot 10^{-5}$ **55.** $7.5 \cdot 10^{-6}$ **57.** $3.8 \cdot 10^{11}$ **59.** $2.9 \cdot 10^{-3}$ **61.** $8.64 \cdot 10^6$ **63.** $2.5 \cdot 10^{-4}$

Pages 210–211
1a. 14; $^{-}20$ **1b.** $^{-}8$; $^{-}6$ **1c.** $^{-}6$ **2a.** $^{-}4$ **2b.** 7 **2c.** $^{-}28$ **2d.** $^{-}10$; $^{-}18$ **2e.** $^{-}18$; $^{-}3$ **2f.** 5; 5; $^{-}15$

Pages 210–211 *(continued)*
3. $^{-}17$ **5.** $^{-}32$ **7.** 21 **9.** $^{-}19$ **11.** $^{-}40$ **13.** 46 **15.** 37 **17.** $^{-}5$ **19.** $^{-}7$ **21.** $^{-}33$ **23.** 5 **25.** 6 **27.** $^{-}14$ **29.** 32 **31.** $^{-}10$ **33.** 7 **35.** $^{-}6$ **37.** 20 **39.** 31 **41.** 21 **43.** $^{-}4$ **45.** 0 **47.** 9 **49.** $^{-}8$ **51.** 0 **53.** $^{-}2$ **55.** A; $^{-}10$ **57.** C; $^{-}50$°F **59.** B; 50 **61.** A; $^{-}10$

Pages 212–213
1a. $^{-}3$; 5 **1b.** $^{-}4$; $^{-}80$ **1c.** $^{-}80$ **2a.** $^{-}8$ **2b.** $^{-}21$ **2c.** $^{-}12$; $^{-}5$ **2d.** $^{-}6$; $^{-}7$ **2e.** $^{-}3$; 15 **2f.** 7; $^{-}5$; $^{-}35$ **3.** $^{-}3$ **5.** 7 **7.** 22 **9.** $^{-}18$ **11.** 30 **13.** 10 **15.** 11 **17.** 8 **19.** $^{-}63$ **21.** 8 **23.** $^{-}11$ **25.** 2 **27.** 0 **29.** 19 **31.** $^{-}12$ **33.** 1 **35.** 10 **37.** $^{-}4$ **39.** 5 **41.** 200 **43.** 14 **45.** 99 **47.** $^{-}1$ **48a.** 8 **48c.** 36

Pages 214–215
1. $^{-}35$ feet **2.** Minutes of descent **3.** $^{-}35$; $^{-}15$ **4.** 7 minutes **5.** 80; 20; $^{-}4$; $^{-}5$ **7.** 8; $^{-}32$; 4; $^{-}128$ **9.** 5 **11.** $^{-}4$ **13.** $^{-}12$ **15.** $^{-}35$ **17.** 5 **19.** $^{-}6$ **21.** $^{-}48$ **23.** 35 **25.** $^{-}4$ **27.** 2 **29.** $^{-}2$ **31.** $^{-}42$ **33.** $^{-}5$ **35.** $^{-}7$ **37.** $^{-}35$ **39.** $^{-}36$ **41.** 2 **43.** 0 **45.** $^{-}3720$

Pages 216–217
1a. lowest; 123 **1b.** $n + 123$; 104 **1c.** $n + 123 = 104$ **1d.** 123 **2.** Yes **3a.** 100 **3b.** 100 **3c.** $^{-}56$ **3d.** 44°F **5.** $d + 9 = {}^{-}7$; $^{-}16$ **7.** $f({}^{-}12) = {}^{-}72$; 6 **9.** $^{-}9 + j = {}^{-}12$; $^{-}3$ **11.** $4t - 8 = {}^{-}32$; $^{-}6$ **13.** $n - 18 = 7$; 25°F

Page 218
1. $\frac{1}{3n}$ **3.** 4 **5.** $1\frac{1}{14}$ **7.** $6z$ **9.** $\frac{9}{10jk}$ **11.** $\frac{3}{n}$ **13.** $\frac{ab}{5}$ **15.** $\frac{2}{m}$ **17.** $1\frac{1}{9}$ **19.** $\frac{4}{15}$ **21.** $1\frac{1}{2}$ **23.** $\frac{3m}{2n}$ **25.** $\frac{2m}{3n^2}$ **27.** $\frac{3ps}{2qr}$ **29.** $\frac{2}{a}$ **31.** 8 **33.** 30 **35.** 20 **37.** 50 **39.** $12\frac{4}{5}$ **41.** $43\frac{3}{4}$ **43.** 27 **45.** 99 **47.** 84 **49.** 6 **51.** 12 **53.** 48 **55.** 88 **57.** 28 **59.** $74\frac{2}{5}$ **61.** 90

Page 219
1. $35,000 **3.** $225,000 **5.** 10:30–midnight **7.** $900 **9.** Take a loss; $750

Chapter 9 Rational Numbers and Equations

Pages 224–225
1. $^{+}\frac{1}{4}$; $^{-}1$ **2.** Kroger **3.** Less than **4a.** Yes

Pages 224–225 *(continued)*

4b. Yes **5.** $^{-}2$ **7.** 3 **9.** $3\frac{1}{3}$ **11.** $\frac{^{-}1}{6}$ **13.** $^{-}6\frac{1}{3}$
15. 6 **17.** $1\frac{1}{2}$ **19.** $^{-}4$ **21.** $1\frac{1}{2}$ **23.** $^{-}5\frac{1}{2}$
25. $\frac{^{-}3}{4}$ **27.** $^{-}6$ **29.** $^{-}1$ **31.** 0 **33.** $1\frac{2}{3}$ **35.** $<$
37. $>$ **39.** $<$ **41.** $>$ **43.** $<$ **45.** $>$ **47.** $<$
49. $>$ **51.** $<$ **53.** $>$ **55.** $<$ **57.** $>$ **59.** Mobil
61. $25 **63.** $^{+}$$25

Pages 226–227

1. Yes **3.** $^{-}1.75$ **5.** $^{-}0.8$ **7.** $^{-}0.\overline{4}$ **9.** 3.5
11. 3.75 **13.** $1.8\overline{3}$ **15.** $0.\overline{45}$ **17.** $1.41\overline{6}$ **19.** $2.08\overline{3}$
21. $^{-}4.\overline{3}$ **23.** $^{-}6.8\overline{3}$ **25.** $\frac{^{-}1}{4}$ **27.** $\frac{3}{4}$ **29.** $\frac{4}{5}$
31. $\frac{12}{25}$ **33.** $\frac{3}{20}$ **35.** $\frac{3}{8}$ **37.** $\frac{^{-}2}{5}$ **39.** $2\frac{1}{4}$ **41.** $2\frac{2}{5}$
43. $9\frac{7}{20}$ **45.** $3\frac{3}{4}$ **47.** $^{-}4\frac{3}{8}$ **49a.** $3\frac{1}{4}$ pounds
49b. $1.05 **49c.** $6 **50a.** $0.\overline{09}$ **50c.** $0.\overline{27}$
50e. $0.\overline{45}$ **51a.** $\frac{6}{11}$ **51c.** $\frac{8}{11}$

Page 229

1. $\frac{^{-}1}{5}$ **3.** $1\frac{1}{16}$ **5.** $\frac{^{-}7}{16}$ **7.** $\frac{^{-}5}{12}$ **9.** $\frac{^{-}3}{10}$ **11.** $\frac{^{-}11}{20}$
13. $1\frac{17}{24}$ **15.** $\frac{^{-}5}{24}$ **17.** $^{-}7\frac{3}{4}$ **19.** 1 **21.** $^{-}2\frac{3}{4}$
23. $^{-}1\frac{19}{20}$ **25.** $1\frac{23}{24}$ **27.** $\frac{^{-}14}{15}$ **29.** $\frac{^{-}13}{18}$ **31.** $\frac{^{-}2}{3}$
33. $\frac{^{-}3}{20}$ **35.** $\frac{^{-}19}{20}$ **37.** $\frac{7}{24}$ **39.** $\frac{^{-}3}{40}$ **41.** $6\frac{4}{5}$
43. $^{-}13\frac{3}{4}$ **45.** $2\frac{1}{15}$ **47.** $2\frac{17}{24}$ **49.** $^{-}18\frac{19}{24}$

Pages 230–231

1a. $\frac{^{-}9}{2}$ **1b.** canceling **1c.** simplest **3.** $\frac{1}{6}$
5. $^{-}2\frac{2}{15}$ **7.** $\frac{^{-}5}{8}$ **9.** 1 **11.** $^{-}6\frac{2}{3}$ **13.** $10\frac{2}{3}$
15. $4\frac{5}{18}$ **17.** $9\frac{13}{18}$ **19.** $^{-}4\frac{2}{3}$ **21.** $^{-}11\frac{23}{32}$
23. $1\frac{1}{2}$ **25.** $^{-}1\frac{1}{3}$ **27.** $1\frac{1}{2}$ **29.** $\frac{^{-}5}{24}$ **31.** $\frac{15}{16}$
33. $^{-}2$ **35.** $\frac{23}{26}$ **37.** $2\frac{5}{32}$ **39.** $^{-}1\frac{5}{24}$ **41.** 2
42a. 22 ft **42c.** 44 ft **43a.** 25 mph **45c.** 55 mph

Page 232

1. 12 **3.** 24 **5.** 24 **7.** $2b$ **9.** $2m^2$ **11.** 4
13. $7\frac{4}{5}$ **15.** $6\frac{2}{3}$ **17.** $\frac{2a}{3b}$ **19.** $\frac{7b}{4}$ **21.** $\frac{7m}{2n}$
23. $\frac{3}{2y}$ **25.** $\frac{10m}{13n^2}$ **27.** $\frac{4}{5ab}$ **29.** 1 **31.** $\frac{1}{3}$ **33.** $\frac{11}{30}$
35. $\frac{4r + 3s}{12}$ **37.** $\frac{4m + 5n}{10}$ **39.** $\frac{6p - 5q}{30}$
41. $\frac{3a - 2b}{4}$ **43.** $\frac{8m - 15n}{18}$ **45.** $\frac{1}{5}$ **47.** $\frac{5}{8}$ **49.** $\frac{1}{5}$

Page 232 *(continued)*

51. $\frac{y}{2}$ **53.** $\frac{2}{5}$ **55.** 1 **57.** $\frac{y}{w}$ **59.** 3 **61.** $\frac{5}{8}$
63. $2\frac{2}{5}$ **65.** $\frac{2c}{b}$ **67.** $\frac{6}{z}$ **69.** $\frac{1}{2}$ **71.** d **73.** $12b$

Page 233

1. $.12 **3.** No **5.** $3n + .18 = 4.68$; Bald Head Wig
7. $1.75v + 1.95 + .29 = 7.49$; 3 Venus Flytraps

Page 235

1a. 12; 5 **1b.** 5; 6 **1c.** 10; 6; $^{-}8$ **3.** 3 **5.** $^{-}1\frac{5}{7}$
7. 4 **9.** $^{-}4\frac{2}{3}$ **11.** $1\frac{1}{8}$ **13.** $1\frac{1}{2}$ **15.** $^{-}1\frac{11}{12}$
17. $\frac{6}{7}$ **19.** $^{-}5$ **21.** $\frac{2}{15}$ **23.** $\frac{^{-}4}{7}$ **25.** 1 **27.** $^{-}2$
29. 9 **31.** $^{-}1\frac{3}{5}$ **33.** 0 **35.** $^{-}10\frac{1}{2}$ **37.** $1\frac{9}{10}$
39. D; $\frac{1}{6}$ **41.** B; $\frac{2}{5}$

Pages 236–237

1a. $^{-}2$ **1b.** 0 **1c.** 1 **3.** $7n$ **5.** $11n - 6$
7. $8n + 3$ **9.** $^{-}8x$ **11.** $5y + 7$ **13.** $9y - 11$
15. $8w - 2$ **17.** $4z - 12$ **19.** $^{-}9r - 15$ **21.** 8
23. $8a + 1$ **25.** $7c$ **27.** 5 **29.** $17m + 2$ **31.** $^{-}18$
33. $^{-}35$ **35.** 0 **37a.** 0 **37c.** 64 **37e.** 0

Pages 238–239

1. combine **2.** $8; yes **3a.** 2; 2 **3b.** 3; $^{-}5\frac{2}{3}$
3c. 16; $^{-}2$ **5.** $^{-}6$ **7.** $\frac{5}{9}$ **9.** $2\frac{3}{7}$ **11.** $^{-}4\frac{2}{3}$
13. $^{-}3\frac{1}{5}$ **15.** $\frac{^{-}1}{8}$ **17.** $1\frac{5}{9}$ **19.** $^{-}2\frac{1}{2}$ **21.** 2
23. 1 **25.** $\frac{1}{11}$ **27.** $^{-}1\frac{1}{2}$ **29.** $\frac{^{-}4}{15}$ **31.** $^{-}2\frac{1}{7}$
33. $\frac{1}{23}$ **35.** $\frac{21}{23}$ **37.** $\frac{^{-}10}{17}$ **39.** $4\frac{6}{7}$ **41.** $^{-}7$ **43.** 0
45. $^{-}1\frac{1}{2}$ **47.** B; $7 **49.** A; $6.50

Pages 240–241

1. combine **2.** $4; yes **3a.** 3; $^{-}2$ **3b.** w; $12\frac{5}{7}$
5. $^{-}1\frac{5}{11}$ **7.** $1\frac{5}{7}$ **9.** $^{-}4\frac{4}{5}$ **11.** $^{-}2\frac{1}{3}$ **13.** $2\frac{2}{3}$
15. $1\frac{5}{12}$ **17.** $\frac{^{-}1}{2}$ **19.** $2\frac{1}{4}$ **21.** $^{-}15$ **23.** 9 **25.** 26
27. $\frac{^{-}4}{5}$

Page 243

1. $4\frac{2}{5}$ **3.** $^{-}7\frac{1}{2}$ **5.** $4\frac{4}{9}$ **7.** 374 miles **9.** 140 miles
11. $37\frac{1}{2}$ minutes

Page 244

1. 15 **3.** 84 **5.** $7\frac{1}{5}$ **7.** $49\frac{1}{2}$ **9.** 30 **11.** 117 **13.** 160 **15.** 105 **17.** 132 **19.** 5 **21.** 96 **23.** 90 **25.** $49\frac{1}{2}$ **27.** $57\frac{1}{7}$ **29.** $1.4 \cdot 10^4$ **31.** $1.2 \cdot 10^5$ **33.** $5.8 \cdot 10^6$ **35.** $1.8 \cdot 10^7$ **37.** $8.3 \cdot 10^{-3}$ **39.** $8.4 \cdot 10^{-4}$ **41.** $1.78 \cdot 10^{-4}$ **43.** $5.286 \cdot 10^{-3}$ **45.** 2 **47.** 0 **49.** $^-63$ **51.** $^-10$ **53.** $^-3$ **55.** $^-36$

Page 245

1. 346.5 calories **3.** 1248 calories **5.** 115.5 more calories **7.** About 9.5 hours

Chapter 10 Ratio, Proportion, and Percent

Pages 250–251

1. $\frac{1}{4}$ **2.** $2a$ **3.** equal **4.** $3x$ **5a.** 3 **5b.** 18 **5c.** b **5d.** $6xy$ **7.** $\frac{1}{4}$ **9.** $\frac{4}{3}$ **11.** $\frac{2}{3}$ **13.** $\frac{8}{3}$ **15.** $\frac{2}{3}$ **17.** $\frac{7}{4}$ **19.** $\frac{2}{3}$ **21.** $\frac{a}{2b}$ **23.** $\frac{d}{c}$ **25.** $\frac{3m}{4n^2}$ **27.** $\frac{3}{2}$ **29.** $\frac{4y}{3z}$ **31.** $\frac{3m}{5n}$ **33.** $\frac{2cd}{3}$ **35.** $\frac{9h}{5j}$ **37.** 24 **39.** 6 **41.** 36 **43.** 9 **45.** 110 **47.** 25 **49.** 20 **51.** 21 **53.** mn **55.** wz^2 **57.** $10j^2k$ **59.** $25m^2$ **61.** $3cd^2$ **63.** $27ab^3$ **65.** $35x^2y^2$ **67.** $\frac{6}{5}$ **69.** 9 stamps **71.** $\frac{10}{3}$

Pages 252–253

1. 5 **2.** 5 feet **3.** No **4.** $15\frac{3}{8}$ feet **5a.** $4\frac{4}{5}$ **5b.** 24 **5c.** 7 **5d.** 4 **7.** 18 **9.** $2\frac{11}{12}$ **11.** $5\frac{8}{11}$ **13.** 36 **15.** $6\frac{1}{4}$ **17.** $15\frac{5}{7}$ **19.** $9\frac{3}{8}$ **21.** 1 **23.** $1\frac{3}{8}$ **25.** 1 **27.** $8\frac{4}{7}$ **29.** 16 **31a.** $1\frac{11}{30}$ feet **31b.** $\frac{11}{12}$ foot **33.** $2\frac{1}{82}$ feet

Page 255

1a. About 8.67 gallons **1b.** 5 gallons **1c.** $9 **1d.** $17.10 **3a.** About 258.33 miles **3b.** About 335.83 miles **3c.** About 15.48 gallons **3d.** About 10.84 gallons **5a.** $150.50 **5b.** About 9.30 days **7.** Yes

Pages 256–257

1. 25% **2.** $16\frac{2}{3}$% **3.** $\frac{1}{4}$; $\frac{1}{6}$ **4a.** $\frac{1}{5}$ **4b.** 75 **4c.** 100 **4d.** $\frac{3}{8}$ **4e.** $\frac{1}{100}$ **4f.** $83\frac{1}{3}$; 250 **5.** $\frac{1}{4}$

Pages 256–257 *(continued)*

7. $\frac{1}{2}$ **9.** $\frac{7}{10}$ **11.** $\frac{3}{20}$ **13.** $2\frac{1}{5}$ **15.** $\frac{11}{25}$ **17.** $\frac{1}{5}$ **19.** $\frac{3}{5}$ **21.** $2\frac{1}{4}$ **23.** $\frac{37}{50}$ **25.** $1\frac{1}{2}$ **27.** $2\frac{1}{2}$ **29.** $\frac{17}{20}$ **31.** $\frac{1}{10}$ **33.** $1\frac{3}{5}$ **35.** $1\frac{1}{10}$ **37.** 4 **39.** $\frac{9}{10}$ **41.** $\frac{9}{20}$ **43.** $2\frac{1}{10}$ **45.** $2\frac{3}{4}$ **47.** $\frac{3}{16}$ **49.** $\frac{13}{16}$ **51.** $\frac{5}{8}$ **53.** $2\frac{1}{16}$ **55.** $1\frac{7}{8}$ **57.** $1\frac{5}{8}$ **59.** $1\frac{3}{8}$ **61.** $\frac{1}{6}$ **63.** $1\frac{1}{3}$ **65.** Recreation and clothing **67.** $\frac{1}{3}$ **69.** $\frac{11}{24}$ **71a.** $6 **71b.** $4 **71c.** $8 **71d.** $3 **71e.** $3

Pages 258–259

1. 12 teams **2.** 24 teams **3.** $\frac{12}{24} = \frac{1}{2}$ **4.** $\frac{16}{24} = \frac{2}{3}$ **5.** 50%; $66\frac{2}{3}$% **6.** Method 1; method 2 **7.** 40% **9.** 90% **11.** 125% **13.** 20% **15.** 80% **17.** 10% **19.** 150% **21.** 140% **23.** 250% **25.** $33\frac{1}{3}$% **27.** 175% **29.** $83\frac{1}{3}$% **31.** $56\frac{1}{4}$% **33.** $55\frac{5}{9}$% **35.** $66\frac{2}{3}$% **37.** $44\frac{4}{9}$% **39.** 62% **41.** $41\frac{2}{3}$% **43.** 28% **45.** $87\frac{1}{2}$% **47.** $62\frac{1}{2}$% **49.** $266\frac{2}{3}$% **51.** $116\frac{2}{3}$% **53.** $91\frac{2}{3}$% **55.** 450% **57.** $233\frac{1}{3}$% **59.** $183\frac{1}{3}$% **61.** $70\frac{5}{6}$% **63.** $66\frac{2}{3}$% **65.** $16\frac{2}{3}$% **67.** $\frac{5}{12}$

Page 260

1. 3^2 **3.** $2^2 \cdot 3$ **5.** 3^3 **7.** 5^2 **9.** $2^4 \cdot 3$ **11.** 2^6 **13.** $2^4 \cdot 3^2$ **15.** $2^4 \cdot 3 \cdot 5$ **17.** $2^5 \cdot 5$ **19.** $2^2 \cdot 3 \cdot 5$ **21.** $2^3 \cdot 3^2$ **23.** $2^3 \cdot 3^2 \cdot 5$ **25.** 1 **27.** 5 **29.** 16 **31.** 1 **33.** y **35.** $8a$ **37.** b **39.** $9f$ **41.** $5wz$ **43.** $8pq^2$ **45.** $\frac{1}{3}$ **47.** $\frac{3}{5}$ **49.** $\frac{2}{3}$ **51.** $\frac{1}{z}$ **53.** $\frac{n}{3m}$ **55.** $\frac{5n}{m}$ **57.** $\frac{3x}{y}$ **59.** $\frac{6}{7q}$ **61.** $\frac{7z^2}{3y}$ **63.** $1.8 \cdot 10^4$ **65.** $3.9 \cdot 10^5$ **67.** $9.64 \cdot 10^6$ **69.** $6.1 \cdot 10^7$ **71.** $1.4 \cdot 10^{-2}$ **73.** $4 \cdot 10^{-4}$ **75.** $2.56 \cdot 10^{-4}$ **77.** $3.13 \cdot 10^{-5}$ **79.** $^-4\frac{1}{5}$ **81.** $^-52$ **83.** 4 **85.** 0 **87.** $^-24$ **89.** $^-54$ **91.** $^-2$ **93.** $^-72$

Page 261

1. 507 km **3.** 754 km **5.** 1222 km **7.** 533 km **9.** 1131 km **11.** 546 km **13.** 871 km **15.** Pittsburgh

Pages 262–263

1. \$15 **2.** 20% **3.** \$42 **4.** 18% **5.** \$3; \$12 **6.** \$7.56; \$34.44 **7a.** 36 **7b.** 47 **7c.** 5 **9.** 10 **11.** 18 **13.** 8 **15.** 24 **17.** 49.92 **19.** 128.7 **21.** 4.025 **23.** 0.375 **25.** 5.4316 **27.** 4.48 **29.** 12.5 **31.** 10 **33.** \$32.76 **35.** \$30.24 **37a.** 36.12 **37c.** 1.0792 **37e.** 9.434

Pages 264–265

1. 80% **2.** 52 questions **3.** More **4.** 65 questions **5a.** 80 **5b.** 150 **5c.** 0.31 **7.** 64 **9.** 200 **11.** 50 **13.** 20.3 **15.** 180 **17.** 350 **19.** 7.1 **21a.** $\frac{3}{4}$ **21b.** 75% **23.** 80 questions **25a.** 24 feet **25c.** 121.5 feet

Pages 266–267

1a. 100; 132 **1b.** 29; n **1c.** $62\frac{1}{2}$; 72; n **3.** 125 **5.** 50 **7.** 500 **9.** 0.075 **11.** 12 **13.** 8 **15.** 48 **17.** 400 **19.** 52 **21.** 144 **23.** 120 **25.** $31\frac{1}{4}$ **27.** $87\frac{1}{2}$ **29.** 6 **31.** 5 **33.** $66\frac{2}{3}$ **35.** 75 **37.** 90 **39.** $41\frac{2}{3}$ **41.** 25% **43.** \$144

Pages 268–269

1a. \$25 **1b.** Increase **1c.** \$50 **2a.** \$175 **2b.** Decrease **2c.** \$50 **3a.** 14 **3b.** 120 **5.** 25% d **7.** 36.2% d **9.** 22.5% d **11.** 19% d **13.** 26.7% d **15.** 40.8% i **17.** 43.8% i **19.** 100% i **21.** 60% d **23.** 46.7% i **25.** $33\frac{1}{3}$% **27a.** \$75 **27b.** \$75 **27c.** No **29.** No **31.** \$99 a week

Page 271

1. \$672 **3.** \$2200 **5.** \$800 **7.** 10% **9.** \$620 **11.** \$372 **13.** \$17,600 **15.** \$3000

Page 272

1. $\frac{1}{9}$ **3.** $\frac{^-5}{12}$ **5.** $\frac{^-7}{10}$ **7.** $\frac{^-13}{32}$ **9.** $1\frac{5}{12}$ **11.** $\frac{^-9}{10}$ **13.** $^-1\frac{17}{24}$ **15.** $\frac{^-1}{24}$ **17.** $\frac{1}{24}$ **19.** $^-2\frac{1}{12}$ **21.** $\frac{7}{10}$ **23.** $^-6$ **25.** $\frac{^-4}{5}$ **27.** $\frac{2}{3}$ **29.** $\frac{^-5}{24}$ **31.** $\frac{^-2}{3}$ **33.** $6x$ **35.** 0 **37.** $^-3w - 3$ **39.** $^-8r - 8$ **41.** $^-7r - 7$ **43.** $1\frac{1}{4}$ **45.** $3\frac{4}{7}$ **47.** $^-5$ **49.** $^-6$ **51.** $\frac{^-1}{3}$ **53.** $1\frac{3}{7}$ **55.** $\frac{^-1}{8}$

Page 273

1. \$1175; \$1325; \$1500 **3.** \$1400; \$1775; \$2225 **5.** 6 years **7.** \$1762.34

Chapter 11 Geometry—Perimeter and Area

Pages 278–279

1. $\angle R$ **2.** $\angle S$ **3.** $\angle T$ **5.** acute **7.** right **9.** acute **11.** right **13.** obtuse **15.** obtuse **17.** 80° **19.** 90° **21.** 48°

Pages 280–281

1. True **3.** False **5.** False **7.** True **9.** True **11.** True **13.** True **15.** False **17.** False **19.** 4 **21.** 8

Pages 282–283

1. Lot D **2.** Lot A **3.** Lot B **4a.** Lot C **4b.** Lot D **4c.** Lots D, E **4d.** Lots B, D, E **4e.** Lot A **4f.** Lot F **5.** Rectangle; parallelogram **7.** Triangle **9.** Hexagon **11.** Trapezoid **13.** Square; rectangle; parallelogram **15.** Triangle **17.** Trapezoid **19.** Lot M—Rita; Lot N—Betty; Lot P—Arlo; Lot R—Cindy; Lot S—David

Pages 284–285

1. m **3.** mm **5.** m **7.** m **9.** km **11.** m **13.** m **15.** m **17.** b **19.** b **21.** b **23.** a **25a.** 691 km **25b.** 321 km

Pages 286–287

1a. 100 **1b.** 10 **2.** Ivan **3a.** 1; 1.825 **3b.** 1000; 9650 **5.** 400 **7.** 0.54 **9.** 25,000 **11.** 3500 **13.** 5800 **15.** 2.5 **17.** 2750 **19.** 7500 **21.** 126 **23.** 0.9 **25.** 84 **27.** 605 **29.** 625 **31.** 5.5 **33.** 0.38 mm **35.** 8.38 m **37.** $100n$ **39.** $1000n$ **41.** $\frac{n}{100}$ **43.** $\frac{n}{10}$

Pages 288–289

1. $P = 4s$; side **2.** $P = 2(l + w)$; length and width **3.** 56 m **5.** 111 cm **7.** 116 km **9.** 24 m **11.** 12 km **13.** 8.8 m **15.** 51 m **17.** 144 mm **19.** 260 cm **21.** 15 m **23.** 83 m

Pages 290–291

1. 3.14 **2.** $2\pi r$ **3.** 36 **4.** 4 **5.** 21.98 ft **7.** 12.56 ft **9.** 9.42 yd **11.** 28.26 yd **13.** 75.36 in. **15.** 251.2 yd **17.** 628 in. **19.** 1.5 yd **21.** 3 in. **23.** 1036.2 ft

Page 292

1. $8c$ **3.** 0 **5.** $^-8d + 4$ **7.** $^-11s - 8$ **9.** $^-10s - 7$ **11.** $^-4k + 5$ **13.** $^-1\frac{4}{5}$ **15.** 0 **17.** 19 **19.** $\frac{^-3}{4}$ **21.** 8 **23.** $1\frac{2}{9}$ **25.** $^-8$ **27.** $^-3$ **29.** $22\frac{1}{2}$ **31.** $^-5$

Page 292 *(continued)*
33. $^{-}2$ **35.** 12 **37.** 20 **39.** 8 **41.** jk **43.** $3rs$
45. $36mn$ **47.** $5wxy$ **49.** $1\frac{3}{7}$ **51.** 4 **53.** 24
55. $12\frac{2}{3}$ **57.** 10 **59.** $2\frac{1}{2}$ **61.** $7\frac{41}{49}$ **63.** $10\frac{2}{3}$

Page 293
1. $4.85 **3.** $4 **5.** 6 rides **7.** C; $2.20 **9.** A; $4.80 **11.** $3j + 4 = 16.30$; $4.10

Pages 294–295
1. 15 **2.** 9 square centimeters **3.** $A = lw$; A is area, l is length, and w is width. **4.** square **5.** 144
7. 6 m^2 **9.** 58.5 m^2 **11.** 810 cm^2 **13.** 3.9 m^2
15. 84 cm^2 **17.** 4 km^2 **19.** 72.25 cm^2 **21.** 11.56 m^2
23. 0.09 km^2 **25.** 12 m **27.** Area; 216 tiles
29. Perimeter; 110 yards **31.** Area; $17.70

Pages 296–297
1. $A = bh$; A is area, b is base, and h is height.
2. centimeters **3.** 25.2 **5.** 30.4 m^2 **7.** 47.46 m^2
9. 450 km^2 **11.** 120 km^2 **13.** 125 cm^2 **15.** 54 m^2
17. 10,000 m^2 **19.** 3 m **21.** 30 km **23.** 46 cm

Pages 298–299
1. height **2.** yards **3.** 54 **5.** 60 $in.^2$ **7.** 15 ft^2
9. $25\frac{1}{2}$ ft^2 **11.** $55\frac{1}{2}$ ft^2 **13.** 180 yd^2 **15.** 36 yd^2
17. 12 ft

Pages 300–301
1a. 36 cm^2 **1b.** 27 cm^2 **2.** Yes **3.** radius **4.** r, r
5. centimeters **6.** 314 **7.** 12.56 cm^2 **9.** 0.785 m^2
11. 113.04 cm^2 **13.** 1256 cm^2 **15.** 4.5216 m^2
17. 2.0096 m^2 **19.** 78.5 cm^2 **21.** 2826 km^2
23. 20,096 cm^2 **25.** 3.14 m^2 **27.** 37.68 m^2
29. 18.24 m^2

Pages 302–303
1a. 12 **1b.** $w + w + 12 + w + w + 12$ **1c.** 96
2. 30 cm; yes **3.** B; 14 cm **5.** A; 20 cm
7. $w + w + 30 + w + w + 30 = 380$; 80 cm
9. $w + 3w + w + 3w = 240$; 30 m
11. $w + 2w + 3 + w + 2w + 3 = 426$; 70 cm
13. $s + s + 3 + s + 4 = 67$; 20 cm

Page 304
1. $\frac{9}{25}$ **3.** $1\frac{11}{25}$ **5.** $\frac{3}{5}$ **7.** 3 **9.** $2\frac{1}{2}$ **11.** $\frac{3}{8}$
13. $\frac{7}{8}$ **15.** $1\frac{5}{8}$ **17.** $2\frac{1}{3}$ **19.** 25% **21.** 50%
23. 75% **25.** 100% **27.** $37\frac{1}{2}\%$ **29.** $62\frac{1}{2}\%$

Page 304 *(continued)*
31. $433\frac{1}{3}\%$ **33.** $183\frac{1}{3}\%$ **35.** $116\frac{2}{3}\%$ **37.** 21
39. 11 **41.** 66.04 **43.** 1.16 **45.** 4.012 **47.** 108
49. 32 **51.** 56 **53.** 32 **55.** 96 **57.** 136 **59.** 32
61. 80 **63.** 200 **65.** 4 **67.** 55 **69.** 120 **71.** $166\frac{2}{3}$

Page 305
1. 260 feet **3.** 30-foot square **5.** $345; $137.50; $29.50; $512 **7.** $567.50

Chapter 12 Surface Area and Volume

Pages 310–311
1. C **2.** E **3a.** E **3b.** B **3c.** A **3d.** C, D, F
5. Square pyramid **7.** Triangular pyramid
9. Triangular prism **11.** Cube **13.** Hexagonal prism
15. Cone

Pages 312–313
1a. 5 pieces **1b.** Triangle A; 28¢ **1c.** Square; 90¢
2. $1.18 **3.** $1.80 **5.** $3 **7.** $1.01 **9.** $1.80
11. $3 **13.** $1.46 **15.** $2.08 **17.** $1.18
19. $2.06 **21.** $3.58 **23.** $4.16 **25a.** D **25b.** E
25c. C

Pages 314–315
1. Jill **2.** back; bottom; right **3.** 2 **4.** 54 **5.** 6
7. 216 $in.^2$ **9.** 48 ft^2 **11.** 54 ft^2 **13.** 150 yd^2
15. 94 pictures **17.** $l = 7$ in.; $w = 6$ in.; $h = 3$ in.

Page 316
1. $\frac{2}{3}$ **3.** 6 **5.** $\frac{2}{3}$ **7.** $\frac{5f}{3g}$ **9.** $\frac{6}{rs}$ **11.** $\frac{y}{2}$ **13.** 1
15. $\frac{19}{24}$ **17.** $\frac{8}{15}$ **19.** $\frac{3r + 2s}{6}$ **21.** $\frac{9m + 4n}{12}$
23. $\frac{3p - 2q}{12}$ **25.** $\frac{10a - b}{8}$ **27.** $\frac{5m - 5n}{6}$ **29.** $2\frac{1}{2}$
31. 1 **33.** $\frac{1}{5}$ **35.** $\frac{y}{4}$ **37.** $1\frac{1}{2}$ **39.** 1 **41.** $\frac{y}{w}$
43. 5 **45.** $\frac{1}{4}$ **47.** $2\frac{2}{3}$ **49.** $\frac{3c}{b}$ **51.** $\frac{18}{z}$ **53.** $\frac{1}{3}$
55. $2d$ **57.** $6b$ **59.** 30 **61.** 42 **63.** 50 **65.** $10\frac{4}{5}$
67. $68\frac{1}{3}$ **69.** $\frac{3}{4}$

Page 317
1. $2.42 **3.** $1.30 **5.** 50¢ **7.** $3.34
9. $79 + 20j = 109$; 1.5 pounds **11.** $3p + p = 12$; 3 cantaloupes

Pages 318–319
1. A **2.** B **3.** 40 cubic centimeters **4.** $V = Bh$ or $V = (lw)h$; V = volume; l = length; w = width;

Pages 318–319 *(continued)*
h = height **5a.** 7; 140 **5b.** 4; 4; 64 **7.** 125 m^3
9. 1260 cm^3 **11.** 238.328 m^3 **13.** 1440 cm^3
15. 780 cm^3 **17.** 1984 cm^3 **19.** 26.88 m^3
21. Perimeter **23.** Area **25.** Perimeter **27.** 14 cm^3

Pages 320–321
1. $V = Bh = (\pi r^2)h$; V is the volume, π is pi, r is the radius, and h is the height. **2.** r, r **3a.** 9; 226.08
3b. 4; 16; 7; 351.68 **5.** 452.16 ft^3 **7.** 769.3 $in.^3$
9. 28.26 $in.^3$ **11.** 226.08 $in.^3$ **13.** 157 ft^3
15. 6437 $in.^3$ **17.** 3.14 yd^3 **19.** 2 in. **21.** 7 ft

Pages 322–323
1. $\frac{1}{3}$ **2.** $\frac{1}{3}$ **3a.** 80 **3b.** $V = \frac{1}{3}Bh = \frac{1}{3}(\pi r^2)h$; V is the volume, π is pi, r is the radius, and h is the height.
5. 105 cm^3 **7.** 1017.36 cm^3 **9.** 628 cm^3
11. 112 cm^3 **13.** 160 cm^3 **15.** 20 m^3
17. 136.5 cm^3 **19.** 235.5 m^3 **21.** 50.2 m^3
23. 803.8 m^3 **25.** 15.2 m^3 **27a.** 34 cm^3
27b. 10 cm^3

Pages 324–325
1. 1000; 1000 **2.** 1000; 1000 **3.** a **5.** b **7.** b
9. a **11.** b **13.** a **15.** 9000 **17.** 125,000
19. 2.875 **21.** 6400 **23.** 25,750 **25.** 0.87
27. 7000 **29.** 28,000 **31.** 1.25 **33.** 4600 **35.** 330
37. 0.575 kg **39.** 5 glasses **41.** 265 g

Pages 326–327
1. 75; 75 **2.** 3; 3 **3.** 8.750; 8.750 **5.** 4.5 L
7. 15.625 L **9.** 6.93 L **11.** 1.02 kg **13.** 8 kg
15. 1.536 kg **17.** 24 cm

Page 329
1. 298 $in.^2$ **3.** 40.26 $in.^2$ **5.** 34.4 $in.^3$
7. $A = lw - \pi r^2$; 129.76 ft^2 **9.** $V = \pi r^2 h + \frac{1}{3}\pi r^2 h$; $1046\frac{2}{3}$ ft^3

Page 330
1. 33 **3.** 33 **5.** 56 **7.** 26 **9.** $28\frac{1}{2}$ **11.** $45\frac{5}{7}$
13. 45 **15.** $20\frac{5}{9}$ **17.** $1\frac{3}{8}$ **19.** $^-10\frac{1}{3}$ **21.** $^-1\frac{4}{15}$
23. $13\frac{1}{2}$ **25.** 2 **27.** $12\frac{3}{5}$ **29.** $3\frac{1}{8}$ **31.** $8\frac{1}{8}$
33. $9\frac{1}{3}$ **35.** $13\frac{3}{4}$ **37.** $45\frac{1}{3}$ **39.** $2\frac{1}{12}$ **41.** 75
43. 250 **45.** $4\frac{2}{3}$ **47.** 52 **49.** 72 **51.** 375
53. 25% i **55.** 100% i **57.** 23.2% i **59.** 250% i
61. 57.1% d

Page 331
1. Family room **3.** 22 feet by 15 feet
5. Bedroom B **7.** 192 ft^2 **9.** $577.50 **11.** $\frac{1}{4}$

Chapter 13 Graphing Equations and Inequalities

Pages 336–337
1. Yes; yes; yes **2.** Yes; yes; yes **3.** No **4.** No
5a. is not **5b.** is **7.** b **9.** e **11.** g **13.** f
15. $n \le {}^-3$ **17.** $n \ge {}^-1$ **19.** $n \le {}^-1\frac{1}{2}$ **21.** $n < \frac{^-3}{4}$
23. $n > {}^-3\frac{3}{4}$

Pages 338–339
1. multiplied **2.** divided **3a.** 5 **3b.** $^-5$ **3c.** $4\frac{1}{2}$
5. Yes **7.** Yes **9.** No **11.** No **13.** $n \ge {}^-11$
15. $n \le {}^-8$ **17.** $n \le 2\frac{1}{2}$ **19.** $n < {}^-15$ **21.** $n < {}^-80$
23. $n \le {}^-18$ **25.** $n < {}^-2\frac{5}{6}$ **27.** $n \ge 8$ **29.** $n \ge {}^-24$
31. $n < 23$ **33.** $y > 2$; c **35.** $y < 1$; b
37. $y \ge 1$; a **39.** $y < {}^-3$; e **41.** $n \ge {}^-2$
43. $n \le {}^-4$ **45.** $n \le 1\frac{2}{5}$ **47.** $n < {}^-6$ **49.** $n > 0$
51. $n \le {}^-19$

Pages 340–341
1. $^-6$; yes **2a.** 5 **2b.** 4; $\le$ **2c.** 1; $\le$ **3a.** No
3b. No **3c.** Yes **3d.** Yes **3e.** No **3f.** Yes
3g. Yes **3h.** No **3i.** No **3j.** Yes **3k.** Yes
3l. Yes **5.** $x > {}^-3$ **7.** $x > {}^-25$ **9.** $x \le 3$
11. $x \le \frac{8}{9}$ **13.** $x > 26$ **15.** $x \le 3$ **17.** $x \ge {}^-21$
19. $x \ge 135$ **21.** $x \le \frac{1}{2}$ **23.** $x \le {}^-2$ **25.** $x \ge {}^-16$
27. $x \le 64$ **29.** $n \le 2$; d **31.** $n \ge \frac{1}{2}$; e **33.** $a \le 1$
35. $r < {}^-3$ **37.** $y < \frac{^-2}{3}$ **39.** $j \ge {}^-1$

Page 342
1. 3^2 **3.** 5^2 **5.** 7^2 **7.** $2^3 \cdot 7$ **9.** 2^4 **11.** 3^4
13. $2^2 \cdot 3^2$ **15.** $2^2 \cdot 17$ **17.** $3^2 \cdot 5$ **19.** 6 **21.** 10
23. 10 **25.** 9 **27.** $3c$ **29.** w **31.** $6n$ **33.** $3b$
35. $\frac{1}{2}$ **37.** $1\frac{7}{12}$ **39.** $\frac{5}{24}$ **41.** $\frac{m + 2n}{16}$ **43.** $\frac{3w + 4z}{15}$
45. $\frac{2x - y}{6}$ **47.** $\frac{2n - 9m}{24}$ **49.** $\frac{10p - 9q}{48}$ **51.** $\frac{3}{32}$
53. $1\frac{1}{8}$ **55.** $\frac{1}{3}$ **57.** $\frac{y}{6}$ **59.** $1\frac{1}{2}$ **61.** 1 **63.** $\frac{2y}{w}$
65. 5 **67.** $1\frac{1}{6}$ **69.** $6\frac{2}{5}$ **71.** $\frac{4m}{n}$ **73.** $\frac{12}{z}$ **75.** $\frac{4z}{3x}$
77. $3d$ **79.** $6n$

Page 343

1. Rhonda **3.** $\frac{1}{10}$ **5.** Kelly **7.** 15% **9.** April or Rhonda

Pages 344–345

1. First coordinate axis **2.** Second coordinate axis **3.** Origin **5.** $(5, {}^-2)$ **7.** $({}^-4, {}^-3)$ **9.** $(6, 0)$ **11.** $(0, 0)$ **13.** $\left(2, {}^-2\frac{1}{2}\right)$ **15.** $\left({}^-2\frac{1}{2}, {}^-1\frac{1}{2}\right)$ **17.** $\left({}^-6\frac{1}{2}, 1\frac{1}{2}\right)$

Pages 346–347

1. *No* **2.** *Yes* **3.** *Yes* **4.** 1 **5.** $({}^-3, {}^-14)$ *and* $\left(\frac{2}{3}, {}^-3\right)$ **6.** $^-3$ **7.** $^-4$; $^-2$; 0; 2; 4 **9.** $^-4$; 1; 6; 11; 16 **19.** 45°*F* **21.** $y = 4x$ **23.** $y = {}^-2x$

Pages 348–349

1. y **2.** 4 **3.** Yes; yes **5.** $^-5$; $^-4$; $^-3$; $^-2$ **7.** $^-3$; $^-1$; 1; 3 **9.** $^-4$; $^-1$; 2; 5 **11.** $^-5$; $^-3$; $^-1$; 1 **21.** $y = 2x - 1$

Pages 350–351

1a. Yes **1b.** Yes **1c.** Yes **1d.** Yes **2.** Yes **3a.** Yes **3b.** Yes **3c.** Yes **3d.** Yes **4.** Yes **5.** below **6.** above **7.** $y \le x + 2$ **9.** $y \ge \frac{1}{3}x + 1$ **11.** $y \ge \frac{1}{3}x + 2$

Pages 352–353

1. $y = {}^-2x - 6$ **2.** $y = \frac{1}{2}x - 1$ **3.** $({}^-2, {}^-2)$ **5.** Yes **7.** Yes **9.** $(1, 1)$ **11.** $({}^-2, 2)$ **13.** $(0, 1)$ **15.** $(2, 2)$ **17.** $(2, 5)$ **19.** $\left(\frac{{}^-2}{3}, 1\frac{2}{3}\right)$

Pages 354–355

1a. Carla; d; $c + d = 12$; $c = 3d$ **1b.** 9, 3; 9; 3 **2.** Yes; yes **3a.** 20; 8 **3b.** 14, 6; 14; 6 **5.** $f + s = 22$; $s + 8 = f$; $f = 15$; $s = 7$ **7.** $f + s = 25$; $4s = f$; $f = 20$; $s = 5$ **9.** $j + k = 26$; $k + 12 = j$; Jim sold 19 tickets; Kelly sold 7 tickets.

Page 356

1. $\frac{2}{5}$ **3.** $\frac{1}{20}$ **5.** $\frac{1}{100}$ **7.** $\frac{9}{50}$ **9.** $1\frac{8}{25}$ **11.** $\frac{16}{25}$ **13.** 4 **15.** $3\frac{1}{2}$ **17.** $\frac{1}{3}$ **19.** 50% **21.** 25% **23.** $16\frac{2}{3}$% **25.** 75% **27.** 150% **29.** $133\frac{1}{3}$% **31.** 175% **33.** $162\frac{1}{2}$% **35.** $41\frac{2}{3}$% **37.** 16 **39.** 78 **41.** 24.03 **43.** 1.86 **45.** 0.41 **47.** 125.8

Page 356 *(continued)*

49. 85 **51.** 56 **53.** 32 **55.** 48 **57.** 96 **59.** 43 **61.** 65 **63.** 250 **65.** 11 **67.** 50 **69.** 152 **71.** $222\frac{2}{9}$

Page 357

1. \$1.83 **3.** No **5.** Kansas City **7.** \$.42 more **9.** $p + 20 = 60$; 40 ounces

Chapter 14 Probability and Statistics

Pages 362–363

1. 3 baseball T-shirts **2.** 3 baseball T-shirts **3.** 6 baseball T-shirts **4.** Red Tigers; green Padres **5.** 6 branches **6.** Yes **7a.** 2 choices; 4 choices **7c.** 8 baseball T-shirts **7e.** 6 baseball T-shirts **9.** 30 outfits **11.** 60 systems

Pages 364–365

1. Carol; David; Alice **2.** CDA, CAD, ACD, ADC, DAC, DCA **3.** 6 ways **4.** 3, 2, and 1 **5a.** 4 people **5b.** 3 people; 2 people; 1 person **5c.** 4, 3, 2, and 1 **5d.** 24 ways **7a.** 5 lifts **7b.** 120 orders **9.** 720 ways **11.** 24 ways **13.** 48 lunches **15.** 720 lunches

Pages 366–367

1. 6 outcomes **2.** Yes **3.** $\frac{1}{6}$ **4.** $\frac{1}{3}$ **5.** $\frac{1}{6}$ **7.** $\frac{1}{2}$ **9.** $\frac{2}{3}$ **11.** $\frac{1}{2}$ **13.** 0 **15.** 1 **17.** $\frac{3}{8}$ **19.** $\frac{1}{8}$ **21.** $\frac{1}{4}$ **23.** $\frac{1}{8}$ **25.** 0 **27.** $\frac{1}{4}$ **29.** $\frac{5}{8}$ **31.** $\frac{1}{2}$ **33.** $\frac{3}{4}$ **35.** $\frac{1}{2}$ **37.** $\frac{1}{6}$ **39.** $\frac{1}{8}$ **41.** $\frac{1}{12}$ **43.** $\frac{23}{24}$

Pages 368–369

1. \$1.00 off **2.** No **3.** 8 outcomes **4.** 2 outcomes **5.** $\frac{1}{4}$ **7.** $\frac{3}{8}$ **9.** $\frac{1}{2}$ **11.** $\frac{3}{4}$ **13a.** $\frac{1}{8}$ **13c.** $\frac{3}{8}$ **13e.** $\frac{7}{8}$ **15a.** $\frac{1}{36}$ **15c.** $\frac{1}{18}$ **15e.** $\frac{5}{12}$ **15g.** $\frac{1}{6}$ **15i.** 0

Pages 370–371

1. $\frac{1}{6}$ **2.** $\frac{1}{2}$ **3.** $\frac{1}{12}$ **4.** $\frac{1}{6}$; $\frac{1}{2}$; $\frac{1}{12}$ **5.** $\frac{1}{12}$ **7a.** $\frac{1}{2}$ **7b.** $\frac{1}{2}$ **7c.** $\frac{1}{4}$ **9.** $\frac{5}{12}$ **11.** $\frac{1}{48}$ **13.** $\frac{5}{48}$ **15.** $\frac{35}{48}$ **17.** $\frac{1}{64}$ **19.** $\frac{1}{64}$ **21.** $\frac{3}{32}$ **23.** $\frac{3}{16}$ **25.** $\frac{15}{32}$ **27.** $\frac{1}{12}$ **29.** $\frac{1}{12}$ **31.** $\frac{2}{9}$ **33.** $\frac{1}{4}$ **35.** $\frac{1}{32}$

Pages 372–373

1. $\frac{1}{10}$ **2.** $\frac{1}{9}$ **3.** multiply **4.** $\frac{1}{90}$ **5.** $\frac{1}{90}$ **7.** $\frac{1}{18}$
9. $\frac{1}{30}$ **11.** $\frac{1}{72}$ **13.** $\frac{1}{9}$ **15.** $\frac{1}{12}$ **17.** $\frac{1}{12}$ **19.** $\frac{1}{4}$
21. $\frac{1}{504}$ **23.** $\frac{1}{3024}$ **25.** $\frac{5}{42}$

Page 374

1. 21 **3.** 27 **5.** 28 **7.** $8\frac{2}{5}$ **9.** $92\frac{1}{4}$ **11.** $15\frac{5}{9}$
13. 18 **15.** 11 **17.** 60 **19.** 160 **21.** 170 **23.** 7
25. 34 **27.** 72 **29.** 30 **31.** $32\frac{4}{7}$ **33.** $29\frac{1}{6}$
35. $40\frac{4}{5}$ **37.** $^{-}6$ **39.** $^{-}10$ **41.** 2 **43.** $^{-}32$ **45.** 32
47. $^{-}7$ **49.** $9x$ **51.** 0 **53.** $^{-}6w + 5$ **55.** $^{-}10n - 9$
57. $^{-}9n - 7$ **59.** $13y + 7$

Page 375

1. $1.20 **3.** 7¢ **5.** $33\frac{1}{3}\%$ **7.** $2c - .51 = 1.39$; $.95

Pages 376–377

1. Yellow; white **2.** 100 gum balls **3.** 500 gum balls **4.** 100 ways; 500 ways **5.** 1 to 5 **6.** 500 ways; 100 ways **7.** 5 to 1 **9.** $\frac{1}{4}$ **11.** $\frac{7}{53}$ **13.** $\frac{13}{17}$
15. $\frac{4}{1}$ **17.** $\frac{53}{7}$ **19.** $\frac{19}{11}$ **21.** 3 to 10 **23.** 1 to 29; 29 to 1 **25.** 35 to 1

Pages 378–379

1. $1 **2.** $\frac{1}{8}$ **3.** $6 **4.** $.75 **5.** Less than **6.** Yes
7. $1.00 or more **9.** $\frac{1}{180}$ **11.** $.67 **13.** A bad deal
15a. $\frac{1}{2}$ **15b.** $3.13 **15c.** Yes **17.** Yes
19. $1.50 for chance on the watch; $1 for chance on the radio

Pages 380–381

1. 41.4 seconds **2.** Mike **3.** Gayle; Nan **4.** Bill's
5. No **6.** 5 students **7.** Bill, Heidi, Nan, Paul
9. 32.3 **11.** 264.6 **13.** 451.8 **15.** 14.2 **17.** 45.2
19. 128.2 **21.** 22.1 **23.** 21.6 **25.** 21.6 **27.** 14.1
29. Bill **31.** Paul **33.** 52.7 seconds **35.** Less

Pages 382–383

1. 75 **2.** Rogers **3.** Manning; Jackson
4. 72; 70; 17 **5.** 8 students; 8 students **6.** Less than
7. 72.6 **8.** Greater than **9.** 11 **11.** 10 **13.** 182.5
15. 6719 **17.** 15; 5 **19.** 66; 16 **21.** 40.5 **23.** 26
25. Manning, Wong, Carlin, Dori, Weaver, Davis, Napes, Lopez, Fallons **27.** 54; 54; 55; 57

Pages 384–385

1. 3 students **3.** 15 students **5.** 24 students
7. $62\frac{1}{2}\%$ **9.** 16 hours **11.** 8 hours **13.** Jan
15. Fourth week **17.** $33\frac{1}{3}\%$ **19.** Bob; Randy
21. 21 records **23.** Loni **25.** Food; savings
27. $3 **29.** $260 **31.** 1982 **33.** 1985

Pages 386–387

1. 6 students **2.** No, because students who ride in a car to school probably live farther than 3 blocks from the school. **3.** Yes **4.** No **5.** Answers will vary. One possible answer: There may be many more male drivers than female drivers living in Lake City.
6. Answers will vary. One possible answer: Most car trips involve starting and ending at one's home.
7. 1981, 60; 1982, 61; 1983, 63; 1984, 64; 1985, 65; 1986, 68 **9.** The first graph **11.** 13.3%

Pages 388–389

1a. 40 students **1b.** 26 students **1c.** 65%
2. 650 students **3a.** 18 people **3b.** 25 people
3c. 72% **3d.** 432 people **5.** 375 people
7. 950 people **9.** 109 families

Page 390

1. 8 **3.** $2\frac{4}{7}$ **5.** $5\frac{1}{3}$ **7.** $^{-}3$ **9.** $^{-}3\frac{4}{5}$ **11.** $\frac{9}{19}$
13. 0 **15.** $1\frac{6}{11}$ **17.** $1\frac{1}{4}$ **19.** 10 **21.** $5\frac{1}{2}$
23. $10\frac{2}{15}$ **25.** 40 **27.** $12\frac{4}{5}$ **29.** 7 **31.** 6
33. $13\frac{1}{11}$ **35.** 20 **37.** 0.63 **39.** 114 **41.** 1650
43. $62\frac{1}{2}$ **45.** 152 **47.** 33.3% d **49.** 50% d
51. 44% i **53.** 32.7% i

Page 391

1. Grade 11 **3.** Grade 2; Band **5.** Graph 1 or 3; 400 students **7.** Graph 3; student participation has been increasing over the past 5 years.

Chapter 15 Similar and Right Triangles

Pages 396–397

1. Side *ST*; side *RT* **2.** $\angle S$; $\angle T$ **3.** 5 cm **5.** 24 mm
7. 27 mm **9.** 1 cm **11.** 3 cm **13.** 3.52 cm
15. 8.125 meters

Pages 398–399

1. 2.0 meters **2.** 1.4 meters **3.** 4.9 meters

Pages 398–399 *(continued)*
4. 7 meters **5.** 15 m **7.** 6 m **9.** 9 m **11.** 14.1 m **13.** 3.33 meters **15.** 50 meters **17.** 2.7 meters **19.** 18.96 meters

Pages 400–401
1. Sides RT and ST; sides WY and XY **2.** 6 units; 9 units **3.** 4 units; 8 units; 12 units **4.** 8 units; 12 units **5.** 3 units; 6 units; 9 units **6.** 0.75 **7a.** 8 **7b.** 12; 0.75 **7c.** $1.\overline{3}$ **7d.** 9; $1.\overline{3}$ **8.** Yes; the measure of the angle **9.** 0.42 **11.** 0.8 **13.** 2.08 **15.** 0.85 **17.** 0.71 **19.** 1.57 **21.** 0.47 **23.** 0.49

Pages 402–403
1. Side AB **2.** Side RS **3.** 5 ft; 13 ft **4.** 0.6; 0.8 **5a.** 0.8 **5b.** 13; 0.38 **5c.** 12; 0.92 **5d.** 0.6 **5e.** 13; 0.92 **5f.** 5; 0.38 **7.** 0.75 **9.** 0.6 **11.** 0.8 **13.** 2.4 **15.** 0.92 **17.** 0.38 **19.** 0.92 **21.** 0.42 **23.** 0.92 **25.** 0.6 **27.** 1.33 **29.** 0.6 **31.** 0.8 **33.** 1.33 **35.** 0.6 **37.** 0.6 **39.** 0.75 **41.** 0.8 **43.** $\frac{12}{13}$ **45.** $\frac{9}{16}$ **47.** $\frac{12}{5}$

Page 404
1. 5 **3.** 7 **5.** 21 **7.** 6 **9.** j **11.** $3y$ **13.** $14c$ **15.** $5xy^3$ **17.** $\frac{7}{6}$ **19.** $\frac{4}{3}$ **21.** $\frac{7}{10}$ **23.** $\frac{4}{3x}$ **25.** $\frac{r}{3}$ **27.** $\frac{5}{7c^2}$ **29.** $\frac{c^2}{9d}$ **31.** $\frac{19k}{4}$ **33.** $\frac{2}{5z}$ **35.** $\frac{9}{20}$ **37.** $1\frac{17}{24}$ **39.** $\frac{2a+b}{6}$ **41.** $\frac{10y+3z}{24}$ **43.** $\frac{3a+10b}{35}$ **45.** $\frac{1}{4}$ **47.** $\frac{5}{36}$ **49.** $\frac{2c-d}{10}$ **51.** $\frac{3j-2k}{24}$ **53.** $\frac{10q-15r}{36}$ **55.** $\frac{1}{4}$ **57.** 1 **59.** $\frac{1}{4}$ **61.** $\frac{2k}{9}$ **63.** $2\frac{1}{3}$ **65.** 1 **67.** $1\frac{1}{2}$ **69.** 5 **71.** $1\frac{1}{2}$ **73.** $13\frac{1}{3}$ **75.** $\frac{2b}{a}$ **77.** $\frac{3}{5}$

Page 405
1. 3; 180 **3.** 1; 180 **5.** 30°; 60° **7.** 20°; 40°, 120° **9.** $n + n + 20 + 90 = 180$; 35°; 55° **11.** $n + 4n + 90 = 180$; 18°; 72°, 90°

Pages 406–407
1. 0.6428 **2.** 0.6428 **3.** 1.0000 **4.** 0.7002; 12.6 **5a.** 0.8660; 17.32 **5b.** 0.7071; 19.0917 **7.** 68.6 ft **9.** 24.6 ft **11.** 18.9 ft **13.** 16.1 ft **15.** 22.9 ft **17.** 10.5 ft **19.** 339.6 ft **21.** 399.3 ft

Pages 408–409
1a. 33° **1b.** 39° **1c.** 36° **2.** 37° **3.** 0.5446 and 0.5592; 0.5592 **4.** 34° **5a.** 38° **5b.** 35° **7.** 71° **9.** 27° **11.** 64° **13.** 51° **15.** 55° **17.** 63° **19.** 320.4 feet **21.** 30°

Pages 410–411
1. Yes **2.** 6 and 7 **3.** 6.5 and 7.1 **4.** 6.8 and 6.8 **5.** 6.8 **7.** 1 **9.** 5 **11.** 8 **13.** 16 **15.** 1.2 **17.** 1.1 **19.** 6.856 **21.** 9.327 **23.** 11.269 **25.** True **27.** True **29.** 20.5 **31.** 27.7

Pages 412–413
1. 16 square units; 25 square units **2.** 25 square units **3.** Yes **4.** Example A; Example B **5.** 11.4 ft **6.** 13.2 ft **7.** 8.6 ft **9.** 12 ft **11.** 8.9 ft **13.** 8 ft **15.** 13.2 ft **17.** 5.7 ft **19.** 8.7 in. **21.** No **23.** No **25.** Yes **27.** No

Pages 414–415
1a. 17; 8 **1b.** 17; b **1c.** 289 **2.** Yes **3.** Drawing A; 12.5 miles **5.** Drawing B; 9.2 feet **7.** 18.0 miles **9.** 127.3 feet **11.** 96.8 feet

Page 416
1. 13 **3.** 32 **5.** 40 **7.** 35 **9.** $16\frac{1}{5}$ **11.** $52\frac{1}{2}$ **13.** 16 **15.** 7 **17.** 160 **19.** 48 **21.** 6 **23.** 22 **25.** 42 **27.** 165 **29.** 56 **31.** 39 **33.** $28\frac{4}{5}$ **35.** $42\frac{6}{7}$ **37.** $10y$ **39.** 0 **41.** $^-15n + 7$ **43.** $^-13t - 15$ **45.** $^-12t - 14$ **47.** $1\frac{1}{3}$ **49.** 44 **51.** $^-3\frac{3}{10}$ **53.** $^-9\frac{1}{3}$

Page 417
1. 28.3 miles **3.** 56.5 miles **5.** More **7.** 178.8 miles **9.** 268.2 miles **11.** 37 miles

Chapter 16 BASIC Programming

Page 423
1. 120 **3.** 10 **5.** 10 **7.** 12 **9.** 43 **11.** 215 **13.** 84

15.
```
120
1000
6
```
17.
```
10002
1000000
50
90
```
19.
```
NEW
10 PRINT 47 + 53 + 9
20 PRINT 4 * 9 + 6
30 END
```
21.
```
NEW
10 PRINT 27 / 5
20 PRINT 7 ↑ 2 + 10
30 END
```
23.
```
9; 6
987; 9; 5
98765; 9; 3
```

Pages 424–425
1. Cost per square foot of construction; square feet of floor space **2.** 1900 **3a.** 45 **3b.** 1900 **3c.** E **4.** 355 345 1750 70 **5.** THE QUOTIENT IS 34

Pages 424–425 *(continued)*

7. THE AREA IS 66.04 SQUARE UNITS **9.** THE AREA IS 2826 SQUARE UNITS **11.** 144 4 .25 15 **13.** THE QUOTIENT IS 240

Pages 426–427

1. Number of hits, number of times at bat, number of walks **2.** Batting average is .28 **3.** Batting average is .333333 **5a.** 15 36 **5b.** 21 36 **5c.** 40 64 **5d.** 33 60 **5e.** $^{-}2$ 28 **5f.** 28 $^{-}32$ **7a.** THE PERIMETER IS 80 UNITS **7b.** THE PERIMETER IS 160 UNITS **7c.** THE PERIMETER IS 84 UNITS **7d.** THE PERIMETER IS 404 UNITS **7e.** THE PERIMETER IS 87.2 UNITS **7f.** THE PERIMETER IS 51.5 UNITS

Pages 428–429

1. 1 orange; 4 oranges; 4 **2.** 4; 16

3.	**5.**	**7.**	**9.**	**11.**
1	3	10	0	60
4	4	9	5	66
9	5	8	10	72
16	6	7	15	78
25	7	6	20	84
36		5		90
49		4		
64		3		
		2		
		1		
		0		

13. AREA IS 3.14 SQUARE UNITS
AREA IS 12.56 SQUARE UNITS
AREA IS 28.26 SQUARE UNITS
AREA IS 50.24 SQUARE UNITS

15. 1
5
9
13
17

17. AREA IS 314 SQUARE UNITS
AREA IS 1256 SQUARE UNITS
AREA IS 2826 SQUARE UNITS

19. Programs will vary. One possible program is:

```
NEW
10  FOR N = 1 TO 10
20  PRINT N ↑ 3
30  NEXT N
40  END
```

Page 430

1. $\frac{2}{5}$ **3.** $\frac{^{-}3}{5}$ **5.** $\frac{^{-}3}{8}$ **7.** $\frac{18}{25}$ **9.** $\frac{3}{20}$ **11.** $2\frac{1}{4}$ **13.** $2\frac{2}{5}$ **15.** $4\frac{11}{20}$ **17.** $3\frac{2}{25}$ **19.** $6\frac{2}{5}$ **21.** $\frac{1}{3}$

Page 430 *(continued)*

23. $\frac{1}{16}$ **25.** $^{-}1\frac{5}{8}$ **27.** $\frac{1}{2}$ **29.** $\frac{^{-}4}{15}$ **31.** $\frac{^{-}3}{20}$ **33.** $^{-}9\frac{7}{8}$ **35.** $\frac{19}{24}$ **37.** $\frac{^{-}2}{15}$ **39.** 1 **41.** 1 **43.** $8\frac{5}{8}$ **45.** $^{-}8$ **47.** $\frac{^{-}1}{9}$ **49.** $\frac{15}{28}$ **51.** $^{-}3\frac{5}{13}$ **53.** 2 **55.** $^{-}1\frac{1}{4}$ **57.** $1\frac{1}{7}$ **59.** $2\frac{1}{2}$ **61.** $^{-}1$ **63.** $14y$ **65.** $4v + 12$ **67.** $^{-}7j + 9$ **69.** $12v - 6$

Page 431

1. $^{-}5$ **3.** 30 **5.** 10 **7.** $^{-}41.8$°F **9.** 107.6°F **11.** Below

Pages 432–433

1. 134 **2.** Jenny **3.** 3 **4.** THE AVERAGE SCORE IS 131; Robin **5a.** THE PRODUCT IS 6000 **5b.** THE QUOTIENT IS 50 **7.** 280 70 **9.** 2 **11.** VOLUME IS 253.44 CUBIC UNITS **13.** PERIMETER IS 8.2 UNITS

Pages 434–435

1a. 30; 5200 **1b.** 156; 224 **1c.** SALARY IS $70
SALARY IS $94
OUT OF DATA IN 10

2a.	**2b.**
25	3
36	9
49	2.4
OUT OF DATA IN 10	OUT OF DATA IN 10

3. 55
134

5. 10 100
11 121
12 144
13 169
14 196

7. COMMISSION IS $248
COMMISSION IS $195.6
COMMISSION IS $207.2

Pages 436–437

1. $1.52 **2.** 0.44 **3.** THE CALL COSTS $1.52
THE CALL COSTS $1.96
OUT OF DATA IN 10

4. 15
36
OUT OF DATA IN 10

5. −3
−4
0

7. 6 > 3
−2 < 7
−7 > −10
7 = 7

9. 20 IF T < 0 THEN 10
6
1.2
75

11. 4 > $^{-}6$
9 < 10
2.1 > 2.09

Pages 438–439

1a. Number of hours worked **1b.** 6.40; 40
2a. \$224 **2b.** \$352 **2c.** \$256 **2d.** \$467.20
3a. 1; M = 4N **3b.** stop **3c.** 4; 8; 12; 16; 20; 24; 28; 32; 36; 40 **5.** 3; 9; 27; 81; 243

7.

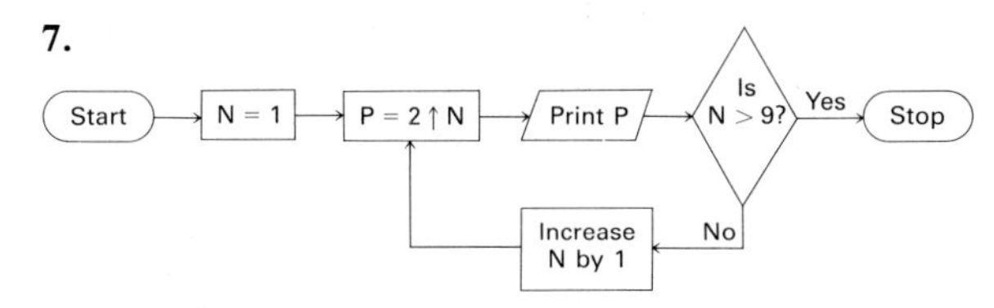

Page 440

1. 5 **3.** $^-23$ **5.** $^-26$ **7.** $^-4$ **9.** 4 **11.** $\frac{^-2}{3}$

13. $\frac{^-1}{3}$ **15.** $\frac{1}{3}$ **17.** $1\frac{5}{13}$ **19.** $1\frac{1}{4}$ **21.** 2 **23.** $4\frac{4}{7}$

25. 10 **27.** $8\frac{4}{5}$ **29.** 60 **31.** 25 **33.** $8\frac{1}{2}$

35. $12\frac{3}{4}$ **37.** $9\frac{9}{23}$ **39.** $12\frac{1}{2}$ **41.** 0.4 **43.** 51

45. 250 **47.** 50% i **49.** 100% i **51.** 50% i
53. 42.9% i **55.** 15.2% i

Page 441

1. Mount Kisco **3.** Highway 20 **5.** 50 mph
7. 3 hours

9. DISTANCE = 135 MILES
DISTANCE = 120 MILES
DISTANCE = 232.2 MILES
OUT OF DATA IN 10

Credits

Photography

Photo Research: Laurel Anderson/Picture Research Consultants

Table of Contents: ***iii** (top to bottom):* Erik Simonson/H. Armstrong Roberts, R. Kruber/H. Armstrong Roberts; ***iv** (top to bottom):* Robert Frerck/Odyssey Productions, Royce Bair and Associates/Uniphoto Picture Agency; ***v** (top to bottom):* Philip Jon Bailey/The Picture Cube, Lou Jones; ***vi** (top to bottom):* Steven Leonard/FPG, Focus on Sports; ***vii** (top to bottom):* Ted Beauden/FPG, Stacy Pick/Stock, Boston; ***viii** (top to bottom):* Grant Heilman Photography, G. R. Richardson/ Taurus Photos; ***ix:** (top to bottom):* Ken Brate/ Photo Researchers, Inc., The Slide Center, Inc.; ***x** (top to bottom):* S. Strickland/FPG, Harald Sund

Chapter 1: ***1:*** Erik Simonson/H. Armstrong Roberts; ***2** (left to right):* Stephen Sherman/The Picture Group, Yoram Kahana/Shooting Star, J. C. Francolon/Gamma-Liaison, Elisa Leonelli/Shooting Star, Roman Iwasiwka/Camera 5; ***4:*** Lee Lockwood/Black Star; ***6:*** Courtesy of Mercedes Benz of North America; ***10, 11, 14:*** Clive Russ; ***19:*** Ellis Herwig/Stock, Boston; ***21:*** Mike Valeri/The Picture Group

Chapter 2: ***27:*** R. Kruber/H. Armstrong Roberts; ***28** (left to right):* Leo De Wys, Inc., Scott Thode/The Stock Market, A. Levenson/ Leo de Wys, Inc., Scott Thode/The Stock Market; ***30** (photos 1–3):* Clive Russ; ***30** (photo 4):* Larry Lawfer; ***34:*** Clive Russ; ***36:*** John Patsch/Nawrocki Stock Photo; ***40:*** Candee Productions/Nawrocki Stock Photo; ***42, 44:*** Clive Russ; ***50:*** David Strick/Black Star

Chapter 3: ***57:*** Robert Frerck/Odyssey Productions; ***58:*** E. M. Bordis/Leo de Wys, Inc.; ***60:*** Clive Russ; ***62:*** Dean Abramson/Stock, Boston; ***65, 66:*** Clive Russ; ***71:*** Paul Johnson; ***72, 76:*** Clive Russ; ***78:*** George J. Marcelonis; ***80:*** P. Chock/Stock, Boston; ***83:*** Jim Wright/Nawrocki Stock Photo; ***84:*** E. M. Bordis/Leo de Wys, Inc.; ***87:*** Donald Smetzer/CLICK, Chicago

Chapter 4: ***91:*** Royce Bair and Associates/Uniphoto Picture Agency; ***95:*** Paul Johnson; ***102:*** Clive Russ; ***107:*** Ellis Herwig/The Picture Cube; ***110:*** Clive Russ; ***112:*** Paul Johnson; ***115:*** Robert Maxham/The Stock Shop, Inc.

Chapter 5. ***119.*** Philip Jon Bailey/The Picture Cube; ***120:*** Clive Russ; ***121:*** Guy Sauvage–Agence Vandstadt/Photo Researchers, Inc.; ***125:*** Franz Kraus/The Picture Cube; ***127:*** P. Grant; ***129:*** Clive Russ; ***130** (left to right):* New York Public Library Picture Collection, D. Goldberg/Sygma, The Bettman Archive, Inc., Ken Regan/Camera 5; ***133:*** Bob Perry, courtesy of Killington Ski Resort; ***136, 138:*** Clive Russ; ***141:*** Candee Productions/Nawrocki Stock Photo

Chapter 6: ***145:*** Lou Jones; ***148** (photos within album):* Lou Jones; ***148** (album):* Clive Russ; ***149:*** Frank Klune, Jr./FPG; ***152:*** Paul Johnson; ***160:*** Walter Frerck/Odyssey Productions; ***162** (left):* H. Armstrong Roberts; ***162** (right):* Robert Frerck/Odyssey Productions; ***164:*** Robert Frerck/Odyssey Productions; ***167:*** Paul Johnson

Chapter 7: ***171:*** Steven Leonard/FPG; ***172, 174:*** Clive Russ; ***175:*** Paul Johnson; ***176:*** Ron Colby/The Stock Market; ***178:*** Walter Frerck/Odyssey Productions; ***181, 182, 184, 185, 186, 187, 191:*** Clive Russ

Chapter 8: ***195:*** Focus on Sports; ***207:*** Paul Johnson; ***208:*** John Dommers/Photo Researchers, Inc.; ***213:*** Focus on Sports; ***214:*** Robert Harding Picture Library; ***216:*** William Curtisinger/Photo Researchers, Inc.; ***219:*** Paul Johnson

Chapter 9: ***223:*** Ted Beaudon/FPG; ***229:*** Clive Russ; ***237:*** Paul Johnson; ***238, 240:*** Clive Russ; ***242–243:*** Barry O'Rourke/The Stock Market; ***245:*** Focus on Sports

Chapter 10: ***249:*** Stacy Pick/Stock, Boston; ***250–251:*** Clive Russ; ***252:*** The Bettman Archive, Inc.; ***254:*** Paul Johnson; ***262, 270:*** Paul Johnson

Chapter 11: ***277:*** Grant Heilman Photography; ***284:*** Geoffrey Gove/Photo Researchers, Inc.; ***286:*** D & J Heston/The Stock Shop; ***290:*** Paul Johnson; ***293:*** Georg Gerster/Photo Researchers, Inc.; ***305:*** Elizabeth Willis

Chapter 12: ***309:*** G. R. Richardson/Taurus Photos; ***310, 314, 317:*** Paul Johnson; ***321, 324:*** Clive Russ; ***331:*** Paul Johnson

Chapter 13: ***335:*** Ken Brate/Photo Researchers, Inc.; ***343:*** Paul Johnson; ***354:*** Richard Hutchings/Photo Researchers, Inc.

Chapter 14: ***361:*** The Slide Center, Inc.; ***362–363:*** Clive Russ; ***364:*** Larry Lawfer; ***366, 367, 369, 370, 371:*** Clive Russ; ***375:*** Stuart Cohen; ***376:*** Susan Lapides; ***378, 379:*** Clive Russ; ***380:*** Paul Johnson; ***382:*** Paulette Crowley; ***386, 388, 389:*** Larry Lawfer; ***391:*** Paul Johnson; ***392:*** Clive Russ

Chapter 15: ***395:*** S. Strickland/FPG; ***396:*** Tom Magno; ***417:*** Robert Frerck/Odyssey Productions

Chapter 16: ***421:*** Harald Sund; ***422, 424:*** Paul Johnson; ***426:*** Burk Uzzle/Woodfin Camp and Associates; ***428:*** Clive Russ; ***431:*** Paul Johnson; ***432:*** Zimmerman/Alpha-FPG

Illustrations

Pages 14, 18, 44, 48, 187, 233, 363 and 365 were produced by Bob Priest. All other illustrations were produced by Dave Hannum/Graphic Ideas.

Acknowledgment

Page 287, exercise 36: from the *Guinness Book of World Records,* published by Sterling Publishing Co., Inc., New York, N. Y., © 1984, by Guinness Superlatives Ltd.